Jonathan Lytton

ANNUAL REVIEW OF BIOPHYSICS AND BIOMOLECULAR STRUCTURE

ANNUAL REVIEW OF BIOPHYSICS AND BIOMOLECULAR STRUCTURE

VOLUME 24, 1995

ROBERT M. STROUD, *Editor*
University of California, San Francisco

WAYNE L. HUBBELL, *Associate Editor*
University of California, Los Angeles

WILMA K. OLSON, *Associate Editor*
Rutgers, The State University of New Jersey

ANNUAL REVIEWS INC. 4139 EL CAMINO WAY P.O. BOX 10139 PALO ALTO, CALIFORNIA 94303-0139

ANNUAL REVIEWS INC.
Palo Alto, California, USA

International Standard Serial Number: 1056-8700
International Standard Book Number: 0-8243-1824-2
Library of Congress Catalog Card Number: 79-188446

Annual Review and publication titles are registered trademarks of Annual Reviews Inc.

∞ The paper used in this publication meets the minimum requirements of American National Standard for Information Sciences—Permanence of Paper for Printed Library Materials, ANSI Z39.48-1984.

Annual Reviews Inc. and the Editors of its publications assume no responsibility for the statements expressed by the contributors to the *Review*.

TYPESET BY MARYLAND COMPOSITION CO., INC.
PRINTED AND BOUND IN THE UNITED STATES OF AMERICA

PREFACE

Einstein's general theory of relativity was questioned in 1994. It could not account for the forces between two infinite planar sheets of mass. Einstein's equations predict no gravitational attraction when space is not distorted. As in physics, molecular biology will continue to be redefined. Any problem that we can now frame will probably be resolved in the next hundred years, but based on the past hundred years, the discoveries to come will reach back to the landmarks of this decade for many key insights and developments. If one series of journals could be passed to our scientific successors in a century, these *Annual Reviews* would best represent the landmarks of this time.

The protein code, how protein molecules mediate their function, lies at the heart of biology. Studies of this central, yet elusive puzzle focus on the progression from sequence to structure, from structure to function, and on to modulation of function. Volume 24 of the *Annual Review of Biophysics and Biomolecular Structure* covers pathways along the evolution of thinking about this essential problem. Questions in focus in this volume include: How do channels in the central nervous system that signal thought and memory react when neurotransmitters bind, how are these channels organized, and how can we design medication for mental disorder? What are the mechanisms of muscle contraction and of cell motility, and how is energy converted so efficiently in living cells? What constitutes the basis of hearing and vision? Which enzymes repair DNA and control DNA transcription and translation? And what types of system track the motion of molecules in living cells?

We are indebted to our author colleagues for intellectual focus and effort, to Amanda Suver for her efforts in the editorial office, and to the staffs at Maryland Composition Company and Book Press for their work on the production of this volume.

ROBERT M. STROUD
EDITOR

Annual Review of Biophysics and Biomolecular Structure
Volume 24, 1995

CONTENTS

SOME RELATED ARTICLES IN OTHER *ANNUAL REVIEWS*

From the *Annual Review of Biochemistry*, Volume 64 (1995):

The Nuclear Pore Complex, L. I. Davis

The Envelope of Mycobacteria, P. J. Brennan and H. Nikaido

Human Carbonic Anhydrases and Carbonic Anhydrase Deficiencies, W. S. Sly and P. Y. Hu

Plasma Lipid Transfer Proteins, A. Tall

Triplex DNA Structures, M. D. Frank-Kamenetskii and S. M. Mirkin

6 Phosphofructo-2-Kinase/Fructose–2,6-Bisphosphatase: A Metabolic Signaling Enzyme, S. J. Pilkis, T. H. Claus, I. J. Kurland, and A. J. Lange

The Catalytic Mechanism and Structure of Thymidylate Synthase, C. W. Carreras and D. V. Santi

Metabolic Coupling Factors in Pancreatic β-Cell Signal Transduction, C. B. Newgard and J. D. McGarry

Structure and Function of Voltage-Gated Ion Channels, W. Catterall

The Multiplicity of Domains in Proteins, R. F. Doolittle

Diversity of Oligonucleotide Functions, L. Gold, B. Polisky, O. Uhlenbeck, and M. Yarus

Protein–RNA Recognition, D. E. Draper

The Small Nucleolar RNAs, E. S. Maxwell and M. J. Fournier

From the *Annual Review of Cell Biology*, Volume 10 (1994):

Protein Serine/Threonine Phosphatases: New Avenues for Cell Regulation, S. Shenolikar

Structure of Actin-Binding Proteins: Insights about Function at Atomic Resolution, T. D. Pollard, S. Almo, S. Quirk, V. Vinson, and E. E. Lattman

Receptor Protein-Tyrosine Kinases and Their Signal Transduction Pathways, P. van der Geer, T. Hunter, and R. A. Lindberg

Dyneins: Molecular Structure and Cellular Function, E. L. F. Holzbaur and R. Vallee

Cell Biology of the Amyloid β-Protein Precursor and the Mechanisms of Alzheimer's Disease, D. J. Selkoe

Structure, Regulation, and Function of NF-κB, U. Siebenlist, G. Franzoso, and K. Brown

viii   (*continued*)

From the *Annual Review of Genetics*, Volume 28 (1994):

Dynamic RNA-RNA Interactions in the Spliceosome, H. D. Madhani and C. Guthrie

Germline p53 Mutations and Heritable Cancer, D. Malkin

Genetic Variability of the Human Immunodeficiency Virus: Statistical and Biological Issues, F. Seillier-Moiseiwitsch, B. Margolin, and R. Swanstrom

The Effects of Inbreeding on Forensic Calculations, B. S. Weir

From the *Annual Review of Microbiology*, Volume 49 (1995):

Polyketide Synthase Gene Manipulation: A Structure-Function Approach in Engineering Novel Antibiotics, C. R. Hutchinson and I. Fujii

Prospects for New Interventions to Treatment and Prevention of Mycobacterial Disease, D. B. Young and K. Duncan

Biocatalytic Syntheses of Aromatics from D-Glucose Renewable Microbial Sources of Aromatic Compounds, J. W. Frost and K. M. Draths

Discovery, Biosynthesis, and Mechanism of Action of the Zaragozic Acids: Potent Inhibitors of Squalene Synthetases, J. D. Bergstrom, C. Dufresne, G. F. Bills, M. Nallin-Omstead, and K. Byrne

Microbiology to 10,500 Meters of the Deep Sea, A. A. Yayanos

From the *Annual Review of Pharmacology and Toxicology*, Volume 35 (1995):

Structural Basis of Selective Cytochrome P450 Inhibition, J.R. Halpert

Nitric Oxide in the Nervous System, J. Zhang and S. H. Snyder

Molecular Strategies for Therapy of Cystic Fibrosis, J. A. Wagner, A. C. Chao, and P. Gardner

Relationships Between Lead-Induced Learning Impairments and Changes in Dopaminergic, Cholinergic, and Glutamergic Neurotransmitter System Functions, D. A. Cory-Slechta

Adenosine Receptor Subtypes: Characterization and Therapeutic Regulation, M. E. Olah and G. L. Stiles

Antagonists of Neuronal Calcium Channels: Structure, Function, and Therapeutic Implications, G. P. Miljanich and J. Ramachandran

From the *Annual Review of Physical Chemistry*, Volume 45 (1994):

Ab Initio Studies of Hydrogen Bonds: The Water Dimer Paradigm, S. Scheiner

Surface Photochemistry, X.-Y. Zhu

Orientation and Alignment of Reaction Products, A. J. Orr-Ewing
and R. N. Zare

Ab Initio Molecular Electronic Structure on Parallel Computers,
R. J. Harrison and R. Shepard

Solid-State NMR Structural Studies of Proteins, S. J. Opella

From the *Annual Review of Physiology*, Volume 57 (1995):

Proteins and Temperature, G. N. Somero

The Evolution of Endothermy in Mammals and Birds: From Physiology to Fossils, J. Ruben

Review of Mechanosensitive Channels, J. Sackin

Molecular Pathology of the Skeletal Muscle Sodium Channel,
R. L. Barchi

The CFTR Chloride Channel of Mammalian Heart, D. C. Gadsby,
G. Nagel, and T.-C. Hwang

The Multifunctional Calcium/Calmodulin-Dependent Protein Kinase: From Form to Function, Andrew P. Braun and H. Schulman

The 5-HT₃ Receptor Channel, M. B. Jackson and J. L. Yakel

Mechanisms of Activation of Glutamate Receptors and the Time Course of Excitatory Synaptic Currents, B. Edmonds, A. J. Gibb,
and D. Colquhoun

Physiological Diversity of Nicotinic Acetylcholine Receptors Expressed by Vertebrate Neurons, D. S. McGehee and L. W. Role

In Defense of the Oral Cavity: Structure, Biosynthesis, and Function of Salivary Mucins, L. A. Tabak

The Hydrophobic Barrier Properties of Gastrointestinal Mucus,
L. M. Lichtenberger

Signal Transduction, Packaging, and Secretion of Mucins, G. Forstner

Mucin Biophysics, R. Bansil, E. Stanley, and J. T. LaMont

Nitric Oxide as a Neurotransmitter in Peripheral Nerves: Nature of Transmitter and Mechanism of Transmission, M. J. Rand and C. G. Li

Nitric Oxide Signaling in the Central Nervous System, J. Garthwaite and C. L. Boulton

Nitric Oxide Synthases: Properties and Catalytic Mechanism,
O. W. Griffith and D. J. Stuehr

For the convenience of readers, a detachable order form/envelope is bound into the back of this volume.

Ephraim Katchalski-
— Katzir

Annu. Rev. Biophys. Biomol. Struct. 1995. 24:1–29

MY LIFE IN AND BEYOND THE LABORATORY

Ephraim Katchalski-Katzir

Department of Membrane Research and Biophysics, Weizmann Institute of Science, Rehovot 76100, Israel

KEY WORDS: autobiographical sketch

CONTENTS

ABSTRACT

Ephraim Katchalski-Katzir grew up in Israel at a time when the State was coming into being, and like many of those of his generation, participated in its creation and defense. He received his scientific education at the Hebrew University of Jerusalem and thereafter at the Polytechnic Institute of Brooklyn, Columbia University, and Harvard University. During and after the establishment of the State, he acted as scientific consultant to the defense leadership, and continued throughout his career to advise the Government of Israel on research and development. His public activities culminated in his election in 1973 as President of the State of Israel.

As one of the founders of the Weizmann Institute of Science, he headed the Department of Biophysics for many years. His research

1

1056-8700/95/0610-0001$05.00

included the study of poly-α-amino acids as protein models, immobilized enzymes, and polymers as chemical reagents. He also carried out theoretical and experimental work on the determination of distance distributions and conformational fluctuations in proteins by nonradiative energy-transfer techniques.

Introduction

I was born in Kiev, in the Ukraine. In 1922, when I was six years old and my brother Aharon nine, the family emigrated to Palestine from Poland. Our first home was in Tel Aviv, then a tiny city taking shape on the sand dunes adjacent to ancient Jaffa. After a year we moved to Jerusalem, and Aharon and I went to the prestigious Gymnasium, where we were lucky enough to be taught by inspiring teachers. Both of us showed special aptitude for the natural sciences, and we decided to continue our studies at the newly established Hebrew University of Jerusalem on Mount Scopus.

Aharon entered the university with the first group of biology students in 1930. I started two years later and very soon realized that I wanted to spend my life in research and teaching. But in high school I had realized that, like all those of my generation, I would have to play my part in activities that had nothing to do with learning but were bound up with the national renaissance. Growing up in Palestine under the British mandate, and especially on the university campus, I was caught up in the ideological and political ferment of that time. Jews were returning to their ancient homeland after 2000 years, filled with the desire to build a democratic state in which we could determine our own future, revive our original language, and revitalize our culture. We were ready to forge a new society, which would be based on the principles of social justice defined by our biblical prophets and would offer a high quality of life enriched by fine moral and spiritual values. In this exhilarating atmosphere, we felt inspired to do our best, and we threw ourselves with great enthusiasm into activities aimed at fulfilling the Zionist dream.

The local Arab population, however, angered by the increasing Jewish presence and the progress in building, agriculture, and other enterprises, had resorted to terrorist attacks against the Jews. Clearly we had to protect ourselves, and this we did by joining the illegal Jewish defense organization, the *Haganah,* which later became the Israel Defense Forces.

Thus, while still a student, I already had quite a clear idea of my goals in life. As well as attempting to do some original research, I felt that I must play my part in raising a new generation of Israeli scientists and help create the physical and intellectual conditions in which science and technology could flourish in this region. I would also do what I could to help establish the State of Israel and to contribute to its security and its social and economic development. I have been lucky enough to spend my life in pursuit of these goals, with some success and considerable satisfaction. In 1973, I became the fourth President of the State of Israel. After serving in this capacity for five years, I was happy to return to my first love, scientific research, and to take up again my work at the Weizmann Institute of Science and embark on new activities at Tel Aviv University.

Not many of my scientific colleagues, I think, have lived through the birth pangs of a new state, or felt the need to throw themselves into a wide range of operations in the national interest, or served as their country's president. Perhaps I may therefore be excused if, while describing my scientific activities, I also give some account here of my life outside science. As this brief survey indicates, I have participated fully, and with great satisfaction, in the most significant areas of life in my country. At the same time, while I have come up against almost insurmountable difficulties, I have been fortunate enough to derive enormous pleasure and fulfillment from my chosen path of research and teaching in the life sciences.

Study and Work at the Hebrew University of Jerusalem

The international tone of Israeli scientific endeavor was set in the early years of the Hebrew University by the excellent teachers, some of them world-famous scientists, who had made their way to Palestine from the great centers of learning in England, Europe, and the United States. After years of solitary research before regular teaching activities started at the university, they were delighted that at last they had someone to teach. We were a small group of students, and they treated us as their friends and future scientific heirs, as they did their best to endow us with all their accumulated knowledge. Professors and students roamed the country together, exploring and recording its flora and fauna, geology, water, and mineral resources.

Our mathematics teacher was Binyamin Amira, who set up the Institute of Mathematics at the university and grew roses in his spare time. Shimon Samburski, professor of physics, gave lectures of extraordinary lucidity. Moshe Weizmann, Chaim Weizmann's younger brother, taught us organic chemistry. I remember him as a rather eccentric character, with an unfortunate tendency to let things slip out of his fingers. We took to hiding the glass utensils, which in those days were hard to replace. Leo Picard, who taught us geology and paleontology, introduced me to a completely new field of knowledge. I remember his handing me a book in English, with instructions to be ready to discuss it with him after two weeks. I had to study day and night, but in the end I had a good idea of English and the geology of the Dead Sea.

A teacher I admired greatly was the Romanian botanist Tchorna Reiss. She used to write her lectures in English and I translated them into Hebrew for her. I remember going with her to Lake Huleh to study its plankton, which I described in my first scientific publication. Alexander Eig, head of the Department of Botany, unlike our other teachers, had not studied at a European center of learning, but was instead self-taught. He was a splendid botanical ecologist with an astonishing knowledge of the plants of Israel. He would take us into the Judean Desert on long field trips, pointing out plant societies and describing their struggles against each other for survival. My second scientific paper, written together with my friend Gideon Orshan, was on plants in the Judean Desert.

Michael Evenari introduced us to a new field of study, plant physiology. Both Aharon and I were enthralled by the subject. Gladly putting aside classification and collection and memorization of details, we tried instead to fathom the secrets of biological processes and the physical and chemical mechanisms that cause them. We also became close friends of the zoologist Shimon Bodenheimer, with whom Aharon wrote in Hebrew a small book about the butterflies of Israel, called *Children of the Sun*. I can still remember my brother running after butterflies and hardly ever catching one.

I soon found myself under the spell of the biological sciences, with botany, zoology, and bacteriology as my major subjects. I was enchanted by the beauty and complexity of living organisms and the intricate ways in which they function. In trying to understand their behavior, however, I soon realized that I would first have to learn chemistry, physics, and mathematics, and so I spent some years in the study of the exact sciences before returning to living organisms. Here my interest was attracted by the large molecules, the macromolecules of the cell, which play a most important role in determining life processes. I was fascinated by the lectures of my biochemistry professor, Andor Fodor, who introduced me to the world of biopolymers. It was particularly intriguing to realize that proteins not only constitute the basic building blocks of elaborate cellular structures, but also act as molecular machines that carry out a multitude of complex reactions within cells and tissues.

The research for my MSc and PhD degrees was done in the Department of Theoretical and Macromolecular Chemistry, headed by the late

Max Frankel. Aharon was by then Frankel's laboratory assistant and was using potentiometric techniques to investigate the interaction of amino acids and peptides with aldehydes and sugars. Understandably, he persuaded me that for my master's thesis I should prepare salt-free basic trifunctional amino acids and investigate their electrochemical properties. These amino acids were not available on the market, so I had to prepare them from red blood cells. For about a year I collected blood from the slaughterhouse, separated and hydrolyzed the red cells, and isolated the basic amino acids lysine, arginine, and histidine from the hydrolysate by means of an elaborate electrophoretic technique. I needed amino acids for my doctoral research as well and was greatly relieved to discover that purchasing them had become possible. But they were expensive, and Prof. Frankel kept a watchful eye on the supplies. Aharon and I overcame this obstacle by quietly emptying the bottles and refilling them with talcum powder. Years later, when I was working at the Weizmann Institute, rumors reached me of an uproar at the Hebrew University—Frankel's amino acids were no longer dissolving in water!

We also kept a low profile regarding our activity with the *Haganah*. I became an officer in this underground organization and for a while commanded a field unit, but was mainly involved, with Aharon and others, in the establishment of the scientific research team that later became the Israeli army's research and development unit. At night we would sneak into the laboratory and manufacture various materials, including tear gas. Occasionally traces of our labors lingered until morning, and sometimes even Frankel himself would shed a tear without knowing why. From our acquaintance with him we knew that he would not take kindly to the underground use of the laboratory, and we preferred not to burden him with our secret. Thus, we had to be doubly secretive about *Haganah* affairs, keeping our activities from the British on the one hand and from the university authorities on the other.

One of the most useful books I came across during my graduate studies was *Proteins, Amino Acids and Peptides,* by Cohn & Edsall (6a), which made me realize that in order to know something about proteins, I would first need to understand the structure and properties, in the solid state and in solution, of various high-molecular-weight polypeptides. Because we were working in a department of macromolecular chemistry, Aharon and I decided to acquaint ourselves with the theoretical and practical information available on synthetic and native polymers, about which we knew very little. We spent many pleasant hours together in a small grove of trees outside the laboratory, poring over whatever articles on polymer chemistry we could lay our hands on, and soon we could practically recite by heart the pioneer works of Hermann Staudinger, Herman Mark, Kurt Meyer, and Paul Flory. Within a year we became the experts on macromolecules in Palestine, and within another year or two found ourselves leading the field in the Middle East. However, we felt completely isolated from the mainstream of scientific activity in Europe and the US. Naturally there was a certain satisfaction in having one's own theories uncontaminated by those of others, but this feeling was rapidly superseded by the need to exchange ideas with colleagues working in related areas.

Staudinger, Meyer, and others had suggested that synthetic high-molecular-weight compounds might serve as useful models in the study of biopolymers. This idea caught my attention. I thought if I could prepare synthetic high-molecular-weight polypeptides consisting of a single or a few amino acid residues, a study of their properties might contribute to the elucidation of the structure-function relationships in proteins. This seemed worth a try.

At the start, I believed it would be possible to prepare amino acid polymers by polymerizing the corresponding amino acid esters. Although I had some success in synthesizing polyglycine and poly-L-alanine by this technique (11, 12), I soon realized that amino acid esters, both in the solid state and in solution, tend to yield diketopiperazines rather than polyamino acids. While perusing the literature in search of a more suitable monomer, I came across Abderhalden's Handbook (1), which contained a description of the work of Leuchs carried out in 1908. After synthesizing N-carboxyglycine anhydride by cyclization of N-carbomethoxyglycyl chloride, Leuchs had found that N-carboxy-glycine-anhydride readily gives off carbon dioxide to yield what he called an anhydroglycine. Suspecting that this product was in fact a linear polyamino acid, I decided to synthesize some additional N-carboxy-α-amino acid anhydrides, study their polymerization, and characterize the corresponding amino acid polymers obtained. As I was particularly interested in preparing a high-molecular-weight, water-soluble polyamino acid, I decided to start with the synthesis of poly-L-lysine. This polypeptide was finally obtained by polymerization of ϵ,N-carbo-benzyloxy-α,N-carboxy-L-lysine anhydride to yield poly-ϵ,N-carbobe-nzyloxy-L-lysine, after removal of the protecting group by suitable means (36, 37). Removal of the protecting group was extremely difficult, and after many attempts I discovered, together with my first PhD student, Izhak Grossfeld, that it could be done with PH_4I. At first we assumed that the benzyl groups of the benzyloxycarbonyl residue are reduced by the liberated PH_3; however, because all of us wept copiously during synthesis, we realized that benzyl iodide was evolving as a result of the HI liberated. Many years later, these findings led Arieh Berger and Dov Ben Ishai in my laboratory at the Weizmann Institute to develop the classic technique for removal of the benzyloxycarbonyl-protecting groups with HBr in glacial acetic acid.

When we sent in our first paper on the synthesis of poly-L-lysine to the *Journal of the American Chemical Society,* it was rejected by the editor, who was not convinced that a polymer had actually been produced. More hard work in the laboratory yielded evidence that persuaded even the most skeptical editor that what we had was indeed a high-molecular-weight, water-soluble polymer of L-lysine. I felt wonderful that we now had our model, which we would be able to use to understand the properties of some of the basic proteins, such as protamines and histones. The technique we developed opened the way for the preparation of linear homopolymers of other bi- and trifunctional amino acids, in which the steric configuration of the amino acid monomer was always retained during polymerization.

Transfer to the Weizmann Institute of Science

In the meantime, our work at the Hebrew University was coming to an end, as our proposed research budgets, each amounting to about $30 a year, were beyond the means of the university's treasury. Both Aharon and I were therefore in a receptive mood when Chaim Weizmann, the distinguished organic chemist who in 1948 became the first President of the State of Israel, invited us in 1946 to join the academic staff of a new scientific center to be named after him.

The planning committee of the new Weizmann Institute of Science was headed by Herman Mark, who in 1947 invited me to spend some time in his world-famous Polymer Center at the Polytechnic Institute of Brooklyn. On the way to Brooklyn, I took the opportunity to spend a couple of months at Columbia University, where the eminent biochemist David Rittenberg, himself a member of the planning committee of the Weizmann Institute, had offered to act as my mentor. From him I learned the new techniques in which isotopically labeled compounds are used to identify and characterize intermediate metabolites. Rittenberg was aware of my work on poly-L-lysine and drew my attention to a recently published short note by Robert Woodward and CM Schramm in the *Journal of the American Chemical Society* (74), describing the synthesis of a copolymer of L-leucine and DL-phenylalanine by copolymerization of the corresponding N-carboxyamino acid anhydrides in benzene. Because of the extremely high viscosity of the resulting solution, Woodward & Schramm had assumed that their copolymer was of extremely high molecular weight, within the limits

1,000,000–15,000,000. When I got hold of their solution, I realized that the authors had erred in their conclusion, as addition of a few drops of formic acid dramatically reduced the viscosity of their polymer in benzene solution. The apparent high viscosity was therefore the result of polypeptide association. This short publication, "Synthesis of protein analogs," nevertheless gave me considerable satisfaction, as the title clearly showed that Woodward & Schramm thought, just as I did, that poly-α-amino acids would be useful as simple high-molecular-weight models for proteins.

At Columbia and Brooklyn I had my first encounters with well-equipped scientific laboratories, and they were indeed splendid places in which to become acquainted with the new theoretical and experimental developments in polymer science. My teachers at Brooklyn were Herman Mark himself, Fred Eirich, and Turner Alfrey. With their help, and thanks to the tools that were placed at my disposal, I showed conclusively, together with my student and collaborator Pnina Spitnik-Elson, that the high-molecular-weight compounds I had synthesized in Jerusalem were in fact amino acid homopolymers.

Herman Mark organized the purchase of the first sophisticated scientific equipment for the Weizmann Institute—an ultracentrifuge, an electron microscope, an electrophoretic apparatus, and an X-ray diffractometer. Palestine at that time (1947) was in turmoil, with the British preparing to leave and our leaders girding themselves for the declaration of the State of Israel. Rather than risk shipping our precious hardware to Rehovot, Mark had it temporarily installed in the laboratories at Brooklyn. He even suggested running the Weizmann Institute as part of the Brooklyn Polytechnic until things settled down, an offer I naturally declined, and within a short time the equipment and I were home in Rehovot.

This was at the beginning of May 1948. Most of my colleagues were by now involved in intensive on-campus research and development activities for the *Haganah*. Other types of research were virtually at a standstill. Aharon and I threw ourselves into whatever had to be done, drawing on all our professional expertise to assist in the defense of the new state. It was painfully clear to all of us that, much as we might aspire to careers in basic research, survival was the first necessity.

The State of Israel was established on May 14, 1948. On the same day, the new State was invaded by five Arab armies and found itself fighting for its existence. I was put in charge of the Israeli army's science corps, and until the end of the war we carried out military research, laying the foundations for *Hemed,* the army's scientific defense unit. With most of the scientists at the Institute in uniform, we felt we were racing against the clock. Day and night the laboratories were in use, and the formerly tranquil campus resounded with the test explosions of new weapons. What we lacked in arms experience we made up for in motivation and a talent for innovation, and this work prepared the way for Israel's future defense industry. The physicists among us—Saul Meiboom, Ephraim Frei, Gideon Yekutieli, and others—helped to develop rockets and electronic systems, while the chemists, including David Vofsi, Yehuda Mazur, Felix Bergmann, and Israel Dostrovsky, worked on the development of modern explosives and propellants. At the same time, because some of the American scientists who were supposed to take charge of departments at the Institute were jittery about coming to Israel, Aharon was asked to be temporary head of the Department of Polymers and I was made acting head of the Department of Biophysics. These two appointments soon became permanent.

Shortly afterwards, in 1951, at the invitation of John Edsall, I first came to Harvard University and its Medical School as a Visiting Scientist and have maintained close contacts with my colleagues there ever since. The department at that time was headed by Edwin Cohn. It took a while, I remember, to become familiar with the Harvard scene and style. After some months, having acquired the courage to come up with my own proposals for research, I would talk them over with John Edsall, who unfailingly encouraged my efforts. Next I would call on Larry Oncley, who unfailingly discouraged them: he would assure me that my ideas could not work, or had already been tried without success. My next sounding-board was Edwin Cohn, who would enthusiastically collar me and deliver lengthy monologues on his own projects. At Harvard I established lasting friendships with Elkan Blout, Paul Doty, Bob Woodward, and Konrad Bloch, all of whom encouraged me to continue with my original research and offered useful critical comments.

Poly-α-Amino Acids as the Simplest Protein Models

Once I had settled into my new quarters at the Weizmann Institute, I continued to extend my work on polyamino acids as protein models. With my colleagues and students I synthesized several other polyamino acids (39) including poly-L-arginine (45), poly-L-histidine (55), poly-L-aspartic acid (3), poly-L-tyrosine (38), poly-L-serine (5, 50), poly-L-cysteine (59), poly-L-proline (4), and poly-L-hydroxyproline (49). We also synthesized amino acid copolymers and multichain polyamino acids (62, 64); in the latter, a suitable polypeptide backbone, such as polylysine, serves for the attachment of several polypeptide chains, resulting in branched macromolecules.

By this time, numerous other groups were also preparing polyamino acids and studying their properties. Within two decades, the 1950s and 1960s, it was possible to clarify the mechanism and kinetics of polymerization of N-carboxyamino acid anhydrides (7, 40), determine the α-helical conformation of some of the polyamino acids in the solid state and in solution (39), detect β-parallel and antiparallel pleated sheets of polyamino acids, and induce helix-coil transitions in the solid state and in solution under appropriate conditions (31). Collaboration between experimentalists and theoreticians facilitated the successful correlation of the macromolecular conformations of polyamino acids in solution with their hydrodynamic properties, optical properties, dipole moments, and nuclear magnetic properties (33, 46, 52, 72).

I was particularly intrigued by the behavior of poly-L-proline in solution (34, 72). Hydrodynamic and optical rotatory studies showed that poly-L-proline can attain two different macromolecular forms in solution. Form I ($[\alpha]D \approx -50°$), which is stabilized in poor solvents such as pyridine and aliphatic alcohols, is characterized by a right-handed helix with all peptide bonds in the *cis* configuration. Form II ($[\alpha]D \approx -540°$), which is stabilized in good solvents such as formic acid and water, is a left-handed helix with all peptide bonds in the *trans* configuration. A series of acid-catalyzed *cis-trans* isomerizations of peptide bonds cause the transformation of the poly-L-proline I helix into the poly-L-proline II helix and vice versa. Because collagen contains a high percentage of proline, finding that the X-ray diffraction spacing of poly-L-proline II and of stretched collagen shows striking similarity was particularly gratifying (8, 61). The predicted conformations for polyglycine II and poly-L-proline II were very useful in the derivation of the structure of collagen by Ramachandran & Kartha (56) and Rich & Crick (57), who proposed that collagen fibers consist of three polypeptide chains of the polyglycine II and poly-L-proline II type coiled about each other in a triple-stranded rope. Our group found that an ordered sequence polymer of the structure H(Pro·Gly·Pro)$_n$OH forms, in the solid state and in solution, a collagen triple helix (9) and thereby proved that the replacement of every third proline residue in poly-L-proline with a glycine residue, leading to the appearance of a CONH group per tripeptide unit, is sufficient to stabilize a collagen-like structure.

In Rehovot, I also investigated the biological properties of polyamino acids (32, 63). To my delight, poly-L-lysine and other homopolyamino acids and amino acid copolymers turned out to be excellent models for investigation of the mechanism of enzymatic protein hydrolysis and transpeptidation. Much of this work was done in the late 1940s. I still remember the excitement with which I followed the rapid hydrolysis of poly-L-lysine by trypsin, using the cumbersome old Van Slyke apparatus. We showed that the specificity of an enzyme acting on a high-molecular-weight polypeptide is often strikingly different from that observed in the presence of low-molecular-weight peptides. Partial hydrolysis of poly-L-lysine yields, as expected, a mixture of lysine oligomers. These were separated chromatographically and investigated immunologically by my former student Arieh Yaron, in Herb Sober's laboratory at the US National Institutes of Health (75, 77). Uptake of these oligomers by *Escherichia coli* was studied by Charles Gilvarg of Princeton University, then a visiting scientist at the Weizmann Institute (16). By using a lysineless mutant of *E. coli*, Gilvarg showed that *E. coli* readily takes up all oligomers up to tetralysine, but no higher, and that these oligomers permit growth of the lysine auxotroph.

In our experiments with a prolineless mutant of *E. coli*, my coworker Sara Sarid observed that the organism can grow on a synthetic medium in which poly-L-proline is substituted for L-proline (60). Clearly, the polymer was being hydrolyzed by an unknown enzyme. Further investigations by Arieh Yaron of the cleavage of various synthetic proline-containing oligo- and polypeptides (76) led to the identification and characterization of a novel enzyme, amino-peptidase P, which subsequent studies showed to be present in other prokaryotes and in eukaryotes.

Poly-L-lysine itself found many additional applications both in our department and in other laboratories. Together with Chana Shalitin, I showed, for example, that poly-L-lysine inhibits multiplication of bacteriophages (66, 67), apparently by interaction with the phage DNA. Earlier, in collaboration with Leah Bichowsky-Slomnicky and Ben Volcani (35), I used polylysine and other polypeptides to investigate the surface charge and agglutination of bacteria, the mechanism of action on bacteria of antibiotic peptides such as gramicidin S, and the mechanism of blood clotting.

An important outgrowth of the studies on synthetic polyamino acids was the development in my laboratory of techniques for the preparation of polypeptidyl proteins (proteins to which polypeptide chains are covalently attached via amide bonds to the free amino groups of the protein). The synthesis of polytyrosyl gelatin and the demonstration that it is antigenic (65), in contrast to the unmodified protein, led in 1960 to the preparation by Michael Sela and Ruth Arnon, then in my department, of the first fully synthetic antigen. In this compound, tyrosine and glutamic acid residues are attached to a multi-poly-DL-alanyl poly-L-lysine. I vividly remember our immunological experiments, in which guinea pigs injected two or three times with polytyrosyl gelatin went into anaphylactic shock—a most unpleasant experience for the guinea pigs and a sobering demonstration to me of how careful one should be in treating living beings with synthetic or even native polymers. Nevertheless, the way was opened for the fundamental and extensive studies of Sela and his coworkers on the chemical and genetic basis of antigenicity. Some of the polypeptidyl enzymes we prepared retained full enzymatic activity. This finding was the basis for our subsequent preparation of a great variety of immobilized enzymes.

Knowledge of the properties of synthetic polypeptides played a decisive role in the work that led in 1961 to the cracking of the genetic code. In their first paper on the subject, Marshall Nirenberg & JH Matthei identified the poly-L-phenylalanine, produced enzymatically in a cell-free system in the presence of polyuridylate used as messenger, with the poly-L-phenylalanine we had synthesized in Rehovot in 1955. As it happens, Michael Sela was at the NIH when Nirenberg was working on the code, and he had informed Nirenberg that the normally insoluble poly-L-phenylalanine could be dissolved in acetic acid saturated with HBr. Soon afterward, Nirenberg & Ochoa identified other homo- and heteropolyamino acids as part of the effort to decipher the genetic code: Poly A was found to code for poly-L-lysine, poly-C for poly-L-proline, and poly-G for polyglycine.

Immobilized Enzymes

My interest in enzyme-polymer conjugates was aroused by the growing body of data indicating that many of the enzymes embedded in organelles or biological membranes within cells act as heterogeneous catalysts. I thought an interesting experiment would be to artificially immobilize enzymes and study their properties, especially their kinetic characteristics, under controlled conditions. Moreover, I felt that such immobilized enzymes could be utilized in the construction of novel enzyme reactors of use in the laboratory, the clinic, and industry.

My first paper on a water-insoluble enzyme was published in 1960 (2), when I described the preparation of a water-insoluble trypsin derivative and its use in a trypsin column. The method involved preparation of a polytyrosyl trypsin derivative containing tyrosyl peptide side chains by means of the polymerization of N-carboxy-L-tyrosine anhydride with trypsin (17) and coupling of the resulting water-soluble derivative with a diazotized copolymer of p-amino phenylalanine and leucine to yield the required water-insoluble trypsin. The trypsin column showed high activity towards benzoyl-L-arginine methyl ester, poly-L-lysine, and other well-known synthetic and native trypsin substrates. Of particular interest was the finding that the enzymatic activity of the water-insoluble trypsin remained practically unaltered in dilute HCl at 2°C. Immobilization prevented autodigestion, and blocking of the ε-amino groups of the enzyme led to a marked decrease in the number of peptide bonds susceptible to trypsin.

These encouraging results prompted us to prepare other immobilized enzymes (30) such as immobilized chymotrypsin (23), urease (58), papain (68), alkaline phosphatase (20), and carboxypeptidase (69), in each case by covalent binding of the enzyme via nonessential side groups to water-insoluble carriers.

Soon after our first experiments with immobilized enzymes, I developed a simple equation, based on the well-known Michaelis-Menten relation, describing the activity of an enzyme column (29). The product yield is, as expected, a function of enzyme and substrate concentrations, height of column, and rate of flow. This simple approach was soon superseded by a more careful analysis of the mode of action and kinetics of immobilized enzymes acting as heterogeneous catalysts, taking into account the rate of diffusion of substrate towards the catalyst, the rate of catalysis, and the diffusion of product from the catalyst into the surrounding medium (23).

Growing interest in immobilized enzymes led to the development by various groups of novel enzyme immobilization techniques in which enzymes were adsorbed or covalently bound to organic or inorganic carriers, or entrapped in gels, fibers, or microcapsules, and systems in which enzymes remained in solution but functioned in a limited space enclosed by an ultrafiltration membrane (6). In a novel enzyme immobilization technique that I developed together with my collaborators at Tel Aviv University's Biotechnology Center, immobilized monoclonal antibodies were used as carriers to combine with their corresponding enzyme antigen (70). With this technique, immobilization did not result in any loss of enzymatic activity.

Thus, we could, within a relatively short period, obtain a great variety of immobilized enzymes as well as enzyme reactors of various types (53), which opened the way for the use of immobilized enzymes in the food, pharmaceutical, and chemical industries.

Another aspect of my work in this field involved the preparation and study of enzymes immobilized in artificial membranes. In 1965, my collaborators and I succeeded in preparing a stable papain membrane on a collodion matrix by adsorbing papain on a collodion membrane and then cross-linking the papain with a cross-linking agent (22). The pH dependence of the enzyme membrane's activity on the concentration of the substrate benzoyl arginine ethyl ester differed from that of crystalline papain. This anomalous behavior was caused by lowering of the local pH within the membrane as a result of the release of acid by the enzymatic hydrolysis of the ester substrate. This latter finding showed that enzymatic reactions within a membrane, leading to accumulation of a product, might alter the environment in which the enzyme acts, and thus lead to an unexpected activity pattern. The availability of papain-collodion membranes enabled us to analyze in detail the kinetic behavior of enzymes immobilized in artificial membranes and calculate the concentrations of substrate and product within the various membrane regions (19, 21).

In attempting to elucidate the function of different carriers on the mode of action of enzymes, we observed that polyelectrolyte carriers markedly affect the pH activity profile of the enzymes to which they are attached (51). In the case of trypsin bound to a copolymer of maleic acid and ethylene, for example, at low ionic strength and with benzoyl-L-arginine ethyl ester serving as the substrate, the pH activity profile was displaced by approximately 2.5 pH units towards more alkaline pH values when compared with native trypsin under similar conditions. At high ionic strength, however, the pH activity curve of the polyelectrolyte-surrounded enzyme shifted to more acid pH values approaching the pH activity of the native enzyme. These findings could be explained in terms of the effect of the electrostatic potential of the polyelectrolyte carrier on the local concentration of H^+ ions in the microenvironment of the bound enzyme molecules. Obviously, then, the microenvironment surrounding an enzyme within an artificial or native membrane might strongly affect its mode of action (44).

In a theoretical analysis of the kinetic behavior of a two-enzyme membrane carrying out a consecutive set of reactions, we showed that, under suitable conditions, the rate of production of the end product at the first stage of the reaction is markedly higher for an immobilized enzyme system than that predicted for the corresponding homogeneous system (18).

The first industrial use of immobilized enzymes was reported in 1967 by Chibata and coworkers of the Tanabe Seiyaku Company in Japan, who developed columns of immobilized *Aspergillus oryzae* aminoacylase for the resolution of synthetic racemic DL-amino acids into the corresponding optically active enantiomers. Around 1970, two other immobilized systems were launched on a pilot plant scale. In England, immobilized penicillin acylase, also referred to as penicillin amidase, was used to prepare 6-amino-penicillanic acid from penicillin G or V, and in the US, immobilized glucose isomerase was used to convert glucose into fructose. These successful industrial applications prompted extensive research in enzyme technology, leading to a steady increase in the number of industrial processes based on sophisticated immobilized enzyme reactors.

The use of immobilized enzymes in industry is now well established (73). I still chuckle when I recall the comment of my good friend, the late Ernst Chain, who told me that I was wasting my time modifying pure, well-characterized enzymes and transforming them into heterogeneous catalysts of no use whatsoever. Happily, he was more successful as a scientist than as a prophet. The intermediate compound 6-amino penicillanic acid, which he employed in the preparation of the semisynthetic penicillin derivatives used as oral antibiotics, is now prepared worldwide by means of an immobilized enzyme process; its estimated production in 1992 was 7500 tons. In the same year, 15,000 tons of acrylamide were produced from acetonitrile by use of immobilized nitrile hydratase, and the production of high-fructose corn syrup from glucose by immobilized glucose isomerase reached 8 million tons (33a).

The Japanese were somewhat more appreciative of my efforts than Professor Chain. In 1985 I was awarded the first Japan Prize for my work on immobilized enzymes.

Polymers as Chemical Reagents

In preparing enzyme-polymer conjugates in which enzymes are bound covalently to polymeric carriers, one needs to prepare chemically active polymers. Not surprisingly, therefore, my group began to think about the possible use of polymers as chemical reagents. Polymers of the type P-A that contain the covalently bound group A, which readily reacts with a low-molecular-weight reagent B, can be used to synthesize compound A-B according to the equation:

$$P - A + B \rightarrow A - B + P.$$

At the end of the reaction the insoluble polymer can be removed by filtration or centrifugation. The filtrate should thus contain only A-B and unreacted B. The most suitable polymers P-A for use as chemical reagents contain relatively large amounts of A, are highly stable when stored, and possess appropriate mechanical properties. Furthermore, the reactivity of a polymer can be markedly modified by the introduction of suitable neighboring side chains.

To examine the possible use of chemically reactive polymers in acylation reactions, we prepared insoluble high-molecular-weight active polyesters of acetic acid and benzoic acid by allowing the corresponding chlorides to react with cross-linked poly-4-hydroxy-3-nitrostyrene. Treatment of the chemically reactive polymer with amines or carboxy-blocked peptides yielded the corresponding acetyl or benzoyl amides or peptide derivatives (13). The successful preparation of active esters of N-blocked amino acids of the above polymer type led to the development of a novel technique for peptide synthesis, enabling the high-yield synthesis of bradykinin and other linear and cyclic peptides (14, 15).

My student and collaborator Avraham Patchornik (54) further developed the use of polymers as chemical reagents. I have no doubt that in due course some of these chemically reactive polymers will be used extensively in organic synthesis.

Effect of Microenvironment on Enzyme Action

The availability of artificial membranes containing immobilized enzymes led us to consider the role of the microenvironment in determining the mode of action of enzymes that are immobilized, singly or as multienzyme complexes, within native or synthetic membranes. In analyzing the influence of the microenvironment on enzyme activity, one can distinguish between effects attributable to the matrix and effects resulting from the enzymatic reaction itself. Our observations in this connection were summarized in a detailed review (44). In considering the effects of various types of biological microenvironments, we took as our reference the model systems consisting of artificial well-characterized membranes in which enzymes are embedded.

Determination of Distance Distributions and Conformational Fluctuations by Nonradiative Energy-Transfer Techniques

As a polymer chemist, I was interested in the behavior of synthetic polymers in solution. Because many of the characteristics of linear polymer solutions are determined by their chain length and flexibility, I thought that partially ordered or flexible structures in peptides and globular proteins should also be described in terms of intramolecular distance distributions and rates of transitions and that these could be determined by a time-resolved long-range dynamic nonradiative energy transfer technique based on Förster's theory (10). First, with Izchak Steinberg, I analyzed the role of diffusion in nonradiative energy transfer as well as in fluorescence quenching and chemical reactions (71). Together with Elisha Haas, we then searched for model oligopeptides in which we could use the energy-transfer technique to determine the distribution of end-to-end distances as well as the Brownian motion of the ends of oligopeptide chains in solution. We synthesized a homologous series of oligopeptides, each consisting of four to nine N^5-(2-hydroxyethyl)-L-glutamine residues and containing at its ends a fluorescent donor and a fluorescent acceptor of electronic excitation energy. The chromophores naphthalene and dansyl, used as donor and acceptor, respectively, fulfilled the conditions necessary for energy transfer according to the Forster mechanism. The kinetics of fluorescence decay of the donor in a highly viscous glycerol solution enabled the derivation of the characteristic end-to-end distribution function between the donor and acceptor (26). Subsequent analysis of the fluorescence decay curves of these oligopeptides in solvents of low viscosity enabled the estimation of the apparent diffusion rate of the molecular ends relative to one another (25, 41).

The nonradiative energy-transfer technique was subsequently extended by Elisha Haas and his students to different proteins specifically labeled with a fluorescent donor and fluorescent acceptor, enabling them to determine intramolecular distances as well as intramolecular dynamics in various proteins such as pancreatic trypsin inhibitor (24) and phosphoglycerate kinase (27). Further theoretical and experimental developments have yielded new information on the denaturation and renaturation of proteins and can be expected to elucidate the mechanisms by which proteins fold during their biosynthesis on ribosomes, as well as the preferential folding of peptide hormones upon binding to their corresponding receptors.

Education and Teaching

As a scientist and a teacher, I have always thought it important to make young people aware of the achievements of modern science and technology and their relevance for everyday life. Early in my career I started to arrange for schoolchildren to meet each week on the university campus with scientists who shared their enthusiasm for experimental work and who often stimulated those young imaginations. This was the beginning of the move towards extramural scientific activities for children and youths. Over the years these programs have become an integral feature of all of Israel's institutes of higher learning, with the support of the Ministry of Education and the active participation of thousands of pupils and of the hundreds of PhD students who serve as instructors. At the Weizmann Institute, thanks to the devoted efforts of my friend, the late Amos de Shalit, an international science summer camp has become a prestigious annual event for scientifically gifted high school seniors, and a science village for schoolchildren was recently opened on campus.

My interest in popularizing science in Hebrew also led me to coedit, together with the late Shlomo Hestrin, one of the first Israeli popular science journals, *Mada,* on which a whole generation of youngsters was raised.

From the early 1950s, several unusually talented young men and women came to work with me and my group in the Department of Biophysics at the Weizmann Institute. Having received such inspiring guidance from my own teachers, and in view of my strong desire to help educate young Israeli scientists, I was more than ready to invest time and effort in nurturing these gifted young people. As a result, instead of concentrating strictly on my own specific research interest, I found myself moving in a number of directions, exploring different—though related—ideas with my students. My aim was to guide each of my students into an area that would enable him or her to tackle specific problems in my laboratory and eventually form independent research groups in which they could continue working on projects of their own. Some of my students went on to achieve remarkable success, which gave me enormous satisfaction. Our collaborations would often continue even after they had left my team and begun work in other disciplines. At one point, former students of mine headed no less than three scientific departments at the Weizmann Institute: Organic Chemistry (Avraham Patchornik), Chemical Immunology (Michael Sela), and Chemical Physics (Izchak Steinberg).

Aharon, My Brother

Of all those who have touched my life, the one who had the greatest personal influence on me was my brother. Aharon Katzir-Katchalsky was known to the world as a distinguished scientist. But to me he was my much-loved, much-admired, older brother—my closest friend and colleague, my guide and leader into the world of polymer research. The work we did together in Prof. Frankel's laboratory in the 1930s launched us on a scientific collaboration that continued for more than 30 years, until his untimely death at the hands of terrorists at Ben Gurion Airport in May, 1972.

Aharon's major scientific interest was in proteins and nucleic acids, and he devoted himself to elucidating the characteristic properties of these most important biopolymers. He developed new approaches to understanding the processes occurring in the living cell. His work on polyelectrolytes, nonequilibrium thermodynamics, and transport phenomena in living organisms, and his extension of network theory from the biological point of view are well known (47).

The scientific group established by Aharon at the Weizmann Institute won the esteem and admiration of scientists throughout the world. His colleagues in Israel and abroad were impressed by his strikingly original ideas and inspired by his enthusiasm and broad-mindedness. He sought to bridge the gap between scientific understanding and ethical insight. Fascinated by all living organisms, in particular by human beings, he believed that "the understanding of living organisms would provide man with a better understanding of himself" and that such understanding would "suggest relationships between human biology and ethical behavior."

After Aharon's death, a group of distinguished scientists from many parts of the world met at my home. We decided to set up a Center in his name, for the promotion of activities in physical biology, macromolecular science, and other scientific areas that fell within his wide-ranging interests. The Aharon Katzir-Katchalsky Center furthers international scientific cooperation through the organization of scientific meetings, lectures that emphasize the impact of scientific and technological advances on human society, and a program that helps young Israeli scientists participate in study courses given abroad. By involving myself in these activities, of which he would have thoroughly approved, I feel that I am continuing my dialogue with my brother.

Serving My Country as State President

As I became more involved in science, I increasingly felt that the academic community had a moral duty to participate in matters of public concern. Because of this sense of obligation, as well as my lifetime involvement with social activities in Israel, in 1966 I accepted the invitation of Prime Minister Levi Eshkol to head a committee charged with advising the government on the organization of its future activities in science and technology. An important result of our work was the appointment, in several government ministries, of Chief Scientists charged with promoting applied research in governmental institutions, in institutes of higher learning, and in industry itself. Our recommendations prompted a marked increase in cooperation between these three sectors. They also led to a dramatic increase in government spending on applied research, leading to a surge in innovative science-based activities, especially in industry and agriculture.

My ongoing involvement as an adviser in government-related activities included participation in various bodies, such as the National Councils for Education and for Research and Development, and a committee that recommended the legal framework covering the rights and obligations of engineers and technicians. In 1967, during the period that culminated in the Six Day War, I served as Chief Scientist of the Defense Ministry. In view of my close association with all sectors of Israel's government and its prime ministers in the course of the above activities,

I was not entirely surprised when Prime Minister Golda Meir approached me to stand for President. I was clearly being offered a unique opportunity to place whatever talents I might possess at the service of my country. In May, 1973, I became the fourth President of the State of Israel and embarked on one of the most interesting periods of my life.

The President is elected by the Knesset, Israel's parliament, for a five-year term. Israelis look to their President for moral rather than political leadership and choose an individual noted for intellectual activities rather than political experience. Running the country is the responsibility not of the President but of the prime minister and his/her cabinet. The President's function, on the other hand, is to represent the state and the people. He therefore serves, both at home and abroad, as a symbol of the State of Israel.

This description may suggest that being President is a rather pleasant pastime, not overly arduous, and requiring not much more than gracious behavior on official occasions. Nothing could be further from the truth. On becoming President, I frequently found myself thinking of my mentor, Chaim Weizmann. A visitor had once asked him how he spent his time as President, to which Weizmann had replied: "Oh, I'm kept very busy—I symbolize and symbolize all day long." I soon came to understand exactly what he had meant. Symbolizing the state means not only supporting it in its successes but also defending it in its failures. It means being a source of moral strength and inspiration, acting sometimes as a father figure and always as an example. It means raising the national morale in times of trouble. I found that symbolizing my country and representing its people was by no means an easy task.

In Israel, the President is relatively accessible to the public, and one of the most demanding—and satisfying—aspects of my office was my contact with hundreds of people from all walks of life who came to *Beit Hanassi*, the presidential residence, to share their ideas and feelings with their President. In the reception rooms, surrounded by the images and symbols of our ancient past and our national rebirth, people talked to me about the lives they wanted to lead, the country they hoped to build, and the state and society to which they would be proud to belong. They talked of their dreams of peace with our Arab neighbors and their hopes for tranquillity within our own borders, echoing the vision of the prophet Isaiah, whose words are inscribed on the frieze framing the ceiling of the President's study: "Nation shall not lift up sword against nation, neither shall they learn war any more."

My involvement, in the course of my presidential duties, with individuals and families in distress reaffirmed my belief in the power of the

President to act as a positive feature in the people's lives. A President who has the humanity and compassion to use his influence wisely may find the means of helping afflicted people in a way that could determine the future course of their lives. I should perhaps mention, however, that with all their esteem for the President, Israelis are not in the habit of indulging any self-importance the President might feel. I well remember being invited to address a lunch-time meeting of the Israel Association of Architects and Engineers, and asking the chairman how long I was expected to talk. "You're the President, sir," he replied. "You can talk for as long as you like. We're leaving at 2 o'clock."

When I accepted the presidential nomination, I realized that I would have to give up my scientific activities for a few years. As any scientist will appreciate, this sacrifice was quite difficult. I expected that I would miss my work in the laboratory, and my fears turned out to be fully justified. I kept up as far as possible with the literature and attended scientific meetings whenever they could be accommodated in my schedule. I also took advantage of my office to promote science and higher education. All too rarely my colleagues, presumably mindful of my other activities and reluctant to make demands on my time, would approach me to review a scientific article. To their astonishment they usually received my comments within a day or two, never realizing with what relish I had fallen upon the work.

Two of the most momentous events in Israel's modern history occurred when I was President. I refer to the Yom Kippur War and the visit of President Anwar Sadat of Egypt to Jerusalem. The first of these occurred six months after I entered office, and the second shortly before I left it, so that the period of my presidency was in one sense defined by those two events.

The Yom Kippur War started on October 6, 1973, when Egypt and Syria launched a surprise attack while Jews were at prayer on Yom Kippur, the holiest day in the Jewish calendar. From the military point of view, Israel gained an impressive victory, but at very great cost. We lost more than 2500 soldiers; many more were wounded and hundreds taken prisoner.

Towards the end of the war, Henry Kissinger appeared on the scene, attempting to mediate between Israel and Egypt, Syria, and Jordan. He covered a good deal of mileage during his trips back and forth between Sadat in Cairo, Assad in Damascus, Hussein in Amman, and Golda Meir in Jerusalem. Progress was slow and the discussions never-ending. I once asked Kissinger whether his earlier experience as a professor of political science at Harvard was of any use to him in his present role as mediator. "Most decidedly," he replied. "As a member of the university senate I often had to sort out differences between obstinate professors who had a talent for presenting an argument in the most lucid and convincing way." As an afterthought he added, "To tell the truth, compared with that my work in the Middle East is child's play."

It was not, however, until Anwar Sadat came to Jerusalem in November 1977 that the way was opened to peace with one of our erstwhile enemies. The visit came at very short notice and took us all by surprise. Its direct outcome was the peace treaty between Egypt and Israel, signed at Camp David in Washington on March 26, 1979. Twelve years passed before other Arab leaders were ready to follow Sadat's courageous example. The Madrid Peace Talks, held under the auspices of the US and Russia, and later the talks held in Oslo, raised a new spirit of optimism and hope for peace in the region. As a result of these talks, a peace agreement was finally signed in 1994 between the Prime Minister of Israel, Yitzhak Rabin, and the chairman of the Palestine Liberation Organization, Yasser Arafat, and autonomous rule was established, as a first step, in Gaza and Jericho. As I write, King Hussein of Jordan has declared his willingness to meet with the Israeli Prime Minister to negotiate peace. There is also hope of future negotiations with Syria. Thus it seems that the process started by the far-sighted Egyptian leader might lead in time to an enduring peace settlement and a new era of cooperation in the Middle East. Enormous potential benefits for the entire region can be expected to follow, given the advanced scientific and technical expertise of Israel, the vast natural resources of some of the Arab states, and the strong motivation of the Palestinian Arabs to improve the conditions of their lives. Thus, the vision of the early Zionist leaders, and our own dreams, may yet become a reality.

Back to Science

When my term of office ended, I was happy to return to the Weizmann Institute, where I enjoyed having the time to think, design research programs, and plan experiments. Also, after a break of some years, I felt ready to move on to new science-related projects. During my presidency I had decided that upon my return to the world of science I would give high priority to the promotion of biotechnological research in Israel. Accordingly, since 1978 I have divided my time between the Department of Biophysics at the Weizmann Institute and the Department of Biotechnology, which I set up at Tel Aviv University. In 1986 I headed a government-appointed committee for biotechnology, which presented some far-reaching recommendations aimed at promoting and supporting research and development in the rapidly growing fields of agricultural, marine, pharmaceutical, and industrial biotechnology.

Because of my conviction that Israel needs a large work force trained to operate in an increasingly high-tech labor market, I agreed to serve as World President of ORT, a Jewish organization established in Russia about 100 years ago as the Organization for Rehabilitation and Training, and today involved in large-scale vocational training at its schools in Israel and abroad. During my term of office, from 1985 to 1990, I helped to establish the first ORT international college in Israel at Carmiel, where young Israelis—Jews, Arabs, and Druze—live and study together with their counterparts from many countries. I am confident that the new college will turn out superbly trained technicians who are well able to take their place in a modern society. I have also involved myself in a move to introduce college education leading to a first degree in the liberal arts or the vocational disciplines. Students wishing to study further could then proceed to a university. Israel's universities are bursting at the seams, and a sensible solution would be to modify the higher-education infrastructure by restricting the universities to students particularly interested in research or especially well suited to creative academic life, while at the same time offering all high school graduates access to the highest educational level to which they may aspire.

Back in the laboratory, the focus of my own scientific interest was now on the factors determining the specificity of antibodies, enzymes, and receptors, and I succeeded in engaging the interest of some of my colleagues in the study of the mode of action of these proteins on a molecular level. Together we developed and used monoclonal antibodies to study protein conformation and conformational alterations, employed peptide libraries to identify peptides that bind to monoclonal antibodies and receptors, and used the findings of crystallographers and theoreticians to explore the interactions between different proteins.

Elucidation of the three-dimensional structure of antibodies and some of the antigen-antibody complexes assured me that it would soon be possible to understand, on a molecular level, interactions between a given antibody and the corresponding epitope on a protein antigen. Furthermore, one could reasonably assume that any conformational alteration occurring at such an epitope would be accompanied by a marked change in its characteristic binding to the corresponding monoclonal antibody (42). Our first observation that monoclonal antibodies can be used as macromolecular probes to detect conformational changes induced in proteins by heat or by adsorption onto solid supports was made at Tel Aviv University during a study of interactions of monoclonal antibodies with lactate dehydrogenase (28). Our group also investigated the interaction of monoclonal antibodies raised against native hen egg white lysozyme (HEL) with the enzyme after its partial reversible denaturation by heating (48). Here, too, the use of different monoclonal antibodies made it possible to demonstrate conformational changes in the enzyme upon heating.

Libraries of synthetic peptides, as well as those consisting of filamentous bacteriophages displaying peptides fused to the minor viral coat protein PIII, are useful tools in the identification of peptides that bind specifically to antibodies and receptors. I therefore decided, together with my collaborators at the Weizmann Institute, Sara Fuchs, Avner Yayon, and David Givol, to use a random phage epitope library in the search for peptides that inhibit the binding of basic fibroblast growth factor to its receptor (78) and the binding of antibody 5.5 to the nicotinic acetylcholine receptor (1a). We found well-characterized inhibitory hexapeptides in both cases. The hexapeptide (DLVWLL) detected in the case of monoclonal antibody 5.5 mimicked a conformation-dependent binding site of the acetylcholine receptor. Bioactivity of the peptide was demonstrated in vivo in hatched chickens by inhibition of the myasthenia gravis–like symptoms caused by injection of monoclonal antibody 5.5.

While continuing to utilize peptide libraries to elucidate the binding specificity of antibodies and receptors, I am trying to clarify the meaning of biological specificity on a molecular level. Some of my ideas on molecular recognition, and those of my colleagues Doron Lancet and Amnon Horovitz, are recorded in an article to be published shortly in a book commemorating the 100th anniversary of the formulation of Emil Fischer's lock-and-key theory. In that article we discuss the meaning of biological specificity as revealed by a single receptor as well as by systems comprised of a repertoire of receptors, the geometric fit between proteins and their ligands, and additivity and nonadditivity in protein-ligand interactions (49a).

A theoretical study of protein recognition reveals that the association of proteins with their ligands involves intricate inter- and intramolecular interactions, solvation effects, and conformational changes. Because of such complexity, we do not yet have a comprehensive and efficient way to predict the formation of protein-ligand complexes from the structure of their free components. With some assumptions, however, such predictions become feasible. One simplifying approach is based on geometric considerations. I was attracted to this approach, as the three-dimensional structure of most protein complexes reveals a close geometric match between contiguous parts of the protein and ligand surfaces. Indeed, the shape and other physical characteristics of the surfaces largely determine the nature of the specific molecular interactions in the complex. In many cases, the three-dimensional structure of the components in the complex closely resembles that of the molecules in their free, native state. Geometric matching thus seems to play an important role in determining the structure of a complex.

Together with my colleagues at the Weizmann Institute, I developed a geometrically based algorithm for predicting the structure of a possible complex between molecules of known structures. Our algorithm is relatively simple and straightforward and relies on the well-established correlation and Fourier transformation techniques used in the field of pattern recognition (43). The algorithm was tested and validated in analyses of the α-β hemoglobin dimer, tRNA synthetase-tyrosinyl adenylate, aspartic proteinase-peptide inhibitor, and trypsin-trypsin inhibitor. The correct relative positions of the complexes within these molecules were successfully predicted.

Concluding Remarks

Like all those of my generation who were a part of that sublime moment in Jewish history, the re-establishment of a Jewish homeland, I feel privileged not only to have witnessed the fulfillment of an ancient dream, but also to have played some part in making it a reality. At the same time, I have had the opportunity to devote much of my life to science. Few activities can be more rewarding than conducting research that leads to a better understanding of the phenomena of life and nature, and indeed my work in all its aspects—research, teaching, collaboration with colleagues, promotion of scientific activities—has brought me great personal fulfillment. Looking back over the years, I can see that my simple protein models, the poly-α-amino acids, have contributed to a better understanding of the secondary structure of proteins and were useful as the first fully synthetic antigens. My work on the transformation of enzymes into heterogeneous catalysts, the immobilized enzymes, has found extensive use in the pharmaceutical, chemical, and food industries. By extension of Förster's theory on nonradiative energy transfer, we were able to work out a way to measure relatively long distances between amino acid residues of a protein or peptide, as well as to determine conformational fluctuations in those molecules. Finally, monoclonal antibodies and peptide libraries continue to be employed as useful tools in the elucidation of protein specificity. If I add to this my contribution to the development of the Weizmann Institute and the establishment of the Biotechnology Center at

Tel Aviv University, my part in raising a new generation of life scientists, and my services as scientific adviser to the Government of Israel, I feel that I have not wasted my life.

Yet my participation over the years in activities outside science has taught me that there is life beyond the laboratory. I have come to understand that if we hope to build a better world, we must be guided by the universal human values that emphasize the kinship of the human race—the sanctity of human life and freedom, peace between nations, honesty and truthfulness, regard for the rights of others, and love of one's fellows.

Moreover, as a scientist I am keenly aware of the power of scientific tools and of their awesome potential both for the good of humankind and for its destruction. The rapid progress of science and technology will continue to raise complicated moral questions. There are no simple answers, and the choices we make will inevitably depend on what we value.

I am still working at the Weizmann Institute. It is here that I was guided, as a young man, by Chaim Weizmann, distinguished scientist and remarkable leader of his people. When he opened the first Knesset in 1949 as first President of the State, he expressed his philosophy in words that I, as fourth President, chose to repeat 24 years later in my own inaugural speech: "All my life I have labored to make science and research the basis of national endeavor, but I have always known full well that there are values higher than science. The only values that offer healing for the ills of humanity are the supreme values of justice and righteousness, peace and love."

Literature Cited

1. Abderhalden E. 1911. *Biochemisches Handlexikon,* Vol. 4. Berlin: Springer-Verlag. 421 pp.
1a. Balass M, Heldman Y, Cabilly S, Givol D, Katchalski-Katzir E, Fuchs S. 1993. Identification of a hexapeptide that mimics a conformation-dependent binding site of acetylcholine receptor by use of a phage-epitope library. *Proc. Natl. Acad. Sci. USA* 90: 10638–42

2. Bar-Eli A, Katchalski E. 1960. A water-insoluble trypsin derivative and its use as a trypsin column. *Nature* 188:856–57
3. Berger A, Katchalski E. 1951. Poly-L-aspartic acid. *J. Am. Chem. Soc.* 73: 4084–88
4. Berger A, Kurtz J, Katchalski E. 1954. Poly-L-proline. *J. Am. Chem. Soc.* 76: 5552–54
5. Bohak Z, Katchalski E. 1963. Synthe-

sis, characterization, and racemization of poly-L-serine. *Biochemistry* 2: 228–37

6. Chibata I, ed. 1978. *Immobilized Enzymes*. New York: Wiley & Sons

6a. Cohn EJ, Edsall JT. 1943. *Proteins, Amino Acids and Peptides. American Chemical Monograph Series*. New York: Reinhold

7. Coombes JD, Katchalski E. 1960. Theoretical analysis of the polymerization kinetics of *N*-carboxy-α-amino acid anhydrides. II. An amine initiated polymerization with a two-stage propagation. *J. Am. Chem. Soc.* 82: 5280–85

8. Cowan PM, McGavin S. 1955. Structure of poly-L-proline. *Nature* 176: 501–3

9. Engel J, Kurtz J, Katchalski E, Berger A. 1966. Polymers of tripeptides as collagen models. II. Conformational changes of poly(L-prolyl-glycyl-L-prolyl) in solution. *J. Mol. Biol.* 17: 255–72

10. Förster T. 1948. Zwischen Moloculare Energiewanderung und Fluoreszenz. *Ann. Phys. Leipzig* 2:55–75

11. Frankel M, Katchalski E. 1942. Poly-condensation of α-amino acid esters. I. Poly-condensation of glycine esters. *J. Am. Chem. Soc.* 64:2264–68

12. Frankel M, Katchalski E. 1942. Poly-condensation of α-amino acid esters. II. Poly-condensation of alanine ethyl ester. *J. Am. Chem. Soc.* 64:2268–71

13. Fridkin M, Patchornik A, Katchalski E. 1966. Use of polymers as chemical reagents. I. Preparation of peptides. *J. Am. Chem. Soc.* 88:3164–65

14. Fridkin M, Patchornik A, Katchalski E. 1968. Use of polymers as chemical reagents. II. Synthesis of bradykinin. *J. Am. Chem. Soc.* 90:2953–57

15. Fridkin M, Patchornik A, Katchalski E. 1972. Peptide synthesis by means of tert-butyloxcarbonylamino acid derivatives of poly(ethylene-co-*N*-hydroxymaleimide). *Biochemistry* 11: 466–71

16. Gilvarg C, Katchalski E. 1965. Peptide utilization in *E. coli*. *J. Biol. Chem.* 240:3093–98

17. Glazer AN, Bar-Eli A, Katchalski E. 1962. Preparation and characterization of polytyrosyl trypsin. *J. Biol. Chem.* 237:1832–38

18. Goldman R, Katchalski E. 1971. Kinetic behavior of a two-enzyme membrane carrying out a consecutive set of reactions. *J. Theor. Biol.* 32:243–57

19. Goldman R, Kedem O, Katchalski E. 1968. Papain-collodion membranes. II. Analysis of the kinetic behavior of enzymes immobilized in artificial membranes. *Biochemistry* 7:4518–31

20. Goldman R, Kedem O, Katchalski E. 1971. Kinetic behavior of alkaline phosphatase-collodion membranes. *Biochemistry* 10:165–72

21. Goldman R, Kedem O, Silman IH, Caplan SR, Katchalski E. 1968. Papain-collodion membranes. I. Preparation and properties. *Biochemistry* 7: 486–500

22. Goldman R, Silman HI, Caplan SR, Kedem O, Katchalski E. 1965. Papain membrane on a collodion matrix: preparation and enzymic behavior. *Science* 150:758–60

23. Goldstein L, Katchalski-Katzir E. 1976. Immobilized enzymes—a survey. In *Immobilized Enzyme Principles*, ed. LB Wingard Jr, E Katchalski-Katzir, L Goldstein, pp. 1–22. New York: Academic

24. Gottfried DS, Haas E. 1992. Nonlocal interactions stabilize compact folding intermediates in reduced unfolded bovine pancreatic trypsin inhibitor. *Biochemistry* 31:12353–62

25. Haas E, Katchalski-Katzir E, Steinberg IZ. 1978. Brownian motion of the ends of oligopeptide chains in solution as estimated by energy transfer between the chain ends. *Biopolymers* 17:11–31

26. Haas E, Wilchek M, Katchalski-Katzir E, Steinberg IZ. 1975. Distribution of end-to-end distances of oligopeptides in solution as estimated by energy transfer. *Proc. Natl. Acad. Sci. USA* 72:1807–11

27. Haran G, Haas E, Szpikowska BK, Mas MT. 1992. Domain motions in phosphoglycerate kinase: determination of interdomain distance distributions by site-specific labeling and time-resolved fluorescence energy transfer. *Proc. Natl. Acad. Sci. USA* 89: 11764–68

28. Hollander Z, Katchalski-Katzir E. 1986. Use of monoclonal antibodies to detect conformational alterations in lactate dehydrogenase isoenzyme 5 on heat denaturation and on absorption to polystyrene plates. *Mol. Immunol.* 23: 927–33

29. Katchalski E. 1962. Water-insoluble enzyme derivatives. Their preparation, properties and use in the study of native macromolecules. *Pontif. Accad. Sci. Scr. Varia* 22:97–107

30. Katchalski E. 1962. Preparation, properties and applications of some water-insoluble derivatives of proteolytic enzymes. In *Polyamino Acids, Polypeptides and Proteins*, ed. MA Stahmann, pp. 283–88. Madison: Univ. Wisconsin Press

31. Katchalski E. 1964. Polyamino acids as protein models. *Proc. Plenary Session Int. Congr. Biochem., 6th, New York*, pp. 80–106

32. Katchalski E. 1965. Use of poly-α-amino acids in biological studies. *Harvey Lect.* 59:243–72

33. Katchalski-Katzir E. 1974. Poly(-amino acids): achievements and prospects. In *Peptides, Polypeptides and Proteins*, ed. ER Blout, FA Bovey, M Goodman, N Lotan, pp. 1–13. New York: Wiley & Sons

33a. Katchalski-Katzir E. 1993. Immobilized enzymes—learning from past successes and failures. *Trends Biotechnol.* 11:471–78

34. Katchalski E, Berger A, Kurtz J. 1963. Behavior in solution of polypeptides related to collagen. *Proc. Int. Symp. Protein Structure and Crystallography, Madras*, pp. 205–39. London: Academic

35. Katchalski E, Bichowski-Slomnitzki L, Volcani BE. 1953. The action of some water-soluble poly-α-amino acids on bacteria. *Biochem. J.* 55:671–80

36. Katchalski E, Grossfeld I, Frankel M. 1947. Poly-lysine. *J. Am. Chem. Soc.* 69:2564–65

37. Katchalski E, Grossfeld I, Frankel M. 1948. Poly-condensation of α-amino acid derivatives. III. Poly-lysine. *J. Am. Chem. Soc.* 70:2094–2101

38. Katchalski E, Sela M. 1953. The synthesis and spectrophotometric study of poly-L-tyrosine and poly-3,5-diiodotyrosine. *J. Am. Chem. Soc.* 75:5284–89

39. Katchalski E, Sela M. 1958. Synthesis and chemical properties of poly-α-amino acids. *Adv. Protein Chem.* 13:243

40. Katchalski E, Shalitin Y, Gehatia M. 1955. Theoretical analysis of the polymerization kinetics of N-carboxy-α-amino acid anhydrides. *J. Am. Chem. Soc.* 77:1925–34

41. Katchalski-Katzir E, Haas E, Steinberg IZ. 1981. Study of conformation and intramolecular motility of polypeptides in solution by a novel fluorescence method. *Ann. N. Y. Acad. Sci.* 366:44–61

42. Katchalski-Katzir E, Kenett D. 1988. Use of monoclonal antibodies in the study of the conformation and conformational alterations in proteins. *Bull. Chem. Soc. Jpn.* 61:133–39

43. Katchalski-Katzir E, Shariv I, Eisenstein M, Friesem AA, Aflalo C, Vakser IA. 1992. Molecular surface recognition: determination of geometric fit between proteins and their ligands by correlation techniques. *Proc. Natl. Acad. Sci. USA* 89:2195–99

44. Katchalski E, Silman I, Goldman R. 1971. Effect of the microenvironment on the mode of action of immobilized enzymes. *Adv. Enzymol.* 34:445–536

45. Katchalski E, Spitnik P. 1949. Poly-arginine. *Nature* 164:1092–97

46. Katchalski E, Steinberg IZ. 1961. Proteins and synthetic polypeptides. *Annu. Rev. Phys. Chem.* 12:433–64

47. Katzir-Katchalsky A. 1976. *Selected Papers, Biophysics and Other Topics*. New York: Academic

48. Kenett D, Fleminger G, Katchalski-Katzir E. 1990. Use of monoclonal antibodies in the detection of structural alterations occurring in lysozyme on heating. *Mol. Immunol.* 27:1–6

49. Kurtz J, Fasman GD, Berger A, Katchalski E. 1958. Poly-hydroxy-L-proline. *J. Am. Chem. Soc.* 80:393–97

49a. Lancet D, Horovitz A, Katchalski-Katzir E. 1994. Molecular recognition in biology: models for analysis of protein/ligand interaction. In *100 Years of the Lock and Key Principle*, ed. JP Lehn. New York: Wiley & Sons. In press

50. Lapidot Y, Katchalski E. 1960. A phosphorylation product of poly-DL-serine. *Bull. Res. Counc. Israel* 9A:63

51. Levin Y, Pecht M, Goldstein L, Katchalski E. 1964. A water-insoluble polyanionic derivative of trypsin. I. Preparation and properties. *Biochemistry* 3:1905–13

52. Lotan N, Berger A, Katchalski E. 1972. Conformation and conformational transitions of poly-α-amino acids in solution. *Annu. Rev. Biochem.* 41:869–902

53. Mosbach K, ed. 1976, 1987, 1988. *Methods in Enzymology*, Vols. 44, 135B, 136C, 137D. New York: Academic

54. Patchornik A. 1982. (see letter by TH Maugh II) "Wolf and Lamb" chemistry. *Science* 217:719–20

55. Patchornik A, Berger A, Katchalski E. 1957. Poly-L-histidine. *J. Am. Chem. Soc.* 79:5227–30

56. Ramachandran GN, Kartha G. 1954. Structure of collagen. *Nature* 174: 269–70
57. Rich A, Crick FHC. 1955. The structure of collagen. *Nature* 176:915–16
58. Riesel E, Katchalski E. 1964. Preparation and properties of water-insoluble derivatives of urease. *J. Biol. Chem.* 239:1521–24
59. Sadeh T, Katchalski E. 1960. Poly-DL-homocysteine, preparation and properties. *Bull. Res. Counc. Israel* 9A:65
60. Sarid S, Berger A, Katchalski E. 1962. Proline iminopeptidase. II. Purification and comparison with iminodipeptidase (prolinase). *J. Biol. Chem.* 237: 2207–12
61. Sasisekharan V. 1959. Structure of poly-L-proline II. *Acta Crystallogr.* 12: 897–903
62. Sela M, Katchalski E. 1955. Branched polyamino acids. *Experientia* 11:62–66
63. Sela M, Katchalski E. 1959. Biological properties of poly-α-amino acids. *Adv. Protein Chem.* 14:391
64. Sela M, Katchalski E, Gehatia M. 1956. Multichain polyamino acids. *J. Am. Chem. Soc.* 78:746–51
65. Sela M, Katchalski E, Olitzki AL. 1956. Anaphylactic shock in guinea pigs sensitized to polytyrosylgelatin. *Science* 123:1129
66. Shalitin C, Danon D, Katchalski E. 1962. Inactivation of *E. coli* bacteriophage T2 by poly-L-lysine. I. Nature of the inactivation process. *Arch. Biochem. Biophys.* 99:494–507
67. Shalitin C, Katchalski E. 1962. Inactivation of *E. coli* bacteriophage T2 by poly-L-lysine. II. Properties of the irreversibly inactivated phage. *Arch. Biochem. Biophys.* 99:508–15
68. Silman IH, Albu-Weissenberg M, Katchalski E. 1966. Some water-insoluble papain derivatives. *Biopolymers* 4: 441–47
69. Solomon B, Koppel R, Katchalski-Katzir E. 1984. Use of a specific monoclonal antibody for the preparation of a highly active immobilized carboxypeptidase A. Research note. *Bio/Technology* 2:709–12
70. Solomon B, Koppel R, Pines G, Katchalski-Katzir E. 1986. Enzyme immobilization via monoclonal antibodies. I. Preparation of a highly active immobilized carboxypeptidase A. *Biotech. Bioeng.* 28:1213–21
71. Steinberg IZ, Katchalski E. 1968. Theoretical analysis of the role of diffusion in chemical reactions, fluorescence quenching and nonradiative energy transfer. *J. Chem. Phys.* 48: 2404–10
72. Steinberg IZ, Sela M, Harrington WF, Berger A, Katchalski E. 1960. The configurational changes of poly-L-proline in solution. *J. Am. Chem. Soc.* 82: 5263–79
73. Tanaka A, Tosa T, Kobayashi T, eds. 1993. *Industrial Application of Immobilized Enzymes.* New York: Marcel Dekker
74. Woodward R, Schramm CM. 1947. Synthesis of protein analogs. *J. Am. Chem. Soc.* 69:1551–52
75. Yaron A, Berger A, Katchalski E, Otey MC, Sober HA. 1964. Preparation and properties of oligolysyl-peptides. *Int. Congr. Biochem. 6th, New York,* p. 190 (Abstr.)
76. Yaron A, Naider F. 1993. Proline-dependent structural and biological properties of peptides and proteins. *Crit. Rev. Biochem. Mol. Biol.* 28(1):31–81
77. Yaron A, Otey MC, Sober HA, Katchalski E, Ehrlich-Rogozinski S, Berger A. 1972. Lysine oligopeptides. Preparation by ion-exchange chromatography. *Biopolymers* 11:607–21
78. Yayon A, Aviezer D, Safran M, Gross JL, Heldman Y, et al. 1993. Isolation of peptides that inhibit binding of basic fibroblast growth factor to its receptor from a random phage-epitope library. *Proc. Natl. Acad. Sci. USA* 90: 10643–47

Annu. Rev. Biophys. Biomol. Struct. 1995. 24:31–57

DESIGN OF MOLECULAR FUNCTION: Channels of Communication

M. Montal

Department of Biology, University of California San Diego, La Jolla,
California 92093-0357

KEY WORDS: de novo protein design, protein folding, membrane-
protein structure, ionic channels, neurotransmitter
receptors, lipid bilayers

CONTENTS

ABSTRACT

The ultimate goal in protein design is to elucidate the fundamental principles that determine structure. With increased understanding of the
molecular basis underlying the sequence-structure relationship may
come the ability to control it and, thereby, to generate proteins with

31

1056-8700/95/0610-0031$05.00

desired specifications. Channel proteins, which mediate cell signaling, are ideally suitable for protein design. Plausible molecular blueprints for the pore-forming structure are bundles of amphipathic α-helices or β-barrels that cluster together to generate a hydrophilic channel. This review focuses on the progress achieved to produce such designs and on the approximation of the synthetic channels to the targeted biological function.

$$* \quad * \quad *$$

The best material model for a cat is another, or preferably the same, cat.

A Rosenblueth &
N Weiner, 1945
(97a)

PERSPECTIVES AND OVERVIEW

Protein design has rapidly become a powerful strategy for the pursuit of the deterministic basis of the sequence-structure relationship. This overview of protein design emphasizes channel proteins, a superfamily of membrane proteins that mediate signaling between the cell and its environment as well as signaling inside the cell. The pore function can be analyzed at the level of single molecular events. However, as no resolved structure for any eukaryotic channel protein is available at the three-dimensional coordinate level, an understanding of the sequence-structure relationship is a challenge. Nevertheless, computational tools have been developed to model protein structure, and NMR spectroscopy has emerged as a technology to determine high-resolution structures of membrane proteins embedded in their bilayer environment. These advances provide an unparalleled opportunity to blend the individual strengths of channel biophysics and structural biophysics.

A central notion in channel-protein design is that, given the primary structure, one can identify functional modules that will fold predictably into stable structural motifs and that will fulfill the desired functional attributes of the authentic system, namely ionic selectivity and specific regulation of channel-open probability (71). A first step is to model only the inner pore-forming element, the most fundamental unit of function of all channel proteins. Bundles of amphipathic α-helices or β-barrels that cluster together to generate a hydrophilic channel can serve as plausible molecular blueprints for the pore-forming structure of channel proteins. The next level of complexity must consider the design of a minimum signal-gated channel that would exhibit the essential properties of ionic selectivity and regulation by transmembrane potential or ligand binding. A modular design envisions these functional units interacting with the fundamental pore structure in a predetermined arrangement, resulting in modulation. Accordingly, the diversity of channel proteins would be determined by sequence specificity, the combinatorial use of folding motifs representing functional modules, and ultimately the oligomeric or subunit organization of the assembly in the environment of the host lipid bilayer membrane. This hypothesis guides channel protein design (71).

Excellent reviews (8, 9, 12, 19, 51, 52, 59, 79, 80, 105) convey the excitement in the channel protein–structure field. There are also surveys of synthetic peptides designed to fold into amphiphilic helices that cluster into a bundle motif, but that are composed of amino acids that lack specific sequence relationships to authentic channels (2).

EVOLUTIONARY CONSERVATION AND SYMMETRY

The notion of a unifying structural motif in the biological design of channel proteins derives from the inferred structural organization; known channel proteins appear to have some fundamentally similar structures: They are symmetric assemblies organized around a central aqueous pore. Members of the superfamilies of channel proteins exhibit extensive amino acid–sequence similarity (8, 19, 51, 52, 59, 79, 80). The possibility that eukaryotic channel proteins evolved from a bacterial ancestor is supported by the recent identification of bacterial homologues of K^+ (69) and mechanosensory channels (109). Similarly, the structural motifs of bacterial membrane proteins may be conserved in eukaryotic homologues. Bacteriorhodopsin (43) and the bacterial photosynthetic reaction centers (24) are bundles of transmembrane α-helices, whereas bacterial porins (22, 120) and the toxin aerolysin (89) are β-barrels. Accordingly, ion channels may be organized as an array of transmembrane α-helices or β-sheets, or as combinations thereof arranged such that amphipathic secondary-structure elements generate a central, hydrophilic pore, while hydrophobic peptide segments surround this inner bundle, serving as an interface with the apolar environment of the membrane. The fact that structural motifs recur in many proteins even though the sequences vary widely led us (51, 71) to surmise that channel proteins are assembled by the combination of individual folding motifs and that these motifs represent specific functional modules of the protein.

THE M2 SEGMENT OF NEUROTRANSMITTER-GATED CHANNELS AS A FOLDING MOTIF AND A FUNCTIONAL MODULE

Among the most extensively investigated channel proteins are those involved in the process of synaptic communication in the nervous system. The superfamily of ionotropic neurotransmitter receptors encompasses receptors (R) for acetylcholine (ACh), the paradigmatic ligand-gated channel; glycine (Gly), the major inhibitory transmitter in spinal cord; and glutamate (Glu), the major excitatory transmitter in the central nervous system (CNS). Nicotinic AChR and GlyR are prototypes of cation-selective and anion-selective ligand-gated channels, respectively. Models for the folding of all these receptor proteins suggest a canonical structure consisting of (a) a large and diverse N-terminal domain, which presumably contains the ligand-binding site and is exposed to the extracellular surface; (b) a transmembrane domain composed of four transmembrane segments, M1–M4, with a long loop connecting M3 and M4 that contains consensus sequences for protein phosphorylation, thereby restricting its location to the cytosol; and (c) a variable C-terminal domain that is presumably constrained to the extracellular face. The transmembrane domain shows high sequence similarity (8, 19, 52, 59, 79, 80).

A remarkable demonstration of the occurrence of independent functional domains was obtained by constructing recombinant chimeras in which the N-terminal domain of the α_7 AChR, which contains the ligand-binding site, was complemented with the C-terminal domain of the serotonin receptor, containing the transmembrane domain. The serotonergic receptor is blocked by Ca^{2+}, whereas the α_7 AChR is permeable to Ca^{2+}. The chimeric receptors were activated by nicotinic ligands but blocked by Ca^{2+}, as expected for a functional coupling of two independent domains (27). The information collected from a variety of approaches is beginning to converge into a proposed pore-forming structure in which the M2 segment is a plausible constituent of the module that lines the pore.

The Acetylcholine Receptor

The AChR from *Torpedo californica* is a pentameric glycoprotein ($M_r \approx 250,000$) with a stoichiometry of $\alpha_2\beta\gamma\delta$, assembled around a cation-conducting pore (19, 52, 59), and that has an effective pore diameter ≤ 7 Å (54a, 116). Theoretical and permeation studies suggest that the vestibules contain a net negative charge, whereas the pore is presumed to be lined with polar, uncharged residues (19, 59, 87). Labeling of the channel with noncompetitive inhibitors such as chlorpromazine (32) and triphenylmethylphosphonium (81) permitted the identification of Ser262 in M2 of the δ subunit (sequence EKMSTAISVLLA-QAVFLLLTSQR) as part of a high-affinity site. Homologous regions from the different subunits contribute to this unique site (19, 96). Additional labeling was discerned on threonine and leucine residues that, when arranged in a helical conformation, would give rise to three sequential rings: a serine-threonine ring, identified in the segment sequence as Ser4; a threonine-serine ring, denoted as T8; and a leucine ring, L11 (19). Photolabeling with uncharged nicotinic antagonist probes confirmed and extended these results (121). M2 is amphipathic (19, 85, 87) and exhibits high similarity both between subunits of the *T. californica* AChR $\alpha_2\beta\gamma\delta$ complex and between species (52, 80). Consequently, M2 is considered to be one of the components lining the AChR channel (19, 52, 59, 71, 80).

Mutagenesis and deletion analysis indicates that changes in M2 distinctly alter the AChR channel permeation properties, whereas mutations in M1 (63) or in M4 (58, 121) affect channel gating but not permeation, and that M4 is exchangeable with hydrophobic segments of the interleukin-2 receptor (113). Mutations of M2 residues that would face the aqueous pore if M2 were an α-helix modulate the ion-permeation properties of the channel (19, 20, 23, 48, 49, 52, 59, 80, 119). Mutations that remove or reduce the charge of the acidic residues at the N- and C-termini lead to a concomitant reduction of single-channel conductance (γ) (48). The AChR affinity for a local anesthetic channel blocker, QX-222, was modulated by selectively increasing or decreasing the polarity of residues in the T8 ring or a S-T ring at the equivalent position, 12, such that reducing polarity of the residue in position 8 increased the equilibrium-dissociation binding constant of QX-222, whereas mutations on site 12 resulted in the opposite effect. Thus, the aromatic moiety of QX-222 presumably interacts preferentially with side chains at position 12, whereas the charged quaternary ammonium recognizes residues at position 8 (20, 59). Residues in position 4 were examined on the mouse α-subunit (119). Of these, γ showed an inverse correlation with the volume of the side chain, such that reduction of volume increased conductance. These results imply that residues in this ring determine aspects of the AChR conduction properties.

Especially striking results have emerged from studies on the neuronal α_7 AChR, which forms functional homooligomers, presumably pentamers, in *Xenopus laevis* oocytes (7, 23, 30). Mutations on the rings of S4, T8, L11, and V15 all affect the permeation properties of the mutant channel, and specific sites alter the pharmacological profile. A case in point is L11 (L247 in α_7, and L251 in *T. californica* α): Mutation L11T increased Ca^{2+} permeability, abrogated the blockade by QX-222, but more drastically decreased the desensitization rate of the agonist-evoked response and increased the sensitivity to agonist. Taken together, the results of photoaffinity labeling and biophysical analysis of mutants point to a direct involvement of M2 in lining the pore of the AChR channel as a bundle of amphipathic α-helices.

Cysteine substitution mutagenesis was used to identify residues of the murine M2α exposed to the pore lumen or to its access pathways (1). Accessibility was probed with small, charged, sulfhydryl-specific methanesulfonate (MTS) derivatives presumed to react only at the water-accessible surface of the protein. AChRs expressed in oocytes were exposed to the MTS reagents in the absence or presence of ACh, and the effect of a test pulse of ACh was determined. Residues S8, L10, and S12 of M2 were accessible to cationic but not anionic MTS derivatives, in both the closed and open states, whereas L11 was accessible in only the open state. The periodicity of reactive residues was interpreted as consistent with a β-strand in the closed conformation of the channel. Alternatively, structural rearrangements resulting from the reaction of the substituted cysteines with the sulfhydryl reagent may account for these observations. This experiment provided no insights into the nature of the conformational change that would explain the exposure of L11 upon channel opening. This study illustrates both the power and the limits of the labeling approach in the absence of detailed protein structures.

The structure of *Torpedo marmorata* AChR was determined with cryoelectronmicroscopy to a resolution of 9 Å (116). The structure shows that the pore is formed by a bundle of five α-helices, one contributed by each subunit, perhaps surrounded by a rim of β-sheets. Unwin suggested that the bundle is formed by M2 helices whereas M1, M3, and M4 may form the rim in which each segment adopts the form of one β-strand or a three-stranded antiparallel β-sheet. This motif is reminiscent of that determined in the crystal structures of three water-soluble bacterial toxins, i.e. the B-subunit pentamers of *Escherichia coli* heat-labile enterotoxin (LT) (104), verotoxin-1 (VT-1) (107), and cholera toxin (CT) (67).

These proteins are members of a large family of bacterial and plant toxins that exhibit a modular organization with an A-domain containing the catalytic activity and a B-domain involved in receptor-membrane interaction and internalization (74). LT, VT-1, and CT are pentamers in which each monomer has one α-helix and two three-stranded antiparallel β-sheets. The outer surface of the pentamer is formed by the antiparallel β-sheets of adjacent monomers, whereas the helices form an inner bundle that lines a central pore. In VT-1, the pore diameter is 11 Å; the pore itself is lined with neutral and nonpolar residues. For LT, the pore diameter is $\sim$12 Å; and the pore itself is lined exclusively with charged residues (104).

This similarity in folding motifs despite nonhomologous amino acid sequences suggests that this motif may also occur in channel proteins confined within the hydrophobic environment of the membrane. The formation of ion channels in lipid bilayers and sensitive cells by the B-domains of several of these toxins may have a functional role. Such channel activity is documented for the agents of diphtheria, cholera, tetanus, and botulism. Moreover, these channels may serve as the conduit for the catalytic moiety of the toxin into the cytosol, where it acts (74).

Designed Channel Proteins

The M2 segment, highly conserved among all members of the superfamily of neurotransmitter-gated channels, is a plausible candidate for the structure that lines the pore. We have used conformational energy calculations to support the suggestion that the ion-conducting pore may be modeled as a parallel homooligomer of five amphipathic α-helices arranged such that polar residues line a central hydrophilic pathway and apolar residues face the hydrophobic bilayer interior (71, 85, 87). Is it possible to design a functional channel protein based on this structural motif? Figure 1 illustrates energy-optimized helical structures for the *T. californica* M2δ monomer (Figure 1*a*, side view). The amphipathic nature of the helix is shown by the predominant segregation of nonpolar residues on one face of the helix and polar residues on the other. A 23-mer peptide with this sequence was reconstituted in lipid bilayers and shown to form channels of heterogeneous conductance and lifetimes. These channels presumably resulted from the self-assembly of conductive oligomers of distinct sizes (82, 85). The channels most frequently formed by the M2δ peptide have primary conductances of 20 and 40 pS (Figure 1*b*). This lack of control over the final product (oligomeric number) is a disadvantage, especially for investigations on the mode of action of channel blockers because the heterogeneity of conductance events renders the interpretation of drug effects ambiguous at best.

A pivotal development for us was our total chemical synthesis of proteins with a putative four- and five-helix bundle topology (73, 82, 83). In these proteins, the M2 channel-forming peptides were covalently attached to a multifunctional carrier template (77). Figures 1*c* and 1*e*

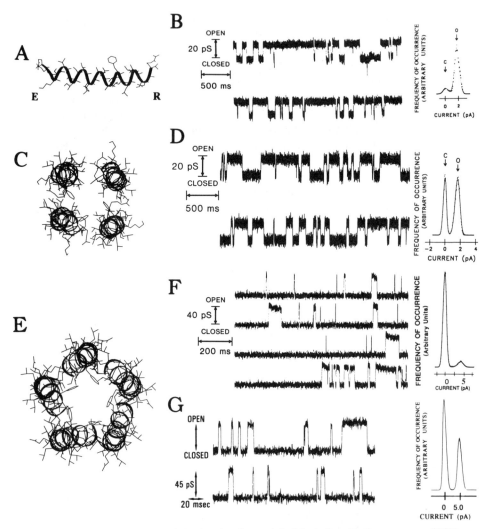

Figure 1 (A) Energy-optimized molecular model of the helix with the sequence of M2δ (side view). The N-terminus is on the left; E and R are the N- and C-terminal residues (83). (C, E) End views of the homotetramer T₄M2δ (C) and the pentamer T₅M2δ (E), with the N-terminus in front (83). (B,D,F,G) Single-channel recordings, and corresponding current histograms, from bilayers containing monomeric M2δ (B) (82), T₄M2δ (D) (82), T₅M2δ (F) (83), and purified *T. californica* AChR (G) (72). The peak centered at zero current corresponds to the closed state (C) and the second peak to the open state (O). For Panel *B*, only the most frequent events are shown, but the distribution of conductances is disperse (73, 82, 85).

show end views of the homotetramer $T_4M2\delta$ and the homopentamer $T_5M2\delta$, respectively (83). Most of the hydrophobic and hydrophilic residues occur on opposite faces of the helices. The lumen of the pore would presumably be lined with polar or neutral residues: Ser4 and Ser8 face the aqueous pore, in accord with chemical labeling experiments and mutational analysis (19, 59). For the tetramer, the pore cross-section is irregular, with dimensions of 4×5 Å; while for the pentamer, the cross-sectional dimension is ~ 7 Å. Such structures, therefore, partly satisfy the requirements for the inner bundle that forms the pore of the nicotinic AChR channel, and the pentamer fulfills the constraints imposed by the pentameric subunit architecture (94).

We synthesized four- and five-helix bundle proteins stepwise by means of solid-phase methods (73, 82, 83) and, more recently, with chemoselective ligation (122). The covalent structure of these proteins, purified with high-performance liquid chromatography (HPLC), was determined with electrospray ionization mass spectrometry: $M_r =$ 11,599 and 14,443 for $T_4M2\delta$ and $T_5M2\delta$, respectively (122). $T_4M2\delta$ (73, 82) and $T_5M2\delta$ (83) form cation-selective channels in lipid bilayers; here, conductance events have homogeneous amplitudes, with $\gamma =$ 20 pS (Figure 1d) and 40 pS (Figure 1f). This observation suggests that the 20- and 40-pS channels recorded with the monomeric M2 peptide (Figure 1b) arise from noncovalently bonded tetrameric and pentameric arrays (85, 87). Overall, similar results were obtained with the M2 sequence of the neuronal α_4 AChR (82), thus supporting the specificity of the M2 sequence.

Amphipathicity of peptides may be sufficient to induce the folding of a bundle in a lipid environment and to express functional activity (38). However, sequence specificity is required to reproduce the targeted biological attributes of selectivity and pharmacological specificity. Indeed, the tethered M2 homooligomeric channels are blocked by QX-222 and by chlorpromazine (73, 82), properties that are characteristic of the authentic AChR (19, 59). Replacing residues modeled to be exposed to the pore lumen (Figures 1a,c,e) affects permeation; the replacement S8 $\rightarrow$ A reduces γ, whereas the substitution F16 $\rightarrow$ A increases γ (82). Apparently, reducing polarity at position 8 decreases γ, whereas increasing polarity at position 16 increases γ, in agreement with mutagenesis results of authentic AChR M2 (19, 20, 59). Peptides consisting of the same amino acid composition as M2δ but that have randomized sequences predicted to retain α-helical structure or to exhibit a two- or a threefold repeat of polar residues do not form channels in bilayers (82), in accord with structural models. A tethered tetramer of M1δ, a highly conserved sequence not considered to line an aqueous channel, does not form channels (73, 82). Sequence specificity is, therefore, deterministic in the design.

The 40-pS channels of $T_5M2\delta$ (Figure 1f) approximate the 45-pS channels of authentic *T. californica* AChR reconstituted in bilayers and recorded under otherwise identical conditions (Figure 1g) (72). The *T. californica* AChR is a heteropentamer, whereas $T_5M2\delta$ is a homopentamer. This feature may explain the observed difference in γ; nevertheless, the approximation is remarkable. The results are consistent with the notion that a five-helix bundle may represent the structural motif underlying the inner bundle that forms the pore of the pentameric AChR channel.

Glycine and GABA Receptors

Two major inhibitory neurotransmitters in the CNS are Gly and γ-amino butyric acid (GABA) (8). GABA is ubiquitous in the CNS, whereas Gly predominates in the spinal cord and brain stem. Agonist binding to these postsynaptic receptors activates a Cl^--conducting channel that, in turn, induces synaptic inhibition by hyperpolarizing the postsynaptic cell. In analogy with the subunit composition and structure of AChR, GlyR is hypothesized to be a heteropentamer of α- and β-subunits in an unknown stoichiometry and arranged pseudosymmetrically around an aqueous pore lined by M2 (8). The M2 segments of GlyR (sequence ARVGLGITTVLTMTTQSSGSRA) and GABAR (sequence ARTVFGVTTVLTMTTLSISARN) are homologous and contain many hydroxyl-containing amino acids, suitable for lining a hydrophilic channel. The occurrence of R at the N- and C-termini of M2 may contribute to the anion selectivity of the pore (8, 11, 57). The conversion of neuronal α_7 AChR from a cation-selective to an anion-selective channel by mutations of three residues on M2 to match those at equivalent positions on GlyR offers compelling evidence for the structural kinship of AChR and GlyR. These changes are: insertion of a P at the N-terminus, the N-terminal mutation $E \rightarrow A$, and the mutation $V_{15} \rightarrow T$ (30).

The GlyR channel in spinal cord neurons is anion selective ($\gamma \approx 45$ pS) and exhibits multiple conductances (10). The occurrence of at least two sequentially occupied anion-binding sites in the channel was inferred from pharmacological results and interpreted to be the functional correlates of basic residues bordering M2 (10). Expression of GlyR α- and β-subunit cDNAs in HEK293 cells showed that homooligomers of α-subunits have a main $\gamma \approx 105$ pS, whereas α/β heterooligomers exhibit a $\gamma \approx 48$ pS. This result suggests that GlyRs in spinal neurons are mainly α/β heterooligomers (11). Homooligomers of α-subunits express glycine-activated Cl^- channels that are blocked by picrotoxin; in contrast, α/β heterooligomers are resistant (93). Notably, a point mutation in a *Drosophila melanogaster* GABAR confers picrotoxin and insecticide resistance. This mutation occurs in M2 at a position postulated to be exposed to the pore lumen, i.e. A_{302} (A4 in the segment sequence), which in the insecticide-resistant mutant is replaced with S (29).

Designed Channel Proteins

Synthetic peptides with the same sequence as M2 of the strychnine-binding α-subunit of GlyR (M2GlyR) form anion-selective channels in bilayers (57, 95). The most frequent events show $\gamma \approx 26$ and 50 pS (95). In contrast, synthetic peptides with sequences of M1 (95) or M4 (57) do not form channels. Furthermore, cation-selective channels are formed by M2GlyR analogues in which Es replace the two flanking Rs at the N- and C-termini of M2 (57, 95). These Rs presumably contribute to the anion selectivity of the channel.

Four-helix bundle proteins, $T_4M2GlyRs$, form homogeneous anion-selective channels with $\gamma = 26$ pS (95). Native GlyR exhibits two predominant conductances of 27 and 46 pS (10), which correlate with the most frequent channels elicited by monomeric M2GlyR, and presumably represent tetramers and pentamers. Because $T_4M2GlyR$ forms channels with $\gamma = 26$ pS, a reasonable inference is that the $\gamma = 45$ pS of native GlyR arises from a pentameric assembly of α- and β-subunits (10). The homomeric $T_4M2GlyR$ channels are blocked by picrotoxin (95), in agreement with the sensitivity of homooligomers of GlyR α-subunits (93), but not by strychnine, an antagonist of GlyR that binds at the ligand-binding domain but does not bind to the channel. Thus, the designed $T_4M2GlyR$ is a functional anion-selective channel, and these findings suggest that a pentameric assembly of α- and β-subunits with a central pore lined by a bundle of M2 would account for several permeation features of the authentic GlyR.

This approach led to the identification of an ion channel–forming motif akin to M2GlyR in the primary structure of a different anion-selective channel, the cystic fibrosis Cl^- channel, CFTR (84, 97). Peptides with sequences of M2 and M6 form anion-selective channels in bilayers, whereas peptides with the sequences of M1, M3, M4, and M5 do not. Conductive heterooligomers of M2 and M6 peptides approximate the γ and anion selectivity that are characteristic of CFTR (84). These results agree with those obtained from CFTR mutants (102). A helical bundle may be the pore motif of the CFTR channel.

Glutamate Receptors

Ionotropic Glu receptors are crucial for concerted synaptic communication in the CNS. NMDARs exhibit high Ca^{2+} permeability and voltage-dependent channel blockade by extracellular Mg^{2+} (16, 56, 76, 79, 98). Asparagine17 on M2 is responsible for these differences (sequence AL-TLSSAMWFSWGVLLNSGIGE). Non-NMDAR, in contrast, have Q or R for GluR1 or GluR2 (15, 47, 118). The presence of Q17 in GluR1 is correlated with an inwardly rectifying I-V relationship and high Ca^{2+} permeability, whereas GluR2 that has R17 exhibits a linear I-V and low Ca^{2+} permeability. Mutations of GluR1 and GluR2 that permute the occurrence of Q or R in these receptors predictably switch the properties of the mutant channels (15, 47, 118). Mutational analysis on both NMDAR and non-NMDAR suggests that, if M2 were helical, residues exposed to the pore lumen would specify the permeation and blockade properties of the receptor (15, 16, 47, 79, 98, 118). Therefore, for GluR, a bundle of M2 helices may also be a plausible framework for the pore-lining structure.

Structure and Transmembrane Orientation of the M2 Segment of Neurotransmitter-Gated Channels Determined by NMR Spectroscopy

^{1}H-NMR spectra of synthetic M2δ, M2GlyR, and M2NMDAR1 peptides in dodecylphosphocholine micelles in H_2O are well resolved and exhibit many interresidue nuclear Overhauser effects (NOEs) characteristic of an α-helix (5, 31). Figure 2a shows that many of the amide hydrogens are in close proximity, which indicates that at least 15–20 residues are in an α-helix (31). The orientation of the helical peptides in oriented lipid bilayers was determined by means of labeling with ^{15}N at positions corresponding to the middle of the helical length—^{15}N-A11M2GlyR (Figure 2b) and ^{15}N-A12M2δ (Figure 2c)—and then measuring the ^{15}N chemical shift with solid-state NMR spectroscopy (5). The key finding is that the N-H bonds of the labeled residues, and those of other residues in the helical peptide, are perpendicular to the plane of the membrane (5). Together, the NMR results provide direct evidence for the helical structure of M2 peptides and their orientation perpendicular to the plane of the bilayer, two features consistent with their pore-forming activity.

NMR substantiates the notion that a bundle of amphipathic α-helices is a plausible structural motif underlying the pore-forming structure of AChR, GlyR, and GluR. Thus, M2 segments of ligand-gated channels fold independently into stable helical structures and can reproduce sev-

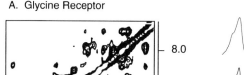

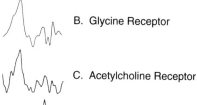

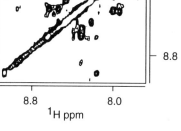

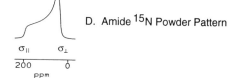

Figure 2   NMR spectra used to determine the secondary structure of M2 peptides in micelles (*A*) and the orientation of the helix in bilayers (*B–D*). (*A*) Two-dimensional homonuclear ^{1}H/^{1}H NOE spectrum of M2GlyR in micelles (31). (*B*) Solid-state ^{15}N NMR spectrum of M2GlyR ^{15}N-labeled at A11 and incorporated in oriented bilayers. (*C*) Same as in *B*, except that the peptide is AChR M2δ ^{15}N-labeled at A12. (*D*) Simulated ^{15}N-amide chemical shift anisotropy powder spectrum (5).

eral of the permeation properties characteristic of the native channel protein, though with a very much broader distribution of conductance. The M2 folding motif may mimic the functional module that lines the pore of neurotransmitter-gated channels. However, whether this folding motif occurs in the context of the fully folded protein is not yet established. The collective evidence is not conclusive, and the hypothesis remains to be validated when the high-resolution structures of the whole protein become available.

MODULAR ORGANIZATION OF TRANSMEMBRANE SEGMENTS IN VOLTAGE-GATED, CATION-SELECTIVE CHANNELS

Voltage-gated channels are responsible for the electrical excitability of neural cells. The pore appears to be formed at the center of a pseudo-symmetric assembly of four internal homologous repeats (for Na^+ and Ca^{2+} channels) or four subunits (for K^+ channels). Each repeat contains six segments (S1–S6) predicted to form transmembrane α-helices and the stretch between S5 and S6. This structure is known as H5 or P and is postulated to traverse part of the membrane as an antiparallel β-hairpin. I refer the reader to recent comprehensive reviews (9, 12, 26, 35, 51, 71, 80, 105).

S1 is essential for the assembly of functional channels, is required for homo- or heterotetramer specification of channel subunits, and appears necessary to stabilize intersubunit interactions in the functional assembly (4, 60, 101). The N-terminal sequence is not essential for functional expression of K^+ channels (3, 117); in contrast, deletion of S1 abolishes expression (4). S1 is primarily hydrophobic (consensus sequence RGI-AIVSVLVILISIVIFCLET), highly conserved, and presumably forms part of an outer, lipid-exposed surface of the array (26, 35, 51, 71).

Ample evidence implicates S4 as a key component of the voltage sensor (9, 12, 26, 35, 36, 51, 61, 64, 65, 71, 88, 91, 105, 108, 114), and several reports (9, 36, 105) also confirm that residues in other segments, probably S2, S3, and S6, are likely to interact electrostatically with the basic residues of S4 to form the energetically favorable ion pairs required for S4 to be embedded in the bilayer hydrophobic core (35, 71). S4 (consensus sequence AILRVIRLVRVFRIFKLSRHSKGL) appears to occur at the center of a clustered structure of high dipole moment. The regularity and conservation of a triad (RXX or KXX) in which X is usually a nonpolar residue is striking (80) and suggests that this recurring structural motif may represent a descendant from a single ancestor of the voltage sensor. If S4 were helical in the context of the whole protein, then the basic residues would be regularly distributed around the helical cylinder, creating potential charged sites for interaction with neighboring segments of the array. The occurrence of highly conserved polar and acidic residues, the sequential and presumably spatial proximity to the voltage-sensing S4, and their amphipathic character designate S2 and S3 as plausible candidates for additional elements of the voltage sensor (35, 36, 71, 105).

S4 of RCK1, a noninactivating K^+ channel, was extensively studied by mutational analysis (cf 105). Mutations of individual charged residues alter the voltage dependence of channel opening to different extents or result in no functional expression. This finding indicates that charged residues of S4 are nonequivalent and that electrostatic interactions are only part of the overall folding energy. Furthermore, conserved substitutions of hydrophobic residues in S4 that would create a cavity in the core of the assembly drastically affect the gating properties of the channel. A case in point: mutations in the Shaker K^+ channel, L375A, L361A, and L382V, produce a remarkable destabilization of the open conformation. This observation indicates that the packing of S4 within the assembly and the short-range interactions with neighboring elements of the array are crucial for the stability of sensor (65). In contrast, little is known about the effect of mutations on S2 (consensus sequence FFIVETLCIIWFTFELLVRFFA) or S3 (consensus sequence NIMNIIDIVAIIPYFITLGTEL). For noninactivating K^+ channels, residue D258 in S3, which is identical in all K^+, Na^+, and Ca^{2+} channels, cannot tolerate change, and mutations at this position that remove, retain, or change charge abolish functional expression of channel currents (36). In contrast, mutations of residue E272 that remove or change charge displace the voltage dependence of channel opening to more depolarizing voltages, reflecting a less stable open conformation (36). The rate of voltage-dependent activation of cardiac and skeletal L-type Ca^{2+} channels is influenced by multiple residues in IS3 and the linker region connecting S3 and S4 (78). This subject is still under investigation, but these results, together with structural considerations and evolutionary conservation, suggest that S2 and S3 are essential elements of the array and may be additional key components of the sensor.

The loop connecting S4 and S5 contains a recognition site for the inactivation particle (50). For Shaker channels, the sequence includes five residues, mutations of which alter channel inactivation: L385, T388, S392, E395, and L396. Mutations of the first four residues also affect permeation properties such as γ and sensitivity to block by internal tetraethylammonium (TEA^+), Ba^{2+}, or Mg^{2+} (106). This information has prompted the notion that such potentially pliable loops may form a vestibule at the inner entry into the pore structure.

The loop connecting S5 and S6 (known as H5 or P) with the consensus sequence P*AFWW***TMTTVGYGD**P, where the asterisk denotes no consensus (69), has come under intense scrutiny. Its role as a structural determinant was initially inferred from mutational and chimeric analysis. Mutations of conserved polar residues alter blockade by TEA, a low-affinity blocker, from the inside or the outside of the pore (124, 125). A chimeric construct in which H5 from the DRK1 channel was replaced with the corresponding segment from the NGK2 channel resulted in a mutant protein that exhibited the γ and TEA sensitivity of the donor NGK2 channel (41).

H5 is the most conserved sequence in all K^+ channels. Indeed, the identification of a putative K^+ channel gene from *E. coli* indicates that this recurring motif, conserved from bacteria to humans (brain), may represent the descendant from a single precursor of a selectivity filter (69). Mutational analysis of Na^+ (42, 112), Ca^{2+} (53, 70, 123), and cyclic nucleotide-gated (34) channels indicates that a similar motif may confer their unique selectivity and permeation properties. The most tantalizing observations were made on Na^+ channels, in which substitutions of residues from repeat III (K1422) and IV (A1714) with E, which occurs in a corresponding position in Ca^{2+} channels, changed the selectivity of the mutant sodium channel to mimic that of Ca^{2+} channels (42).

Similar experiments examined Ca^{2+} channels, in which mutations of conserved glutamates in each of the four repeats were introduced to remove charge (E $\rightarrow$ Q) or change charge (E $\rightarrow$ K) (53, 70, 123). Affinity was inferred from the efficacy of block by Ca^{2+} and Cd^{2+} on inward Li^+ and Ba^{2+} currents through expressed Ca^{2+} channels. Each of the four glutamates contributes distinctly to the characteristic high-affinity binding of Ca^{2+} and Cd^{2+} (53, 70, 123). Replacements in repeat III had the strongest effects (123). Drastic changes (up to 1000-fold) in the affinity of the channel for Ca^{2+} were measured, suggesting that these conserved glutamates are involved in forming the high-affinity calcium-binding site within the pore. Concomitantly, the selectivity of the channel for monovalent cations markedly increased, switching the apparent selectivity profile from divalent to monovalent (53, 70, 123). The H5 sequence, therefore, provides a ring of negatively charged residues at the entrance to the channel and may be a major structural determinant of Ca^{2+} selectivity. The motif is reminiscent of ones present in annexin (6, 14) and, at the most reductionist level, in chelating compounds such as EGTA (99).

The collective information is consistent with the view that the loop between S5 and S6 forms a vestibule at the pore entrance that modulates the selectivity and toxin sensitivity (33, 112) of the pore-forming structure. Two plausible candidates for the pore-forming structure are S5 (consensus sequence ELGLLIFFLFIGVILFSSAVYFAE) and S6 (consensus sequence GKIVGSLCAIAGVLTIALPVPVIVSN). Domain-swapping constructs have highlighted the involvement of S6 in forming part of the pore. Chimeras in which S6 of the Shaker channel was replaced with that of the NGK2 channel displayed the permeation properties characteristic of the donor NGK2 channel, namely, larger γ, 100-fold higher sensitivity to external block by TEA, and 10-fold lower sensitivity to internal block by TEA (66). A single residue, L472, of S6 appears to account for the different sensitivities to internal TEA block by the distinct K^+ channels. A double chimera involving the cytoplasmic halves of S5 and S6 conferred to the acceptor channel the characteristic features of, and sensitivity to, channel blockade by internal 4-aminopyridine of the donor channel (54). These results implicate S5, H5, and S6 as major structural constituents of the pore-lining of voltage-gated channels. But do these segments constitute a functional module?

A novel family of K^+ channels, the inward rectifiers (IRK), display a canonical topology consisting of only two transmembrane segments, M1 and M2, and a connecting loop that exhibits ~44% identity to the K^+ channel H5 (44, 55). Inward rectifiers are physiologically important in maintaining prolonged depolarizations (55). Rectification arises primarily from open channel blockade by intracellular Mg^{2+} (110). The two best-characterized members of the family, IRK1 and ROMK1 (renal outer medulla K^+ channel), are especially interesting in that their H5 sequences differ by only two residues (I6 → L, T10 → V) yet their γ and sensitivity to Mg^{2+} block mismatch: IRK1 has lower γ and higher affinity to Mg^{2+} block. Remarkably, sole exchange of the C-terminus of IRK1 with that of ROMK1 conferred to the latter distinctly higher affinity to Mg^{2+} blockade and reduced γ, whereas H5 domain–swapping experiments between the two channels did not (110). Thus, the C-terminal end of inward rectifiers is a key determinant of these pore properties.

Inward rectifiers may be structurally related to the canonical voltage-gated channels, as inferred from constructs in which deletion of the protein domain encompassing S1–S4 of an outward rectifier K^+ channel, where the N-terminal end is religated to S5, produces a mutant channel with properties characteristic of inward rectifiers (115). How the S1–S4 domain switches the S5-H5-S6 module from inward to outward rectification is an intriguing question. However, the findings suggest that a module consisting of M1, H5, and M2 (inward rectifiers) or S5, H5, and S6 (voltage-gated K channels) may represent a unit of function and perhaps a folding motif, such as a helix-loop-helix motif.

Such are the broad considerations that lead the design. In the emergent picture, S1 is the insertion sequence; S2, S3, and S4 are key elements of the voltage sensor; S5 and S6 are components of the pore-forming structure; and H5 forms a vestibule at the outer pore entrance.

Inferences About Cation-Selective Channel Structure Derived from the Atomic Structure of Annexin V

Annexins may be viewed as a model for the structure of channel proteins (6, 14). They are involved in a variety of calcium-mediated cellular processes ranging from membrane fusion to the inhibition of coagulation and inflammation. Annexin binding to membranes depends on calcium and acidic lipid; binding to lipid bilayers leads to the formation of transmembrane channels (6, 14). The crystal structure of annexin V, determined to 2-Å resolution, shows that this protein is almost entirely α-helical (6, 14). Four repeats are arranged around a central hydrophilic pore; each consists of four parallel α-helices and a fifth perpendicular helix that connects adjacent repeats. The helices that form the pore are ~15 amino acids in length (~22 Å), which is not long enough to span the bilayer core. The exterior of the molecule is polar and charged, with nonpolar residues at the cores of the individual domains, as expected for a water-soluble protein. The convex surface contains Ca^{2+}-binding sites that may mediate its binding to acidic lipids in membranes. Also, the central pore is formed by a bundle of four helices, IIA, IIB, IVA, and IVB, and contains a ring of negatively charged residues exposed to the pore lumen. All these features suggest that annexin conforms to a water-soluble version of a channel protein. Annexin V forms cation-selective channels in bilayers containing acidic lipid (6). An $E \rightarrow S$ mutation in the annexin central pore reduces the channel Ca^{2+} permeability, which supports the tenet that this ring of acidic residues is exposed to the luminal face of the pore, as inferred from the crystal structure. This structural information, therefore, provides a basis for a four-helix bundle as a framework for an ion-conducting pore protein and for a ring of acidic residues as a determinant of the Ca^{2+} selectivity of the pore.

Designed Channel Proteins

Efforts at protein design have focused on the pore-forming structure. The strategy involves initial identification of candidate pore-lining segments presumably contributed by each repeat or subunit to generate a tetrameric array. A detailed study considered the dihydropyridine (DHP)-sensitive, voltage-gated, L-type calcium channel (68, 75, 111): a systematic analysis involved the synthesis of monomeric peptides representing each one of the predicted transmembrane sequences for one repeat, IV, (or subunit) and their reconstitution in lipid bilayers for the determination of channel activity (37, 39). Peptides with sequences of S2 and S3 form discrete cation-selective channels, whereas peptides with the sequences of S1, S4, S5, H5, and S6 do not. These five peptides do incorporate into bilayers, as evidenced by erratic fluctuations in membrane current that reflect transient perturbations of membrane stability. A monomeric peptide with the sequence of the Na^+ channel IS3 also forms cation-selective channels (86). Thus, the S2 and S3 sequences are amphipathic, have the inherent ability to form channels in membranes, and may fulfill this functional role in the context of the whole protein.

An additional constraint of the design was to generate the tetrameric organization of the authentic channel, which was accomplished by tethering channel-forming sequences to a carrier template (37, 39, 77). Proteins with a four-α-helix–bundle topology, $T_4CaIVS2$ and $T_4CaIVS3$, form cation-selective channels in bilayers (37). Amphipathicity of peptide modules is, therefore, sufficient to generate a functional ion-conducting protein (38). However, the pore properties of the $T_4CaIVS3$ channel are closer to those of authentic calcium channels in terms of γ saturation, blockade by Ca^{2+} and Cd^{2+}, and stereospecific modulation by enantiomers of DHP (37, 39). These results underscore the sequence requirement for ionic selectivity and for specific drug action. The fact that the designed proteins are functional channels indicates that the four-helix bundle motif may be a blueprint for a functional pore unit. Qualification is required, however, because this minimum motif, incomplete as it may be, is unlikely to represent the more complex structural organization of authentic Ca^{2+} channels. The issue is further complicated by the deterministic nature of the H5 sequence in specification of the high-affinity Ca^{2+}-binding site (53, 70, 123).

The four-helix bundle of the annexin pore exposes a ring of negatively charged residues to the lumen (6, 14), and the energy-minimized structure of the designed four-helix bundle protein $T_4CaIVS3$ indicates that a ring of aspartates (D7), which is absolutely conserved in all voltage-gated Ca^{2+} channels, is the narrowest region of pore (4.2 Å) and may provide a high-affinity binding site for permeant cations (39). If a ring of acidic residues were a structural determinant of Ca^{2+} permeability, introduction of such a determinant into the pore structure of a channel protein might confer Ca^{2+}-selectivity to an inherently nonselective pore. Indeed, the mutation T244 → D in M2 of the homomeric α_7 AChR (at position 8 of the M2 segment sequence) generates a ring of negatively charged residues exposed to the pore lumen of the oligomeric receptor. This ring causes the AChR channel to be more permeable to divalent cations (28).

A peptide with the sequence of IVS4 extended to include the S45 linker (13) from the *Electrophorus electricus* Na^+ channel produced channels with $\gamma = 8$ and 5 pS in neutral and negatively charged bilayers, respectively. No control sequences were reported. Using circular dichroism (CD) and Fourier-transform infrared (FT-IR) spectroscopy, another study examined a peptide with the sequence of H5 from Shaker K^+ channels and a tetramer of this sequence obtained by tethering four of these peptides onto a branching lysine core (40). Both forms of the H5 sequence were predominantly α-helical in aqueous dispersions of lysophosphatidylcholine and in phospholipid vesicles. Both peptides form channels in bilayers, and the monomer γ ranges from 12–50 pS while the tetramer $\gamma = 13$ pS (40).

In contrast, a different group concluded that the H5 sequence was a mixture of α-helix, β-strand, β-turn, and random coil and that it formed anion-selective channels with a γ value larger than that of authentic Shaker (103). The H5 sequences of either Shaker (90) or IRK1 (100) in hydrophobic environments were predominantly not helical but tended to self-associate in the membrane-bound state. Similar results were obtained with assigned H5 sequences from repeats I (92), III (92), and IV (21) of the *E. electricus* Na^+ channel. The latter sequence forms channels in bilayers, with $\gamma = 6$ pS. In contrast, IVH5 of L-type Ca^{2+} channels inserts into bilayers but does not form channels (37). Collectively, the information about secondary structure of H5 sequences is inconclusive, and the bilayer data only indicate that H5 sequences partition into membranes.

All these results converge to point to a significant issue in the design strategy, namely, the structure of these peptide segments in the context of the environment in which they are studied (e.g. helix-promoting solvents such as trifluoroethanol or lipid membranes) and the potentially different folding of these independent modules in the context of the whole protein. Thus, at present, these hypotheses regarding protein structure have produced more questions than answers.

Is there room for improvement? The design of helical bundles tethered to a carrier template mandates that the final product be a discontinuous molecule because the helical modules are attached on one end to a preformed template and free at the other. The simultaneous assembly of peptide blocks further constrains the modules in a parallel orientation with respect to the helical axis. In contrast, biological design dictates that the modular components of a protein be connected, thereby generating a continuous, linear molecule. For a helical bundle, this implies that the helical modules are connected by loops or turns, yielding an antiparallel orientation of helices. This could be accomplished by engineering genes designed to direct the synthesis and expression of a four-helix bundle motif representing a putative pore-forming structure, or a helix-loop-helix motif representing a functional unit for a voltage-gated, cation-selective channel, such as the presumed structure of inward rectifiers (M1, H5, M2). Such strategies that more closely follow the biological design, could produce proteins that could be characterized functionally by single-channel recordings in bilayers or in oocytes and structurally by NMR or X-ray diffraction.

CLOSING REMARKS

How close have we come to designing a functional channel protein? The structural information available indicates that the helical-bundle pore motif, either surrounded by helices, as in annexin, or by antiparallel β-sheets, as in certain bacterial toxins, occurs in eukaryotic channel proteins. The tethered five-helix bundle $T_5M2\delta$ approximates some of the permeation properties of the AChR channel, and NMR analysis is consistent with the M2 segment being a transmembrane α-helix. This is probably the best candidate for a functional folding motif. For voltage-gated channel proteins, the four-helix bundle design we describe led to the mimicry of some of the functional channel proteins. The evidence concerning designs based on the putative H5 β-hairpin is ambiguous at best. The remarkable plasticity of channel proteins revealed by the successful construction of chimeras (27, 34, 41, 46, 54, 66, 78, 110) implies that channels can be restructured to create novel features.

From the context of the canonical folding topology of channel proteins, one wonders if we can reach an understanding of why a complex whole has properties its parts lack, and of how the parts are altered by the context in which they reside. The fascinating and complex biology of channel proteins appears matched by their diversity. Efforts to mimic such exquisite designs will undoubtedly foster our understanding of how channel proteins work at a molecular level. Thus, the search will continue for the elusive structure, which becomes ever more notorious for its absence.

ACKNOWLEDGMENTS

Space limitations prevented me from referring to multiple significant contributions to the field; I apologize. I thank the colleagues who shared their work in progress, my graduate students, postdoctoral fellows, and collaborators for their involvement, and A Ferrer-Montiel, S Opella, and M Oblatt for valuable comments. Our research is supported by grants from the US Public Health Service (GM-49711), the Office of Naval Research (ONR N000 14-89-J1489), the Department of the Army Medical Research (DAMD 17-93-C-3100), and a Research Scientist Award from the Alcohol, Drug Abuse, and Mental Health Administration (MH-00778) to MM.

Literature Cited

1. Akabas MH, Stauffer DA, Xu M, Karlin A. 1992. Acetylcholine receptor channel structure probed in cysteine-substitution mutants. *Science* 258:307–10

2. Akerfeldt KS, Lear JD, Wasserman ZR, Chung LA, DeGrado WF. 1993. Synthetic peptides as models for ion channel proteins. *Acc. Chem. Res.* 26:191–97

3. Attali B, Lesage F, Ziliani P, Guil-
lemare E, Honore E, et al. 1993. Multiple mRNA isoforms encoding the
mouse cardiac Kv1.5 delayed rectifier K^+ channel. *J. Biol. Chem.* 268:
24283–89

4. Babila T, Moscucci A, Wang H,
Weaver FE, Koren G. 1994. Assembly of mammalian voltage-gated
potassium channels: evidence for
an important role of the first
transmembrane segment. *Neuron* 12:
615–26

5. Bechinger B, Kim Y, Chirlian LE,
Gesell J, Neumann JM, et al. 1991.
Orientations of amphipathic helical
peptides in membrane bilayers determined by solid-state NMR spectroscopy *J. Biomol. NMR* 1:167–73

6. Berendes R, Voges D, Demange P,
Huber R, Burger A. 1993. Structure-
function analysis of the ion channel
selectivity filter in human annexin V.
Science 262:427–30

7. Bertrand D, Galzi JL, Devillers-
Thiery A, Bertrand S, Changeux JP.
1993. Mutations at two distinct sites
within the channel domain M2 alter
calcium permeability of neuronal α_7
nicotinic receptor. *Proc. Natl. Acad.
Sci. USA* 90:6971–75

8. Betz H. 1992. Structure and function
of inhibitory glycine receptors. *Q.
Rev. Biophys.* 25:381–94

9. Bezanilla F, Stefani E. 1994. Voltage-
dependent gating of ionic channels.
Annu. Rev. Biophys. Biomol. Struct.
23:819–46

10. Bormann J, Hamill OP, Sakmann B.
1987. Mechanism of anion permeation through channels gated by glycine and γ-amino butyric acid in
mouse cultured spinal neurones. *J.
Physiol.* 385:243–86

11. Bormann J, Rundström N, Betz H,
Langosch D. 1993. Residues within
transmembrane segment M2 determine chloride conductance of glycine
receptor homo- and hetero-oligo-
mers. *EMBO J.* 12:3729–37

12. Brown AM. 1993. Functional bases
for interpreting amino acid sequences
of voltage-dependent K^+ channels.
Annu. Rev. Biophys. Biomol. Struct.
22:173–98

13. Brullemans M, Helluin O, Dugast JY,
Molle G, Duclohier H. 1993. Implication of segment S45 in the permeation pathway of voltage-dependent sodium channels. *Eur. Biophys. J.* 23:
39–49

14. Burger A, Voges D, Demange P,
Perez CR, Huber R, Berendes R.

1994. Structural and electrophysiological analysis of annexin V mutants. Mutagenesis of human annexin
V, an in vitro voltage-gated calcium
channel, provides information about
the structural features of the ion pathway, the voltage sensor and the ion
selectivity filter. *J. Mol. Biol.* 237:
479–99

15. Burnashev N, Monyer H, Seeburg
PH, Sakmann B. 1992. Divalent ion
permeability of AMPA receptor
channels is dominated by the edited
form of a single subunit. *Neuron* 8:
189–98

16. Burnashev N, Schoepfer R, Monyer
H, Ruppersberg JP, Günther W, et al.
1992. Control by asparagine residues
of calcium permeability and magnesium blockade in the NMDA receptor. *Science* 257:1415–19

17. Deleted in proof

18. Deleted in proof

19. Changeux JP, Galzi JL, Devillers-
Thiéry A, Bertrand D. 1992. The
functional architecture of the acetylcholine nicotinic receptor explored
by affinity labeling and site-directed
mutagenesis. *Q. Rev. Biophys.* 25:
395–432

20. Cohen BN, Labarca C, Davidson N,
Lester HA. 1992. Mutations in M2
alter the selectivity of the mouse nicotinic acetylcholine receptor for organic and alkali metal cations. *J. Gen.
Physiol.* 100:373–400

21. Cosette P, Brullemans M, Duclohier
H. 1994. Peptide modelling and functional assays of the P-region of voltage-dependent sodium channels. *Biophys. J.* 66:A281

22. Cowan SW, Schirmer T, Rummel G,
Steiert M, Ghosh R, Pauptit RA, et
al. 1992. Crystal structures explain
functional properties of two *E. coli*
porins. *Nature* 358:727–33

23. Devillers-Thiéry A, Galzi JL, Bertrand S, Changeux JP, Bertrand D.
1992. Stratified organization of the nicotinic acetylcholine receptor channel. *Neuroreport* 3:1001–4

24. Diesenhofer J, Michel H. 1991. High-
resolution structures of photosynthetic reaction centers. *Annu. Rev.
Biophys. Biophys. Chem.* 20:247–66

25. Deleted in proof

26. Durell SR, Guy HR. 1992. Atomic
scale structure and functional models
of voltage-gated potassium channels.
Biophys. J. 62:238–47

27. Eisele JL, Bertrand S, Galzi JL, Devillers-Thiéry A, Changeux JP, Bertrand D. 1993. Chimaeric nicotinic-

serotonergic receptor combines distinct ligand binding and channel specificities. *Nature* 366:479–83

28. Ferrer-Montiel AV, Montal M. 1993. A negative charge in the M2 transmembrane segment of the neuronal α_7 acetylcholine receptor increases permeability to divalent cations. *FEBS Lett.* 324:185–90

29. ffrench-Constant RH, Rocheleau TA, Steichen JC, Chalmers AE. 1993. A point mutation in a *Drosophila* GABA receptor confers insecticide resistance. *Nature* 363:449–51

30. Galzi JL, Devillers-Thiéry A, Hussy N, Bertrand S, Changeux JP, Bertrand D. 1992. Mutations in the channel domain of a neuronal nicotinic receptor convert ion selectivity from cationic to anionic. *Nature* 359:500–5

31. Gesell J, Opella SJ, Sun W, Montal M. 1992. Multidimensional NMR studies of the channel-lining peptide segments of the acetylcholine and glycine receptors. *Symp. Protein Soc., 6th. San Diego, Calif.* S33:52. New York: Cambridge Univ. Press

32. Giraudat J, Dennis M, Heidmann T, Chang JY, Changeux JP. 1986. Structure of the high affinity binding site for non-competitive blockers of the acetylcholine receptor: serine 262 of the δ-subunit is labeled by [^{3}H] chlorpromazine. *Proc. Natl. Acad. Sci. USA* 83:2719–23

33. Goldstein SAN, Pheasant DJ, Miller C. 1994. The charybdotoxin receptor of a *Shaker* K$^+$ channel: peptide and channel residues mediating molecular recognition. *Neuron* 12:1377–88

34. Goulding EH, Tibbs GR, Liu D, Siegelbaum SA. 1993. Role of H5 domain in determining pore diameter and ion permeation through cyclic nucleotide-gated channels. *Nature* 364:61–64

35. Greenblatt RE, Blatt Y, Montal M. 1985. The structure of the voltage-sensitive sodium channel: inferences derived from computer aided analysis of the *Electrophorus electricus* channel primary structure. *FEBS Lett.* 193:125–34

36. Gross GJ, Lacro RV, Logothetis DE. 1993. Identification of negatively charged elements of the voltage sensor in a potassium channel. *Biophys. J.* 64:A313

37. Grove A, Iwamoto T, Tomich JM, Montal M. 1993. Design of a functional calcium channel protein: inferences about an ion channel-forming motif derived from the primary structure of voltage-gated calcium channels. *Protein Sci.* 2:1918–30

38. Grove A, Mutter M, Rivier JE, Montal M. 1993. Template assembled synthetic proteins designed to adopt a globular four-helix bundle conformation form ionic channels in lipid bilayers. *J. Am. Chem. Soc.* 115:5919–24

39. Grove A, Tomich JM, Montal M. 1991. A molecular blueprint for the pore-forming structure of voltage-gated calcium channels. *Proc. Natl. Acad. Sci. USA* 88:6418–22

40. Haris PI, Ramesh B, Sansom MSP, Kerr ID, Srai KS, Chapman D. 1994. Studies of the pore-forming domain of a voltage-gated potassium channel protein. *Protein Eng.* 7:255–62

41. Hartmann HA, Kirsch GE, Drewe JA, Taglialatela M, Joho RH, Brown AM. 1991. Exchange of conduction pathways between two related K$^+$ channels. *Science* 251:942–44

42. Heinemann SH, Terlau H, Stühmer W, Imoto K, Numa S. 1992. Calcium channel characteristics conferred on the sodium channel by single mutations. *Nature* 356:441–43

43. Henderson R, Baldwin JM, Ceska TA, Zemlin F, Beckmann E, Downing KH. 1990. Model for the structure of bacteriorhodopsin based on high-resolution electron cryo-microscopy. *J. Mol. Biol.* 213:899–929

44. Ho K, Nichols CG, Lederer WJ, Lytton J, Vassilev PM, et al. 1993. Cloning and expression of an inwardly rectifying ATP-regulated potassium channel. *Nature* 362:31–38

45. Deleted in proof

46. Hong K, Driscoll M. 1994. A transmembrane domain of the putative channel subunit MEC-4 influences mechanotransduction and neurodegeneration in *C. elegans*. *Nature* 367:470–73

47. Hume RI, Dingledine R, Heinemann SF. 1991. Identification of a site in glutamate receptor subunits that controls calcium permeability. *Science* 253:1028–31

48. Imoto K, Busch C, Sakmann B, Mishina M, Konno T, et al. 1988. Rings of negatively charged amino acids determine the acetylcholine receptor channel conductance. *Nature* 335:645–48

49. Imoto K, Konno T, Nakai J, Wang F, Mishina M, Numa S. 1991. A ring of uncharged polar amino acids as a component of channel constriction in the nicotinic acetylcholine receptor. *FEBS Lett.* 289:193–200

50. Isacoff EY, Jan YN, Jan LY. 1991. Putative receptor for the cytoplasmic inactivation gate in the *Shaker* K$^+$ channel. *Nature* 353:86–90

51. Jan LY, Jan YN. 1992. Structural elements involved in specific K$^+$ channel functions. *Annu. Rev. Physiol.* 54:537–55

52. Karlin A. 1993. Structure of nicotinic acetylcholine receptors. *Curr. Opin. Neurobiol.* 3:299–309

53. Kim MS, Morii T, Sun LX, Imoto K, Mori Y. 1993. Structural determinants of ion selectivity in brain calcium channel. *FEBS Lett.* 318:145–48

54. Kirsch GE, Shieh CC, Drewe JA, Vener DF, Brown AM. 1993. Segmental exchanges define 4-aminopyridine binding and the inner mouth of K$^+$ pores. *Neuron* 11:503–12

54a. Kistler J, Stroud RM, Klymkowsky MW, Lalancette RA, Fairclough RH. 1982. Structure and function of an acetylcholine receptor. *Biophys. J.* 37:371–83

55. Kubo Y, Baldwin TJ, Jan YN, Jan LY. 1993. Primary structure and functional expression of a mouse inward rectifier potassium channel. *Nature* 362:127–33

56. Kutsuwada T, Kashiwabuchi N, Mori H, Sakimura K, Kushiya E, et al. 1992. Molecular diversity of the NMDA receptor channel. *Nature* 358:36–41

57. Langosch D, Hartung K, Grell E, Bamberg E, Betz H. 1991. Ion channel formation by synthetic transmembrane segments of the inhibitory glycine receptor—a model study. *Biochim. Biophys. Acta* 1063:36–44

58. Lee Y-H, Li L, Lasalde J, Rojas L, McNamee M, Ortiz-Miranda S, Pappone P. 1994. Mutations in M4 of *Torpedo californica* acetylcholine receptors dramatically alter ion-channel function. *Biophys. J.* 66:646–53

59. Lester HA. 1992. The permeation pathway of neurotransmitter-gated ion channels. *Annu. Rev. Biophys. Biomol. Struct.* 21:267–92

60. Li M, Jan YN, Jan LY. 1992. Specification of subunit assembly by the hydrophilic amino-terminal domain of the Shaker potassium channel. *Science* 257:1225–30

61. Liman ER, Hess P, Weaver F, Koren G. 1991. Voltage-sensing residues in the S4 region of a mammalian K$^+$ channel. *Nature* 353:752–56

62. Deleted in proof

63. Lo DC, Pinkham JL, Stevens CF. 1991. Role of a key cysteine residue in the gating of the acetylcholine receptor. *Neuron* 6:31–40

64. Logothetis DE, Kammen BF, Lindpainter K, Bisbas D, Nadal-Ginard B. 1993. Gating charge differences between two voltage-gated K$^+$ channels are due to the specific charge content of their respective S4 regions. *Neuron* 10:1121–29

65. Lopez GA, Jan YN, Jan LY. 1991. Hydrophobic substitution mutations in the S4 sequence alter voltage-dependent gating in *Shaker* K$^+$ channels. *Neuron* 7:327–36

66. Lopez GA, Jan YN, Jan LY. 1994. Evidence that the S6 segment of the *Shaker* voltage-gated K$^+$ channel comprises part of the pore. *Nature* 367:179–82

67. Merritt EA, Sarfaty S, van den Akker F, L'Hoir C, Martial JA, Hol WGJ. 1994. Crystal structure of cholera toxin B-pentamer bound to receptor G$_{M1}$ pentasaccharide. *Protein Sci.* 3:166–75

68. Mikami A, Imoto K, Tanabe T, Niidome T, Mori Y, et al. 1989. Primary structure and functional expression of the cardiac dihydropyridine-sensitive calcium channel. *Nature* 340:230–33

69. Milkman R. 1994. An *Escherichia coli* homologue of eukaryotic potassium channel proteins. *Proc. Natl. Acad. Sci. USA* 91:3510–14

70. Mikala G, Bahinski A, Yatani A, Tang S, Schwartz A. 1993. Differential contribution by conserved glutamate residues to an ion-selectivity site in the L-type Ca^{2+} channel pore. *FEBS Lett.* 335:265–69

71. Montal M. 1990. Molecular anatomy and molecular design of channel proteins. *FASEB J.* 4:2623–35

72. Montal M, Anholt R, Labarca P. 1986. The reconstituted acetylcholine receptor. In *Ion Channel Reconstitution,* ed. C Miller, pp. 157–204. New York: Plenum

73. Montal M, Montal MS, Tomich JM. 1990. Synporins-synthetic proteins that emulate the pore structure of biological ionic channels. *Proc. Natl. Acad. Sci. USA* 87:6929–33

74. Montecucco C, Papini E, Schiavo G. 1994. Bacterial protein toxins penetrate cells via a four-step mechanism. *FEBS Lett.* 346:92–98

75. Mori Y, Friedrich T, Kim MS, Mikami A, Nakai J, et al. 1991. Primary structure and functional expression

from complementary DNA of a brain calcium channel. *Nature* 350:398–402

76. Moriyoshi K, Masu M, Ishii T, Shigemoto R, Mizuno N, Nakanishi S. 1991. Molecular cloning and characterization of the rat NMDA receptor. *Nature* 354:31–37

77. Mutter M, Hersperger R, Gubernator K, Muller K. 1989. The construction of new proteins. V. A template-assembled synthetic protein (TASP) containing both a 4-helix bundle and β-barrel-like structure. *Proteins Struct. Funct. Genet.* 5:13–21

78. Nakai J, Adams BA, Imoto K, Beam KG. 1994. Critical roles of the S3 segment and S3-S4 linker of repeat I in activation of L-type calcium channels. *Proc. Natl. Acad. Sci. USA* 91: 1014–18

79. Nakanishi S, Masu M. 1994. Molecular diversity and functions of glutamate receptors. *Annu. Rev. Biophys. Biomol. Struct.* 23:319–48

80. Numa S. 1989. A molecular view of neurotransmitter receptors and ionic channels. *Harvey Lect.* 83:121–65

81. Oberthur W, Hucho F. 1988. Photoaffinity labeling of functional states of the nicotinic acetylcholine receptor. *J. Protein Chem.* 7:141–50

82. Oblatt-Montal M, Buhler LK, Iwamoto T, Tomich JM, Montal M. 1993. Synthetic peptides and four helix bundle proteins as model systems for the pore-forming structure of channel proteins. I. Transmembrane segment M2 of the nicotinic cholinergic receptor channel is a key pore-lining structure. *J. Biol. Chem.* 268:14601–7

83. Oblatt-Montal M, Iwamoto T, Tomich JM, Montal M. 1993. Design, synthesis and functional characterization of a pentameric channel protein that mimics the presumed pore structure of the nicotinic cholinergic receptor. *FEBS Lett.* 320:261–66

84. Oblatt-Montal M, Reddy GL, Iwamoto T, Tomich JM, Montal M. 1994. Identification of an ion channel-forming motif in the primary structure of CFTR, the cystic fibrosis chloride channel. *Proc. Natl. Acad. Sci. USA* 91:1495–99

85. Oiki S, Danho W, Madison V, Montal M. 1988. M2 δ, a candidate for the structure lining the ionic channel of the nicotinic cholinergic receptor. *Proc. Natl. Acad. Sci. USA* 85: 8703–7

86. Oiki S, Danho W, Montal M. 1988. Channel protein engineering: synthetic 22-mer peptide from the primary structure of the voltage-sensitive sodium channel forms ionic channels in lipid bilayers. *Proc. Natl. Acad. Sci. USA* 85:2393–97

87. Oiki S, Madison V, Montal M. 1990. Bundles of amphipathic transmembrane α-helices as a structural motif for ion-conducting channel proteins: studies on sodium channels and acetylcholine receptors. *Proteins Struct. Funct. Genet.* 8:226–36

88. Papazian DM, Timpe LC, Jan YN, Jan LY. 1991. Alteration of voltage-dependence of *Shaker* potassium channel by mutations in the S4 sequence. *Nature* 349:305–10

89. Parker MW, Buckley JT, Postma JP, Tucker AD, Leonard K, et al. 1994. Structure of the *Aeromonas* toxin proaerolysin in its water-soluble and membrane-channel states. *Nature* 367:292–95

90. Peled H, Shai Y. 1993. Membrane interaction and self-assembly within phospholipid membranes of synthetic segments corresponding to the H-5 region of the Shaker K⁺ channel. *Biochemistry* 32:7879–85

91. Perozo E, Santacruz-Toloza L, Stefani E, Bezanilla F, Papazian DM. 1994. S4 mutations alter gating currents of *Shaker* K⁺ channels. *Biophys. J.* 66:345–54

92. Pouny Y, Shai Y. 1994. Secondary structure, membrane interaction and assembly within phospholipid membranes of synthetic H-5 segments of voltage-gated sodium channel. *Biophys. J.* 66:A103

93. Pribilla I, Takagi T, Langosch D, Bormann J, Betz H. 1992. The atypical M2 segment of the β subunit confers picrotoxinin resistance to inhibitory glycine receptor channels. *EMBO J.* 11:4305–11

94. Raftery MA, Hunkapiller MW, Strader CD, Hood LE. 1980. Acetylcholine receptor: complex of homologous subunits. *Science* 208:1454–56

95. Reddy GL, Iwamoto T, Tomich JM, Montal M. 1993. Synthetic peptides and four-helix proteins as model systems for the pore-forming structure of channel proteins. II. Transmembrane segment M2 of the brain glycine receptor is a plausible candidate for the pore-lining structure. *J. Biol. Chem.* 268:14608–15

96. Revah F, Galzi JL, Giraudat J, Haumont PY, Lederer F, Changeux JP. 1990. The noncompetitive blocker

[^{3}H] chlorpromazine labels three amino acids of the acetylcholine receptor γ-subunit: implications for the α-helical organization of regions MII and for the structure of the ion channel. *Proc. Natl. Acad. Sci. USA* 87: 4675–79

97. Riordan JR. 1993. The cystic fibrosis transmembrane conductance regulator. *Annu. Rev. Physiol.* 55:609–30

97a. Rosenblueth A, Wiener N. 1945. The role of models in science. *Philos. Sci.* 12:316–21

98. Sakurada K, Masu M, Nakanishi S. 1993. Alteration of Ca^{2+} permeability and sensitivity to Mg^{2+} and channel blockers by a single amino-acid substitution in the N-methyl-D-aspartate receptor. *J. Biol. Chem.* 268:410–15

99. Schauer CK, Anderson OP. 1987. Calcium-selective ligands. 2. Stucture and spectroscopic studies on calcium and cadmium complexes of $EGTA^{4-}$. *J. Am. Chem. Soc.* 109: 3646–56

100. Shai Y, Ben-Efraim I. 1994. Molecular recognition between membrane-located synthetic segments of K^+ ion channels. *Biophys. J.* 66:A 427

101. Shen NV, Chen X, Boyer MM, Pfaffinger PJ. 1993. Deletion analysis of K^+ channel assembly. *Neuron* 11: 67–76

102. Sheppard DN, Rich DP, Ostegaard LS, Gregory RJ, Smith AE, Welsh JM. 1993. Mutations in CFTR associated with mild disease form Cl^- channels with altered pore properties. *Nature* 362:160–64

103. Shinozaki K, Anzai K, Kirino Y, Lee S, Aoyagi H. 1994. Ion channel activity of a synthetic peptide with a primary structure corresponding to the presumed pore-forming region of the voltage dependent potassium channel. *Biochem. Biophys. Res. Commun.* 198:445–50

104. Sixma TK, Stein PE, Hol WG, Read RJ. 1993. Comparison of the B-pentamers of heat-labile enterotoxin and verotoxin-1: two structures with remarkable similarity and dissimilarity. *Biochemistry* 32:191–98

105. Sigworth FJ. 1993. Voltage gating of ion channels. *Q. Rev. Biophys.* 27: 1–40

106. Slesinger PA, Jan YN, Jan LY. 1993. The S4-S5 loop contributes to the ion-selective pore of potassium channels. *Neuron* 11:739–49

107. Stein PE, Boodhoo A, Tyrrell GJ, Brunton JL, Read RJ. 1992. Crystal structure of the cell-binding B oligomer of verotoxin-1 from *E. coli. Nature* 355:748–50

108. Stühmer W, Conti F, Suzuki H, Wang XD, Noda M, et al. 1989. Structural parts involved in activation and inactivation of the sodium channel. *Nature* 339:597–603

109. Sukharev SI, Blount P, Martinac B, Blattner FR, Kung C. 1994. A large conductance mechanosensitive channel in *E. coli* encoded by *mscL* alone. *Nature* 368:265–68

110. Taglialatela M, Wible BA, Caporaso R, Brown AM. 1994. Specification of pore properties by the carboxyl terminus of inwardly rectifying K^+ channels. *Science* 264:844–47

111. Tanabe T, Takeshima H, Mikami A, Flockerzi V, Takahashi H, et al. 1987. Primary structure of the receptor for calcium channel blockers from skeletal muscle. *Nature* 328:313–18

112. Terlau H, Heinemann SH, Stuhmer W, Pusch M, Conti F, et al. 1991. Mapping the site of block by tetrodotoxin and saxitoxin of sodium channel II. *FEBS Lett.* 293:93–96

113. Tobimatsu T, Fujita Y, Fukuda K, Tanaka K, Mori Y, et al. 1987. Effects of substitution of putative transmembrane segments on nicotinic acetylcholine receptor function. *FEBS Lett.* 222:56–62

114. Tytgat J, Nakazawa K, Gross A, Hess P. 1993. Pursuing the voltage sensor of a voltage-gated mammalian potassium channel. *J. Biol. Chem.* 268:23777–79

115. Tytgat J, Vereecke J, Carmeliet E. 1994. A possible structural link between voltage-gated and inward rectifier K^+ channels. *Biophys. J.* 66: A425

116. Unwin N. 1993. Nicotinic acetylcholine receptor at 9 Å resolution. *J. Mol. Biol.* 229:1101–24

117. VanDongen AM, Frech GC, Drewe JA, Jobo RH, Brown AM. 1990. Alteration and restoration of K^+ channel function by deletions at the N^- and C^- termini. *Neuron* 5:433–43

118. Verdoorn TA, Burnashev N, Monyer H, Seeburg PH, Sakmann B. 1991. Structural determinants of ion flow through recombinant glutamate receptor channels. *Science* 252: 1715–18

119. Villarroel A, Herlitze S, Koenen M, Sakmann B. 1991. Location of a threonine residue in the α-subunit M2 transmembrane segment that deter-

mines the ion flow through the acetyl-
choline receptor channel. *Proc. R. Soc. London* 243:69–74

120. Weiss MS, Schulz GE. 1992. Structure of porin refined at 1.8 Å resolution. *J. Mol. Biol.* 227:493–509

121. White BH, Cohen JB. 1992. Agonist-induced changes in the structure of the acetycholine receptor M2 regions revealed by photoincorporation of an uncharged nicotinic noncompetitive antagonist. *J. Biol. Chem.* 267: 15770–83

122. Yamakazi M, Dawson S, Kent SBH, Montal M. 1994. Synthesis by chemoselective ligation of membrane proteins that emulate the pore structure of ligand-gated ionic channel proteins. *Protein Sci.* 3:113 (Abstr. 354M)

123. Yang J, Ellinor PT, Sather WA, Zhang JF, Tsien RW. 1993. Molecular determinants of Ca^{2+} selectivity and ion permeation in L-type Ca^{2+} channels. *Nature* 366:158–61

124. Yellen G, Jurman ME, Abramson T, MacKinnon R. 1991. Mutations affecting internal TEA blockade identify the probable pore-forming region of a K^+ channel. *Science* 251:939–42

125. Yool AJ, Schwartz TL. 1991. Alteration of ionic selectivity of a K^+ channel by mutation of the H5 region. *Nature* 349:700–4

Annu. Rev. Biophys. Biomol. Struct. 1995. 24:59–83
Copyright © 1995 by Annual Reviews Inc. All rights reserved

GATING-SPRING MODELS OF MECHANOELECTRICAL TRANSDUCTION BY HAIR CELLS OF THE INTERNAL EAR

Vladislav S. Markin and A. J. Hudspeth

Howard Hughes Medical Institute and Center for Basic Neuroscience Research, University of Texas Southwestern Medical Center, Dallas, Texas 75235-9117

KEY WORDS: auditory system, equilibrium, hearing, ion channel, vestibular system

CONTENTS

1056-8700/95/0610-0059$05.00

ABSTRACT

A sensory receptor of the internal ear, or hair cell, responds to sound or acceleration when this mechanical stimulus deflects the cell's mechanosensitive organelle, or hair bundle. The gating-spring model posits that mechanoelectrical transduction occurs as mechanical force is transmitted through an elastic element, or gating spring, to the molecular gate of each transduction channel; increased tension in the gating spring then promotes the channel's transition from a closed to an open state. Electrophysiological and micromechanical data from a variety of hair cells, both in vivo and in vitro, confirm that the stimulus dependence of channel open probability and bundle stiffness are quantitatively consistent with the model. The results accord still better, however, with an extended formulation including channel transitions among one open and two closed states. In addition to providing a derivation of this three-state model, this review delineates several experimentally testable predictions of gating-spring models.

PERSPECTIVES AND OVERVIEW

Hair cells, sensory receptors that are, in effect, biological strain gauges, conduct mechanoelectrical transduction in the acoustical, vestibular, and lateral-line organs of vertebrates. A hair cell is sensitive to deflection of its hair bundle, an erect cluster of a few dozen to a few hundred nearly parallel, cylindrical processes termed *stereocilia*. The hair bundle owes its mechanical sensitivity to transduction channels, an ensemble of cation-specific ion channels located near the stereociliary tips.

The behavior of transduction channels can largely be explained by the gating-spring model, which proposes that the hair cell's transduction channels are opened by elastic elements, the gating springs, that are stretched when the hair bundle is deflected toward its tall edge (5, 19, 20, 21). These gating springs are probably the tip links, which are fine filaments that connect the tip of each stereocilium to the side of the longest neighboring process (2, 35).

The initial part of this review provides a précis of the gating-spring model and an evaluation of the experimental data that bear upon it. To delineate similarities and differences between the transduction machineries in various receptor organs and in different species, we analyze the results of in vitro experiments from several laboratories.

The hair cells of greatest importance to humans are those of the cochlea, the mammalian hearing organ. The review's second section concerns the stimuli that impinge upon cochlear hair cells and provides evidence that the sensitivity of these cells in vivo is similar to that measured in experimental systems in vitro. The data not only indicate that the gating-spring model applies to hair cells in general but also suggest that the molecules involved in mechanoelectrical transduction are similar throughout the vertebrates.

The most detailed formulations of the gating-spring model published to date (19, 20) have considered only two states of the transduction channel. Although a two-state model provides a satisfactory qualitative explanation of the behavior of hair cells, a three-state model offers improved quantitative agreement with experimental observations. In the final portion of this review, we provide a compact, general derivation of the relevant equations for the three-state model. We demonstrate the applicability of the model to experimental results from several laboratories and apply the extended formulation to phenomena such as hair-bundle entropy, mechanical fluctuations, and distortion products in the cochlea.

THE TWO-STATE GATING-SPRING MODEL

General Features of Two-State Mechanosensitive Channels

The gating-spring model is a specific case of a more general model for the gating of mechanically sensitive channels (20). In the simplest instance, a mechanosensitive channel includes two states, closed and open. A transition between these two states results from external mechanical action, such as hydrostatic pressure (P), membrane tension (σ), or linear force (f). During the transition between the closed and open states, the mechanosensitive channel must change its configuration. This change may include an alteration in the channel's molecular volume (v), in the area occupied by the channel (a), or in the position of the channel's gate (B).[1] These parameters, each of which is positive in sign, are called, respectively, the *gating volume, gating area*, and *gating distance*.

If the force parameter is held constant during the process of channel opening, then the channel experiences a change in energy, ΔE, given by

---

[1] The gating distance, as measured along the gating spring, was earlier denoted d (19). Because this designation led to confusion with the differential operator, the comparable parameter is now designated B, the gating distance as measured in terms of displacement of the bundle's top.

the product of the force parameter and the conjugate gating parameter:

$$\Delta E = vP, \ \Delta E = -a\sigma, \ \text{or} \ \Delta E = -Bf. \qquad 1.$$

The signs of these expressions reflect the fact that pressure tends to close channels, whereas membrane tension or linear force promotes channel opening. The Boltzmann distribution provides the channel's equilibrium probability of being open, p_o, or closed, p_c; the ratios of these probabilities are (21, 50)

$$\frac{p_o}{p_c} = \exp\left[-\left(\frac{\Delta\mu^0 + vP}{kT}\right)\right]; \qquad 2.$$

$$\frac{p_o}{p_c} = \exp\left[-\left(\frac{\Delta\mu^0 - a\sigma}{kT}\right)\right]; \qquad 3.$$

$$\frac{p_o}{p_c} = \exp\left[-\left(\frac{\Delta\mu^0 - Bf}{kT}\right)\right]. \qquad 4.$$

In each instance, the parameter $\Delta\mu^0$ includes any other free-energy changes, aside from mechanical work, incurred by the channel in the process of opening; k and T are, respectively, the Boltzmann constant and absolute temperature.

The open probability of mechanosensitive channels is usually studied as a function of a force parameter and has the familiar form

$$p_o = \frac{1}{1 + \exp\left(\dfrac{\Delta\mu^0 + \Delta E}{kT}\right)}, \qquad 5.$$

in which ΔE represents the change in a transduction element's internal energy upon opening. The midpoint of the transition, at which $p_o = 0.5$, characterizes the magnitude of the force parameter at which the free energies of the channel in its open and closed states are equal.

The Two-State Model for Gating in Hair Cells

The gating-spring model for transduction by hair cells (5) supposes that the molecular gate of each active transduction channel is attached to an elastic gating spring (Figure 1a). This spring bears some tension when the hair bundle is in its resting position; consequently, the channel has a finite resting probability of being open. When the hair bundle is deflected towards its tall edge, a direction defined as positive in sign

a   b   c

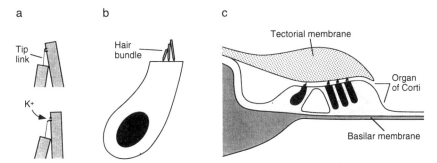

Figure 1   The mechanoelectrical-transduction process of vertebrate hair cells. *(a)* The molecular gate of each transduction channel is thought to be attached to a filament, or tip link, that electron microscopy shows as stretching between adjacent stereocilia *(upper panel)*. Each channel rapidly flickers between its closed and open states; mechanical stimulation of the hair bundle *(lower panel)* increases the tension in the tip link, enhances the channel's open probability, and augments the flow of K^+ and other cations into the cell. *(b)* A hair cell is an epithelial cell surmounted by a hair bundle containing 20–300 stereocilia. These cylindrical processes systematically vary in length across the cell's apical surface; displacement of the bundle towards its tall edge excites the cell by opening transduction channels. *(c)* A cross-section of the mammalian cochlea depicts four rows of hair cells lying in an epithelial strip, the organ of Corti, upon the elastic basilar membrane. The hair bundles of three rows of outer hair cells insert into the gelatinous tectorial membrane; the bundles of a single row of inner hair cells are free of this membrane. When sound drives the basilar membrane up and down, shearing motion of the tectorial membrane deflects the hair bundles and thus stimulates the hair cells.

(49), shear between adjacent stereocilia increases the tension in the gating spring and the channel's open probability consequently increases. Conversely, negative stimuli decrease tension and promote channel closure.

The two-state model can be formulated in either of two frames of reference. First, the analysis may take into account the entire hair bundle, as measured at the bundle's top (Figure 1*b*). This convention requires no assumptions about the precise site of transduction and offers the advantage that the parameters correspond to directly measureable features of the bundle, such as its position and stiffness. The alternative approach is to formulate a theory in terms of the individual transduction element (20), that is, the transduction channel and its associated gating spring. Although this approach clarifies the relation between theoretical concepts and their molecular interpretations, it requires an assumption about the identity of a gating spring. In this article, we use the first approach in derivations; by convention, the parameters of the resultant models are expressed in capital letters. When an examination of the molecular implications of results is needed, we introduce the corresponding single-channel parameters.

The two-state model indicates that the steady-state probability of a channel's being open, p_o, is related to the hair bundle's displacement from its resting position, X, by a single Boltzmann function (5, 16),

$$p_o = \frac{1}{1 + \exp\left\{-\left[\frac{Z(X - X_0)}{kT}\right]\right\}},$$ 6.

in which X_0 is the midpoint of the opening transition (Figure 2a). The gating sensitivity, Z, provides a measure of the transduction channel's mechanical responsiveness. This parameter may also be called the single-channel gating force because it indicates the change in the external force that must be applied to hold a hair bundle stationary when a single channel opens (21).

As a transduction channel opens, the associated gating spring shortens and the tension that it bears consequently decreases. Because the gating springs contribute nearly half of a bundle's resistance to motion (18, 19, 21, 26, 48), the gating-spring model indicates that hair-bundle stiffness should decline over the range of bundle displacements in which the channels open and close (19). For the two-state form of the model, a hair bundle's slope stiffness, K_{hb}, is given by

$$K_{hb} = K_s + K_g - \frac{NZ^2}{4kT}\left\{\cosh\left[\frac{Z(X - X_0)}{2kT}\right]\right\}^{-2}.$$ 7.

Here K_s is the stiffness of the stereociliary pivots, K_g that of the ensemble of gating springs, and N the number of transduction elements. The final term in this relation, which represents a reduction in the bundle's slope stiffness as the transduction channels are mechanically gated, is termed the *gating compliance*. The bundle's stiffness is plotted as a function of displacement in Figure 2b.

The investigation of hair cells provides a unique opportunity to analyze the opening of the channel as a function of bundle displacement. As shown in Equation 6, the channel's open probability assumes a form containing the gating sensitivity Z. This term, which represents the change in gating-spring tension during channel opening with the hair bundle's displacement held constant, is independent of displacement: The gating springs are of constant stiffness. The product of the gating sensitivity, Z, and gating displacement, B, is of the order of magnitude of kT.

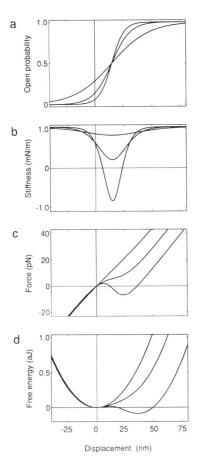

Figure 2 Characteristics of mechanoelectrical transduction by hair cells, as calculated from a two-state model. In each panel, results are displayed for three values of the gating sensitivity, Z: 250, 500, and 750 fN. *(a)* The equilibrium open probability for transduction channels as a function of bundle displacement. Higher values of the gating sensitivity produce successively steeper displacement-response relations. *(b)* The slope stiffness of a hair bundle. The opening and closing of transduction channels causes a local decrease in stiffness—the gating compliance—near the bundle's resting position. As the gating sensitivity increases, the gating compliance grows until the bundle's slope stiffness becomes negative. *(c)* The relation between the force required to displace a hair bundle and the extent of the deflection. When the gating sensitivity is low, the bundle exhibits nearly linear behavior. A high gating sensitivity, however, results in a sharply inflected curve with a region of negative slope. *(d)* The free energy of a hair bundle as a function of bundle position. The energy profile is nearly parabolic when the gating sensitivity is small. A high gating sensitivity, on the other hand, leads to a function with two energy minima.

Negative Hair-Bundle Stiffness

The gating compliance confers upon hair bundles a peculiar property (10) whose physiological significance remains unknown. Figure 2*c* shows the dependence of bundle stiffness on displacement for three different values of the gating sensitivity, Z. Around the midpoint of the gating transition, these curves display a drop whose depth depends upon the sharpness of the gating transition and hence on the value of the gating sensitivity. For very sensitive transduction channels, i.e. when

$$\frac{NZ^2}{4kT} > K_s + K_g, \qquad 8.$$

the bundle displays a negative slope stiffness. This peculiarity also manifests itself graphically as a negative slope in a plot of force, F_{hb}, vs bundle displacement (Figure 2c). In terms of hair-bundle energy, a sufficiently negative stiffness indicates the presence of two energy minima and hence of two possible stable states of the bundle (Figure 2d). If it actually occurs in hair cells, negative bundle stiffness could give rise to such interesting effects as hysteresis in hair-bundle movement, rebound motion, bistability, and oscillations.

Force Fluctuations

In the preceding sections, we have considered the average characteristics of the hair bundle. In actuality, the number of open channels and the force produced by a given bundle displacement both fluctuate. The distribution of channels between different states determines the magnitude of these fluctuations. To simplify the analysis of force fluctuations, we assume that, for a given position of the hair bundle, all N channels are independent and have identical probabilities of occupying their different states. The average number of channels in the open state, $\langle N_o \rangle$, is accordingly

$$\langle N_o \rangle = Np_o, \qquad\qquad 9.$$

while the actual number of channels open at any instant is a random number with a binomial distribution. The variance of this number, $\sigma_{N_o}^2$, is

$$\sigma_{N_o}^2 = Np_o p_c = Np_o(1 - p_o), \qquad\qquad 10.$$

which reaches a maximum at the transition's midpoint. The fluctuation in the number of open channels manifests itself as electrical noise in the transduction current and receptor potential (16).

The mechanical noise resulting from channel gating in a hair bundle can be measured either as a fluctuation of force at a given bundle displacement or as a fluctuation of bundle position during application of a constant force (11). The actual force corresponding to a displacement X is

$$F(X) = F_o(X) + N_c Z, \qquad\qquad 11.$$

in which F_o is the force needed to hold the bundle at position X with all the channels open and N_c is the number of channels in the closed state. From this equation, one can ascertain that the variance of the force, σ_F^2, is

$$\sigma_F^2 = Z(\langle F \rangle - F_o) - \frac{(\langle F \rangle - F_o)^2}{N}. \qquad\qquad 12.$$

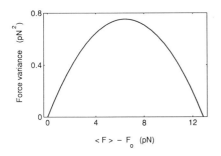

Figure 3 Variance in hair-bundle force due to stochastic channel gating. The force required to maintain a bundle at a particular position fluctuates as individual transduction channels open and close. The variance, or noise, in the force is negligible when the channels are almost always open or shut; the noise is maximal when the open probability is one half.

The variance in the force can be considered a function of the difference ($\langle F \rangle - F_o$). This dependence, which is presented in Figure 3, is of parabolic form. The maximal force variance, $NZ^2/4$, occurs at the position $(\langle F \rangle - F_o) = NZ/2$, the midpoint of the transition between the closed and open states.

COMPARISON OF EXPERIMENTAL RESULTS WITH THEORY

Most of the experimental data on the gating of hair cells have come from studies of hair cells dissected from receptor organs of the internal ear and stimulated with mechanical probes (22). In vitro studies permit the application of a broad range of biophysical and electrophysical techniques that are not readily deployed against hair cells in the intact ear. Nevertheless, we should be certain that the conclusions reached with isolated hair cells apply to those in the intact hearing organ. For this reason, we first evaluate data obtained in vitro, then examine those from experiments on relatively intact cochleae.

Mechanosensitivity of Hair Cells

A simple means of estimating the mechanical sensitivities of hair bundles facilitates consideration of experimental data on hair cells. This metric should reflect the range of hair-bundle displacements over which transduction channels move from their closed to their open states and should also describe the range of stimulation in which gating compliance is significant. Such a measure, whose values are denominated in meters, in effect constitutes a space constant for channel gating.

For the Boltzmann relation that characterizes transduction-channel gating (Equation 6), the space constant should reflect the slope of the relation between bundle displacement and channel open probability. A convenient means of characterizing the width of this relation is by determining the tangent line of greatest slope and extrapolating it to the baseline, for which $p_o = 0$, as well as to the line corresponding to $p_o = 1$. The distance along the abscissa between the two intersections, the effective width of the gating transition, defines the space constant, Λ:

$$\Lambda = 4kT/Z. \qquad\qquad 13.$$

As a hair bundle is displaced by $\pm \Lambda/2$ about the midpoint of its operating range, the channels' open probability varies between about 0.12 and 0.88.

The range of hair-bundle sensitivities estimated from the space constants of gating is quite broad. In one extensively studied experimental system, the epithelial preparation of a bullfrog saccular hair cell (19), a space constant of $\Lambda \approx 56$ nm corresponds to the average gating sensitivity of $Z \approx 290$ fN. Solitary hair cells isolated from the same source exhibit a larger space constant and hence a lower sensitivity of 50–90 fN (1, 14). Cells isolated from turtle basilar papilla display approximately half that sensitivity (6), whereas those from chick ear are still less responsive by a similar factor (32).

Hair cells in epithelial preparations of cultured mouse cochleae have yielded the greatest mechanical sensitivity. From this work, the estimated $Z \approx 210$ fN for an inner hair cell (44) and $Z \approx 610$–845 fN for outer hair cells (43, 44). Outer hair cells presumably exert the dominant effect on the mechanical properties of the organ of Corti, the epithelial strip lying along the elastic basilar membrane and containing the hair cells (Figure 1c). Outer hair cells outnumber inner hair cells by about fourfold and are directly attached to the tectorial membrane, whereas inner hair cells are only hydrodynamically coupled. In analyses of hair bundles' contribution to the basilar membrane's mechanical properties, we may therefore assume that $Z \approx 700$ fN in the mammalian cochlea.

Each gating spring is probably one of the morphologically demonstrated tip links between contiguous stereocilia (2, 35). If so, then the gating sensitivity may be interpreted in terms of individual tip links. Because of the hair bundle's geometrical arrangement, tip-link extension is related to hair-bundle displacement by a mechanical gain factor, γ (19). Although this factor is actually a complex function of hair-bundle displacement, it is nearly constant for bundle movements within the physiological range of stimulation (13, 25, 34). More specifically, one can express this relationship with $\gamma \approx s/h$, in which successive stereocilia are separated along the bundle's plane of mirror symmetry by distance s, and the average stereociliary height in the bundle is h (19, 25).

Using published data on the dimensions of hair bundles, one can gauge the effects of bundle geometry on gating sensitivity: for outer hair cells in the apical turn of mouse cochlea, $h \approx 3.5$ μm (43); for those in the basal turn of chinchilla cochlea, $h \approx 1.0$ μm (31); for an outer hair cell of guinea pig cochlea, $s \approx 0.9$ μm (33); and for one in the cochlear basal turn of guinea pig or gerbil, $s \approx 1.1$ μm (12). If we take these dimensions as typical for cochlear hair cells, the γ value in the cochlea is in the range 0.26–1.1, with a best estimate about three times the bullfrog sacculus γ value of 0.14 (19).

In the gating-spring model, $Z = \gamma \kappa_g b$, where κ_g is the stiffness of an individual gating spring and b is the displacement associated with opening of a single channel's gate. The lower-case parameters here indicate measurements with respect to an individual transduction element, rather than to the entire hair bundle. A given hair bundle's gating sensitivity, Z, thus depends directly upon its geometrical arrangement. Therefore, the two- or threefold sensitivity difference between hair cells in epithelial preparations of the cochlea and sacculus may have a geometrical origin; the greater mechanosensitive of cochlear hair cells may originate from the length and spacing of the stereocilia and may belie similar values of κ_g and b. The molecular properties of tip links and transduction channels may therefore be conserved throughout vertebrate hair cells.

Relation Between Basilar-Membrane Motion and Hair-Bundle Deflection

The gating-spring model has proven useful in our understanding of mechanoelectrical transduction on the basis of responses acquired from in vitro experiments. One goal is clearly to understand whether the same ideas apply in vivo to intact acousticolateralis organs, and especially to the mammalian cochlea. In order to gain an appreciation of the range of hair-bundle motions encountered during acoustical stimulation, we next analyze data on cochlear mechanical and electrical responses.

The 16,000 hair cells of a human cochlea reside in the organ of Corti (Figure 1c). Each frequency component of a sound causes a portion of the basilar membrane to oscillate and this motion is conveyed to, and transduced by, the hair bundles of the overlying receptor cells. The amplitude of basilar-membrane motion at various frequencies of stimulation has been measured by use of several techniques, especially measurement of Doppler shifts from moving Mössbauer-radiation sources and laser interferometry. Data are available for a range of sound-pressure levels,[2] from about 20 dB, the lowest level at which reliable measurements have been made (38), to approximately 65 dB, above which nonlinearities of the middle ear begin to distort responses (24). On the assumption that experimental conditions tend to degrade cochlear performance, the highest observed sensitivities from each study are considered most likely to reflect the performance of the intact cochlea.

Three general conclusions emerge from the data on basilar-membrane motion. First, recent experiments employing interferometry provide estimates of sensitivity that generally exceed those obtained earlier by either the Mössbauer or the interferometric technique. Second, the best results yield sensitivities that are not wildly discrepant despite differences in technique, species, and characteristic frequency (3, 37, 39, 40). Finally, because of a compressive nonlinearity in the basilar membrane's response near the characteristic frequency, the estimate of sensitivity profoundly depends upon the sound-pressure level. For chinchilla, the relation between peak sound-pressure level and basilar-membrane motion is characterized by a near-threshold sensitivity approaching $30 \ \mu\text{m}\cdot\text{Pa}^{-1}$ (39). Evidently, the cat basilar membrane is still more responsive, with a maximal sensitivity exceeding $100 \ \mu\text{m}\cdot\text{Pa}^{-1}$ (3).

If the basilar membrane is modeled as an elastic sheet and if the organ of Corti and tectorial membrane are considered rigid bodies that pivot at their edges, we can estimate the mechanical gain between vertical motion at the center of the basilar membrane and shear motion at the tops of hair bundles (36). Values measured in cat ears (30) indicate that this factor ranges from about 0.4 at the cochlear apex to as much as 2–3 at the base. For the frequency used in laser-interferometric measurements of distortion products in the chinchilla (38, 39)—approximately 8 kHz—the gain in cat cochleae is near 0.65. Taking into account the mechanical gain of the organ of Corti, we may use the approximate sensitivity factors of $8.2 \ \mu\text{m}\cdot\text{Pa}^{-1}$ at 20 dB, $1.6 \ \mu\text{m}\cdot\text{Pa}^{-1}$ at 40 dB, $0.5 \ \mu\text{m}\cdot\text{Pa}^{-1}$ at 60 dB, and $0.1 \ \mu\text{m}\cdot\text{Pa}^{-1}$ at 80 dB to relate hair-bundle motion to sound-pressure level in chinchilla cochleae.

The results above also allow estimation of the threshold for mechanical responsiveness of hair cells. If the chinchilla's behavioral threshold for 9-kHz stimuli is 10 dB, the basilar-membrane excursion is ± 2.7 nm, and the hair-bundle motion approximately ± 1.7 nm, at threshold in that species. The threshold for single-fiber activation in cat corresponds to a basilar-membrane motion of roughly ± 0.7 nm at 30 kHz

---

[2] By convention, sound-pressure levels are reported on a logarithmic scale referenced to a standard root-mean-square pressure of 20 μPa.

(3) and hence to a hair-bundle motion of ± 1.0 nm. The threshold for the guinea pig's compound action potential lies at a basilar-membrane motion of ± 0.18 nm (47) and therefore at a hair-bundle motion of about the same magnitude; if other criteria for threshold are employed, the threshold displacement may be smaller still (47). In any event, the results suggest that a hair cell's threshold corresponds to subnanometer hair-bundle displacements.

Corroborative Results

If hair cells in the intact cochlea have the same sensitivity as those in vitro, a direct examination of the relation between sound-pressure level and a hair cell's electrical response should corroborate these estimates. For this purpose, we must interpret a cell's receptor potential in terms of channel open probability. This procedure has obvious risks; in particular, membrane rectification upon depolarization or hyperpolarization would lead to an overestimate of sensitivity.

In two results from inner hair cells of guinea pig cochlea (41, 45), the relations between sound pressure and apparent open probability have maximal slopes averaging 2.4 Pa^{-1}. In a third investigation (9), the displacement-response relation of a guinea pig inner hair cell displayed a maximal slope of 16.1 Pa^{-1}, and that of an outer hair cell had a maximal slope of 10.3 Pa^{-1}. On the assumption that $Z \approx 210$ fN for an inner hair cell, the conversion factor that relates hair-bundle motion to peak sound-pressure level has an average of 0.57 $\mu m \cdot Pa^{-1}$ for inner hair cells. For the outer hair cell, the conversion factor is 0.25 $\mu m \cdot Pa^{-1}$ on the basis of an assumed value of $Z \approx 700$ fN.

Although sound intensities as great as 90 dB (± 0.89 Pa) were used in these studies, stimulation at 60 dB produced the maximal slopes in all three instances (9, 41, 45). Under this circumstance, the sensitivity factor is 0.5 $\mu m \cdot Pa^{-1}$. The direct estimate of sensitivity (from guinea pigs) and the indirect estimate (from chinchillas) accordingly agree extraordinarily well, especially in view of the species differences and numerous assumptions involved.

THE THREE-STATE GATING-SPRING MODEL

Although the two-state gating-spring model successfully explains the basic features of mechanotransduction in hair cells, it fails to account for several experimental observations. First, the channel open probability, as estimated from the transduction current or receptor potential, consistently displays a more complicated form than that predicted by the two-state model. In data from hair cells of several species, the relation between bundle displacement and electrical response saturates abruptly for negative displacements but more slowly for positive ones (5, 6, 16, 22, 28, 32). Next, the experimentally observed stiffness of a hair bundle is somewhat greater before than after channel opening (19, 28). Finally, mechanical and electrical measurements place the point of channel opening at slightly different bundle positions (19). These experimental findings all suggest the existence of two closed states of the channel.

In order to accommodate the experimental results not expected on the basis of the two-state model, we have developed a more general three-state model that simultaneously accounts for both the displacement-current and displacement-stiffness relations of mechanotransducing channels. We derive below the equations that pertain to this extended model for mechanoelectrical transduction by hair cells.

Suppose that each hair bundle includes N identical transduction channels, each of which is supposed to occupy any of three states, a first closed state 1, a second closed state 2, or an open state 3; these configurations are related by the state diagram $1 \leftrightarrow 2 \leftrightarrow 3$. When a channel passes from the first to the second closed state, the length of the gating spring changes by B_{12}; when the channel's gate opens, the spring's length decreases by an amount B_{23}. In previous versions of the two-state model, the elasticity of the gating springs was not supposed to change upon channel gating. Although including an elastic gate in the formulation would not be difficult (29, 46), the experimental data presently available suggest that such an addition is unnecessary (4); we thus retain the simpler formulation for the transition $2 \leftrightarrow 3$. During the transition $1 \leftrightarrow 2$, however, we suppose that the stiffness of a single transduction element changes from K_1/N to K_2/N. The difference in stiffness is $\Delta K/N$, in which $\Delta K = K_2 - K_1$. To visualize this change in stiffness, we suppose that, when a particular channel is in the first closed state, a portion of its gating spring is immobilized so that this portion of the spring's tension is not transmitted to the gate. This state is accordingly less compliant than are the subsequent states in which the channel is successively closed, then open.

General Equations

N transduction elements and the combined springs of the stereociliary pivots produce the mechanical resistance of a hair bundle. When the channels pass from one state to another, the altered tension in the gating springs manifests itself as a change in bundle stiffness. The thermodynamic properties of a hair bundle are determined by the distribution of channels between different states and hence by the energy of these states. The most convenient way to assess these properties is to calculate the partition function of the system. If the energy of a channel in state m is E_m, then the partition function, q, for an individual channel is

$$q = \sum_m \exp(-E_m/kT), \qquad\qquad 14.$$

in which the sum is taken over all states of a channel. The stereociliary pivot is supposed to have only one state with energy E_s; its partition function is accordingly $\exp(-E_s/kT)$. The partition function of a whole hair bundle, Q, can thus be presented as follows:

$$Q = q^N \exp(-E_s/kT). \qquad\qquad 15.$$

We can now determine the Helmholtz free energy, A, of a hair bundle:

$$A = -kT \ln Q. \qquad\qquad 16.$$

If all other conditions are maintained constant, the Helmholtz free energy of a hair bundle is presumably a function of temperature, T, and of bundle displacement, X. The differential of the Helmholtz free energy therefore assumes the form

$$dA = -SdT + F_{hb}dX, \qquad\qquad 17.$$

in which S is the entropy of the system and F_{hb} is an external force acting on the hair bundle. This force is defined by the relation

$$F_{hb} \equiv \left(\frac{\partial A}{\partial X}\right)_T = -kT\left(\frac{\partial \ln Q}{\partial X}\right)_T. \qquad\qquad 18.$$

The hair bundle's slope stiffness (19, 21) may now be obtained as the derivative of this force with respect to displacement:

$$K_{hb} = \left(\frac{\partial F_{hb}}{\partial X}\right)_T = -kT\left(\frac{\partial^2 \ln Q}{\partial X^2}\right)_T. \qquad\qquad 19.$$

We must also establish the probability, p_m, that a channel will occupy each of its different states; this probability is given by the Boltzmann distribution,

$$p_m = \frac{1}{q}\exp\left(-\frac{E_m}{kT}\right). \qquad\qquad 20.$$

Energy

The equations presented above provide a general description of a gating-spring model with an arbitrary number of states. We must next introduce a specific dependence of energy on hair-bundle displacement. Using experimental results (8, 17, 18, 19, 26), one can describe the stereociliary pivots as an ensemble of Hookean springs with a combined stiffness K_s. Their total energy E_s depends on X in the following way (19, 20):

$$E_s = \frac{K_s}{2} (X_s^{\tau} + X)^2,$$

21.

in which X_s^{τ} is the extension of a pivot spring at the resting position of a hair bundle.

One can calculate the energy of a single channel and gating spring in a similar way. Let the length X_2^{τ} be the extension of a gating spring when the hair bundle is in its resting position and the channel is in its closed state. When the bundle is deflected from its resting position by a distance X, the extension of a gating spring in the latched state is then $X_2^{\tau} + X + B_{12}$; that in the closed state is $X_2^{\tau} + X$; and that in the open state is $X_2^{\tau} + X - B_{23}$. The energies of the latched, closed, and open states of a channel are, therefore:

$$E_1 = \frac{K_1}{2N} (X_2^{\tau} + X + B_{12})^2 + \mu_1^0;$$

22.

$$E_2 = \frac{K_2}{2N} (X_2^{\tau} + X)^2 + \mu_2^0;$$

23.

$$E_3 = \frac{K_3}{2N} (X_2^{\tau} + X - B_{23})^2 + \mu_3^0.$$

24.

The final equations require only the differences between these energy values. Thus, we introduce the energy of unlatching, $\Delta E_{12} = E_2 - E_1$, and the energy of channel opening, $\Delta E_{23} = E_3 - E_2$, together with the difference in standard free energies between states 2 and 3, $\Delta \mu_{23}^0 = \mu_3^0 - \mu_2^0$.

The transition between the closed and open states is determined by the difference in energy between them, ΔE_{23}. If this difference is positive and large, the channel is nearly always closed; if the difference is zero, the channel is open half of the time, and so on. The energy difference changes with bundle displacement; the rate of its change, $-d\Delta E_{23}/dX$, describes the channel's sensitivity to hair-bundle displacement. If the stiffness of the hair bundle is the same in the closed and open states ($K_2 = K_3$), the energy difference for the transition $2 \leftrightarrow 3$ is

$$\Delta E_{23} = -\frac{K_2 B_{23}}{N}(X - X_{23}),$$ 25.

and thus the transition's displacement sensitivity is

$$-\frac{d\Delta E_{23}}{dX} = \frac{K_2 B_{23}}{N} \equiv Z_{23}.$$ 26.

Note that this sensitivity is independent of the hair bundle's displacement.

The derivative of energy with respect to a coordinate is the force acting along that coordinate. In the present case, $d\Delta E_{23}/dX$ is the difference between the forces acting in the hair bundle in the closed and open states. In other words, this expression represents the change in the spring tension after opening of the gate while the bundle's displacement is held constant.

The parameter

$$X_{23} \equiv -X_2^\tau + \frac{B_{23}}{2} + \frac{N\Delta\mu_{23}^0}{K_2 B_{23}} = -X_2^\tau + \frac{B_{23}}{2} + \frac{\Delta\mu_{23}^0}{Z_{23}}$$ 27.

provides the hair-bundle displacement at which the energy difference between the closed and open states is zero. At this deflection of the hair bundle, the populations of states 2 and 3 are equal. The energy of channel opening, ΔE_{23}, depends linearly on hair-bundle displacement; as a result, the gating force is a constant independent of bundle position.

The energy of unlatching is

$$\Delta E_{12} = -Z_{12}(X - X_{12}) - \frac{\Delta K}{2N}(X^2 - X_{12}^2),$$ 28.

in which Z_{12}, a parameter that may be regarded as the unlatching force, is given by

$$Z_{12} = \frac{K_1 B_{12} + \Delta K X_2^\tau}{N} = \frac{K_2 B_{12} + \Delta K(X_2^\tau + B_{12})}{N}.$$ 29.

The parameter X_{12} represents the hair-bundle displacement at which the energy difference between the closed state and the latched one becomes zero. It is a cumbersome function of many parameters including the difference in standard free energies of the closed and latched states, $\Delta\mu_{12}^0 = \mu_2^0 - \mu_1^0$.

The Gating Spring's Slackening Point

Because gating springs are supposed to resist extension but not compression, the hair bundle can reach a negative displacement at which the springs slacken. Experiments on gating kinetics (5) and hair-bundle stiffness (19, 42) provide evidence for such a phenomenon. The position of the slackening point depends upon the state of each channel. After this point is reached, the elastic energy associated with the gating spring becomes zero and the channel's total energy becomes independent of displacement. The energy of the channel in an arbitrary state m after the slackening point therefore remains constant and equal to

$$E_m = \mu_m^0. \qquad\qquad 30.$$

For the closed state 1, the slackening point occurs at a displacement equal to $X = -X_2^{\tau} - B_{12}$. The corresponding point for the closed state 2 lies at $X = -X_2^{\tau}$, and that for the open state 3 occurs at the displacement $X = B_{23} - X_2^{\tau}$.

Channel Open Probability

We may now determine the probabilities of occurrence of a channel's three different states:

$$p_1 = \cfrac{1}{1 + \exp\left[\dfrac{Z_{12}(X - X_{12}) + \Delta K(X^2 - X_{12}^2)/(2N)}{kT}\right]}$$
$$\times \left\{1 + \exp\left[\dfrac{Z_{23}(X - X_{23})}{kT}\right]\right\}, \qquad 31.$$

$$p_2 = \cfrac{1}{1 + \exp\left[\dfrac{Z_{23}(X - X_{23})}{kT}\right]}$$
$$+ \exp\left\{-\left[\dfrac{Z_{12}(X - X_{12}) + \Delta K(X^2 - X_{12}^2)/(2N)}{kT}\right]\right\}, \qquad 32.$$

$$p_3 = \cfrac{1}{1 + \exp\left\{-\left[\dfrac{Z_{23}(X - X_{23})}{kT}\right]\right\}}$$
$$\times \left(1 + \exp\left\{-\left[\dfrac{Z_{12}(X - X_{12}) + \Delta K(X^2 - X_{12}^2)/(2N)}{kT}\right]\right\}\right). \qquad 33.$$

Equation 33, which expresses the channel's open probability, p_3, is more complicated than that derived in the two-state model. This function, as estimated from the dependence of the receptor potential upon bundle movement, is presented in Figure 4a for a hair cell from bullfrog

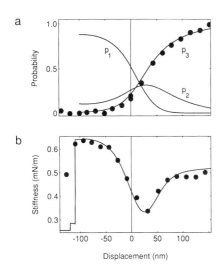

Figure 4 Predictions of the three-state model for mechanoelectrical transduction. *(a)* The equilibrium probabilities of a channel's occurring in the latched state (p_1), the closed state (p_2), or the open state (p_3), as a function of hair-bundle displacement. The calculated open probability, which saturates more abruptly upon stimulation in the negative than in the positive direction, differs from that predicted from a two-state model (Figure 1*a*) but agrees well with experimental data derived from the receptor potentials of hair cells from the internal ear of the frog *(points)*. *(b)* The calculated slope stiffness of a hair bundle as a function of bundle displacement. The stiffness of the bundle falls when large negative stimuli slacken the gating springs. As a consequence of gating compliance, the stiffness also declines near the bundle's resting position. In contrast to the result expected from a two-state model (Figure 2*b*), the slope stiffnesses calculated for positive and negative bundle deflections are not equal. Experimental results from a hair bundle of a bullfrog sacculus are shown for comparison *(points)*.

sacculus. This asymmetrical displacement-response relation provides a good fit to the experimental data on hair cells from several species (5–7, 16, 28, 32, 42).

Entropy

Another interesting parameter of a hair bundle is the entropy of the mechanoelectrical transduction apparatus. Because the number of states accessible to the system changes as channels open and close, the entropy depends upon hair-bundle position (23). For the three-state system, the entropy of each channel, S, is given by

$$S = -Nk(p_1 \ln p_1 + p_2 \ln p_2 + p_3 \ln p_3).\qquad 34.$$

For a large negative or positive bundle displacement, the entropy is low because most of the channels are found in only a single state (Figure 4*a*). At intermediate bundle positions, the entropy increases by the order of magnitude Nk. Over the full range of gating transitions, a hair cell accordingly exchanges with the surrounding medium an amount of heat on the order of NkT.

Force and Stiffness

To displace the hair bundle by a distance X, we must apply to the bundle an external force, F_{hb}, given by

$$F_{hb} = p_1 F_1(X) + p_2 F_2(X) + p_3 F_3(X)$$

$$= [K_2 + K_s + \Delta K p_1(X)] X \qquad\qquad 35.$$

$$- NZ_{23}[p_3(X) - p_3(0)] + NZ_{12}[p_1(X) - p_1(0)],$$

in which $F_m(X)$ is the force that would be needed if all the channels were in state m. When deriving this equation, we accounted for the fact that the externally applied force must be zero at the bundle's resting position. The equation consequently relates the channels' probabilities of occupying various states with the bundle in a given position to those probabilities with the bundle at its resting position.

The difference between the forces $F_2(X)$ and $F_3(X)$ is equal to the combined gating force of all the bundle's channels,

$$F_2(X) - F_3(X) = NZ_{23}, \qquad\qquad 36.$$

a value that does not depend on the bundle's position.

We may now determine the slope stiffness of the hair bundle:

$$K_{hb} = K_s + K_2 - \frac{Np_3(1 - p_3)Z_{23}^2}{kT}$$

$$- \frac{Np_1(1 - p_1)}{kT}\left(Z_{12} + \frac{X\Delta K}{N}\right)^2 \qquad\qquad 37.$$

$$- \frac{2Np_1p_3Z_{23}}{kT}\left(Z_{12} + \frac{X\Delta K}{N}\right) + p_1\Delta K.$$

This function is presented in Figure 4b together with experimental measurements from a bullfrog hair cell. The figure demonstrates that the three-state model gives very satisfactory agreement between theory and experimental observations. With appropriately adjusted parameter values, this model also accurately fits other data on hair-bundle stiffness (19, 42).

Distortion Products

Distortion products occur in the human auditory sensation evoked by a pair of pure primary tones, f_1 and f_2. Discovered by the violinist

Tartini and the organist Sorge early in the eighteenth century, these phantom tones are conspicuous enough that they were employed to carry melodies in musical compositions. The frequencies of distortion products are given by combinations of the primary frequencies, such as the difference tone $f_2 - f_1$, the sum tone $f_2 + f_1$, and the cubic distortion products $2f_1 - f_2$ and $2f_2 - f_1$. Combination tones of higher order, such as $3f_1 - 2f_2$ and $4f_1 - 3f_2$, have also been reported.

Distortion tones appear at relatively low intensities of stimulation; their psychophysically perceived intensities then grow over a large range in proportion to the intensities of the primary tones (15). These results are inconsistent with an ordinary power-series nonlinearity, in which the amplitude of the cubic term, for example, would increase rapidly with the intensity of the input primaries. Distortion tones arise instead from an essential nonlinearity in the cochlea.

The variation in a hair bundle's stiffness with position constitutes a mechanical nonlinearity that can give rise to two-tone distortion products (27). The mechanical resistance afforded by a stimulated hair bundle may be approximated by the instantaneous relation of forced to bundle displacement (Equation 35; Figure 2c). If two sinusoidal displacement signals are simultaneously applied to the hair bundle, such that

$$X(t) = A_1 \sin(2\pi f_1 t) + A_2 \sin(2\pi f_2 t), \qquad\qquad 38.$$

Fourier analysis reveals numerous components in the response. Expanding the force-displacement relation as a Taylor series,

$$F_{hb}(X) = \sum_{m=1}^{\infty} r_m X^m, \qquad\qquad 39.$$

in which a_m is the numerical coefficient of the mth term. This expansion reveals that the force exerted by the stimulated hair bundle should contain distortion products with frequencies $m_1 f_1 \pm m_2 f_2$:

$$F_{hb}(t) = \sum_{m_1,m_2} A(m_1,m_2)\sin[2\pi(m_1 f_1 + m_2 f_2)t + \phi(m_1,m_2)], \qquad 40.$$

in which $A(m_1,m_2)$ is the amplitude of the harmonic with combination numbers m_1 and m_2, and $\phi(m_1,m_2)$ is this harmonic's phase. The summation in this expression is taken over both positive and negative combination numbers. The order of a harmonic, M, is determined by the sum of the absolute values of its combination numbers:

$$M = |m_1| + |m_2|. \qquad\qquad 41.$$

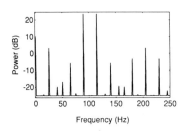

Figure 5 Distortion products anticipated on the basis of a three-state model of mechanoelectrical transduction. If a hair bundle is stimulated by the simultaneous imposition of sinusoidal deflections at two frequencies, here 90 Hz and 115 Hz, the force produced by the bundle should display distortion products of the frequencies and magnitudes shown. The results are displayed in a power spectrum of relative bundle force vs frequency. The predicted results accord well with those measured when hair bundles from bullfrog sacculus are stimulated with elastic probes.

In general, the larger the order of a harmonic, the smaller is its amplitude; nonetheless, this dependence fluctuates.

Figure 5 provides a specific example of the distortion products anticipated as a result of the gating compliance of a hair bundle from a frog sacculus. Although gating compliance causes distortion products whether a two- or a three-state model is used, the latter formulation better fits the experimental results. Mechanical measurements of the force produced by individual hair bundles reveal distortion products at the frequencies, and of the amplitudes, predicted from application of the three-state model (27). However, whether these distortion products in fact account for the psychophysically observed phantom tones remains unknown.

SUMMARY

The three-state model for mechanoelectrical transduction by hair cells represents a generalization of the original two-state formulation. The augmented model thus contains the original version as a particular case: If we move the midpoint of the transition between the two closed states far in the negative direction, the original equations apply. Generally, however, the behavior of the three-state model is more complicated. The three-state model explains why the hair bundle's stiffness before channel opening can exceed that after opening: The gating compliance stems from two transitions, whereas the receptor potential results from only one, and the midpoints of these two phenomena need not be identical. The receptor potential is proportional to the channels' open probability, whose description requires a function more complicated than a simple two-state Boltzmann relation. In good agreement with the experimental observations, the curve describing open probability becomes shallower at larger displacements. Although the three-state model contains more parameters than the earlier formulation, we do not enjoy complete latitude in assigning values to the parameters. Simultaneous fitting of both mechanical and electrical data instead places strong restrictions on these values.

ACKNOWLEDGMENTS

We thank EA Lumpkin, ME Benser, NP Issa, and CE Stewart for critical comments on the manuscript. DP Corey, PG Gillespie, and J Howard joined the authors in formulating a mutually acceptable, and internally consistent, nomenclature for the parameters employed in the present work. This review, as well as the original work from our laboratory on which it is based, was supported by grants DC00241 and DC00317 from the National Institutes of Health.

Literature Cited

1. Assad JA, Hacohen N, Corey DP. 1989. Voltage dependence of adaptation and active bundle movement in bullfrog saccular hair cells. *Proc. Natl. Acad. Sci. USA* 86:2918–22
2. Assad JA, Shepherd GMG, Corey DP. 1991. Tip-link integrity and mechanical transduction in vertebrate hair cells. *Neuron* 7:985–94
3. Cooper NP, Rhode WS. 1992. Basilar membrane mechanics in the hook region of cat and guinea-pig cochleae: sharp tuning and nonlinearity in the absence of baseline position shifts. *Hearing Res.* 63:163–90
4. Corey DP, Howard J. 1994. Models for ion channel gating with compliant states. *Biophys. J.* 66:1254–57
5. Corey DP, Hudspeth AJ. 1983. Kinetics of the receptor current in bullfrog saccular hair cells. *J. Neurosci.* 3: 962–76
6. Crawford AC, Evans MG, Fettiplace R. 1989. Activation and adaptation of transducer currents in turtle hair cells. *J. Physiol.* 419:405–34
7. Crawford AC, Fettiplace R. 1981. Non-linearities in the responses of turtle hair cells. *J. Physiol.* 315:317–38
8. Crawford AC, Fettiplace R. 1985. The mechanical properties of ciliary bundles of turtle cochlear hair cells. *J. Physiol.* 364:359–79
9. Dallos P. 1986. Neurobiology of cochlear inner and outer hair cells: intracellular recordings. *Hearing Res.* 22: 185–98
10. Denk W, Keolian RM, Webb WW. 1992. Mechanical response of frog saccular hair bundles to the aminoglycoside block of mechanoelectrical transduction. *J. Neurophysiol.* 68:927–32
11. Denk W, Webb WW. 1992. Forward and reverse transduction at the limit of sensitivity studied by correlating electrical and mechanical fluctuations in frog saccular hair cells. *Hearing Res.* 60:89–102
12. Forge A, Davies S, Zajic G. 1988. Characteristics of the membrane of the stereocilia and cell apex in cochlear hair cells. *J. Neurocytol.* 17:325–34
13. Geisler CD. 1993. A model of stereociliary tip-link stretches. *Hearing Res.* 65:79–82
14. Gillespie PG, Hudspeth AJ. 1993. Adenine nucleoside diphosphates block adaptation of mechanoelectrical transduction in hair cells. *Proc. Natl. Acad. Sci. USA* 90:2710–14
15. Goldstein JL. 1967. Auditory nonlinearity. *J. Acoust. Soc. Am.* 41:676–89

16. Holton T, Hudspeth AJ. 1986. The transduction channel of hair cells from the bull-frog characterized by noise analysis. *J. Physiol.* 375:195–227
17. Howard J, Ashmore JF. 1986. Stiffness of sensory hair bundles in the sacculus of the frog. *Hearing Res.* 23: 93–104
18. Howard J, Hudspeth AJ. 1987. Mechanical relaxation of the hair bundle mediates adaptation in mechanoelectrical transduction by the bullfrog's saccular hair cell. *Proc. Natl. Acad. Sci. USA* 84:3064–68
19. Howard J, Hudspeth AJ. 1988. Compliance of the hair bundle associated with gating of mechanoelectrical transduction channels in the bullfrog's saccular hair cell. *Neuron* 1:189–99
20. Howard J, Roberts WM, Hudspeth AJ. 1988. Mechanoelectrical transduction by hair cells. *Annu. Rev. Biophys. Biophys. Chem.* 17:99–124
21. Hudspeth AJ. 1992. Hair-bundle mechanics and a model for mechanoelectrical transduction by hair cells. In *Sensory Transduction*, ed. D PCorey, SD Roper, pp. 357–70. New York: Rockefeller Univ. Press
22. Hudspeth AJ, Corey DP. 1977. Sensitivity, polarity, and conductance change in the response of vertebrate hair cells to controlled mechanical stimuli. *Proc. Natl. Acad. Sci. USA* 74:2407–11
23. Hudspeth AJ, Roberts WM, Howard J. 1989. Gating compliance, a reduction in hair-bundle stiffness associated with the gating of transduction channels in hair cells from the bullfrog's sacculus. In *Cochlear Mechanisms: Structure, Function and Models. NATO Advanced Science Institutes Series*, ed. JP Wilson, DT Kemp, 164: 117–23. New York: Plenum
24. Humes LE. 1980. On the nature of two-tone auditory nonlinearity. *J. Acoust. Soc. Am.* 67:2073–83
25. Jacobs RA, Hudspeth AJ. 1990. Ultrastructural correlates of mechanoelectrical transduction in hair cells of the bullfrog's internal ear. *Cold Spring Harbor Symp. Quant. Biol.* 55:547–61
26. Jaramillo F, Hudspeth AJ. 1993. Displacement-clamp measurement of the forces exerted by gating springs in the hair bundle. *Proc. Natl. Acad. Sci. USA* 90:1330–34
27. Jaramillo F, Markin VS, Hudspeth AJ. 1993. Auditory illusions and the single hair cell. *Nature* 364:527–29
28. Kros CJ, Rüsch A, Richardson GP.

1992. Mechano-electrical transducer currents in hair cells of the cultured neonatal mouse cochlea. *Proc. R. Soc. London Ser. B* 249:185–93
29. Lecar H, Morris CE. 1993. Biophysics of mechanotransduction. In *Mechanoreception by the Vascular Wall*, ed. GM Rubanyi, pp. 1–11. Mount Kisco: Futura
30. Liberman MC. 1982. The cochlear frequency map for the cat: labeling auditory-nerve fibers of known characteristic frequency. *J. Acoust. Soc. Am.* 72:1441–49
31. Lim DJ. 1980. Cochlear anatomy related to cochlear micromechanics. A review. *J. Acoust. Soc. Am.* 67: 1686–95
32. Ohmori H. 1987. Gating properties of the mechano-electrical transducer channel in the dissociated vestibular hair cell of the chick. *J. Physiol.* 387: 589–609
33. Osborne MP, Comis SD, Pickles JO. 1988. Further observations on the fine structure of tip links between stereocilia of the guinea pig cochlea. *Hearing Res.* 35:99–108
34. Pickles JO. 1993. A model for the mechanics of the stereociliar bundle on acousticolateral hair cells. *Hearing Res.* 68:159–72
35. Pickles JO, Comis SD, Osborne MP. 1984. Cross-links between stereocilia in the guinea pig organ of Corti, and their possible relation to sensory transduction. *Hearing Res.* 15:103–12
36. Rhode WS, Geisler CD. 1967. Model of the displacement between opposing points on the tectorial membrane and reticular lamina. *J. Acoust. Soc. Am.* 42:185–90
37. Robles L, Ruggero MA, Rich NC. 1986. Basilar membrane mechanics at the base of the chinchilla cochlea. I. Input-output functions, tuning curves, and response phases. *J. Acoust. Soc. Am.* 80:1364–74
38. Robles L, Ruggero MA, Rich NC. 1991. Two-tone distortion in the basilar membrane of the cochlea. *Nature* 349:413–14
39. Ruggero MA. 1992. Responses to sound of the basilar membrane of the mammalian cochlea. *Curr. Opin. Neurobiol.* 2:449–56
40. Ruggero MA, Robles L, Rich NC, Recio A. 1992. Basilar membrane responses to two-tone and broadband stimuli. *Philos. Trans. R. Soc. London Ser. B* 336:307–15
41. Russell IJ, Kössl M. 1991. The voltage

responses of hair cells in the basal turn of the guinea-pig cochlea. *J. Physiol.* 435:493–511

42. Russell IJ, Kössl M, Richardson GP. 1992. Nonlinear mechanical responses of mouse cochlear hair bundles. *Proc. R. Soc. London Ser. B* 250:217–27

43. Russell IJ, Richardson GP. 1987. The morphology and physiology of hair cells in organotypic cultures of the mouse cochlea. *Hearing Res.* 31:9–24

44. Russell IJ, Richardson GP, Cody AR. 1986. Mechanosensitivity of mammalian auditory hair cells *in vitro*. *Nature* 321:517–19

45. Russell IJ, Sellick PM. 1983. Low-frequency characteristics of intracellularly recorded receptor potentials in guinea-pig cochlear hair cells. *J. Physiol.* 338:179–206

46. Sachs F, Lecar H. 1991. Stochastic models for mechanical transduction. *Biophys. J.* 59:1143–45

47. Sellick PM, Patuzzi R, Johnstone BM. 1982. Measurement of basilar membrane motion in the guinea pig using the Mössbauer technique. *J. Acoust. Soc. Am.* 72:131–41

48. Shepherd GMG, Corey DP. 1994. The extent of adaptation in bullfrog saccular hair cells. *J. Neurosci.* In press

49. Shotwell SL, Jacobs R, Hudspeth AJ. 1981. Directional sensitivity of individual vertebrate hair cells to controlled deflection of their hair bundles. *Ann. N. Y. Acad. Sci.* 374:1–10

50. Zimmerberg J, Parsegian VA. 1986. Polymer inaccessible volume changes during opening and closing of a voltage-dependent ionic channel. *Nature* 323:36–39

Annu. Rev. Biophys. Biomol. Struct. 1995. 24:85–116
Copyright © 1995 by Annual Reviews Inc. All rights reserved

MOLECULAR AND STRUCTURAL BASIS OF TARGET RECOGNITION BY CALMODULIN

Anna Crivici and Mitsuhiko Ikura

Division of Molecular and Structural Biology, Ontario Cancer Institute and Department of Medical Biophysics, University of Toronto, Toronto, Ontario, Canada M4X 1K9

KEY WORDS: calcium binding, conformational change, molecular model, regulation, signal transduction

CONTENTS

ABSTRACT

Calmodulin (CaM) acts as an intracellular calcium sensor that translates the Ca^{2+} signal into a variety of cellular processes. Ca^{2+}-CaM recogni-

85

tion of a short polypeptide segment in target proteins induces conformational changes in both CaM and the target, enabling the target protein to become functionally active. The solution and crystal structures of Ca^{2+}-CaM bound to peptides derived from three CaM-dependent enzymes reveal structural features that are common in target recognition by Ca^{2+}-CaM. Phosphorylation of the target proteins at sites in or near the CaM-binding region modulates binding of CaM, thereby providing an additional mechanism of functional regulation. The structural aspects of target recognition by Ca^{2+}-CaM are discussed using mainly the three-dimensional structural information obtained with nuclear magnetic resonance spectroscopy and X-ray diffraction methods.

PERSPECTIVES AND OVERVIEW

Calmodulin (CaM) is a small (148 residues), ubiquitous, highly conserved protein that is an integral modulator of many calcium-dependent processes in virtually every eukaryotic cell type. It functions as a cytosolic calcium receptor and binds four calcium ions with high affinity (K_d 10^{-5} to 10^{-6} M) in response to a variety of extracellular signals (reviewed in 39, 75). Saturation of the calcium-binding sites induces a conformational change that enables Ca^{2+}-CaM to recognize and bind target proteins with high affinity (K_d 10^{-7} to 10^{-11} M) (75). Interaction of CaM with its targets further induces a conformational change in Ca^{2+}-CaM and the target to yield an activated target protein complex. A number of natural peptides also bind CaM with high affinity, including several hormones, neurotransmitters, and venoms (91–93). Because these are either exogenous or secreted peptides, the physiological relevance of these interactions is unclear.

Many Ca^{2+}-CaM–dependent proteins are involved in cell signaling through phosphorylation or dephosphorylation of intracellular proteins or participate in signal transduction by modulating levels of intracellular second messengers such as Ca^{2+}, cAMP, cGMP, and nitric oxide (e.g. 21, 48, 49, 88, 141). Another important area of CaM regulation involves the regulation of cytoskeletal elements (e.g. 2, 127, 139). New cellular targets of CaM are continuously being identified, but their functions and the role of their interactions with CaM often remain unknown. Biochemical characterization of various CaM-binding proteins have defined a role for CaM as an integrator of several different signal-transduction pathways as well as a mediator of Ca^{2+}-dependent cellular events.

The functional role of the interaction of CaM with target proteins and the molecular and structural features of the mode of recognition and regulation by CaM are intriguing. Although no single consensus sequence for CaM recognition exists, the complexes formed are highly specific and of high affinity. Activation of the majority of CaM-dependent proteins requires Ca^{2+} (see section on calcium-independent calmodulin-target interactions for exceptions). The Ca^{2+}-saturated form of CaM is conformationally distinct from the Ca^{2+}-free form, which adds to the complexity of the mode of target recognition because the formation of the ternary complex requires adjustments in the structure of CaM as well as a conformational change in the target that elicits activation.

Because most of the target proteins are large and multimeric, CaM-target complexes have been difficult to study at the molecular level. Consequently, much of the structural information available has been obtained from the study of CaM complexed with peptide venoms (72, 91, 93), model peptides (24, 32, 112), and peptide fragments of the CaM-binding domains of several target proteins (e.g. 14, 63, 100, 101, 134, 157). Functional studies (e.g. 42, 69, 72, 79, 121, 128, 146) using structurally modified CaM have also contributed to the elucidation of the different modes of recognition and complex formation found in different types of targets.

Several comprehensive reviews describing structural (24, 113, 153, 163) and functional (103, 124) aspects of CaM are available, including collections edited by Cohen & Klee (26), Means & Conn (102), and Carafoli & Klee (18). This review includes a description of the current model of CaM-target interaction and focuses on the structural and conformational features required for recognition and activation by CaM and their relevance to the biological activities of this protein and its targets. We briefly discuss the results of investigations into the regulation of CaM-target interactions by structural modifications; this examination defines a role for CaM in the integration of different intracellular signal-transduction pathways.

CALMODULIN-DEPENDENT ENZYMES AND PROTEINS

Protein Kinases and Phosphatases

CaM-dependent protein kinases and phosphatases, which include both dedicated and multifunctional enzymes, seem to share a common mode of CaM recognition and regulation. The best-studied members of this group include skeletal- and smooth-muscle myosin light chain kinases (MLCKs) (14, 89, 124), multifunctional CaM-dependent protein kinase II (CaMKII) (27, 29, 50, 120), CaM-dependent protein phosphatase-2B

(25), calcineurin (the major protein phosphatase in the brain) (25, 52), and phosphorylase kinase (33). These enzymes are generally regulated by a form of intrasteric inhibition (Figure 1) by which, in the absence of Ca^{2+}-CaM, substrate binding is competitively inhibited by a pseudo-substrate inhibitory domain of the enzyme. Under conditions of high intracellular Ca^{2+} concentration, the interaction of Ca^{2+}-CaM with the enzyme, typically at a site near the inhibitory domain of the target, induces a conformational change that relieves the autoinhibition, allowing full enzyme activity to proceed. Constitutive Ca^{2+}-CaM-independent activity can be induced in vitro by proteolytic cleavage of the full regulatory domain, which includes the autoinhibitory and the CaM-binding domains) or by cleavage of the autoinhibitory domain only (reviewed in 26). The autoinhibitory and CaM-binding domains overlap in the MLCKs and CaMKII (28) but are separated by 50–60 residues within the A subunit of calcineurin (the B subunit of calcineurin is also a CaM-like Ca^{2+}-binding protein) (25, 52).

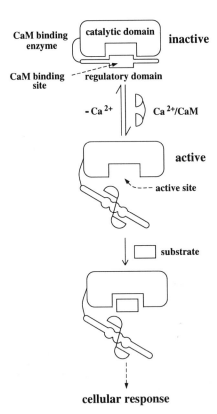

Figure 1   A general model of regulation of a target enzyme by intrasteric inhibition and activation by CaM.

Proteins Involved in Second-Messenger Generation

CaM-dependent cyclic nucleotide phosphodiesterase (PDE) (21, 111), type I adenylyl cyclase (83, 160), plasma membrane Ca^{2+}-ATPase (35, 159), and nitric oxide synthase (88, 160) are all CaM-dependent enzymes involved in signal transduction through generation or regulation of intracellular second messengers. In addition, inositol trisphosphate receptors bind CaM, but the role of CaM binding is presently unclear (41).

The molecular mechanism of CaM regulation has not been defined for all of these proteins but may follow a general mode of regulation analogous to those of the protein kinases and phosphatases. For example, interaction of CaM with the CaM domain of PDE relieves inhibition caused by an autoinhibitory domain (22). The CaM-binding domain of Ca^{2+}-ATPase likely interacts with two discontinuous sites on the energy-transduction domain (which couples Ca^{2+} transport to the ATPase activity) in the latent state, restricting the mobility of the cytoplasmic domain. Interaction with Ca^{2+}-CaM induces a conformational change that dissociates the CaM-binding and transduction domains, allowing Ca^{2+} transport and ATPase activity to proceed (35). Interaction between Ca^{2+}-CaM and these proteins enables cross-talk between the Ca^{2+}-CaM pathway and other signal-transduction pathways.

Proteins Involved in Regulation of Cytoskeletal Elements

The molecular basis of CaM regulation and the functional relevance of CaM interaction with cytoskeletal proteins and their regulatory proteins is not clearly defined. CaM-binding proteins thought to participate in various cytoskeleton-mediated events such as motility, cell growth and development, and morphogenesis include spectrin (149, 150), β-adducin (139), caldesmon (59, 94, 169), brush border myosin-I (BBMI) (30, 154), and the myristoylated alanine-rich C kinase substrate (MARCKS) (2, 12) and a related protein, F52 (12, 13). Details on the interaction of CaM with BBMI and MARCKS are described in later sections (Calcium-Independent Calmodulin-Target Interactions and Phosphorylation of Target Proteins, respectively).

STRUCTURAL ASPECTS OF CALMODULIN-TARGET INTERACTIONS

Calmodulin-Binding Domains on Target Proteins

The identification of calmodulin-target proteins among Ca^{2+}-dependent proteins has largely been based on binding affinity and a functional requirement for CaM (26, 113). CaM dependency is characterized by activation constants in the nanomolar range (75) and by a sensitivity to inhibition by CaM-binding drugs (26, 70) and high-affinity peptide targets of CaM (6, 34).

The CaM-binding domains of the targets have generally been mapped using limited proteolysis or by means of deletion, truncation, and site-directed mutagenesis. Extensive mapping is also carried out using synthetic peptides and proteolytic fragments that incorporate full or partial sequences of the protein segment of interest. Positive identification of a sequence as a CaM-binding domain requires that the synthetic peptide retain a high affinity for CaM, with a K_d value comparable to those of the intact target protein (26) and with an ability to inhibit CaM binding to the native target protein as well as the native protein's CaM-dependent activity (26). In some cases, the precise boundaries of the binding domain have not been positively determined because of the complexity in the regulatory mechanisms of these target proteins.

Examination of the CaM-binding sequences of various target proteins reveals that the CaM-binding domain is limited to a short region of 14–26 residues that has a propensity to form a basic amphiphilic α-helix (reviewed in 113). DeGrado and coworkers (34) have developed a computer algorithm that can be used to examine cDNA libraries or protein sequences for potential CaM-binding domains. This technique involves a quantitative evaluation of a sequence on the basis of its electronic and hydrophobic properties and secondary-structure propensity to identify putative basic amphiphilic α-helical motifs (reviewed in 113). This approach has been used to correctly predict several CaM-binding domains (e.g. 4, 15, 20, 160) but has also identified regions that do not have high CaM affinity when reproduced within a synthetic peptide (33, 73, 94). However, residues in the primary sequence of known CaM-binding domains do not always exhibit a propensity to form an amphipathic α-helix (Table 1). In phosphorylase kinase, one segment of the CaM-binding domain, reproduced in the synthetic peptide PhK13, is predicted to form an extended β-turn–β-sheet structure (33).

Structure of Ca^{2+}-Calmodulin

The crystal structure of Ca^{2+}-CaM, first solved by Babu et al in 1985 (9), subsequently solved by Kretsinger et al (81), and further refined by several groups (8, 23, 130), has provided a starting point for the development of a model of the Ca^{2+}-CaM–target protein complex and for describing the conformational changes that must occur upon Ca^{2+} binding to CaM and upon target complexation. The crystal form of

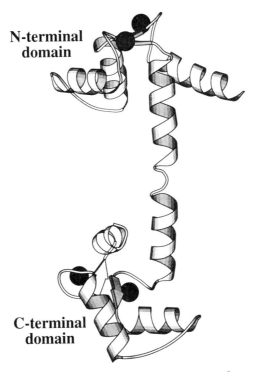

N-terminal
domain

C-terminal
domain

Figure 2   X-ray crystal structure of Ca^{2+}-CaM determined at 2.2-Å resolution. Residues
78–81 of the interconnecting helix (residues 65–93) show some deviations from ideal
helix geometry (8, 23). The structure was reproduced from atomic coordinates deposited
by Babu et al (8) in the Brookhaven Protein Data Bank (structure code 3CLN).

Ca^{2+}-CaM (Figure 2) is a dumbbell-shaped molecule, approximately
65 Å long, with N- and C-terminal globular domains or lobes (25 × 20
× 20 Å) separated by an interconnecting helix of approximately eight
turns. Each globular domain contains two Ca^{2+}-binding sites of the
EF-hand (helix-loop-helix) type related by a two-fold axis of symmetry.
The globular lobes are cup shaped and have a concave hydrophobic
surface in the center of each and negatively charged residues at the
rims. The extreme ends of the interconnecting helix form part of the
helix-loop-helix Ca^{2+} sites, and the central six residues (76–82) are
solvent exposed. NMR studies (10, 67) indicate that, in solution, residues 78–81 adopt a nonhelical conformation with considerable flexibility. In the refined crystal structure, residues 79–81 show some deviations from ideal helix geometry and contain some of the highest
temperature factors in the molecule (8, 23).

Table 1 Primary sequences of some known and putative calmodulin binding domains of protein and peptide calmodulin targets

Target[a]	Sequence[b]	Reference
skMLCK (M13)[c]	KRRWKKNFIAVSAANRFKKISSSGAL	14
smMLCK (smMLCKp)	ARRKWQKTGHAVRAIGRLSS	88
CaMKII	ARRKLKGAILTTMLATRNFS	111
Caldesmon	GVRNIKSMWEKGNVFSS	169
Calspermin	ARRKLKGAILTTMLATRNFS	120
PFK (M11)	FMNNWEVYKLLAHIRPPAPKSGSYTV	15
Calcineurin	ARKEVIRNKIRAIGKMARVFSVLR	74
PhK (PhK5)	LRRLIDAYAFRIYGHWLKKGQQNRG	33
(PhK13)	RGKFKVICLTVLASVRIYYQYRRVKPG	33
Ca²⁺-ATPase (C28W)	LRRGQILWFRGLNRIQTQIKVVNAFSSS	159
59-kDa PDE	RRRKHLQRPIFRLRCLVKQLEK	160
60-kDa PDE	TEKMWQQRLKGILRCLLVKQLMGQ	111
NOS (NO-30)	KRRAIGFKKLAEAVKFSAKLMGQ	160
Type I AC (AC-28)	IKPAKRMKFKTVCYLLVQLMHCRKMFKA	160
Bordetella pertussis AC	IDLLWKIARAGARSAVGTEA	118
Neuromodulin	KAHKAATKIQASFRGHITRKKLKGEKK	20
Spectrin	KTASPWKSARLMVHTVATFNSIKE	85
MARCKS	KKKKKRFSFKKSFKLSGFSFKKSKK	45

	Sequence[b]	[c]
F52 or MacMARCKS	K K K K K F S F K K P F K L S G L S F K R N R K	13
β-Adducin	K Q Q K E K T R W L N T P N T Y L R V N V A D E V Q R N M G S	139
HSP90α	K D Q V A N S A F Q E R L R K H G L E V I	106
HIV-1 gp160	Y H R L R D L L L I V K R I V E L L G R R	147
BBMHCI	Q Q L A T L I Q K T Y R G W R C R T H Y Q L M Q	104
Dilute MHC	R A A C I R I Q K T I R G W L L R K R Y L C M Q	104
Mastoparan	I N L K A L A A L A K K I L	93
Melittin	G I G A V L K V L T T G L P A L I S W I K R K R Q Q	93
Glucagon	H S Q G T F T S D Y S K Y L D S R R A Q D F V Q W L M N T	92
Secretin	H S D G T F T S E L S R L R D S A R L Q R L L Q G L V	92
VIP	H S D A V F T D N Y T R L R K Q M A V K K Y L N S I L N	92
GIP	Y A D G T F I S D Y S A I M N K I R Q Q D F V N W L L A Q Q Q K S	92
Model peptide CBP2	W K K L L K L L K K L L K L G	34

[a] Abbreviations: AC, adenylyl cyclase; BBMHCI, brush-border myosin heavy chain–I; CaMKII, calmodulin kinase II; CBP2, calmodulin binding peptide–2; GIP, gastrin inhibitory peptide; HIV-1 gp160, human immunodeficiency virus envelope glycoprotein 160; HSP, heat-shock protein; MARCKS, myristoylated alanine-rich C kinase substrate; MHC, myosin heavy chain; NOS, nitric oxide synthase; PDE, phosphodiesterase; PFK, phosphofructokinase; PhK, phosphorylase kinase; sk–, skeletal muscle– and smooth muscle–myosin light chain kinase; VIP, vasoactive intestinal peptide.

[b] Alignment of the CaM domains was made by visual inspection based on alignment of the putatively conserved major (bold and underlined) and minor (bold) hydrophobic anchors that interreact with the hydrophobic patches of the C- and N-terminal domains of CaM (63), and on the alignment of the conserved basic residue (bold and italicized) analogous to that residue of MLCK that is required for activation by CaM (100, 101). Precise boundaries of the CaM-binding domain are not known for all targets.

[c] Names in parentheses are those used in the literature for the synthetic peptides containing the sequences listed.

Studies of Ca^{2+}-CaM by small-angle X-ray scattering and fluorescence techniques have also indicated the presence of an equilibrium between several conformational substates in solution. The results of these measurements reflect an average conformation that is more compact than the elongated crystal structure, in which the distance between the globular domains varies over a range of values (55, 142).

Conformational Changes upon Ca^{2+} Binding

Solution techniques, such as NMR (e.g. 10, 36, 62–64, 66, 68, 134, 143, 166, 172), fluorescence (e.g. 19, 91–93, 112, 115, 146) and CD spectroscopy (e.g. 54, 76, 97), and small-angle X-ray scattering (e.g. 15, 30, 31, 54, 55, 71, 73, 76, 78), have also been carried out to elucidate the Ca^{2+}-induced conformational changes in CaM that occur in the first step in the transduction of the Ca^{2+} signal by CaM. Early NMR studies (5, 38, 65, 66, 77) indicated a two-step conformational change in CaM upon binding Ca^{2+} and clearly demonstrated that the C- and N-terminal domains contain high- and low-affinity sites for Ca^{2+}, respectively. Both the affinity and cooperativity of Ca^{2+} binding is affected by target-complex formation. K_d values for Ca^{2+} can increase significantly in the presence of target peptides (75). Changes in the cooperativity of Ca^{2+} binding suggest that some conformational communication occurs between the globular domains of CaM when this molecule is complexed to a target protein or peptide (64, 86, 167). This type of communication has also been observed in studies of CaM containing mutations in the Ca^{2+}-binding sites that affect the protein's ability to bind Ca^{2+}. These mutations influence both binding and activation of target proteins (42, 97, 98, 108, 148).

In addition to measuring changes in Ca^{2+}-binding properties, solution experiments using small-angle X-ray scattering (55, 142) and fluorescence anisotropy measurements of photo-cross-linked CaM (146) indicate that CaM is more compact in the Ca^{2+}-free state. Upon saturation with Ca^{2+}, the molecule becomes more elongated, and CD measurements indicate that the helical content also increases (56, 79, 95). The elongation of CaM upon binding Ca^{2+} may be necessary to expose the hydrophobic surfaces on the globular domains to enable target binding (16, 58, 70, 84, 153, 156, 161).

Models of the Calmodulin-Target Complex

The dumbbell-shaped conformation of Ca^{2+}-bound CaM, whether fully elongated as found in the crystal structure or more compact as indicated by the solution studies, has been difficult to reconcile with the high affinities of either CaM-protein or CaM-peptide complexes. Several important observations have contributed to the structural models of CaM-target complexes based on the crystal structure of Ca^{2+}-CaM and on structural and functional studies of CaM–target peptide complexes in solution. Large conformational changes both in CaM and in peptide targets have been evidenced by small-angle X-ray and neutron scattering studies of CaM in complexes with several natural and synthetic peptides (reviewed in 157) and by ^1H NMR studies that indicate major perturbations in the chemical-shift patterns of the complex (76). Although many of the peptide targets are unstructured in solution (e.g. 76, 169, 170), they adopt a helical conformation within the complex (e.g. 63, 76, 100, 101, 134, 169, 170). Klevit et al (76) first made this observation from CD measurements that showed a significant increase in the helical content of the CaM-M13 complex that was greater than that expected from the sum of contributions from the individual components. NMR studies reveal that both melittin (143) and a peptide derived from smMLCK (134) are helical when bound to CaM. DeGrado and coworkers (115) carried out fluorescence studies of CaM complexed with model tryptophan-containing peptides and showed that the emission maxima of these complexes were consistent with a helical conformation of the peptide. Cross-linking experiments of CaM have suggested that both of the globular N- and C-terminal domains of CaM interact with the target (112, 114) and can be in close proximity to each other (72, 96, 123). Proteolytic cleavage of Ca^{2+}-CaM yields independent globular domains that can bind target peptides and proteins with reduced affinity but that cannot activate all target enzymes (69, 125).

The most difficult problem in developing models of CaM–target peptide complexes involves the integrity of the central helical linker found in the crystal structure of Ca^{2+}-CaM. The refined crystal structure includes some deviations from ideal geometry in the central portion of this helix (9). Mutations and deletions in this region are tolerated in many CaM-target complexes with respect to both binding and activation (122, 129). As previously noted, NMR experiments indicate that residues 78–81 adopt a nonhelical structure with a high degree of flexibility (10, 67).

Persechini & Kretsinger (124), and subsequently O'Neil & DeGrado (113), proposed that each globular domain of CaM could interact with one of two hydrophobic patches approximately 180° apart in the helical form of the skMLCK peptide, M13. The main concept of this model, which uses the central helix as a flexible tether, proved to be correct (see below), but the detailed mode of interaction between the peptide and the globular domains of CaM could not be accurately predicted.

Strynadka & James (153) proposed a model for the complex of CaM and mastoparan, a peptide venom similar in sequence to that of helix A of troponin C (151, 152). Although, unlike Kretsinger's model, no attempt was made to alter the conformation of the central helix, the relative orientation of the mastoparan helix and the C-terminal domain of CaM in this model is very similar to that found in NMR- and X-ray–derived structures of the CaM-M13 complex (see below) (63, 100).

Structure of the Calmodulin–Target Peptide Complex

In 1992, the three-dimensional structure of CaM complexed with M13 was solved by using multidimensional NMR techniques (Figure 3) (63). The conformations of the globular domains are nearly identical to those of the crystal structure of Ca^{2+}-CaM, but the interconnecting central helix (residues 65–93) is disrupted into two smaller helices (residues 65–73 and 83–93), which form part of the helix-loop-helix Ca^{2+}-binding sites. The flexible region in the central helix of Ca^{2+}-CaM (residues 78–81) is expanded in the complex to include residues 74–82, which do not appear to form any important contacts with the target peptide or with the globular domains. The overall shape of the molecule is more compact than the crystal structure of Ca^{2+}-CaM. The globular domains lie close to one another and, along with the flexible linker, form a hydrophobic channel that passes through the molecule at an approximate 45° angle relative to its long axis. The channel is occupied by the target peptide that adopts a helical conformation. Residues 3–21 of the 26-residue M13 peptide make up the helix and form contacts with the globular domains of CaM. The remaining residues of M13 are disordered and lie outside of the channel.

The target peptide M13 contains two important hydrophobic residues, Trp4 and Phe17, that form numerous contacts with the C- and N-terminal domains of CaM, respectively (Figure 4). These two residues establish hydrophobic interactions between the target and CaM and may represent anchors that determine the relative orientation of the target within the channel formed by the globular domains (Figure 5). Other hydrophobic residues of the peptide, Phe8, Ile9, Ala10, Val11, Ala13, and Ala14, also contribute to the hydrophobic contacts with the globular domains of CaM (Figure 4). In addition to the hydrophobic interactions, several possible electrostatic interactions can be deduced from the NMR-derived structure (63).

Almost at the same time that the NMR solution structure of CaM-M13 was solved, the crystal structure of the analogous complex with a peptide from smMLCK (smMLCKp) was determined by Meador et al (100). The overall features of the complex are very similar to those of the solution structure of Ikura et al (63). The orientation of the helical

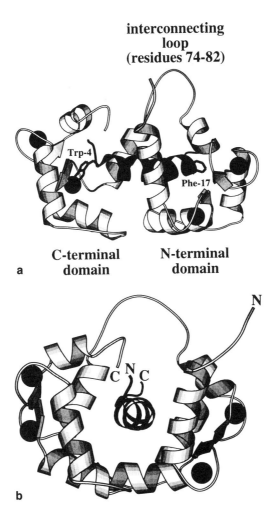

Figure 3 (*a*) NMR solution structure of Ca^{2+}-CaM (*light ribbon*) complexed with the skMLCK peptide, M13 (*dark ribbon*). The major hydrophobic anchors of the peptide, Trp4 and Phe17, interact with the C-terminal and N-terminal domains of CaM, respectively. (*b*) Structure is rotated to illustrate the hydrophobic channel formed by the terminal domains of CaM that enclose the target peptide. Side chains have been omitted for clarity. The structures were reproduced from atomic coordinates deposited by Ikura et al (63) in the Brookhaven Protein Data Bank (structure code 2BBM).

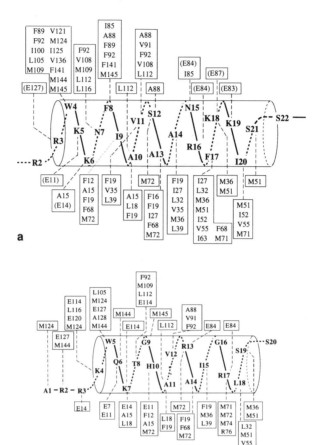

Figure 4 (*a*) Schematic summary of the intermolecular nuclear Overhauser effect (NOE) interactions (<5-Å distances) between residue pairs in M13 (residues indicated in the schematic helix) and Ca^{2+}-CaM (residues written above and below the helix) observed in the NMR solution structure (63). Potential electrostatic interactions between M13 and glutamic acid residues of CaM are inferred from the three-dimensional structure. (*b*) Schematic summary of the interactions (<4-Å distances) between the residues of the peptide smMLCKp and Ca^{2+}-CaM as observed in the crystal structure of the complex reported by Meador et al (100). (*c*) Schematic summary of the interactions (<4-Å distances) between the residues of the peptide fragment of CaMKII and Ca^{2+}-CaM as observed in the crystal structure of the complex reported by Meador et al (101). Major hydrophobic anchors of the peptide targets: (*a*) Trp4 and Phe17, (*b*) Trp5 and Leu18, and (*c*) Leu10 and Leu19.

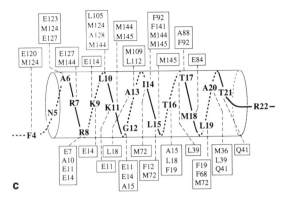

Figure 4   (continued)

peptide within the complex is nearly identical to that of the CaM-M13 complex, with analogous residues of smMLCKp making similar contacts with the globular domains of CaM. A major difference between the structures lies in the conformation of the loop that connects the globular domains of CaM. In the crystal structure, residues 73–77 are found within an extended but well-defined loop that separates shorter helices on either side that make up a part of the helix-loop-helix Ca^{2+}-binding sites. Note that residues 74–82 are nonhelical and flexible in the solution NMR structure of the CaM-M13 complex (10, 63, 67). Several hydrophobic interactions between CaM and smMLCKp appear in the crystal structure (Figure 4).

The crystal structure of Ca^{2+}-CaM complexed with a 25-residue peptide fragment of CaMKII, recently reported by Meador et al (101), represents the third CaM-target complex solved to date. The overall topology of the structure is similar to that of the MLCK peptide complexes: As observed in the MLCK peptide complexes, the terminal domains of CaM are wrapped around the helical target peptide, enclosing the peptide in a hydrophobic channel within a globular core, and the interconnecting linker region of CaM is partially extended to form a loop joining the terminal domains. In addition, the hydrophobic patches of the terminal domains of CaM are anchored at two hydrophobic residues of the target peptide. However, a significant difference is that the major hydrophobic anchors within the CaM-binding domain of CaMKII, Leu10, and Leu19 (Figure 4) are approximately one turn of a helix closer together than those analogous residues in the MLCK peptides M13 and smMLCKp. The relative positions of the minor hy-

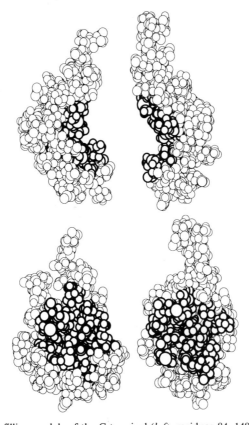

Figure 5 Space-filling models of the C-terminal (*left*, residues 84–148) and N-terminal (*right*, residues 1–72) domains of CaM extracted from the average NMR solution structure of Ca^{2+}-CaM complexed with M13 (63). The structures in the lower part of the diagram are rotated to show the surface of CaM that forms the hydrophobic channel and interacts directly with M13. The dark circles represent atoms of the hydrophobic residues of CaM that are adjacent to those hydrophobic residues of the peptide target, as determined from the NOEs observed in the NMR studies (63). The highlighted atoms are those of the hydrophobic residues of CaM listed in Figure 4*a*.

drophobic anchors (Table 1) are unchanged with respect to those in the MLCK peptides.

The arrangement of hydrophobic residues in CaM-binding domains may be an important determinant in the mode of CaM recognition of its targets. The positions of the major (residues 4 and 17) and minor (residues 8 and 11) hydrophobic anchors of M13 are conserved in many of the known CaM-binding domains of target proteins (Table 1). Recently, synthetic peptide analogues of melittin and a smMLCK peptide, which contain hydrophobic anchoring sites separated by 12 residues, were prepared using all D-amino acids (36). Both peptides formed complexes with Ca^{2+}-CaM that spectroscopically resembled those prepared with the native forms of the target peptides. Truncated peptides that are lacking in one of the terminal hydrophobic residues analogous to Trp4 or Phe17 of M13 bind to CaM with reduced affinity (73) because they may only form contacts with one of the globular domains. Failure to bind both domains simultaneously may result in an elongated rather than a compact complex structure, as has been observed in small-angle X-ray scattering studies of peptide fragments of the CaM-binding domain of Ca^{2+}-ATPase (73).

In addition to hydrophobic interactions between the target peptides and CaM, the crystal structures of Ca^{2+}-CaM complexed with smMLCKp and the CaMKII peptide reveal important electrostatic interactions that involve salt bridges between the basic residues of the peptide and glutamic acid residues in the N- and C-terminal domains of CaM (100, 101). Arg17 of smMLCKp appears to be particularly important because it establishes hydrogen bonds and electrostatic interactions with Glu84 and Arg74 and van der Waals contacts with Met71, Met72, and Met76. These residues are in the interconnecting loop region of CaM and may therefore be critical for establishing and maintaining the bend required to bring the globular domains close together (101).

Two major features of CaM may therefore be important in the interaction of Ca^{2+}-CaM with target peptides of varying primary sequence. In many of the known cases, the target peptide adopts a helical conformation upon complex formation (e.g. 63, 76, 100, 101, 169, 170), but the length of the helical region bound by the terminal domains of CaM may vary. Helices of varying length may be accommodated by the flexibility of the interconnecting linker region of CaM, which acts as a hinge (43), joining the globular domains as they fold around the target peptide. The length of the target peptide helix and the relative position of the hydrophobic anchors on the target peptide is reflected in the distance separating the terminal lobes of CaM in the globular structure of the complex. Although many of the known primary sequences of CaM-binding domains (Table 1) contain residues that may act as the major hydrophobic anchors that are separated by 12 residues (as found in the MLCK peptide complexes), other target domains, such as that of caldesmon (169), may more closely resemble the CaM-binding domain of CaMKII, in which the hydrophobic anchors are separated by eight residues. The terminal domains of Ca^{2+}-CaM may recognize and bind to different target amphipathic α-helices by making adjustments in the conformations of the flexible, hydrophobic methionine side chains (113, 161, 168, 169) and acidic glutamic acid side chains that interact with the basic residues of the target peptide (100, 101). CaM is unique in that it contains numerous methionine residues (nine in total: residues 36, 51, 71, 72, 76, 109, 124, 144, and 145), which is unusual for a protein of this size.

The structures of CaM complexed with the three different peptides may be representative of the mode of interaction of CaM with its targets and can be used to explain much of the experimental data obtained for CaM-target complexes. The results of cross-linking studies between the globular domains of CaM, and between CaM and a bound peptide, can be explained by the close proximity of the cross-linked residues in the structures. Mutations and deletions in the flexible linker of CaM can be accommodated without destroying the activity of CaM because these residues form few contacts with the target domain and may only be important in allowing the globular domains to move close together upon complexation (71, 80, 90, 121). The NMR structure, which shows that only residues 3–21 of M13 are in contact with CaM, supports binding studies indicating that only 17 residues of M13 are required to bind CaM (14, 89). The inaccessibility of the CaM-binding domain to proteolysis while CaM is bound (14) can be explained by the manner in which the target domain is enclosed within the hydrophobic channel.

The interactions between the light and heavy chains of the regulatory domain of scallop adductor (165) and of chicken skeletal muscle myosin (131) represent an analogous mode of target recognition. The essential and regulatory light chains, which share a sequence homology with CaM, form hydrophobic interactions with helical segments of the so-called IQ-motif of the heavy chain, particularly at two hydrophobic residues that are located 12 residues apart in the primary sequence. The regulatory light chain–binding region of the heavy chain has a kink in the middle of it.

The mode of interaction (described above) in the α-helical target model may not apply to all CaM-binding proteins and peptides. We have preliminary evidence that the complex formed between Ca^{2+}-CaM and a peptide fragment of the MARCKS-related protein, F52, which binds CaM in a Ca^{2+}-dependent manner in a 1:1 complex, does not involve a helical conformation of the peptide target (T Porumb, A Crivici, PJ Blackshear & M Ikura, in preparation). The α-helical target model also does not readily accommodate the interaction between Ca^{2+}-CaM and target proteins believed to contain a sequentially discontinuous CaM-binding domain, such as phosphorylase kinase (33), Ca^{2+}-ATPase (35), and caldesmon (94). Because Ca^{2+} is required for the formation of the hydrophobic patches necessary to bind to the hydrophobic face of the target peptides, the model described above does not account for the target recognition of CaM in a Ca^{2+}-independent manner.

Calcium-Independent Calmodulin-Target Interactions

Several proteins have been identified that bind CaM in the Ca^{2+}-free state, but all are believed to be sensitive to Ca^{2+} concentration. These proteins can be divided into three groups. The first case is represented by neuromodulin, which binds one molecule of CaM with higher affinity in the absence of Ca^{2+} than in the presence of Ca^{2+} under conditions of low ionic strength (3, 4, 6). The functional significance of this observation is not clear, but the finding suggests a role for neuromodulin as a plasma membrane–associated CaM trap that releases CaM into the cytosol in response to increases in Ca^{2+} concentration (87).

The second group of proteins includes those that contain CaM as an integral subunit that does not dissociate even at low Ca^{2+} concentration. Phosphorylase kinase (PhK) contains CaM as an integral subunit of the multimeric enzyme complex, which has an $(\alpha\beta\gamma\delta)_4$ subunit composition (33). CaM, the δ subunit, remains tightly associated with the complex under conditions of low Ca^{2+} concentration, but activation of the catalytic subunit is Ca^{2+} dependent (33). CaM may be bound to the γ subunit in its Ca^{2+}-free conformation, thereby forming numerous intersubunit contacts (158). Knowledge of the conformation of CaM in the PhK complex may be important to our understanding of the mode of target recognition because two discrete segments of the γ subunit are thought to bind to CaM simultaneously (158). These discontinuous segments have been reproduced in the peptides PhK5 and PhK13 (158). Solution X-ray scattering studies of synthetic CaM-domain peptides complexed with CaM showed that the complex between CaM and PhK13, or between CaM and both PhK5 and PhK13, forms an extended complex whose conformational parameters are similar to those of Ca^{2+}-CaM (33, 158).

The CaM-dependent adenylyl cyclase of *Bordetella pertussis* may also contain two distinct CaM-binding segments that form a single CaM-binding domain (83). This extracellular bacterial enzyme, which may be involved in the pathogenesis of whooping cough (reviewed in 26), binds CaM in vitro in the presence and absence of Ca^{2+} (48). Interestingly, Ca^{2+}-stimulated CaM-dependent activation is not reversible by Ca^{2+} chelators (48, 83). Like PhK, a PDE isolated from bovine lung contains CaM as an integral subunit (145). The mechanism of Ca^{2+}-CaM regulation of these latter two proteins is currently unclear because of the limited structural information available.

Brush border myosin-I (BBMI) represents a third example of a Ca^{2+}-independent CaM-target association. This protein functions by coupling ATP hydrolysis to actin binding to enable the movement of the plasma membrane along the cytoskeleton in a CaM-dependent manner (127). This myosin-I–type protein consists of a single myosin heavy chain and three or four closely associated CaM molecules with low Ca^{2+} affinity, referred to as the light chains. The activating or inhibitory effect of Ca^{2+} on this protein is the subject of debate. Several groups have reported that Ca^{2+} induces the dissociation of CaM (30, 31), suggesting an inhibitory role for Ca^{2+}, whereas others have shown that Ca^{2+} is required for both ATPase activity and motility (107). More recent studies suggest that BBMI activity is sensitive to subtle changes in Ca^{2+} concentration within its normal physiological ranges. The four bound CaM molecules can be categorized into three groups that display unique Ca^{2+}- and temperature-dependent affinities for the myosin heavy chain subunit (154). Ca^{2+}-induced dissociation of one CaM stimulates the activity of this protein through a putative conformational change in the ATPase- and actin-binding sites. Dissociation of the first CaM is also believed to influence the binding of two of the three remaining molecules so that Ca^{2+}- or temperature-dependent dissociation of this second group results in a complete loss of activity (154).

POSTTRANSLATIONAL MODIFICATIONS OF CALMODULIN AND TARGET PROTEINS

Phosphorylation of Target Proteins

Studies of the phosphorylation-dephosphorylation cycle of CaM-dependent enzymes have only recently led to the identification of the sites of phosphorylation. Many CaM-dependent enzymes are frequently sensitive to phosphorylation by serine/threonine kinases (e.g. 17, 25, 45, 53, 61, 99, 105) and are phosphorylated in vitro by one or more of the three major multifunctional serine/threonine kinases: cyclic AMP–dependent protein kinase (cAPK), CaMKII, and protein kinase C (PKC) (e.g. 7, 45, 51, 60, 61, 155). As with the general mode of regulation by CaM, CaM-binding proteins seem to share a common mechanism of regulation by phosphorylation, with some variations and exceptions. In many cases, phosphorylation of a target residue in or near the CaM-binding domain reduces CaM affinity and inhibits CaM-induced activation of the enzyme activity. Conversely, phosphorylation is inhibited when CaM is bound to the regulatory domain.

This basic mode of regulation has been found in MLCK phosphorylation by cAPK, CaMKII, and PKC, which all modify the same serine residue at the C-terminal end of the CaM-binding domain (1, 60, 61, 110). Calcineurin A is phosphorylated by CaMKII and PKC at a serine residue at the C-terminal end of the CaM-binding domain (17,53). This phosphorylation is inhibited by bound CaM, although CaM can still bind to the phosphorylated domain (17, 51, 53). Different isozymes of CaM-dependent PDE are targets of different kinases. Phosphorylation of the 60-kDa isozyme by cAPK is inhibited by CaM, but CaM can still bind to phospho-PDE (144). CaMKII phosphorylates the 63-kDa isozyme at two major sites, which reduces the enzyme affinity for CaM (111, 144). The phosphorylation sites of these isoforms of PDE have not been determined, and the CaM-binding domains do not contain the necessary kinase consensus sequences.

CaMKII exhibits an interesting variation on this theme. Phosphorylation occurs at a primary site through intersubunit autophosphorylation. This site, Thr286, is located in the autoinhibitory domain, which is N-terminal to the boundary of the overlapping CaM-binding domain (28). Phosphorylation of this threonine residue has the opposite effect on both CaM-binding and enzyme activity compared with the examples mentioned above. Autophosphorylation is activated by CaM, which relieves the intrasteric inhibition on the catalytic site. Dissociation of the inhibitory domain exposes the target threonine, and phosphorylation inhibits the reassociation of this segment with the catalytic domain, thus producing a CaM-independent active form of the enzyme. A secondary effect of this modification is a 1000-fold increase in the CaM-binding affinity (105); hence this form of CaMKII has one of the highest affinities of all known CaM-binding proteins. If CaM is dissociated by the addition of Ca^{2+} chelators, autophosphorylation of a secondary site can occur, which reduces the enzyme affinity for CaM. Not surprisingly, this secondary site, Thr306, is located within the CaM-binding domain. A recent study also showed that CaMKII is a substrate of PKC in vitro and that phosphorylation occurs at Thr286 in the autoinhibitory domain (162).

Several CaM-binding cytoskeletal proteins are also substrates of serine/threonine protein kinases, and in all known cases phosphorylation occurs within the CaM-binding domain. Phosphorylation of β-adducin by cAPK, CaMKII, and PKC on a serine or threonine residue at the C-terminal end of the CaM-binding domain inhibits CaM binding (139), but the functional significance of this modification is not known. MARCKS and the related protein F52 contain multiple serine residues within the CaM-binding domain that are phosphorylated by PKC (2), a process that reduces CaM-binding affinity and is inhibited by bound CaM (46). Another important effect of phosphorylation involves the translocation of the plasma membrane–anchored MARCKS to the cytosol, where it interacts with actin (2, 12). The phosphoprotein can bind to actin but cannot cross-link it. Dephosphorylation in the absence of actin causes MARCKS to revert to the membrane-bound form and, in the presence of actin, allows MARCKS to participate in actin-filament cross-linking. CaM binding to MARCKS, like phosphorylation, inhibits actin cross-linking but, unlike phosphorylation, does not result in translocation of the plasma membrane–associated form of the protein.

In addition to cross-linking actin, MARCKS may function as a CaM store by sequestering CaM at the plasma membrane in the absence of PKC activity (12). Release of Ca^{2+} to the cytosol in response to some extracellular signal may be mediated by the activity of PKC (12). A similar function has been proposed for neuromodulin (119), which is anchored to the plasma membrane through a palmitic acid residue (44) and binds CaM in a Ca^{2+}-independent manner. Phosphorylation of a serine residue in neuromodulin near the N-terminal end of the CaM-binding domain reduces the affinity for CaM (4, 11). Thus, mobilization of neuromodulin-associated CaM may be directly mediated through an increase in Ca^{2+} concentration, which reduces CaM affinity for neuromodulin, or through the kinase activity of PKC.

Regulation of the majority of the CaM-dependent protein functions described above can likely be explained on the basis of the destabilizing effects on the interaction with CaM, a largely hydrophobic protein, caused by the introduction of a negatively charged phosphate group into or near the CaM-binding domain on the target. Steric effects cannot be discounted in the putative destabilization of the CaM–phosphoprotein complex.

Secondary conformational effects induced by phosphorylation may also be important. In the case of CaMKII, the observed increase in CaM affinity for the Thr286-phosphorylated form of the protein may arise from a direct or indirect interaction between the phosphorylated inhibitory domain and the CaM–target domain complex, inducing some conformational change in CaM, its binding domain, or both components, with the result that additional interactions between the proteins increase the affinity of CaMKII for CaM. An alternative explanation may be that CaM does not optimally bind to its target domain in the dephosphoprotein because of some direct or indirect influence of the inhibitory domain on the conformational accessibility of the CaM domain. Phosphorylation may release this constraint and allow the CaM domain to bind CaM with higher affinity. The effect of mutating the target threonine residue to an aspartic acid in the native protein mimics the autophosphorylation by inducing Ca^{2+}-CaM–independent activity (37). These results suggest that the introduction of a negative charge is sufficient to generate this activity; however, how this change in the electronic properties of this domain enhances CaM-binding affinity is unknown. Further structural studies are required to identify the structural basis of this enhanced binding.

Posttranslational Modification of Calmodulin

Less attention has been paid to endogenous posttranslational modifications of CaM itself and the implications of the molecular and structural effects of these changes on CaM-target recognition. Studies have shown that posttranslational modifications of CaM have both a physiological basis and effects on the activation of various CaM targets. The effects on target protein activation, however, appear to be quite specific. Much, but not all, of the calmodulin isolated from higher organisms contains an ϵ-trimethyllysine residue at position 115 (26, 102), but unmethylated calmodulin can activate most known target proteins, except for NAD kinase, which is significantly more sensitive to activation by unmethylated CaM (116, 117, 132, 133, 140). The structural basis for this biological effect is not known (171).

A much rarer modification, glycation of one or more lysine side chains of CaM, reduces CaM's ability to bind Ca^{2+} and to activate several target enzymes (79) but does not appear to be associated with a major structural rearrangement, as determined by CD spectroscopy and small-angle X-ray scattering (79). Although glyco-CaM is not normally found, it has been isolated from diabetic individuals and may be involved in the histopathological development of this disease (78).

Phosphorylation of CaM at the serine and threonine residues of the central linker region by multifunctional casein kinase II results in a reduction in the activation of smMLCK but does not prevent CaM from binding to this target (135). The same modifications to CaM reduced the binding affinity of CaM for PDE without changing the activation kinetics (135). Tyr99 phosphorylation generates a form of CaM that more effectively activates PDE and has a greater affinity for this target than the wild-type CaM (164). The conformational effects of these forms of CaM phosphorylation are not known.

Phospho-CaM has been isolated from several tissues (109, 126) and has been shown to be a substrate of the insulin receptor tyrosine kinase in vitro (47, 136–138) and of several serine/threonine kinases in vitro (57, 82, 109, 126) and in intact cells (40, 109, 126). Because the effects of phosphorylation appear to be target specific, this type of modification may represent not only a form of regulation that modulates the ability of CaM to recognize and activate target proteins, but also a mechanism by which CaM differentially regulates targets within a single cell. The effects of these structural modifications on CaM may provide some insights into an alternate regulatory pathway that can influence target protein response to Ca^{2+}-dependent signals.

SUMMARY AND FUTURE DIRECTIONS

These and other observations have raised some questions concerning the universality of a single mode of interaction between CaM and its targets. Current investigations focusing on the primary, secondary, and tertiary structural features required for CaM recognition are addressing the following questions: (*a*) Is a basic amphiphilic α-helix the only structural motif recognized by CaM? Although many of the known peptide fragments of CaM-binding domains apparently bind Ca^{2+}-CaM as an α-helix, several examples suggest other modes of interaction in which CaM recognizes and binds to nonhelical or discontinuous segments of the primary sequence. Unknown are the conformations of these CaM-binding regions in the intact, native proteins and the relevant conformational changes that occur within these targets that enable CaM recognition or that result from CaM binding. (*b*) How does CaM accommodate such a diverse selection of target sequences with such high affinity? The interconnecting linker region of CaM acts as a hinge that allows the terminal lobes of CaM to wrap around a target to varying degrees, depending on the length and three-dimensional structure of the target domain. The hydrophobic patches in the terminal domains of CaM contain many flexible residues, particularly methionine residues, that can optimize the contact between the CaM domains and the hydrophobic faces of a variety of targets.

Finally, recent studies of posttranslational modifications of CaM and its targets have prompted investigations into the role and mechanism of regulation of CaM and its targets by secondary regulatory pathways, as well as of the effects of structural modifications of both components on complex formation.

ACKNOWLEDGMENTS

We thank Tim Harvey for his expert assistance in producing the figures, and all members of our laboratory for comments on the manuscript. Research in our laboratory is supported by the Medical Research Council of Canada (MRC). AC and MI are the recipients of an MRC Postdoctoral Fellowship and an MRC Scholarship, respectively.

Any *Annual Review* chapter, as well as any article cited in an *Annual Review* chapter, may be purchased from the Annual Reviews Preprints and Reprints service.

1-800-347-8007;415-259-5017;email:arpr@class.org

Literature Cited

1. Adelstein RS, Conti MA, Hathaway DR, Klee CB. 1978. Phosphorylation of smooth muscle myosin light chain kinase by the catalytic subunit of adenosine 3':5'-monophosphate-dependent protein kinase. *J. Biol. Chem.* 253:8347

2. Aderem A. 1992. Signal transduction and the actin cytoskeleton: the roles of MARCKS and profilin. *Trends Biochem. Sci.* 17:438

3. Alexander A, Cimler BM, Meier KE, Storm DR. 1987. Regulation of calmodulin binding to P-57, a neurospecific calmodulin binding protein. *J. Biol. Chem.* 262:6108

4. Alexander KA, Wakim BT, Doyle GS, Walsh KA, Storm DR. 1988. Identification and characterization of the calmodulin-binding domain of neuromodulin, a neurospecific calmodulin-binding protein. *J. Biol. Chem.* 263:7544

5. Andersson A, Drakenberg T, Thulin E, Forsen S. 1983. A ^{113}Cd and ^{1}H NMR study of the interaction of calmodulin with D600, trifluoperazine and some other hydrophobic drugs. *Eur. J. Biochem.* 134:459

6. Andreasen TJ, Keller CH, LaPorte DC, Edelman AM, Storm DR. 1981. Preparation of azidocalmodulin: a photoaffinity label for calmodulin-binding proteins. *Proc. Natl. Acad. Sci. USA* 78:2782

7. Apel ED, Byford MF, Au D, Walsh KA, Storm DR. 1990. Identification of the protein kinase C phosphorylation site in neuromodulin. *Biochemistry* 29:2330

8. Babu YS, Bugg CE, Cook WJ. 1988. Structure of calmodulin refined at 2.2 Å resolution. *J. Mol. Biol.* 204:191

9. Babu YS, Sack JS, Greenhough TJ, Bugg CE, Means AR, Cook WJ. 1985. Three dimensional structure of calmodulin. *Nature* 315:37

10. Barbato G, Ikura M, Kay LE, Pastor RW, Bax A. 1992. Backbone dynamics of calmodulin studied by ^{15}N relaxation using inverse detected two-dimensional NMR spectroscopy: the central helix is flexible. *Biochemistry* 31:5269

11. Baudier J, Deloulme JC, Dorsselaer AV, Black D, Matthes HWD. 1991. Purification and characterization of a brain-specific protein kinase C substrate, neurogranin. *J. Biol. Chem.* 266:229

12. Blackshear PJ. 1993. The MARCKS family of cellular protein kinase C substrates. *J. Biol. Chem.* 268:1501

13. Blackshear PJ, Verghese GM, Johnson JD, Haupt DM, Stumpo DJ. 1992. Characteristics of the F52 protein, a MARCKS homologue. *J. Biol. Chem.* 267:13540

14. Blumenthal DK, Krebs EG. 1987. Preparation and properties of the calmodulin binding domain of skeletal muscle myosin light-chain kinase. *Methods Enzymol.* 139:115

15. Buschmeier B, Meyer HE, Mayr GW. 1987. Characterization of the calmodulin-binding sites of muscle phosphofructokinase and comparison with known calmodulin binding domains. *J. Biol. Chem.* 262:9454

16. Cachia PJ, Gariepy J, Hodges RS. 1985. Structural studies on calmodulin and troponin C. In *Calmodulin Antagonists and Cellular Physiology,* ed. H Hidaka, DJ Hartshorne, pp. 63–88. New York: Academic

17. Calalb MB, Kincaid RL, Soderling TR. 1990. Phosphorylation of calcineurin: effect on calmodulin binding. *Biochem. Biophys. Res. Commun.* 172:551

18. Carafoli E, Klee C, eds. 1992. New developments in the calmodulin field. *Cell Calcium* 13:353

19. Chapman ER, Alexander K, Vorherr T, Carafoli E, Storm DR. 1992. Fluorescence energy transfer analysis of calmodulin-peptide complexes. *Biochemistry* 31:12819

20. Chapman ER, Au D, Alexander KA, Nicolson TA, Storm DR. 1991. Characterization of the calmodulin binding domain of neuromodulin. *J. Biol. Chem.* 266:207

21. Charbonneau H. 1990. Structure-function relationships among cyclic nucleotide phosphodiesterases. In *Cyclic Nucleotide Phosphodiesterases: Structure, Regulation and Drug Action*, ed. J Beavo, MD Houslay, pp. 267–96. New York: Wiley & Sons

22. Charbonneau H, Kumar S, Novack JP, Blumenthal DK, Griffith PR, et al. 1992. Evidence for domain organization within the 61-kDa calmodulin-dependent cyclic nucleotide phosphodiesterase from bovine brain. *Biochemistry* 30:7931

23. Chattopadhyaya R, Meador WE, Means AR, Quiocho FA. 1992. Calmodulin structure refined at 1.7 Å resolution. *J. Mol. Biol.* 228:1177

24. Clore GM, Bax A, Ikura M, Gronenborn AM. 1994. Structure of calmodulin-target peptide complexes. *Curr. Opin. Struct. Biol.* 3:838

25. Cohen P. 1989. The structure and regulation of protein phosphatases. *Annu. Rev. Biochem.* 58:453

26. Cohen P, Klee CB, eds. 1988. *Calmodulin*. Amsterdam: Elsevier

27. Colbran RJ, Schworer CM, Hashimoto Y, Fong YL, Rich DP, et al. 1989. Calcium/calmodulin-dependent protein kinase II. *Biochem. J.* 258:313

28. Colbran RJ, Smith M, Schworer CM, Fong YL, Soderling TR. 1989. Regulatory domain of calcium/calmodulin-dependent protein kinase II. *J. Biol. Chem.* 264:4800

29. Colbran RJ, Soderling TR. 1990. Calcium/calmodulin-dependent protein kinase II. *Curr. Topics Cell. Reg.* 31:181

30. Collins K, Sellers JR, Matsudaira P. 1990. Calmodulin dissociation regulates brush border myosin I (110-kD-calmodulin) mechanochemical activity in vitro. *J. Cell. Biol.* 110:1137

31. Coluccio LM, Bretscher A. 1987. Calcium-regulated cooperative binding of the microvillar 110K-calmodulin complex to F-actin: formation of decorated filaments. *J. Cell. Biol.* 105:325

32. Cox JA, Comte M, Fitton JE, DeGrado WF. 1985. The interaction of calmodulin with amphiphilic peptides. *J. Biol. Chem.* 260:2527

33. Dasgupta M, Honeycutt T, Blumenthal DK. 1989. The γ-subunit of skeletal muscle phosphorylase kinase contains two noncontiguous domains that act in concert to bind calmodulin. *J. Biol. Chem.* 264:17156

34. DeGrado WF, Prendergast F, Wolfe HR, Cox JA. 1985. The design, synthesis, and characterization of tight-binding inhibitors of calmodulin. *J. Cell. Biochem.* 29:83

35. Falchetto R, Vorherr T, Carafoli E. 1992. The calmodulin-binding site of the plasma membrane Ca^{2+} pump interacts with the transduction domain of the enzyme. *Protein Sci.* 1:1613

36. Fisher PJ, Prendergast FG, Ehrhardt MR, Urbauer JL, Wand JL, et al. 1994. Calmodulin interacts with amphiphilic peptides composed of all D-amino acids. *Nature* 368:651

37. Fong Y-L, Taylor WL, Means AR, Soderling TR. 1989. Studies of the regulatory mechanism of Ca^{2+}/calmodulin-dependent protein kinase II. *J. Biol. Chem.* 264:16759

38. Forsen S, Andersson A, Drakenberg T, Teleman O, Thulin E, Vogel HJ. 1983. ^{25}Mg, ^{43}Ca and ^{113}Cd NMR studies of regulatory calcium binding proteins. In *Calcium-Binding Proteins*, ed. B de Bernard, GL Sottocasa, G Sandri, E Carafoli, AN Taylor, et al, pp. 121–31. Amsterdam: Elsevier

39. Forsen S, Linse S, Drakenberg T, Kordel J, Akke M, et al. 1991. Ca^{2+} binding in proteins of the calmodulin superfamily: cooperativity, electrostatic contributions and molecular mechanisms. In *Protein Conformations*, ed. DJ Chadwick, K Widdows, pp. 222–36. Chichester: Wiley & Sons

40. Fukami Y, Nakamura T, Nakayama A, Kanehisa T. 1986. Phosphorylation of tyrosine residues of calmodulin in Rous sarcoma virus–transformed cells. *Proc. Natl. Acad. Sci. USA* 83:4190

41. Furuichi T, Kohda K, Miyawaki A, Mikoshiba K. 1994. Intracellular channels. *Curr. Opin. Neurobiol.* 4:294

42. Gao ZH, Krebs J, VanBerkum MFA, Tang WJ, Maune JF, et al. 1993. Activation of four enzymes by two series of calmodulin mutants with point mutations in individual Ca^{2+} binding sites. *J. Biol. Chem.* 268:20096

43. Gerstein M, Lesk AM, Chothia C.

1994. Structural mechanisms for domain movement in proteins. *Biochemistry* 33:6739

44. Gorgels TGMF, Van Lookeren Champagne M, Oestreicher AB, Gribnau AAM, Gispen WH. 1989. B-50/GAP43 is localized at the cytoplasmic side of the plasma membrane in developing and adult rat pyramidal tract. *Neuroscience* 9:3861

45. Graff JM, Rajan RR, Randall RR, Nairn AC, Blackshear PJ. 1991. Protein kinase C substrate and inhibitor characteristics of peptides derived from the myristoylated alanine-rich C kinase substrate (MARCKS) protein phosphorylation site domain. *J. Biol. Chem.* 266:14390

46. Graff JM, Young TM, Johnson JD, Blackshear PJ. 1989. Phosphorylation-regulated calmodulin binding to a prominent cellular substrate for protein kinase C. *J. Biol. Chem.* 264:21818

47. Graves CB, Gale RD, Laurino JP, McDonald JM. 1986. The insulin receptor and calmodulin: calmodulin enhances insulin-mediated receptor kinase activity and insulin stimulates phosphorylation of calmodulin. *J. Biol. Chem.* 261:10429

48. Greenlee DV, Andreas TJ, Storm DR. 1982. Calcium-independent stimulation of *Bordetella pertussis* adenylate cyclase by calmodulin. *Biochemistry* 21:2759

49. Guerini D, Krebs J, Carafoli E. 1987. Stimulation of the erythrocyte Ca^{2+}-ATPase and of bovine brain cyclic nucleotide phosphodiesterase. *Eur. J. Biochem.* 170:35

50. Hanson PI, Schulman H. 1992. Neuronal Ca^{2+}/calmodulin-dependent protein kinases. *Annu. Rev. Biochem.* 61:559

51. Hashimoto Y, King MM, Soderling TR. 1988. Regulatory interactions of calmodulin-binding proteins: phosphorylation of calcineurin by autophosphorylated Ca^{2+}/calmodulin-dependent protein kinase II. *Proc. Natl. Acad. Sci. USA* 85:7001

52. Hashimoto Y, Perrino BA, Soderling TR. 1990. Identification of an autoinhibitory domain in calcineurin. *J. Biol. Chem.* 265:1924

53. Hashimoto Y, Soderling TR. 1989. Regulation of calcineurin by phosphorylation. *J. Biol. Chem.* 264:16524

54. Heidorn DB, Seeger PA, Rokop SE,

Blumenthal DK, Means AR, et al. 1989. Changes in the structure of calmodulin induced by a peptide based on the calmodulin-binding domain of myosin light-chain kinase. *Biochemistry* 28:6757

55. Heidorn DB, Trewhella J. 1988. Comparison of the crystal and solution structures of calmodulin and troponin C. *Biochemistry* 27:909

56. Hennessey JP, Parthasarathy M, Johnson WC. 1981. Conformational transitions of calmodulin as studied by vacuum-UV CD. *Biopolymers* 26:561

57. Heppel LA, Newton DL, Klee CB, Pinna LA. 1988. The phosphorylation of calmodulin and calmodulin fragments by kinase fractions from bovine brain. *Biochim. Biophys. Acta* 972:69

58. Herzberg O, Moult J, James MNG. 1986. A model for the Ca^{2+}-induced conformational transition of troponin C. *J. Biol. Chem.* 261:2638

59. Ikebe M. 1990. Phosphorylation of smooth muscle caldesmon by calmodulin dependent protein kinase II. *J. Biol. Chem.* 265:17607

60. Ikebe M, Inagaki M, Kanamura K, Hidaka H. 1985. Phosphorylation of smooth muscle myosin light chain kinase by Ca^{2+}-activated, phospholipid-dependent protein kinase. *J. Biol. Chem.* 260:4547

61. Ikebe M, Reardon S. 1990. Phosphorylation of smooth muscle light chain kinase by smooth muscle Ca^{2+}/calmodulin-dependent multifunctional protein kinase. *J. Biol. Chem.* 265:8975

62. Ikura M. 1986. Proton nuclear magnetic resonance studies on the kinetics of tryptic fragments of calmodulin upon calcium binding. *Biochim. Biophys. Acta* 872:195

63. Ikura M, Clore GM, Gronenborn AM, Zhu G, Klee CB, Bax A. 1992. Solution structure of a calmodulin-target peptide complex by multidimensional NMR. *Science* 256:632

64. Ikura M, Hasegawa N, Hikichi K, Aimoto S, Yazawa M, Yagi K. 1989. [113]Cd-NMR evidence for cooperative interaction between the amino- and carboxyl-terminal domains of calmodulin. *Biochem. Biophys. Res. Commun.* 161:1233

65. Ikura M, Hiraoki T, Hikichi K, Mikuni T, Yazawa M, Yagi K. 1983. Nuclear magnetic resonance studies on

calmodulin: calcium-induced conformational change. *Biochemistry* 22:2573

66. Ikura M, Hiraoki T, Minowa O, Yamaguchi H, Yazawa M, Yagi K. 1984. Nuclear magnetic resonance studies on calmodulin: calcium-dependet spectral change of proteolytic fragments. *Biochemistry* 23:3124

67. Ikura M, Kay LE, Krinks M, Bax A. 1991. Triple-resonance multidimensional NMR study of calmodulin complexed with the binding domain of skeletal muscle myosin light-chain kinase: indication of a conformational change in the central helix. *Biochemistry* 30:5498

68. Ikura M, Minowa O, Hikichi K. 1985. Hydrogen bonding in the carboxyl-terminal half-fragment 78–148 of calmodulin as studied by two-dimensional nuclear magnetic resonance. *Biochemistry* 24:4264

69. Izumi Y, Wakita M, Yoshino H, Matsushima N. 1992. Structure of the proteolytic fragment F34 of calmodulin in the absence and presence of mastoparan as revealed by solution X-ray scattering. *Biochemistry* 31:12266

70. Jarrett HW. 1984. The synthesis and reaction of a specific affinity label for the hydrophobic drug-binding domains of calmodulin. *J. Biol. Chem.* 259:10136

71. Kataoka M, Head JF, Persechini A, Kretsinger RH, Engelman DM. 1991. Small angle X-ray scattering studies of calmodulin mutants with deletions in the linker region of the central helix indicate that the linker region retains a predominantly α-helical conformation. *Biochemistry* 30:1188

72. Kataoka M, Head JF, Seaton BA, Engelman DM. 1989. Melittin binding causes a large calcium dependent conformational change in calmodulin. *Proc. Natl. Acad. Sci. USA* 86:6944

73. Kataoka M, Head JF, Vorherr T, Krebs J, Carafoli E. 1991. Small-angle X-ray scattering study of calmodulin bound to two peptides corresponding to parts of the calmodulin-binding domain of the plasma membrane Ca^{2+} pump. *Biochemistry* 30:6247

74. Kincaid RL, Nightingale MS, Martin BM. 1988. Characterization of a cDNA clone encoding the calmodulin binding domain of mouse calcineurin. *Proc. Natl. Acad. Sci. USA* 85:8983

75. Klee CB. 1988. Interaction of calmodulin with Ca^{2+} and target proteins. See Ref. 26, pp. 36–56

76. Klevit RE, Blumenthal DK, Wemmer DE, Krebs EG. 1985. Interaction of calmodulin with a calmodulin-binding peptide from myosin light chain kinase: major spectral changes in both occur as a result of complex formation. *Biochemistry* 24:8152

77. Klevit RE, Vanaman TC. 1984. Azidotyrosylcalmodulin derivatives: specific probes for protein-binding domains. *J. Biol. Chem.* 259:15414

78. Kowluru A, Kowluru RA, Bitensky MW. 1987. Nonenzymatic glycosidation of erythrocyte cytoskeletal proteins in diabetes mellitus. *Front. Diabetes* 8:190

79. Kowluru RA, Heidorn DB, Edmonson SP, Bitensky MW, Kowluru A, et al. 1989. Glycation of calmodulin: chemistry and structural and functional consequences. *Biochemistry* 28:2220

80. Kretsinger RH. 1992. The linker of calmodulin—to helix or not to helix. *Cell Calcium* 13:363

81. Kretsinger RH, Rudnick SE, Weisman LJ. 1986. Crystal structure of calmodulin. *J. Inorg. Biochem.* 28:289

82. Kubo M, Strott CA. 1988. Phosphorylation of calmodulin on threonine residue(s) by cytosol prepared from the adrenal cortex. *Biochem. Biophys. Res. Commun.* 156:1333

83. Ladant D. 1988. Interaction of *Bordetella pertussis* adenylate cyclase with calmodulin. *J. Biol. Chem.* 263:2612

84. Laporte PC, Wierman BM, Storm DR. 1980. Calcium-induced exposure of a hydrophobic surface on calmodulin. *Biochemistry* 19:3814

85. Leto TL, Pleasic S, Forget BG, Benz EJ, Harchesi VT. 1989. Characterization of the calmodulin-binding site of nonerythroid α-spectrin. *J. Biol. Chem.* 264:5826

86. Linse S, Drakenberg T, Forsen S. 1986. Mastoparan binding induces a structural change affecting both the N-terminal and C-terminal domains of calmodulin: a ^{113}Cd-NMR study. *FEBS Lett.* 199:28

87. Liu Y, Storm DR. 1990. Regulation of free calmodulin levels by neuromodulin: neuron growth and regeneration. *Trends Pharmacol. Sci.* 11:107

88. Lowenstein CJ, Snyder SH. 1992. Nitric oxide, a novel biologic messenger. *Cell* 70:705

89. Lukas TJ, Burgess WH, Prendergrast FG, Lau W, Watterson DM. 1986. Calmodulin binding domains: characterization of a phosphorylation and calmodulin binding site from myosin light chain kinase. *Biochemistry* 25: 1458

90. Mackall J, Klee CB. 1991. Calcium-induced sensitization of the central helix of calmodulin to proteolysis. *Biochemistry* 30:7242

91. Malencik DA, Anderson SR. 1982. Binding of simple peptides, hormones, and neurotransmitters by calmodulin. *Biochemistry* 21:3481

92. Malencik DA, Anderson SR. 1983. Binding of hormones and neuropeptides by calmodulin. *Biochemistry* 22: 1995

93. Malencik DA, Anderson SR. 1983. High affinity binding of the mastoparans by calmodulin. *Biochem. Biophys. Res. Commun.* 114:50

94. Marston SB, Fraser IDC, Huber PAJ, Pritchard K, Gusev NB, Torok K. 1994. Location of two contact sites between human smooth muscle caldesmon and Ca^{2+}-calmodulin. *J. Biol. Chem.* 269:8134

95. Martin SR, Bayley PM. 1986. The effects of Ca^{2+} and Cd^{2+} on the secondary and tertiary structure of bovine testis calmodulin. *Biochem. J.* 238:485

96. Matsushima N, Izumi Y, Matsuo T, Yoshino H, Ueki T, Miyake Y. 1989. Binding of both Ca^{2+} and mastoparan to calmodulin induces a large change in the tertiary structure. *J. Biochem.* 105:883

97. Maune JF, Beckingham K, Martin SR, Bayley PM. 1992. Circular dichroism studies on calcium binding to two series of Ca^{2+} binding site mutants of *Drosophila melanogaster* calmodulin. *Biochemistry* 31:7779

98. Maune JF, Klee CB, Beckingham K. 1992. Ca^{2+} binding and conformational change in two series of point mutations to the individual Ca^{2+}-binding sites of calmodulin. *J. Biol. Chem.* 267:5286

99. McIlroy BK, Walters JD, Blackshear PJ, Johnson JD. 1991. Phosphorylation-dependent binding of a synthetic MARCKS peptide to calmodulin. *J. Biol. Chem.* 266:4959

100. Meador WE, Means AR, Quiocho FA. 1992. Target enzyme recognition by calmodulin: 2.4 Å structure of a calmodulin-peptide complex. *Science* 257:1251

101. Meador WE, Means AR, Quiocho FA. 1993. Modulation of calmodulin plasticity in molecular recognition on the basis of X-ray structures. *Nature* 262:1718

102. Means AR, Conn PM, eds. 1987. Cellular regulator. Part A. Calcium- and calmodulin-binding proteins. *Methods Enzymol.* 139:1–917

103. Means AR, VanBerkum MFA, Bagchi I, Lu KP, Rasmussen CD. 1991. Regulatory functions of calmodulin. *Pharmacol. Ther.* 50:255

104. Mercer JA, Seperack PK, Strobel MC, Copeland NG, Jenkins NA. 1991. Novel myosin heavy chain encoded by murine dilute coat colour locus. *Nature* 349:709

105. Meyer T, Hanson PI, Stryer L, Schulman H. 1992. Calmodulin trapping by calcium/calmodulin-dependent protein kinase. *Science* 256:1199

106. Minami Y, Kawasaki H, Suzuki K, Yahara I. 1993. The calmodulin-binding domain of the mouse 90-kDa heat shock protein. *J. Biol. Chem.* 268: 9604

107. Mooseker MS, Conzelman KA, Coleman TR, Heuser JE, Sheetz MP. 1989. Characterization of intestinal microvillar membrane disks: detergent-resistant membrane sheets enriched in associated brush border myosin I (110K-calmodulin). *J. Cell. Biol.* 109:1153

108. Mukherjea P, Beckingham K. 1993. Calcium binding mutants of calmodulin adopt abnormal conformation in complex with model target peptides. *Biochem. Mol. Biol. Int.* 29:555

109. Nakajo S, Hayashi K, Daimatsu T, Tanaka M, Nakaya K, Nakamura Y. 1986. Phosphorylation of rat brain calmodulin in vivo and in vitro. *Biochem. Int.* 13:687

110. Nishikawa M, Shirakawa S, Adelstein RS. 1982. *J. Biol. Chem.* 260: 8978

111. Novack JP, Charbonneau H, Bentley JK, Walsh KA, Beavo JA. 1991. Sequence comparison of the 63-, 61-, and 59-kDa calmodulin-sensitive cyclic nucleotide phosphodiesterases. *Biochemistry* 30:7940

112. O'Neil KT, DeGrado WF. 1989. The interaction of calmodulin with fluorescent and photoreactive model peptides: evidence for a short interdomain separation. *Proteins* 6:284

113. O'Neil KT, DeGrado WF. 1990. How calmodulin binds its targets: sequence independent recognition of

amphiphilic α-helices. *Trends Biochem. Sci.* 15:59

114. O'Neil KT, Erickson-Viitanen S, DeGrado WF. 1989. Photolabeling of calmodulin with basic, amphiphilic α-helical peptides containing p-benzoylphenylalanine. *J. Biol. Chem.* 264:14571

115. O'Neil KT, Wolfe HR, Erickson-Viitanen S, DeGrado WF. 1987. Fluorescence properties of calmodulin-binding peptides reflect α-helical periodicity. *Science* 236:1454

116. Oh S-H, Roberts DM. 1990. Analysis of the state of posttranslational calmodulin methylation in developing pea plants. *Plant Physiol.* 93:880

117. Oh S-H, Steiner H-Y, Dougall DK, Roberts DM. 1992. Modulation of calmodulin levels, calmodulin methylation and calmodulin binding proteins during carrot cell growth and embryogenesis. *Arch. Biochem. Biophys.* 297:28

118. Oldenburg DJ, Gross MK, Wong CS, Storm DR. 1992. High-affinity calmodulin binding is required for the rapid entry of *Bordetella pertussis* adenylyl cyclase into neuroblastoma cells. *Biochemistry* 31:8884

119. Paudel HK, Zwiers H, Wang JH. 1993. Phosphorylase kinase phosphorylates the calmodulin-binding regulatory proteins of neuronal tissue-specific proteins B-50 (GAP-43) and neurogranin. *J. Biol. Chem.* 268:6207

120. Payne ME, Fong YL, Ono T, Colbran RJ, Kemp BE, et al. 1988. Calcium/calmodulin-dependent protein kinase II. *J. Biol. Chem.* 263:7190

121. Persechini A, Blumenthal DK, Jarrett HW, Klee CB, Hardy DO, Kretsinger RH. 1989. The effects of deletions in the central helix of calmodulin on enzyme activation and peptide binding. *J. Biol. Chem.* 264:8052

122. Persechini A, Hardy DO, Blumenthal DK, Jarrett HW, Kretsinger RH. 1988. The effects of genetically engineered amino acid deletions in the calmodulin long helix. *Biophys. J.* 53:252a

123. Persechini A, Kretsinger RH. 1988. The central helix of calmodulin functions as a flexible tether. *J. Biol. Chem.* 263:12175

124. Persechini A, Kretsinger RH. 1988. Toward a model of the calmodulin-myosin light-chain kinase complex: implications for calmodulin function. *J. Cardiovasc. Pharm.* 12(Suppl. 5):S1

125. Persechini A, McMillan A, Leakey P. 1994. Activation of myosin light chain kinase and nitric oxide synthase activities by calmodulin fragments. *J. Biol. Chem.* 269:16148

126. Plancke YD, Lazarides E. 1983. Evidence for a phosphorylated form of calmodulin in chicken brain and muscle. *Mol. Cell. Biol.* 3:1412

127. Pollard TD, Doberstein SK, Zot HG. 1991. Myosin-I. *Annu. Rev. Physiol.* 53:653

128. Putkey JA, Draetta GF, Slaughter GR, Klee CB, Cohen P, et al. 1986. Genetically engineered calmodulins differentially activate target enzymes. *J. Biol. Chem.* 261:9896

129. Putkey JA, Ono T, VanBerkum MFA, Means AR. 1988. Functional significance of the central helix in calmodulin. *J. Biol. Chem.* 263:1242

130. Rao ST, Wu S, Satyshur KA, Ling KY, Kung C, Sundaralingam M. 1993. Structure of *Paramecium tetraurelia* calmodulin at 1.8 Å resolution. *Protein Sci.* 2:436

131. Rayment I, Rypniewski WR, Schmidt-Base RS, Tomchick DR, Benning MM, et al. 1994. Three-dimensional structure of myosin subfragment-1: a molecular motor. *Science* 261:50

132. Roberts DM, Besl L, Oh SH, Masterson RV, Schell J, Stacey G. 1992. Expression of a calmodulin methylation mutant affects the growth and development of transgenic tobacco plants. *Proc. Natl. Acad. Sci. USA* 89:8394

133. Roberts DM, Rowe PM, Siegel FL, Lukas TJ, Watterson DM. 1986. Trimethyllysine and protein function: effect of methylation and mutagenesis of lysine-115 of calmodulin on NAD kinase activation. *J. Biol. Chem.* 261:1491

134. Roth SM, Schneider DM, Strobel LA, VanBerkum MFA, Means AR, Wand AJ. 1991. Structure of the smooth muscle myosin light-chain kinase calmodulin-binding domain peptide bound to calmodulin. *Biochemistry* 30:10078

135. Sacks DB, Davis HW, Williams JP, Sheehan EL, Garcia JGN, McDonald JM. 1992. Phosphorylation by casein kinase II alters the biological activity of calmodulin. *Biochem. J.* 283:21

136. Sacks DB, Fujita-Yamaguchi Y, Gale RD, McDonald JM. 1989. Tyrosine-specific phosphorylation of calmodulin by the insulin receptor kinase puri-

fied from human placenta. *Biochem. J.* 263:803

137. Sacks DB, McDonald JM. 1988. Insulin-stimulated phosphorylation of calmodulin by rat liver insulin receptor preparations. *J. Biol. Chem.* 263:2377

138. Sacks DB, McDonald JM. 1989. Calmodulin as substrate for insulin-receptor kinase. Phosphorylation by receptors from rat skeletal muscle. *Diabetes* 38:84

139. Scaramuzzino DA, Morrow JS. 1993. Calmodulin-binding domain of recombinant erythrocyte-adducin. *Proc. Natl. Acad. Sci. USA* 90:3398

140. Schaefer WH, Lukas TJ, Blair IA, Schultz JE, Watterson DM. 1987. Amino acid sequence of a novel calmodulin from *Paramecium tetraurelia* that contains dimethyllysine in the first domain. *J. Biol. Chem.* 262:1025

141. Schmidt HHHW, Pollock JS, Nakane M, Forstermann U, Murad F. 1992. Ca^{2+}/calmodulin-regulated nitric oxide synthases. *Cell Calcium* 13:427

142. Seaton BA, Head JF, Engelman DM, Richards F. 1985. Calcium induced increase in the radius of gyration and maximum dimension of calmodulin measured by small angle scattering. *Biochemistry* 24:6740

143. Seeholzer SH, Cohn M, Putkey JA, Means AR, Crespi HL. 1986. NMR studies of a complex of deuterated calmodulin with melittin. *Proc. Natl. Acad. Sci. USA* 83:3634

144. Sharma RK. 1991. Phosphorylation and characterization of bovine heart calmodulin-dependent phosphodiesterase. *Biochemistry* 30:5963

145. Sharma RK, Wang J-H. 1986. Purification and characterization of bovine lung calmodulin-dependent cyclic nucleotide phosphodiesterase, an enzyme containing calmodulin as a subunit. *J. Biol. Chem.* 261:14160

146. Small EW, Anderson SR. 1988. Fluorescence anisotropy decay demonstrates calcium-dependent shape changes in photo-cross-linked calmodulin. *Biochemistry* 27:419

147. Srinivas SK, Srinivas RV, Anantharamaiah GM, Compans RW, Segrest JP. 1993. Cytosolic domain of the human immunodeficiency virus envelope glycoproteins binds to calmodulin and inhibits calmodulin-dependent proteins. *J. Biol. Chem.* 268:22895

148. Starovasnik MA, Su D-R, Beckingham K, Klevit RE. 1992. A series of point mutations reveal interactions between the calcium-binding sites of calmodulin. *Protein Sci.* 1:245

149. Steiner JP, Walke HT Jr, Bennett V. 1989. Calcium/calmodulin inhibits direct binding of spectrin to synaptosomal membranes. *J. Biol. Chem.* 264:2783

150. Stromqvist M, Berglund A, Shanbhag VP, Backman LJ. 1988. Influence of calmodulin on the human red cell membrane skeleton. *Biochemistry* 27:1104

151. Strynadka NCJ, James MNG. 1988. Two trifluoroperazine-binding sites on calmodulin predicted from comparative modelling with troponin C. *Proteins* 3:1

152. Strynadka NCJ, James MNG. 1989. Crystal structures of the helix-loop-helix calcium-binding proteins. *Annu. Rev. Biochem.* 58:951

153. Strynadka NCJ, James MNG. 1990. Model for the interaction of amphiphilic helices with troponin C and calmodulin. 1990. *Proteins* 7:234

154. Swanljung-Collins H, Collins JH. 1991. Ca^{2+} stimulates the Mg^{2+}-ATPase activity of brush border myosin I with three or four calmodulin light chains but inhibits with less than two bound. *J. Biol. Chem.* 266:1312

155. Tan JL, Ravid S, Spudich JA. 1992. Control of non-muscle myosins by phosphorylation. *Annu. Rev. Biochem.* 61:721

156. Tanaka T, Hidaki H. 1980. Hydrophobic regions function in calmodulin-enzyme interactions. *J. Biol. Chem.* 255:11078

157. Trewhella J. 1992. The solution structures of calmodulin and its complexes with synthetic peptides based on target enzyme binding domains. *Cell Calcium* 13:377

158. Trewhella J, Blumenthal DK, Rokop SE, Seeger PA. 1990. Small-angle scattering studies show distinct conformations of calmodulin in its complexes with two peptides based on the regulatory domain of the catalytic subunit of phosphorylase kinase. *Biochemistry* 29:9316

159. Vorherr T, James P, Krebs J, Enyedi A, McCormick DJ, et al. 1990. Interaction of calmodulin with the calmodulin binding domain of the plasma membrane Ca^{2+} pump. *Biochemistry* 29:355

160. Vorherr T, Knopfel L, Hofmann F, Mollner S, Pfeuffer T, Carafoli E. 1993. The calmodulin binding domain of nitric oxide synthase and adenylyl cyclase. *Biochemistry* 32:6081

161. Walsh M, Stevens FC, Oikawa K, Kay CM. 1978. Chemical modification studies on the Ca^{2+}-dependent protein modulator: the role of methionine residues in the activation of cyclic nucleotide phosphodiesterase. *Biochemistry* 17:3924

162. Waxham MN, Aronowski J. 1993. Ca^{2+}/calmodulin-dependent protein kinase II is phosphorylated by protein kinase C in vitro. *Biochemistry* 32:2923

163. Weinstein H, Mehler EL. 1994. Ca^{2+}-binding and structrual dynamics in the functions of calmodulin. *Annu. Rev. Physiol.* 56:213

164. Williams J, Jo H, McDonald JM. 1991. Phosphotyrosyl calmodulin has increased affinity for cyclic nucleotide phosphodiesterase. *FASEB J.* 5: 448a

165. Xie X, Harrison DH, Schlichting I, Sweet RM, Kalabokis VN, et al. 1994. Structure of the regulatory domain of scallop myosin at 2.8 Å resolution. *Nature* 368:306

166. Yazawa, M, Ikura M, Hikichi K, Luan Y, Yagi K. 1987. Communication between two globular domains of calmodulin in the presence of mastoparan or caldesmon fragment: Ca^{2+} binding and ^{1}H NMR. *J. Biol. Chem.* 262:10951

167. Yazawa M, Ikura M, Hikichi K, Ying L, Yagi K. 1987. Communication between two globular domains of calmodulin in the presence of mastoparan or caldesmon fragment: Ca^{2+} binding and ^{1}H NMR. *J. Biol. Chem.* 262:10951

168. Zhang M, Li M, Wang JH, Vogel HJ. 1994. The effect of Met→Leu mutations on calmodulin's ability to activate cyclic nucleotide phosphodiesterase. *J. Biol. Chem.* 269:15546

169. Zhang M, Vogel HJ. 1994. The calmodulin binding domain of caldesmon binds to calmodulin in an α-helical conformation. *Biochemistry* 33: 1163

170. Zhang M, Vogel HJ. 1994. Characterization of the calmodulin-binding domain of rat cerebellar nitric oxide synthase. *J. Biol. Chem.* 269:981

171. Zhang M, Vogel HJ. 1994. Characterization of trimethyllysine-115 in calmodulin by nitrogen-14 and carbon-13 NMR spectroscopy. *J. Biol. Chem.* 269:5099

172. Zhang M, Vogel HJ. 1994. Two-dimensional NMR studies of selenomethionyl-calmodulin. *J. Mol. Biol.* 239:545

Annu. Rev. Biophys. Biomol. Struct. 1995. 24:117–40

MASS SPECTROMETRY OF NUCLEIC ACIDS: The Promise of Matrix-Assisted Laser Desorption-Ionization (MALDI) Mass Spectrometry

Michael C. Fitzgerald and Lloyd M. Smith

Department of Chemistry, University of Wisconsin, Madison, Wisconsin 53706

KEY WORDS: oligonucleotides, oligodeoxynucleotides, DNA, RNA, matrices

CONTENTS

ABSTRACT

In the past several years, significant progress has been made in the application of matrix-assisted laser desorption-ionization (MALDI) mass spectrometry to the analysis of large biopolymers, including nu-

117

1056-8700/95/0610-0117$05.00

cleic acids. By isolating analyte molecules in an appropriate matrix and irradiating the sample with a high-intensity, pulsed laser beam, MALDI can generate intact, gas-phase ions of these analytes. Primarily used with time-of-flight mass spectrometers, this relatively new, soft ionization technique has allowed for the routine analysis of oligonucleotides up to 60 or so nucleotides in length. Recent results have also shown that base specific, matrix-dependent fragmentation is an important factor in the MALDI analysis of oligonucleotides. Further extension of the technique to longer oligonucleotides will rely on both the continued search for new matrix materials and an increased understanding of the desorption and ionization process in MALDI.

HISTORICAL PERSPECTIVE AND OVERVIEW

A revolution in mass spectrometry promises to challenge the speed, accuracy, and sensitivity of existing bioanalytical techniques for the characterization of both natural and synthetic biopolymers. The recent development of soft ionization techniques such as matrix-assisted laser desorption-ionization (MALDI) has significantly extended the application of mass spectrometry to the analysis of increasingly high-molecular-weight biopolymers, including nucleic acids. Prior to 1970, the mass spectral analysis of nucleic acids and other large biopolymers was restricted by traditional ionization methods such as electron or chemical ionization. The limited ability of such harsh ionization techniques to generate intact, gas-phase ions from these samples made gaining useful molecular-weight or structural information difficult. However, since the advent of the first soft ionization techniques in the 1970s, the role of mass spectrometry in structural biology has increased. The first techniques included ^{252}Cf plasma desorption (PD), fast atom bombardment (FAB), and secondary ion mass spectrometry (SIMS) (1, 10, 35). Initially exploited for their ability to ionize peptides and proteins, these techniques have also been applied to the analysis of small nucleic acids. By bombarding the analyte with high energy (50–100 MeV) fission fragments emitted from a ^{252}Cf source, the PD technique is useful for the analysis of nucleic acids up to 12 nucleotides long (38). Still larger nucleic acid samples (up to 24 nucleotides) have been ionized using the FAB and SIMS techniques in which energetic atoms and ions cause the desorption of analyte ions from a low-volatility liquid matrix (13, 22, 23, 58).

More recently, the development of electrospray ionization extended the applicability of mass spectrometry to even higher-molecular-weight biopolymers in excess of 100,000 amu (34, 48). The electrospray ionization technique depends on dispersing an analyte solution into small, charged droplets from which charged ions desorb into the gas phase, and it has proved very useful for the analysis of a wide variety of proteins and oligonucleotides. However, the electrospray ionization process produces a series of multiply charged, molecular ions for a given analyte. This multiple charging phenomenon has limited the application of the electrospray technique to relatively pure samples and has complicated the mass analysis of larger nucleic acid samples. For instance, although multiply charged molecular ions of oligonucleotides as large as 76 residues have been detected using the technique, the formation of multiple salts often obscures the useful molecular-weight information contained in these spectra (48).

MALDI, the youngest and most rapidly evolving of these new soft ionization techniques, has been widely employed for the mass spectrometric analysis of biopolymers and has shown great potential for nucleic acid analysis (25, 28). This technique generates intact, gas-phase ions of high-molecular-weight analytes by isolating analyte molecules in an appropriate crystalline matrix (usually a small organic molecule) and irradiating the sample with a laser tuned to an absorption band of the matrix. Subsequent mass analysis of these ions using conventional time-of-flight mass spectrometers has allowed the determination of molecular masses with accuracies up to 0.010%.

The roots of MALDI can be traced to early experiments by Karas et al characterizing the laser desorption and ionization of amino acids and dipeptides (29). These authors observed that the laser irradiance required for direct desorption and ionization of these analytes varied according to the absorption characteristics of the sample at the laser wavelength. Amino acids with strong resonant absorption at the laser wavelength were not only desorbed and ionized at low threshold irradiances but also did not suffer extensive decomposition during the process. On the other hand, the very high irradiances required for nonresonant desorption and ionization of nonabsorbing analytes induced a high degree of fragmentation. More significantly, these authors observed that nonabsorbing analytes could be desorbed and ionized at much lower laser irradiances and without severe fragmentation if they were analyzed in the presence of a highly absorbing sample, or matrix. For example, Karas et al (25) reported that irradiation of a 1:1 mixture of alanine and tryptophan not only produced intact ions of the absorbing analyte, tryptophan, but also generated molecular ions of alanine that were not observable when alanine was analyzed alone under similar conditions.

Karas & Hillenkamp (31) and Tanaka et al (52) reported the first

MALDI results with higher-molecular-weight analytes in 1988. In separate experiments, both groups demonstrated that intact protein molecules could be desorbed, ionized, and subsequently mass analyzed by isolating analyte molecules in an absorbing matrix and irradiating the sample with a high-intensity, pulsed laser beam. Karas & Hillenkamp used a nicotinic acid matrix and 266-nm radiation output from a frequency-quadrupled Nd:YAG laser, while Tanaka and coworkers used cobalt powder dispersed in glycerol and 337-nm radiation output from a nitrogen laser. Neither group observed any significant fragmentation of the analyte. Interestingly, Karas & Hillenkamp's sample preparation technique required only picomole quantities of analyte, whereas Tanaka and coworkers obtained their results with nanomolar quantities. The superior results observed with nicotinic acid prompted the search for other organic solids that might be even more effective matrices and stimulated interest in analyzing other classes of compounds with MALDI.

Since the technique emerged in 1988, several useful compounds have been identified as effective matrices for the MALDI analysis of various analytes, including glycopeptides, carbohydrates, oligosaccharides, and oligonucleotides in addition to both polar and nonpolar synthetic polymers. The vast majority of matrices reported to date have been organic solids with strong absorption characteristics at the wavelength used for desorption-ionization. However, several liquid matrices as well as frozen water have also proven effective for the desorption and ionization of different biomolecules (14, 41, 46).

Different classes of compounds have enjoyed varying degrees of success with the MALDI technique. Clearly one of the most successful applications is the analysis of proteins. The discovery of appropriate matrix compounds has enabled the analysis of many high-molecular-weight proteins (up to 500,000 amu) with no apparent limitations resulting from primary, secondary, or tertiary structure. In sharp contrast, the MALDI analysis of oligonucleotides has been limited to relatively small molecules (<29,000 amu) and strongly depends upon base composition and choice of matrix.

Although MALDI analysis of oligonucleotides has not yet achieved the same generality and lack of size limitations available for proteins, significant progress has been made in the past several years. Here, we review the current status of MALDI mass spectrometry for the analysis of nucleic acids. The role of the matrix is discussed along with several important observations that have helped define the size, sequence, and matrix dependence of MALDI results with nucleic acids. We also summarize the unique problems related to the fragmentation of nucleic acids in MALDI. Finally, important applications to the characterization of modified oligonucleotides and to DNA sequencing are discussed within the framework of the current limitations associated with the MALDI analysis of nucleic acids.

THE MATRIX

The matrix is a key part of the MALDI technique. By isolating analyte molecules in an appropriate matrix and irradiating the sample with a high intensity, pulsed laser beam, one can generate intact, gas-phase ions of the analyte. The role of the matrix in this process is generally thought to be threefold: (*a*) cocrystallization of the analyte and a large molar excess of the matrix serves to incorporate analyte molecules within matrix crystals; (*b*) matrix absorption of the energy from each laser pulse results in the ejection of both matrix and analyte molecules into the gas phase; and (*c*) the matrix plays a role in the ionization of analyte molecules, most probably through gas-phase matrix-analyte interactions (2, 16, 30, 61, 62).

Condensed-Phase Matrix-Analyte Interactions

The preparation of an appropriate analyte-matrix deposit is a critical factor in MALDI. For solid matrices, sample preparation typically involves mixing a dilute solution of analyte ($\sim 1\ \mu$M) with a concentrated solution of matrix ($\sim$1–5 mM) prior to depositing several microliters of this mixture onto a stainless steel support. Evaporation of the solvent then results in formation of a solid mixture containing the analyte and matrix crystals. Although the matrix-analyte interactions in this condensed phase have not yet been fully characterized, several studies have examined them.

Noncovalently associated dyes have been used with some success to follow the incorporation of different analytes in matrix crystals. For example, Coomassie Brilliant Blue has been used to examine the inclusion of proteins in matrix crystals, and acridine orange has been used to follow the incorporation of short oligonucleotides (3, 47). In these experiments, matrix-analyte crystallization in the presence of dye yielded intensely colored matrix crystals, whereas crystals formed from solutions containing only matrix and dye did not become colored. These results suggest that analytes are fairly homogeneously distributed throughout matrix crystals and that analyte molecules are somehow incorporated into the crystal structure of the matrix.

The experimental observation that hundreds of MALDI spectra can be obtained from the same spot of a given crystal provides additional evidence for the homogeneous distribution of analyte molecules in matrix crystals (51). Experiments by Strupat et al with 2,5-dihydroxybenzoic acid matrix crystals grown in the presence of small quantities of cytochrome c also substantiate the notion that analyte molecules end up embedded in the crystal lattice of the matrix after sample preparation in MALDI (51). In these experiments, single matrix crystals were cleaved and protein signals were easily detected from the newly exposed inner surface of the matrix crystal. Interestingly, the authors also noted that X-ray crystallographic data for 2,5-dihydroxybenzoic acid matrix crystals containing a protein analyte (cytochrome c) did not show any evidence of defects in the crystal structure.

Desorption-Ionization Mechanisms

The wide range of experimental parameters (laser power, wavelength, pulse width, choice of matrix) used in MALDI experiments has greatly hampered the development of a unified model for MALDI. Difficulties associated with decoupling the desorption and ionization process further complicate modeling efforts. Matrix absorption of the energy from each laser pulse in MALDI clearly results in the ejection of both ions (positive and negative) and neutrals of matrix and analyte molecules (39). Experimental evidence also strongly indicates that the desorption-ionization event is collective in nature (17). Ens and coworkers (17) carefully studied the production of insulin molecular ions using a sinapinic acid matrix and found that the process either generated numerous molecular ions ($\sim 10^4$) or none at all. These results provide a dramatic illustration of the steep threshold behavior of MALDI. Moreover, ion yields are very sensitive to photon flux. Below a certain laser irradiance, the ion yield is zero; above this threshold, the ion yield increases rapidly.

Attempts have also been made to quantitate the relative ionization efficiencies of the matrix and analyte in the MALDI process. Results for alkyl amine analytes desorbed from various MALDI matrices have indicated that the formation of analyte ions and neutrals in MALDI can vary according to the matrices and laser irradiances used for desorption and ionization (39). However, in this work, matrices that produced large amounts of analyte ions also produced a significant number of neutral analyte molecules, and the ratio of analyte neutrals to ions was generally more than 10,000 to 1 when desorption irradiances were near the threshold for ion generation. Aside from the few reports described above, very few experimental data describing details of the MALDI process are available, and current theories on the desorption and ionization of intact, high-molecular-weight analytes in MALDI are largely based on only a few very general experimental observations.

Despite the lack of experimental data, several different models have been developed to help explain the lack of analyte degradation during the desorption process, which is a distinguishing feature of the technique. The desorption step in MALDI is generally characterized by rapid heating of the matrix followed by a phase change of the matrix-analyte mixture from a solid to gas. The result of this phase change is the ejection of analyte molecules, along with intact and fragmented matrix molecules, into the gas phase. Beavis & Chait have proposed that the desorption process occurs quickly enough to allow the formation of a very dense gas that expands adiabatically into the vacuum, creating a supersonic jet (8). According to this model, the analytes are not fragmented because these molecules are sufficiently cooled in the expanding jet. Experimental measurements of the velocity distributions of different peptide and matrix ions produced by MALDI provide some support for this model (7). The observation that peptide ions of various sizes possess similar velocity distribution does suggest the presence of a supersonic jet expansion.

Another hypothesis, referred to as the homogeneous bottleneck model (HBM), has also been proposed to account for the production of internally cold analyte molecules and ions in MALDI (59). According to the HBM, absorption of laser light by the matrix results in homogeneous sample heating followed by bulk sample evaporation. Analyte molecules escape damage primarily because of an inefficient vibrational energy coupling between the analyte and the matrix lattice. The model argues that the high-energy-density matrix lattice is cooled efficiently by sublimation rather than by energy transfer to analyte molecules.

Ion formation in MALDI is generally thought to take place promptly after desorption and to result from gas-phase interactions between the matrix and analyte. Other ionization mechanisms such as preformation of ions in the condensed phase and thermal ionization have been considered but are probably not very important. Thermal ion formation is unlikely because the high temperature required for the ionization of large molecules would most likely destroy the analyte, and because ion formation in the condensed phase is not very efficient. The intense ion signals for protonated and deprotonated analyte molecules observed in MALDI spectra suggest that proton transfer reactions are important in the ionization process.

The ionization process has yet to be fully characterized, and the reactive protons on the different matrices have yet to be unambiguously identified. Most matrix materials contain carboxylic acid functional groups, but whether this group is involved in proton transfer reactions is unclear. For example, the methyl ester of sinapinic acid is just as good a matrix as sinapinic acid itself (20). A few useful matrices that lack acidic functional groups have also been reported (4, 18, 20). Gimon and coworkers (20) have suggested that ion formation results from proton-transfer reactions between the analyte and electronically excited matrix molecules (20). Indeed, proton-transfer reactions between analytes and matrix molecules in excited states appear to be very important in MALDI, as suggested by investigations of Wu et al (62) using 3-hydroxypicolinic acid and several structural isomers of this compound, including 2-hydroxynicotinic acid, 2-hydroxypyridine-5-carboxylic acid, and 6-hydroxynicotinic acid. These compounds all displayed strong UV absorption characteristics and facile desorption, as well as the formation of similar ions upon laser desorption. However, only 3-hydroxypicolinic acid is an effective MALDI matrix. The lack of success with the other isomers may result from a decrease, caused by hydroxypyridine-pyridinone tautomerism, in the excited state acidity of the OH group in these compounds.

Common MALDI Matrices

The search for effective MALDI matrices has been ongoing since the birth of the technique. However, the properties required of a matrix are not well defined, and the discovery of MALDI matrices has largely relied upon empirical methods. The most basic requirement, that the matrix have a strong absorption at the wavelength of the irradiating laser, has prompted the testing of numerous highly substituted, aromatic compounds with absorption characteristics at wavelengths commonly used for MALDI (266 nm, 308 nm, 337 nm, 355 nm, and 10.6 μm). The vast majority of MALDI work to date has focused on the analysis of proteins, for which a variety of different compounds have been identified as effective matrices. The more commonly used protein matrices include 2,5-dihydroxybenzoic acid and α-cyano-4-hydroxycinnamic acid, as well as several cinnamic acid derivatives such as ferulic, caffeic, and sinapinic acids (5, 9, 51). Figure 1 shows the chemical structures of several of these compounds. Many of these protein matrices have also proven useful for the MALDI analysis of other classes of compounds, such as glycopeptides, carbohydrates, and oligosaccharides, as well as both polar and nonpolar synthetic polymers. Juhasz et al (27) provide an excellent summary of the matrices employed for the MALDI analysis of these different classes of compounds.

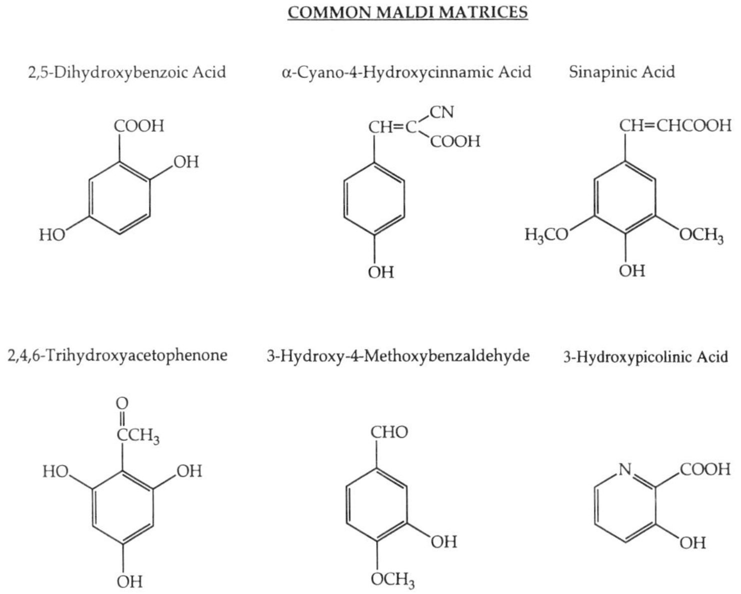

COMMON MALDI MATRICES

2,5-Dihydroxybenzoic Acid   α-Cyano-4-Hydroxycinnamic Acid   Sinapinic Acid

2,4,6-Trihydroxyacetophenone   3-Hydroxy-4-Methoxybenzaldehyde   3-Hydroxypicolinic Acid

Figure 1 The chemical structures of six commonly used matrix materials are shown. The top three compounds are most often used for the MALDI analysis of proteins; the bottom three compounds have proved especially useful in the analysis of nucleic acids.

However, most of the matrices commonly used for the MALDI analysis of proteins are not well suited to the analysis of nucleic acids. Therefore, over the past few years, much research has focused on the search for novel matrices for the MALDI analysis of oligonucleotides; and a few compounds have been identified as effective matrices for the desorption and ionization of these analytes. The most successful matrices used with UV radiation include 2,4,6-trihydroxyacetophenone, 3-hydroxy-4-methoxybenzaldehyde, and 3-hydroxypicolinic acid (see Figure 1) (15, 45, 63). However, high quality results with nucleic acids have also been obtained using IR radiation with the matrices succinic acid and urea (43). Some of the best MALDI results for oligodeoxynucleotides have been generated by using 3-hydroxypicolinic acid, which has proven especially useful for the efficient desorption and ionization of single-stranded, mixed-base molecules ranging in length from 10–89 nucleotides (62). Investigators have also used 3-hydroxypicolinic acid to analyze double-stranded DNA in this same size range, although the ion signals correspond to the molecular weights of the single strands (55).

Investigations involving the desorption and ionization of oligodeoxy-nucleotides from a thin, frozen layer of water deposited on a metallic substrate have also met with some success. In this method, the analyte is dispersed in a matrix consisting of a frozen-water film, and the sample is irradiated with a laser tuned to an absorption band of the metallic substrate. Early experiments have indicated that this approach can be used to desorb intact DNA fragments as large as several hundred thousand atomic mass units (40). Moreover, the technique can generate high-quality mass spectra of single-stranded, mixed-base oligodeoxynucleotides as large as 60 nucleotides (46). A double-stranded oligodeoxynucleotide 28 nucleotides in length has also been detected in its native state by using an ice matrix (41). Clearly, use of a frozen-water matrix can produce high quality spectra, but the reported irreproducibility of the technique has hindered its development.

INSTRUMENTATION

The MALDI technique was developed for and is used primarily with time-of-flight (TOF) mass spectrometers. Figure 2 shows the basic design of a MALDI TOF mass spectrometer. Ions form in the ion source after each laser pulse and are then accelerated to a fixed kinetic energy by an electric potential. The ions then traverse the length of the flight tube and ultimately arrive at the detector at a time characteristic of their mass. This time period is roughly proportional to the square root of the ion's mass-to-charge ratio, or $(m/z)^{1/2}$, and can be used to calculate the mass of the ion. The MALDI experiment is especially well suited for use with TOF mass spectrometers because the desorption-ionization event takes place at a specific point in space and time, and each laser pulse serves as a convenient start time for the experiment. TOF mass analyzers also allow an entire mass spectrum to be recorded in less than a millisecond.

The use of several different lasers has also met with success in MALDI. The following pulsed UV and IR lasers have all been used with appropriately absorbing matrices for desorption and ionization: nitrogen (337 nm), excimer (193, 248, 308, and 351 nm), frequency-doubled excimer-pumped dye (220–300 nm), Q-switched frequency-tripled and quadrupled Nd:YAG (355 and 266 nm, respectively), TEA-CO_2 (10.6 μm), and Er:YAG (~3 μm). Laser irradiances required for MALDI vary with different matrix and wavelength combinations but are typically in the range of 10^6 to 10^8 W/cm^2.

Several different ion-source configurations have been developed, but in most MALDI TOF instruments ions are accelerated in one or two

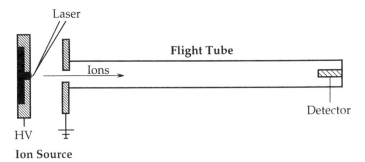

Figure 2 Diagram of a time-of-flight mass spectrometer used for MALDI.

stages through a total potential of 1–30 kV. Ion-flight path lengths can range from 0.1 m to 3 m. Ions are usually detected with an electron multiplier after they are converted to electrons at a conversion electrode. In some cases the velocity of high mass ions is not enough to generate secondary electrons efficiently, and a postacceleration stage at the end of the flight tube is used to stimulate secondary electron emission (31).

Fourier-transform mass spectrometry (FTMS) instruments are also easily coupled to pulsed-ionization schemes, but their success in combination with MALDI has been limited. FTMS, an ion trap technique, relies on trapping ions in an analyzer cell prior to detection. Because MALDI ions are initially formed with high kinetic energies, they are not easily trapped. However, the inherently high mass resolution of FTMS has stimulated interest in approaches that might avoid this problem. Several groups have used high trapping potentials and various collisional cooling schemes to increase the trapping efficiency of MALDI ions in FTMS (12, 36, 49). These approaches have been successful in the FTMS detection of peptides and proteins of up to about 12,000 amu. Ion detection in FTMS is also especially sensitive to fragmentation because ions are typically detected tens to hundreds of milliseconds after they form. Fragmentation has proved to be an important issue in the MALDI analysis of nucleic acids with FTMS, and the abundance of fragment ions in FTMS spectra of oligonucleotides is higher than in TOF spectra (24).

MALDI ANALYSIS OF OLIGONUCLEOTIDES

Typical Results with DNA

Figure 3 shows the MALDI mass spectrum of a single-stranded, mixed-base oligomer of DNA. The spectrum was obtained using the matrix

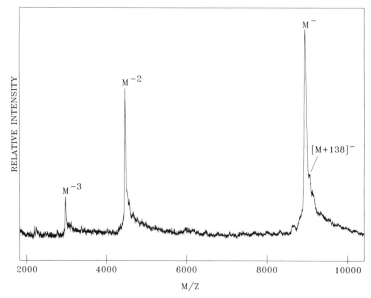

Figure 3   Negative-ion MALDI mass spectrum of a single-stranded, mixed-base 29-mer of sequence d[GTAAAACGACGGCCAGTGAATTCGAGCTC] (8936.6 amu) generated with 355-nm radiation using 3-hydroxypicolinic acid as the matrix.

3-hydroxypicolinic acid and is characteristic of a MALDI result. The signal-to-noise ratio is high, and analyte fragmentation seems absent. The three major signals observed in the spectrum correspond to singly, doubly, and triply charged ions of the analyte that arise from the loss of one, two, or three hydrogens from the intact molecule. These hydrogens are presumably lost from the phosphate backbone. The poorly resolved, weak high-mass shoulders associated with each of the three major peaks in Figure 3 are apparently caused by formation of an analyte-matrix adduct. The relative intensity of matrix adducts varies from spectrum to spectrum and matrix to matrix. The significance of the low-intensity signals in the baseline is not clear. These signals may result from ion fragmentation, sample impurities, and/or instrumental noise. The spectrum does not show low-molecular-weight ion signals ($m/z < 500$ amu) of the matrix. The spectrum in Figure 3 was generated in a negative-ion mode, although the positive-ion mode can yield similar results with this matrix and analyte. Positive-ion formation results from the protonation of analyte molecules; however, the most likely position of the positive charge is less clear when positive rather than negative ions are used. In all likelihood, positive-ion formation results from protonation of the nucleobases. Unfortunately, the mechanisms of positive- or negative-ion formation in MALDI are not yet well understood, and the actual location of charge remains to be definitively determined.

One of the strengths of the MALDI technique is its sensitivity. The spectrum in Figure 3 was generated with a total of 1 pmol of oligonucleotide loaded onto the sample probe. Good-quality oligonucleotide spectra have also been reported with as little as a 0.1 pmol total loading (47) as well as with 50 fmol of protein (32). These similar sensitivities suggest that the desorption-ionization process can operate with comparable efficiency for both oligonucleotides and proteins.

Mass resolution in TOF mass spectrometry is generally expressed as the mass, m, of a given ion divided by Δm, which is defined as the full width of the signal at half the maximum intensity. For example, the mass resolution ($m/\Delta m$) of the major peak in Figure 3 is 138. Mass resolutions of up to 1000 can be achieved with TOF instruments. However, in MALDI, several important factors limit mass resolutions. The ion production time, initial velocity distribution, and adduct formation all contribute to peak broadening and decrease mass resolution, and mass resolutions greater than 300 are rarely obtained for high-molecular-weight ion signals in MALDI TOF instruments.

Generally, very little analyte purification is required prior to MALDI analysis, and samples can be prepared directly in common buffers containing phosphate, Tris, and/or EDTA. However, the presence of even trace amounts of alkali cations such as sodium or potassium ions can dramatically reduce spectral quality. The replacement of hydrogen ions with other cations such as sodium and potassium at multiple sites along the phosphate backbone can severely limit signal intensities, mass resolution, and mass accuracy in the analysis of larger samples. Different distributions of these counterions can produce a complex series of salts for a given analyte; with higher-molecular-weight analytes, these multiple salt peaks are usually not well resolved and contribute to peak broadening. Therefore, investigators have taken several approaches to remove alkali cations from nucleic acid samples prior to sample deposition. In one, a cation exchange resin is used to replace alkali ions with ammonium ions. Subsequent desorption of the ammonium salts of oligonucleotides results in proton transfer to the phosphate group and the loss of a neutral ammonia molecule (43). A large excess of various ammonium salts has also been included in sample preparations to suppress salt formation (15, 45). The lack of multiple salt peaks in the mass spectrum in Figure 3 reflects the pretreatment of the matrix and analyte solutions with a cation-exchange resin.

Size, Sequence, and Matrix Dependence

Numerous potential matrices for the MALDI analysis of nucleic acids have been screened despite the trial-and-error nature of the process. Initial MALDI investigations with nucleic acids primarily involved testing established protein matrices for their ability to effectively desorb and ionize intact oligodeoxynucleotides. After the initial discovery of nicotinic acid as a protein matrix, several authors reported that this compound was also effective for the MALDI analysis of small oligodeoxynucleotides (two to six bases) as well as of a much larger yeast tRNA (24,952 amu) (50). Several other matrices useful for the analysis of proteins, including sinapinic acid and 2,5-dihydroxybenzoic acid, also proved successful at generating intact ions of various oligonucleotides. However, the use of these matrices has generally been limited to homopolymers of thymine and relatively small mixed-base samples (less than 10 nucleotides in length) (26, 44, 57). Other homopolymers and longer mixed-base sequences do not generally yield high-quality results. Therefore, much attention remains focused on the search for new matrices for the analysis of nucleic acids that would hopefully provide the same generality and lack of size limitations offered by the MALDI analysis of proteins.

More recently, Pieles and coworkers (45) discovered that 2,4,6-trihydroxy-acetophenone is useful for the mass analysis of natural and modified oligonucleotides 2–24 nucleotides in length. Currie & Yates (15) have tested approximately 30 different potential matrix compounds and found that a 3-hydroxy-4-methoxybenzaldehyde matrix was useful for the analysis of large, mixed-base oligomers, including a single-stranded oligodeoxynucleotide 60 nucleotides in length. Schneider & Chait (47) report testing 48 different matrix compounds for their ability to generate laser desorption mass spectra of several different homopolymer oligodeoxynucleotides. In this work, favorable results with a $d(T)_{18}$ sample were obtained with 20 of these matrices, but no discernible molecular ion signal for $d(G)_{18}$ was detected using any of the 48 matrices. The most successful oligonucleotide matrix to date is 3-hydroxypicolinic acid, which has been used effectively for the MALDI analysis of single-stranded, mixed-base oligonucleotides as large as 89 nucleotides in length (62, 63).

Several important observations can be made from the nucleic acid MALDI results reported to date. Of the numerous compounds that have been screened as potential MALDI matrices for oligonucleotide analysis, only a few have proved useful. This result is similar to that observed in the search for MALDI matrices for protein analysis. The factors that determine matrix utility remain undefined for both proteins and nucleic acids. However, most protein matrices discovered to date have proven useful for the analysis of various proteins in a broad mass range and containing different amino acid sequences. In contrast to these observations with proteins, the MALDI matrices currently used for nucleic acid analysis have only been effective for mixed-base oligonucleotides in a relatively limited size range that varies from matrix to matrix. Also peculiar to the analysis of nucleic acids is the apparent sequence dependence. For example, the results of several studies have indicated that one can use several different matrices to analyze homopolymers of thymidine, but results with other homopolymers and mixed-base sequences have been limited (26, 53, 56).

These limitations of size and base composition in the MALDI analysis of nucleic acids have generated significant interest in characterizing the unique problems associated with the application of the technique to oligonucleotide analysis. As the MALDI process itself is not very well understood, it has been difficult to pinpoint the problems with oligonucleotide analysis. However, three possible causes for the length-, sequence-, and matrix-dependent results observed for oligonucleotides have been considered. These are low ionization efficiency, poor incorporation into matrix crystals, and fragmentation during the MALDI process. The successful MALDI results reported for polythymidilic acids suggest that the desorption-ionization process for oligonucleotides can be efficient. Similarly, the favorable MALDI results obtained with small homopolymers of adenine, cytosine, and guanosine indicate that an inherently low ionization efficiency for these bases is not likely to be responsible for failures to observe MALDI signals from longer stretches of these homopolymers or other mixed-base analytes (47; L Zhu, MC Fitzgerald, GR Parr & LM Smith, submitted).

Some evidence also indicates that inadequate incorporation of oligonucleotide analytes into matrix crystals is not responsible for the poor results obtained with some samples. Schneider & Chait's experiment using acridine orange to follow the incorporation of oligonucleotides into sinapinic acid crystals was performed with both $d(T)_{18}$ and $d(G)_{18}$ (47). Significantly, no macroscopic differences between crystals grown in the presence of the dye and $d(T)_{18}$ or $d(G)_{18}$ were observed. Colored crystals were obtained in both cases. Further quantitation of these results also indicated that sinapinic acid matrix crystals contained similar amounts of $d(T)_{18}$ and $d(G)_{18}$. These findings indicate that the lack of $d(G)_{18}$ incorporation is probably not the primary reason for the poor MALDI results obtained with this analyte.

Fragmentation Behavior

The details of mass spectral results obtained from different oligonucleo-tides using various matrices have indicated that fragmentation may limit the MALDI analysis of some oligonucleotide samples. MALDI results with a $d(G)_7$ sample using the matrix 2,5-dihydroxybenzoic acid showed a substantial amount of fragmentation along the sugar-phosphate back-bone during MALDI analysis (47). Fragmentation of the N-glycosidic bond of deoxyguanosine, deoxyadenosine, and deoxycytosine during the MALDI analysis of oligodeoxynucleotides up to 30 nucleotides in length has also been observed (42). Studies of the MALDI behavior of a variety of poly dT samples with internal guanosine, adenosine, or cytosine residues have been particularly helpful in elucidating the frag-mentation behavior of oligodeoxynucleotides during the MALDI pro-cess (L Zhu, MC Fitzgerald, GR Parr & LM Smith, submitted).

Figures 4a and 4b show negative-ion mass spectra obtained in the MALDI analysis of an oligodeoxynucleotide sample $d(T_4GT_{10})$ using the matrices 2,5-dihydroxybenzoic acid and 3-hydroxypicolinic acid. The analysis of $d(T_4GT_{10})$ with 3-hydroxypicolinic acid yielded almost exclusively singly and multiply charged ions of the intact analyte (Fig-ure 4a). However, when the same analyte was analyzed with 2,5-dihy-droxybenzoic acid, several prominent ion signals caused by fragmenta-tion products were also detected (Figure 4b). The m/z ratio of the major peak in Figure 4b is consistent with the formation of a pT_{10} ion resulting from cleavage of the 3' C-O bond along the phosphodiester backbone at the guanosine residue (identified as site I in the schematic shown with Figure 4). The two other fragment-ion signals correspond to the parent ion from which a guanine base has been lost and to a [T_4G-3'OH-Gbase] fragment ion. This latter ion is formed through cleavage at site I.

Fragmentation results reported for other samples, such as $d(T_4G_4T_{10})$, $d(T_4C_4T_{10})$, $d(T_4A_4T_{10})$, and $d(T_7G_4T_4)$, were similar to those described above for $d(T_4GT_{10})$ and have provided important clues about fragmentation behavior in MALDI. The major spectral peaks in each case generally include the intact ion, the intact ion from which a base (adenine, cytidine, or guanine) has been lost, the intact 3'-end product of phosphodiester bond cleavage at site I, and the 5'-end prod-uct of phosphodiester bond cleavage at site I, which is missing a base (adenine, cytidine, or guanine). Significantly, the spectra include nei-ther peaks corresponding to the 3'-end fragmentation products missing a base, nor the 5'-end fragmentation products containing all the bases. These observations suggest that base loss is a prerequisite to phosphate

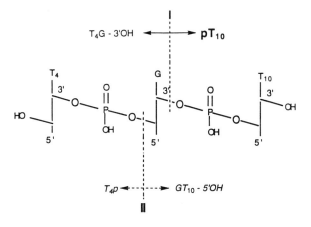

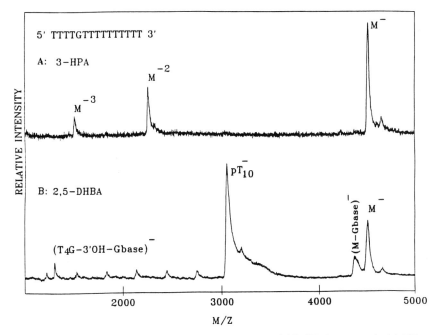

Figure 4   (*Bottom*) Negative-ion MALDI mass spectra of d(T$_4$GT$_{10}$) generated with 355-nm radiation using the matrices 3-hydroxypicolinic acid (*A*) and 2,5-dihydroxybenzoic acid (*B*). No fragmentation is observed in spectrum *A*. The major fragments in spectrum *B* arise from phosphate backbone cleavage at site I as defined in the schematic (*top*). From L Zhu, MC Fitzgerald, GR Parr & LM Smith, submitted.

backbone cleavage in the MALDI analysis of these analytes. Interestingly, McLuckey and coworkers (37) proposed a similar two-step fragmentation pathway for the collision-induced dissociation of small, multiply charged, gas-phase, oligonucleotide ions. The decomposition of these samples also involved base loss and subsequent cleavage of the 3' C-O bond of the phosphodiester linkage of the sugar from which the base was eliminated; interestingly, however, these investigations with collisional fragmentation showed not only guanine base loss but adenine, cytosine, and thymine base losses as well.

Fragmentation events in MALDI TOF mass spectrometry can occur anywhere along the ion path from the accelerating region to the end of the flight tube. Decompositions that occur in the accelerating region of the instrument are of particular importance in MALDI experiments. Fragmentation events that occur promptly after ionization (before the ion undergoes any substantial acceleration) will produce ion fragments that are accelerated the entire distance of the source and that yield flight times consistent with their nominal m/z value. On the other hand, fragments generated during acceleration of the ion will acquire flight times slower than those predicted from their respective m/z values, as these ions were initially accelerated as slower, higher-mass metastable species. Therefore, the signals for these fragment ions would be detected at larger m/z values than expected and contribute to asymmetric peak shapes.

The spectral features of the fragment ion peaks detected in the MALDI spectrum shown in Figure 4b are consistent with those expected from fragmentation events that occur in the accelerating region of the spectrometer. The fragment-ion signals in the spectrum are highly asymmetric, with a steep leading edge and a high-mass tail. Generally, the leading edge of these peaks corresponds to the m/z value predicted for the respective fragment ions, and the tails extend up to an additional 600 m/z units.

Because the desorption and ionization step in MALDI is not well characterized, studying the mechanism of fragment-ion formation has been difficult. However, the reported matrix and sequence dependences of fragmentation have provided some insight. Proton transfer reactions between matrix and analyte molecules may lead to the elimination of a protonated base through cleavage of the N-glycosidic bond; another possibility is that proton transfer from the phosphodiester groups to the ionizable bases may catalyze base elimination (42; L Zhu, MC Fitzgerald, GR Parr & LM Smith, submitted). In either case, the preferential loss of guanine over the other bases might be explained by the relatively high proton affinity of guanosine. Gas-phase proton affinities for deoxyribonucleotides (dN) have been reported as 234.4, 233.6, 233.2, and 224.9 kcal/mol for dG, dA, dC, and dT, respectively (21). Similarly, pK values for deoxyguanosine, deoxyadenosine, deoxy-cytidine, and deoxythymidine nucleosides are 3.2, 3.5, 4.2, and 9.9, respectively (11), although the deoxythymidine pK value refers to a deprotonation rather than a protonation reaction. The potential artifact of fragment generation by means of acid hydrolysis of oligonucleotides in the condensed phase during sample preparation is insignificant, as shown by HPLC analysis of oligonucleotide samples before and after MALDI sample preparation (42; L Zhu, MC Fitzgerald & LM Smith, submitted). In these reports, matrix-analyte interactions in the condensed phase did not adversely affect the stability of these analytes, at least on the time scale of sample preparation and analysis in MALDI. Apparently, the desorption-ionization process induces fragmentation in the gas phase.

APPLICATIONS

DNA Sequencing

MALDI permits the rapid analysis, with high sensitivity and reasonable mass accuracy, of multicomponent mixtures. These characteristics have generated substantial interest in using MALDI mass spectrometry for the size-separation step in DNA sequence analysis. In this scenario, the four nested sets of DNA fragments generated in Sanger sequencing reactions and that terminate in dideoxynucleotides A, C, G, or T would each be subjected to MALDI analysis; then the centroid of each peak would be determined, and the four mass spectra overlaid. The order of the peaks would correspond to the sequence. Conventional approaches rely on denaturing polyacrylamide gel electrophoresis coupled with radioactive or fluorescence-based detection schemes for the separation and detection of DNA fragments that are produced in enzymatic termination reactions. A mass spectrometry–based method would significantly increase the speed of the separation, detection, and data-acquisition processes for sequence analysis, which is critical to the success of large-scale sequencing projects such as the Human Genome Initiative.

The results of a mock sequencing experiment have shown that accurate sequence information is attainable using the MALDI mass spectrometry approach outlined above (Figure 5). In this experiment, MALDI was used to analyze mixtures of synthetic oligonucleotides chosen to match the first 24 DNA fragments generated in typical sequencing reactions using standard M13mp19 template and primer (19).

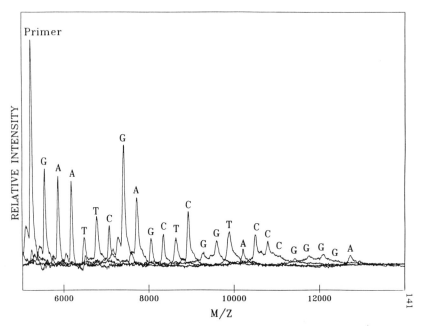

Figure 5 Negative-ion MALDI mass spectrum of synthetic oligonucleotides corresponding to A, C, G, and T sequencing reactions. The mass spectrum of each mock sequencing reaction was recorded separately, and the results obtained after overlaying the four spectra are shown. A total of 0.5 pmol of each of the mixture components was analyzed using the matrix 3-hydroxypicolinic acid. Reprinted with permission from Ref. 19.

Negative-ion mass spectra of each mixture were recorded separately, and the results obtained after overlaying the four spectra are shown. A total of 0.5 pmol of each of the mixture components was analyzed using the matrix 3-hydroxypicolinic acid. For comparison, standard fluorescence-based sequencing reactions utilize approximately 1.0 pmol of template DNA and generate about 1–25 fmol of extension products. The results in Figure 5 highlight the potential of MALDI-based DNA sequencing (the data shown take only several hundred microseconds to acquire), as well as the considerable challenge (more than an order of magnitude increase is needed in both mass range and sensitivity) that must be met before the method will be competitive with existing approaches.

Characterization of Modified Oligonucleotides

The structural analysis of oligonucleotides containing modified nucleotides is often difficult and in some cases is impossible by conventional methods that rely on enzymatic degradation followed by gel electrophoresis or HPLC. MALDI mass spectrometry offers a convenient way of confirming and sometimes identifying the presence of various modifications. Generally, the behavior of modified oligonucleotides is similar to that of normal nucleic acids in MALDI, and matrices commonly used for the analysis of normal oligonucleotides have proved just as useful with modified samples. For example, a fluorescein oligonucleotide conjugate was easily analyzed using the matrix 2,4,6-trihydroxyacetophenone; determination of the correct molecular weight verified the covalent attachment of the dye (45). Oligonucleotides containing modified bases such as uracil glycol, bromoguanine, and O^6-butylguanine have also proven amenable to MALDI analysis using 3-hydroxypicolinic acid as a matrix (60).

In some cases, MALDI has been used in the sequence determination of short, modified polynucleotides. Sequence verification of short, synthetic methylphosphonate oligodeoxyribonucleotides has been accomplished by MALDI analysis of crude synthetic mixtures containing the intact product and a distribution of failed sequences that differ in length by successive methylphosphonate deoxyribonucleotides (33). In this approach, the sequence is easily determined once the mass differences between adjacent signals from failure-sequence molecular ions have been determined. MALDI has also been used to directly analyze partial digestions of modified oligonucleotides by 5' and 3' exonucleases (45). Mass differences between the various cleavage products were then used to assign the sequence.

CONCLUSIONS

In the past four years, substantial progress in the application of MALDI to the mass analysis of nucleic acids has been made. The discovery of new matrix materials has allowed the routine analysis of single-stranded oligonucleotides up to 60 or so nucleotides in length. The continued search for MALDI matrices will likely lead to even more effective matrix materials for the analysis of nucleic acids. However, a better understanding of the desorption and ionization process in MALDI is clearly needed to expedite this search. Current efforts to understand the fundamental processes at work in MALDI promise to greatly assist the continued development of this method into a powerful and robust tool for nucleic acid analysis.

Literature Cited

1. Barber M, Bordoll RS, Elliott GJ, Sedgwick RD, Tyler AN. 1982. Fast atom bombardment mass spectrometry. *Anal. Chem.* 54:645A
2. Beavis R. 1992. Matrix-assisted ultraviolet laser desorption: evolution and principles. *Org. Mass Spectrom.* 27: 653
3. Beavis RC, Bridson JN. 1993. Epitaxial protein inclusion in sinapic acid crystals. 1993. *J. Phys. D. Appl. Phys.* 26:442
4. Beavis RC, Chait BT. 1989. Factors affecting the ultraviolet laser desorption of proteins. *Rapid Commun. Mass Spectrom.* 3:233
5. Beavis RC, Chait BT. 1989. Cinnamic acid derivatives as matrices for ultraviolet laser desorption mass spectrometry of proteins. *Rapid Commun. Mass Spectrom.* 3:432
6. Deleted in proof
7. Beavis RC, Chait BT. 1991. Velocity distributions of intact high mass polypeptide molecule ions produced by matrix assisted laser desorption. *Chem. Phys. Lett.* 181:479
8. Beavis RC, Chait BT. 1991. Investigations of matrix isolated, (uv) laser induced polymer sublimation using a time-of-flight mass spectrometer. In *Methods and Mechanisms for Producing Ions from Large Molecules*, ed. KG Sanding, W Ens. pp. 134–39. New York: Plenum. 334 pp.
9. Beavis RC, Chaudhary T, Chait BT. 1992. α-Cyano-4-hydroxycinnamic acid as a matrix for matrix-assisted laser desorption mass spectrometry. *Org. Mass Spectrom.* 27:156 (Lett.)
10. Benninghoven A, Sichtermann WK. 1978. Detection, identification and structural investigation of biologically important compounds by secondary ion mass spectrometry. *Anal. Chem.* 50:1180
11. Blackburn GM, Gait MJ, eds. 1990. In *Nucleic Acids in Chemistry and Biology*, p. 21. New York: IRL Press. 446 pp.
12. Castoro JA, Wilkins CL. 1993. Ultrahigh resolution matrix-assisted laser desorption/ionization of small proteins by Fourier transform mass spectrometry. *Anal. Chem.* 65:2621
13. Cerny RL, Tomer KB, Gross ML, Grotjahn L. 1987. Fast atom bombardment combined with tandem mass spectrometry for determining structures of small oligonucleotides. *Anal. Biochem.* 165:175

14. Cornett DS, Duncan MA, Amster IJ. 1993. Liquid mixtures for matrix-assisted laser desorption. *Anal. Chem.* 65:2608
15. Currie GJ, Yates JT III. 1993. Analysis of oligodeoxynucleotides by negative-ion matrix-assisted laser desorption mass spectrometry. *J. Am. Soc. Mass Spectrom.* 4:955
16. Ehring H, Karas M, Hillenkamp F. 1992. Role of photoionization and photochemistry in ionization processes of organic molecules and relevance for matrix-assisted laser desorption ionization mass spectrometry. *Org. Mass Spectrom.* 27:472
17. Ens W, Mao Y, Mayer F, Standing KG. 1991. Properties of matrix-assisted laser desorption. Measurements with a time-to-digital converter. *Rapid Commun. Mass Spectrom.* 5:117
18. Fitzgerald MC, Parr GR, Smith, LM. 1993. Basic matrices for the matrix-assisted laser desorption/ionization mass spectrometry of proteins and oligonucleotides. *Anal. Chem.* 65:3204
19. Fitzgerald MC, Zhu L, Smith LM. 1993. The analysis of mock DNA sequencing reactions using matrix-assisted laser desorption/ionization mass spectrometry. *Rapid Commun. Mass Spectrom.* 7:895
20. Gimon ME, Preston, LM, Solouki T, White MA, Russell DH. 1992. Are proton transfer reactions of excited states involved in uv laser desorption ionization? *Org. Mass Spectrom.* 27:827 (Lett.)
21. Greco F, Liguori A, Sindona G, Uccella N. 1990. Gas-phase proton affinity of deoxyribonucleosides and related nucleobases by fast atom bombardment tandem mass spectrometry. *J. Am. Chem. Soc.* 112:9092
22. Grotjahn L, Frank R, Blöcker H. 1982. Ultrafast sequencing of oligodeoxyribonucleotides by FAB-mass spectrometry. *Nucleic Acids Res.* 10:4671
23. Grotjahn L, Taylor LCE. 1985. The use of signal averaging techniques for the quantitation and mass measurement of high molecular weight compounds using fast atom bombardment mass spectrometry. *Org. Mass Spectrom.* 20:146
24. Hettich R, Buchanan M. 1991. Structural characterization of normal and modified oligonucleotides by matrix-assisted laser desorption Fourier transform mass spectrometry. *J. Am. Soc. Mass Spectrom.* 2:402

25. Hillenkamp F, Karas M, Beavis RC, Chait BT. 1991. Matrix-assisted laser desorption/ionization mass spectrometry of biopolymers. *Anal. Chem.* 63: 1193A

26. Huth-Fehre T, Gosine JN, Wu KJ, Becker CH. 1992. Matrix-assisted laser desorption mass spectrometry of oligodeoxythymidylic acids. *Rapid Commun. Mass Spectrom.* 6:209

27. Juhasz P, Costello CE, Biemann K. 1993. Matrix-assisted laser desorption ionization mass spectrometry with 2-(4-hydroxyphenylazo)benzoic acid matrix. *J. Am. Soc. Mass Spectrom.* 4:399

28. Karas M, Bachmann D, Bahr U, Hillenkamp F. 1987. Matrix-assisted ultraviolet laser desorption of non-volatile compounds. *Int. J. Mass Spectrom. Ion Phys.* 78:53

29. Karas M, Bachmann D, Hillenkamp F. 1985. Influence of the wavelength in high-irradiance ultraviolet laser desorption mass spectrometry of organic molecules. *Anal. Chem.* 57:2935

30. Karas M, Bahr U, Giessmann U. 1991. Matrix-assisted laser desorption ionization mass spectrometry. *Mass Spectrom. Rev.* 10:335

31. Karas M, Hillenkamp F. 1988. Laser desorption ionization of proteins with molecular masses exceeding 10,000 daltons. *Anal. Chem.* 60:2299

32. Karas M, Ingendoh A, Bauh R, Hillenkamp F. 1989. Ultraviolet-laser desorption/ionization mass spectrometry of femtomolar amounts of large proteins. *Biomed. Environ. Mass Spectrom.* 18:841

33. Keough T, Baker TR, Dobson RLM, Lacey MP, Riley TA, et al. 1993. Antisense DNA oligonucleotides. II. The use of matrix-assisted laser desorption/ionization mass spectrometry for the sequence verification of methylphosphonate oligodeoxyribonucleotides. *Rapid Commun. Mass Spectrom.* 7:195

34. Loo JA, Udseth HR, Smith RD. 1989. Peptide and protein analysis by electrospray ionization-mass spectrometry and capillary electrophoresis-mass spectrometry. *Anal. Biochem.* 179: 404

35. Macfarlane RD, Torgerson DF. 1976. ^{151}Cf-plasma desorption time-of-flight mass spectrometry. *Int. J. Mass Spectrom. Ion Phys.* 21:81

36. McIver RT Jr, Li Y, Hunter RL. 1994. Matrix-assisted laser desorption/ionization with an external ion source Fourier-transform mass spectrometer.

Rapid Commun. Mass Spectrom. 8: 237

37. McLuckey SA, Habibi-Goudarzi S. 1993. Decompositions of multiply charged oligonucleotide anions. *J. Am. Chem. Soc.* 115:12085

38. McNeal CJ, Ogilvie KK, Theriault NY, Nemer MJ. 1982. A new method for sequencing fully protected oligonucleotides using 252-Cf-plasma desorption mass spectrometry. 2. Negative ions of subunits in the stepwise synthesis of a heptaribonucleotide. *J. Am. Chem. Soc.* 104:976

39. Mowry CD, Johnston MV. 1993. Simultaneous detection of ions and neutrals produced by matrix-assisted laser desorption. *Rapid Commun. Mass Spectrom.* 7:569

40. Nelson RW, Rainbow MJ, Lohr DE, Williams P. 1989. Volatilization of high molecular weight DNA by pulsed laser ablation of frozen aqueous solutions. *Science* 246:1585

41. Nelson RW, Thomas RM, Williams P. 1990. Time-of-flight mass spectrometry of nucleic acids by laser ablation and ionization from a frozen aqueous matrix. *Rapid Commun. Mass Spectrom.* 4:348

42. Nordhoff E, Cramer R, Karas M, Hillenkamp F, Kirpekar F, et al. 1993. Ion stability of nucleic acids in infrared matrix-assisted laser desorption/ionization mass spectrometry. *Nucleic Acids Res.* 21:3347

43. Nordhoff E, Ingendoh A, Cramer R, Overberg A, Stahl B, et al. 1992. Matrix-assisted laser desorption/ionization mass spectrometry of nucleic acids with wavelengths in the ultraviolet and infrared. *Rapid Commun. Mass Spectrom.* 6:771

44. Parr GR, Fitzgerald MC, Smith LM. 1992. Matrix-assisted laser desorption/ionization mass spectrometry of synthetic oligodeoxyribonucleotides. *Rapid Commun. Mass Spectrom.* 6: 369

45. Pieles Y, Zürcher W, Schär M, Moser HE. 1993. Matrix-assisted laser desorption ionization time-of-flight mass spectrometry: a powerful tool for the mass and sequence analysis of natural and modified oligonucleotides. *Nucleic Acids Res.* 21:3191

46. Schieltz DM, Chou CW, Luo CW, Thomas RM, Williams P. 1992. Mass spectrometry of DNA mixtures by laser ablation from frozen aqueous solution. *Rapid Commun. Mass Spectrom.* 6:631

47. Schneider K, Chait BT. 1993. Matrix-assisted laser desorption mass spectrometry of homopolymer oligodeoxyribonucleotides. Influence of base composition on the mass spectrometric response. *Org. Mass Spectrom.* 28: 1353

48. Smith RD, Loo JA, Edmonds CG, Barinaga CJ, Udseth HR. 1990. New developments in biochemical mass spectrometry: electrospray ionization. *Anal. Chem.* 62:882

49. Solouki T, Russell DH. 1992. Laser desorption studies of high mass biomolecules in Fourier-transform ion cyclotron resonance mass spectrometry. *Proc. Natl. Acad. Sci. USA* 89:5701

50. Spengler B, Pan Y, Cotter RJ. 1990. Molecular weight determination of underivatized oligodeoxyribonucleotides by positive-ion matrix-assisted ultraviolet laser-desorption mass spectrometry. *Rapid Commun. Mass Spectrom.* 4:99

51. Strupat K, Karas M, Hillenkamp F. 1991. 2,5-dihydroxybenzoic acid: a new matrix for laser desorption-ionization mass spectrometry. *Int. J. Mass Spectrom. Ion Phys.* 111:89

52. Tanaka K, Waki H, Ido Y, Akita S, Yoshida Y, Yoshida T. 1989. Protein and polymer analysis up to m/z 100,000 by laser ionization time-of-flight mass spectrometry. *Rapid Commun. Mass Spectrom.* 3:351

53. Tang K, Allman SL, Chen CH. 1992. Mass spectrometry of laser-desorbed oligonucleotides. *Rapid Commun. Mass Spectrom.* 6:365

54. Deleted in proof

55. Tang K, Allman SL, Chen CH, Chang LY, Schell M. 1993. Matrix-assisted laser desorption/ionization of restriction enzyme-digested DNA. *Rapid Commun. Mass Spectrom.* 2:183

56. Tang K, Allman SL, Jones RB, Chen CH, Araghi S. 1993. Laser mass spectrometry of oligonucleotides with isomer matrices. *Rapid Commun. Mass Spectrom.* 7:63

57. Tang K, Allman SL, Jones RB, Chen CH, Araghi S. 1993. Laser mass spectrometry of polydeoxyribothymidylic acid mixtures. *Rapid Commun. Mass Spectrom.* 7:63

58. van Breemen RB, Martin LB, Le JC. 1984. Continuous-flow fast atom bombardment mass spectrometry of oligonucleotides. *J. Am. Soc. Mass Spectrom.* 2:157

59. Vertes A, Gijbels R, Levine RD. 1990. Homogeneous bottleneck model of matrix-assisted ultraviolet laser desorption of large molecules. *Rapid Commun. Mass Spectrom.* 4:28

60. Wang BH, Biemann K. 1994. Matrix-assisted laser desorption/ionization time-of-flight mass spectrometry of chemically modified oligonucleotides. *Anal. Chem.* 66:1918

61. Wang BH, Dreisewerd K, Bahr U, Karas M, Hillenkamp F. 1993. Gas-phase cationization and protonation of neutrals generated by matrix-assisted laser desorption. *J. Am. Soc. Mass Spectrom.* 4:393

62. Wu KJ, Shaler TA, Becker CH. 1994. Time-of-flight mass spectrometry of underivatized single-stranded DNA oligomers by matrix-assisted laser desorption. *Anal. Chem.* 66:1637

63. Wu KJ, Steding A, Becker CH. 1993. Matrix-assisted laser desorption time-of-flight mass spectrometry of oligonucleotides using 3-hydroxypicolinic acid as an ultraviolet-sensitive matrix. *Rapid Commun. Mass Spectrom.* 7: 142

Annu. Rev. Biophys. Biomol. Struct. 1995. 24:141–65
Copyright © 1995 by Annual Reviews Inc. All rights reserved

THERMODYNAMICS OF PARTLY FOLDED INTERMEDIATES IN PROTEINS

Ernesto Freire

Department of Biology and Biocalorimetry Center, The Johns Hopkins University, Baltimore, Maryland 21218

KEY WORDS: protein folding, folding intermediates, molten globule, thermodynamics, calorimetry

CONTENTS

ABSTRACT

Until recently, the energetics of protein-folding intermediates eluded direct measurement by high-sensitivity microcalorimetric techniques. But during the past year, the direct measurement of thermodynamic parameters for folding intermediates of α-lactalbumin, apomyoglobin, cytochrome *c,* and staphylococcal nuclease has provided new insights on the nature of the forces involved in the stabilization of nascent pro-

141

tein structures. In this review, I summarize those results and discuss the structural implications of the observed thermodynamic behavior.

INTRODUCTION

The study of protein-folding intermediates in general and equilibrium intermediates in particular has grown considerably in recent years, mainly because of the availability of new methods for evaluating the structural features and energetics of these protein states. An increasing body of evidence suggests that kinetic and equilibrium intermediates share common structural characteristics. Recent studies have shown that the kinetic intermediate that exists during the folding of apomyoglobin is structurally similar to the equilibrium intermediate that becomes populated at low pH values (26, 31). This situation appears to be the same for α-lactalbumin (27), staphylococcal nuclease (28, 65), and other proteins. During the past few years, evidence has emerged that under certain solvent conditions some proteins exhibit a significant population of equilibrium folding intermediates (17, 29, 30, 35, 63). The experimental access to folding intermediates that become populated under equilibrium conditions facilitates detailed structural studies and accurate measurements of their energetics.

Numerous partly folded states can be obtained through heat denaturation, which provides an opportunity for direct energetic measurements with highly sensitive differential-scanning calorimetric techniques. Under certain solvent conditions, the heat-denatured state of some proteins does not resemble a fully hydrated random coil but rather a compact state exhibiting a significant hydrophobic core and different degrees of residual secondary structure (see 9, 35, 53 for recent reviews). This state, often referred to as a compact-denatured or molten-globule state, is the subject of this review. Both terms are used interchangeably and denote a protein state characterized by (a) significant secondary structure, (b) significant compactness resulting from the presence of a sizable hydrophobic core, and (c) a tertiary structure reminiscent of the native fold but that does not necessarily exhibit the packing of the native state. These characteristics have been discussed elsewhere (22).

Structural Features of Molten Globules

Experimental evidence obtained primarily by using NMR seems to indicate that the so-called molten-globule states of various proteins are composed of regions that are folded and regions that are disordered (see e.g. 3, 26, 28, 31, 54, 56). This view contrasts with the classical view of the molten globule, in which the entire protein was considered to exist in a compact, liquid-like state [see the commentary by Skolnick et al (60)]. The elements of secondary structure present in these partly folded states are native-like and largely preserve the native tertiary fold, even though they generally lack the native state's tight packing (8, 11, 47, 56, 62). In general, the exact amount of secondary structure is not the same for all molten globules: Some of them have as much secondary structure as the native state, and other ones more closely resemble the unfolded state (56). In this emerging view, the molten globule is at first glance somewhat analogous to a partly folded state of a protein composed of several domains or subdomains in which some are folded and other unfolded. The main differences between molten globules and partly folded states of multidomain proteins appear to center around the structural packing of the folded regions.

In partly folded states of multidomain proteins, the folded domains do not usually lose their nativeness when the other domains are unfolded. In fact, crystallographic, NMR, and calorimetric studies of domains obtained in isolated form by partial proteolysis or genetic engineering have shown that the domains preserve their native structure and internal packing (7, 15, 43, 50, 55, 57). The native packing of a domain is determined by intradomain rather than interdomain interactions. As a result, isolated domains undergo folding-unfolding transitions as cooperative as those observed in the intact protein, even though their stability might be affected by the lack of interactions with the remaining domain(s). On the other hand, packing interactions in the folded regions of molten globules appear to be highly disrupted and, judging by NMR data, are characterized by significant side-chain flexibility and disorder (see e.g. 3, 10, 29, 59). The folded regions of the molten globule apparently require the remaining regions of the protein to achieve native packing. In this case, interactions within the subdomain are not sufficient. This limitation was recently demonstrated for α-lactalbumin, in which the recombinant α-helical domain by itself does not achieve the extensive and specific side-chain packing of the native state (47).

The cooperativity of molten-globule transitions is usually less than that of native protein structures. It is tempting to speculate that the cooperativity is linked to the extent and uniqueness of the atomic packing of the molecule. At this point, whether the cooperativity is a rather smooth function of packing or whether it shows an abrupt change of character at some critical packing density is not clear. This chapter reviews the experimental evidence already available, which seems to indicate varying degrees of cooperativity in the molecules studied. Here, I primarily address issues dealing with the energetics and the nature of the thermal transitions observed in molten globules and the first attempts at predicting the structural determinants of molten globules from the structure of the native state.

EXPERIMENTAL ENERGETICS

The most fundamental quantity required to account for the stability and folding behavior of a monomeric protein is the partition function, Q, defined as the sum of the statistical weights of all the states accessible to the protein:

$$Q = \sum_{i=0}^{N} \exp(-\Delta G_i/RT),   \qquad 1.$$

where the statistical weights or Boltzmann exponents $[\exp(-\Delta G_i/RT)]$ are defined in terms of the Gibbs free energy ΔG_i for each state i; R is the gas constant; and T is the absolute temperature.

$$\Delta G_i = \Delta H_i(T_R) + \Delta C_{p,i} \cdot (T - T_R) - T \cdot [\Delta S_i(T_R) + \Delta C_{p,i} \cdot \ln(T/T_R)], \qquad 2.$$

where $\Delta H_i(T_R)$ and $\Delta S_i(T_R)$ are the relative enthalpy and entropy of state i at the reference temperature T_R, and $\Delta C_{p,i}$ is the relative heat capacity of that state. For convenience, the native state is chosen as the reference state to express all relative thermodynamic parameters. Equation 1 can be written as:

$$Q = 1 + \sum_{i=1}^{N-1} \exp(-\Delta G_i/RT) + \exp(-\Delta G_N/RT), \qquad 3.$$

where the terms under the summation sign include all intermediates that become populated during the transition. The first and last terms are the statistical weights of the native and unfolded states, respectively. The population of molecules in state i (P_i) is equal to the ratio of the statistical weight of that state over the partition function $[P_i = \exp(-\Delta G_i/RT)/Q]$. In principle, the number of terms within the summation is astronomical, but in practice, folding-unfolding transitions are highly cooperative, and most of those terms are negligible (13, 14). In fact, under many experimental conditions, the entire summation in Equation 3 is negligible, and the folding-unfolding transition is well approximated by the two-state partition function $[Q = 1 + \exp(-\Delta G_N/RT)]$ (22). Under certain experimental conditions (e.g. extreme pH values, mild concentration of denaturants, extreme ionic strengths) or with certain mutations, some proteins exhibit significant populations of stable, partly folded intermediates (13, 22, 24–26, 29, 30, 34).

For several years, a direct calorimetric determination of the energetics of the molten-globule state could not be obtained, partly because of the lack of differential scanning calorimeters with the required sensitivity and baseline stability. Therefore, the magnitude and sign of the quantities (ΔH, ΔS, ΔC_p) that defined the state's Gibbs free energy were not known. This fact precluded a precise evaluation of the forces that contribute to the stabilization of the molten-globule state. Fortunately this situation has changed somewhat during the past year.

Heat-Capacity Differences

Until recently, the heat capacities of the unfolded and molten-globule states were erroneously thought to be identical (48, 68). Recent direct experimental evidence drawn from cytochrome c (20), α-lactalbumin (18), apomyoglobin (19), and staphylococcal nuclease (5, 6, 65) indicate that there are substantial heat-capacity differences between the native, molten-globule, and unfolded states. Table 1 summarizes the experimental results.

As indicated in Table 1, the relative heat capacities of the molten-globule states are intermediate between those of the native and unfolded states. They amount to 30–70% of the total difference between the native and unfolded states. Because the positive heat-capacity change associated with protein unfolding is known to be associated with the exposure of hydrophobic groups to water, these results are

Table 1 Relative heat capacities for equilibrium-folding intermediates[a]

Protein	$\Delta C_{p,N\to U}$ kcal(K mol)$^{-1}$	$\Delta C_{p,N\to I}$ kcal(K mol)$^{-1}$	$\Delta C_{p,I\to U}$ kcal(K mol)$^{-1}$	$\mathcal{R}$[a]
α-Lactalbumin[b]	1.8	0.9	0.9	0.5
Staphylococcal nuclease (P117G)[c]	2.1	1.3	0.8	0.65
Cytochrome c[d]	1.3	0.9	0.4	0.69
Apomyoglobin[e]	1.5	0.5	1.0	0.33

[a] $\Delta C_{p,N\to U}$ is the heat capacity difference between the unfolded and native states. $\Delta C_{p,N\to I}$ is the heat capacity difference between the intermediate and native states. $\Delta C_{p,I\to U}$ is the heat capacity difference between the unfolded and intermediate states. $\mathcal{R}$ is the ratio between the relative heat capacities of the intermediate state and the unfolded state. $\mathcal{R}$ is roughly proportional to the fractional degree of unfolding of the hydrophobic core of the molecule in the molten-globule state.
[b] From Griko et al (18).
[c] From Xie et al (65).
[d] From Hagihara et al (20).
[e] Taken from Figure 6 in Ref. 19.

consistent with the notion that the molten globule preserves a hydrophobic core devoid of water molecules and that hydrophobic interactions are important in the stabilization of molten globules (22, 35).

In recent years, several groups have established quantitative correlations between heat-capacity changes and changes in polar and apolar solvent-accessible surface areas (ASA in equations) (42, 61). The heat-capacity difference between arbitrary conformational states of a protein can be expressed as a linear combination of the differences in polar (ΔASA_{pol}) and apolar (ΔASA_{ap}) solvent-accessible surface areas between those states (42, 43, 61):

$$\Delta C_p = a' \cdot \Delta ASA_{ap} + b' \cdot \Delta ASA_{pol} \qquad \text{4a.}$$

$$\Delta C_p = 0.45 \cdot \Delta ASA_{ap} - 0.26 \cdot \Delta ASA_{pol}, \qquad \text{4b.}$$

where 0.45 and -0.26 are the elementary contributions in cal(K mol)$^{-1}$ per square Ångstrom of apolar and polar area that become exposed to water. The absolute values of the coefficients depend on the exact algorithm used to perform the calculations. In our case, all of our accessible surface area calculations of protein structures and partly folded states were analyzed as described previously (42) by implementing the Lee & Richard's algorithm (36) in the program ACCESS (Scott R Presnell, Univ. Calif., San Francisco), with a probe radius of 1.4 Å and a slice width of 0.25 Å.

The heat capacity changes listed in Table 1 indicate that the molten-globule states of those proteins maintain a variable portion of the hydrophobic core existing in the native state. Apparently, the molten globule obtained by acetylation of cytochrome c preserves the smallest proportion of the native hydrophobic core, whereas the molten globule of apomyoglobin preserves the largest fraction. A correlation between the relative change in heat capacity and the change in the degree of compactness between the molten-globule and the native state would seem logical. The change in heat capacity is elicited by the hydration of side chains and backbone, and as such it requires water penetration coupled to the expansion of those regions. In this respect, Nishii et al (46) recently published the radius of gyration measured by small angle X-ray scattering for the native and molten-globule states of apomyoglobin and cytochrome c. Their results indicate that for cytochrome c the radius of gyration increases approximately 26% (13.5 to 17.0 Å) upon the transition from the native to the molten-globule state, whereas for apomyoglobin it increases only 10% (20.1 to 22.2 Å). The helical content of cytochrome c remains almost constant during this process, whereas that of apomyoglobin decreases by about 10%, as judged by ellipticity measurements (46). The molten globule of cytochrome c appears to be more expanded and therefore exposes a larger fraction of residues to water.

Enthalpy Differences

Until recently, the molten-globule and unfolded states were also believed to be enthalpically equivalent (68). This view has been challenged both experimentally and on purely thermodynamic grounds. From a thermodynamic standpoint, two states characterized by different heat capacities cannot be enthalpically equal at all temperatures, because the enthalpy of a state is equal to the temperature integral of the heat capacity of that state (22, 64). The relative enthalpies of the molten-globule states of cytochrome c (20), α-lactalbumin (18), and staphylococcal nuclease (5, 6, 65) have been measured recently using high-sensitivity differential-scanning calorimetry. Figure 1 summarizes the results.

The results presented in Figure 1 clearly indicate that in all cases the relative enthalpies of the molten-globule and unfolded states are different. In general, at high temperatures, the unfolded state is enthalpically higher. At lower temperatures, however, the enthalpies become closer in magnitude and eventually the molten globule becomes the higher enthalpic state. The reason for this behavior is the stronger temperature dependence of the enthalpy of the unfolded state, which is determined by its higher heat capacity. The temperature at which the enthalpies of the molten-globule and unfolded states are the same is called the inversion temperature T_{inv}. For α-lactalbumin, staphylococcal nuclease, and other proteins not shown (KP Murphy, AD Robertson, ND Meadow, S Roseman & E Freire, in preparation), the inversion temperature occurs at temperatures above 25°C. For the molten globule obtained by acetylation of the amino groups of cytochrome c, the inversion temperature is below 0°C, according to the data of Hagihara et al (20).

In the absence of, or after correction for, protonation effects, the enthalpy change for unfolding can also be parametrized as a linear combination of the changes in ΔASA_{ap} and ΔASA_{pol} (42, 43). At any arbitrarily chosen reference temperature T_R, the enthalpy change $\Delta H(T_R)$ can be written as:

$$\Delta H(T_R) = a(T_R) \cdot \Delta ASA_{ap} + b(T_R) \cdot \Delta ASA_{pol}, \qquad 5.$$

where the coefficients $a(T_R)$ and $b(T_R)$ are functions of temperature. The most convenient reference temperature appears to be 60°C, which corresponds to the median unfolding temperature in the protein thermo-

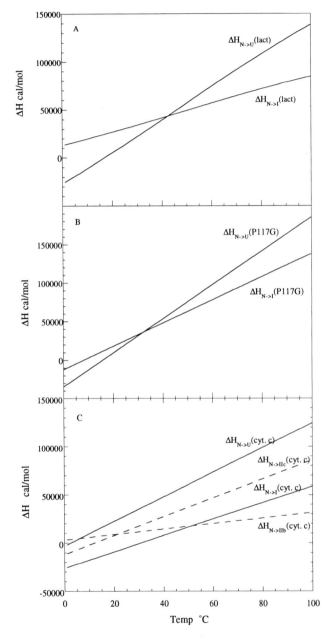

Figure 1 (A) Temperature dependence of the relative enthalpies of the molten-globule and unfolded states of α-lactalbumin. At temperatures lower than 45°C, the molten globule is enthalpically higher than the unfolded state. The data used for this graph are from

dynamic database and therefore involves the smallest temperature extrapolation of the experimental data. The coefficients $a(60)$ and $b(60)$ are equal to -8.44 and 31.4 cal(mol-$\mathring{A}^2$)$^{-1}$ respectively (66, 67). By avoiding long temperature extrapolations, the calculated enthalpy values become less dependent on errors in ΔC_p. Also, the calculated values in the temperature range of interest ($<60°C$) become independent of the decrease in ΔC_p at high temperatures (39, 65). The average error in the calculated ΔH values is 6% at the reference temperature of 60°C. The enthalpy change at any other temperature is obtained by means of the standard thermodynamic relationship:

$$\Delta H(T) = \Delta H(60) + \Delta C_p \cdot (T - 60). \qquad 6.$$

Under most conditions, Equation 6 accounts for over 90% of the enthalpy change of unfolding at the experimental transition temperatures, because the enthalpies associated with protonation and other ionic effects are relatively small. Nevertheless, these additional contributions and those of specific ligands must be taken into account explicitly, especially at low temperatures, where the contribution from Equation 5 is close to zero. By performing experiments in buffers with different enthalpies of ionization, one can uncouple the conformation and ionization contributions to the total enthalpy change (45, 52).

Equations 4–6 establish a one-to-one correspondence between the enthalpy and heat-capacity changes, and the polar and apolar solvent accessibilities:

$$\Delta ASA_{ap} = [b(60) \cdot \Delta C_p - b' \cdot \Delta H(60)]/[a' \cdot b(60) - a(60) \cdot b'] \qquad 7.$$

$$\Delta ASA_{pol} = [a(60) \cdot \Delta C_p - a' \cdot \Delta H(60)]/[a(60) \cdot b' - a' \cdot b(60)], \qquad 8.$$

and provide a way of estimating solvent accessibility changes directly from thermodynamic parameters. For complete unfolding, the difference between ΔASA values obtained from calorimetric data and the crystallographic structure of the proteins in the thermodynamic database has a standard deviation of 2.8% for the polar and 3.6% for the apolar areas.

Application of Equations 7 and 8 to the data in Table 1 and Figure

---

Griko et al (18). (*B*) Temperature dependence of the relative enthalpies of the molten-globule and unfolded states of staphylococcal nuclease P117G. At temperatures lower than 41°C, the molten-globule state is enthalpically higher than the unfolded state. The data used for this graph are from Xie et al (65). (*C*) Temperature dependence of the relative enthalpies of the molten globules IIb and IIc (34), the acetylated molten globule (20), and the unfolded states of cytochrome *c*.

1 indicates that for both α-lactalbumin and staphylococcal nuclease P117G, a larger percentage of polar than of apolar interactions is disrupted in the molten-globule state. According to the data of Hagihara et al (20), the situation is different for the molten globule induced by the acetylation of the lysyl ϵ-amino groups of cytochrome c. In this case, a larger proportion of apolar than polar interactions becomes disrupted in the molten globule. This behavior appears to be consistent with the observation that the native helical content of cytochrome c remains approximately constant in the molten globule and with the known tendency of cytochrome c to form rather extended intermediates that are not primarily stabilized by hydrophobic interactions (29, 30).

Different partly folded states of the same protein do not expose to the solvent the same proportion of polar and apolar surface because the distribution of polar and apolar groups within the protein is not uniform. This structural property is reflected in the energetics and ultimately in the probability that a particular partly folded state will become populated.

Molten-Globule Stabilization

The observation originally made for α-lactalbumin that the molten-globule state is enthalpically higher than the unfolded state immediately raised important questions and set rigorous thermodynamic constraints on possible mechanisms of stabilization (18).

Because the probability of a state becoming populated is determined by its Gibbs free energy, a high positive enthalpy would clearly contribute unfavorably to the state's stability; therefore, to become stable, the molten-globule state must have a relative entropy higher than that of the unfolded state, i.e. the term $-T\Delta S$ in the Gibbs free-energy equation should not only compensate but should overcome the unfavorable ΔH term. Figure 2 illustrates this situation with the data obtained calorimetrically for staphylococcal nuclease P117G (65). In panel A, the relative entropies of the molten-globule and unfolded states have been plotted as a function of temperature. As shown in the figure, at temperatures below 35°C the entropy of the molten-globule state is larger than that of the unfolded state. This characteristic behavior results in the Gibbs free-energy function shown in panel B. At temperatures between 5 and 60°C, the molten-globule state has a lower free energy and therefore is more stable than the unfolded state. Also, immediately after thermal denaturation, the molten globule, not the unfolded state, is the most stable state. This situation continues up to about 65°C, at which the unfolded state becomes the most highly populated state.

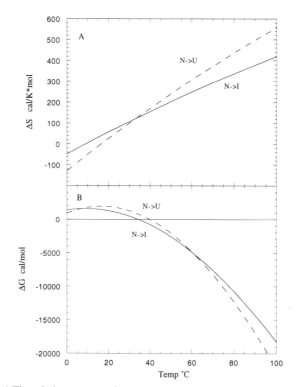

Figure 2   (*A*) The relative entropy of the molten globule and unfolded states of staphylococcal nuclease P117G. (*B*) The Gibbs free energy of the molten-globule and unfolded
states of staphylococcal nuclease P117G. The data used for this graph are from Xie et
al (65).

α-Lactalbumin exhibits entropies similar to those shown in Figure 2
(18, 66), and this situation likely occurs in the stabilization of all molten
globules exhibiting a higher enthalpy than the unfolded state. In general,
this condition is expected for molten globules that are highly compact
and stabilized primarily by hydrophobic interactions. The situation appears to be different for some of the partly folded states identified for
cytochrome *c,* as shown in Figure 1*C.*

The Relative Entropy of the Molten Globule

According to the experimental data for the molten globules of α-lactal-
bumin and staphylococcal nuclease P117G, their stabilization at low
temperatures (e.g. room temperature) has an entropic origin because
the enthalpy contributes unfavorably to their free energy of stabiliza-

tion. If this is the case, how does the molten-globule state, which is by definition more ordered than the unfolded state, become entropically more favorable than the unfolded state? To answer this question, the different contributions to the entropy change must be examined.

The relative entropy of any arbitrary protein state can be written as:

$$\Delta S(T) = \Delta S(385.15) + \Delta C_p \ln(T/385.15), \qquad\qquad 9.$$

where the reference temperature of 385.15 K (112°C) is used. This temperature offers a convenient reference because at that point the entropy associated with the hydration of apolar groups is negligible (2). Because ΔC_p can be effectively parametrized, as discussed above, an investigation of the magnitude of $\Delta S(385.15)$ is important. In general, several factors contribute to this term:

$$\Delta S(385.15) = \Delta S_{conf} + \Delta S_{H^+} + \Delta S_{bind} + \Delta S_{pol} + \Delta S_{vib} + \Delta S_{other}. \qquad 10.$$

The term ΔS_{conf} is the conformational entropy and includes backbone as well as side-chain entropy changes. ΔS_{H^+} and ΔS_{bind} are the terms associated with protonation or other binding events; these two terms can usually be determined experimentally. ΔS_{pol} and ΔS_{vib} are the terms contributed by polar hydration and vibrational degrees of freedom, respectively, and ΔS_{other} contains all the contributions unaccounted for by the previous terms. In Equation 10, all terms are evaluated at 385.15 K; this temperature was not explicitly written for simplicity. Experiments have shown that after correction for protonation or other binding effects $\Delta S(385.15)$ is equal or very close to the value expected for the conformational entropy (37, 42, 49, 51). The immediate implication of this observation is that the remaining terms (ΔS_{pol}, ΔS_{vib}, etc) are either negligible or cancel each other.

Analysis of the experimental data for α-lactalbumin and staphylococcal nuclease P117G indicates that the main source of stabilization of the molten globule of these proteins is the so-called solvent-related entropy [$\Delta C_p \ln(T/385.15)$], which originates primarily from the hydration of apolar groups (i.e. the hydrophobic effect). By maintaining a sizable hydrophobic core, the molten globule does not expose a large apolar surface to water and therefore gains a significant amount of entropy relative to the unfolded state. At room temperature, the solvent-related entropy more than compensates for the larger conformational entropy of the unfolded state. Additional terms, such as protonation as the molten globule is stabilized at low pH, also help overcome its unfavorable enthalpy.

TEMPERATURE-INDUCED TRANSITIONS

An important characteristic of some molten-globule states is the absence of a thermally induced transition. Originally this observation was made for α-lactalbumin and interpreted as a proof that the molten-globule and unfolded states of α-lactalbumin were enthalpically equivalent (48, 68). From a strict thermodynamic point of view, temperature cannot induce a transition between two enthalpically equivalent states; however, the converse is not true—the absence of a transition does not imply that two states of a protein are enthalpically equivalent. Furthermore, we now know that the molten globule and the unfolded state are enthalpically different. Why then are thermal transitions absent in some molten globules? The simplest and most trivial reason is that under some conditions some molten globules are significantly more stable than the unfolded state, and these proteins do not unfold within the experimentally accessible range, which is usually between 0 and 100°C. Some rearrangements might occur as a function of temperature within the molten globule itself, but the globule remains in a compact state without exhibiting a significant hydration of the groups that are buried away from the solvent. Figure 3 presents an example of this behavior, as shown by the staphylococcal nuclease variant P117G. At pH 3.5 and low salt concentrations, the protein remains in the molten-globule or compact-denatured state after thermal denaturation, as demonstrated by the value of the state's heat capacity after heat denaturation. At high salt concentration, a second transition that represents the thermal unfolding of the molten globule occurs. At low salt concentration, the molten globule does not unfold even at high temperatures and does not exhibit a transition. This example clearly indicates that the absence or existence of a transition within the experimentally accessible temperature range can be modulated by solvent conditions.

Under certain conditions, molten globules do in fact undergo thermal transitions. Besides the transition for the staphylococcal nuclease P117G molten globule (65), calorimetrically determined thermal transitions have been reported for the molten globules of α-lactalbumin (18), cytochrome c (20), apomyoglobin (19), and a monomeric insulin analogue (23). The main question arising from these studies deals with the character and the cooperativity of the transition because not all of them show the same thermodynamic characteristics. The thermal transition of the molten globule of staphylococcal nuclease P117G approaches the behavior of a two-state transition (16, 65). According to the calorimetric data of Hagihara et al (20), the thermal transition of the molten

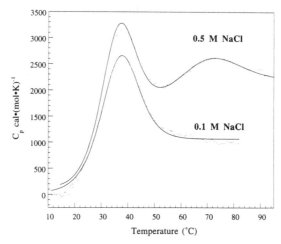

Figure 3 Temperature dependence of the excess heat capacity of staphylococcal nuclease P117G at pH 3.5 and two different NaCl concentrations. At 0.1 M NaCl, the state existing after thermal denaturation is not completely unfolded and displays a lower heat capacity than the unfolded state, which indicates that the former state preserves a hydrophobic core. At 0.5 M NaCl, the heat-capacity function exhibits two clearly distinguishable peaks. The first peak corresponds to the transition between the native state and the molten-globule state and is not affected by the change in ionic strength. The second peak corresponds to the transition between the molten-globule and the unfolded state. Adapted from Xie et al (65).

globule of cytochrome c is characterized by a van't Hoff–to–calorimetric enthalpy ratio ($\Delta H_{vH}/\Delta H$) of ~0.5–0.7, which suggests that the thermal transition is not as cooperative as a two-state transition. The molten globule of α-lactalbumin undergoes a gradual transition characterized by poor cooperativity ($\Delta H_{vH}/\Delta H$ of ~0.4). On the other hand, the thermal transition of the molten globule of apomyoglobin appears to exhibit a strange behavior characterized primarily by an increase in heat capacity with no appreciable heat effect (19).

According to the existing data, the cooperativity of the molten-globule transition is not similar for all proteins studied. As mentioned before, protein structures referred to as molten globules in the literature are characterized by the presence of both folded and unfolded regions. Whether helical or β-sheet structures define the folded regions does not seem to be an issue. In α-lactalbumin, for example, helices A, B, and C define the folded subdomain, whereas the β-sheet structure is unfolded. For staphylococcal nuclease, the opposite is true—the β-sheet subdomain is largely intact while the helical structure is missing. In apomyoglobin, on the other hand, helices A, G, and H are folded in the molten-globule state. So, the cooperative behavior of molten-globule transitions cannot be directly associated with the type of secondary-structure elements present in the molten globule.

The cooperativity of a transition is related to the number of states that become populated during the transition. Usually, partly folded states have very low probabilities because they expose to the solvent a relatively large amount of hydrophobic surface without a parallel increase in the conformational entropy to compensate. This uncompensated exposure occurs primarily at the so-called complementary regions (13), i.e. those surfaces in the folded regions that are structurally complementary and are buried away from the solvent by the regions that become unfolded in the partly folded state (Figure 4). It is not surprising that the partly folded states that become populated expose to the solvent an anomalously large polar area (see discussion above) while keeping a significant hydrophobic core buried. This situation is possible because polar and apolar residues are not homogeneously distributed within the protein; therefore, some states can expose a larger fraction of the polar buried residues. The hydrophobic core need not be a unique quasispherical structure within a protein; instead it may be a branched structure containing two or more subcores, in which case a cooperative breakdown is possible.

A potential mechanism of stabilization for a partly folded state such as the one shown in Figure 4 could be elicited by a relaxation in the packing density, provided that water does not penetrate and that the partial loss in van der Waals interactions is more than compensated by

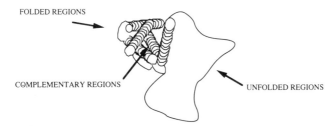

Figure 4 Schematic representation of a partly folded state. Partly folded states are composed of folded and unfolded regions. The folded regions include regions that were already exposed to the solvent in the native state, and those (complementary regions) that become exposed to the solvent as a result of the unfolding of part of the protein. Relative to the native state, a partly folded intermediate exposes to the solvent two distinct regions: (*a*) the portions of the protein that are unfolded and (*b*) the complementary surfaces located in the regions of the protein that remain folded. In the molten-globule state, the folded regions preserve the native tertiary fold but usually lack the tight packing of side chains found in the native state.

the gain in conformational entropy resulting from the lower packing density. A relaxation in packing density will have a negative effect on the enthalpy of stabilization that primarily results from reduced van der Waals interactions and a positive effect on the entropy change resulting from the gain of new degrees of freedom by the amino acid side chains as the atomic packing loosens. A net stabilization will be obtained if the favorable $T\Delta S$ term is larger in magnitude than the unfavorable ΔH term. If this is the case, the thermal denaturation of the native state will lead to the unfolding of some regions of the protein and a relaxation of the native packing in the regions that remain folded. Depending on the resulting packing characteristics of the regions that remain folded, a second cooperative transition may or may not occur. This appears to be the situation for partly folded states that have been characterized as molten globules structurally and thermodynamically.

At this point, quantitative evaluations of the degree to which the native packing is disrupted are not available. Two extreme models for the packing of side chains have been envisioned [see Bromberg & Dill (4)]: one, the jigsaw puzzle model, in which the side chains are precisely interlocked and another, the nuts and bolts model, in which the side chains exhibit multiple nonspecific interactions and organize themselves like nuts and bolts in a jar. The first model is somewhat analogous to that of Shakhnovich & Finkelstein (58) and predicts a jump in the side-chain entropy at some critical packing density. The second model predicts a monotonic increase in side-chain entropy upon decreasing packing density. Of course, the packing of side chains in a protein need not be uniform and may exhibit characteristics of the first model in some regions and of the second model in other regions. Heterogeneities in packing density might also lead to the appearance of high and low packing density regions. van der Waals interactions will be stronger in regions of higher packing density and may define areas that are stabilized primarily by interactions within the region rather than by interactions with other regions of the molecule.

STRUCTURAL DETERMINANTS OF THE MOLTEN GLOBULE

Recently, a combinatorial algorithm aimed at predicting the structural determinants of molten globules from the high-resolution structure of the native state was proposed (65–67). The combinatorial algorithm considers the protein as formed by an arbitrary number of folding units. Each folding unit can be either folded or unfolded. The computer generates protein states in a combinatorial way by folding and unfolding the folding units in all possible combinations (66). The total number of states (N) that is generated is proportional to the number of folding units (N_f) and is equal to $N = 2^{N_f}$. The number of folding units determines the resolution of the analysis. In principle, each amino acid residue can be considered as a folding unit; in practice, however, this choice will generate a computationally intractable number of states. A reasonable approach is to begin the analysis with a few units and coarse partitioning and progressively increase the number of folding units in order to increase the resolution. Usually, secondary-structure elements are used as the starting point for partitioning. The resolution of the partitioning grid is then increased by further subdividing the protein into smaller units comprising only parts of secondary-structure elements. This process can be carried out to the desired level of resolution.

Currently, the calculations assume that the folded regions in partly folded states preserve the native fold and the native packing. This is certainly an oversimplification and is expected to introduce errors of different magnitudes in the calculated thermodynamic parameters. The calculated heat capacity should not be significantly affected as far as water does not penetrate into the interior of the folded regions. If the native packing is disrupted in the partly folded states, the calculated enthalpy values will most likely be overestimated, and the conformational entropy will be underestimated. However, the errors in enthalpy and entropy can be expected to partially compensate for each other, which will result in an overall smaller error in the estimated free energy. At this point, the limited size of the database prevents us from assessing the magnitude of the errors. For example, for staphylococcal nuclease, the ΔC_p of the intermediate is estimated accurately, whereas the ΔH is underestimated by 8 kcal mol^{-1}, or about 25%.

By definition, all the states generated by the combinatorial algorithm are native-like. Nonnative partly folded states can also be stable under certain solvent conditions. In this respect, Liu et al (38) recently reported that the acid-denatured state of the predominantly β-sheet protein CRABP has a larger helical content than the native state. The role of nonnative intermediates in the protein-folding process is, however, still unclear (40). Because the ensemble of partly folded states generated by the combinatorial algorithm does not include nonnative intermediates, their relative probabilities cannot be evaluated.

Once the ensemble of states is generated, the energetics of each state is calculated (see 65–67 for details). The criteria used to select molten-globule candidates from the entire ensemble of partly folded states are based on the relative enthalpy, entropy, heat capacity, and the free energy of each state. These parameters are calculated for each state with Equations 4–6. Currently, the enthalpy and heat capacities (or solvent-related entropies) are the quantities that can be predicted with the highest accuracy, whereas the conformational entropy of unfolding can only be approximated by a mean-value type of calculation using an empirical-area scaling of the form $\Delta S_{conf} \approx [0.028*(\Delta ASA_{ap} + 2.42 \Delta ASA_{pol}) \pm 3\%]$, in which the variation of $\pm 3\%$ can be used to account for changes in denaturation temperature. On a per residue basis, this formula yields an average ΔS_{conf} of 4.3 cal(K mol)$^{-1}$ per amino acid residue, as expected (37).

The free energies can be used to calculate the partition function for the ensemble of states generated by the combinatorial algorithm and to calculate the population of each state as a function of temperature. Other thermodynamic functions such as the average enthalpy or the excess heat-capacity function can be calculated using standard thermodynamic equations (see e.g. 12, 41).

Application of Combinatorial Unfolding Algorithm to Staphylococcal Nuclease P117G

This section illustrates the combinatorial unfolding algorithm with staphylococcal nuclease. This protein consists of a β-barrel subdomain formed by two three-stranded β-sheets and an α-helical subdomain composed of three α-helices. Several partitionings of the protein were considered for the purpose of applying the combinatorial unfolding algorithm (65). The initial partitioning (scheme A) consisted of seven folding units corresponding to the following elements of secondary structure:

A: {6, 37} {38, 51} {52, 70} {71, 98} {99, 109} {110, 120} {121, 141},

where the boundaries of each unit are enclosed in brackets. In the structure of P117G, the first five residues are disordered. The first unit includes three β-strands: β1 (residues 10–19), β2 (residues 22–27), and β3 (residues 30–36). The second unit corresponds to a loop (residues 38–51), and the third unit is defined by the first α-helix (residues 54–68). Three β-strands, β4 (residues 71–76), β5 (residues 88–95), and β6 (residues 97–98), form the fourth unit. The fifth unit corresponds to the second α-helix (residues 99–106). The sixth unit is an 11-residue loop (residues 110–120), and the last unit includes the third α-helix (residues 135–141).

The definition of the boundaries of each folding unit constitutes an element of uncertainty in any partitioning scheme. For this reason, the boundaries of each folding unit are shifted upwards and downwards in sequence by one and two amino acid residues, and the results are compared. Next, the resolution of the initial partitioning is increased by dividing the folding units into smaller units. In the case of P117G, the following schemes were considered:

B: {6, 27} {28, 37} {38, 51} {52, 70} {71, 82} {83, 98} {99, 109} {110, 120} {121, 141}

C: {6, 27} {28, 37} {38, 51} {52, 60} {61, 70} {71, 82} {83, 98} {99, 109} {110, 120} {121, 141}

D: {6, 19} {20, 27} {28, 37} {38, 51} {52, 60} {61, 70} {71, 82} {83, 95} {96, 98} {99, 109} {110, 120} {121, 141}.

Scheme B is composed of nine folding units in which two additional units were created by considering $\beta 3$ and $\beta 4$ as two separate units. In scheme C, one additional unit was created by breaking the long helix (residues 54–68) into two separate units. This strategy is used to test whether helices behave as cooperative units and are found either completely folded or completely unfolded. In scheme D, each β-strand constitutes a separate folding unit, which results in consideration of twelve folding units and a total of 4096 states. For P117G, the results obtained with all these schemes were very similar, i.e. the regions of the protein predicted to be folded or unfolded were the same regardless of the scheme used.

Results of Molten-Globule Search for α-Lactalbumin and Staphylococcal Nuclease P117G

Figure 5 shows the calculated intrinsic free-energy values at different temperatures for all the states generated by the combinatorial algorithm for α-lactalbumin and staphylococcal nuclease P117G. The figure clearly shows that at low temperature the native state is the one with the lowest free energy and therefore the one most significantly populated. Immediately after thermal denaturation, however, the unfolded state does not become populated, as indicated by the lower free energies of several partly folded states. All the states in this group share common structural features, as shown in Tables 2 and 3. At higher temperatures, the unfolded state progressively becomes the lowest free-energy state and therefore the most significantly populated. Figure 6 illustrates the conserved structural characteristics of the partly folded states that are predicted to be the most highly populated after thermal denaturation. For α-lactalbumin, helices A, B, and C are predicted to be folded, and for staphylococcal nuclease P117G the β-sheet subdomain is predicted to be folded.

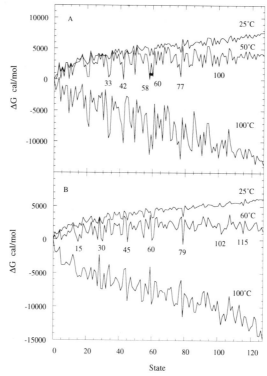

Figure 5 (*A*) The Gibbs free energy of the 128 states generated by the combinatorial unfolding algorithm for α-lactalbumin at 25°C, 50°C, and 100°C. At low temperatures, the native state has the lowest free energy and is the one most significantly populated. At 50°C, a temperature immediately above the denaturation temperature, the group of partly folded states summarized in Table 2 becomes populated. The states in this group share common structural features and define the molten-globule state. Only at higher temperatures (100°C) does the unfolded state become significantly populated. (*B*) The Gibbs free energy of the 128 states generated for staphylococcal nuclease P117G at 25°C, 60°C, and 100°C. At low temperatures, the native state is the one most significantly populated. Immediately above the denaturation temperature, the group of partly folded states summarized in Table 3 becomes populated. As in the case of α-lactalbumin, the states in this group share common structural features and define the molten-globule state. Only at higher temperatures (100°C) does the unfolded state become significantly populated. The lines in the figure are only a guide to the eye, since each state is a discrete entity.

The structural features predicted by the thermodynamic calculations agree well with direct structural measurements of the molten-globule state of α-lactalbumin by NMR and CD spectroscopy. Hydrogen-exchange experiments with guinea pig α-lactalbumin indicate that the

α-Lactalbumin   SNase P117G Mutant

Figure 6 (*Left*) The structural characteristics of the predicted molten globule of α-lactalbumin (state 77, binary representation: 0011011; see Table 2). (*Right*) The structural characteristics of the predicted molten globule of staphylococcal nuclease P117G (state 79, binary representation: 0110111; see Table 3). In both figures, the black areas represent the folded regions of the protein molecule and the light areas the unfolded regions. Both states summarize the regions that have the higher probabilities of being folded and unfolded in the molten-globule state. Both figures were generated with the program Molscript (33).

most protected protons are located in the B and C helices (3, 8). In bovine α-lactalbumin, the C helix is also the most stable region (1). Furthermore, the experiments suggest that the persistent structure in the A state is native like. The small protection factors for the protons located in the β-sheet indicate that this structure is absent in the A state. An X-ray analysis of the low-pH and high-pH crystallographic struc-

Table 2 Structural characteristics of molten-globule candidates of α-lactalbumin[a]

Folding units	1	2	3	4	5	6	7		
residues	1–18	19–33	34–67	68–82	83–104	105–113	114–122		
2° structure	A helix	B helix	β-sheet	3_{10} helix	C helix	D helix	3_{10} helix		

State #			Binary code					$N_{U,i}$[b]	$\Delta C_{p,i}$ kcal $(K\ mol)^{-1}$
33	0	0	1	0	0	1	0	43	0.7
42	0	0	1	1	0	0	0	49	0.68
58	0	0	1	1	0	1	0	58	0.8
60	0	0	1	1	0	0	1	58	0.86
77*	0	0	1	1	0	1	1	67	0.95
100	0	1	1	1	0	1	1	82	1.3
127	1	1	1	1	1	1	1	122	1.8

[a] Protein states are designated by a unique binary code in which a folded unit is represented by a 0 and an unfolded unit by a 1.
[b] $N_{U,i}$ is defined as the number of unfolded residues in state i.

Table 3 Structural characteristics of molten-globule candidates of staphylococcal nuclease P117G variant

Folding units	1	2	3	4	5	6	7		
residues 2°	6–37	38–51	52–70	71–98	99–109	110–120	121–141		
structure	β-sheet	Loop	A helix	β-sheet	B helix	Loop	C helix		
State #				Binary code				$N_{U,i}$	$\Delta C_{p,i}$ kcal $(K \, mol)^{-1}$
15	0	0	0	0	0	1	1	32	0.65
30	0	1	0	0	0	1	1	46	0.91
45	0	1	0	0	1	1	1	57	1.1
60	0	1	1	0	1	0	1	65	1.3
79	0	1	1	0	1	1	1	76	1.3
102	0	1	1	1	1	0	1	83	1.9
115	0	1	1	1	1	1	1	104	2.0
127	1	1	1	1	1	1	1	136	2.3

tures of human α-lactalbumin suggests that residues 104–111 appear to be disordered at low pH (21). NMR hydrogen-exchange experiments on the kinetic folding intermediates of the structurally similar protein, hen egg white lysozyme (54), also indicate that the A, B, and C helices are the earliest structural elements that become protected in pulse-label experiments, whereas the β-sheet is unfolded. Finally, Peng & Kim (47) have recently shown that the isolated α-domain (A, B, and C helices) can form by itself the molten globule of α-lactalbumin. These structural features coincide with the structural properties predicted by the simulated molten-globule candidates.

The results of the analysis for staphylococcal nuclease P117G indicate that the most probable structure of the intermediate is one in which the β-subdomain is intact or almost intact while the other parts of the molecule are unfolded. This conclusion is supported by CD experiments that demonstrate the absence of significant helical structure in the intermediate. More interestingly, this structure is also very close to that of a kinetic folding intermediate of P117G revealed by NMR hydrogen-exchange experiments (28). This observation suggests that the stable compact denatured state is the kinetic intermediate undergoing further stabilization. A similar phenomenon has also been observed for other proteins (27, 31, 32).

The results discussed above and those found for other proteins (barnase, III^{Glc}, T4 lysozyme, interleukin 1β, and 434 repressor) (67) suggest the feasibility of accurate predictions of the structural features of molten-globule intermediates.

ACKNOWLEDGMENTS

Supported by grants from the National Institutes of Health (RR04328, GM37911, and NS24520) and the National Science Foundation (MCB-9118687). The author thanks Dr. Dong Xie, Dr. Peter Privalov, and all the members of the Biocalorimetry Center for many helpful discussions and for providing an exciting environment for protein research.

Literature Cited

1. Alexandrescu AT, Evans PA, Pitkeathly M, Baum J, Dobson CM. 1993. Structure and dynamics of the acid-denatured molten globule state of alpha-lactalbumin: a two-dimensional NMR study. *Biochemistry* 32:1707–18
2. Baldwin RL. 1986. Temperature dependence of the hydrophobic interaction in protein folding. *Proc. Natl. Acad. Sci. USA* 83:8069–72
3. Baum J, Dobson CM, Evans PA, Hanley C. 1989. Characterization of a partly folded protein by NMR methods: studies of the molten globule state of guinea-pig α-lactalbumin. *Biochemistry* 28:7–13
4. Bromberg S, Dill KA. 1994. Side-chain entropy and packing in proteins. *Protein Sci.* 3:997–1009
5. Carra JH, Anderson EA, Privalov PL. 1994. Thermodynamics of staphylococcal nuclease denaturation. I. The acid-denatured state. *Protein Sci.* 3:944–51
6. Carra JH, Anderson EA, Privalov PL. 1994. Thermodynamics of staphylococcal nuclease denaturation. II. The A state. *Protein Sci.* 3:952–59
7. Chothia C. 1984. Principles that determine the structure of proteins. *Annu. Rev. Biochem.* 53:537–72
8. Chyan C-L, Wormald C, Dobson CM, Evans PA, Baum J. 1993. Structure and stability of the molten globule state of guinea-pig alpha-lactalbumin: a hydrogen exchange study. *Biochemistry* 32:5681–91
9. Dill KA, Shortle D. 1991. Denatured states of proteins. *Annu. Rev. Biochem.* 60:795–825
10. Dobson CM. 1991. Characterization of protein folding intermediates. *Curr. Opin. Struct. Biol.* 1:22–27
11. Dobson CM. 1992. Unfolded proteins, compact states and molten globules. *Curr. Opin. Struct. Biol.* 2:6–12
12. Freire E. 1994. Statistical thermodynamic analysis of DSC data: structural deconvolution of the heat capacity function of proteins. *Methods Enzymol.* 240:502–30
13. Freire E, Haynie DT, Xie D. 1993. Molecular basis of cooperativity in protein folding. IV. CORE: a general cooperative folding model. *Proteins Struct. Funct. Genet.* 17:111–23
14. Freire E, Murphy KP. 1991. The molecular basis of cooperativity in protein folding. *J. Mol. Biol.* 222:687–98
15. Freire E, Murphy KP, Sanchez-Ruiz JM, Galisteo ML, Privalov PL. 1992. The molecular basis of cooperativity in protein folding. Thermodynamic dissection of interdomain interactions in phosphoglycerate kinase. *Biochemistry* 31:250–56
16. Gittis AG, Stites WE, Lattman EE. 1993. The phase transition between a compact denatured state and a random coil state in staphylococcal nuclease is first-order. *J. Mol. Biol.* 232:718–24
17. Goto Y, Nishikiori S. 1991. Role of electrostatic repulsion in the acidic molten globule of cytochrome *c*. *J. Mol. Biol.* 222:679–86
18. Griko Y, Freire E, Privalov PL. 1994. Energetics of the alpha-lactalbumin states. A calorimetric and statistical thermodynamic study. *Biochemistry* 33:1889–99

19. Griko YV, Privalov PL. 1994. Thermodynamic puzzle of apomyoglobin unfolding. *J. Mol. Biol.* 235:1318–25

20. Hagihara Y, Tan Y, Gotto Y. 1994. Comparison of the conformational stability of the molten globule and native states of cytochrome *c*: effects of acetylation, urea and guanidine-hydrochloride. *J. Mol. Biol.* 237:336–48

21. Harata K, Muraki M. 1992. X-ray structual evidence for a local helix-loop transition in α-lactalbumin. *J. Biol. Chem.* 267:1419–21

22. Haynie DT, Freire E. 1993. Structural energetics of the molten globule state. *Proteins Struct. Funct. Genet.* 16:115–40

23. Hua QH, Ladbury JE, Weiss MA. 1993. Dynamics of a monomeric insulin analogue: testing the molten-globule hypothesis. *Biochemistry* 32:1433–42

24. Hughson FM, Baldwin RL. 1989. Use of site-directed mutagenesis to destabilize native apomyoglobin relative to folding intermediates. *Biochemistry* 28:4415–22

25. Hughson FM, Barrick D, Baldwin RL. 1991. Probing the stability of a partly folded apomyoglobin intermediate by site-directed mutagenesis. *Biochemistry* 30:4113–18

26. Hughson FM, Wright PE, Baldwin RL. 1990. Structural characterization of a partly folded apomyoglobin intermediate. *Science* 249:1544–48

27. Ikeguchi M, Kuwajima K, Sugai S. 1986. Ca^{2+}-induced alteration in the unfolding behavior of α-lactalbumin. *J. Biochem. Tokyo* pp. 1191–1201

28. Jacobs MD, Fox RO. 1994. Staphylococcal nuclease folding intermediate charaterized by hydrogen exchange and NMR spectroscopy. *Proc. Natl. Acad. Sci. USA* 91:449–53

29. Jeng M-F, Englander SW. 1991. Stable submolecular folding units in a noncompact form of cytochrome *c*. *J. Mol. Biol.* 221:1045–61

30. Jeng M-F, Englander SW, Elöve GA, Wand AJ, Roder H. 1990. Structural description of acid-denatured cytochrome *c* by hydrogen exchange and 2D NMR. *Biochemistry* 29:10433–37

31. Jennings PA, Wright PE. 1993. Formation of a molten globule intermediate early in the kinetic folding pathway of apomyoglobin. *Science* 262:892–96

32. Kippen AD, Sancho J, Fersht AR. 1994. Folding of barnase in parts. *Biochemistry* 33:3778–86

33. Kraulis PJ. 1991. MOLSCRIPT: a program to produce both detailed and schematic plots of protein structures. *J. Appl. Crystallogr.* 24:946–50

34. Kuroda Y, Kidokoro S-i, Wada A. 1992. Thermodynamic characterization of cytochrome *c* at low pH. Observation of the molten globule state and of the cold denaturation process. *J. Mol. Biol.* 223:1139–53

35. Kuwajima K. 1989. The molten globule state as a clue for understanding the folding and cooperativity of globular-protein structure. *Proteins Strut. Funct. Genet.* 6:87–103

36. Lee B, Richards FM. 1971. The interpretation of protein structures: estimation of static accessibility. *J. Mol. Biol.* 55:379–400

37. Lee KH, Xie D, Freire E, Amzel LM. 1994. Estimation of changes in side chain configurational entropy in binding and folding: general methods and application to helix formation. *Proteins Struct. Funct. Genet.* 19:291–301

38. Liu Z-P, Rizo J, Gierasch LM. 1994. Equilibrium folding studies of cellular retinoic acid binding protein, a predominantly β-sheet protein. *Biochemistry* 33:134–42

39. Makhatadze G, Privalov PL. 1993. Contribution of hydration to protein folding thermodynamics. I. The enthalpy of hydration. *J. Mol. Biol.* 232:639–59

40. Matthews CR. 1993. Pathways of protein folding. *Annu. Rev. Biochem.* 62:653–83

41. Montgomery D, Jordan R, McMacken R, Freire E. 1993. Thermodynamic and structural analysis of the folding/unfolding transitions of DnaK. *J. Mol. Biol.* 232:680–92

42. Murphy KP, Bhakuni V, Xie D, Freire E. 1992. The molecular basis of co-operativity in protein folding. III. Identification of cooperative folding units and folding intermediates. *J. Mol. Biol.* 227:293–306

43. Murphy KP, Freire E. 1992. Thermodynamics of structural stability and cooperative folding behavior in proteins. *Adv. Protein Chem.* 43:313–61

44. Deleted in proof

45. Murphy KP, Xie D, Garcia KC, Amzel LM, Freire E. 1993. Structural energetics of peptide recognition: angiotensin II/antibody binding. *Proteins Struct. Funct. Genet.* 15:113–20

46. Nishii I, Kataoka M, Tokunaga F, Goto Y. 1994. Cold denaturation of the

molten globule states of apomyoglobin and a profile for protein folding. *Biochemistry* 33:4903–9

47. Peng Z-y, Kim PS. 1994. A protein dissection study of a molten globule. *Biochemistry* 33:2136–41

48. Pfeil W, Bychkova VE, Ptitsyn OB. 1986. Physical nature of the phase transition in globular proteins. Calorimetric study of human α-lactalbumin. *FEBS Lett.* 198:287–91

49. Privalov PL. 1979. Stability of proteins: small globular proteins. *Adv. Protein Chem.* 33:167–239

50. Privalov PL. 1982. Stability of proteins: proteins which do not present a single cooperative system. *Adv. Protein Chem.* 35:1–104

51. Privalov PL, Gill SJ. 1988. Stability of protein structure and hydrophobic interaction. *Adv. Protein Chem.* 39:191–234

52. Privalov PL, Griko YV, Venyaminov SY, Kutyshenko VP. 1986. Cold denaturation of myoglobin. *J. Mol. Biol.* 190:487–98

53. Ptitsyn O. 1992. The molten globule state. In *Protein Folding*, ed. TE Creighton, pp. 243–300. New York: Freeman

54. Radford SE, Dobson CM, Evans PA. 1992. The folding of hen lysozyme involves partially structured intermediates and multiple pathways. *Nature* 358:302–7

55. Ramsay G, Freire E. 1990. Linked thermal and solute perturbation analysis of cooperative domain interactions in proteins. The structural stability of diphtheria toxin. *Biochemistry* 29:8677–83

56. Redfield C, Smith RA, Dobson CM. 1994. Structural characterization of a highly-ordered "molten globule" at low pH. *Struct. Biol.* 1:23–29

57. Richards FM. 1977. Areas, volumes, packing and protein structure. *Annu. Rev. Biophys. Bioeng.* 6:151–76

58. Shakhnovich EI, Finkelstein AV. 1989. Theory of cooperative transitions in protein molecules. I. Why denaturation of a globular protein is a 1st

order phase transition. *Biopolymers* 28:1667–80

59. Shortle D, Abergunawardana C. 1993. NMR analysis of the residual structure in the denatured state of an unusual mutant of staphylococcal nuclease. *Curr. Biol.* 1:121–34

60. Skolnick J, Kolinski A, Godzik A. 1993. From independent modules to molten globules: observations on the nature of protein folding intermediates. *Proc. Natl. Acad. Sci. USA* 90:2099–2100

61. Spolar RS, Livingstone JR, Record MT Jr. 1992. Use of liquid hydrocarbon and amide transfer data to estimate contributions to thermodynamic functions of protein folding from the removal of nonpolar and polar surfaces from water. *Biochemistry* 31:3947–55

62. Woodward C. 1993. Is the slow-exchange core the protein folding core? *Trends Biol. Sci.* 18:359–60

63. Xie D, Bhakuni V, Freire E. 1991. Calorimetric determination of the energetics of the molten globule intermediate in protein folding: apo-α-lactalbumin. *Biochemistry* 30:10673–78

64. Xie D, Bhakuni V, Freire E. 1993. Are the molten globule and the unfolded states of apo-a-lactalbumin enthalpically equivalent? *J. Mol. Biol.* 232:5–8

65. Xie D, Fox R, Freire E. 1994. Thermodynamic characterization of a staphylococcal nuclease folding intermediate. *Protein Sci.* In press

66. Xie D, Freire E. 1994. Molecular basis of cooperativity in protein folding. V. Thermodynamic and structural conditions for the stabilization of compact denatured states. *Proteins Struct. Funct. Genet.* 19:291–301

67. Xie D, Freire E. 1994. Structure based prediction of protein folding intermediates. *J. Mol. Biol.* 242:62–80

68. Yutani K, Ogasahara K, Kuwajima K. 1992. Absence of the thermal transition in apo-α-lactalbumin in the molten globule state. *J. Mol. Biol.* 228:347–50

Annu. Rev. Biophys. Biomol. Struct. 1995. 24:167–83

DNA ANALOGUES WITH NONPHOSPHODIESTER BACKBONES

Peter E. Nielsen

Center for Biomolecular Recognition, Department of Medical Biochemistry and Genetics, Biochemistry Laboratory B, University of Copenhagen, The Panum Institute, Blegdamsvej 3, DK-2200 Copenhagen N, Denmark

KEY WORDS: DNA mimic, antisense reagents, antigene reagents, triple helix, strand invasion, DNA structure

CONTENTS

ABSTRACT

This review discusses the recent developments of DNA analogues with nonphosphodiester backbones in terms of DNA structure and antisense and antigene potential. A larger number of derivatives are now available in which the phosphodiester linkage has been replaced but the deoxyribose retained. However, only a few of these (e.g. the ones having a

167

thioformacetal or a carboxamide linkage) appear to be good structural DNA mimics. Two successful attempts to replace the entire deoxyribose phosphate backbone have been reported, the morpholino derivatives and the peptide nucleic acids (PNA), which contain an *N*-(2-aminoethyl)glycine–based pseudopeptide backbone. Most information is available on the PNA, which is a very promising DNA mimic. In conclusion, the deoxyribose phosphate backbone is not essential for a potent structural DNA mimic and not even required for a helical duplex structure.

INTRODUCTION

The first report that oligonucleotides could specifically suppress gene expression by antisense binding to a sequence of complementary messenger RNA (74) started a veritable chemical quest for DNA analogues of improved efficacy. The goal was and still is to make a DNA analogue suitable for antisense-drug development. The immediate aim was to make biologically stable (nuclease-resistant) analogues that retained the RNA hybridization properties of natural DNA but that also had improved cellular-uptake properties.

Chemically speaking, DNA consists of units (Figure 1), each composed of a nucleobase (adenine, cytosine, guanine, or thymine) attached to a pentose sugar (deoxyribose) via a glycosidic linkage, with a phosphate ester linking successive sugar rings. Thus, modifications of DNA may be divided into those involving (*a*) the nucleobase, (*b*) the sugar, and/or (*c*) the phosphate diester.

During the past 20 years, numerous such DNA analogues have been synthesized, and this is still an active research area. However, most efforts have been devoted to the often cumbersome chemical synthesis

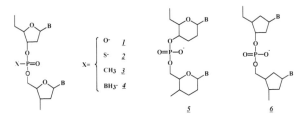

Figure 1 Chemical structures of normal phosphodiester DNA (analogue 1), phosphorothioate (analogue 2), methylphosphonate (analogue 3), boranophosphonate (analogue 4), homo-DNA (analogue 5), and a pentacarbocyclic DNA (analogue 6). B is a nucleobase, either adenine, guanine, cytosine, or thymine. Underlined numerals in figures correspond to "analogue *n*" in the text.

of these compounds, and only in a few cases has the chemistry reached a stage that allows for a more thorough biochemical, biological, and pharmacokinetic evaluation of the analogues.

Several recent reviews have covered the chemistry of DNA analogues and the potential use of these molecules as antisense or antigene drugs, and I refer the reader to these papers for further background material (e.g. 8, 21, 43, 44, 59, 66, 67). This review focuses on recent advances in the development of DNA analogues in which the phosphodiester linkage or the entire backbone has been replaced with an alternative, structurally homomorphous chemical entity.

DNA ANALOGUES

Phosphate Modifications

The methylphosphonates (analogue 3) and especially the phosphorothioates (analogue 2) are as yet the best-studied oligonucleotide analogues. The first drugs to reach clinical trials were developed from them (9, 10). Although both phosphorothioate and methylphosphonate oligonucleotides have advantages over unmodified oligonucleotides (e.g. nuclease resistance), in terms of antisense drug candidates, they are only the first generation. The second generation is eagerly awaited.

Other modifications of the phosphate include phosphoramidates, phosphorodithioates, and phosphotriesters (43, 67), but none of these seem to have major advantages, either as antisense drugs or as DNA mimics in general. However, the recently described boranophosphates (analogue 4) appear to have very interesting properties, especially in relation to DNA technology (61, 63). An enzymatic synthesis of an analogue in which the 5'-oxygen is replaced with a methylene group has also been reported (2). This analogue is nuclease resistant and thus has an antisense potential.

Ribose Modifications

Several laboratories are pursuing strategies involving the replacement of the ribose moiety of the backbone. These modifications include, for example, hexose (homo-DNA) (analogue 5) (19) and carbocyclically derived phosphodiester backbones (analogue 6) (57; H Moser, personal communication). The results so far show that, whereas pentacarbocyclic DNA has retained DNA-like hybridization properties (H Moser, personal communication), the structure-related behavior of homo-DNA distinctly differs from that of natural DNA (i.e. linear duplexes are formed), and this molecule also exhibits altered base-pairing properties (19).

Phosphodiester Mimics

A major part of the ongoing synthetic efforts in many laboratories involves structural mimicking of the entire phosphodiester linkage (including the 5'-methylene group of the deoxyribose), with the aim of developing a backbone linkage that is charge neutral (to increase the stability of DNA hybrid complexes), relatively hydrophobic (to increase cellular uptake), and achiral (to obtain stereochemical purity). Chemically speaking, this task consists of replacing four atoms in the linkage chain (Figure 2) and can be accomplished in numerous ways depending on the imagination and skill of the organic chemist (Figure 3). Unfortunately, as discussed below, the DNA molecular designer lacks a solid theoretical foundation—apart from some guidelines—on which to build (vide infra). Thus, one way (which is being followed) to arrive at designer rules is to synthesize various derivatives and characterize them in terms of hybridization and pharmacological properties, similar to the way traditional medicinal chemists derivatize model compounds and refine these structures to produce medically useful drugs.

The phosphate diester mimics reported so far (Figure 3) include alkanes (analogue 7) (42), ethers (analogues 8, 9) (4), thioethers (analogues 10, 11) (4), amines (analogues 12, 13) (42), ketones (analogue 14) (42), formacetals (analogue 15) (34), thioformacetals (analogues 16, 17) (5, 34), amides (analogues 18–20) (32, 40–42), carbamates (analogues 21, 22) (70), ureas (analogue 23) (71), hydroxylamines (analogues 24, 25) (12, 69), sulfamates (analogue 26) (58), sulfamides (analogue 27) (58), sulfones (analogue 28) (29, 33), glycinyl amides (analogue 29) (62, 67, 68), and others (43, 67). These analogues have all been prepared as dinucleotide building blocks compatible with normal phosphodiester oligonucleotide synthesis, and the resulting oligomers are thus composed of, at best, alternating phosphodiester and modified internucleoside linkages. In most cases only one or a few modified linkages have been incorporated into a 10- to 15-mer phosphodiester oligonucleotide. Therefore, the physical measurements obtained reflect the effect of a modified backbone in a phosphodiester context. These data bear on

Figure 2 The phosphodiester linkage (including the 5'-methylene group of the ribose) consists of four atoms (X, Y, Z, and W). These have been the subject of numerous modifications (see Figure 3).

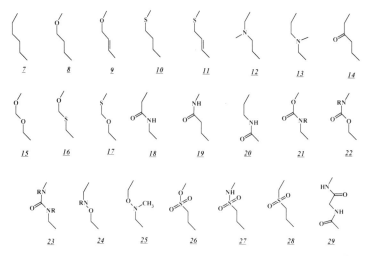

Figure 3 Oligonucleotide backbone modifications according to the X, Y, Z, and W substitution (cf Figure 2).

the phosphodiester structure that directly mimics properties of the linkage, but even if a linkage cannot be accommodated within a phosphodiester environment, an oligomer made up entirely of a modified backbone could adopt a conformation that allows for Watson-Crick base pairing (hybridization) with a complementary oligonucleotide.

The effect of sequence context must also be considered when comparing the merits of various backbone modifications, because different laboratories use different test sequences for evaluation of new backbones.

Nevertheless, we can already conclude that only very few of the above backbone modifications are good phosphodiester linkage mimics. Thermal stability measurements on hybrids with complementary DNA or RNA indicate that the most promising analogues are the 3'-thioformacetal (analogue 17) (34) and the 5'-amido derivative (analogue 18) (41, 61), but a proper evaluation must await additional biophysical and biological results.

What Makes a Good Phosphodiester-Linkage Mimic?

The answer to this question is the heart of the game and has still not emerged. However, several guidelines or key parameters can be considered: geometry, flexibility, and hydrophobicity. The right geometry is obviously essential because the helical parameters of the base pairs in the duplex are determined by the type of double helix—A, B, or some intermediate form. Thus, the conformational flexibility of the two connected sugars is limited. The evaluation of the adequate geometry of a proposed new backbone can largely be performed using computer modeling or physical model building. At a minimum, such an analysis will reveal if the structure is sterically reasonable.

The backbone must be flexible to adopt the right conformation. However, the linkage should not be too flexible because the entropy cost of freezing out the conformation required for hybridization will then be very high. Thus, the trick seems to be to impose restricted conformational flexibility on the backbone in a way that favors the hybridization-competent conformation. Jones, Matteucci, and coworkers may have achieved such flexibility in triplex formation through a 2',3'-cyclic riboacetal linkage (analogue 30; Figure 4) (35). Their results indicate that oligonucleotides containing such riboacetal linkages form more stable triplexes with double-stranded DNA targets than do normal oligonucleotides. However, at least part of the effect may result from the concomitant reduction of negative charge (35). Finally, lipophilicity of the linkage plays a role. Primarily, the water solubility of oligonucleotide analogues relies heavily on the solubility of the backbone because the nucleobases are largely hydrophobic in nature. Thus, analogues with backbones composed solely of very hydrophobic linkages, such as analogues 7, 8, 9, 10, 11, and 14, will most probably be only slightly soluble in water, as is also seen for methylphosphonates (analogue 3). A hydrophilic backbone is also expected to be superior because this is the part of the oligomer that is exposed to the aqueous solvent upon formation of a duplex. However, biological considerations such as cellular uptake may favor more hydrophobic backbones.

Backbone Replacement

Only a few attempts to replace the entire (deoxy)ribose-phosphate backbone, retaining just the nucleobases, have been successful. One

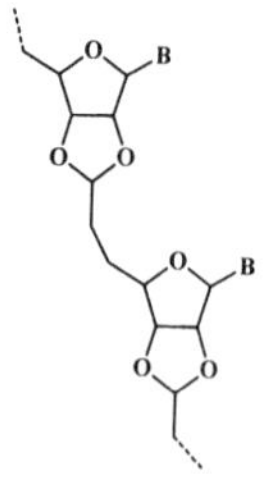

Figure 4 Structure of the bicyclic riboacetal analogue.

30

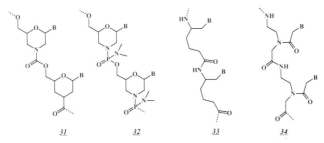

Figure 5 Oligonucleotide backbone replacements 31 and 32 are morpholino derivatives, and analogue 34 is PNA (peptide nucleic acid).

attempt involves the conversion of ribonucleosides to the corresponding morpholino compounds and oligomerization of these via carbamate linkages (analogue 31; Figure 5) (64). Although such morpholino carbamates showed some promise as DNA mimics (64), members of the second generation of morpholino-DNA connected via phosphor amidate linkages (analogue 32) (J Summerton, D Stein, S-B Huang, D Weller, J Puma & D Weller, personal communication) reportedly form much more thermally stable hybrids with complementary oligonucleotides and are also potent antisense reagents in an in vitro assay (J Summerton, D Stein, S-B Huang, D Weller, J Puma & D Weller, personal communication).

Analogues with amide or peptide-like backbones have also been devised (e.g. analogues 33, 34) (28, 50). The peptide nucleic acid (PNA), which has an achiral, noncharged backbone composed of N-(2-aminoethyl)glycine units (analogue 34), turned out to be a very good structural mimic of DNA (17, 37; recently reviewed in 53). In fact, hybrids between PNA and complementary DNA or RNA exhibit the highest thermal stability per base pair of any oligonucleotide analogue studied so far (17). The increase in thermal stability over that of DNA·DNA duplexes is ~1.5°C per base pair at physiological ionic strength; this increase is almost exclusively ascribed to the lack of interstrand electrostatic repulsion due to the noncharged backbone of the PNA (17). Furthermore, base-pair mismatch discrimination with PNA is as good as or better than that observed with natural DNA (17).

The potential of PNA as a source of antisense or antigene drugs and biomolecular probes has led to intense study of this type of DNA analogue, and apart from the early phosphate-modified oligonucleotides, phosphorothioates, and methylphosphonate, PNA is presently the most widely studied DNA analogue (e.g. 1, 3, 23, 53).

PNA has several attractive properties for drug development, but it is also the first example of a DNA-like molecule that retains only the nucleobases, i.e. the genetic information bearing part of DNA. This feature makes PNA relevant for discussions on DNA structure-function and evolution (17, 49, 53). Furthermore, the binding of PNA to double-stranded DNA takes place not by triple-helix formation, but by strand invasion upon the formation of P-loop strand–displacement complexes (8, 17, 53), which have unique biological properties (46).

ANTISENSE DRUGS

Numerous recent reviews have discussed the antisense strategy (9–11, 24, 27, 43, 44, 48), which is well beyond the scope of this chapter. However, a brief discussion of the basis of this technology is relevant, particularly in relation to new developments in oligonucleotide analogue chemistry.

The principle of antisense drugs is attractively simple: An oligonucleotide (mimic) is targeted to the messenger RNA (mRNA) of the gene exploiting nucleobase complementarity, and upon binding of the antisense drug, the mRNA is inactivated and therefore does not direct the synthesis of the protein gene product. Inactivation can result from direct blockage of the translational machinery (ribosomes and other protein factors) or from triggering of mRNA degradation by RNase H, an enzyme that specifically degrades the RNA strand of RNA·DNA duplexes. Thus, for any potential antisense oligonucleotide analogue, one should determine if it promotes RNase H activity or if an antisense effect must rely on direct interference with translation. Only analogues that are chemically closely related to DNA such as phosphorothioates (analogue 2) promote RNase H activity. Finally, the very complex issue of cellular uptake and pharmacokinetics must be considered. Therefore, developing a biologically stable oligonucleotide analogue with superior hybridization capacity is only a first small, but nonetheless crucial, step towards an efficient antisense drug. As discussed earlier, several of the oligonucleotide analogues described so far qualify as this first step, and the next major hurdle will be in cellular biology and pharmacology.

At this stage, predicting which analogues will have the brighter prospects as second-generation antisense drugs (after phosphorothioates and methylphosphonates) is difficult, if not impossible.

ANTIGENE DRUGS

The genome—double-stranded DNA itself—can also act as a target for oligonucleotides and their analogues because these may bind to homopurine or homopyrimidine sequences by means of triple-helix formation (14, 25) or, in the case of PNA, through strand invasion (51, 53, 54). Although in vitro experiments have indicated that gene transcription can be inhibited by oligonucleotides bound to promoter regions of the gene (16, 22, 38, 73), and by using PNA we can even activate transcription (46), the synthesis of antigene drugs based on oligonucleotides and their analogues is probably even further into the future than the production of antisense drugs.

TRIPLE HELIX

For over 30 years, investigators have known that one homopurine and two homopyrimidine polynucleotide strands can form a helical triplex structure (20). The interest in such triplex DNA was revived by the demonstration that short oligonucleotides ($\sim$15 nt) under appropriate ionic conditions can also form triple helices via Hoogsteen base pairing (Figure 6a) with a longer double-stranded DNA molecule (36, 47) and that such oligonucleotides may act as sequence-specific DNA-binding agents (14, 26). The triple-helix propensity of novel oligonucleotide analogues is therefore also of interest, although such data for almost all of the derivatives discussed here, with the exception of 3'-thioformacetal (analogue 16) and riboacetal (analogue 28), are not yet available. Very interestingly, the riboacetal appears particularly well suited for triplex formation; it yields a thermal stabilization of $\sim$4°C per unit in a triplex structure (35) compared with unmodified DNA, although it does not stand out as an exceptional DNA mimic. It actually causes a decrease in duplex T_m of $\sim$1°C per riboacetal (35). These results probably reflect how the backbone structures of the strands in a duplex differ from the structure of the third strand in a triplex. Thus, a good duplex DNA mimic may not necessarily be a good triplex binder and vice versa.

STRAND INVASION

The discovery that binding of PNA to a double-stranded DNA target did not occur via triplex formation but rather through strand invasion came as a surprise (7, 50). Subsequent experiments revealed that this binding mechanism is favored because of the formation of extremely stable PNA$_2$-DNA triplexes involving both Watson-Crick and Hoogsteen hydrogen bonding (55) (Figure 6b).

In terms of sequence recognition, PNA targeting is still subject to the constraints imposed by the Hoogsteen base pairing of the second PNA strand, i.e. much the same sequence constraints imposed on tri-

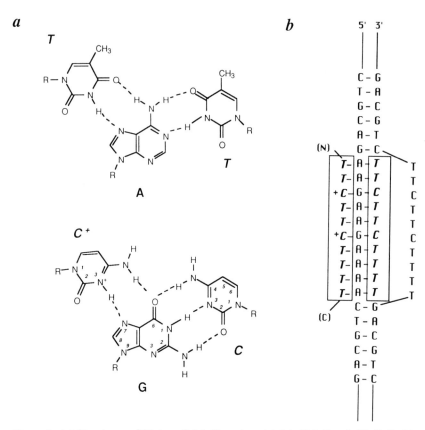

Figure 6 (*a*) Structures of Watson-Crick-Hoogsteen triplets T·A-T and C⁺·G-C. (*b*) Schematic structure of a PNA strand–displacement loop. The two PNA strands are shown in boxes. N and C denote the amino and carboxy termini of the PNA.

plex-forming oligonucleotides. However, because half of the recognition occurs through Watson-Crick base pairing of the first PNA strand, mere stabilization through the second PNA strand—even without strong sequence recognition—may well be able to stabilize the complex enough to allow it to bind even mixed-sequence, double-stranded DNA targets. The development of dimeric PNAs containing both of the PNA strands required for binding (M Egholm, L Christensen, K Dueholm, O Buchardt, J Coull & PE Nielsen, submitted) is an important step towards this goal.

The mechanism for strand invasion has not been elucidated yet, but the available evidence supports a mechanism involving an unstable duplex-invasion complex (which is the rate-limiting step). The inherent breathing of the DNA double helix promotes this invasion, and this thermodynamically unstable complex is subsequently trapped by the binding of the second PNA. This binding model is also consistent with the observation that the binding decreases drastically at increasing ionic strength (6, 52, 56). In vitro transcription-inhibition experiments have shown that PNA strand–displacement complexes are more powerful than DNA triple helices because they cause efficient arrest of the elongating RNA polymerase at the site of binding (23, 51, 54), and shorter targets can be used (51, 54). Even more interestingly, PNA strand–displacement loops function as transcription start sites for RNA polymerase in vitro (46). Thus, PNA-binding sites mimic biological promoters, and PNA serves as an artificial transcription factor. These results open the possibility of developing specific gene-activating drugs based on PNA or other sequence-selective, strand-invasive reagents. Other potent DNA mimics with uncharged backbones should also form very stable triplexes with homopurine DNA targets and thereby invade the two strands of the double helix.

BIOMOLECULAR TOOLS

Early on, research showed that reagents that bind sequence specifically to double-stranded DNA can be employed as tools in DNA technology for gene-sequence mapping and analyses (14, 26). Whether oligonucleotide analogues in general will have any advantages over deoxyoligonucleotides in such applications is not clear, but the special properties of PNA can be exploited. Strand displacement binding has, for instance, been used to promote sequence-specific, double-strand cleavage by the otherwise relatively sequence-neutral, single strand–specific nuclease S1 (13). PNA has also been used as a sequence-specific blocker of the polymerase chain reaction (PCR) for development of a point-mutation PCR assay, because PNA itself does not serve as a primer for the DNA polymerase (55a).

DNA STRUCTURE

As the carrier of genetic information, DNA (and to a minor extent RNA) is one of the central molecules of life; some considered it *the* molecule of life. Because genetic information resides in the sequence of the nucleobases, questions surround the role of the deoxyribose-phosphate backbone. The studies of oligonucleotide analogues with modified backbones could contribute considerably to elucidate this problem. Relevant questions include: How much can the phosphate or the ribose be changed without affecting the "functional" DNA structure? How much can the phosphodiester linkage be changed? Is the sugar-phoshate backbone required at all? And why is double-stranded DNA helical? Naturally, these questions can be asked both in a biological/enzymatic and in a structural nucleobase/recognition context. I restrict the discussion to the latter.

Clearly, moderate substitutions of the nonphosphodiester oxygens of the phosphate group will not seriously affect the hybridization properties of the DNA [e.g. phosphorothioates (analogue 2) or methylphosphonates (analogue 3)]. Likewise, the entire phosphodiester linkage can be replaced, provided the new linkage fulfills some yet rather poorly understood geometry and flexibility requirements. Changes that may seem rather insignificant to the chemist, such as moving a sulfur from the 3' (analogue 15) to the 5' (analogue 16) position, can make the difference between a good and a bad DNA mimic (4, 39). The position of an amide bond between the two sugars is also important: analogue 17 is a fairly good DNA mimic whereas analogues 18 or 19 are not (32, 40, 41).

The ribose ring can also be replaced; again the proper geometry is essential (compare analogues 5 and 6). However, other rings besides pentacyclic ones can produce this geometry—as exemplified by the morpholino derivatives 30 and 31—provided that the linkage is right. Finally, as shown by the results of the morpholino derivatives 30 and 31 and of PNA, chemical replacement of the entire deoxyribose-phosphate backbone can result in efficient structural DNA mimics. Thus, neither the phosphate diester linkage nor the (deoxy)ribose is essential for a functional DNA structure in terms of nucleobase recognition (hybridization).

This finding brings us to the question of DNA (or RNA) helicity. The results obtained with homo-DNA, and structural considerations regarding the stereochemistry of the ribose (19), serve as the basis for the argument that the ribose is a major determinant for the helical structure of double-stranded DNA (or RNA) (19). The length of the phosphodiester linkage (in combination with the sugar geometry) also promotes a helical conformation (6). However, Watson-Crick complementary PNA oligomers form duplexes, and circular dichroism measurements indicate that these duplexes adopt a helical conformation reminiscent of that of DNA (72). These results show that the ribose is not essential for a helical duplex structure. We must yet determine to what extent helicity is dictated by optimal base-stacking overlap of the base pairs themselves and what is the influence of the backbone on interbase distance.

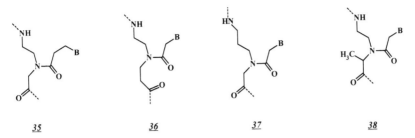

<u>35</u>   <u>36</u>   <u>37</u>   <u>38</u>

Figure 7   PNA derivatives. The derivatives with extended backbone were constructed using a propionyl linker to the nucleobase (analogue 35) (30, 31), replacing glycine with β-alanine (analogue 36) (30, 31) or replacing aminoethyl with aminopropyl (analogue 37) (30, 31). A chiral backbone was constructed using *d*- or *l*-alanine instead of glycine (analogue 38) (15). PNAs containing the *d/l*-alanine backbone retained the DNA-mimicking properties of PNA (15).

Studies on PNA may also shed light on these questions. The introduction of PNA derivatives with backbone extensions (analogues 35–37; Figure 7) greatly reduces the DNA hybridization properties of the PNA oligomers, an observation that again stresses the importance of the right geometry of the backbone, of constrained flexibility, or of both. However, it remains to be seen if homo-duplexes of such modified PNAs form and if so what their structure is.

Finally, all of the above results clearly show that DNA-like molecules do not need to contain a phosphodiester backbone, and each of these molecules, by virtue of its nucleobase sequence, potentially carries genetic information. Thus, in terms of the early evolution and earthly origin of life, the primordial genetic material may not necessarily have contained a phosphodiester-(deoxy)ribose backbone, but could have had, for example, a peptide-like backbone (49). The study of inherently achiral DNA mimics like PNA may also provide model systems with which we can ask questions about the origin of chirality in the biological world (60). For example, a recent study showed that "seeding" of left or right handedness into a PNA$_2$ duplex can be accomplished via one covalently attached chiral amino acid (72).

PROSPECTS

Clearly, the possibilities for making DNA analogues containing non-phosphodiester backbones are far from exhausted, and the encouraging results, especially with PNA, suggest that totally novel backbone-re-placement structures can be devised. Nevertheless, one should keep the objective in mind. Exploring DNA in terms of structural space is of fundamental interest, but the drive behind most of the studies discussed here has been a desire to make more potent antisense and antigene drugs, and the implicit aim has been to make enzyme-resistant DNA analogues that form the most stable hybrids with complementary DNA or RNA. I think it is time to modify this thinking, especially because many such analogues are now at hand, and focus more on biological parameters such as cellular uptake, bioavailability, and general pharmacokinetics. This is the next major challenge in terms of therapeutic applications, and these are the problems that require solutions before the next generation of antisense and antigene drugs is born.

However, we should not forget that by studying the properties of DNA analogues, we may gain insight into the structural and biological properties of DNA itself, and we may even get clues to why DNA has evolved as the major genetic material and to the identity of its primordial predecessor.

Literature Cited

1. Almarsson Ö, Bruice TC, Kerr J, Zuckermann RN. 1993. Molecular mechanics calculations of the structures of polyamide nucleic acid DNA duplexes and triple helical hybrids. *Proc. Natl. Acad. Sci. USA* 90:7518–22
2. Breaker RR, Gough GR, Gilham PT. 1993. Synthesis and properties of adenosine oligonucleotide analogues containing methylene groups in place of phosphodiester 5'-oxygens. *Biochemistry* 32:9125–28
3. Brown SC, Thomson SA, Veal JM, Davis, DG. 1994. NMR solution structure of a peptide nucleic acid complexed with RNA. *Science* 265:777–80
4. Cao X, Matteucci MD. 1994. Oligodeoxynucleotides containing 3'-allylether, 3'-allylsulfide and their saturated derivatives as phosphate mimics. *Tetrahedr. Lett.* 35:2325–28
5. Cao X, Matteucci MD. 1994. Preparation, characterization and binding properties of an oligodeoxynucleotide containing the 3'-ribothioformacetal phosphate analog. *Bioorg. Med. Chem. Lett.* 4:807–10
6. Calladine CR, Drew HR. 1992. *Under-*

standing DNA. The Molecule & How It Works. New York: Academic
7. Cherny DY, Belotserkovskii BP, Frank-Kamenetskii MD, Egholm M, Buchardt O, et al. 1993. DNA unwinding upon strand displacement of binding of PNA to double stranded DNA. *Proc. Natl. Acad. Sci. USA* 90: 1667–70
8. Cook PD. 1991. Medicinal chemistry of antisense oligonucleotides—future opportunities. *Anticancer Drug Des.* 6:585–607
9. Crook ST. 1992. Oligonucleotide therapy. *Curr. Opinion Biotechnol.* 3: 656–61
10. Crook ST. 1993. Therapeutic potential of oligonucleotides. *Curr. Opin. Invest. Drugs* 2:1045–48
11. Crook ST. 1992. Therapeutic applications of of oligonucleotides. *Annu. Rev. Pharmacol. Toxicol.* 32:329–76
12. Debart F, Vasseur JJ, Sanghvi YS, Cook PD. 1992. Synthesis and incorporation of methyleneoxy(methylimino) linked thymidine dimer into antisense oligonucleosides. *Biorg. Med. Chem. Lett.* 2:1479–82

13. Demidov V, Frank-Kamenetskii MD, Egholm M, Buchardt O, Nielsen PE. 1993. Sequence selective double strand DNA cleavage by PNA targeting using nuclease S1. *Nucleic Acids Res.* 21:2103–7

14. Dervan PB. 1992. Reagents for the site-specific cleavage of megabase DNA. *Nature* 359:87–88

15. Dueholm K, Petersen KH, Jensen DK, Egholm M, Nielsen PE, Buchardt O. 1994. Peptide nucleic acid (PNA) with a chiral backbone based on alanine. *Bioorg. Med. Chem. Lett.* 4: 1077–80

16. Duval-Valentin G, Thuong N, Helene C. 1992. Specific inhibition of transcription by triple helix-forming oligonucleotides. *Proc. Natl. Acad. Sci. USA* 89:504–8

17. Egholm M, Buchardt O, Christensen L, Behrens C, Freier SM, et al. 1993. PNA hybridizes to complementary oligonucleotides obeying the Watson-Crick hydrogen bonding rules. *Nature* 365:556–68

18. Deleted in proof

19. Eschenmoser A, Loewenthal E. 1992. Chemistry of potentially prebiological natural products. *Chem. Soc. Rev.* 21: 1–16

20. Felsenfeld G, Davies DR, Rich A. 1957. Formation of a three-stranded polynucleotide molecule. *J. Am. Chem. Soc.* 79:2023–24

21. Goodchild J. 1990. Conjugates of oligonucleotides and modified oligonucleotides: a review of their synthesis and properties. *Bioconjug. Chem.* 1: 165–87

22. Grigoriev M, Praseuth D, Guieysse AL, Robin P, Thuong NT, et al. 1993. Inhibition of gene expression by triple helix–directed DNA cross-linking at specific sites. *Proc. Natl. Acad. Sci. USA* 90:3501–5

23. Hanvey JC, Peffer NC, Bisi JE, Thomson SA, Cadilla R, et al. 1992. Antisense and antigene properties of peptide nucleic acids. *Science* 258: 1481–85

24. Hélène C. 1991. Rational design of sequence-specific oncogene inhibitors based on antisense and antigene oligonucleotides. *Eur. J. Cancer* 27: 1466–71

25. Hélène C. 1991. The anti-gene strategy: control of gene expression by triplex-forming-oligonucleotides. *Anticancer Drug Des.* 6:569–84

26. Hélène C. 1993. Sequence-selective recognition and cleavage of double-helical DNA. *Curr. Opin. Biotechnol.* 4:29–36

27. Hélène C, Toulmé J-J. 1990. Specific regulation of gene expression by antisense, sense and antigene nucleic acids. *Biochim. Biophys. Acta* 1049: 99–125

28. Huang S-B, Nelson JS, Weller DD. 1991. Acyclic nucleic acid analogues: synthesis and oligomerization of 4-diamino - 2 - oxo - 1(2H) - pyrimidinepentanoic acid and δ,4-diamino-2-oxo-1(2H)-pyrimidinehexanoic acid. *J. Org. Chem.* 56:6007–18

29. Huang Z, Schneider KC, Benner SA. 1993. Oligonucleotide analogs with dimethylenesulfide, -sulfoxide, and -sulfone groups replacing phosphodiester linkages. *Methods Mol. Biol.* 20: 315–53

30. Hyrup B, Egholm M, Nielsen PE, Wittung P, Norden B, Buchardt O. 1994. Structure-activity studies of the binding of modified peptide nucleic acids (PNA) to DNA. *J. Am. Chem. Soc.* 116:7964–70

31. Hyrup B, Egholm M, Rolland M, Nielsen PE, Berg RH, Buchardt O. 1993. Modification of the binding affinity of peptide nucleic acids (PNA). PNA with extended backbones consisting of 2-aminoethyl-β-alanine or 3-aminopropylglycine units. *J. Chem. Soc. Chem. Commun.* pp. 518–19

32. Idziak IJG, Damha MJ, Giannaris PA. 1993. Synthesis and hybridization properties of amide-linked thymidine dimers incorporated into oligodeoxynucleotides. *Tetrahedron Lett.* 34: 5417–20

33. Jenny TF, Benner SA. 1993. Preparation of enantiomerically pure analogs of purine nucleosides for the synthesis of sulfone-linked oligonucleotide analogs. *Helv. Chim. Acta* 76:826–41

34. Jones R, Lin K-Y, Milligan JF, Wadwani S, Matteucci MD. 1993. Synthesis and binding properties of pyrimidine oligodeoxynucleoside analogs containing neutral phosphodiester replacements: the formacetal and 3'-thioformacetal internucleoside linkages. *J. Org. Chem.* 58:2983–91

35. Jones RJ, Swaminathan S, Milligan JF, Wadwani S, Froehler BC, Matteucci MD. 1993. Oligonucleotides containing a covalent conformationally restricted phosphodiester analog for high-affinity triple helix formation: the riboacetal internucleotide linkage. *J. Am. Chem. Soc.* 115:9816

36. Le Doan T, Perrouault L, Praseuth D,

Habhoub N, Decout JL, et al. 1987. Sequence-specific recognition photo-crosslinking and cleavage of the DNA double helix by an oligoα-thymidylate covalently linked to an azidoprofla-vine derivative. *Nucleic Acids Res.* 15: 7749–60

37. Leijon M, Gräslund A, Nielsen PE, Buchardt O, Norden B, et al. 1994. Structural characterization of PNA-DNA duplexes by NMR. Evidence for DNA in a B-like conformation. *Biochemistry* 33:9820–25

38. Maher LJ, Wold B, Dervan PB. 1991. Oligonucleotide-directed DNA triple-helix formation: an approach to artificial repressors? *Antisense Res. Dev.* 1: 277–81

39. Matteucci M, Lin K-Y, Butcher S, Moulds C. 1991. Deoxyoligonucleo-tides bearing neutral analogues of phosphodiester linkages recognize duplex DNA via triple-helix germination. *J. Am. Chem. Soc.* 113:7767

40. Mesmaeker AD, Lebreton J, Waldner A, Fritsch V, Wolf RM, Freier SM. 1993. Amides as substitute for the phosphodiester linkage in antisense oligonucleotides. *SynLett* pp. 733–36

41. Mesmaeker AD, Waldner A, Lebreton, J, Hoffman P, Fritsch V, et al. 1994. Amides as a new type of back-bone modification in oligonucleotides. *Angew. Chem. Int.* 33:226–29

42. Mesmaeker AD, Waldner A, Sanghvi YS, Lebreton J. 1994. Comparison of rigid and flexible backbones in anti-sense oligonucleotides. *Bioorg. Med. Chem. Lett.* 4:395–98

43. Milligan JF, Matteucci MD, Martin JC. 1993. Current concepts in anti-sense drug design. *J. Med. Chem.* 36: 1923–37

44. Mirabelli CK, Bennett CF, Anderson K, Crooke ST. 1991. In vitro and in vivo pharmacologic activities of anti-sense oligonucleotides. *Anticancer Drug Des.* 6:647–61

45. Deleted in proof

46. Møllegaard NE, Buchardt O, Egholm M, Nielsen PE. 1994. PNA-DNA strand displacement loops as artificial transcription promoters. *Proc. Natl. Acad. Sci. USA* 91:3892–95

47. Moser HE, Dervan PB. 1987. Sequence-specific cleavage of double helical DNA by triple helix formation. *Science* 238:645–50

48. Neckers L, Whitesell L, Rosolen A, Geselowitz DA. 1992. Antisense inhibition of oncogene expression. *Crit. Rev. Oncog.* 3:175–231

49. Nielsen PE. 1993. Peptide nucleic acid (PNA). A model structure for the pri-mordial genetic material. *Orig. Life* 23: 323–27

50. Nielsen PE, Egholm M, Berg RH, Buchardt O. 1991. Sequence selective recognition of DNA by strand dis-placement with a thymine-substituted polyamide. *Science* 254:1497–1500

51. Nielsen PE, Egholm M, Berg RH, Buchardt O. 1993. Peptide nucleic acids (PNA). Potential antisense and anti-gene agents. *Anticancer Drug Des.* 8: 53–63

52. Nielsen PE, Egholm M, Berg RH, Buchardt O. 1993. Sequence specific inhi-bition of restriction enzyme cleavage by PNA. *Nucleic Acids Res.* 21: 197–200

53. Nielsen PE, Egholm M, Buchardt O. 1994. Peptide nucleic acids (PNA). A DNA mimic with a peptide backbone. *Bioconj. Chem.* 5:3–7

54. Nielsen PE, Egholm M, Buchardt O. 1994. Sequence specific transcription arrest by PNA bound to the template strand. *Gene* In press

55. Nielsen PE, Egholm M, Buchardt O. 1994. Evidence for (PNA)₂/DNA tri-plex structure upon binding of PNA to dsDNA by strand displacement. *J. Mol. Recognit.* 7:165–70

55a. Ørum H, Nielsen PE, Egholm M, Berg RH, Buchardt O, Stanley C. 1993. Single base pair mutation analy-sis by PNA directed PCR clamping. *Nucleic Acids Res.* 21:5332–36

56. Peffer NJ, Hanvey JC, Bisi JE, Thom-son, SA, Hassman FC, et al. 1993. Strand-invasion of duplex DNA by peptide nucleic acid oligomers. *Proc. Natl. Acad. Sci. USA* 90:10648–52

57. Perbost M, Lucas M, Chavis C, Pom-pon A, Baumgartner H, et al. 1989. Sugar modified oligonucleotides. I. Carbo-oligodeoxynucleotides as po-tential antisense agents. *Biochem. Bio-phys. Res. Commun.* 165:742

58. Reynolds RC, Crooks PA, Maddry JA, Akhtar MS, Montgomery JA, Secrist JA. 1992. Synthesis of thymidine di-mers containing internucleoside sulfo-nate and sulfonamide linkages. *J. Org. Chem.* 57:2983–85

59. Sanghvi YS, Cook PD. 1993. Towards second-generation synthetic back-bones for antisense oligonucleosides. In *Nucleosides and Nucleotides as Antitumor and Antiviral Agents,* ed. CK Chu, DC Baker, pp. 311–23. New York: Plenum

60. Schwartz AW. 1994. The origin of

macromolecular chirality. *Curr. Biol.* 4:758–60

61. Shaw BR, Madison J, Sood A, Spielvogel BF. 1993. Oligonucleoside boranophosphate. *Methods Mol. Biol.* 20:225–43

62. Singh AK, Varma RS. 1992. Ruthenium tetroxide: a mild reagent for the oxidation of 2',3'-O-isopropylidene purine nucleosides. *Tetrahedron Lett.* 33:2307

63. Sood A, Shaw BR, Spielvogel BF. 1990. Boron-containing nucleic acids. 2. Synthesis of oligodeoxynucleoside boranophosphates. *J. Am. Chem. Soc.* 112:9000–1

64. Stirchak EP, Summerton JE, Weller DD. 1989. Uncharged stereoregular nucleic acid analogues. 2. Morpholino nucleoside oligomers with carbamate internucleoside linkages. *Nucleic Acids Res.* 17:6129–41

65. Deleted in proof

66. Uhlmann E, Peyman A. 1990. Antisense oligonucleotides: a new therapeutic principle. *Chem. Rev.* 90:544

67. Varma RS. 1993. Synthesis of oligonucleotide analogues with modified backbones. *SynLett* pp. 621–37

68. Varma RS, Hogan ME. 1992. Ruthenium tetraoxide catalyzed oxidation of nucleosides: a facile synthesis of 5'-carboxylic acid derivatives. *Tetrahedron Lett.* 33:7719–20

69. Vasseur J-J, Debart F, Sanghvi YS, Cook PD. 1992. Oligonucleotides: synthesis of a novel methylhydroxylamine-linked nucleoside dimer and its incorporation into antisense sequences. *J. Am. Chem. Soc.* 114:4006–7

70. Waldner A, Mesmaeker AD, Lebreton J. 1994. Synthesis of oligodeoxyribonucleotides containing dimers with carbamate moieties as replacement of the natural phosphodiester linkage. *Bioorg. Med. Chem. Lett.* 4:405–8

71. Waldner A, Mesmaeker AD, Lebreton J, Fritsch V, Wolf RM. 1994. Ureas as backbone replacements for the phosphodiester linkage in oligonucleotides. *SynLett* pp. 57–62

72. Wittung P, Nielsen PE, Buchardt O, Egholm M, Norden B. 1994. Double helix formation by complementary PNA. Direct observation of helical seeding. *Nature* 368:561–63

73. Young SL, Krawczyk SH, Matteucci MD, Toole JJ. 1991. Triple helix formation inhibits transcription elongation in vitro. *Proc. Natl. Acad. Sci. USA* 88:10023–26

74. Zamecnik PC, Stephenson ML. 1978. Inhibition of rous sarcoma virus replication and cell transformation by a specific oligodeoxynucleotide. *Proc. Natl. Acad. Sci. USA* 75:280–84

Annu. Rev. Biophys. Biomol. Struct. 1995. 24:185–208
Copyright © 1995 by Annual Reviews Inc. All rights reserved

STRUCTURE AND MECHANISM OF DNA TOPOISOMERASES

Dale B. Wigley

Laboratory of Molecular Biophysics, Rex Richards Building, University of Oxford, South Parks Road, Oxford, OX1 3QU, United Kingdom

KEY WORDS: DNA gyrase, antibiotics, supercoiling

CONTENTS

ABSTRACT

DNA topoisomerases are ubiquitous enzymes that control the level of supercoiling of DNA in cells. There are several classes, each with distinct properties, which are briefly discussed in this review. High-resolution X-ray crystallographic structures have been obtained for fragments of two classes of these enzymes, which when combined with biochemical data, reveal a great deal about the gymnastics that the enzymes undergo during catalysis and provide fascinating snapshots of their mechanisms. These mechanisms are discussed in detail. Finally, the

1056-8700/95/0610-185$05.00

first structure of a topoisomerase in a complex with an antibiotic was recently solved. This structure is briefly discussed with regard to the biochemical activity of the compound.

PERSPECTIVES AND OVERVIEW

DNA topoisomerases are the enzymes responsible for controlling the level of DNA supercoiling in cells. Mechanistically, they can be divided into two main classes: type I enzymes, which cleave a single strand of DNA during the course of the reaction, and type II enzymes, which cleave both strands. These two families contain several other subgroups consisting of variants of these two general classes. Topoisomerases are ubiquitous and are implicated in most biological processes that involve DNA. Clearly, the mechanisms of both enzyme classes involve DNA cleavage and DNA strand passage through the break, followed by religation of the cleaved DNA. The precise manner by which such a complicated series of concerted events can be carried out by a single molecule poses many interesting questions, the answers to which are just beginning to come to light.

TYPE I ENZYMES

The type I enzyme family can be divided into three subgroups—I, III, and V. The enzymes operate by cleaving a single-stranded section of DNA that then becomes covalently attached to the enzyme through a phospho-tyrosine linkage. A single strand (or in some cases double strand) of DNA is then passed through the single-stranded break, at which point, one cycle of DNA relaxation has occurred. Although each of these different subgroups cleave only one strand of DNA, their cleavage mechanisms are less similar than they appear at first and are discussed in more detail below. The type I enzymes can catalyze several different reactions, including the relaxation of supercoiled DNA and the formation of double-stranded DNA from complementary single-stranded circles. They can also catenate or decatenate double-stranded circles, provided that one of the circles contains a single-stranded nick or gap.

Because of the importance of DNA topoisomerases, much effort has gone into finding specific inhibitors that might be useful as pharmaceutical compounds. Although no such compounds are known for bacterial topoisomerase I, the eukaryotic enzymes are a useful target for camptothecin, an anticancer compound.

Bacterial Topoisomerase I

The first topoisomerase discovered was originally named the ω-protein (37) but was later renamed *Escherichia coli* topoisomerase I, after the discovery of other topoisomerase activities in cells. The bacterial type I enzymes are monomeric proteins that have a subunit molecular weight of approximately 100,000. They can relax negatively supercoiled DNA by changing the linking number (or degree of supercoiling) in steps of one. In order to do this, the enzymes require magnesium ions, but no other cofactors. The phospho-tyrosine linkage is via the free 5' end of the cleaved DNA strand.

Structure of a 67-kDa Fragment of E. coli Topoisomerase I

A 67-kDa N-terminal fragment of *E. coli* topoisomerase I has been crystallized (16), and its structure has been reported at 2.2-Å resolution (17). The protein comprises four domains (Figure 1), which contact each other to give a structure with overall dimensions of

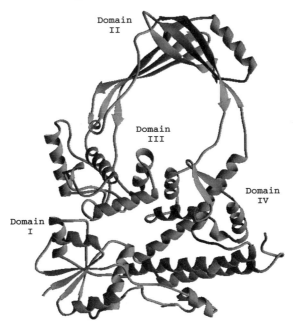

Figure 1 Ribbon diagram of the 67-kDa fragment of *E. coli* topoisomerase I showing the domain structure of the protein (modified from Ref. 17), produced from coordinates kindly provided by A Mondragon.

67 × 43 × 96 Å. These structural domains surround a large cavity running through the fragment that, with a diameter of over 25 Å, can easily accommodate a regular B-form DNA double helix. In addition, another cleft runs approximately perpendicularly to the large hole through the structure, and a smaller hole runs parallel to the large hole. All of these features are thought to be important for the mechanism of the enzyme. The C-terminal residue of the fragment is located on one side of the structure; the missing DNA-binding domain of the intact protein may also be located in this region, adjacent to the cleft across the protein surface.

The path taken by the polypeptide chain is very tortuous indeed. It begins in domain I, passes into domain IV, moves on to domain II, then to domain III before returning to domain II and finishing up in domain IV again. This linkage between the domains may well be important in that it provides a firm scaffold for this remarkably open structure and is likely to be important for the contortions that the protein must undergo during catalysis. The interactions made by domain III with domains I and IV are thus noncovalent, which suggests that a simple rigid body movement during enzyme catalysis could pull them apart. The active site can be identified by the location of Tyr319 in the structure. This residue occupies a position adjacent to the cleft and small hole described above, at the tip of domain III. The other residues in this region are highly conserved, as one would expect for the active-site region. Interestingly, a cluster of acidic residues in domain I (Asp111, Asp113, and Glu115) have a spatial arrangement similar to that of the acidic residues that coordinate two magnesium ions in the Klenow fragment of DNA polymerase I (3). Magnesium ions are implicated in the cleavage reaction of bacterial topoisomerase I, but the suggested magnesium-binding sites have not been confirmed by means of crystallization in the presence of magnesium ions or the more electron-dense manganese ions.

Mechanism

The structure of the 67-kDa fragment is fascinating, but what does it allow us to deduce about the molecular mechanism of DNA relaxation by topoisomerase I? The 67-kDa fragment retains the ability to cleave single-stranded DNA (16), but it cannot catalyze DNA relaxation. Nevertheless, the crystal structure clearly indicates that Tyr319 is buried at the center of the structure between domains I and III and is therefore inaccessible to single-stranded DNA. This observation strongly implies that a structural change must occur that exposes Tyr319 and allows it to attack and cleave the DNA substrate. The protein structure suggests that this conformational change could involve a rigid body movement of domains II and III to expose the active site. Because no cofactors (other than magnesium ions) are required by the enzyme, this conformational change is thought to be triggered by interactions with DNA. The binding site for double-stranded DNA substrates appears to be the large cleft that runs adjacent to the active-site tyrosine residue and continues across domain IV. Electrostatic calculations certainly suggest that this region carries a large positive potential, as one might expect for a DNA-binding site. In the intact protein, domain IV continues to form the C-terminal domain that contains several zinc-binding sites thought to be involved in DNA binding. The large cavity that runs through the 67-kDa fragment also carries a large positive electrostatic potential. The wide diameter (27.5 Å) of the cavity could accommodate either single or double-stranded DNA without steric hindrance.

Consequently, a topological mechanism for the catenation and decatenation of DNA circles, where one circle has a single-stranded nick or gap, has been proposed (17). Figure 2 summarizes this mechanism. In the first step, the enzyme opens up from the closed conformation observed in the crystal structure and allows a double-stranded section of DNA to pass into the central hole of the protein. At the same time, the single-stranded region of the nicked circle (solid part of dashed curve) binds to domain I of the protein. In step 2, the enzyme closes again and cleaves the DNA while phospho-tyrosine linkages to the active-site tyrosine residue form at the tip of the extended arm-like structure that ends with domain III. In step 3, this arm then lifts away from domains I and IV to form a DNA gate, through which the translocated double strand passes (step 4). At this point, catenation of the DNA circles has occurred. After the strand-passage event, domain III reassociates with domains I and IV; the DNA break is resealed; and the protein-DNA complex can dissociate (step 5). Finally, the DNA-protein complex dissociates. Decatenation occurs if the reaction proceeds in the opposite direction. The model accounts well for the catenation reaction, but it is less clear how the relaxation activity of topoisomerase I is accounted for by this model.

Topoisomerases III and V

The eukaryotic type III enzymes differ from the bacterial type I enzymes in that their activity is independent of magnesium ions. They can relax both negatively and positively supercoiled DNA, and during the reaction, a covalent link is made between the protein and the 3'

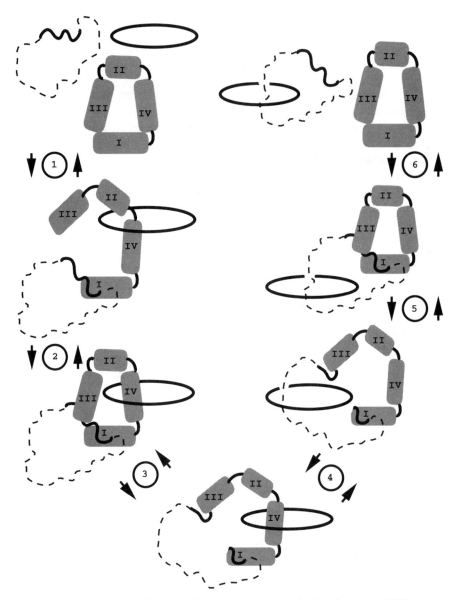

Figure 2 A mechanism for catenation and decatenation by topoisomerase I (17). An explanation of the diagram is provided in the text.

end of the cleaved DNA strand rather than the 5' end. Like the bacterial enzymes, their activity is independent of ATP. All of these properties are shared by the type V topoisomerases, which were recently discovered in hyperthermophilic bacteria (34). Interestingly, the type V topoisomerase from *Methanopyrus kandleri* is recognized by antibodies raised against human type III topoisomerase, but not by antibodies against the type I enzyme from *E. coli,* suggesting that type V is indeed more closely related to the eukaryotic than to the bacterial enzymes. Type III enzymes are also known as eukaryotic type I enzymes.

Vaccinia virus encodes its own DNA topoisomerase that has similar properties to eukaryotic type III enzymes (30). One major difference, however, is that the vaccinia enzyme is resistant to the antitumor drug camptothecin. It is also considerably smaller, being monomeric and having a subunit molecular weight of 32,000, which is approximately one third that of the eukaryotic enzymes. In addition, unlike most topoisomerases, the vaccinia enzyme shows significant sequence specificity with a marked preference for (C/T)CCTT (33).

Reverse Gyrase

Reverse gyrase is an enzyme capable of introducing positive supercoils into DNA circles (12). It is found in organisms that live in extreme environments (e.g. temperatures above 70°C), and it is thought to have a role in stabilizing DNA under these harsh conditions. Sequence analysis of the cloned *Sulpholobus acidocaldarious* reverse gyrase gene suggests that the single polypeptide chain comprises two functional domains: an ATP-dependent DNA helicase and a domain that has significant homology with bacterial type I DNA topoisomerase (6). Less is known about this enzyme than other topoisomerases, but it probably creates a region of DNA that is underwound locally by the helicase activity and that is then relaxed by the type I topoisomerase domain. The combined activity is ATP-dependent positive supercoiling (6).

TYPE II ENZYMES

The type II family contains three main subgroups—topoisomerases II and IV and DNA gyrase. The molecular weights and subunit structures of these enzymes at first appear to vary greatly, but comparisons of DNA and protein-sequence data (Figure 3) indicate that the enzymes are in fact very similar: The multimeric enzymes are equivalent to the larger proteins, but the polypeptide chain is broken into separate parts. This observation in itself suggests a domain structure for the proteins, a feature that has been exploited for structural and biochemical analysis.

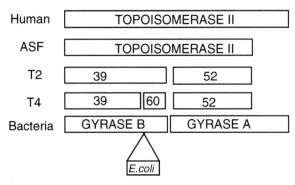

Figure 3 Sequence homology alignments of the type II topoisomerases. The blocks represent the linear amino acid sequence beginning with the N-terminus at the left. ASF, African swine fever virus; T2, T4, bacteriophages T2 and T4.

The enzymes can catalyze several different reactions, including supercoiling or relaxation of DNA, knotting or unknotting, and catenation or decatenation of double-stranded DNA circles. All are ATP-dependent enzymes capable of relaxing supercoiled DNA, with a requirement for magnesium ions, and cleave both DNA strands during the course of the reaction. The cleaved DNA becomes attached to the enzyme through covalent phospho-tyrosine linkages with the 5′ ends of the cleaved DNA. The generally favored mechanism then requires a double-stranded section of DNA be passed between the cleaved ends of the DNA break, which must consequently move apart by at least 20 Å (the diameter of a double-stranded DNA helix). The cleaved DNA is then religated. Each strand-passage event alters the linking number by two. Such a mechanism implies that large conformational changes in the DNA, the protein, or both, must take place during the course of the enzyme-catalyzed reaction.

Eukaryotic and Viral Topoisomerase II

Although the eukaryotic and viral type II enzymes share the greatest degree of mechanistic similarity, they show the greatest variability in sequence and subunit composition. The eukaryotic enzymes are all homodimeric enzymes and have a subunit molecular weight of up to 180,000. They also show a reasonable degree of similarity in both sequence and molecular weight. Two iso-enzymes, termed p170 and p180 because of their apparent molecular masses on SDS polyacrylamide gel electrophoresis (7), occur in humans, although their individual functions still need to be fully resolved. The eukaryotic and viral type II enzymes require ATP, yet can relax only supercoiled DNA, an energetically favorable reaction. The reason for this remains an enigma. The DNA-binding site covers approximately 16 base pairs (20), and DNA cleavage takes place at the center of this region. The eukaryotic enzymes are inhibited by several different compounds, many of which have clinical applications (see 18 for a review). Most of these compounds appear to stabilize the cleaved DNA intermediate on the enzyme. The compounds in this large group vary in structure enormously but most share the feature of a large planar moiety that may intercalate between the cut ends of the DNA and prevent religation. However, one group of inhibitors appears to be different and to act by stabilizing the closed form of the ATP-operated DNA clamp (27).

The degree of sequence homology across the various classes of type II topoisomerases is quite good, except for a region at the C-terminus of the proteins (see Figure 3). This region can be removed by proteolysis to release a truncated enzyme that is as active as (or more active than) the full-length protein (31). This region of the eukaryotic enzymes is also a domain that, when phosphorylated, signals that the protein should be transported from the cytoplasm to the nucleus (32). A similar function has been described for regions in other nuclear proteins and may be a common feature of eukaryotic DNA-binding proteins.

The type II topoisomerase from the eukaryotic virus responsible for African swine fever (ASF) has been cloned and sequenced (2). It is shorter than the eukaryotic enzymes because it lacks the C-terminal phosphorylation domain (Figure 3). Presumably, it lacks this domain because it does not need to be transported into the nucleus but instead must remain in the cytoplasm where viral DNA replication takes place.

The bacteriophages T2 and T4 both encode type II DNA topoisomerases (19). These enzymes are more complex with respect to their subunit composition than the eukaryotic enzymes. The T2 enzyme comprises two copies each of two polypeptide chains. The gene 39 product has sequence homology with the N-terminal region of the eukaryotic enzymes and is responsible for the ATPase activity of the complex. The gene 52 product contains the active-site tyrosine residue that becomes covalently attached to DNA during the enzyme reaction. This protein is also the major DNA-binding site of the active complex. In the T4 enzyme, the gene 39 product is shorter than its T2 counterpart, although it retains similar activities. However, a third protein (the product of gene 60) provides the region equivalent to the C-terminus of the T2 gene 39 protein. The gene 52 proteins of both phages appear to be very similar.

DNA Gyrase

DNA gyrase has the unique ability to introduce negative supercoils into closed circular DNA (8). This energetically unfavorable activity is coupled to the hydrolysis of ATP. Curiously, in contrast to the eukaryotic enzymes, DNA gyrase can also relax supercoiled DNA in an ATP-independent manner. Because DNA gyrase is only found in prokaryotes and is an essential enzyme, compounds that inhibit it have been developed as antibiotics. Although the quinolones (e.g. norfloxacin, ciprofloxacin) are used clinically, they cannot be used to treat young children or expectant mothers because of side effects. The severity of the side effects associated with the coumarins (e.g. novobiocin, coumermycin A1) preclude their clinical use. Consequently, a greater understanding of the structure and mechanism of DNA gyrase may allow it to be developed as a more successful antibacterial drug target.

The active gyrase complex is a heterotetramer comprising two proteins. The A protein has a molecular weight of ~97 kDa and is the target of the quinolone antibiotics. It is also the major DNA-binding site. The free A protein forms a tight-binding dimer in solution.

The B protein shows a greater variability between bacterial species than the A protein, but appears to fall into two classes, one with a molecular weight of 90 kDa and another of 70 kDa. The most studied is the class of B protein found in *E. coli,* which is of the higher-molecular-weight species. A comparison of amino acid and DNA sequences from a variety of bacterial species (see Figure 3) reveals that the difference between the two classes of protein mainly results from a large insertion, ~170 amino acids, in the region of residue 560 in the *Bacillus subtilis* sequence that gives rise to the larger *E. coli* protein. This large insertion has been discovered in the B proteins from several bacterial species, but its sequence does not appear to be conserved between these species. Gyrase B proteins that lack the insertion are active, and the precise role of this part of the protein remains unclear. However, the major role of the B protein is clear—namely, the hydrolysis of ATP.

DNA gyrase is unique among the type II topoisomerases in that it can catalyze the energetically unfavorable introduction of negative supercoils into closed circular DNA; a process driven by the free energy of hydrolysis of ATP. The ATPase activity of the B protein is inhibited by both the coumarin class of antibiotics (22) (Figure 4) and by the recently discovered cyclothialidines (23) (Figure 4). The inhibition by both classes of compound is thought to be competitive, a surprising feature given their lack of structural similarity to ATP. In the absence of the A protein, both classes of B protein appear to be monomeric in solution.

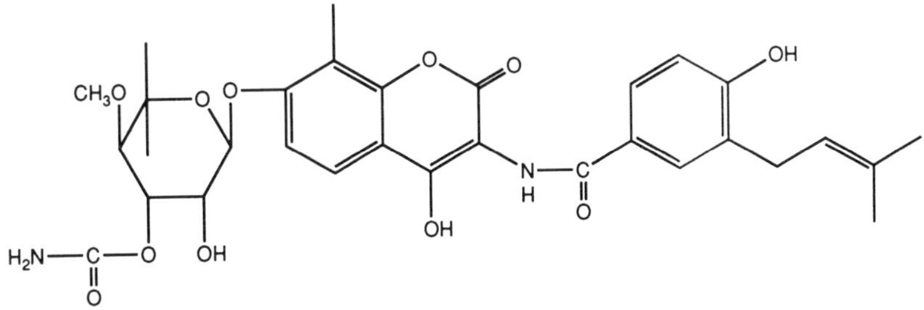

Novobiocin

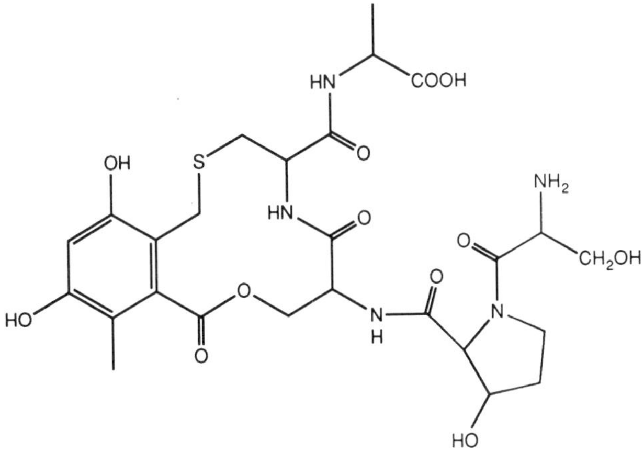

Cyclothialidine

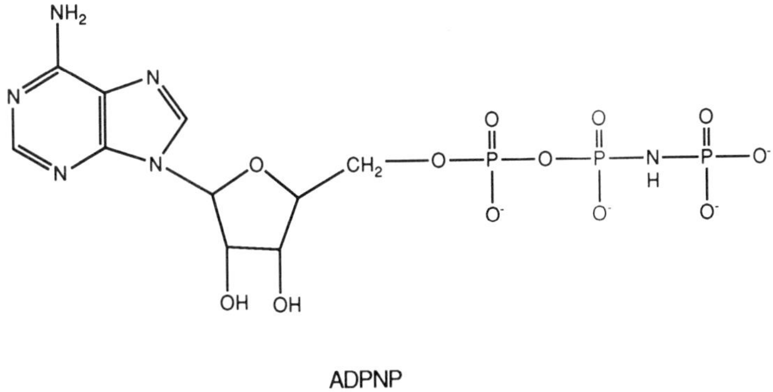

ADPNP

Figure 4 Structures of several gyrase B protein inhibitors. All of these compounds appear to be competitive inhibitors of ATP in spite of the lack of structural homology.

The mechanism of supercoiling by DNA gyrase has been studied using a variety of biochemical and biophysical techniques (13, 14). These studies show that the A_2B_2 complex is not a very compact structure and probably contains channels or cavities likely to play important roles in the DNA supercoiling activity of gyrase. The mechanism of supercoiling by gyrase probably involves several distinct steps. First, gyrase binds to relaxed DNA with a right-handed wrap of approximately 120 base pairs. This wrap is effectively cleaved at the center, producing a four-base-pair staggered cut. The cut ends of the DNA then become covalently attached to a tyrosine residue on each of the A subunits. A DNA strand is then passed through this double-stranded break (which must move apart by at least 20 Å to allow this), at which point two supercoils have been introduced into the DNA. This is probably the step that is coupled to the hydrolysis of ATP, as only limited supercoiling is observed when ATP is replaced by the nonhydrolyzable analogue 5'-adenylyl-β,γ-imido-diphosphate (ADPNP). This limited supercoiling has been interpreted as evidence that only one cycle of supercoiling occurs before the enzyme becomes trapped at some point in the catalytic cycle that requires hydrolysis of ATP to release it (35). DNA gyrase is highly processive and introduces many supercoils before dissociation from the DNA.

The work of Kirchhausen et al (13) exemplifies studies of DNA gyrase by electron microscopy. In this study, gyrase proteins, intact A_2B_2 complexes, and gyrase-DNA complexes were sprayed onto mica and visualized by rotary shadowing with platinum. Three-dimensional reconstruction methods were used to produce images similar to electron-density maps obtained from X-ray crystallography, although the effective resolution of these electron-microscopy images is only on the order of 30 Å. In spite of this low resolution, the images clearly showed that the A protein is V-shaped and that the B proteins wrap around the A proteins to produce a heart-shaped complex. Images of the complex between protein and DNA were interpreted as having the DNA bound within the boundaries of the molecule, which is consistent with other biochemical and biophysical data.

Although much about the structure and mechanism of DNA gyrase has been learned from these experiments, the details about the molecular mechanism of supercoiling by gyrase will have to come from other techniques. The most obvious source of this information is X-ray crystallography, but attempts to obtain crystals of gyrase proteins suitable for X-ray diffraction studies have met with little success. The large size of the gyrase proteins indicates that they likely comprise more than one functional domain. The work of various groups (4, 25, 26) has yielded information about this domain structure, and the evidence clearly shows that the proteins do indeed comprise functional domains associated with distinct biochemical activities (Figure 5).

Limited proteolysis of the A protein yields two fragments that remain very tightly associated even after proteolysis (25). The larger fragment (64 kDa), comprising residues 5–571, when complexed with the B protein, retains the ability to bind to the B protein and to cleave and religate DNA. The complex can also catalyze supercoiling of DNA, albeit with reduced efficiency. The smaller C-terminal fragment (33 kDa) binds to DNA and, when bound in sufficiently high density, induces a right-handed twist in the DNA (26). The conclusion from these experiments was that the 64-kDa fragment contained the site of DNA breakage and reunion, whereas the 33-kDa fragment was the major DNA-binding region of the complex and is responsible for the larger size of this DNA-binding site compared with that of the eukaryotic enzymes. These fragments have now been overexpressed in *E. coli,* and crystallization experiments with the purified 64-kDa fragment have resulted in crystals that diffract weakly to 4.5-Å resolution (24).

Evidence for a domain structure within the B protein came initially from the observation that a mutant strain of *E. coli* produced a truncated version of the B protein (4). Sequence analysis revealed that the protein had lost the first 394 residues at the N-terminus. This shortened B protein could form a complex with the A protein and support the ATP-independent relaxation of supercoiled DNA. However, it could not hydrolyze ATP nor supercoil DNA. These data led to the inference that the C-terminal region of the protein was responsible for interactions with the A protein, but that the N-terminal region contained the ATP-hydrolyzing activity. Overexpression of the N-terminal region in *E. coli* confirmed these deductions (1). Although the 43-kDa N-terminal

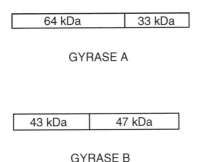

Figure 5 Functional domains of the gyrase proteins as identified by limited proteolysis studies (25, 26) or in mutant proteins (4). The N-terminus of the proteins is at the left.

fragment retains the ability to bind coumarin antibiotics and to hydrolyze ATP, it can no longer form a complex with the A protein. Like the intact B protein, the free 43-kDa fragment is a monomer in solution as well as in the presence of novobiocin or ADP (1). However, in the presence of the nonhydrolyzable ATP analogue, ADPNP, the fragment becomes a dimer. Crystals suitable for X-ray–diffraction analysis have been obtained for this dimeric complex (10), and the crystal structure has been solved at 2.5-Å resolution (38).

Structure of a 43-kDa Fragment of the E. coli DNA Gyrase B Protein

The 43-kDa protein monomer comprises two crystallographic domains (Figure 6). The first of these domains (residues 2–220) contains an eight-stranded β-sheet and several α-helical regions on one side of the sheet. A remarkable feature of this domain is the N-terminal arm of 15 residues that extend from the main body of the protein. The second domain (residues 221–393) contains a four-stranded β-sheet and α-helices on both sides of the sheet. Some of the helical regions are quite long, particularly residues 343–393, which are all in an α-helical conformation except for a proline residue at position 365 that changes the direction of the helix. The remainder of the intact B protein would, of course, continue from the end of this helix.

The ATP-binding site can be located from electron density corresponding to the bound ADPNP. This site is found at the center of the first domain (Figure 6). Magnesium ions are thought to be required for ATP hydrolysis, and a potential Mg^{2+} ion was identified in the electron-density maps. Its position has been confirmed by cocrystallization experiments in which magnesium ions were replaced with the more electron-dense manganese ions (RJ Lewis & DB Wigley, unpublished data).

The mechanism of hydrolysis of ATP that is utilized by other ATPases insures "in-line" attack by a water molecule on the γ-phosphate of the ATP. This mechanism has been investigated for DNA gyrase by site-specific mutagenesis (9). Various mutant enzymes were made to assess the roles of two residues—His38 and Glu42—that are close to the γ-phosphate moiety. Using the results obtained from these mutant proteins, a mechanism for hydrolysis of ATP was proposed in which Glu42 acts as a general base by extracting a proton from a water molecule that then attacks the γ-phosphate group and induces hydrolysis of ATP. His38 was proposed to align and polarize this glutamate residue and hence aid catalysis.

No nucleotide other than ATP supports supercoiling by DNA gyrase, except perhaps 2'-deoxy ATP, for which there are conflicting reports

(8, 35). In any case, the 2'-deoxy ATP is certainly not as good a cofactor as ATP. This specificity of the enzyme for ATP results from interactions between the nucleotide-binding pocket and the adenine ring. The interaction between the six-amino group of the base and Asp73 contributes most to this specificity, which probably explains the specificity for ATP over GTP. Other interactions that provide specificity include Tyr109 with the nitrogen at the N3 position of the purine ring and Lys103 with the β-phosphate moiety of ADPNP. Affinity-labeling studies had previously implicated Lys103 in ATP binding (36). Additional residues that interact with the bound nucleotide include Gln335, Lys337, and Tyr5, which are discussed below.

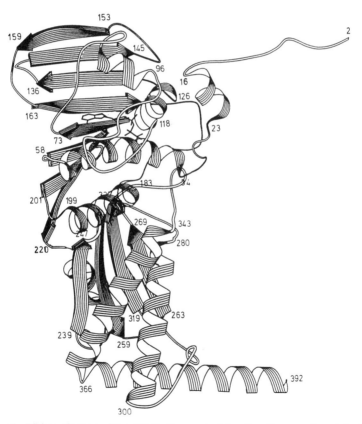

Figure 6 Ribbon diagram of the 43-kDa fragment of the *E. coli* gyrase B protein. The bound ADPNP molecule is overlaid in a black stick representation. Numbers refer to the beginning and end of secondary structural elements.

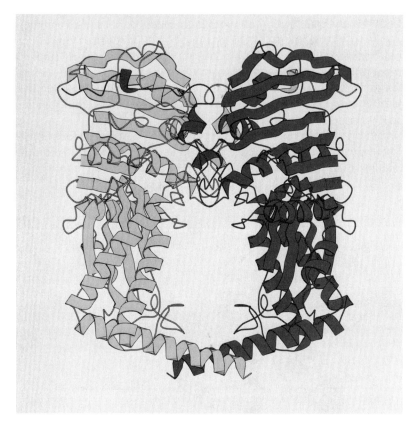

Figure 7   The structure of a dimer of the 43-kDa fragment of the gyrase B protein. This figure was kindly prepared by M Noble using his program XOBJECTS.

Mechanism

Our discussion of the crystal structure has so far been restricted to the crystallographic asymmetric unit that comprises a single subunit of the 43-kDa fragment. However, the N-terminus of the protein clearly forms an extension that wraps around an adjacent subunit in the crystal lattice (Figure 7). The two subunits are related by a crystallographic two-fold axis, and so, by symmetry, the N-terminal arm of the adjacent subunit is in turn wrapped around the first subunit. These two subunits represent a dimeric unit and prompted sedimentation-equilibrium experiments to investigate the oligomeric state of the 43-kDa protein under a variety of conditions. These studies showed that the free protein was monomeric but formed dimers in the presence of ADPNP (1).

Further investigation of the dimer contacts in the crystal structure reveals some interesting features. First, the N-terminal arm from each subunit not only forms contacts with its partner in the dimer but also with the bound ADPNP. Thus, both subunits contribute to each ATP-binding site. Second, the dimer interface is surprisingly hydrophilic for a subunit contact. Finally, and most interesting of all, a large channel runs between the subunits. This channel is approximately 20 Å in diameter and is lined with arginine residues. In fact, every single arginine residue present in the lower half of the protein protrudes into this channel. Taken together, these observations strongly suggest that this channel may be a DNA-binding site, and given that the A proteins are known to be the major DNA-binding site in the complex, it seems likely that this channel is involved instead in the DNA strand–passage event.

However, in order to be involved in strand passage, the channel would have to open and close, so the crystal structure was examined for a plausible mechanism for this process. In order for the channel to close, there have to be interactions that are stabilized in the dimer. The N-terminal arm from one subunit provides links with the ATP-binding site on the adjacent subunit. Closer examination reveals that one residue, Tyr5, plays a very important role in this interaction. The phenolic hydroxyl of the tyrosine side chain forms a hydrogen bond with the 2'-hydroxyl of the ribose sugar of the bound ADPNP. Substituting 2'-deoxy ATP for ATP in a supercoiling assay, thereby eliminating the interaction between ADPNP and the side chain, reduces activity, which indicates that this interaction is important for the supercoiling activity of gyrase. Sedimentation-equilibrium analysis of the 43-kDa protein in the presence and absence of ADPNP shows that this nucleotide induces dimerization, which is also evident from the crystal structure. In addition, the ATPase activity of the 43-kDa protein shows a greater than first-order dependence upon protein concentration (1). Taken together, these data suggest that binding of ATP controls the association and dissociation of the interface between the N-terminal domains of the gyrase B protein, which may be one aspect of the opening and closing mechanism for a molecular gateway involved in DNA strand passage. However, such a gateway requires a hinge, that is, a region of the protein must be flexible enough to allow the gate to open and close. As one might expect, this hinge region resides between the two domains of the 43-kDa protein at residues 220 and 221. That these are both glycine residues indicates a region of high conformational flexibility.

But this cannot be the whole story—how does the hydrolysis of ATP fit into the picture? If binding of ATP to the protein induces closing of the gateway, how does it open again? Further examination of the ATP-binding site answers these questions. Two residues (Gln335 and Lys337) interact with the γ-phosphate moiety of the ATP. These residues are in the second domain of the protein and protrude into the ATP-binding site in the upper domain. Consequently, the ATP-binding site is formed from residues from both domains of one subunit as well as from the N-terminal arm of the other subunit in the dimer, and these contacts will probably depend greatly upon whether the bound nucleotide is ATP or ADP. This is especially true for Gln335 and Lys337, which only interact with the γ-phosphate group of ATP, because these contacts will be lost after ATP hydrolysis to ADP, and the links between the ATP-binding site and the second domain will be broken. Thus, the ATP-binding site serves as a focus for interactions between domains within a monomer as well as for interactions between subunits, and it may act as a central control point. Indeed, ATP hydrolysis may set off events throughout the molecule that lead to destabilization of the dimer interface and reopening of the gateway. In this scheme, the molecular mechanism by which ATP hydrolysis is coupled to strand passage is quite clear: The free energy available from the hydrolysis of ATP is utilized as binding energy in the enzyme-ATP complex to distort the enzyme to an energetically unfavorable conformation (closing of the gateway). Subsequent hydrolysis of the ATP then destabilizes the closed gateway and allows the enzyme to relax back to its most favorable conformation by releasing ADP, and hence the gateway reopens.

Sequence analysis indicates that the eukaryotic enzymes are highly homologous to DNA gyrase, particularly in the N-terminal region encompassing the 43-kDa fragment of the gyrase B protein. Consequently, the structure of this region is probably similar in both classes of enzyme, and the mechanistic implications of the structure can be applied to both groups of enzyme. A series of elegant experiments by Roca, Wang, and colleagues has provided biochemical evidence that supports the structural model presented above. The first series of experiments (28) showed that the yeast topoisomerase II operates via an ATP-dependent protein clamp that is irreversibly closed upon binding of the nonhydrolyzable ATP analogue, ADPNP. This clamp is almost certainly the region of the yeast enzyme that corresponds to the 43-kDa fragment of the gyrase B protein. Additional studies using a group of antitumor drugs (27) indicate that these compounds (which contain approximate two-fold symmetry) bind more tightly to the yeast enzyme in the presence of ADPNP. This suggests that they sit at the interface between the ATP-binding N-terminal domains of the protein dimer and thus trap the closed form of the ATP-operated gateway. More recent experiments (29) have provided evidence for a second gateway that opens upon binding of ADPNP. This second gateway is the means of escape for the DNA strand that has been trapped by the ATP-dependent clamp. It also allows this translocated strand to pass out of the cavity between the N-terminal domains and to leave the complex through the (at least) 20-Å double-stranded break created by the protein. Thus, the binding of nucleotide controls the opening and closing of gateways, which allows the translocated DNA strand to pass through the protein.

Figure 8 shows a topological mechanism for the catenation of two double-stranded DNA circles by DNA gyrase, although the same mechanism could apply equally to other type II topoisomerases. In the first

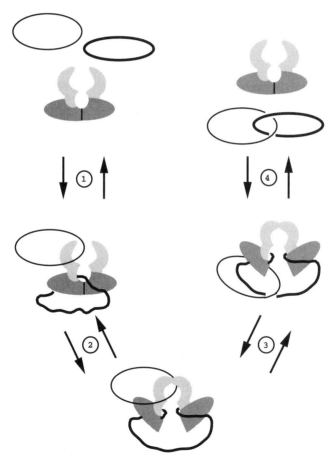

Figure 8   A mechanism for DNA catenation and decatenation by DNA gyrase. The diagram is explained in the text.

step, two double-stranded DNA circles bind to the enzyme, one to the A proteins (which involves a considerable wrap around the protein) and a second less extensively to the B proteins. Upon binding of ATP (step 2), the N-terminal domains of the B protein associate to close the ATP-dependent gateway and thus capture the DNA strand that is to be translocated in the cavity between these domains. At the same time (or shortly thereafter), the second gateway opens up between the A proteins; the DNA circle bound to the A proteins is cleaved; and the ends become covalently attached to the active-site tyrosine residues. In the third step, the translocated DNA strand passes from the cavity between the B proteins and leaves the protein complex through the gap between the A proteins. At this point catenation has taken place. The final step involves religation of the cleaved DNA and release of the products. Decatenation could occur by a reversal of this process. A similar mechanism could also account for the relaxation and supercoiling activities of the type II enzymes.

Binding of Antibiotics

One of the many questions still unanswered about DNA gyrase is the molecular mechanism by which coumarin drugs inhibit the ATPase activity of the B protein. Recent work (5) has attempted to address this question in a novel way. This study has utilized derivatized phospholipids in which novobiocin is attached to the head group. These phospholipids spontaneously form bilayers, and when intact *E. coli* B protein is added to the phospholipid, two-dimensional crystals can be obtained. These crystals were subjected to analysis by electron diffraction and three-dimensional image reconstruction techniques. The images obtained were at 11-Å resolution for two-dimensional projections and at 27-Å resolution for three-dimensional images. These images, from a structural viewpoint, were consistent with the earlier electron-microscopy studies (13) described above. However, the recent study has the advantage that the point of attachment of the B protein to the phospholipid bilayer could be presumed to be close to the novobiocin-binding site. Biochemical studies had already shown that the novobiocin-binding site was likely to be contained within the 24-kDa domain of the B protein comprising the first 220 amino acids, a conclusion also supported by genetic studies involving novobiocin-resistant bacterial strains (see 21 for a review). Superposition of the X-ray crystal structure of the 43-kDa fragment of the B protein on the electron-diffraction images reveals that the point of attachment to the phospholipid bilayer does indeed involve the N-terminal region of the protein and furthermore was in the region of the ATP-binding site determined by X-ray

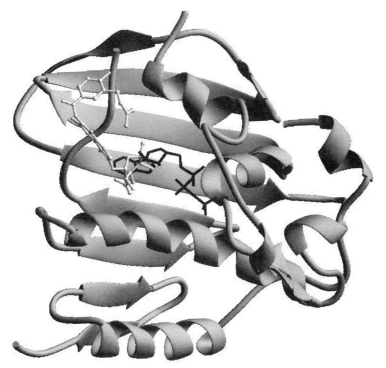

Figure 9 Overlap of the ATP- and novobiocin-binding sites within the first domain of the gyrase B protein. Novobiocin is represented in light gray and ADPNP in black. The sites overlap only in the region of the adenine-binding pocket, but this overlap is sufficient to explain the inhibitory effect of novobiocin.

crystallography. This result is in good agreement with biochemical data that indicate that the coumarin drugs are competitive inhibitors of the ATPase activity of DNA gyrase. However, X-ray crystallography must still provide molecular details about the interaction between the coumarin drugs and DNA gyrase. To this end, several crystal forms have now been obtained of coumarin drugs complexed with N-terminal fragments of gyrase B proteins (15), and structures of complexes with novobiocin and cyclothialidines have been solved at high resolution (RJ Lewis & DB Wigley, unpublished data). These structures reveal that both compounds do indeed bind at the ATP-binding site (Figure 9), in spite of their lack of similarity either to each other or to ATP. Details about the interactions between these drugs and their binding sites in gyrase will provide the impetus for renewed effort to improve inhibitors of DNA gyrase.

Topoisomerase IV

Topoisomerase IV is a bacterial enzyme that appears to be closely related to DNA gyrase (11). It was identified from mutations that led to a deficiency in the partition phase of bacterial replication. The role of this enzyme may be to unlink the catenated daughter chromosomes prior to partition. Sequence alignments show that the *parC* gene product is very similar to the gyrase A protein, whereas the *parE* gene product corresponds to the B protein. Interestingly, in spite of the obvious sequence homology with DNA gyrase, topoisomerase IV cannot catalyze supercoiling of DNA—it can only catalyze its relaxation by a mechanism that requires the hydrolysis of ATP. This feature makes topoisomerase IV more akin to the eukaryotic type II enzymes than to DNA gyrase. Consequently, the answer to the question of how gyrase alone can couple the hydrolysis of ATP to drive supercoiling is locked away in the sequence (and hence structural) differences between gyrase and topoisomerase IV. Precisely which of those differences provides the key remains a mystery at present.

CONCLUDING REMARKS

Evidence for the mechanisms proposed for both type I and II DNA topoisomerases has now been provided by the crystal structures of fragments of both classes of enzyme. Even though the amount of structural information on both classes of enzyme is limited at present, some common features are already apparent. The crystal structures have provided fascinating glimpses of the contortions that both classes of enzyme have to undergo in order to catalyze their respective reactions and have shown that the enzymes possess remarkable structures that allow them to accomplish their tasks. These tantalizing snapshots have provided a basis for part of the molecular mechanism of topoisomerase activity, but we clearly do not yet have the full story for either class of enzyme. Future structural work will surely help to fill in the gaps.

Literature Cited

1. Ali JA, Jackson AP, Howells AJ, Maxwell A. 1993. The 43-kilodalton N-terminal fragment of the DNA gyrase B protein hydrolyzes ATP and binds coumarin drugs. *Biochemistry* 32: 2717–24

2. Bayliss SA, Dixon LK, Vydelingum S, Smith GL. 1992. African swine fever

virus encodes a gene with extensive homology to type II DNA topoisomerases. *J. Mol. Biol.* 228:1003–10

3. Beese LS, Steitz TA. 1991. Structural basis for 3′-5′ exonuclease activity of *E. coli* DNA polymerase I: a two metal ion mechanism. *EMBO J.* 10:25–33

4. Brown PO, Peebles CL, Cozzarelli NR. 1979. A topoisomerase from *E. coli* related to DNA gyrase. *Proc. Natl. Acad. Sci. USA* 76:6110–14

5. Celia H, Hoermann L, Schultz P, Lebeau L, Mallouh V, et al. 1994. Three-dimensional model of *E. coli* gyrase B subunit crystallized in two-dimensions on novobiocin-linked phospholipid films. *J. Mol. Biol.* 236:618–28

6. Confalonieri F, Elie C, Nadal M, Bouthier de la Tour C, Forterre P, Duguet M. 1993. Reverse gyrase: a helicase-like domain and a type I topoisomerase in the same polypeptide. *Proc. Natl. Acad. Sci. USA* 90:4753–57

7. Drake FH, Zimmerman JP, McCabe FL, Bartus HF, Per SR, et al. 1987. Purification of topoisomerase II from amsacrine-resistant P388 leukemia cells. *J. Biol. Chem.* 262:16739–47

8. Gellert M, Mizuuchi K, O'Dea MH, Nash HA. 1976. DNA gyrase: an enzyme that introduces superhelical turns into DNA. *Proc. Natl. Acad. Sci. USA* 73:3872–76

9. Jackson AP, Maxwell A. 1993. Identifying the catalytic residue of the ATPase reaction of DNA gyrase. *Proc. Natl. Acad. Sci. USA* 90:11232–36

10. Jackson AP, Maxwell A, Wigley DB. 1991. Preliminary crystallographic analysis of the ATP-hydrolysing domain of the *E. coli* DNA gyrase B protein. *J. Mol. Biol.* 217:15–17

11. Kato J, Nishimura Y, Imamura R, Niki H, Hiraga S, Suzuki H. 1990. New topoisomerase essential for chromosome segregation in E. coli. *Cell* 63:393–404

12. Kikuchi A, Asai K. 1984. Reverse gyrase—a topoisomerase which introduces positive superhelical turns into DNA. *Nature* 309:677–81

13. Kirchhausen T, Wang JC, Harrison SC. 1985. DNA gyrase and its complexes with DNA: direct observation by electron microscopy. *Cell* 41:933–43

14. Kreuger S, Zaccai G, Wlodawer A, Langowski J, O'Dea M, 1990. Neutron and light-scattering studies of DNA gyrase and its complex with DNA. *J. Mol. Biol.* 211:211–20

15. Lewis RJ, Singh OMP, Smith CV, Maxwell A, Skarzynski T, 1994. Crystallization of inhibitor complexes of an N-terminal fragment of the DNA gyrase B protein. *J. Mol. Biol.* 241:128–30

16. Lima CD, Wang JC, Mondragon A. 1993. Crystallization of a 67kDa fragment of *E. coli* DNA topoisomerase I. *J. Mol. Biol.* 232:1213–16

17. Lima CD, Wang JC, Mondragon A. 1994. Three-dimensional structure of the 67K N-terminal fragment of *E. coli* DNA topoisomerase I. *Nature* 367:138–46

18. Liu LF. 1989. DNA topoisomerase poisons as antitumor drugs. *Annu. Rev. Biochem.* 58:351–75

19. Liu LF, Liu CC, Alberts BM. 1979. T4 DNA topoisomerase: a new ATP-dependent enzyme essential for initiation of T4 bacteriophage DNA replication. *Nature* 281:456–61

20. Lund K, Anderson AH, Christiansen K, Svejstrup JQ, Westergaard O. 1990. Minimal DNA requirement for topoisomerase II–mediated cleavage in vitro. *J. Biol. Chem.* 265:13856–63

21. Maxwell A. 1993. The interaction between coumarin drugs and DNA gyrase. *Mol. Microbiol.* 9:681–86

22. Mizuuchi K, O'Dea MH, Gellert M. 1978. DNA gyrase: subunit structure and ATPase activity of the purified enzyme. *Proc. Natl. Acad. Sci. USA* 75:5960–63

23. Nakada N, Shimada H, Hirata T, Aoki Y, Kamiyama T, et al. 1993. Biological characterization of cyclothialidine, a new DNA gyrase inhibitor. *Antimicrob. Agents Chemother.* 37:2656–61

24. Reece RJ, Dauter Z, Wilson KS, Maxwell A, Wigley DB. 1990. Preliminary crystallographic analysis of the breakage-reunion domain of the *E. coli* DNA A protein. *J. Mol. Biol.* 215:493–95

25. Reece RJ, Maxwell A. 1989. Tryptic fragments of the *E. coli* DNA gyrase A protein. *J. Biol. Chem.* 264:19648–53

26. Reece RJ, Maxwell A. 1991. The C-terminal domain of the *E. coli* DNA gyrase A subunit is a DNA-binding protein. *Nucleic Acids Res.* 19:1399–1405

27. Roca J, Ishida R, Berger JM, Andoh T, Wang JC. 1994. Antitumor bisdioxopiperazines inhibit yeast DNA topoisomerase II by trapping the enzyme in the form of a closed protein clamp. *Proc. Natl. Acad. Sci. USA* 91:1781–85

28. Roca J, Wang JC. 1992. The capture

of a DNA double helix by an ATP-dependent protein clamp: a key step in DNA transport by type II topoisomerases. *Cell* 71:833–40

29. Roca J, Wang JC. 1994. DNA transport by a type II DNA topoisomerase: evidence in favor of a two-gate mechanism. *Cell* 77:609–16

30. Shaffer R, Traktman P. 1987. Vaccinia virus encapsidates a novel topoisomerase with the properties of a eukaryotic type I enzyme. *J. Biol. Chem.* 262: 9309–15

31. Shiozaki K, Yanagida M. 1991. A functional 125-kDa core polypeptide of fission yeast DNA topoisomerase II. *Mol. Cell. Biol.* 11:6093–6102

32. Shiozaki K, Yanagida M. 1992. Functional dissection of the phosphorylated termini of fission yeast DNA topoisomerase II. *J. Cell. Biol.* 119: 1023–36

33. Shuman S, Prescott J. 1990. Specific DNA cleavage and binding by vaccinia virus DNA topoisomerase. *J. Biol. Chem.* 265:17826–36

34. Slesarev AI, Stetter KO, Lake JA, Gellert M, Krah R, Kozyavkin SA. 1993. DNA topoisomerase V is a relative of eukaryotic topoisomerase I from a hyperthermophilic prokaryote. *Nature* 364:735–37

35. Sugino A, Higgins NP, Brown PO, Peebles CL, Cozzarelli NR. 1978. Energy coupling in DNA gyrase and the mechanism of action of novobiocin. *Proc. Natl. Acad. Sci. USA* 75: 4838–42

36. Tamura JK, Gellert M. 1990. Characterization of the ATP-binding site on *E. coli* DNA gyrase. Affinity labeling of lys-103 and lys-110 of the B subunit by pyridoxal 5'- diphospho-5'-adenosine *J. Biol. Chem.* 265:21342–49

37. Wang JC. 1971. Interaction between DNA and an *E. coli* protein, ω. *J. Mol. Biol.* 55:523–33

38. Wigley DB, Davies GJ, Dodson EJ, Maxwell A, Dodson GG. 1991. Crystal structure of an N-terminal fragment of the DNA gyrase B protein. *Nature* 351:624–29

Annu. Rev. Biophys. Biomol. Struct. 1995. 24:209–37
Copyright © 1995 by Annual Reviews Inc. All rights reserved

NMR SPECTROSCOPIC STUDIES OF PARAMAGNETIC PROTEINS: Iron-Sulfur Proteins

Hong Cheng

Department of Pharmacology, Mayo Clinic and Mayo Foundation, Rochester, Minnesota 55905

John L. Markley

Department of Biochemistry, University Wisconsin-Madison, 420 Henry Mall, Madison, Wisconsin 53706

KEY WORDS: electron-nucleus interactions, ferredoxin, rubredoxin, HiPIP, isotopic labeling

CONTENTS

ABSTRACT

Newer NMR methods, particularly in conjunction with stable isotope labeling, offer exciting approaches to structure-function studies of para-

1056-8700/95/0610-0209$05.00

magnetic proteins. This review examines progress in NMR spectroscopy of iron-sulfur proteins. The application of multidimensional multinuclear NMR spectroscopy to iron-sulfur proteins and the optimization of NMR pulse sequences for rapidly relaxing spins have allowed investigators to determine sequence-specific assignments for numerous NMR signals in rubredoxins, ferredoxins, and high-potential iron proteins, including those from the cysteine residues that ligate iron ions or iron-sulfur clusters. These advances enable one to interpret the wealth of information derived from NMR parameters, such as the temperature and pH dependence of chemical shifts and the relaxation properties of the resonances that report on interactions between nuclei and between nuclei and unpaired electron density. This information is being used to test theoretical descriptions of electron distribution within these molecules and to model the structures and dynamic properties of the proteins in solution. Mutagenesis of these proteins, in conjunction with NMR studies, is beginning to reveal which residues are important for cluster formation and stability and which residues play a role in electron transfer to and from redox partner proteins.

PERSPECTIVES AND OVERVIEW

Paramagnetic proteins are those that contain one or more unpaired electrons in at least one of their oxidation states. Although the unpaired electron may reside on an amino acid free radical, the paramagnetic center more often is a cofactor such as a flavin, a heme with bound metal, or a metal cluster. A given paramagnetic protein may contain more than one such paramagnetic center.

Figure 1 shows various iron-sulfur bonding patterns found in proteins as identified by X-ray crystallography. Rubredoxins contain the simplest unit, a single iron ion coordinated tetrahedrally by four cysteines. Ferredoxins are classified by their redox potentials and cluster types, which consist of two, three, or four iron ions and either two or four inorganic sulfides. The [2Fe-2S] clusters have two oxidation states: oxidized, with Fe(III) as both metals, and reduced, with one Fe(III) and one Fe(II); the [4Fe-4S] clusters can have three oxidation states: 3Fe(III)/1Fe(II), 2Fe(III)/2Fe(II), and 1Fe(III)/3Fe(II). In high-potential iron proteins (HiPIPs), only the first two are accessible as the oxidized and reduced states, respectively; in ferredoxins only the last two are accessible as the oxidized and reduced states. The iron ions in clusters can be ferromagnetically or antiferromagnetically coupled (for reviews, see 13, 30, 33, 66, 75, 123, 126, 129). In rubredoxins, ferredoxins, and HiPIPs, each iron or iron-sulfur cluster is covalently attached

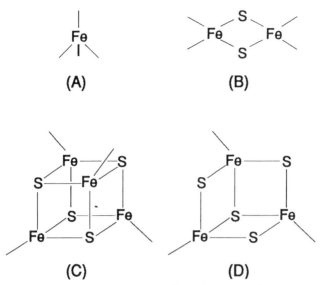

Figure 1   Four forms of iron-sulfur clusters found by means of X-ray crystallography in iron-sulfur proteins. In all cases, the ligands from the protein are cysteinyl sulfur atoms. As indicated in the figure, all but the three-iron cluster have four cysteinyl ligands; the three-iron cluster is ligated by three cysteines. (*A*) One-iron center found in rubredoxins. (*B*) [2Fe-2S] cluster found in plant-type, respiratory, and 2Fe bacterial ferredoxins. (*C*) [4Fe-4S] cluster found in bacterial 4Fe ferredoxins, in high-potential iron proteins (HiPIPs), as one of the clusters in 7Fe ferredoxins, and as both of the two clusters in 8Fe ferredoxins. (*D*) [3Fe-4S] cluster found as one of the clusters in 7Fe ferredoxins and in aconitase.

to the sulfur atoms of four cysteine residues (Figure 1). In other classes of iron-sulfur proteins, other amino acids serve as cluster ligands (e.g. Rieske proteins have two histidines and two cysteines) (61).

Although the fundamental biological function of rubredoxins, ferredoxins, and HiPIPs is electron transfer, other classes of iron-sulfur proteins play different roles, such as enzymic catalysis (aconitase) and gene regulation (iron-responsive element binding protein) (62, 109). Because of their structural similarities to the gene-regulatory proteins, investigators have speculated that some ferredoxins (91, 130) and rubredoxins (1, 91) may also play important roles in gene regulation.

Iron-sulfur proteins were among the first proteins studied by means of NMR spectroscopy (reviewed in 100–102) and have since represented fruitful subjects for NMR investigations (14, 22, 76). Iron-sulfur proteins figure prominently in discussions of the fundamentals of NMR spectroscopy of paramagnetic proteins (5, 14, 22, 24, 69, 74, 112). The

electron-nuclear interactions, which provide much interesting information about the cluster and how it interacts with the protein, complicate
the acquisition and analysis of NMR spectra of iron-sulfur proteins
(92–94). Unpaired electrons present in the paramagnetic center interact
with nuclei either by a contact mechanism through chemical bonds
or by a pseudocontact mechanism through space. These interactions
provide efficient nuclear relaxation mechanisms that broaden the NMR
signals and/or provide new chemical-shift mechanisms that give rise to
hyperfine-shifted resonances located well outside the normal diamagnetic chemical-shift range for a given type of spin. The paramagnetism
can hinder the determination of sequence-specific assignments, particularly to resonances from amino acid residues that ligate the iron-sulfur
cluster. These, of course, may be the most important assignments,
because they are needed to interpret the hyperfine-shifted signals. Efficient proton relaxation mechanisms mediated by the paramagnetic center may make it difficult or impossible to determine proton-proton cross
relaxation (the nuclear Overhauser effect, or NOE) in the neighborhood
of the cluster except for very short interproton distances. Because the
NOE is the most important kind of information used in determining
solution structures of small proteins by NMR spectroscopy, the paramagnetism can severely limit the structural resolution attainable in the
vicinity of the cluster.

This review focuses on newer developments in NMR studies of rubredoxins, ferredoxins, and HiPIPs. We first introduce NMR methods
used in the study of paramagnetic proteins and present current strategies for assigning NMR resonances. Then we discuss the interpretation
of the temperature dependence and relaxation rates of hyperfine-shifted
resonances. Finally, we survey the remarkable progress made in determining the secondary structures and full three-dimensional structures
of iron-sulfur proteins in solution from NMR data.

SAMPLE PREPARATION AND NMR METHODS

Ferredoxins, HiPIPs, and rubredoxins are small acidic proteins whose
molecular weights range between 6000 and 14,000. Protein sequences
and sequence comparisons from numerous species are available (12).
Iron-sulfur proteins of low molecular mass tend to be easy to isolate
from their organism or tissue of origin and can be purified to homogene-
ity. Protein stability is rarely an issue, although some ferredoxins are
less stable than others, particularly in the reduced state. Some iron-
sulfur proteins do not tolerate lyophylization, and so ultrafiltration is
the method most frequently used for protein concentration or buffer

exchange. Genes have been isolated or synthesized and heterologous expression systems in *Escherichia coli* and yeast have been developed for several iron-sulfur proteins (2, 46, 49, 51, 78, 99, 108, 111, 113, 127, 131). Some ferredoxins are expressed mainly as apoproteins that can be reconstituted in vitro by adding Fe(II) ion, sulfide, and a redox buffer such as dithiothreitol (46, 79). Some iron-sulfur proteins have been prepared chemically by means of peptide synthesis followed by cluster regeneration (119, 120).

Direct chemical synthesis and chemical modification (59, 95) provide routes for selective isotopic labeling. More commonly, however, iron-sulfur proteins are labeled biosynthetically (39, 40, 43, 96, 97; for general review see 77). Uniform labeling (ul) of a recombinant protein with ^{13}C and/or ^{15}N can be carried out by growing the host cells of the expression system on a minimal medium containing [ul ^{13}C]glucose and/or $^{15}NH_4Cl$ as the sole carbon and nitrogen sources, respectively (35, 46). Growing the host cells on a defined medium containing an appropriate mixture of unlabeled and labeled amino acids results in biosynthetic selective labeling. For some labeling patterns, adding an excess amount of the labeled amino acid(s) to be incorporated to a minimal medium is sufficient (41, 44, 45, 47); in other cases an auxotrophic host strain must be used to avoid migration of the label to other amino acid types (45, 46).

Iron-sulfur proteins generally should be kept under anaerobic conditions. Sodium dithionite ($Na_2S_2O_4$) is commonly used as the reducing reagent in the preparation of reduced proteins; its disadvantage is that its reduction potential is pH dependent (79) so that it is difficult to reduce a protein at low pH. Alternative reducing agents include methyl viologen (46, 117, 118) and sodium borohydride ($NaBH_4$) (86, 87). Reducing agents can mediate electronic self-exchange between a protein in two oxidation states, and different rates have been reported for various reducing reagents (117, 126). Potassium ferricyanide [$K_3Fe(CN)_6$] can be used as a reagent to oxidize the protein (88). In order to preserve the oxidation state of the protein during NMR data acquisition, the NMR tube can be flame-sealed after the protein has been reduced or oxidized.

Basically, all of the NMR methods used in the studies of diamagnetic proteins (for reviews, see 48, 55, 134) can be adapted to the study of paramagnetic proteins. These must be supplemented with specialized experiments that deal with nuclei that are relaxed rapidly by the paramagnetic center and those that experience large hyperfine shifts.

Small nuclear Overhauser effects from hyperfine-shifted resonances can be detected from one-dimensional (1D) or two-dimensional (2D)

NOE experiments with short irradiation (mixing) times, on the order of the shorter T_1 of two interacting spins (45). The short irradiation periods are needed for optimal signal detection. Under such conditions, spin diffusion effects among proton nuclei are negligible, and proton-proton distances can be estimated from NOE buildup curves (89).

Cross-peaks between pairs of hyperfine-shifted resonances and between hyperfine-shifted and diamagnetic resonances have been observed in magnitude COSY and TOCSY spectra. Because hyperfine-shifted resonances relax too rapidly to permit coherence transfer between two proton nuclei, cross-peaks seen in such spectra must arise from cross-correlation between dipole-dipole relaxation and Curie relaxation (23, 132). These results suggest that additional experiments designed to optimize the detection of cross-correlation effects may be useful in studies of iron-sulfur proteins.

Early studies of isotopically labeled iron-sulfur proteins utilized homologous expression and suffered from low yields and limited prospects for selective labeling (38, 40–43, 93–97). Nevertheless, they provided useful information about the feasibility of such studies. Current molecular biological methods allow one to prepare uniformly labeled proteins relatively inexpensively and to incorporate ^2H, ^{13}C, or ^{15}N selectively in residue types of interest (46, 77). Since the magnetogyric ratios of ^{13}C and ^{15}N are smaller than that of ^1H ($\gamma_{^{13}C}/\gamma_{^1H} = 0.25$ and $\gamma_{^{15}N}/\gamma_{^1H} = -0.101$), the broadening experienced by a resonance from a ^{13}C or ^{15}N nucleus should be considerably smaller than that from a ^1H nucleus at the same distance from the paramagnetic center. In addition, the larger coupling constants for these nuclei (e.g. $^1J_{C-C} = 35–70$ Hz, $^1J_{C-H} = 120$ Hz, and $^1J_{N-H} = 60$ Hz) lead to efficient magnetic coherence transfers that can be exploited by means of 2D or 3D NMR experiments designed to provide data for spin system analyses and sequential assignments. In addition, ^1H and ^{13}C resonances of ^{13}C-labeled cysteine residues in ferredoxins have been correlated using 1D decoupling difference spectroscopy (73, 46) and 2D heteronuclear multiple quantum spectroscopy (HMQC) (45, 46).

Electronic self-exchange takes place between oxidized and reduced species in iron-sulfur proteins; the exchange can be intermolecular, or in cases of ferredoxins with more than one cluster, intramolecular. The electron self-exchange rates can be measured by means of either 1D or 2D (homonuclear or heteronuclear) NMR magnetization exchange experiments (3, 21, 118) on a sample containing a mixture of oxidized and reduced protein, provided that the electronic exchange rate is slow enough so that separate (hyperfine-shifted) signals are seen for the oxidized and reduced forms of the protein yet fast enough so that the lifetimes of the states are not much longer than the T_1 values of the spins being observed.

RESONANCE ASSIGNMENTS

Hyperfine-Shifted Resonances

Early NMR studies of iron-sulfur proteins focused on the well-resolved, hyperfine-shifted resonances and sought to classify various types of paramagnetic centers on the basis of patterns of isotropic shifts (41, 71, 72, 116, 100–102, 106) and comparisons with spectra of model clusters (65). However, in the absence of assignments to particular amino acids in the protein sequence, the information obtained was of limited utility.

Early attempts to assign hyperfine-shifted resonances of ferredoxins by conventional NMR methods were unsuccessful. A breakthrough came with the realization that 1D NOE spectroscopy could be used to detect cross relaxation between pairs of hyperfine-shifted spins and between hyperfine-shifted and diamagnetic spins (53). Shortly thereafter, investigators found that by using 2D NOE methods optimized for the rapidly relaxing spins they could extend such studies to more highly overlapped regions of the spectrum (118). Most of the cysteinyl α- and β-proton resonances in reduced plant-type ferredoxins could be assigned by comparing distances derived from the NOE data with those from the X-ray structures of ferredoxins and by making use of theoretical descriptions of their chemical shifts (53, 118). Assignments could then be extended to cysteinyl resonances in the oxidized ferredoxin by means of a 2D magnetization exchange experiment (118).

The steps typically used in assigning hyperfine-shifted resonances are as follows: First, the largest hyperfine-shifted signals observed in the ^1H NMR spectrum of a ferredoxin are assumed to come from the cysteinyl α- and β-protons and that for a given cysteine residue, the β-protons (3 bonds from the Fe) have larger isotropic shifts than the α-proton (5 bonds from the Fe). In addition, the proton resonances from a given cysteinyl ligand to the cluster should have the same kind of temperature dependence. On the basis of these assumptions, the α-, and β-proton spin systems from each cysteinyl ligand are identified using data from magnitude COSY, TOCSY, 1D NOE (saturation transfer), and/or 2D NOESY (with fast repetition rates and short mixing times). Then, by comparison with an available crystal structure, sequence-specific assignments for the cysteinyl proton resonances are derived from NOEs detected between cysteinyl protons and those of other amino acid residues. In some cases, it has been possible to make stereospecific assignments to the individual prochiral β-protons (Cys $H^{\beta 2}$ and Cys $H^{\beta 3}$). This general strategy has yielded assignments for the cysteinyl proton resonances of several ferredoxins and HiPIPs (6–8, 10, 15–21, 31, 32, 45, 50, 53).

Except perhaps in the assignment of some HiPIPs, whose hyperfine signals are sharp enough to yield enough NOEs for assignments independent of an X-ray structure (L Banci, personal communication), this strategy requires a highly refined X-ray structure to ensure the correctness of the assignments. Moreover, the structure in solution is assumed to be the same as that in the crystal. Because no X-ray structure for a reduced [2Fe-2S] ferredoxin is available, in making assignments for these proteins investigators have also assumed that the structure in the reduced state is similar to that in the oxidized state. Also, as the result of spin delocalization, well-resolved hyperfine-shifted resonances may arise from residues other than cysteine in the vicinity of the iron-sulfur cluster. For example, two of the seven well-resolved, hyperfine-shifted peaks (peaks F' and F'') in the ^{1}H NMR spectra of *Pseudomonas putida* and *Azotobacter vinelandii* 7Fe ferredoxins were not from cysteinyl α- or β-protons (44, 45). Also, one of the hyperfine-shifted proton peaks (peak K) in the spectrum of reduced *Anabaena* 7120 vegetative ferredoxin did not arise from cysteine (46, 118). Thus, the investigator should make use of selective isotopic labeling to verify assignments of hyperfine-shifted resonances deduced with the above assumptions (45–47).

Biosynthetic isotopic labeling provides a direct way of determining the origins of hyperfine-shifted resonances by residue type and position. Complete sequence-specific assignments are possible by more laborious chemical syntheses. Because of their low natural abundance, selective labeling with ^{2}H, ^{13}C, or ^{15}N results in NMR spectra that are simple and relatively easy to interpret. The earliest application of this approach to an iron-sulfur protein was a study by Packer et al (98) in which [^{2}H$^\beta$]cysteine was incorporated into *Clostridium acidi-urici* 8Fe ferredoxin. The first selective ^{13}C enrichment of an iron-sulfur protein was the incorporation of [^{13}C$^\beta$]cysteine into the 7Fe ferredoxin from *P. putida* ferredoxin (45), and the first selective ^{15}N labeling of cysteine in an iron-sulfur protein was that of *Anabaena* 7120 vegetative ferredoxin (46) discussed below.

In studies of *Anabaena* 7120 vegetative ferredoxin, the ferredoxin was labeled selectively with [^{2}H$^\alpha$]cysteine, [^{2}H$^{\beta 2,\beta 3}$]cysteine, [^{13}C$^\beta$]cysteine, and [^{15}N]cysteine (46, 47). The hyperfine-shifted cysteinyl α- and β-proton, β-carbon, and backbone nitrogen resonances were observed in ^{1}H, ^{13}C, and ^{15}N NMR spectra of the oxidized and reduced states of the protein (in single oxidation states and in mixtures of the two). Figure 2 shows representative 1D ^{15}N NMR spectra. With the exception of the two most rapidly relaxing cysteinyl β-proton resonances, all the cysteinyl β-proton and β-carbon resonances were correlated by means of 1D decoupling and 2D HMQC experiments. Furthermore, ^{2}H NMR spectroscopy was introduced in this work as a method for studying cysteine hydrogens. Although ^{2}H is a quadrupolar nucleus, and the contribution of a quadrupolar term in the relaxation cannot be ignored, particularly with larger proteins, the smaller magnetogyric ratio of ^{2}H ($\gamma_{^1H}/\gamma_{^2H} = 6.51$) reduces the paramagnetic effect on line broadening for ^{2}H resonances. Dipeptide-selective double labeling of the backbone amide (70) was introduced as a method for assigning hyperfine-shifted nitrogen resonances. A sample of *Anabaena* 7120 vegetative ferredoxin was produced with incorporated [^{13}C′]Ala and [^{15}N]Cys. The decoupling difference ^{13}C NMR spectrum of this sample showed a signal when the frequency of one of the four hyperfine-shifted nitrogen resonances was irradiated. Because the protein contains only one Ala-Cys linkage, at residues 45 and 46, the nitrogen signal was assigned to Cys46 (46). This approach should also serve in the assignment of cysteinyl carbonyl carbons, which could then be extended to C^α and C^β by detection of single-bond coupling in a sample incorporating uniformly ^{13}C-enriched cysteine.

Several studies have made use of 1D saturation transfer or 2D exchange spectroscopy (EXCSY) with iron-sulfur proteins of mixed oxidation state to extend assignments from spectra in one oxidation state to another (17, 21, 46, 118). If more than one magnetization-exchange process is present in the protein, we must consider the possibility of their interaction. This can be a serious problem when a sample of an iron-sulfur protein with more than one cluster is present as a mixture of oxidized and reduced forms. For example, in *Clostridium pasteurianum* ferredoxin, which contains two [4Fe-4S] clusters, intramolecular electronic exchange between clusters is fast on the NMR time scale, whereas intermolecular electronic exchange is slow (58). In such cases, caution must be used in cross-assigning resonances between oxidation states from 2D exchange spectra (17, 115).

Diamagnetic Resonances

Several early assignments of diamagnetic signals from ferredoxins were made on the basis of comparisons of spectra of variants from different species with limited sequence changes (e.g. 37, 39). This approach has

A.

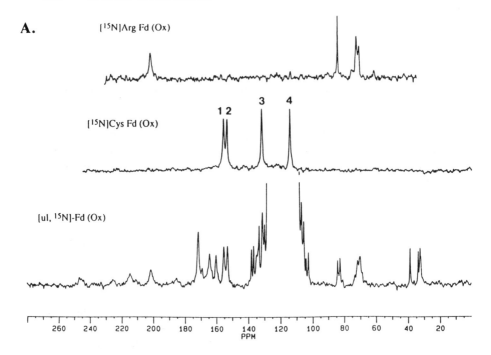

B.

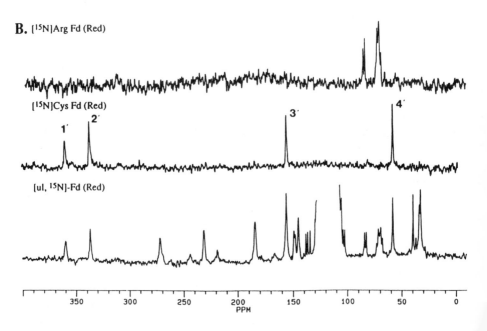

been used more recently to assign histidine signals in spectra of verte-brate ferredoxins (60, 81, 82) and has been augmented by the use of chemical modification (83) and site-directed mutagenesis (135).

Generalized sequence-specific NMR resonance assignment strate-gies have been developed for use with diamagnetic proteins as large as 30 kDa (for reviews see 48, 55, 134). The major problem introduced by a paramagnetic center, as seen in the analysis of spectra of *Anabaena* 7120 ferredoxins, is the efficient relaxation of spins from nuclei in its vicinity (within about 8 Å of the iron atoms for an oxidized [2Fe-2S] ferredoxin), which leads to loss of cross peaks in conventional multidi-mensional NMR spectra (35, 92). Similar problems have been encoun-tered in the sequence-specific assignment of other ferredoxins (35, 57, 88, 128, 136). These gaps in the data work against sequential assignment strategies (such as NOESY) that rely heavily on nearest-neighbor con-nectivities (134). Better strategies for iron-sulfur proteins are those that make use of through-bond coupling with double-labeled proteins and those that can make use of selective labeling for identifying starting points or anchors in the analysis of the data. The detection of connectiv-ities from rapidly relaxing spins requires more specialized methods, such as NOESY with fast repetition rates and short mixing times, TOCSY with reduced spin-lock duration (57, 88, 128), or multidimen-sional heteronuclear NMR spectroscopy (35).

Anabaena 7120 vegetative ferredoxin was the first iron-sulfur protein to be double-labeled uniformly with ^{13}C (to 26%) and ^{15}N (ul 98%) (93, 94). In addition to the routinely used proton homonuclear experiments, COSY, NOESY, and TOCSY, the heteronuclear experiments of single-bond and multiple-bond $^1H\{^{13}C\}$ correlation, $^1H\{^{15}N\}$ correlation, and $^{13}C\{^{15}N\}$ correlation were also used in the spin-system identification. This approach led to nearly complete assignments of the diamagnetic NMR signals (92, 94).

←————————————————————————————————————

Figure 2 Comparison of ^{15}N NMR spectra (60.802 MHz, at 298 K) of (*A*) oxidized and (*B*) reduced samples of *Anabaena* 7120 ferredoxin labeled uniformly with nitrogen-15 ([ul, ^{15}N]-Fd) and labeled selectively by incorporation of enriched cysteine ([^{15}N]Cys Fd) and by incorporation of enriched arginine ([^{15}N]Arg Fd) (adapted from Reference 46). The ^{15}N peaks from the backbone nitrogen of each of the four iron-ligated cysteines are resolved in spectra of the ferredoxin in both oxidation states. The ^{15}N signal from the backbone nitrogen of Arg42 is observed as a hyperfine-shifted resonance (~200 ppm) in the spectrum of the oxidized protein, but no signal from this nitrogen is resolved in the spectrum of the reduced ferredoxin. These results provide direct evidence that the backbone NH of Arg42 hydrogen bonds to the cluster, as suggested by the X-ray structure (62, 108).

Following the development of an overexpression system for the protein, *Anabaena* 7120 heterocyst ferredoxin was labeled uniformly with ^{15}N and/or ^{13}C (both at levels >98%) (35). These labeling patterns made it possible to use newer three-dimensional (3D) NMR methods in assigning its spectrum. ^{15}N-edited interresidue $(^1H^\alpha)_i/(^1H^N)_{i+1}$ NOE connectivities were obtained from a 3D NOESY-HMQC experiment, and spin systems of individual residues were identified from HMQC and the TOCSY-HMQC spectra of the sample labeled uniformly with ^{15}N. Triple-resonance experiments that make use of efficient couplings along the peptide backbone [HNCA, HNCO, and HN(CO)CA] provided more assignments than standard NOESY or 3D (^{1}H, ^{15}N) NOESY-HMQC data (35). Figure 3 shows an example of 3D HNCA data from an oxidized [2Fe-2S] ferredoxin. Comparison of the NMR results with the X-ray structure of the same protein (68) revealed minor structural differences probably resulting from crystal packing (35).

An alternative way of dealing with paramagnetism in a protein is to eliminate it, for example, by substituting a diamagnetic metal ion for a paramagnetic transition metal ion. This approach was used in NMR studies of selenium-substituted clostridial ferredoxin (58) and zinc-substituted rubredoxin (27) Although zinc substitution is also possible with ferredoxins, the low stability of zinc-substituted protein may preclude extensive NMR studies (T Pochapsky, personal communication).

Identification of Hydrogen Bonds

Hydrogen bonding in proteins is generally inferred from NMR data on the basis of slowed rates of hydrogen exchange. Hydrogen bonding associated with regular secondary structure is deduced from patterns of NOEs (134) and chemical shifts (133) in conjunction with slowed hydrogen exchange. The question of hydrogen bonding to the cluster is an important issue, because such interactions are thought to be partly responsible for differences in reduction potentials observed in different proteins that have the same kind of cluster. Hyperfine-shifted proton resonances have been detected for several iron-sulfur proteins in H_2O solvent that disappear when the protein is transferred to ^2H_2O, presumably as the result of hydrogen exchange, and these resonances have been assigned to hydrogen bonds to the cluster (e.g. 72).

Hyperfine shifting and broadening of ^{15}N resonances are indicative of an excellent method for studying hydrogen bonding to an iron-sulfur cluster. Perhaps the clearest example of the use of ^{15}N NMR to study hydrogen bonding is provided by Arg42 of *Anabaena* 7120 vegetative ferredoxin (46). Selective incorporation of [^{15}N]arginine into the protein identified the single arginyl residue (Arg42) as the source of one of

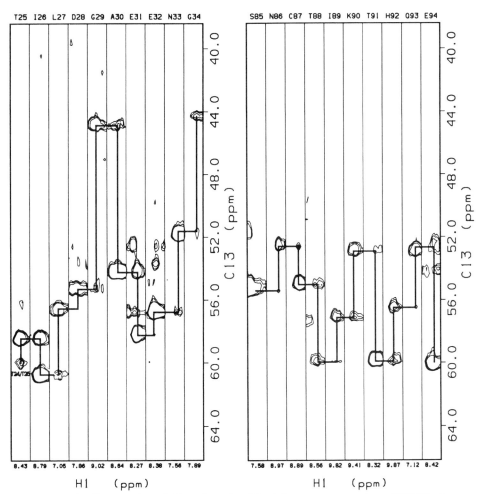

Figure 3 Contour plots of slices through a 3D triple-resonance spectrum (HNCA) of oxidized *Anabaena* 7120 heterocyst ferredoxin labeled uniformly with ^{13}C and ^{15}N (adapted from Ref. 35). The 3D HNCA experiment correlates $^1H_i^N$, $^{15}N_i$, and $^{13}C_i^\alpha$ and $^{13}C_{i-1}^\alpha$ resonances along the backbone. Each strip is taken at a different $^{15}N_i$ frequency (not indicated), and the cross peaks indicate $(^1H_i^N, \, ^{13}C_{i-1}^\alpha)$ and $(^1H_i^N, \, ^{13}C_i)$ connectivities that provide sequential assignments along the backbone. The results shown here assign backbone resonances from Thr25 to Cys34 (*left*) and from Ser85 to Glu94 (*right*); the triple-resonance 3D data enabled peaks to be assigned that could not be assigned by proton only or proton-nitrogen experiments.

the hyperfine-shifted nitrogens in the spectrum of the protein labeled uniformly with ^{15}N (Figure 2). This signal was present at about 200 ppm (75-ppm isotropic shift) in the spectrum of the oxidized protein, but did not show up in the spectrum of the reduced protein (Figure 2), probably because it is broadened further and/or shifted beyond the examined spectral region by the greater paramagnetism. The results strongly suggest that the arginine is hydrogen bonded to the iron-sulfur cluster in solution in both the oxidized and reduced states, as suggested by the X-ray structure of the same protein in its oxidized state, which shows that the backbone amide nitrogen of Arg42 is within hydrogen-bonding distance of sulfide atom S1 of the cluster (64, 110).

Hydrogen bonding also has been detected by observation of Fermi contact coupling through a heteronuclear-correlation experiment. In NMR studies of ^{113}Cd-substituted rubredoxin from *Pyrococcus furiosus,* H-bond–mediated scalar coupling was observed in the ^{1}H-^{113}Cd heteronuclear spin-echo difference NMR spectrum for the backbone amide protons of Ile7, Cys8, Ile40, and Cys41, but not for Trp10 and Ala43 (26). The results suggest that the backbone amide protons of Ile7, Cys8, Ile40, and Cys41 are involved in hydrogen bonding with the iron atom, in agreement with the X-ray structure.

INTERPRETATION OF DATA FROM HYPERFINE RESONANCES

Once assignments have been made for hyperfine-shifted signals, the information from their NMR parameters (chemical shift, temperature and pH dependence of the shift, linewidth, and longitudinal relaxation rate) can be interpreted in molecular terms. Considerable progress has been made in the theoretical understanding of these NMR parameters, but gaps remain between experimental results and their explanation.

Isotropic Shifts

The isotropic shift is the component of the chemical shift of a nuclear spin attributable to interactions between the nucleus and unpaired electrons. Thus the hyperfine shift is the sum of the diamagnetic shift (the shift the nuclear spin would experience in the absence of the paramagnetic center) and the isotropic shift. The isotropic shift has two principal components: the Fermi contact shift and the pseudocontact shift. The Fermi contact shift arises from the presence of unpaired electron density at the nucleus through electron delocalization along the chemical bonds. The pseudocontact shift arises from dipole-dipole interactions between unpaired electron spins and the nuclear spin. Qualitative analyses of these two types of isotropic shifts have been discussed in the literature (80).

In comparison to the predominant Fermi contact shift, the pseudocontact shift can be neglected when interpreting the hyperfine chemical shifts of iron-sulfur proteins (5). Thus, the temperature dependence observed for the hyperfine-shifted resonances arises from a shift in the Boltzmann distribution of the allowed magnetic spin levels of the unpaired electron. Moreover, the isotropic shift is proportional to the spin magnetization $\langle S_z \rangle$.

An interpretation of the chemical shifts of the cysteinyl hyperfine-shifted resonances and their temperature dependence was first proposed by Dunham et al (54) and further developed by Banci et al (11). The Curie law predicts that the absolute value of $\langle S_z \rangle$ decreases with increasing temperature, in agreement with the expectation from Boltzmann statistics. Resonances that follow this temperature dependence are termed *Curie*. Experimentally, some hyperfine-shifted signals are seen to have the opposite temperature dependence. Those whose isotropic shifts increase with increasing temperature are termed *anti-Curie*. At sufficiently high temperature, anti-Curie spins must reverse their temperature dependence and approach the diamagnetic shift value. An anti-Curie spin should therefore have a region in which its temperature dependence follows the Curie law; this region is termed *pseudo-Curie* (11).

The theoretical model is based on the spin-Hamiltonian treatment of exchange coupling in 2Fe and 4Fe clusters. The model enables one to identify the oxidation state of an iron in the cluster as Fe(III) or Fe(II) on the basis of the characteristic temperature dependence of its coordinated cysteine β-proton resonances. Basically, the characteristic temperature dependence results from the antiferromagnetic coupling between two unequal intermediate spin vectors, S_A and S_B, either from two iron ions in distinct spin states [i.e. Fe(III) and Fe(II)] or from partially coupled pairs of iron ions with intermediate spin states (where $S_A = S_1 + S_2$, $S_B = S_3 + S_4$, and S_i represents the spin state of each ion). In the ground state, the larger spin S_A is parallel to the direction of the external magnetic field, and the smaller spin S_B is antiparallel to the external magnetic field as the result of antiferromagnetic coupling. This situation leads to positive spin density for the cysteines that are coordinated to the ion with S_A, and resonances from these cysteines are in turn shifted downfield (relative to the diamagnetic region). In contrast, negative spin density is expected for the cysteines that are coordinated to the ion with S_B; their resonances are shifted upfield. As the temperature increases, the two intermediate spins become more uncoupled. If kT is larger than J (the coupling constant between S_A and S_B), the two spins (S_A and S_B) are uncoupled, and both are then parallel to the external field.

The dependence of $\langle S_z \rangle_A$ and $\langle S_z \rangle_B$ on the reciprocal temperature (T^{-1}) can be characterized by three cases:

1. $kT > J$ (region 1 in Figure 4). At high temperature, where $kT > J$, the intermediate spins $\langle S_z \rangle_A$ and $\langle S_z \rangle_B$ are completely decoupled. Both $\langle S_z \rangle_A$ and $\langle S_z \rangle_B$ show temperature dependence of the same sign ($\langle S_z \rangle_A$ Curie and $\langle S_z \rangle_B$ pseudo-Curie), and all resonances are shifted downfield (positive isotropic shifts).
2. $kT \approx J$ (region 2 in Figure 4). When $kT \approx J$, $\langle S_z \rangle_B$ changes sign and shows anti-Curie behavior; $\langle S_z \rangle_A$ shows Curie temperature dependence; and all resonances are shifted downfield.

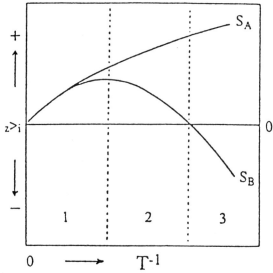

Figure 4 Qualitative schematic representation of the temperature dependence of the spin magnetization $\langle S_z \rangle$ for the two intermediate spin states, S_A and S_B, which couple to yield the total cluster spin state S_T (S_T equals to one of $S_A - S_B$, . . . ,$S_A + S_B$, assuming $|S_A| > |S_B|$) (from 32, with permission). The three regions are: 1. $kT > J$, where $\langle S_z \rangle_A$ and $\langle S_z \rangle_B$ are decoupled. Both exhibit temperature dependence with positive slope, and both have hyperfine shifts of the same sign (+). 2. $kT \approx J$, where $\langle S_z \rangle_A$ has Curie temperature dependence while $\langle S_z \rangle_B$ has anti-Curie temperature dependence, and both have hyperfine shifts of the same sign (+). 3. $kT < J$, where $\langle S_z \rangle_A$ and $\langle S_z \rangle_B$ are coupled. $\langle S_z \rangle_A$ has Curie temperature dependence and $\langle S_z \rangle_B$ has pseudo-Curie temperature dependence, and the two have isotropic shifts of opposite sign.

3. $kT < J$ (region 3 in Figure 4). When $kT < J$, spins $\langle S_z \rangle_A$ and $\langle S_z \rangle_B$ are antiferromagnetically coupled; $\langle S_z \rangle_A$ exhibits Curie behavior, and $\langle S_z \rangle_B$ exhibits pseudo-Curie behavior. $\langle S_z \rangle_A$ and $\langle S_z \rangle_B$ have opposite sign, and resonances from nuclei sensing $\langle S_z \rangle_A$ are shifted downfield, whereas those sensing $\langle S_z \rangle_B$ are shifted upfield.

   This theoretical model (11, 54) yields a satisfactory interpretation of the temperature dependence of paramagnetic cysteinyl β-proton resonances in NMR spectra of many ferredoxins: reduced [2Fe-2S] ferredoxins (53, 106, 116–118), oxidized HiPIPs that contain one [4Fe-4S] cluster (6–8, 10, 18–20), *C. pasteurianum* 2[4Fe-4S] ferredoxin (15–17, 31), and oxidized [3Fe-4S] ferredoxins (32). For reduced [2Fe-2S] ferredoxins ([2Fe-2S]$^{1.0+}$, $S = 1/2$), the intermediate spins for the iron pairs are $S_A = 5/2$ for the ferric and $S_B = 2$ for the ferrous ion. Since $J = 100$ cm^{-1}, which is equivalent to kT at room temperature, the β-proton resonances of cysteines ligated to Fe(III) are shifted downfield and exhibit Curie temperature dependence, and the β-proton resonances of cysteines ligated to Fe(II) are also shifted downfield but exhibit anti-Curie temperature dependence. For oxidized HiPIPs ([4Fe-4S]$^{3.0+}$, $S = 1/2$), the intermediate spins for the iron pairs are $S_A = 7/2$ for the 2Fe$^{2.5+}$ and $S_B = 3$ for the 2Fe$^{3.0+}$ (84, 85, 90, 107). The β-protons of cysteines ligated to the 2Fe$^{2.5+}$ have downfield-shifted, Curie-like resonances, whereas the β-protons of cysteines ligated to the 2Fe$^{3.0+}$ have either downfield-shifted, anti-Curie resonances or upfield-shifted, pseudo-Curie resonances. For oxidized [3Fe-4S] ferredoxins ([3Fe-4S]$^{1.0+}$, $S = 1/2$), the intermediate spins are $S_A = 5/2$ for the lone Fe$^{3.0+}$ and $S_B = 2$ for the paired 2Fe$^{3.0+}$. As a consequence, the β-protons of the cysteine ligated to Fe$^{3.0+}$ have downfield-shifted, Curie resonances, and the β-protons of the cysteines ligated to the paired 2Fe$^{3.0+}$ have downfield-shifted, anti-Curie resonances.

   On the basis of this model and NOE data, one can assign which cysteine residues ligate Fe(II) and which ligate Fe(III). For all reduced plant-type ferredoxins investigated, Fe(II) is ligated by Cys41 and Cys46, and Fe(III) is ligated by Cys49 and Cys79 (53, 118). In the case of HiPIPs, the NMR results show that the pattern of ligation of irons of different oxidation states by specific cysteines (as determined by sequence similarity) is not conserved among different variants (6–8, 10, 18–20). These results for HiPIPs have been explained (10) in terms of sequence effects on an equilibrium between two species of [4Fe-4S]$^{3.0+}$ that have interchange between one Fe$^{3.0+}$ and one Fe$^{2.0+}$. Such an explanation fits with the observed nonlinearity of the temperature dependence of hyperfine-shifted resonances and EPR parameters. A similar variability in the electron distribution in [3Fe-4S] ferredoxins from different species has been suggested from analysis of patterns of contact shifts (32).

Despite its other successes, the model discussed above fails to explain the anti-Curie temperature dependence observed for the cysteine hyperfine-shifted resonances in oxidized [2Fe-2S] ferredoxins. This effect has been attributed to anti-Curie contributions from excited paramagnetic states, which the model ignores. Moreover, the model fails to predict the observed temperature dependence of the cysteinyl carbon and nitrogen resonances. Whereas the resonances of the cysteinyl β-carbon and its attached protons have the same temperature dependence in NMR spectra of oxidized *P. putida* 7Fe ferredoxin (45), the temperature dependence of cysteinyl carbon and nitrogen resonances differed from that of the protons of the same residue in reduced *Anabaena* 7120 vegetative ferredoxin (46).

Mouesca et al (85) have presented a quantitative model that describes the hyperfine-shifted resonances in NMR spectra of oxidized HiPIPs. In their work, they first measured the hyperfine tensors of the eight protons in the synthetic cluster model, $[N(C_2D_5)]_2[Fe_4S_4(SCH_2C_6D_5)_4]$, using ENDOR. The hyperfine tensors were analyzed into two parts, isotropic and anisotropic. From this, the spin state of the $[4Fe-4S]^{3+}$ paramagnetic center in its ground state was determined to be $|7/2, 3, 1/2\rangle$. The isotropic hyperfine couplings of the eight protons were derived from their isotropic hyperfine tensors, and their chemical shifts were then calculated quantitatively from the isotropic hyperfine couplings. Their formulation indicates that cysteinyl β-proton resonances with positive isotropic shifts arise from cysteines coordinated to irons of the mixed-valence pair, whereas those with negative isotropic shifts arise from cysteines coordinated to the two Fe(III) (85). This conclusion is consistent with assignments in NMR spectra of *Chromatium vinosum* HiPIP made on the basis of the measured temperature dependence of the cysteinyl β-proton resonances.

Differences in isotropic shifts observed for the prochiral cysteinyl $^1H^{\beta2}$ (*pro-S*) and $^1H^{\beta3}$ (*pro-R*) resonances have been attributed to their different orientation with respect to the iron-sulfur cluster. An empirical equation was derived from the results of NMR studies of cluster models in which electron-nuclear interactions resulted from spin delocalization (56, 63, 67, 105, 124). In this model, the isotropic chemical shift is given by

$$\delta = A + B\cos2\theta, \qquad\qquad 1.$$

where A and B are constants, $A \ll B$, and θ is the dihedral angle between the H-C$^\beta$-S and C$^\beta$-S-Fe planes. However, predictions of isotropic shifts of cysteine ^{1}H$^{\beta 2}$ and ^{1}H$^{\beta 3}$ resonances of ferredoxins from Equation 1, in which the dihedral angles were derived from X-ray structures, were far from the experimental results (15, 31). The situation in ferredoxins is more complex than this model allows. Contributions to spin delocalization probably come from unpaired electrons located on the $3d$ orbitals of the iron as well as π and σ delocalization.

Mouesca et al (85) then improved the model for isotropic shifts. The empirical equation they used was

$$\delta^* = A + B\cos(\theta_i + \theta_o) + C\cos 2(\theta_i + \theta_o), \qquad\qquad 2.$$

where A, B, and C are constants, δ^* is the normalized isotropic shift, θ_i is the dihedral angle between the H-C$^\beta$-S and C$^\beta$-S-Fe planes, and θ_o is a supplementary reference angle. In this model, contributions from both π and σ spin delocalizations are considered. Patterns of isotropic shifts predicted from this model for the cysteinyl β-protons of HiPIPs were in good agreement with experimental data (31, 85).

The hyperfine-shifted cysteinyl proton resonances can serve as probes for investigations of electron distribution within the iron-sulfur cluster and its environment. An example of a ^{1}H NMR study of this kind concerns the 7Fe ferredoxin from A. vinelandii, which contains one [4Fe-4S] cluster with a reduction potential of -647 mV at pH 7.8 and one [3Fe-4S] cluster with a higher reduction potential (-425 mV at pH 7.8). Cheng et al (44) suggested that the pH$_{mid}$ value of 5.4 exhibited by three of the cysteinyl β-proton peaks arises from protonation of Asp15. Movement of the negatively charged Asp15 upon reduction was observed in X-ray diffraction data collected at high pH (pH 8) but not in data collected at low pH (pH 6) (125). Mutation of Asp15 to Asn led to a change in the reduction potential for the [3Fe-4S] cluster at high pH. Results from electrochemical studies have shown that protonation of the [3Fe-4S] cluster at acidic pH affects reduction or oxidation of the [3Fe-4S] cluster and that Asp15 plays a key role in this proton transfer. Because the Asp15→Asn mutation led to a reduced rate of cell growth, this proton-transfer reaction appears to be physiologically important (114).

Spin Relaxation

Hyperfine-shifted spins have very short longitudinal (T_1) and transverse (T_2) relaxation times because of their interactions with single and multiple unpaired electrons. Contact and dipolar mechanisms are the most important processes in nuclear relaxation, and the Curie component can be neglected. The nuclear relaxation times, T_1 and T_2, can be expressed by a simplified Solomon-Bloembergen equation (29, 121, 122):

$$T_{1,2}^{-1} = (B\gamma_1^2 R_{\text{Fe}}^{-6} + C A_{\text{con}}^2) T_{1e}, \qquad\qquad 3.$$

where B and C are constants for a protein, A is the hyperfine coupling constant, R_{Fe} is the distance to the nearest (coordinated) Fe, and T_{1e} is the metal electronic longitudinal relaxation time. The first term arises from the dipolar mechanism, and the second term arises from the contact mechanism.

According to Equation 3, the nuclear resonance linewidth, which is inversely proportional to the nuclear transverse relaxation time (T_2), is proportional to the electronic relaxation time (T_{1e}). This implies that longer electronic relaxation times give broader hyperfine-shifted resonances, and shorter electronic relaxation times give narrower NMR resonances. Thus, the linewidths of nuclei close to Fe(III) ($T_{1e} = 10^{-11}$ s) are broader than those the same distance from Fe(II) ($T_{1e} = 10^{-12}$ s). Another important feature of this expression is that paramagnetic effects on the linewidth are larger for nuclei with larger magnetogyric ratios than for those with smaller magnetogyric ratios.

In general, the analysis of nuclear relaxation is complex for paramagnetic proteins that contain more than one metal ion, where antiferromagnetic coupling between different metal ions gives rise to new electron-spin energy levels. However, one may still be able to deduce the oxidation states of the iron ions on the basis of relaxation times of cysteinyl nuclear spins. In oxidized *Anabaena* 7120 vegetative ferredoxin, the β-carbon resonances from the four cysteines, all ligated to Fe(III), had similar T_1 relaxation times (~ 2 ms). When the protein was reduced, the T_1 relaxation times of the β-carbons assigned to the two cysteines ligated to Fe(III) (Cys49 and Cys79) were largely unchanged (2.4 and 2.9 ms, respectively), but those from β-carbons assigned to the two cysteines ligated to Fe(II) (Cys41 and Cys46) became much longer (29 and 19 ms, respectively) (46). This observation must be attributed to the difference in T_{1e} of Fe(III) and Fe(II) in the reduced cluster. Because nuclear spins relax from nuclear-electron contact and dipolar interactions, the limited contribution from the contact interaction can be estimated from the isotropic shifts and the X-ray structure (31).

Preliminary results from measurements of T_1 values for the hyperfine-shifted ^{15}N resonances of *Anabaena* 7120 vegetative and heterocyst ferredoxins indicate that the relaxation mechanism is predominantly dipolar. Correlations of assigned resonances with distances from the irons of the cluster derived from the X-ray structures of the two proteins suggest that ^{15}N T_1 values may provide accurate distances for nitrogens that are between 4.5 and 8.5 Å of the nearest iron (36). The linear relationship with the inverse sixth-power of the distance did not hold for the cysteinyl ligand nitrogens or for other residues with nitrogens closer than 4.5 Å to an iron; the simple dipolar model appears not be applicable to these spins, either because the point-dipole approximation breaks down at short distances or because delocalization of spin density from the iron ions to other atoms has been neglected.

NMR SOLUTION STRUCTURES

When sequence-specific resonance assignments of an iron-sulfur protein have been completed, the protein secondary structure can be identified from patterns of NOEs or chemical shifts, as is routinely done with diamagnetic proteins (35, 57, 88, 92, 128, 136). Distance constraints derived from 2D NOEs and coupling constants can be used in modeling the three-dimensional structure of the protein. In general with iron-sulfur proteins, detailed information is lacking for the region directly surrounding the cluster. Some of the missing information can be supplied from knowledge of the covalent geometry of the cluster from X-ray structures or by using relaxation data as loose distance constraints to the iron atoms (34). Approaches of this kind have been used to model the three-dimensional solution structures of oxidized *Anabaena* 7120 vegetative ferredoxin (34) and putidaredoxin, a [2Fe-2S] ferredoxin from *Pseudomonas putida* (104). Figure 5 shows the family of structures for putidaredoxin that are compatible with the NMR data. In studies of the reduced HiPIP I from *Ectothiorhodospira halophila*, investigators were able to determine a large number of distance constraints from residues near the [4Fe-4S]; these measurements have permitted the determination of a more highly refined solution structure from NMR data for this protein than is possible with [2Fe-2S] ferredoxins (4).

The solution structure of Zn-substituted *P. furiosus* rubredoxin has been reported (28). Replacement of the iron with a diamagnetic ion sidesteps the problems inherent in NMR spectroscopy of paramagnetic proteins. However, one must consider the possibility that the modification may change structural features of the protein that are important to its function. Comparison of the structure of the Zn-substituted rubredoxin with the X-ray structures of *P. furiosus* rubredoxin in its oxidized and reduced states revealed distinct changes in structural parameters around the paramagnetic center as well as subtle changes within the protein framework (25, 52).

Figure 5 Backbone (α-carbon) connectivities for a family of 10 NMR structures generated for oxidized putidaredoxin (from 104, with permission). A pairwise rms deviation of 1.14 from the average atomic positions was obtained for all backbone atoms, and a 1.80 pairwise rms deviation from the average structure was obtained for all nonhydrogen atoms.

Molecular dynamics calculations were employed in a study in which NMR data were used to refine the X-ray structure of oxidized HiPIP from *C. vinosum* (9). Molecular dynamics simulations with distances from NOE measurements as constraints led to structures that were more consistent with the NMR data than the original X-ray structure.

CONCLUSION

NMR studies of ferredoxins, HiPIPs, and rubredoxins have provided unique information about their structures in solution, their electron distribution from iron ions onto protein atoms, and their electron-transfer reactions. The inherent paramagnetism of iron-sulfur proteins contributes additional chemical-shift (isotropic shifts) and relaxation mechanisms to nuclear spins near clusters. This results in difficulties in determining sequence-specific assignments and high-resolution 3D solution structures. Much progress has been made already in adapting

NMR methodology to the solution of these problems. Advances also have been made in the theoretical framework needed to interpret parameters derived from studies of hyperfine-shifted resonances: the isotropic shift, its pH and temperature dependence, the linewidth, the T_1 relaxation time, and cross-relaxation and chemical-exchange rates. Because hyperfine-shifted resonances are usually resolved from the diamagnetic envelope, even in relatively large proteins, they represent useful probes for the investigation of fundamental biological problems (42, 103). The increasing importance being attached to the family of iron-sulfur proteins, coupled with the current intense interest in NMR spectroscopy of iron-sulfur proteins and paramagnetic proteins in general, forecasts continued rapid development of this exciting field.

ACKNOWLEDGMENTS

This review is dedicated to the memory of Dr. William D Phillips. Grant support from the National Science Foundation (MCB-9115142) and National Institutes of Health (RR02301) is gratefully acknowledged. The authors thank their collaborators who have participated in the studies reviewed here and recognize their debt to the many other workers in this field.

Literature Cited

1. Adman ET, Sieker LC, Jensen LH, Bruschi M, LeGall J. 1977. A structure model of rubredoxin from *Desulfovibrio vulgaris* at 2 Å resolution. *J. Mol. Biol.* 112:113–20
2. Agarwal A, Tan J, Eren M, Tevelev A, Lui SM, et al. 1993. Synthesis, cloning and expression of a synthetic gene for high potential iron protein from *Chromatium vinosum. Biochem. Biophys. Res. Commun.* 197: 1357–62
3. Alexandrescu AT, Loh SN, Markley JL. 1990. Chemical exchange spectroscopy based on carbon-13. Applications to protein folding and enzymology. *J. Magn. Reson.* 87:523–35
4. Banci L. 1994. 3D structure of HiPIPs through NMR and molecular dynamics. *Proc. NATO Advanced Workshop on Nuclear Magnetic Resonance of Paramagnetic Macromolecules, Sintra, Portugal, June*

4–8, p. 20. Dordrecht: Kluwer. (Abstr.)
5. Banci L, Bertini I, Briganti F. 1991. The electronic structure of paramagnetic polynuclear metal clusters in proteins studied through ^{1}H NMR spectroscopy. *New J. Chem.* 15: 467–77
6. Banci L, Bertini I, Briganti F, Luchinat C, Scozzafava A, et al. 1991. ^{1}H NMR spectra of oxidized high-potential iron-sulfur protein (HiPIP) from *Rhodocyclus gelatinosus*. A model for oxidized HiPIPs. *Inorg. Chem.* 30:4517–24
7. Banci L, Bertini I, Briganti F, Scozzafava A, Oliver MV. 1991. [1]H NOE studies of oxidized high potential iron sulfur protein II from *Ectothiorhodospira halophila. Inorg. Chim. Acta* 180:171–75
8. Banci L, Bertini I, Capozzi F, Carloni P, Ciurli S, et al. 1993. The iron-sulfur

cluster in the oxidized high-potential iron protein from *Ectothiorhodospira halophila*. *J. Am. Chem. Soc.* 115: 3431–40

9. Banci L, Bertini I, Carloni P, Luchinat C, Orioli PL. 1993. Molecular dynamics simulations on HiPIP from *Chromatium vinosum* and comparison with NMR data. *J. Am. Chem. Soc.* 114:10683–89

10. Banci L, Bertini I, Ciurli S, Ferretti S, Luchinat C, et al. 1993. The electronic structure of $[Fe_4S_4]^{3+}$ cluster in proteins. An investigation of the oxidized high-potential iron-sulfur protein II from *Ectothiorhodospira vacuolata*. *Biochemistry* 32:9387–97

11. Banci L, Bertini I, Luchinat C. 1990. The ^1H NMR parameters of magnetically coupled dimers—the Fe_2S_2 proteins as an example. *Struct. Bond.* 72: 113–36

12. Barker WC, George DG, Srinivasarao GY, Yeh LS. 1992. Database of protein sequence alignments. *Biophys. J.* 61:A348 (Abstr. #2000)

13. Beinert H. 1990. Recent developments in the field of iron-sulfur proteins. *FASEB J.* 4:2483–91

14. Bertini I, Banci L, Luchinat C. 1989. Proton magnetic resonance of paramagnetic metalloprotein. *Methods Enzymol.* 177:246–64

15. Bertini I, Briganti F, Luchinat, Luchinat C, Scozzafava A. 1990. ^1H NMR studies of the oxidized and partially reduced 2(4Fe-4S) ferredoxin from *Clostridium pasteurianum*. *Inorg. Chem.* 29:1874–80

16. Bertini I, Briganti F, Luchinat C, Messori L, Monnanni R, et al. 1991. 2D ^1H NMR studies of oxidized 2(Fe_4S_4) ferredoxin from *Clostridium pasteurianum*. *FEBS Lett.* 289: 253–56

17. Bertini I, Briganti F, Luchinat C, Messori L, Monnanni R, et al. 1992. ^1H-NMR studies on partially and fully reduced 2(4Fe-4S) ferredoxin from *Clostridium pasteurianum*. *Eur. J. Biochem.* 204:831–39

18. Bertini I, Capozzi F, Ciurli S, Luchinat C, Messori L, Piccioli M. 1992. Identification of the iron ions of high potential iron protein from *Chromatium vinosum* within the protein frame through two-dimensional NMR experiments. *J. Am. Chem. Soc.* 114: 3332–40

19. Bertini I, Capozzi F, Luchinat C, Piccioli M. 1993. ^1H-NMR investigation of oxidized and reduced high-poten-tial iron-sulfur protein from *Rhodopseudomonas globiformis*. *Eur. J. Biochem.* 212:69–78

20. Bertini I, Capozzi F, Luchinat C, Piccioli M, Oliver V. 1992. NMR is a unique and necessary step in the investigation of iron sulfur protein: the HiPIP from *R. gelatinosus* as an example. *Inorg. Chim. Acta* 198–200: 483-91

21. Bertini I, Gaudemer A, Luchinat C, Piccioli M. 1993. Electron self-exchange in high-potential iron-sulfur proteins. Characterization of protein I from *Ectothiorhodospira vacuolata*. *Biochemistry* 32:12887–93

22. Bertini I, Luchinat C. 1986. *NMR of Paramagnetic Molecules in Biological Systems*. Menlo Park, CA: Benjamin/Cummings

23. Bertini I, Luchinat C, Tarchi D. 1993. Are true scalar connectivities ever measured in COSY spectra of paramagnetic molecules? *Chem. Phys. Lett.* 203:445–49

24. Bertini I, Turano P, Vila A. 1993. Nuclear magnetic resonance of paramagnetic metalloproteins. *Chem. Rev.* 93:2833–2932

25. Blake PR, Day MW, Hsu BT, Joshua-Tor L, Park J-B, et al. 1992. Comparison of the X-ray structure of native rubredoxin from *Pyrococcus furiosus* with the NMR structure of the zinc-substituted protein. *Protein Sci.* 1: 1522–25

26. Blake PR, Park J-B, Adams MWW, Summers MF. 1992. Novel observation of NH . . . S(Cys) hydrogen-bond-mediated scalar coupling in ^{113}Cd-substituted rubredoxin from *Pyrococcus furiosus*. *J. Am. Chem. Soc.* 114:4931–33

27. Blake PR, Park J-B, Bryant FO, Aono S, Magnuson JK, et al. 1991. Determinants of protein hyperthermostability: purification and amino acid sequence of rubredoxin from the hyperthermophilic archaebacterium *Pyrococcus furiosus* and secondary structure of the zinc adduct by NMR. *Biochemistry* 30:10885–95

28. Blake PR, Park J-B, Zhou ZH, Hare DR, Adams MWW, et al. 1992. Solution-state structure by NMR of zinc-substituted rubredoxin from the marine hyperthermophilic archaebacterium *Pyrococcus furiosus*. *Protein Sci.* 1:1508–21

29. Bloembergen N. 1957. Proton relaxation times in paramagnetic solutions. *J. Chem. Phys.* 27:572–73

30. Bruschi M, Guerlesquin F. 1988. Structure, function and evolution of bacterial ferredoxins. *FEMS Microbiol. Rev.* 54:155–76

31. Busse SC, La Mar GN, Howard JB. 1991. Two-dimensional NMR investigation of iron-sulfur cluster electronic and molecular structure of oxidized *Clostridium pasteurianum* ferredoxin. *J. Biol. Chem.* 266:23714–23

32. Busse SC, La Mar GN, Yu LP, Howard JB, Smith ET, et al. 1992. Proton NMR investigation of the oxidized three-iron clusters in the ferredoxins from the hyperthermophilic Archae *Pyrococcus furiosus* and *Thermococcus litoralis*. *Biochemistry* 31:11952–62

33. Cammack R, Rao KK, Hall DO. 1985. Ferredoxins: structure and function of a ubiquitous group of proteins. *Physiol. Vég.* 23:649–58

34. Chae YK. 1994. *Multinuclear, multidimensional NMR studies of Anabaena 7120 vegetative and heterocyst ferredoxins*. PhD thesis. Univ. Wisc., Madison

35. Chae YK, Abildgaard F, Mooberry ES, Markley JL. 1994. Multinuclear, multidimensional NMR studies of *Anabaena* 7120 heterocyst ferredoxin. Sequence-specific resonance assignments and secondary structure of the oxidized form in solution. *Biochemistry* 33:3287–95

36. Chae YK, Markley JL. 1994. Analysis of hyperfine-shifted nitrogen-15 resonances in the oxidized form of *Anabaena* 7120 ferredoxins. *Biochemistry*. In press

37. Chan T-M, Hermodson MA, Ulrich EL, Markley JL. 1983. Nuclear magnetic resonance studies of two-iron-two-sulfur ferredoxins. 2. Determination of the sequence of *Anabaena variabilis* ferredoxin II, assignment of aromatic resonances in proton spectra, and effects of chemical modifications. *Biochemistry* 22:5988–95

38. Chan T-M, Markley JL. 1982. Heteronuclear (^{1}H, ^{13}C) two-dimensional chemical shift correlation NMR spectroscopy of a protein. Ferredoxin from *Anabaena variabilis*. *J. Am. Chem. Soc.* 104:4010–11

39. Chan T-M, Markley JL. 1983. Nuclear magnetic resonance studies of two-iron-two-sulfur ferredoxins. 1. Properties of the histidine residues. *Biochemistry* 22:5982–87

40. Chan T-M, Markley JL. 1983 Nuclear magnetic resonance studies of two-iron-two-sulfur ferredoxins. 3. Heteronuclear (^{13}C,^{1}H) two-dimensional NMR spectra, ^{13}C peak assignments, and ^{13}C relaxation measurements. *Biochemistry* 22:5996–6002

41. Chan T-M, Markley JL. 1983. Nuclear magnetic resonance studies of two-iron-two-sulfur ferredoxins. 5. Hyperfine-shifted peaks in ^{1}H and ^{13}C spectra. *Biochemistry* 22:6008–10

42. Chan T-M, Ulrich EL, Markley JL. 1983. Nuclear magnetic resonance studies of two-iron-two-sulfur ferredoxins. 4. Interactions with redox partners. *Biochemistry* 22:6002–7

43. Chan T-M, Westler WM, Santini RE, Markley JL. 1982. Carbon-13 NMR subspectra of a protein based on the number of attached protons. Ferredoxin from *Anabaena variabilis*. *J. Am. Chem. Soc.* 104:4008–10

44. Cheng H, Grohmann K, Sweeney W. 1990. The downfield resonances in the ^{1}H NMR spectra of *Azotobacter vinelandii* and *Pseudomonas putida* seven-iron ferredoxins. *J. Biol. Chem.* 265:12388–92

45. Cheng H, Grohmann K, Sweeney W. 1992. NMR studies of *Azotobacter vinelandii* and *Pseudomonas putida* seven-iron ferredoxins. Direct assignment of β-cysteinyl carbon NMR resonances and further proton NMR assignments of cysteinyl and aromatic resonances. *J. Biol. Chem.* 267:8073–80

46. Cheng H, Westler WM, Xia B, Oh B-H, Markley JL. 1994. Protein expression, selective isotopic labeling, and analysis of hyperfine-shifted NMR signals of *Anabaena* 7120 vegetative [2Fe-2S] ferredoxin. *Arch. Biochem. Biophys*. In press

47. Cheng H, Xia B, Reed GH, Markley JL. 1994. Optical, EPR, and ^{1}H NMR spectroscopy of serine-ligated [2Fe-2S] ferredoxin produced by site-directed mutagenesis of cysteine residues in recombinant *Anabaena* 7120 vegetative ferredoxin. *Biochemistry* 33:3155–64

48. Clore GM, Gronenborn A. 1991. Applications of three- and four-dimensional heteronuclear NMR spectroscopy to protein structure determination. *Prog. Nucl. Magn. Reson. Spectrosc.* 23:43–92

49. Coghlan VM, Vickery LE. 1989. Expression of human ferredoxin and assembly of the [2Fe-2S] center in *E. coli*. *Proc. Natl. Acad. Sci. USA* 86:835–39

50. Cowan JA, Sola M. 1990. ¹H NMR studies of oxidized high-potential iron protein from *Chromatium vinosum*. Nuclear Overhauser effect measurements. *Biochemistry* 29:5633–37

51. Davasse V, Moulis J-M. 1992. Design and functional expression in *Escherichia coli* of a synthetic gene encoding *Clostridium pasteurianum* 2[4Fe-4S] ferredoxin. *Biochem. Biophys. Res. Commun.* 185:341–49

52. Day MW, Hsu BT, Joshua-Tor L, Park J-B, Zhou ZH, et al. 1992. X-ray crystal structure of the oxidized and reduced forms of the rubredoxin from the marine hyperthermophillic archaebacterium *Pyrococcus furiosus*. *Protein Sci.* 1:1494–1507

53. Dugad LB, La Mar GN, Banci L, Bertini I. 1990. Identification of localized redox states in plant-type two-iron ferredoxins using the nuclear Overhauser effect. *Biochemistry* 29: 2263–71

54. Dunham WR, Palmer G, Sands RH, Bearden AJ. 1971. On the structure of the iron-sulfur complex in the two-irons ferredoxins. *Biochim. Biophys. Acta* 253:373–84

55. Edison AS, Abildgaard F, Westler WM, Mooberry ES, Markley JL. 1994. Practical introduction to the theory and implementation of multi-nuclear, multidimensional NMR experiments. *Methods Enzymol.* 239: 3–79

56. Fitzgerald RJ, Drago RS. 1968. Contact-shift studies, delocalization mechanisms, and extended Hückel calculations of nickel(II)-alkylamine complexes. *J. Am. Chem. Soc.* 90: 2523–27

57. Gaillard J, Albrand J-P, Moulis J-M, Wemmer DE. 1992. Sequence-specific assignments of ¹H nuclear magnetic resonance spectra of reduced high-potential ferredoxin (HiPIP) from *Chromatium vinosum*. *Biochemistry* 31:5632–39

58. Gaillard J, Moulis JM, Meyer J. 1987. Hydrogen-1 nuclear magnetic resonance of selenium substituted clostridial ferredoxins. *Inorg. Chem.* 26: 320–24

59. Gluck M, Sweeney MV. 1990. ¹³C-NMR of *Clostridium pasteurianum* ferredoxin after reductive methylation of the amines using [¹³C]formaldehyde. *Biochim. Biophys. Acta* 1038:146–51

60. Greenfield NJ, Wu X, Jordan F. 1989. Proton magnetic resonance spectra of adrenodoxin: features of the aromatic region. *Biochim. Biophys. Acta* 995: 246–54

61. Gurbiel RJ, Batie CJ, Sivaraja M, True AE, Fee JA, et al. 1989. Electron-nuclear double resonance spectroscopy of ¹⁵N-enriched phthalate dioxygenase from *Pseudomonas cepacia* proves that two histidines are coordinated to the [2Fe-2S] Rieske-type clusters. *Biochemistry* 28:4861–71

62. Hentze MW, Argos P. 1991. Homology between IRE-BP, a regulatory RNA-binding protein, aconitase, and isopropylmalate isomerase. *Nucleic Acid Res.* 19:1739–40

63. Ho FF-L, Reilley CN. 1969. Conformational studies of chelated ethylenediamines by nuclear magnetic resonance. Paramagnetic nickel(II) complexes of *N*-alkylethylenediamines. *Anal. Chem.* 41:1835–41

64. Holden HM, Jacobson BL, Hurley JK, Tollin G, Oh B-H, et al. 1994. Structure-function studies of [2Fe-2S] ferredoxins. *J. Bioeng. Biomembr.* 26:67–88

65. Holm RH, Phillips WD, Averill BA, Mayerle JJ, Herskovitz T. 1974. Synthetic analogs of the active sites of iron-sulfur proteins. V. Proton resonance properties of the tetranuclear clusters [Fe₄S₄(SR)₄]²⁻. Evidence for dominant contact interactions. *J. Am. Chem. Soc.* 96:2109–17

66. Howard JB, Rees DC. 1991. Perspective on non-heme iron protein chemistry. *Adv. Protein Chem.* 42:199–208

67. Heller C, McConnell HM. 1969. Radiation damage in organic crystals. II. Electron spin resonance of (CO₂H)CH₂CH(CO₂H) in β-succinic acid. *J. Chem. Phys.* 32:1535–39

68. Jacobson BL, Chae YK, Markley JL, Rayment I, Holden HM. 1993. Molecular structure of the oxidized, recombinant, heterocyst [2Fe-2S] ferredoxin from *Anabaena* 7120 determined to 1.7 resolution. *Biochemistry* 32:6788–93

69. Jardetzky O, Roberts GCK. 1981. Paramagnetic perturbations of NMR spectra. In *NMR in Molecular Biology*. New York: Academic

70. Kainosho M, Tsujii T. 1982. Assignment of the three methionyl carbonyl carbon resonances in *Streptomyces subtilisin* inhibitor by a carbon-13 and nitrogen-15 double-labeling technique. A new strategy for structural studies of proteins in solution. *Biochemistry* 21:6273–79

71. Krishnamoorthi R, Markley JL, Cusanovich MA, Przysiecki CT. 1986.

Hydrogen-1 nuclear magnetic resonance investigation of *Clostridium pasteurianum* rubredoxin. Location and assignment of resonances from the coordinating cysteinyl residues. *Biochemistry* 25:50–54

72. Krishnamoorthi R, Markley JL, Cusanovich MA, Przysiecki CT, Meyer TE. 1986. Hydrogen-1 nuclear magnetic resonance investigation of high potential iron-sulfur proteins from *Ectothiorhodospira halophila* and *Ectothiorhodospira vacuolata*. 1. A comparative study of hyperfine shifted resonances. *Biochemistry* 25: 60–67

73. Kupče E, Freeman R. 1992. Indirect detection of fast-relaxing, insensitive nuclei. *J. Magn. Reson.* 98:217–22

74. La Mar GN, Horrocks WD, Holm RH, eds. 1973. *NMR of Paramagnetic Molecules*. New York: Academic

75. Lovenberg W, ed. 1973. *Iron-Sulfur Proteins*, Vol. 3. New York: Academic

76. Markley JL, Chan T-M, Krishnamoorthi R, Ulrich EL. 1986. Nuclear magnetic resonance studies of structure-function relationships in iron-sulfur proteins. In *Iron-Sulfur Protein Research*, ed. H Matsubara, Y Katsube, K Wada, pp. 167–81. Tokyo/Berlin: Springer-Verlag

77. Markley JL, Kainosho M. 1993. Stable isotope labeling and resonance assignments in larger proteins. In *NMR of Biological Macromolecules: A Practical Approach*, ed. GCK Roberts, pp. 101–52. Oxford, UK: Oxford Univ. Press

78. Mathieu I, Meyer J, Moulis J-M. 1992. Cloning, sequencing and expression in *Escherichia coli* of the rubredoxin gene from *Clostridium pasteurianum*. *Biochem. J.* 285: 255–62

79. Mayhew SG. 1978. The redox potential of dithionite and SO_2^- from equilibrium reactions with flavodoxins, methyl viologen, and hydrogen plus hydrogenase. *Eur. J. Biochem.* 85: 535–47

80. McConnell HM, Chesnut DB. 1958. Theory of isotropic hyperfine interactions in π-electron radicals. *J. Chem. Phys.* 28:107–17

81. Miura S, Ichikawa Y. 1991. Conformational change of adrenodoxin induced by reduction of iron-sulfur cluster. *J. Biol. Chem.* 266:6252–58

82. Miura S, Ichikawa Y. 1991. Proton nuclear magnetic resonance investigation of adrenodoxin. Assignment of aromatic resonances and evidence for a conformational similarity with ferredoxin from *Spirulina platensis*. *Eur. J. Biochem.* 197:747–57

83. Miura S, Tomita S, Ichikawa Y. 1991. Modification of histidine 56 in adrenodoxin with diethyl pyrocarbonate inhibited the interaction with cytochrome P-450scc and adrenodoxin reductase. *J. Biol. Chem.* 266:19212–16

84. Mouesca J-M, Lamotte B, Rius G. 1991. Comparison between spin population distributions in two different $[Fe_4S_4]^{3+}$ clusters by proton ENDOR in single crystals of a synthetic model compound. *Inorg. Biochem.* 43:251

85. Mouesca J-M, Rius G, Lamotte B. 1993. Single-crystal proton ENDOR studies of the $[Fe_4S_4]^{3+}$ cluster: determination of the spin population distribution and proposal of a model to interpret the ^1H NMR paramagnetic shifts in high-potential ferredoxins. *J. Am. Chem. Soc.* 115:4714–31

86. Nagayama K, Ohmori D, Imai T, Oshima T. 1983. Proton magnetic resonance studies of 7Fe ferredoxins. Lower potential of the [4Fe-4S] redox center than the [3Fe-3S] cluster. *FEBS Lett.* 158:208–12

87. Nagayama K, Ohmori D, Imai T, Oshima T. 1986. NMR studies of 7Fe ferredoxins: redox states and structural changes in two iron-sulfur clusters. In *Iron-Sulfur Proteins*, ed. J Matsubara, Y Kateube, K Wada, pp. 125–38. Tokyo/Berlin: Springer-Verlag

88. Nettesheim D, Scott RH, Feinberg BA, Otvos J. 1992. Sequential resonance assignments of oxidized high-potential iron-sulfur protein from *Chromatium vinosum*. *Biochemistry* 31:1234–44

89. Neuhaus D, Williamson M. 1989. *The Nuclear Overhauser Effect*. New York: VCH

90. Noodleman L. 1988. A model for the spin states of high-potential $[Fe_4S_4]^{3+}$ proteins. *Inorg. Chem.* 27: 3677–79

91. O'Halloran TV. 1993. Transition metals in control of gene expression. *Science* 261:715–25

92. Oh B-H, Markley JL. 1990. Multinuclear magnetic resonance studies of the 2Fe-2S ferredoxin from *Anabaena* species strain PCC 7120. 1. Sequence-specific hydrogen-1 resonance assignments and secondary structure in solution of the oxidized form. *Biochemistry* 29:3993–4004

93. Oh B-H, Markley JL. 1990. Multinuclear magnetic resonance studies of the 2Fe-2S ferredoxin from *Anabaena* species strain PCC 7120. 3. Detection and characterization of hyperfine-shifted nitrogen-15 and hydrogen-1 resonances of the oxidized form. *Biochemistry* 29:4012–17

94. Oh B-H, Mooberry ES, Markley JL. 1990. Multinuclear magnetic resonance studies of the 2Fe-2S ferredoxin from *Anabaena* species strain PCC 7120. 2. Sequence-specific carbon-13 and nitrogen-15 resonance assignments of the oxidized form. *Biochemistry* 29:4004–11

95. Packer EL, Sternlicht H, Lode ET, Rabinowitz JC. 1975. The use of ^{13}C nuclear magnetic resonance of aromatic amino acid residues to determine the midpoint oxidation-reduction potential of each iron-sulfur cluster of *Clostridium acidi-urici* and *Clostridium pasteurianum* ferredoxins. *J. Biol. Chem.* 250:2062–72

96. Packer EL, Sternlicht H, Rabinowitz JC. 1972. The possible role of aromatic residues of *Clostridium acidi-urici* ferredoxin in electron transport. *Proc. Natl. Acad. Sci. USA* 69:3278–82

97. Packer EL, Sternlicht H, Rabinowitz JC. 1973. The possible structural and functional role of aromatic residues in bacterial ferredoxins. *Ann. NY Acad. Sci.* 222:824–37

98. Packer EL, Sweeney WV, Rabinowitz JC, Sternlicht H, Shaw EN. 1977. Direct assignment of the cysteinyl, the slowly exchangeable, and the aromatic ring ^1H nuclear magnetic resonances in clostridial-type ferredoxins. *J. Biol. Chem.* 252:2245–53

99. Palin M-F, Berthiaume L, Lehoux J-G, Waterman MR, Jurgen Sygusch J. 1992. Direct expression of mature bovine adrenodoxin in *Escherichia coli*. *Arch. Biochem. Biophys.* 295:126–31

100. Phillips WD. 1973. Biological applications. See Ref. 74, pp. 421–78

101. Phillips WD, Poe M. 1972. Contact shifts and magnetic susceptibilities in iron-sulfur proteins as determined from nuclear magnetic resonance spectra. *Methods Enzymol.* 24:304–17

102. Phillips WD, Poe M. 1973. NMR spectroscopy of the iron-sulfur proteins. In *Iron-Sulfur Proteins*, ed. W Lovenberg, 2:255–84. New York: Academic

103. Pochapsky T, Ratnaswamy G, Patera A. 1994. Redox-dependent ^1H NMR spectral features and tertiary structural constraints on the C-terminal region of putidaredoxin. *Biochemistry* 33:6433–41

104. Pochapsky T, Ye XM, Ratnaswamy G, Lyons T. 1994. An NMR-derived model for the solution structure of oxidized putidaredoxin, a 2-Fe, 2-S ferredoxin from *Pseudomonas*. *Biochemistry* 33:6424–32

105. Pratt L, Smith BB. 1969. Proton resonance spectra of some nickel complexes in aqueous solution. *Trans. Faraday Soc.* 65:915–27

106. Ratnaswamy G, Pochapsky TC. 1993. Characterization of hyperfine-shifted ^1H resonances in oxidized and reduced putidaredoxin, A 2-Fe 2-S ferredoxin from *Pseudomonas putida*. *Magn. Reson. Chem.* 31:S73–S77

107. Rius G, Lamotte B. 1989. Single-crystal ENDOR study of a ^{57}Fe-enriched iron-sulfur $[Fe_4S_4]^{3+}$ cluster. *J. Am. Chem. Soc.* 111:2464–69

108. Rogers WJ, Hodges M, Decottignies P, Schmitter J-M, Gadal P, et al. 1992. Isolation of a cDNA fragment coding for *Chlamydomonas reinhardtii* ferredoxin and expression of the recombinant protein in *Escherichia coli*. *FEBS Lett.* 310:240–45

109. Rouault TA, Stout CD, Kaptain S, Harford JB, Klausner RD. 1991. Structural relationship between an iron-regulated RNA-binding protein (IRE-BP) and aconitase functional implications. *Cell* 64:881–83

110. Rypniewski WR, Breiter DR, Benning MM, Wesenberg G, Oh B-H, et al. 1991. Crystallization and structure determination to 2.5 resolution of the oxidized 2Fe-2S ferredoxin isolated from *Anabaena* 7120. *Biochemistry* 30:4126–31

111. Sagara Y, Har T, Ariyasu Y, Ando F, Tokunaga M, et al. 1992. Direct expression in *Escherichia coli* and characterization of bovine adrenodoxins with modified amino-terminal region. *FEBS Lett.* 300:208–12

112. Satterlee JD. 1990. Fundamental concepts of NMR in paramagnetic systems. *Concepts Magn. Res.* 2:69–79; 119–29

113. Seaton BL, Vickery LE. 1992. Expression of human ferredoxin in *Saccharomyces cerevisiae*: mitochondrial import of the protein and assembly of the [2Fe-2S] center. *Arch. Biochem. Biophys.* 294:603–8

114. Shen B, Martin LL, Butt JN, Armstrong FA, Stout CD, et al. 1993. *Azotobacter vinelandii* ferredoxin I: aspartate 15 facilitates proton transfer to the reduced [3Fe-4S] cluster. *J. Biol. Chem.* 268:25928–99

115. Skjeldal L, Hårklau H, Ljones T, Markley JL. 1994. NMR of ferredoxin from *Clostridium pasteurianum*. *Proc. NATO Advanced Workshop on Nuclear Magnetic Resonance of Paramagnetic Macromolecules, Sintra, Portugal, June 4–8.* p. 70. Dordrecht: Kluwer. (Abstr.)

116. Skjeldal L, Markley JL, Coghlan VM, Vickery LE. 1991. ^{1}H NMR spectra of vertebrate [2Fe-2S] ferredoxins. Hyperfine resonances suggest different electron delocalization patterns from plant ferredoxins. *Biochemistry* 30:9078–83

117. Skjeldal L, Westler WM, Markley JL. 1990. Detection and characterization of hyperfine-shifted resonances in the proton nuclear magnetic resonance spectrum of *Anabaena* 7120 ferredoxin at high magnetic fields. *Arch. Biochem. Biophys.* 278:482–85

118. Skjeldal L, Westler WM, Oh B-H, Krezel AM, Holden H, et al. 1991. Two-dimensional magnetization exchange spectroscopy of *Anabaena* 7120 ferredoxin. Nuclear Overhauser effect and electron self-exchange cross peaks from amino acid residues surrounding the 2Fe-2S cluster. *Biochemistry* 30:7363–68

119. Smith ET, Feinberg BA, Richards JH, Tomich JM. 1991. Physical characterization of a totally synthetic 2[4Fe-4S] clostridial ferredoxin. *J. Am. Chem. Soc.* 113:688–89

120. Smith ET, Tomich JM, Iwamoto T, Richards JH, Mao Y, et al. 1991. A totally synthetic histidine-2 ferredoxin: thermal stability and redox properties. *Biochemistry* 30:11669–76

121. Solomon I. 1955. Relaxation processes in a system of two spins. *Phys. Rev.* 99:559–65

122. Solomon I, Bloembergen N. 1956. Nuclear magnetic interactions in the HF molecule. *J. Chem. Phys.* 25:261–66

123. Spiro TG, ed. 1982. *Iron Sulfur Proteins,* Vol. 4. New York: Wiley

124. Stone EW, Maki AH. 1962. Hindered internal rotation and ESR spectroscopy. *J. Chem. Phys.* 37:1326–1841

125. Stout CD. 1993. Crystal structures of oxidized and reduced *Azotobacter vinelandii* ferredoxin at pH 8 and 6. *J. Biol. Chem.* 268:25920–27

126. Sweeney WV, Rabinowitz JC. 1980. Proteins containing 4Fe-4S clusters: an overview. *Annu. Rev. Biochem.* 49:139–61

127. Tang C, Henry HL. 1993. Overexpression in *Escherichia coli* and affinity purification of chick kidney ferredoxin. *J. Biol. Chem.* 268:5069–76

128. Teng Q, Zhou ZH, Smith ET, Smith ET, Busse SC, et al. 1994. Solution ^{1}H NMR determination of secondary structure for the three-iron form of ferredoxin from the hyperthermophilic archaeon *Pyrococcus furiosus.* *Biochemistry* 33:6316–26

129. Thompson AJ. 1985. Iron-sulfur proteins. In *Metalloproteins,* Part 1, ed. P Hanson, pp. 79–120. Weinheim: Verlag Chemie

130. Thomson AJ. 1991. Does ferredoxin I (*Azotobacter*) represent a novel class of DNA-binding proteins that regulate gene expression in response to cellular iron(II)? *FEBS Lett.* 285:230–36

131. Ulamnn H, Beckert V, Schwarz D, Bernhardt R. 1992. Expression of bovine adrenodoxin in *E. coli* and site-directed mutagenesis of [2Fe-2S] cluster ligands. *Biochem. Biophys. Res. Commun.* 188:1131–38

132. Wimperis S, Bodenhausen G. 1989. Relaxation-allowed cross-peaks in two-dimensional NMR correlation spectroscopy. *Mol. Phys.* 66:897–919

133. Wishart DS, Sykes BD. 1994. The ^{13}C chemical shift index: a simple method for the identification of protein secondary structure using ^{13}C chemical shifts. *J. Biomol. NMR* 4:171–80

134. Wüthrich K. 1986. *NMR of Proteins and Nucleic Acids.* New York: Wiley

135. Xia B, Cheng H, Skjeldal L, Coghlan VM, Vickery LE, Markley JL. 1994. Multinuclear magnetic resonance and mutagenesis studies of the histidines of human mitochondrial ferredoxin. *Biochemistry.* In press

136. Ye XM, Pochapsky TC, Pochapsky SS. 1992. ^{1}H NMR sequential assignments and identification of secondary structural elements in oxidized putidaredoxin, an electron-transfer protein from *Pseudomonas.* *Biochemistry* 31:1961–68

Annu. Rev. Biophys. Biomol. Struct. 1995. 24:239–67

APPLICATIONS OF PARALLEL COMPUTING TO BIOLOGICAL PROBLEMS

B. Ostrovsky

Electical, Computer, and Systems Engineering Department, Boston University, Boston, Massachusetts 02215

M. A. Smith

MIT Laboratory for Computer Science, Cambridge, Massachusetts 02139

Y. Bar-Yam

Electical, Computer, and Systems Engineering Department, Boston University, Boston, Massachusetts 02215

KEY WORDS: cellular automata, polymer dynamics, polymer melts, polymer collapse

CONTENTS

1056-8700/95/0610-0239$05.00

ABSTRACT

Parallel computers should provide the greatest processing power and memory for scientific simulations in the coming decades. This review discusses general strategies and specific algorithms for the use of various parallel architectures in simulations of biological and artificial polymers. General strategies include space partitioning (domain decomposition cell methods) and distributed independent simulations. Specific algorithms include cellular automata for efficient abstract polymer simulation. One algorithm, the two-space algorithm, is particularly efficient both for parallel and serial computation. Three applications, 2D melts, gel electrophoresis, and polymer collapse, are described. Simulations of high-density melts in 2D show that contrary to expectations, polymers do not completely segregate at the highest densities; instead, polymer interpenetration is significant. Preliminary simulations of gel electrophoresis show its behavior in the diffusive regime and demonstrate the use of Cellular Automaton Machines (CAMs). Polymer collapse is studied in the regime of large departures from good solvent conditions. In this regime, kinetics plays a significant role. Collapse is dominated (nucleated) by migration of the chain ends.

INTRODUCTION TO PARALLEL COMPUTING

The modeling and simulation of complex biological systems will likely consume a large fraction of computational resources in the upcoming years. The elucidation of many such systems has only recently become feasible with the use of computers, and other systems remain just beyond our reach. In particular, the dynamic properties of natural polymers (proteins, DNA) as well as synthetic polymeric systems are of intense academic and industrial interest. Theoretical understanding of how the behavior of these systems arises from their microscopic structure is a fundamental problem of the field. Computer simulations play a central role because intuitive arguments are difficult to make and analytic results are virtually impossible to obtain. However, the considerable number of conformations of long polymers, as well as the large amount of memory required, limit the usefulness of conventional computer simulations. The advent of parallel computation promises to enable many breakthroughs in this field.

At this point, advances in very large-scale integration (VLSI) technology have reduced the cost of microprocessors, but their performance remains limited by the physical limitations of the speed of light and packing densities. Nevertheless, inexpensive individual microprocessors now approach the performance of the fastest conventional serial computers (21). Parallel processing attempts to combine the power of conventional microprocessors in a system where such microprocessors, often called processing nodes or processing elements, work together on a certain problem in parallel. This arrangement should give a programmer proportionally larger sizes of memory and, in theory, allow a program to achieve a speedup equal to the number of processing elements. Even higher speedups are possible for problems that can be addressed using cooperative parallel algorithms that are not discussed here. The full speedup, unfortunately, is generally not achieved, for several reasons. One is the need for communication between the processors to coordinate the execution of a program and/or to exchange data between them. This communication often has a severe impact on the performance of a program, and therefore, it can also occupy much of the programmer's efforts. Another reason for nonperfect speedups is that many fast serial algorithms are not easily parallelizable, which leads to the development of new algorithms specially tailored for parallel computers. However, these algorithms may not be efficient, and the speedups they achieve are often such that the performance improvement is negligible compared with the investment in both development time and money.

Unlike programming a serial computer, creating an algorithm for a parallel machine, as well as programming it, often requires knowledge of an underlying architecture. Thus certain algorithms can be easily (and effectively) implemented on some machines and will perform poorly on others. According to Flynn (17), all computers can be categorized into four groups, depending on the type of program that each processor runs and the type of data it operates on. The first group, SISD (single instruction single data) computers, represent the usual serial machines. Another class is SIMD (single instruction multiple data) machines, in which all processors synchronously execute the same set of instructions that are broadcast by a special control unit. Examples of SIMD computers are Thinking Machines CM-2, MasPar MP-1 and MP-2, and Goodyear MPP. The third class, MIMD (multiple instructions multiple data) computers, offer a programmer the ability to run an independent program on each of the nodes and to exchange messages between them. Examples of computers belonging to this group are nCUBE, Thinking Machines CM-5, and Intel Paragon. The last category, MISD (multiple instruction single data), has not found general use and is rarely considered.

A variety of experimental parallel architectures are also under development. Of particular interest for spatially distributed systems are experimental Cellular Automata Machines (CAMs) (24), which were developed at the MIT Laboratory for Computer Science. The recently completed CAM-8 is an indefinitely scalable multiprocessor optimized for fine-grained, discrete modeling of spatially distributed systems, such as lattice-gas simulations of fluid flows. CAM-8 implements a uniform three-dimensional (3D) space of cells, each of which can be thought of as a simple processor connected to nearby neighbors.

In addition to inherently parallel computers, networks of workstations may also be used. Such workstations are usually connected together via ethernet and can be thought of as a very loosely coupled MIMD machine. These systems are much less expensive than currently available parallel computers, are easily expandable and maintainable, and allow a user to write programs that can be ported from one workstation type to another with no or very minimal modifications—something very uncommon among parallel computers. Several software packages allow one to connect multiple workstations into a system. PVM (Parallel Virtual Machine) from the Oak Ridge National Laboratory is one of the most popular of these packages. The drawback of this approach is that the speed of communication between workstations is extremely slow, thus allowing only applications that require infrequent communication.

For a particular architecture, algorithms may be constructed to take advantage of its particular strengths. Alternatively, the choice of architecture may also be based on the available algorithms. One of the central issues influencing the choice of the architecture is the granularity of the algorithm. An algorithm is usually considered fine grained when it can be subdivided into large number of very simple homogeneous tasks that can be processed concurrently (usually these tasks consist of a few arithmetic statements). This sort of algorithm maps well onto SIMD computers consisting of many simple processors. On the other hand, an algorithm is coarse grained if the tasks into which the problem can be subdivided are rather complicated. These algorithms are suited for MIMD machines, which have more powerful processors than do SIMD machines, but usually fewer of them.

For various reasons, including the high power of single processors, the majority of recent architectures are MIMD. As described below, simulations of complex biological polymers can sometimes be formulated using fine-grained algorithms. Their efficient implementation on MIMD machines (or workstation networks) requires an additional step of coarse graining.

The most generally applicable approach to parallel processing of a single simulation in spatially distributed systems, including complex polymer simulations, is known as the space-partitioning, domain-decomposition, or cell method (36, 37). In this approach, individual processors are assigned to regions of space. Such domain decomposition–based computing strategies have various applications (18). As discussed below, this approach is often preferred over assigning processors to specific atoms or monomers.

Most scientific studies require a statistical analysis of many independent simulations. This need motivates a second strategy for parallel processing, termed distributed independent simulation, in which different processors are assigned to independent simulations. The simulations might vary only by their starting point or by the values of random numbers used during the simulation to represent thermal reservoirs. The disadvantage of this approach is that a study is limited by the length of the longest simulation and by the memory required. From a programming point of view, after serial implementation the additional effort required is to broadcast (scatter) and retrieve (gather) the simulation results. Interprocessor communication is necessary only at broadcast and retrieval. This approach is well suited to MIMD architectures or networks of workstations as a collection of (almost) independent serial computers. These computers perform independent simulations, and the results are later collected by some central node, which performs statistical analysis. This method allows a program to avoid large amounts of communication and yet exploits the capacity of powerful serial computers.

APPLICATIONS TO POLYMER SIMULATIONS

Conventional simulations of polymer systems are of two types: molecular dynamics (25) and Monte Carlo (1). Molecular-dynamics simulations are suggestive of realistic Newtonian dynamics of polymers and are implemented by moving all atoms with small steps according to forces calculated from modeled interatomic forces. Monte Carlo simulations represent the dynamics of an ensemble of polymers with steps that take into account thermodynamic-transition probabilities. Both techniques give the same results for structure, conformational change, and diffusion.

All atoms can be moved in parallel (at the same time) in molecular dynamics; hence this method appears to be ideal for use with parallel-processing computers (3). However, with a processor attached to each atom, calculation of the forces requires much communication between processors. As mentioned above, connections between processors are the limiting feature of parallel computers.

Monte Carlo simulation can be more efficient than molecular dynamics because it allows larger displacements, and thus, in effect, it allows larger time steps. However, when processors are assigned to individual atoms, parallelization becomes difficult because of the joint effects of simultaneous movement of different atoms.

We can overcome the problem of large numbers of force computations in molecular dynamics or of interactions in Monte Carlo. As the distance between two atoms increases, the interactions between them rapidly diminish, so that after a certain distance, called the cutoff distance, the interactions can be safely assumed to be zero. When long-range Coulomb forces are present, multipole expansion averages can be used to include longer-range interactions, though efficient implementation of such algorithms is not easy.

If each atom interacts with only a few other atoms—those within the cutoff distance from it—the number of necessary force calculations (and hence interprocessor communication) is greatly reduced. However, to take full advantage of this reduction, we must know, without relying upon interprocessor communications, which atoms are close to each other at a particular time. Therefore, a family of algorithms sometimes called cell or domain-decomposition methods have been developed in which a system is spatially subdivided into a number of cells. An atom is assumed to interact only with atoms that are inside its own cell and in any of this cell's 26 nearest neighbors (in a 3D cubic cellular system). This approach is of general interest in molecular-dynamics simulations, not just in polymer simulations, and has been implemented on both SIMD (26) and MIMD (23) platforms. Cell methods are often used in combination with Verlet neighbor tables (39), in which each molecule keeps a table of its neighbors.

Applications of space partitioning or cell methods to polymer simulations are few and quite recent. Smith et al (36, 37) discuss an abstract Monte Carlo polymer model that was then applied by Smith & Bar-Yam (35) to gel electrophoresis simulations and by Ostrovsky & Bar-Yam (29) to polymer collapse. These studies are described in the following sections.

Esselnik & Hilbers (15) describe an implementation of the cell algorithm on a MIMD network of transputers. They applied this approach to a simulation of the crystallization of short polymer chains.

Lin et al (22) give a very detailed description of a direct approach to the parallelization of CHARMM—a widely used molecular simulation program developed primarily for biomolecular systems—on the MIMD Intel iPSC/860. The focus of the parallelization was the partitioning of the core loops in each of the four (serial) stages of the computation. The results achieved showed that on the 32-processor system the overall speedup was 4.3, which is substantially lower than linear. The less-than-optimal results may be attributed to communication overhead since additional processors did not improve performance. Commuincation overhead tends to grow with the number of processors.

Brooks et al (4) use a different approach for parallelizing CHARMM. Their simulations were performed on the eight-processor Cray Y-MP and made use of the Verlet neighbor list method. They independently parallelize the SHAKE algorithm used to implement local bonding constraints so as to eliminate high-frequency motions. In the same paper, the implementation of long-range Coulomb interactions, in a particular model of polarizibility, is described without limiting the range of the interactions so that all pairs of interactions are included. The implementation is on a 32K processor CM-2.

Cohen (9) describes implementation of a parallel algorithm for modeling the degradation of the heparin polymer by the enzyme heparinase. This model is not spatially based; instead it uses a list to represent the types of bonds along the polymer. The simulation was performed on Goodyear's MPP and was implemented in SIMD mode.

Camp & Plimpton (5) review several domain-decomposition simulation strategies and discuss a limited simulation of liquid crystal–like molecules.

Two research efforts in the area of polymer simulations have made explicit and large-scale use of multiple processors for distributed independent simulations. Nakanishi et al (28) used up to 128 heterogeneous workstations, spread over the country and connected into a single system by the EcliPSe tool kit, to study the conformational properties of polymer chains in disordered media. A comparison of the performance of the EcliPSe system with that of a CRAY Y-MP running the same problem demonstrated the superior overall execution time as well as the greater cost effectiveness of networked workstations over large vector supercomputers such as the CRAY. Paul et al (2, 31) used a similar method in their simulations of semidilute polymer solutions. For their work they used a Meiko Computing Surface composed of 80 processors.

PARALLEL ALGORITHMS

General Considerations

The general space-partitioning approach to parallel-processing dynamics developed for polymer simulations can be used for both molecular-dynamics and Monte Carlo simulations. We have developed dynamic models that replicate the simplicity of highly successful abstract models for high-molecular-weight polymers (10, 13). As Monte Carlo simulations do not require the specification of artificial forces in the abstract model, we describe and implement the approach in the language of Monte Carlo step dynamics.

In Monte Carlo simulations of abstract polymer structure and dynamics (1), a long chain of monomers is represented by the coordinates of each monomer. The methods for describing the local structure of the polymer and the process of each move are numerous. However, quite generally, a simulation step consists of selecting a monomer $\langle i \rangle$ from the polymer chain and performing a move subject to the following constraints: (a) The move does not break the polymer connectivity, that is, monomer $\langle i \rangle$ does not dissociate itself from its nearest neighbors along the chain (NNCs), and (b) the move does not violate excluded volume, that is, monomer $\langle i \rangle$ does not overlap the volume of any other monomer $\langle j \rangle$.

In naive parallel processing, a set of processors is assigned one-to-one to perform the movement of a set of monomers. Each processor does not know the outcome of the movement of the other monomers; it can only know their position before the current step. Constraints a and b generally are considered to preclude systematic parallel processing of polymer dynamics because movement of different monomers at the same time is likely to lead to dissociation or overlap. The former constraint only restricts the parallel motion of nearest neighbors and thus can be overcome using simple algorithms. In contrast, the nonlocal excluded volume constraint restricts the parallel motion of any two monomers, presenting a fundamental difficulty for parallel processing.

We can overcome this difficulty by recognizing that polymer interactions are local in space. The polymer can coil so as to bring any two monomers into contact, yet at any particular time, the only possible interactions are between spatially neighboring monomers. As a general rule, monomers sufficiently distant in space from each other can be moved in parallel without interference in that particular step. Two monomers can move independently if the distance between them is greater than $2(l+r)$, where l is the step length and r is the excluded volume radius. These requirements are met by partitioning the space as in Figure 1. In each shaded region, we select a monomer (whose center lies in that shaded region) and then move all the selected monomers independently. Finally, we shift the shaded regions before the next selection process. This describes the total modification of an existing nonparallel algorithm into a parallel one. However, the tabulation

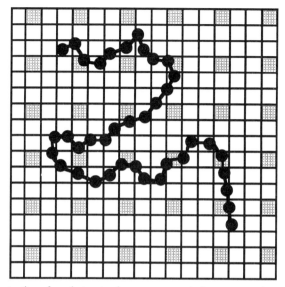

Figure 1   Illustration of an abstract polymer composed of monomers that are connected to neighbors and do not overlap excluded volumes. The motion of monomers is restricted so that they do not detach from neighbors or overlap with any other monomer. Moving any two monomers at the same time can lead to inadvertent overlapping. However, if only one monomer is selected from each shaded region, the monomers selected can be moved at the same time without accidental overlap. The shaded regions can then be shifted so that all monomers can be moved.

of monomers in each region, which must be updated with each move, constitutes an additional computational task. This update can be performed efficiently and in parallel.

Introduction to Cellular Automata

The idea of space-oriented dynamics is manifest in the very general category of dynamic models known as cellular automata (CA) (41). An automaton consists of a rule for specifying the state of a system after a time interval (defined to be one unit of time) in terms of its previous state. In a simplified form, dividing space into cells and considering each cell to have only two possible values, ON and OFF, the state of a cell is determined by the condition of its neighborhood at the previous time. Different rules for determining the state of the cell describe different dynamics. The cellular automaton is a sufficiently general construction to capture the essence of dynamic systems for formal investigations (16, 41). Specific automata have been used to model systems of interest in biology, chemistry, and physics. CA are ideal for simulation on parallel computers. Cellular Automata Machines (CAMs) (38) are computers designed to simulate a cellular automaton for study and analysis.

Standard CA are not well suited to the description of systems with constraints or conservation laws. For example, if we want to conserve the number of ON sites, we must establish a rule whereby turning off one site is tied to turning on another site. Margolus dynamics (38) represents a modification of CA developed to describe such systems; in this approach, the rule updates a whole neighborhood rather than a single cell. Then, a conservation law that holds in the neighborhood update (the number of ON sites) also holds globally.

Cellular Automata for Polymer Dynamics

We have developed a CA Margolus dynamics approach for the simulation of polymers (36, 37). In two dimensions, ON cells represent monomers, and a polymer is described by a set of monomers that touch either at corners or on edges of the cells. In a chain polymer (Figure 2), each monomer has two such neighbors except for the ends, which

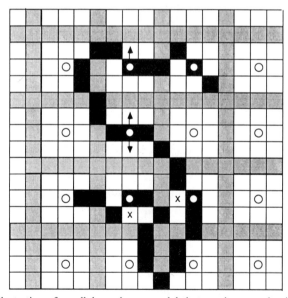

Figure 2 Illustration of a cellular polymer model that can be moved using Margolus cellular automaton dynamics. In this model, monomers are considered attached if they are touching at either faces or corners. Moves can only originate in the squares marked by central circles in the middle of 3 × 3 neighborhoods separated by buffers. Arrows denote allowed moves. An X in the target square marks moves not allowed because of excluded volume.

have only one. We select a sublattice of cells (illustrated by circles in Figure 2) separated by three cells in each direction. If a monomer is located in one of these cells, it can be moved up, down, right, or left as permitted by the constraints of maintaining connectivity and excluded volume. In Figure 2, arrows illustrate permitted movements, whereas Xs indicate movements not allowed by excluded volume. A movement corresponds to an update of the 3×3 plaquette around a selected site; the information for the update is contained in a larger 5×5 region. All 3×3 plaquettes can be updated simultaneously. Finally, the selected sublattice (circles in Figure 2) is shifted before the next set of update steps (preferably randomly to avoid possible correlations in the motion).

In the simulation of long polymers, the high-molecular-weight limit should be realized for moderate numbers of monomers in the model. As for real polymers, the long-length behavior is reached when the details of the local properties become unimportant. Thus we choose the local dynamics to minimize the influence of local constraints on the dynamics. A polymer has two characteristic types of local dynamic behavior: motion perpendicular to the polymer and motion along the polymer contour (which involves local length changes in the long polymer). An effective approach to minimize the influence of local structure is to allow local changes in polymer length. To enable monomers to be more flexible in their motion, we have generalized the CA dynamics just described.

In a generalized formulation of polymer dynamics, we define a region V of cells around each monomer as its bonding neighborhood. A polymer is constructed in which each monomer has its NNCs in the region V about it. The dynamics is defined simply by requiring that the motion of a monomer be allowed only if its movement to a new position (selected at random from a movement region M around it) does not change its NNCs. This restriction preserves both connectivity (preventing loss or change of a neighbor) and excluded volume (preventing the addition of a neighbor). In the original CA dynamics (Figure 2), V was the 3×3 region around the monomer. Using the general formulation, V can be larger, for example, a 5×5 region. NNCs no longer need to be adjacent in space: The bonded neighbors of a monomer are defined solely by being within V. Then monomers can separate by one space and remain NNCs, as in the fluctuating-bond method (6). Thus, local length changes are possible, which improves the simulation of high-molecular-weight polymers. For parallel processing, monomers can be moved independently at a distance from which two monomers can be moved towards each other without one entering the other's bonding neighborhood V.

Two-Space Algorithm

The consideration of more flexible polymer dynamics leads us to a second general class of dynamics enabling a different partitioning of the polymer for simulations. The simplest way to describe this dynamics in two dimensions (2D) is to consider a polymer on two parallel planes (see Figure 3). The monomers of the polymer alternate between the planes so that odd-numbered monomers are on one plane and even-numbered monomers are on the other. The polymer and its dynamics are described as in the preceding paragraph except that the NNCs of a monomer are located in the other plane, and excluded volume with respect to non-NNC monomers is only enforced with respect to monomers in that other plane. The bonding neighborhood (see above) of a monomer in one plane is located entirely in the other plane. This approach allows additional flexibility because neighboring monomers can be on top of each other so that even a 3 × 3 neighborhood dynamics allows local expansion and contraction. More interestingly, this dynamics allows all of the monomers in one plane to be moved at the same time without concern for mutual interference because both connectivity and excluded volume are implemented through interactions with the other plane. Thus, half the monomers can be simultaneously updated. To preserve detailed balance, we must choose at random which of the two planes to update at each step.

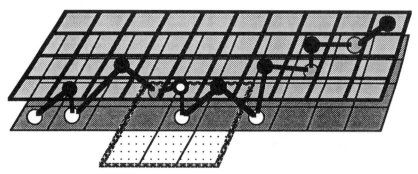

Figure 3 Schematic illustration of a two-plane polymer used in two-plane polymer dynamics described in the text. Monomers on the upper plane are shown as filled circles; monomers on the lower plane are shown as open circles. Monomers are attached only to monomers in the other plane. The bonding neighborhood of each monomer is a 3 × 3 region of cells located in the opposite plane. A lightly shaded region indicates the bonding neighborhood of the black monomer marked with a white dot. Its two neighbors are located in the bonding neighborhood. Bonds are indicated by line segments between monomers.

Because of its inherent fine-grained parallelism, the two-space algorithm lends itself to implementation on various massively parallel architectures. Two distinct paradigms for parallelism in this algorithm correspond to space and polymer assignment. Spatial assignment is particularly efficient for high-density melts, whereas polymer assignment is useful for dilute systems or for problems in which the polymer is embedded in a medium.

We can implement the two-plane algorithm in three dimensions by assuming that the polymer is in a double space. The two-plane or space polymer dynamics can be mapped onto a single-plane or space dynamics with an unusual implementation of excluded volume. This difference in the local interaction does not affect the asymptotic structural and dynamic behavior; therefore, the 3D two-space model is in the same universality class as other abstract polymer models (12). The radius of gyration of polymers of the two-space algorithm is shown in Figure 4, and the relaxation time is shown in Figure 5 as a function of length, $L = N - 1$, where N is the number of monomers.

The two-space algorithm was compared (37) with the bond-fluctuation method (6). The two-space algorithm excels in four ways: step speed (computer time per time step), relaxation rate (short polymer relaxation time), inherent parallelism, and simplicity. The intrinsic speed is quantified by the polymer relaxation times shown in Figure 5. The slopes of the dotted lines follow the scaling result, $\tau \sim L^{5/2}$. The two-space algorithm is intrinsically 2.5 times faster. The overall speed

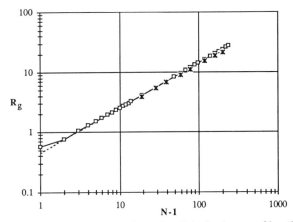

Figure 4   2D simulations of the radius of gyration (R_g) of polymers of length L, testing the two-space algorithm on a conventional computer (*squares*) and on CAM-6, a cellular automata machine (*asterisks*). The straight line shows the exact result for long polymers, $R_g \sim L^{0.75}$.

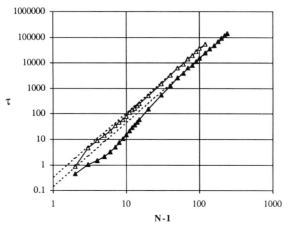

Figure 5   2D simulations of the Rouse relaxation time τ of polymers of length L for both the two-space algorithm (*filled triangles*) and the bond-fluctuation algorithm (*open triangles*). Both curves obey the $t \sim L^{5/2}$ scaling law, but the prefactors differ by a factor of 2.5. Relaxation of the two-space algorithm is 2.5 times faster. Thus the two-space algorithm is fast even for implementations on serial computers.

advantage, which is more than 7, is the product of the step speed and the relaxation rate ratios. Thus the two-space algorithm is fast even on serial machines. Formulation of the two-space algorithm as a CA ensures the parallelizability of the algorithm from the outset. In contrast, great effort is required to vectorize bond-fluctuation simulations (40). The simplicity of the two-space algorithm can be fully appreciated when it is extended to three dimensions. In the bond-fluctuation method, such an extension requires careful consideration of polymer crossing. In contrast, the two-space algorithm automatically does not allow crossing.

IMPLEMENTATION

We can make two-space polymer simulations parallel by means of two general approaches: space partitioning, in which each processor is assigned to several lattice sites, and polymer partitioning, in which a processor is assigned to a set of monomers. Within each of the parallelization schemes, processor assignment may take advantage of the full parallelization (fine graining) or of task aggregation (coarse graining). In fine-grained space partitioning, each processor is assigned to one double-space lattice site. This method is well suited to dense systems in which the fraction of occupied sites is high. Parallel architectures suited for fine-grained simulations require fast intersite communication and large numbers of processors, while the processing elements themselves do not necessarily have to be very powerful. If the number of processors is too small, a compiler may create so-called virtual processors that allow the user to treat each site as assigned to a separate dedicated processor. When coarse graining is used, a whole region of lattice is assigned to a single processor; hence this method requires fewer, more powerful processors.

The fine-grained approach to polymer partitioning would assign each monomer to a separate processor, whereas for coarse graining each processor would be responsible for a group of monomers, whether successive along the chain or gathered together under some other rules. Even though parallel processing is possible using this approach, extensive interprocessor communication of monomer locations is needed either directly or to construct a poster space that represents monomer locations. Thus far, polymer partitioning for the two-space algorithm has not been implemented on parallel architectures. In the following sections, we describe implementation of the two-space algorithm for fine and coarse graining in space partitioning (30).

Fine-Grained Parallelism

Fine-grained implementation assumes each lattice site is assigned a dedicated processor, thus allowing the algorithm to be easily implemented on SIMD machines. The system is updated in three steps: (*a*) The even or odd plane is selected at random; (*b*) for each occupied site, one of four compass directions is chosen at random; (*c*) a Monte Carlo step is performed subject to two constraints in the other plane, connectivity and excluded volume (Figure 6).

For each step, a processor (lattice site) requires communication with six other processors to determine whether the move is allowed. The total number of communications depends on the connectivity of the processors. Assuming single-step communication with any of the eight

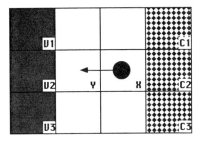

Figure 6   In fine-grained simulation, one processor is assigned to a site. Assume the processor assigned to site X has a monomer in its odd plane that has elected to move westward. In order to make the step, processor X must determine that there is nothing in the even plane of processors C1, C2, and C3 (to preserve connectivity) and nothing in the even plane of processors V1, V2, and V3 (to preserve excluded volume).

nearest neighbors, the total number of communications is nine. If the same operations are applied to all processors, the total number of operations to enable movement of monomers in all four directions would be 36. This number can be decreased by gathering the information in two stages (see Figure 6). First, the data from C1, C2, and C3 are combined into C2, and V1, V2, and V3 data are combined into V2, totaling four communications per plane update. Then, the information may be transferred in three steps to X. The same information may be used either at X for moving west or at Y for moving east. Thus, data is collected in vertical and horizontal strips. The result of vertical (or horizontal) data gathering is shifted left and right (or up and down). The total number of communications per plane update is $4 + (4 \cdot 3) = 16$ (compare with the 36 communications, above). Note that with this optimization, only NEWS (north east west south) communications are needed. Finally, four more communications are needed to move the monomers, for a total of 20. We emphasize the number of communications because the communication-to-computation ratio is generally large and, therefore, minimizing communications is extremely important. In the fine-grained implementation, computation requires only random-number generation, evaluation of a compound logical expression using communicated data, and clearing a variable when a monomer leaves the site.

The fine-grained approach is especially efficient when dense systems are simulated. Figure 7 compares the performance of the algorithm on a parallel computer (MP-1) with that of a serial machine (IBM RS/6000) by showing the time required to execute 10^4 space updates as a function of the number of polymers of length 30. As the density of the system

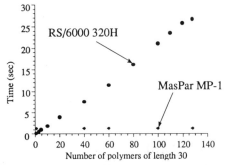

Figure 7 Comparison of serial (IBM RS/6000 320H) and parallel (MP-1) architectures performing increasing density simulations of 10^4 space updates of a 128×64 lattice. List processing was used on the serial computer, fine-grained space processing on the MP-1.

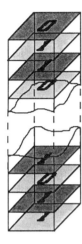

Figure 8   Bit-plane parallelism on SIMD computers makes use of each bit of the longest data type for an independent simulation (see text).

increases, the advantage of a parallel simulation becomes more and more pronounced.

Another kind of parallelization may be implemented when the existence of a monomer on the lattice is represented by only one bit. In this case, a lattice plane of the algorithm can be represented as a single-bit plane. More than one system can be simulated simultaneously (see Figure 8) by programming the algorithm as a number of bitwise operations. This bit-wise parallelism enables an internal form of distributed simulation. For example, if the largest integer type on a computer is 64 bits (as in MP-1), then 64 systems can be updated in a single step. The speedup, however, is much less. We achieved a 12-fold speedup on the MP-1 because of two factors: Communication time for 64-bit numbers is larger than it is for 32-bit numbers, and the generation of a 64-bit random number takes twice as long as for a 32-bit number.

Coarse-Grained Parallelism

In architectures with powerful individual processors, task aggregation by means of coarse graining enhances the performance, which is particularly important for machines with relatively slow communication and networks of workstations. For coarse-grained space partitioning, each processor is assigned to a region of the lattice rather than to a single site. Figure 9 shows the basic structure (for simplicity these regions are assumed to be rectangular). Individual processors are assigned to regions X and N1–N8. Each space is updated in four steps: (*a*) One of two spaces is chosen at random. (*b*) All processors synchronize. (*c*) Each processor updates the piece of lattice to which it is assigned by

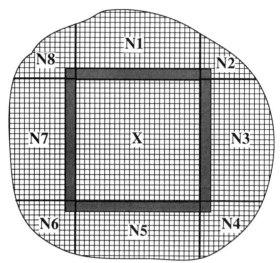

Figure 9 Schematic drawing of the processor assignment for coarse-grained simulations by space partitioning (see text).

either scanning all lattice sites in the region or processing the list of monomers that belong to that region. The former method is efficient for dense systems and is similar in its implementation to fine graining. The latter is better for dilute systems. (*d*) Processor X receives information from its eight neighbors N1–N8 about moves performed on monomers within two lattice units from its boundaries (shaded area in Figure 9). In list processing, monomer lists are updated to keep track of monomers entering and leaving the region.

This implementation of the algorithm in which each processor works independently during the space update is well suited to MIMD architectures. Because communication between processors only describes the boundary regions, the frequency and amount of communication is reduced. Moreover, all of the information transferred between two processors before each space update may be combined into one message. However, adequately fast synchronization is required. Unlike in SIMD, in which each step is synchronous, in MIMD explicit synchronization must be performed between space updates and must be taken into account when performance issues are considered.

EXAMPLES OF APPLICATIONS

2D Melts

A unique feature of polymer solutions in 3D compared to other states of condensed matter is the existence of a semidilute regime of polymer concentration in which chains interpenetrate and become entangled with each other. This condition occurs when the volume fraction c of the space occupied by the polymers exceeds the overlap volume fraction c^*, which can be arbitrarily small for high-molecular-weight polymers ($c^* \propto N/R_0^d \approx 1/N^{d\nu-1}$, where N is the number of chain monomers, R_0 the isolated chain radius, ν the Flory exponent, and d the dimension of space). In 3D, polymers interpenetrate, and intrachain excluded-volume interactions are screened by the presence of the other polymers. It is usually assumed that because of stronger excluded-volume repulsions, interpenetration does not take place in 2D. The chains are believed to become progressively segregated into compact disks as concentration is increased above c^* (7). However, we showed by simulations that the 2D melt behavior cannot be so simply described. Instead there appears to be a behavior intermediate between complete segregation and interpenetration whose precise nature remains undetermined.

As melt density increases, the radius of gyration R_g of a polymer decreases. In 3D, the decrease in size has been described as the result of the screening of excluded volume interactions between monomers of the same polymer. This screening causes the polymer to shrink to a size characteristic of a random walk, which is smaller than the random walk with excluded volume. Thus, for interpenetrating polymers, the structural properties are independent of excluded volume and correspond to isolated polymers without excluded volume. This behavior is quite different from the behavior expected in 2D, since contraction to a collapsed disk implies that the excluded volume plays the essential role in the size of the polymer. However, in 2D two theoretical exponents for the behavior of the radius of gyration coincide. Both a collapsed disk and a random walk have the same scaling $R_g \sim N^\nu$ with $\nu = 1/2$. Hence, more subtle effects may play a role in the polymer structure.

We performed detailed computer simulations of 2D polymer solutions on a MasPar MP-1. The runs were done on a 128×64 periodic lattice. The maximal concentration (area fraction) allowed by the two-space algorithm is $\rho_{max} = 3/4$ because of local excluded volume constraints. Therefore, the concentration in the simulation was defined as $c = \rho/\rho_{max} = (4/3)QN/(128 \times 64)$, where Q is the number of polymers on the lattice. Runs were performed in the concentration range $0.163 < c < 0.651$ and for chain lengths of $50 < N < 333$.

The results of our simulations appear in Figures 10–13, which display various properties of the polymer as a function of polymer length and density. At high densities, the radius of gyration follows a power law scaling behavior as a function of N. The exponent can be seen in Figure 10a, which shows the nearly constant R_g^2/N consistent with either ran-

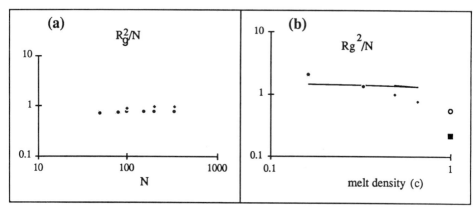

Figure 10 Average radius of gyration of polymers in a 2D melt. The scaling R_g $\propto N^{1/2}$, predicted both for segregated compact disks and random walks, is apparent when R_g^2 is divided by chain length N as shown here. (*a*) The N dependence is very weak (*circles, c* = 0.65; *diamonds, c* = 0.48). (*b*) Concentration dependence (*closed circles, N* = 200; *diamonds, N* = 333, which nearly overlap). Two points are shown at concentration c = 1. The open circle is an extrapolation of the measured values. The solid square shows the value expected for compact disks. The extrapolated value is approximately 2.5 times higher. The nearly horizontal line shows the values expected from a random walk. It varies slightly with density because of changes in the probabilities of locations of nearest neighbors along the chain. The line is approximately 2.5 times higher than the extrapolated value. Other results also indicate that the behavior of polymers at high density lies between compact disks and random walks.

dom walk or disk structure. As a function of density (Figure 10*b*), the polymers decrease rapidly in size.

A first indication that the behavior of the polymers does not reach the expected compact disk limit arises from consideration of the limit of the polymer size at maximal density. In Figure 10*b*, the horizontal axis is the concentration c, so the maximum possible value corresponds to unity. At high densities, the behavior of the polymer radius of gyration R_g^2/N must reach a universal constant. This constant can be calculated for the compact disk as well as for the random walk. For a compact disk: $R_g^2/N = 1/2\pi\rho_{\max} = 0.21$, using $\rho_{\max} = 3/4$. For random walks, the radius of gyration can be written as: $R_g^2/N = \sigma^2 = P_1 + 2P$, where σ is the root mean square distance traveled in an elementary step, P_1 is the probability of moving along a horizontal or vertical lattice direction, and P is the probability of moving along diagonals. These values were calculated during the simulations and are weak functions of the density. At low densities, $\sigma^2 \approx 1.4$, whereas at the highest densities we studied $\sigma^2 \approx 1.3$. Figure 10b shows that the measured extrapolated density is quite distinct from the value expected for either compact disk or random walk. It lies half way (on a logarithmic scale) between the two expected values.

To make further progress, the polymer properties that can clearly distinguish the degree of polymer interpenetration must be measured. For this we use a measure of the polymer structure that considers the area compared to the perimeter of the region of space occupied by the polymer. The shape factor S is defined by the ratio of the perimeter squared of the polymer divided by its area, $S = P^2/A$. This quantity should be much smaller for a system of segregated disks than for interpenetrating polymers. To measure it, we use an algorithm that fills in the area surrounding each of the polymers until all of the spaces in the plane are occupied. Then the perimeters of the spaces associated with each polymer are counted, as is the area. The procedure is discussed in detail elsewhere (34).

The average shape factor shown in Figure 11 is normalized so that the minimum possible value is unity. The important observation is that the shape factor increases as a function of density. From the probability distribution of shape factors shown in Figure 12, we see that both the maximum and the width of the distribution increase with increasing density. The long tail of the shape factor most clearly shows the significant interpenetration of polymers at the highest density, and the in-

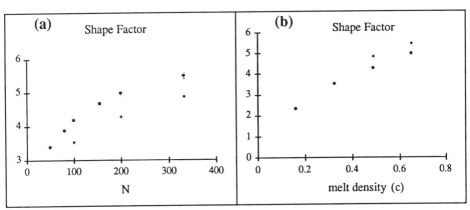

Figure 11   The shape factor S is plotted (linear axes) as a function of the same parameters used in Figure 10. The shape factor measures directly polymer interpenetration. It is expected to be unity for completely segregated disks, and this is the lowest possible value. The increasing shape factor as a function of polymer density indicates that significant interpenetration occurs and increases as a function of density.

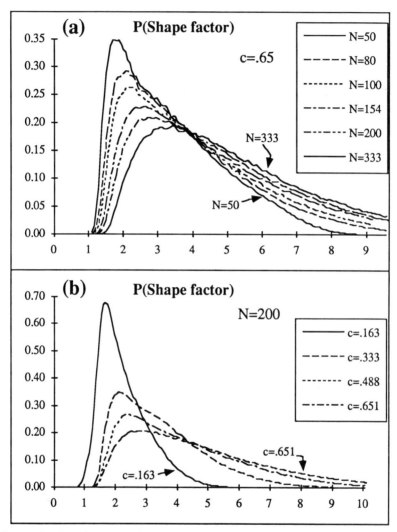

Figure 12 Plots of the probability distribution of shape factors found for 2D melts (*a*) for constant concentration *c* = 0.65 and varying lengths as indicated and (*b*) for constant length *N* = 200 and varying concentrations as indicated. The plots indicate that the tail of the distribution becomes larger for higher densities or longer polymers at the same density. This result reinforces the conclusion that significant interpenetration of polymers occurs.

crease in this tail with density suggests that such interpenetration does not disappear in the high-density limit. For segregated disks or even various segregated shapes of polymers, a sharp cutoff should occur in the shape-factor distribution.

Figure 13 shows a frame taken from a simulation of polymers of length $N = 333$ at the highest density $c = 0.65$. Distinct individual

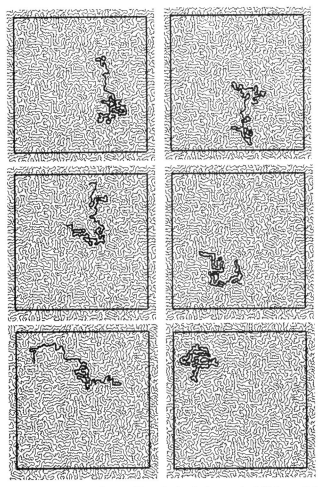

Figure 13   A frame snapshot from a 2D melt simulation on the MP-1 parallel computer showing polymers of length 333 at a density of 0.65. Each picture highlights a distinct polymer. Contrary to expectations that polymers will segregate into compact disks at high densities, the chains adopt both compact and expanded conformations. This observation is consistent with the analysis of averaged quantities described in Figures 10–12.

polymers are highlighted in each of the six illustrations. There is clear indication that the polymers are sometimes compact and sometimes expanded. Time lapse pictures show that polymers change from expanded to contracted.

Gel Electrophoresis

The use of pulsed fields has greatly enhanced the separation of DNA chains of varying length by gel electrophoresis in recent years (32, 33). Of special note is the importance of this technique to the Human Genome Project. Prior to this development, separation was only effective on relatively short chains because longer chains become oriented and exhibit velocities that are independent of chain length. Simulations of the motion of polymers in media have demonstrated the processes of entanglement and disentanglement, which lead to the effectiveness of pulsed fields. Extensive large-scale simulations that can probe the effect of realistic models of the gel medium and investigate the diffusion of polymers under variable fields would enhance our understanding and may potentially influence the design of improved gels and field-induced separation techniques.

The polymer dynamics described above can be modified to give the polymers a net drift velocity. The simplest method is to assign unequal probabilities of performing steps in different directions. Alternatively, one can, at regular intervals, choose a definite direction of movement (say, to the right) for all the monomers. The bias in motion generated by either method corresponds to the effect of an electric field. In physical systems, in the diffusive regime, an electric field causes such a drift on top of the random Brownian motion. This modification of the two-space algorithm can be used to model aspects of pulsed-field gel electrophoresis (PFG). However, the motion of polymers in PFG is believed to depend on tension and sliding (14) that is not contained in monomer diffusion. A more basic modification of the simulations would be necessary to include these features.

Our model simulations in the diffusive regime were performed on CAM-6 using simple gel models. The gel was implemented directly in the initial conditions of the space. The simplest gel model is a fixed set of obstacles. These obstacles can be thought of as polymer strands that intersect the two-dimensional plane. Such immovable obstructions can be made out of monomers arranged in a block, and therefore no further modifications to the dynamic rule are necessary. It turns out that a 2 $\times$ 2 block of even monomers superimposed on a similar block of odd monomers (eight monomers total) forms a tightly bound block that cannot move. Moreover, a one-cell excluded volume surrounds each block, so that no other monomers can enter this 4×4 volume. The 4×4 excluded volume of each block reduces the pore size accordingly. Frames from the simulations and a more detailed discussion are given elsewhere (35).

Polymer Collapse

The flexible polymer coil-to-globule transition is an extensively investigated and fundamental aspect of the properties of polymers in dilute solution. Analytic arguments as well as Monte Carlo simulations have been used to investigate the structure of various model polymers as a function of the effective temperature or relative solvent affinity through the transition (θ-point). The study of model polymers is not relevant to the problem of determining the end structure in biopolymer collapse. However, the relevance of the kinetics of the coil-to-globule transition has increased with the development of the molten globule concept (19). According to the most general form of this idea, the polymer initially collapses into a globule that then reorganizes into a specific structure. It is the initial collapse that may be modeled by the kinetics of the coil-to-globule transition. Despite extensive investigations of the thermodynamics of collapse (8), little is known about the kinetics of this transition. Nucleation may play a role in the kinetics, whereas it plays no role in the thermodynamics.

deGennes has developed a mean field kinetic theory for homopolymer collapse during slight departures from the θ-point (11). He suggests that under these conditions the polymer initially collapses into a sausage shape. Then diffusion thickens the sausage uniformly as the ends contract. As the length N of the polymer increases, the collapse time slows dramatically as N^2. Grosberg et al (20) have extended this model by discussing the influence of topological constraints on the later stages of the collapse. Simulations of the kinetics of the collapse of realistic polymer models have been limited to investigations of very short polymers (27).

As described previously, not only does the two-space algorithm have inherent parallelism, but it performs more efficiently than other algorithms on conventional serial computers. This advantage has led to the investigation of polymer collapse by slightly modifying the existing two-space algorithm. The simulations were performed on a serial computer; however, parallel implementation is also possible.

To model the kinetics of collapse, Ostrovsky & Bar-Yam (29) assumed that monomers that encounter each other can stick together, forming a cluster. Once formed, aggregates are moved as a unit, but their diffusion constant scales by Stokes' law for spherical bodies in

d-dimensions, $D \propto 1/M^{1/d}$. The diffusion constant of the aggregate can be implemented as the probability of an elementary step. Polymer dynamics are simulated by selecting an aggregate (monomers are included as aggregates of mass 1) and by moving the aggregate in one of four compass directions with a probability given by the diffusion constant and only if connectivity constraints allow—the aggregate does not leave any neighbors behind. The excluded volume constraint is eliminated to allow sticking.

For parallel implementation, the difference between the new algorithm and the original one is that monomers are now replaced by aggregates with changing mass. This difference precludes implementation of the parallel version of the algorithm as before, because some mechanism is required to keep track of the masses. To solve this problem, a special feature of many SIMD computers that allows each element of

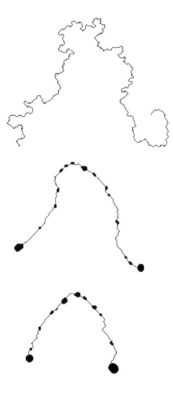

Figure 14 Frame snapshots of the collapse of a single polymer of length $N = 500$ monomers in two dimensions. The plot is constructed by placing dots of area $M^{1/2}$ for an aggregate of mass M. This area does not reflect the excluded volume of the aggregates, which is zero during collapse. Successive snapshots are taken at intervals of approximately 1/4 of the collapse time with the initial configuration shown at the top. The results demonstrate the end-dominated collapse process by which the ends diffuse along the contour of the polymer, thereby accreting small aggregates.

a parallel structure to send a value to another element can be used. When two elements send their values to the same destination, an arithmetic operation can be performed on these values. In the polymer simulation, aggregation occurs when two aggregates move to the same site. Thus, parallelism can be achieved by having each element of the parallel structure send the value of its mass to the destination site. Upon collision, the masses add.

Our simulations (29) to date were performed on a conventional computer. Figure 14 shows frames of the simulations in 2D. These frames illustrate the central result—the dominance of aggregation at the polymer ends is the mechanism of collapse. Some small aggregates forming along the contour of the polymer are then accreted by the ends. This observation has been confirmed for various abstract polymer models in both 2D and 3D. More realistic models with excluded volume and reversible aggregation during collapse display the same behavior. The dominance of end motion in collapse is reasonable because the aggregates along the contour are constrained. They cannot readily move to aggregate with their neighbors because of the bonds to the neighbor on the other side. End aggregates do not suffer from this constraint.

CONCLUSIONS

The use of large-scale parallelism for simulations presents many opportunities for fundamental advances in our understanding of the microscopic dynamics of polymers in both artificial and biological systems. However, with few exceptions, applications have not yet realized this promise. Simulations of polymers scale as a high power of the system size and the use of parallel machines does not change this. Nevertheless, various problems have been just beyond the reach of serial machines and can be solved by parallel architectures. This past year has marked the first time that the speed of parallel machines has surpassed that of the fastest serial machines. While such benchmarks are only suggestive, the systematic shift of high-end–system manufacturers, such as IBM and CRAY, to the production of parallel machines indicates that more and more state-of-the-art simulations will be performed on parallel architectures or networks of workstations.

We have described several systematic methodologies for implementing existing or novel polymer simulation algorithms on parallel architectures. Even the seemingly special-purpose two-space algorithm provides opportunities for generalization. Also, an efficient parallel algorithm can give rise to efficient implementation on serial machines.

More generally, domain decomposition can be an effective simulation strategy for a variety of spatially distributed systems.

Literature Cited

1. Binder K. 1987. *Applications of Monte-Carlo Methods in Statistical Physics*. Berlin: Springer-Verlag. 2nd ed.
2. Binder K. 1991. Simulation of dense polymer systems in two and three dimensions. *Int. J. Mod. Phys. C. Phys. Comput.* 2:263–66
3. Boghosian BM. 1990. Computational physics on the Connection Machine. *Comput. Phys.* 4:14
4. Brooks CL III, Young WS, Tobias DJ. 1991. Molecular simulations on supercomputers. *Int. J. Supercomput. Appl.* 5:98–112
5. Camp WJ, Plimpton SL. 1993. MIMD massively parallel methods for engineering and science problems. *Proc. 1993 Simulation Multiconf. High Performance Computing*, pp. 127–42. San Diego: SCS
6. Carmesin I, Kremer K. 1988. The bond fluctuation method: a new effective algorithm for the dynamics of polymers in all spatial dimensions. *Macromolecules* 21:2819–23
7. Carmesin I, Kremer K. 1990. Static and dynamic properties of two-dimensional polymer melts. *J. Phys. France* 51:915–32
8. Chan HS, Dill KA. 1991. Polymer principles in protein structure and stability. *Annu. Rev. Biophys. Biophys. Chem.* 20:447–90
9. Cohen DM. 1989. Suitability of simulation of a population of chemical polymers on the massively parallel processor. *Proc. Symp. Frontiers of Massively Parallel Computation, 2nd,* pp. 241–47 Washington, DC: IEEE Comput. Sci.
10. deGennes PG. 1979. *Scaling Concepts in Polymer Physics*. Ithaca: Cornell Univ. Press
11. deGennes PG. 1985. Kinetic collapse for a flexible coil. *J. Phys. Lett.* 46: L639–42
12. des Cloizeaux J, Jannink G. 1987. *Le Polymers en Solution: Leur Modelisation et Leur Structure*. Paris: Ed. Phys.
13. Doi M, Edwards SF. 1986. *Theory of Polymer Dynamics*. Oxford: Oxford Sci.
14. Duke TAJ, Viovy JL. 1992. Simulation of megabase DNA undergoing gel electrophoresis. *Phys. Rev. Lett.* 68: 542–45
15. Esselink K, Hilbers PAJ. 1992. Parallel molecular dynamics on a torus network. *Proc. Scalable High Performance Computing Conf.*, pp. 106–22. Los Alamitos: IEEE Comput. Sci.
16. Farmer D, Toffoli T, Wolfram S. 1984. *Cellular Automata*. Amsterdam: North-Holland
17. Flynn MJ. 1972. Some computer organizations and their effectiveness. *IEEE Trans. Comput.* C-21:948–60
18. Fox GC, Otto SW. 1984. Algorithms for concurrent processors. *Phys. Today* 37(May):50–59
19. Freire E. 1995. Thermodynamics of partly folded intermediates in proteins. *Annu. Rev. Biophys. Biomol. Struct.* 24:141–65
20. Grosberg AY, Nechaev SK, Shakhnovich EI. 1988. The role of topological constraints in the kinetics of collapse of macromolecules. *J. Phys. France* 49:2095–2100
21. Kumar V, Grama A, Gupta A, Karypis G. 1994. *Introduction to Parallel Computing. Design and Analysis of Algorithms*. Menlo Park, CA: Benjamin-Cummings
22. Lin SL, Mellor-Crummey J, Pettitt BM, Phillips GN Jr. 1992. Molecular dynamics on a distributed-memory processor. *J. Comput. Chem.* 13: 1022–35
23. Lomdahl PS, Tamayo P, Gronbech-Jensen N, Beazley DM. 1993. 50 Gflops molecular dynamics on the Connection Machine 5. *Proc. Supercomputing '93 Conf.*, pp. 520–27. Los Alamitos: IEEE Comput. Sci.
24. Margolus N, Toffoli T. 1990. Cellular Automata Machines. In *Lattice Gas Methods of Partial Differential Equations*, ed. GD Doolen, U Frisch, B

Hasslacher, S Orszag, S Wolfram., pp. 219–48. Reading, PA: Addison-Wesley

25. McCammon JA, Harvey SC. 1987. *Dynamics of Proteins and Nucleic Acids.* Cambridge: Cambridge Univ. Press

26. Melcuk AI, Giles RC, Golud H. 1991. Molecular dynamics simulation of liquids on the Connection Machine. *Comput. Phys.* May/June:311

27. Miller R, Danko CA, Fasolka MJ, Balazs AC, Chan HS, Dill KA. 1992. Folding kinetics of proteins and copolymers. *J. Chem. Phys.* 96:768–80

28. Nakanishi H, Rego V, Sunderam S. 1992. Superconcurrent simulation of polymer chains on heterogenious networks. *Proc. Supercomputing '92,* pp. 561–69. Los Alamitos: IEEE Comput. Sci.

29. Ostrovsky B, Bar-Yam Y. 1994. Irreversible polymer collapse in 2 and 3 dimensions. *Europhys. Lett.* 25: 409–14

30. Ostrovsky B, Smith MA, Biafore M, Bar-Yam Y, Rabin Y, et al. 1993. Massively parallel architectures and polymer simulation. *Proc. SIAM Conf. Parallel Processing for Scientific Computing, 6th,* p. 193. Philadelphia: SIAM

31. Paul W, Binder K, Heermann DW, Kremer K. 1991. Crossover scaling in semidilute polymer solutions: a Monte-Carlo test. *J. Phys. II* 1:37–60

32. Schwartz DC, Cantor CR. 1984. Sepa-

ration of yeast chromosome-sized DNA's by pulsed field gradient gel electrophoresis. *Cell* 37:67–75

33. Smith CL. 1991. Separation and analysis of DNA by electrophoresis. *Curr. Opin. Biotechnol.* 2:86–91

34. Smith MA. 1994. *Cellular automata methods in mathematical physics.* PhD thesis. MIT, Cambridge, MA

35. Smith MA, Bar-Yam Y. 1993. Cellular automaton simulation of pulsed field gel electrophoresis. *Electrophoresis* 14:337–43

36. Smith MA, Bar-Yam Y, Rabin Y, Bennett CH, Margolus N, Toffoli T. 1992. Cellular automata simulation of polymers. *MRS Symp. Proc.* 248:483–88

37. Smith MA, Bar-Yam Y, Rabin Y, Ostrovsky B, Bennett CH, et al. 1992. Parallel processing simulation of polymers. *J. Comp. Polymer Sci.* 2:165–71

38. Toffoli T, Margolus N. 1987. *Cellular Automata Machines: A New Environment for Modeling.* Cambridge: MIT Press

39. Verlet V. 1967. Computer "experiments" on classical fluids. I. Thermodynamical properties of Lennard-Jones molecules. *Phys. Rev.* 159:98

40. Wittmann HP, Kremer K. 1990. Vectorized version of the bond fluctuation method for lattice polymers. *Comput. Phys. Commun.* 61:309–30

41. Wolfram S. 1986. *Theory and Applications of Cellular Automata.* Singapore: World Sci.

Annu. Rev. Biophys. Biomol. Struct. 1995. 24:269–91

THE CYSTINE-KNOT GROWTH-FACTOR SUPERFAMILY[1]

Peter D. Sun

National Institute of Allergy and Infectious Diseases, National Institutes of Health, Bethesda, Maryland 20892

David R. Davies

National Institute of Diabetes, Digestive and Kidney Diseases, National Institutes of Health, Bethesda, Maryland 20892

KEY WORDS: X-ray structure; common cytokine fold; comparison of TGF-β, PDGF, NGF, and hCG; disulfide motif

CONTENTS

ABSTRACT

Four recent crystal structures of growth factors—nerve growth factor, transforming growth factor-β, platelet-derived growth factor, and human chorionic gonadotropin—from four separate superfamilies revealed that these proteins are structurally related and share a common overall topology. These proteins have very little sequence homology, but they all have an unusual arrangement of six cysteines linked to form a "cystine-knot" conformation. The active forms of these proteins are dimers, either homo- or heterodimers. Despite the overall topological similarity between the monomers, the interfaces used to form the dimer are in each case quite different. Because the surfaces used for dimer formation are mostly hydrophobic, the uniqueness of each dimer accounts for the lack of sequence homology and raises questions about the effectiveness of reverse sequence fitting in this kind of structure as a predictor of structural homology.

INTRODUCTION

Growth factors compose a group of diverse protein molecules that regulate cell growth, differentiation, and cell-cell communications. Although the molecular mechanisms that govern growth factor–mediated processes remain largely unknown, growth factors can be generally classified into several superfamilies based on their structural and functional similarities. Examples of these superfamilies include: (a) the hematopoietic growth factors, such as growth hormone, IL-2, IL-4, G-CSF, and CNTF, which all possess a four-helix-bundle structural motif (10, 26, 94); (b) the β-trefoil family members, such as IL-1β, IL-1α, FGF, and keratinocyte growth factor, which all share a common β-trefoil fold (28, 91, 99); (c) the EGF-like growth factors such as EGF and TGF-α, which all have an immunoglobulin-like domain in their structure (66).

The number of new growth factor structures available is increasing, and a new growth-factor fold, the so-called cystine-knot growth-factor fold, has unexpectedly emerged. NGF, TGF-β, PDGF, and glycoprotein hormones serve as prototypes of this superfamily (22, 60, 67, 68, 86). Unlike other growth factor families, the protomer structures of all members of this fold have a cystine-knot motif located in topologically equivalent positions, but otherwise, they share no significant sequence homology. As a result, it is often difficult to recognize a member of this superfamily before its three-dimensional (3D) structure is known. For the same reason, this is the only superfamily in which the knowledge of a 3D structure becomes the most definite and sometimes the only way to define a member. Although they bind to quite different receptor families, the remarkable structural similarity between these growth factors suggests that they have probably evolved from a common ancestor. Another unique feature of this superfamily is that they all function in a dimeric form, and sometimes both hetero- and homodimers can be formed.

In this review, we summarize the structural and functional properties of this superfamily and compare the crystal structures of four of the family's prototypes, TGF-β, NGF, PDGF, and hCG.

BIOLOGICAL FUNCTIONS

TGF-β Family

The TGF-β family consists of a set of growth factors that share at least 25% sequence identity in their mature amino acid sequence. Members in this gene family include the transforming growth factors, TGF-β1–5 (4, 19, 27, 40, 41, 45, 87); inhibins and activins (inhibin A, inhibin B, activin A, and activin AB) (30, 53, 56, 89); bone morphogenic proteins, BMP-2–7 (17, 71, 95); the decapentaplegic gene complex, DPP-C (72); Vgl (93); vgr-1 (55); Müllerian inhibiting substance, MIS (16); a growth-differentiation factor, GDF-1 (49); and dorsalin-1, dsl-1 (8). Most of these factors exist as either homo- or heterodimers (Table 1).

The best-studied factors of this gene family are the transforming growth factors. They form homodimeric proteins with a molecular weight of 25,000. Five isoforms of TGF-βs have been isolated to date from different species, and the mature peptide sequences of these proteins share 64–82% homology. TGF-β1–3 are found in mammalian cells, TGF-β3 and 4 in chicken embryos, and TGF-β5 in *Xenopus laevis* (57, 85). They can be found in virtually any cell type and throughout the developmental stages of any given species.

The diverse biological activities of TGF-β in cell growth and regulation can be classified as: (*a*) effects on the cell cycle, (*b*) effects on the extracellular matrix, and (*c*) effects on other peptide growth factors. Many of the cell growth–inhibitory effects of TGF-β directly result from its ability to interrupt the cell cycle during late G_1 phase, preventing induction of DNA synthesis and progression into S phase. For example, TGF-β1 exhibits potent growth- and differentiation-inhibitory effects in many endothelial and epithelial cells and is a negative regulator during myogenesis (88), osteogenesis (18), and embryogenesis (35). In mesenchymal cells, TGF-β increases cell accumulation and their

Table 1 Members of the cystine knot growth factor superfamily

Family	Active form	Family	Active form
TGF-β		PDGF	
TGF-β1–5	Homodimer	PDGF-AA	Homodimer
Inhibin A	α,βA dimer	PDGF-AB	Heterodimer
Inhibin B	α,βB dimer	PDGF-BB	Homodimer
Activin A	βA homodimer	v-sis	Homodimer
Activn AB	βA,βB dimer	VEGF	Homodimer
BMP-2,3,4,5,6,7	Homo- or heterodimer		
DPP-C		Glycoprotein hormone	
Vg1		hCG	α,β dimer
vgr-1		LH	α,β dimer
GDF-1		FSH	α,β dimer
dsl-1		TSH	α,β dimer
MIS	Homodimer		
Neurotrophin			
NGF	Homodimer		
BDNF	Homodimer		
NT-3,4	Homodimer		

response to extracellular-matrix components, including type I, III, IV, and V collagen; tenascin; and elastin (54, 73, 90). TGF-β can also promote or inhibit cell growth by modulating the secretion of other growth factors. For example, it stimulates the growth of fibroblasts by increasing the level of PDGF secretion (78).

Three types of TGF-β receptors, I, II, and III, are expressed on the cell surface in order to mediate the growth-factor signal (100–103). Types I and II are members of the Ser/Thr kinase receptor family, whereas the type III receptor, a proteoglycan whose function is to present TGF-βs to the type I and II receptors, does not have a functional cytoplasmic domain.

Neurotrophic Factors

The neurotrophins represent a family of growth factors that control the development and survival of certain neurons in both the peripheral (PNS) and the central nervous systems (CNS). The members of this family include nerve growth factor (NGF) (51), brain-derived neurotrophic factor (BDNF) (32, 50), neurotrophin-3 (NT-3), neurotrophin-4 (NT-4), and neurotrophin-5 (NT-5) (6, 13, 33). Among them, NGF is the prototypical neurotrophin that defines the properties and functions of this class of growth factors.

NGF is synthesized and released from target tissues in both the PNS and CNS. In the PNS, the target tissues are typically nonneuronal cells while in the CNS the targets are neurons such as the sympathetic, sensory, and cholinergic basal forebrain neurons (52). The role of NGF as a survival reagent during nerve development comes mainly from its ability to rescue some neurons from naturally occurring cell death, thus preventing nerve degeneration (7). In adult tissues, the function of NGF is less well understood.

There are two different classes of neurotrophin receptors, a low-affinity receptor, p75^{NGFR}, which serves as a common receptor for all the known neurotrophins, and a high affinity receptor, p140^{trk}, which belongs to the trk family of tyrosine kinase receptors and is different for each neurotrophic factor (43, 62).

PDGF Family

Platelet-derived growth factor (PDGF) is a major mitogenic factor for cells of mesenchymal origin. It promotes the growth and differentiation of fibroblasts and smooth muscle cells during development and embryo-genesis. It also functions as a chemotactic reagent for inflammatory cells during wound healing (36). Two forms of the PDGF gene are expressed, PDGF-A and PDGF-B, resulting in three isoforms of the dimeric growth factor, PDGF-AA, PDGF-AB, and PDGF-BB. All three have similar biological functions as cell mitogens, but they differ in the activation of the receptor isoforms. Like the growth factor itself, the gene for the receptor also takes two forms, PDGF-α and -β receptors (58, 82), which results in three functional dimeric receptor isoforms, ⟨aa⟩, ⟨ab⟩, and ⟨bb⟩. Both forms of the receptor have an intracellular tyrosine kinase domain, but they respond differently to the different isoforms of PDGF (12, 37): PDGF-AA only complexes with the ⟨aa⟩ receptor; PDGF-AB complexes with the ⟨aa⟩ or ⟨ab⟩ receptor; and PDGF-BB can complex with all three receptor isoforms, ⟨aa⟩, ⟨ab⟩, and ⟨bb⟩ (34, 84).

Other members the PDGF family include the vascular endothelial growth factor (VEGF) and the v-sis oncogene product of p28$^{v\text{-}sis}$, a transforming protein of simian sarcoma virus (SSV). The p28$^{v\text{-}sis}$ sequence is 90% homologous to that of PDGF-B and 50% homologous to PDGF-A (11, 77). It binds to and activates both the α and β PDGF receptors (48).

Glycoprotein Hormones

Glycoprotein hormones refer to a set of four related glycopeptides: human chorionic gonadotropin (hCG), follicle-stimulating hormone

(FSH), luteinizing hormone (LH), and thyroid-stimulating hormone (TSH). They are dimers of two noncovalently linked α- and β-subunits (69, 75). All four glycoprotein hormones share a common α-subunit, whereas each has its unique β-subunit that determines its specific hormone activity (14, 29). hCG is thought to maintain the early stages of pregnancy, acting to prolong corpus luteum function. In mammalian systems, LH and hCG bind to the same receptor and possess similar biological functions, whereas FSH and TSH bind to structurally similar but distinct receptors. Interestingly, the level of FSH in pituitary cells and the level of hCG in human placenta cells are modulated by the inhibins and activins, members of the TGF-β family (30, 56).

THREE-DIMENSIONAL STRUCTURE DETERMINATIONS

Human Transforming Growth Factor $\beta 2$ (TGF-$\beta 2$)

Daopin et al (25) and Schlunegger & Grütter (80) simultaneously reported the crystal structure of TGF-$\beta 2$ at 2.1 and 2.2 Å resolution, respectively. Both groups crystallized the mature form of the protein, 112 amino acids, in a space group of $P3_2 21$ with the cell dimensions $a = b = 60.6$ and $c = 75.3$ Å. Later, structural comparison showed that the two structures are essentially identical (23). The structure from Davies' group was then refined to 1.8-Å resolution (24) and that from Grütter's group was refined to 1.95-Å resolution (81). At about the same time, an NMR characterization of the secondary structure of TGF-$\beta 1$ was also reported, and the predicted tertiary NOEs were in agreement with the crystal structure obtained from Davies' group (2, 3).

The structure shows TGF-$\beta 2$ as a disulfide-linked dimer in which the overall dimensions of each monomer are $60 \times 20 \times 15$ Å (Figure 1a). The secondary structure of the protomer consists mainly of four irregular antiparallel β-strands (labeled as 1, 2, 3, and 4 in Figure 1a) and an 11-residue α-helix between the second and the third strand. Of the nine cystines in each monomer, eight of them form four intrachain disulfides, and one, cystine 77, forms an interchain disulfide with the same cystine of another monomer. The four intrachain disulfide bonds are between Cys7 and Cys16, Cys15 and Cys78, Cys44 and Cys109, and Cys48 and

---

Figure 1 Ribbon diagrams of the 3D structures. The two monomers are shaded differently and the knotted disulfides are shown in solid bonds. (*A*) TGF-$\beta 2$; (*B*) β-NGF; (*C*) PDGF-BB; (*D*) hCG-α (*shaded subunit*) and hCG-β. Molscript was used to prepare the figure (46).

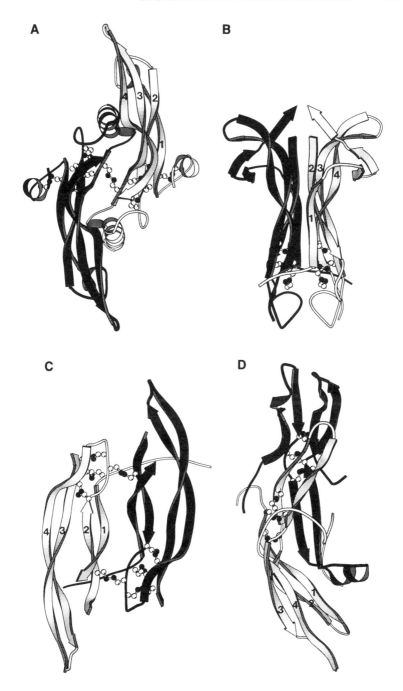

Table 2 List of disulfide bonds

Cystine knot	β-NGF	TGF-β2	PDGF-BB	hCG-α	hCG-β
I–IV	15–80	15–78	16–60	10–60	9–57
II–V	58–108	44–109	49–97	28–82	34–88
III–VI	68–110	48–111	53–99	32–84	38–90
Interchain	None	77–77	43–52		
			52–43		
Other		7–16		7–31	23–72
				59–87	26–110
					93–100

Cys111. The latter three, Cys15-Cys78, Cys44-Cys109, and Cys48-Cys111, define a topological cystine knot in which the Cys15-Cys78 disulfide passes through a ring bounded by the Cys44-Cys109 and Cys48-Cys111 disulfides together with the connecting polypeptide backbone, residues 44–48 and 109–111 (Table 2).

The two monomers form a head-to-tail dimer with the residues on the long helix (residues 58–68) packed against the residues near the end of the β-sheets. The molecular interface between the dimer of TGF-β2 is largely hydrophobic, burying a total area of 2600 Å^2.

Murine Nerve Growth Factor (β-NGF)

McDonald et al (59) and Holland et al (39) determined the crystal structure of β-NGF, the first structure found of the cystine-knot family of growth factors. The crystals from McDonald et al belonged to the space group P6$_5$22 and had the unit cell parameters $a = b = 56.48$ Å and $c = 182.39$ Å and one monomer in each asymmetric unit (59). The structure was determined at 2.3-Å resolution (Figure 1b). The protomer structure consists mainly of four irregular antiparallel β-strands (labeled as 1, 2, 3, and 4 in Figure 1b) with an insertion of two shorter strands between the first and the second strand. The overall dimension of the molecule is roughly 60 × 25 × 15 Å. Six cystines in each monomer form the knotted disulfide bonds (Cys15-Cys80, Cys58-Cys108, and Cys68-Cys110) clustered at the one end of all the β-strands. The dimer is formed between the two flat faces of the four-stranded β-sheets, burying a total of 2300 Å^2 of surface area. The interface again is characterized as largely hydrophobic. In the work of Holland et al, five crystallographically unique monomers were present and solved in two different space groups (39). Although the core of the molecule (the disulfide knot and the four β-strands) was nearly identical in all five copies,

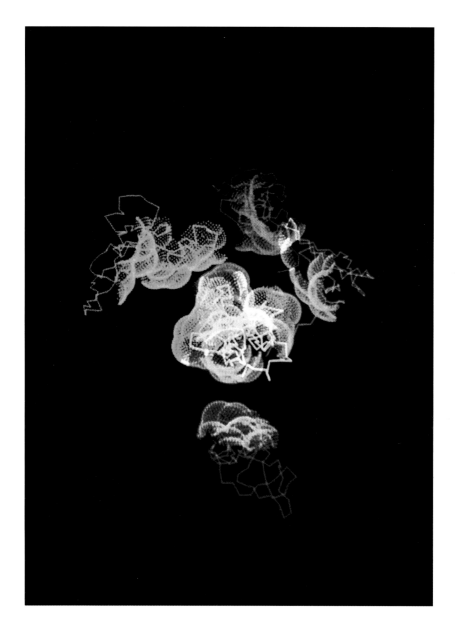

Figure 5 The dimerization modes of the four growth factors. Shown in the center is a generic monomer and surrounding it are the monomers of the TGF-β2 (*green*), β-NGF (*purple*), PDGF-BB (*blue*), and hCG-α (*orange*), which are in their dimerization orientations with respect to the monomer at the center. The dotted surfaces indicate the dimer contact surfaces color coded for each dimer pair. The dimer interface of hCG partially overlaps with that of TGF-β2 and PDGF-BB.

significant flexibility was observed in the loop regions between the four β-strands.

Human Platelet-Derived Growth Factor BB (PDGF-BB)

Oefner et al (70) determined the crystal structure of the mature homodimeric isoform of human platelet-derived growth factor, PDGF-BB, at 3.0-Å resolution. The crystals belong to space group C2 with unit cell dimensions $a = 147.3$ Å, $b = 31.8$ Å, $c = 90.1$ Å, and $\beta = 98.7°$. The protomer has 109 amino acids and consists of four irregular antiparallel β-strands and a 17-residue N-terminal tail (Figure 1c). Of the eight disulfide-bonded cysteines, six, Cys16-Cys60, Cys49-Cys97, and Cys53-Cys99, form the knotted arrangement and two, Cys43-Cys52, form two interchain disulfide bonds (Table 2). The edges of the four-stranded β-sheet form the dimer, which results in the majority of inter-subunit contacts being between the first two strands of the β-sheet and with the N-terminal tail. The total surface area buried is estimated to be 2200 Å^2, and most of the buried residues are hydrophobic in nature.

Human Chorionic Gonadotropin (hCG)

The most recent addition to the cystine-knot superfamily structures is the determination of the crystal structure of human chorionic gonadotropin by Lapthorn et al (47) and Wu et al (97). Unlike NGF, TGF-β, and PDGF-BB, which are homodimers, hCG is a heterodimer (Figure 1d). The α-subunit contains five disulfide bonds, three of which, Cys10-Cys60, Cys28-Cys82, and Cys32-Cys84, adopt the knotted configuration (Table 2). Except for a short three-turn α-helix located between residues 40 and 47, most of the secondary structures in the α-subunit are irregular β-strands and β-hairpin loops. The β-subunit contains six disulfide bonds; among them, Cys9-Cys57, Cys34-Cys88, and Cys38-Cys90 form the topological cystine knot.

Two unique features have been observed in the dimer formation between the α- and β-subunits. First, the segments of well-defined β-sheet structure near the cystine knot in each subunit are brought together upon dimerization to form a short seven-stranded β-barrel, resulting in an interface that has both hydrophobic and hydrogen-bonding interactions. Second, the so-called seat-belt loop, from Cys90 to Cys110 of the β-subunit, is wrapped around the midsection of the α-subunit in the heterodimer to increase the contact surface. The dimerization buries a total of 4525 Å^2 of surface area, according to Lapthorn et al (47), and 3860 Å^2, according to Wu et al (97).

STRUCTURE COMPARISONS

Comparison of the Protomer Structures

Because of the lack of sequence homology, the structural similarity among the four growth factors was not predicted prior to the solution of the 3D structures. It is now clear that the protomer structures of all four families of growth factors share a common fold.

NONGLOBULAR SHAPE OF THE PROTOMER STRUCTURES   Each protomer assumes a curled sheet-like nonglobular structure with overall dimensions of approximately $60 \times 20 \times 15$ Å. As a result, they lack a well-defined hydrophobic core. The face of the sheet is formed by four irregular antiparallel β-strands, and near one end of the strands, the most rigid and least exposed part of the molecule, lies a cluster of disulfide bonds in the topological knotted configuration shown in Figure 2. Comparison of the cystines of the knot, for example TGF-β2 and NGF (22), clearly shows that not only are the connectivities of these half cystines identical among all four structures, but their positions are also readily superimposable, resulting in a root-mean-square (rms) agreement of 0.5–1.5 Å between different growth factors for all the atoms in the six half cystines (Table 3, upper diagonal).

COMMON MOTIFS IN SEQUENCE   As also noted by McDonald & Hendrickson (60) and Murry-Rust et al (67), some common patterns emerge from the sequence alignment provided by the structural superpositions: (a) The spacing of the last two cystines is always CXC—with only one residue between CysV and CysVI. (b) The size of the cystine ring depends on the spacing between CysII and CysIII, which varies from 3 to 15. Among the five peptide chains in the structures of TGF-β2,

Table 3 rms agreement among the cystines and the sequence identity between the growth factors[a]

	TGF-β2	PDGF-BB	β-NGF	hCG-α	hCG-β
TGF-β2		0.81	1.54	0.67	0.85
PDGF-BB	12		1.36	0.56	0.73
β-NGF	10	10		1.43	1.31
hCG-α	13	17	9		0.57
hCG-β	13	12	9	9	

[a] The upper diagonal shows the rms agreement in Ångstroms, calculated using all the atoms of the six knotted half-cystine residues, and the lower diagonal shows the number of identical residues based on the 3D structural alignment. All structural alignments are done with the program ALIGN (79).

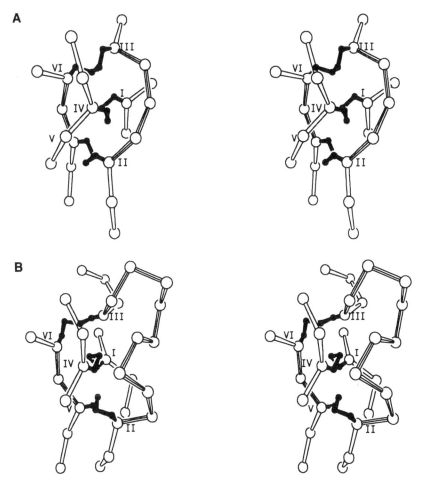

Figure 2   Stereo representation of the cystine knot. The six cystines participating in the three disulfide bonds are sequentially named CysI through CysVI. The disulfide pairings are between CysI and CysIV, CysII and CysV, and CysIII and VI. The topological knot is formed by passing the I-IV disulfide bond through the ring bounded by the II-V and III-VI disulfides and the connecting peptide backbones (only the C_α atoms are shown) in between (*shaded bonds*). (*A*) The eight-membered ring cystine knot, as observed in the structures of TGF-β2, PDGF, and hCG. (*B*) The 14-membered ring observed in the NGF cystine knot. ORTEP was used to prepare the figure (42). Although the C_αs of the cysteines of the proteins in the ring (*A*) superimpose on those in NGF (*B*), the conformations of their three disulfide bridges have the opposite chirality (67).

PDGF-BB, β-NGF, and hCG, four have an 8-membered cystine ring and one, β-NGF, has a 14-membered cystine ring (Figure 2*b*). Where only three residues lie between CysII and CysIII, as is the case for all members of the TGF-β and PDGF families and glycoprotein hormones, the middle residue between the two cystines is always a Gly, i.e. a CXGXC pattern. The conservation of this Gly residue has a simple structural explanation, namely that any other amino acid in this position would imply severe steric hindrance with the backbone of CysI, whose position is fixed by means of disulfide bonding with CysIV. The requirement of a Gly residue is relaxed when the cystine ring becomes larger, as in the case of the NGF family. Furthermore, the rms differences among all the half cystines appear to correlate well with the size of the cystine-knot ring, as shown in Table 3. That is, the rms differences among TGF-β2, PDGF-BB, hCG-α, and hCG-β, which all have an eight-membered ring, and the CXGXC pattern are less than the rms differences between them and NGF, which has a 14-membered ring.

SIMILARITY IN β-STRANDS   Apart from the cystine residues, the different families show little sequence similarity. Among TGF-β2, NGF, PDGF, and hCG, the sequence identities are well below 20% (see Table 3, lower diagonal). Nevertheless, the backbone conformations of these growth factors are remarkably similar, especially in the regions near the disulfide knot (Table 4). The results of Table 4, in which the backbone α-carbons have been superimposed, show that a large fraction of the C_α atoms can be paired to within 3.0 Å in most of the comparisons. Figure 3 illustrates the part of the backbone structure that can be superimposed among different growth factors, including a conserved twist in the middle of the fourth strand.

The conservation of the cystine-knot motif among these growth factors clearly indicates the importance of the disulfide bridges. They provide much of the fold's framework. Mutational analysis of TGF-β1 and PDGF (15, 31), in which the cystine residues are sequentially mutated throughout the sequence, showed loss of biological activity of the growth factor upon mutation of any of the six cysteine residues. In contrast, the cysteines that form intersubunit disulfide bonds are in

Table 4 Structure superposition among the alpha carbons[a]

	TGF-β2	PDGF-BB	β-NGF	hCG-α	hCG-β
TGF-β2		3.2	3.16	2.0	2.6
PDGF-BB	72		3.51	1.98	1.40
β-NGF	73	59		3.57	3.70
hCG-α	64	56	45		2.35
hCG-β	89	64	42	68	

[a] The upper diagonal shows the rms agreement in Ångstroms, and the lower diagonal shows the number of alpha-carbon pairs used in the alignments.

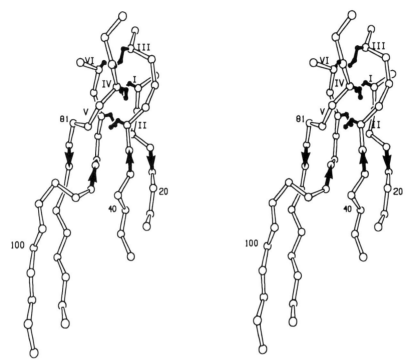

Figure 3 An α-carbon representation of the structurally conserved regions among TGF-β2, NGF, PDGF, and hCG. It includes the central cystine knot (*solid bonds*) and a four-stranded irregular antiparallel β-sheet (*open bonds*). A twist between the third and fourth strand is also observed in all four growth-factor structures. Arrows indicate the direction of the strands. ORTEP was used to prepare the figure.

some cases dispensable, e.g. the Cys43-Cys52 intersubunit disulfide bond of PDGF (44).

Apart from the disulfide knot and the conserved region of the four β-strands, the four growth factors share no structural resemblance. The N-terminal tail region and the regions between the conserved strands differ greatly. For example, in the region between the second and third conserved β-strands (or between CysIII and CysIV), all four monomers differ both in size and in conformation. PDGF-BB has the shortest connection in this region, only a six-residue β-hairpin loop. NGF has a longer and more complicated loop, an 11-residue loop, in between CysIII and CysIV. This region in both TGF-β2 and hCG has regular secondary structures. In TGF-β2, they are mostly helical, whereas both the hCG-α and hCG-β-subunits have a pair of long antiparallel β-strands. Sequence analysis reveals that these regions are also less conserved within each individual family and thus may adopt different conformations even among the members of the same growth-factor family (24).

OTHER KNOTTED DISULFIDE STRUCTURES   Besides the knotted disulfide structure assumed in these growth factors, other protein structures also have knotted disulfide arrangements. Examples are the potato carboxypeptidase A inhibitor (76), the scorpion neurotoxin, and the trypsin inhibitor EETI II (1, 20), which all have three knotted disulfides with the same pairing as the disulfides observed in the growth-factor structures, namely the I-IV, II-V, and III-VI cystine bondings. However, each forms its own unique 3D knot. Topologically, in all the growth-factor situations, the disulfide I-IV threads through a ring formed by II-V and III-VI. This threading disulfide is III-VI in the potato carboxypeptidase A inhibitor and the trypsin inhibitor EETI II structures, and II-V in the scorpion neurotoxin structure.

Comparison of the Dimer Structures

When the structures of NGF and TGF-β2 were published, a comparison revealed two interesting features (22). First, their protomer structures exhibit striking similarity, despite the lack of any sequence homology. Second, in contrast, their modes of dimer association differ profoundly. Since the publication of these reports, the structures of PDGF-BB and hCG have been added to the fold family, and each of these also has unique dimerization modes.

DIMER INTERFACE IS EXTENSIVE AND HYDROPHOBIC   All members of the TGF-β, NGF, PDGF, and glycoprotein hormone families of growth factors form dimers, either homo- or heterodimers. Some dimers, such as the members of the TGF-β and PDGF families, are connected by one or two covalent disulfide linkages, and others, such as those of the NGF and glycoprotein hormone families, are connected by noncovalent, mostly van der Waals, interactions (Table 2). The amount of interface area buried in each dimer is very extensive, measuring 2600, 2340, 2200, and 4525 Å^2 (from 47) and 3860 Å^2 (from 97) for TGF-β2, NGF, PDGF-BB, and hCG, respectively. The excessively large interface area buried in an hCG dimer partly results from an additional separate interface formed between the so-called seat-belt loop of the β-subunit and the α-subunit. Most of the interface area in the structures of the four growth factors is hydrophobic in nature, which suggests that the main driving force for the formation of a stable dimer is the hydrophobic interaction.

STABILITY OF A MONOMER VS A DIMER   Given the overall flatness and lack of a defined hydrophobic core of the protomer structure, we predict that a monomeric form of these growth factors is unlikely to assume a stable native conformation in solution. This prediction can be rationalized by comparing the area of the buried hydrophobic core of a monomer with that of a dimer. The calculated surface area shows that the monomers of TGF-β2, NGF, and PDGF bury approximately a total of 44, 43, and 33%, respectively, of their nonpolar surface area, whereas the dimers bury a total of 58, 57, and 54%, respectively. Miller et al surveyed the percentage of nonpolar surface area buried in 40 well-refined protein structures and found that protein molecules bury on average 55 $\pm$ 5% of their nonpolar surface area (64). Because the hydrophobic interaction, which is best measured by the amount of buried nonpolar surface, is the main stabilizing force of a protein structure, Miller et al's findings would argue that the three monomers lack sufficient hydrophobic stabilization to sustain their native conformations, whereas the dimeric forms bury a typical amount of nonpolar surface and thus are stable in solution. The monomeric forms of glycoprotein hormones may provide more buried nonpolar surface than those of TGF-β2, NGF, and PDGF because they are heavily glycosylated upon expression and thus may exist as stable monomeric forms in solution.

THE UNIQUENESS OF THE DIMERIZATION MODES   The dimers whose 3D structures have been characterized so far all differ both in the orientations of their respective monomers and in the locations of their dimer interfaces. One (NGF) dimerizes in a head-to-head orientation, and the other three, TGF-β2, PDGF-BB, and hCG, dimerize in head-to-tail orientations (Figure 4). In terms of the locations of their interfaces (Figure 5, color plate), NGF uses the relatively uncurled face of the four-stranded β-sheet to form the contact surface. TGF-β2, in contrast to NGF, adopts the opposite side of the β-sheet, the curled up face, as its dimer interface. PDGF-BB, on the other hand, dimerizes on the side of the β-sheet so that most of the interface area is mediated by the first two strands of the β-sheet and its N-terminal tail. Finally, the dimer interface of human chorionic gonadotropin appears to be located partly on the curled up face of the β-sheet and partly on the side of the β-sheet's first strand, resulting in an overlap of the contact area with that of TGF-β2 and PDGF-BB. These very different dimer formations result in very different locations for the hydrophobic residues in their respective protomer structures. Consequently, all the existing 3D-1D profile–based, sequence-alignment algorithms fail to show any similarity between the monomers. This makes predicting a member of this superfamily fold from the sequence alone particularly challenging.

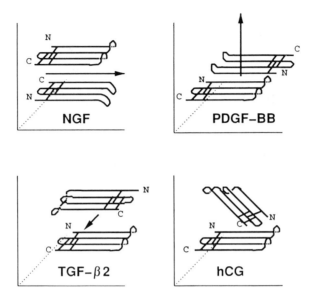

Figure 4   Schematic representation of the different dimer forms. Each protomer is represented by a set of three knotted disulfide bonds and a four-stranded antiparallel β-sheet. N and C label the N and C termini. The molecular two-fold axis that relates two monomers is shown with an arrow in each case except hCG, in which there is only a pseudo two-fold axis between the α- and β-subunits.

Finally, most of these growth factors, with the possible exception of glycoprotein hormones, are expressed first as latent forms with propeptides similar to or larger than the mature growth factors themselves (63, 83). The functions of these propeptides remain largely unknown, although they are believed to take part in the activation regulatory processes controlled by the cell surface proteases (65, 92). Given the fact that the monomers lack well-defined hydrophobic cores, protein folding and dimerization become a highly cooperative process. Therefore, propeptides may also function as chaperones to facilitate the folding of the mature peptides.

RECEPTORS AND RECEPTOR BINDING

The structural similarity among these growth factors does not extend to either the extracellular ligand-binding domain or the intercellular kinase domain.

Extracellular Binding Domain

No sequence homology has been observed in the ligand-binding domain of these growth-factor receptors, and no 3D structure for them has been determined. Three major forms of TGF-β receptors, types I, II, and III TGFβR, have been cloned (100–103). Types I and II, which have intracellular kinase domains, are the signal-transducing receptors. The major ligand-binding receptor, type II TGFβR, has a relatively small ligand-binding domain of 136 amino acids that contains cysteine-rich segments. These receptors exhibit no recognizable sequence homologies with other receptor families.

NGF has two forms of receptor, the low-affinity (LNGFR, p75^{NGFR}) and the high-affinity form (HNGFR, p140^{trkA}). The extracellular domain of p75^{NGFR}, which can bind to NGF, BDNF, NT-3, and NT-4, has four cysteine-rich regions similar to those in TNF receptors, and the extracellular part of the high-affinity receptor P140^{trkA}, a member of the *trk* protooncogene family, has two cysteine-rich domains and two immunoglobulin domains.

The extracellular portion of the PDGF receptor consists of 5 immunoglobulin-like domains, whereas the extracellular part of hCG receptor contains 14 leucine-rich repeats (LRRs) (61). The sequence of the ribonuclease inhibitor has a similar number of LRRs (97); the structure of these receptors assumes a horseshoe shape.

Receptor Dimerization

Ligand-induced receptor dimerization has been observed crystallographically in two growth factor–receptor systems. One is the human growth hormone system, in which one molecule of hGH binds to two receptor molecules asymmetrically and thus facilitates the receptor dimerization (26). The other example is the recent solution of the complex structure between TNF and TNF receptor. In this case, TNF itself exists as a trimer, and it binds symmetrically to a receptor trimer (5). Because all the cystine-knot growth factors are dimers, the signal-transduction mechanism may involve the growth factor–induced receptor dimerization. In fact, in the inhibition of cell growth signaled by TGF-β, evidence indicates that the binding of TGF-β1 to its cell surface type II receptor—the high-affinity receptor—causes the receptor to dimerize with the type I TGF-β receptor—the low-affinity receptor—and it is this receptor complex that leads to the subsequent kinase activation (9, 96). The PDGF and NGF receptor systems represent similar cases (12, 21, 38, 62).

The location of most of the proposed receptor-binding sites remain largely speculative because of insufficient mutagenic analysis and the absence of a ligand-receptor complex structure. These proposed sites reside in the loop regions between the four structurally conserved β-strands and are outside the cystine-knot motif. Because these growth-factor regions differ greatly at both the sequence and structure level, different families of growth factors probably recognize their receptors in entirely different manners.

FUTURE PERSPECTIVES

The situation in which the promoter sequences of all four growth factors share extensive structural resemblance and yet lack any significant sequence homology represents an extreme example of divergent evolution. The sequence divergence is nearly complete, except for the six knotted cystine residues. However, the 3D fold is preserved throughout evolution. By which process did these growth factors evolve? What was the earliest form, a dimer or a monomer? Another interesting issue is that all the members of this cystine-knot superfamily exist primarily in dimeric forms. Are there other forms apart from the four known dimers? Furthermore, many dimers can form both homo- and hetero-dimers that have different biological activities. For example, the activins and inhibins, members of the TGF-β family, are formed by differential dimerization of three polypeptide chains, α, βA, and βB. When the α-chain pairs with βA or βB, it produces either inhibin A or inhibin B, which inhibit the production of pituitary FSH, gonadal sex steroids, and placental hormones (98). However, when βA forms a homodimer or dimerizes with βB, two activin molecules result that have an effect on growth regulation opposite to that of the inhibins (74). Whether this intrinsic property of differential dimerization is part of the cell regulatory machinery remains unknown. In some situations, such as PDGF, the isoform population does appear to be regulated (37). Finally, a very challenging question is how to predict, based on sequence information, other members of this superfamily fold. How many more growth factors are there that assume the same fold? The answer to this question requires a better understanding of the fold, especially the determinants of the fold other than the cystine residues. Our current knowledge based on the four growth factor structures has not yet provided a tool to accomplish this goal.

ACKNOWLEDGMENTS

We thank Dr. NW Isaacs for making hCG coordinates available to us, Dr. GH Cohen for discussions related to the structural alignment, and

Drs. A Roberts and S-W Chen for their helpful comments on the manuscript.

Literature Cited

1. Almassy RJ, Fontecilla-Camps JC, Suddath FL, Bugg CE. 1983. Structure of variant-3 scorpion neurotoxin from *Centruroides sculpturatus* Ewing, refined at 1.8 Å resolution. *J. Mol. Biol.* 170:497–510

2. Archer SJ, Bax A, Roberts AB, Sporn MB, Ogawa Y, et al. 1993. Transforming growth factor β1: NMR signal assignments of the recombinant protein expressed and isotopically enriched using Chinese hamster ovary cell. *Biochemistry* 32:1152–63

3. Archer SJ, Bax A, Roberts AB, Sporn MB, Ogawa Y, et al. 1993. Transforming growth factor β1: secondary structure as determined by heteronuclear magnetic resonance spectroscopy. *Biochemistry* 32:1164–71

4. Assoian RK, Komoriya A, Meyers CA, Miller DM, Sporn MB. 1983. Transforming growth factor-beta in human platelets. *J. Biol. Chem.* 258:7155–60

5. Banner DW, D'Arcy A, Wolfgang J, Gentz R, Schoenfeld H, et al. 1993. Crystal structure of soluble human 55 kd TNF receptor–human TNFβ complex: implications for TNF receptor activation. *Cell* 73:431–45

6. Barde YA. 1989. Trophic factors and neuronal survival. *Neuron* 2:1525–34

7. Barker PA, Murphy RA. 1992. The nerve growth factor receptor: a multicomponent system that mediates the actions of the neurotrophin family of proteins. *Mol. Cell Biol.* 110:1–15

8. Basler K, Edlund T, Jessell TM, Yamada T. 1993 Control of cell pattern in the neural tube: regulation of cell differentiation by dorsalin-1, a novel TGFβ family member. *Cell* 73:687–702

9. Bassing CH, Howe DJ, Segarini PR, Donahoe PK, Wang X-F. 1994. A single heteromeric receptor complex is sufficient to mediate the biological effects of TGF-β. *J. Biol. Chem.* 269:14861–64

10. Bazan JF. 1990. Haemopoietic receptors and helical cytokines. *Immunol. Today* 11:350–54

11. Bejcek BE, Hoffman RM, Lipps D, Li DY, Mitchell CA, et al. 1992 The v-sis oncogene product but not platelet-derived growth factor (PDGF) A homodimers activate PDGF alpha and beta receptors intracellularly and initiate cellular transformation. *J. Biol Chem.* 267:3289–93

12. Benito M, Lorenzo M. 1993. Platelet derived growth factor/tyrosine kinase receptor mediated proliferation. *Growth Regul.* 3:172–79

13. Berkemeier LR, Winslow JW, Kaplan DR, Nikolics K, et al 1991. Neurotrophin-5: a novel neurotrophic factor that activates *trk* and *trkB*. *Neuron* 7:857–66

14. Boothby R, Ruddon RW, Anderson C, McWilliams D, Boime I. 1981. A single gonadotropin α-subunit gene in normal tissue and tumor-derived cell lines. *J. Biol. Chem.* 256:5121–25

15. Brunner AM, Lioubin MN, Marquardt H, Malacko AR, Wang WC, et al. 1992. Site-directed mutagenesis of glycosylation sites in the transforming growth factor-beta 1 (TGF-β1) and TGF-β2 (414) precursors and of cysteine residues within mature TGF-β1: effects on secretion and bioactivity. *Mol. Endocrinol.* 6:1691–1700

16. Cate RL, Mattaliano RJ, Hession C, Tizard R, Farber NM, et al. 1986. Isolation of the bovine and human genes for Mullerian inhibiting substance and expression of the human gene in animal cells. *Cell* 45:685–98

17. Celeste AJ, Iannazzi JA, Taylor RC, Hewick RM, Rosen V, et al. 1990. Identification of transforming growth factor beta family members present in bone-inductive protein purified from bovine bone. *Proc. Natl. Acad. Sci. USA* 87:9843–47

18. Centrella M, McCarthy TL, Canalis E. 1988. Skeletal tissue and trans-

forming growth factor-β. *FASEB J.* 2:3066–73

19. Cheifetz S, Weatherbee JA, Tsang MLS, Anderson JK, Mole JE, et al. 1987. The transforming growth factor-β system, a complex pattern of cross-reactive ligands and receptors. *Cell* 48:409–15

20. Chiche L, Gaboriaud C, Heitz A, Mornon JP, Castro B, Kollman PA. 1989. Use of restrained molecular dynamics in water to determine three-dimensional protein structure: prediction of the three-dimensional structure of *Ecballium elaterium* trypsin inhibitor. *Proteins* 6:405–20

21. Daniel T, Kumjian DA. 1992. Platelet-derived growth factor receptors and phospholipase C activation. *Kidney Int.* 41:575–80

22. Daopin S, Cohen GH, Davies D. 1992. Structural similarity between transforming growth factor-$\beta 2$ and nerve growth factor. *Science* 258:1160–61

23. Daopin S, Davies DR, Schlunegger MP, Grütter MG. 1994. Comparison of two crystal structures of TGF-$\beta 2$: the accuracy of refined protein structures. *Acta Crystallogr. D* 50:85–92

24. Daopin S, Li M, Davies DR. 1993. Crystal structure of TGF-$\beta 2$ refined at 1.8 Å resolution. *Proteins* 17:176–92

25. Daopin S, Piez KA, Ogawa Y, Davies DR. 1992. Crystal structure of transforming growth factor-$\beta 2$: an unusual fold for the superfamily. *Science* 257:369–73

26. DeVos AM, Ultsch M, Kossiakoff AA. 1992. Human growth hormone and extracellular domain of its receptor: crystal structure of the complex. *Science* 255:306–12

27. Derynck R, Lindquist PB, Lee A, Wen D, Tamm J, et al. 1988. A new type of transforming growth factor-β, TGF-$\beta 3$. *EMBO J.* 7:3737–43

28. Eriksson AE, Cousens LS, Weaver LH, Matthews BW. 1991. Three-dimensional structure of human basic fibroblast growth factor. *Proc. Natl. Acad. Sci. USA* 88:3441–45

29. Fiddes JC, Goodman HM. 1981. The gene encoding the common alpha subunit of the four human glycoprotein hormones. *J. Mol. Appl. Genet.* 1:3–7

30. Forage RG, Ring JM, Brown RW, McInerney BV, Cobon GS, et al. 1986. Cloning and sequence analysis of cDNA species coding for the two subunits of inhibin from bovine follicular fluid. *Proc. Natl. Acad. Sci. USA* 83:3091–95

31. Giese NA, Robbins KC, Aaronson SA. 1987. The role of individual cysteine residues in the structure and function of the v-sis gene product. *Science* 236:1315–18

32. Hohn A, Leibrock J, Bailey K, Barde YA. 1990. Identification and characterization of a novel member of the nerve growth factor/brain–derived neurotrophic factor family. *Nature* 344:339–41

33. Hallböök F, Ibàñez CF, Persson H. 1991. Evolutionary studies of the nerve growth factor family reveal a novel member abundantly expressed in *Xenopus* ovary. *Neuron* 6:845–58

34. Hart CE, Forstrom JW, Kelly JD, Seifert RA, Smith RA, et al. 1988. Two classes of PDGF receptor recognize different isoforms of PDGF. *Science* 240:1529–31

35. Heine UI, Flanders K, Roberts AB, Munoz EF, Sporn MB. 1987. Role of transforming growth factor-β in the development of the mouse embryo. *J. Cell Biol.* 105:2861–76

36. Heldin C-H. 1992. Structural and functional studies on platelet-derived growth factor. *EMBO J.* 11:4251–59

37. Heldin C-H, Ostman A, Eriksson A, Siegbahn A, Claesson-Welsh L, Westermark B. 1992. Platelet-derived growth factor: isoform-specific signalling via heterodimeric or homodimeric receptor complexes. *Kidney Int.* 41:571–74

38. Hempstead BL, Martin-Zanca D, Kaplan DR, Parada LF, Chao MV. 1991. High-affinity NGF binding requires coexpression of the *trk* proto-oncogene and the low-affinity NGF receptor. *Nature* 350:678–83

39. Holland DR, Cousens LS, Meng W, Matthews BW. 1994. Nerve growth factor in different crystal forms displays structural flexibility and reveals zinc binding sites. *J. Mol. Biol.* 239:385–400

40. Jakowlew SB, Dillard PJ, Kondaiah P, Sporn MB, Roberts AB. 1988. Complementary deoxyribonucleic acid cloning of a novel transforming growth factor-β messenger ribonucleic acid from chick embryo chondrocytes. *Mol. Endocrinol.* 2:747–55

41. Jakowlew SB, Dillard PJ, Sporn MB, Roberts AB. 1988. Complementary deoxyribonucleic acid cloning of an mRNA encoding transforming

growth factor-β4 from chicken embryo chondrocytes. *Mol. Endocrinol.* 2:1186–95

42. Johnson CK. 1970. *ORTEP: a fortran thermal-ellipsoid plot program for crystal structure illustrations.* Oak Ridge, TN: Oak Ridge National Lab.

43. Kaplan DR, Martin-Zanca D, Parada LF. 1991. Tyrosine phosphorylation and tyrosine kinase activity of the *trk* proto-oncogene product induced by NGF. *Nature* 350:158–60

44. Kenney WC, Haniu M, Herman AC, Arakawa T, Costigan VJ, et al. 1994. Formation of mitogenically active PDGF-B dimer does not require interchain disulfide bonds. *J. Biol. Chem.* 269:12351–59

45. Kondaiah P, Sands MJ, Smith JM, Fields A, Roberts AB, et al. 1990. Identification of a novel transforming growth factor-β (TGF-β5) mRNA in *Xenopus laevis. J. Biol. Chem.* 265: 1089–93

46. Kraulis P. 1991. Molscript: a program to produce both detailed and schematic plots of protein structures. *J. Appl. Crystallogr.* 24:946–50

47. Lapthorn AJ, Harris DC, Littlejohn A, Lustbader JW, Canfield RE, et al. 1994. Crystal structure of human chorionic gonadotropin. *Nature* 369: 455–61

48. Lee BA, Donoghue DJ. 1991. Membrane-anchored form of v-sis/PDGF-B induces mitogenesis without detectable PDGF receptor autophosphorylation. *J. Cell. Biol.* 113:361–70

49. Lee S-J. 1991. Expression of growth/differentiation factor 1 in the nervous system: conservation of a bicistronic structure. *Proc. Natl. Acad. Sci. USA* 88:4250–54

50. Leibrock J, Lottspeich F, Hohn A, Hofer M, Hengerer B, et al. 1989. Molecular cloning and expression of brain-derived neurotrophic factor. *Nature* 341:149–52

51. Levi-Montalcini R. 1987. The nerve growth factor: thirty-five years later. *EMBO J.* 6:1145–54

52. Lewin GR, Mendell LM. 1993. Nerve growth factor and nociception. *Trends Neurosci.* 16:353–59

53. Ling N, Ying SY, Ueno N, Shimasaki S, Esch F, et al. 1986. Pituitary FSH is released by a heterodimer of the β-subunits from the two forms of inhibin. *Nature* 321:779–82

54. Liu J-M, Davidson JM. 1988. The elastogenic effect of recombinant transforming growth factor-β on porcine aortic smooth muscle cells. *Biochem. Biophys. Res. Commun.* 154: 895–901

55. Lyons K, Graycar JL, Lee A, Hashmi S, Lindquist PB, et al. 1989. Vgr-1, a mammalian gene related to *Xenopus* Vg-1, is a member of the transforming growth factor gene superfamily. *Proc. Natl. Acad. Sci. USA* 86:4554–58

56. Mason AJ, Hayflick JS, Ling N, Esch F, Ueno N, et al. 1985. Complementary DNA sequences of ovarian follicular fluid inhibin show precursor structure and homology with transforming growth factor-β. *Nature* 318: 659–63

57. Massagué J. 1990. The transforming growth factor-β family. *Annu. Rev. Cell Biol.* 6:597–641

58. Matsui T, Heidaran M, Miki T, Popescu N, La Rochelle W, et al. 1989. Isolation of a novel receptor cDNA establishes the existence of two PDGF receptor genes. *Science* 243:800–4

59. McDonald NQ, Lapatto R, Murray-Rust J, Gunning J, Wlodawer A, Blundell TL. 1991. New protein fold revealed by a 2.3 Å resolution crystal structure of nerve growth factor. *Nature* 354:411–14

60. McDonald NQ, Hendrickson WA. 1993. A structural superfamily of growth factors containing a cystine knot motif. *Cell* 73:421–24

61. McFarland KC, Sprengel R, Phillips HS, Kohler M, Seeburg PH, et al. 1989. Lutropin-choriogonadotropin receptor: an unusual member of the G protein-coupled receptor family. *Science* 245:494–99

62. Meakin SO, Shooter EM. 1992. The nerve growth factor family of receptors. *Trends Neurosci.* 15:323–31

63. Miller DM, Ogawa Y, Iwata KK, Ten Dijke P, Purchio AF, et al. 1992. Characterization of the binding of transforming growth factor-β1, -β2, and -β3 to recombinant β1-latency-associated peptide. *Mol. Endocrinol.* 6:694–702

64. Miller S, Janin J, Lesk AM, Chothia C. 1987. Interior and surface of monomeric proteins. *J. Mol. Biol.* 196: 641–56

65. Miyazono K, Hellman U, Wernstedt C, Heldin C-H. 1988. Latent high molecular weight complex of transforming growth factor β1. *J. Biol. Chem.* 263:6407–15

66. Moy FJ, Li YC, Rauenbuehler P,

Winkler ME, Scheraga HA, et al. 1993. Solution structure of human type-alpha transforming growth factor determined by heteronuclear NMR spectroscopy and refined by energy minimization with restraints. *Biochemistry* 32:7334–53

67. Murray-Rust J, McDonald NQ, Blundell TL, Hosang M, Oefner C, et al. 1993. Topological similarities in TGF-β2, PDGF-BB and NGF define a superfamily of polypeptide growth factors. *Structure* 1:153–59

68. Murzin AG, Chothia C. 1992. Protein architecture: new superfamilies. *Curr. Opin. Struct. Biol.* 2:895–903

69. Odell WD, Griffin J, Grover S, Carrell DT. 1992. Human chorionic gonadotropin-like proteins: secretion in nonpregnant humans and production by bacteria. *Trans. Am. Clin. Climatol. Assoc.* 103:238–54

70. Oefner C, D'Arcy A, Winkler FK, Eggimann B, Hosang M. 1992. Crystal structure of human platelet-derived growth factor BB. *EMBO J.* 11:3921–26

71. Ozkaynak E, Schnegelsberg PNJ, Jin DF, Clifford GM, Warren FD, et al. 1992. Osteogenic protein-2: a new member of the transforming growth factor-β superfamily expressed early in embryogenesis. *J. Biol. Chem.* 267:25220–27

72. Padgett RW, St Johnston RD, Gelbart WM. 1987. A transcript from a *Drosophila* pattern gene predicts a protein homologous to the transforming growth factor-β family. *Nature* 325:81–84

73. Pearson CA, Pearson D, Shibahara S, Hofsteenge J, Chiquet-Ehrismann R. 1988. Tenascin: cDNA cloning and induction by TGF-β. *EMBO J.* 7:2677–81

74. Petraglia F, Vaughan J, Vale W. 1989. Inhibin and activin modulate the release of gonadotropin-releasing hormone, human chorionic gonadotropin, and progesterone from cultured human placenta cells. *Proc. Natl. Acad. Sci. USA* 86:5114–17

75. Pierce JG, Parsons TF. 1981. Glycoprotein hormones: structure and function. *Annu. Rev. Biochem.* 50:465–75

76. Rees DC, Lipscomb WN. 1982. Refined crystal structure of the potato inhibitor complex of carboxypeptidase A at 2.5 Å resolution. *J. Mol. Biol.* 160:475–98

77. Robbins KC, Leal F, Pierce JH, Aaronson SA. 1985. The v-sis/PDGF2 transforming gene product localizes to cell membranes but is not a secretory protein. *EMBO J.* 4:1783–92

78. Roberts AB, Anzano MA, Wakefield LM, Roche NS, Stern DF, Sporn MB. 1985. Type beta transforming growth factor: a bifunctional regulator of cellular growth. *Proc. Natl. Acad. Sci. USA* 82:119–23

79. Satow Y, Cohen GH, Padlan EA, Davies DR. 1986. Phosphocholine binding immunoglobulin Fab McPC603. An X-ray diffraction study at 2.7 Å. *J. Mol. Biol.* 190:593–604

80. Schlunegger MP, Grütter MG. 1992. An unusual feature revealed by the crystal structure at 2.2 Å resolution of human transforming growth factor-β2. *Nature* 358:430–34

81. Schlunegger MP, Grütter MG. 1993. Refined crystal structure of human transforming growth factor beta 2 at 1.95 Å resolution. *J. Mol. Biol.* 231:445–58

82. Seifert RA, Hart CE, Phillips PE, Forstrom JM, Ross R, et al. 1989. Two different subunits associate to create isoform-specific platelet-derived growth factor receptors. *J. Biol. Chem.* 264:8771–78

83. Sha X, Yang L, Gentry LE. 1991. Identification and analysis of discrete functional domains in the pro region of pre-pro-transforming growth factor beta 1. *J. Cell Biol.* 114:827–39

84. Sorkin A, Westermark B, Heldin C-H, Claesson-Welsh L. 1991. Effect of receptor kinase inactivation of the rate of internalization and degradation of PDGF and the PDGF β-receptor. *J. Cell Biol.* 112:469–78

85. Sporn MB, Roberts AB. 1990. The transforming growth factor betas. In *Peptide Growth Factors and Their Receptors.* 1:419–72. New York: Springer-Verlag

86. Swindells MB. 1992. Structural similarity between transforming growth factor-β2 and nerve growth factor. *Science* 258:1160–61

87. Ten Dijke P, Hansen P, Iwata KK, Pieler C, Foulkes JG. 1988. Identification of another member of the transforming growth factor type β gene family. *Proc. Natl. Acad. Sci. USA* 85:4715–19

88. Thompson NL, Flanders KC, Smith M, Ellingsworth LR, Roberts AB, Sporn MB. 1989. Expression of transforming growth factor-β1 in specific cells and tissues of adult and neonatal mice. *J. Cell Biol.* 108:661–69

89. Vale W, Rivier J, Vaughan J, McClin-

tock R, Corrigan A, et al. 1986. Purification and characterization of an FSH releasing protein from porcine ovarian follicular fluid. *Nature* 321: 776–79

90. Varga J, Rosenbloom J, Jimenez SA. 1987. Transforming growth factor-β causes a persistent increase in steady-state amounts of type I and type III collagen and fibronectin mRNAs in normal human dermal fibroblasts. *Biochem J.* 247:597–604

91. Veerapandian B, Gilliland GL, Raag R, Svensson AL, Masui Y, et al. 1992. Functional implications of interleukin-1 beta based on the three-dimensional structure. *Proteins* 12: 10–23

92. Wakefield LM, Smith DM, Flanders KC, Sporn MB. 1988. Latent transforming growth factor-β from human platelets. *J. Biol. Chem.* 263:7646–54

93. Weeks DL, Melton DA. 1987. A maternal mRNA localized to the vegetal hemisphere in *Xenopus* eggs codes for a growth factor related to TGF-β. *Cell* 51:861–67

94. Wlodawer A, Pavlovsky A, Gustchina A. 1993. Hematopoietic cytokines: similarities and differences in the structures, with implications for receptor binding. *Protein Sci.* 2: 1373–82

95. Wozney JM, Rosen V, Celeste AJ, Mitsock LM, Whitters MJ, et al. 1988. Novel regulators of bone formation: molecular clones and activities. *Science* 242:1528–34

96. Wrana JL, Attisano L, Carcamo J, Zentella A, Doody J, et al. 1992. TGF-β signals through a heteromeric protein kinase receptor complex. *Cell* 71:1003–14

97. Wu H, Lustbader JW, Liu Y, Can-field RE, Hendrickson WA. 1994. Structure of human chorionic gonadotropin at 2.6 Å resolution from MAD analysis of the selenomethionyl protein. *Structure* 2:545–58

98. Ying S-Y, Becker A, Ling N, Ueno N, Guillemin R. 1986. Inhibin and beta type transforming growth factor (TGF-β) have opposite modulating effects on the follicle stimulating hormone (FSH) induced aromatase activity of cultured rat granulosa cells. *Biochem. Biophys. Res. Commun.* 136:969–75

99. Zhang JD, Cousens LS, Barr PJ, Sprang SR. 1991. Three-dimensional structure of human basic fibroblast growth factor, a structural homolog of interleukin 1 beta. *Proc. Natl. Acad. Sci. USA* 88:3446–50; 1991. Erratum. *Proc. Natl. Acad. Sci. USA* 88(12):5477

100. Ebner R, Chen R-H, Shum L, Lawler S, Zioncheck TF, et al. 1993. Cloning of a type I TGF-β receptor and its effect on TGF-β binding to the type II receptor. *Science* 260:1344–48

101. Lin HY, Wang X-F, Ng-Eaton E, Weinberg RA, Lodish HF. 1992. Expression cloning of the TGF-β type II receptor, a functional transmembrane serine/threonine kinase. *Cell* 68:775–85

102. Ten Dijke P, Yamashita H, Ichijo H, Franzen P, Laiho M, et al. 1994. Characterization of type I receptors for transforming growth factor-β and activin. *Science* 264:101–4

103. Wang X-F, Lin HY, Ng-Eaton E, Downward J, Lodish HF, Weinberg RA. 1991. Expression cloning and characterization of the TGF-β type III receptor. *Cell* 67:797–805

Annu. Rev. Biophys. Biomol. Struct. 1995. 24:293–318

STRUCTURE AND FUNCTION OF DNA METHYLTRANSFERASES

Xiaodong Cheng

W. M. Keck Structural Biology Laboratory, Cold Spring Harbor Laboratory, Cold Spring Harbor, New York 11724

KEY WORDS: DNA methylation, C5-cytosine methyltransferase, extrahelical base, base-flipping mechanism, N6-adenine and N4-cytosine methylation

CONTENTS

ABSTRACT

In prokaryotes, the major role of DNA methylation is to protect host DNA against degradation by restriction enzymes. In eukaryotes, DNA methylation has been implicated in the control of several cellular processes, including differentiation, gene regulation, and embryonic devel-

opment. Structural work on *Hha*I DNA methyltransferase demonstrates that the substrate nucleotide is completely flipped out of the
helix during the modification reaction and has provided much insight
into the enzymatic properties of *S*-adenosyl-L-methionine (SAM)–dependent DNA-modifying enzymes. Structural comparison of three enzymes, *Hha*I C5-cytosine methyltransferase, *Taq*I N6-adenine methyltransferase, and catechol *O*-methyltransferase, reveals a striking similarity in protein folding and indicates that many SAM-dependent
methyltransferases have a common catalytic-domain structure. This
feature permits the prediction of tertiary structure for other DNA,
RNA, protein, and small-molecule methyltransferases from their amino
acid sequences, including the eukaryotic C_pG methyltransferases.

PERSPECTIVES AND OVERVIEW

Hotchkiss first described methylation in calf thymus DNA in 1948 (25).
Arber & Dussoix (1) and Srinivasan & Borek (69) uncovered its possible
physiological roles in prokaryotes and eukaryotes, respectively, in 1962
and 1964. Since then, investigators have found DNA methylation in
many different genes in bacteria, viruses, fungi, vertebrates, and plants.
   In prokaryotes, DNA methylation protects the bacteria's DNA
against degradation by restriction enzymes (1) and corrects errors in
DNA replication by means of the mismatch repair system (50). In 1964,
Gold & Hurwitz identified the first DNA methyltransferase (Mtase) in
Escherichia coli (16). Subsequently, restriction and modification systems from many bacterial species were isolated, and their recognition
sites were identified (for review, see 59). The availability of sequence-
specific restriction enzymes and Mtases led to a major breakthrough
in the field of molecular biology.
   In eukaryotes, DNA methylation appears to have a different and
more diversified role. It has been implicated in the control of several
cellular processes, including differentiation and gene regulation (see
32). A series of discoveries over the past few years has generated new
interest in DNA methylation. In particular, mouse DNA Mtase is essential for normal embryonic development (43) and is associated with DNA
replication foci (42). Cytosine methylation may also contribute to C-T
transition mutations, accounting for about one-third of all somatic and
germline mutations in humans (for review, see 7).
   A central issue underlying the biology of DNA methylation is its
associated enzymology. The determination of the crystal structure of
the *Hha*I Mtase (M.*Hha*I) marks a turning point in our understanding
of the chemistry behind DNA methylation (11, 12, 33). This structure

reveals how the active nucleophile reaches its target, directly supports the proposed enzymatic mechanisms, and illustrates a novel mode of sequence-specific DNA recognition. This review discusses some enzymatic and chemical properties of DNA Mtases from a structural standpoint.

DNA METHYLATION

Types of DNA Methylation

Two major classes of DNA Mtases differ in the nature of the modification introduced (Figure 1). The members of one class (e.g. M.*Hha*I)

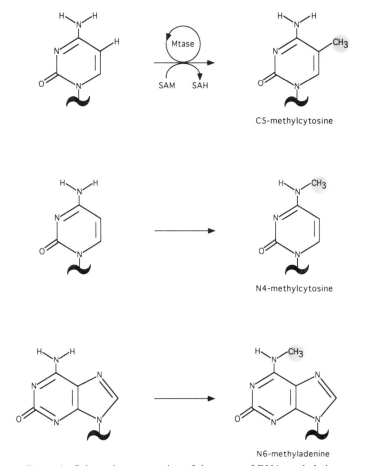

Figure 1   Schematic presentation of the types of DNA methylation.

methylate a ring carbon and form C5-methylcytosine. Members of the second class methylate exocyclic nitrogens and form either N4-methyl-cytosine (e.g. M.*Pvu*II) or N6-methyladenine (e.g. M.*Taq*I). Both classes of Mtases utilize the cofactor *S*-adenosyl-L-methionine (SAM) as the methyl donor and are active as monomeric enzymes. Only one of the DNA strands is methylated during each methylation event. This observation is consistent with the fact that the natural substrate for most methylations inside the cell is newly replicated hemimethylated DNA. De novo methylation, on the other hand, is a two-step process in which hemimethylated DNA is an intermediate reaction product (24, 61). In bacterial type II systems, methylation and restriction of DNA by Mtases and endonucleases occur within the same DNA target, con-sisting of up to eight base pairs of palindromic sequences (see 59). In eukaryotes, the modification of cytosine at carbon-5 occurs predomi-nantly at the C_pG dinucleotide (see 32). In addition, plant DNA is meth-ylated in C_pN_pG trinucleotides, where N can be any base (18).

C5-Cytosine Methyltransferases

C5-cytosine Mtases can be found in both prokaryotes and eukaryotes, whereas the exocyclic Mtases have been isolated mainly from pro-karyotes.

CONSERVED SEQUENCE MOTIFS   The genes for more than 100 different Mtases have been cloned and many of their primary sequences charac-terized (for review, see 77). These studies have facilitated comparisons among Mtases to help distinguish between conserved sequence motifs and variable sequence elements (12, 37, 41, 57, 67). C5-cytosine Mtases, including the C-terminal 500 amino acids of the eukaryotic C_pG Mtases, share a set of 10 conserved blocks of amino acids (12, 37, 57). That these conserved motifs have the same linear order simplifies their identification from primary sequences. Figure 2 shows amino acids of M.*Hha*I with the conserved motifs highlighted using the nomenclature of Posfai et al (57).

Before the structural work on DNA Mtases, two motifs were thought to have roles common to the chemistry of these enzymes. Motif I (Phe-XGlyXGly or a close relative) is presumed to be part of the cofactor-binding site. This assignment was based on the presence of this consen-sus sequence in a wide variety of SAM-dependent Mtases, including N6-adenine and N4-cytosine Mtases and RNA, protein, and small-mol-ecule Mtases (26, 35, 65, 78). Motif IV contains an invariant dipeptide Pro-Cys known to be part of the catalytic site (see below).

In contrast, a comparison of 16 sequences of N6-adenine and 3 N4-

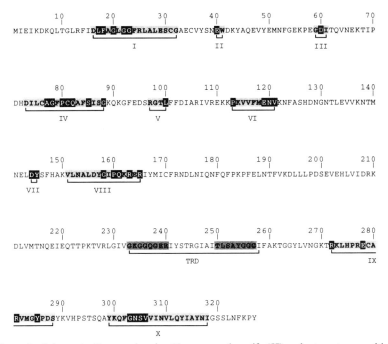

Figure 2 Schematic diagram showing 10 conserved motifs (57) and a target recognition domain (TRD) (41) in the M.*Hha*I sequence.

cytosine Mtases revealed only 2 conserved segments, namely AspX-PheXGlyXGly and AspProProTyr, corresponding to motifs I and IV in C5-cytosine Mtases, respectively (35). As described below, alignments based on three-dimensional structures with M.*Hha*I reveal more conserved motifs in M.*Taq*I, an N6-adenine Mtase (54).

VARIABLE REGION AND TARGET-RECOGNITION DOMAIN   The variable region between motifs VIII (GlnXArgXArg) and IX (ArgGlu) defines the DNA sequence specificity of both monospecific (34, 47) and multispecific C5-cytosine Mtases (3, 71, 74, 76). Hybrid construction between the monospecific Mtases established that this variable region determines the DNA sequence specificity (34) as well as the base to be methylated within the target sequence (47).

For the multispecific enzymes, those that recognize several target sequences, Trautner and coworkers defined and eventually deleted, rearranged, and exchanged target recognition domains (TRDs) within the variable region (for review, see 53). Sequence comparisons of various putative TRDs from multi- and monospecific Mtases revealed that

TRDs are tandemly arranged, nonoverlapping stretches, each spanning approximately 40–50 amino acids, with a consensus sequence of Thr(Val/Ile/Leu)$X_{5\ or\ 6}$Gly(Val/Leu) in the C-terminal portion (see 53).

Catalytic Mechanism

Wu & Santi (80, 81) analyzed the reaction mechanism of M.*Hha*I, which is analogous to uridine methylation by thymidylate synthase (20, 46) and tRNA(Uracil-5) methylase (62). This study led to the proposal that C5-cytosine methylation proceeds through the formation of a transient, covalent protein-DNA complex and that 5-methyldeoxycytidine is produced from deoxycytidine via a dihydrocytosine intermediate (Figure 3). A key feature of this process involves nucleophilic attack on the carbon-6 of the target cytosine by the thiol group of a cysteine. The formation of the covalent bond leads to the addition of a methyl group to the carbon-5 of cytosine followed by elimination of the 5-position proton and release of the covalent intermediate. The mechanism is directly supported by the identification of the cysteine in conserved motif IV covalently attached to DNA in the trapped intermediates formed with the suicide substrate 5-fluoro-2'-deoxycytosine [M.*Hae*III (9), M.*Eco*RII (14), human Mtase (66), *Dcm* (19)]. The mechanism is also supported by the loss of functional mutations of this cysteine in several Mtases [M.*Eco*RII (83), M.*Hha*I (48), M.*Hae*III (10)]. In the trapped intermediate, the methyl group has transferred to the carbon-5 of cytosine, but the elimination step cannot proceed because the fluorine on carbon-5 cannot be released as F^+, unlike H^+ (Figure 3, *bottom*).

In Wu & Santi's scheme, the carbon-5 of the covalent intermediate is a resonance-stabilized carbanion that can take up the methyl group from SAM to leave behind *S*-adenosyl-L-homocysteine (SAH). A modification of this scheme was proposed that involves N3 protonation. Baker et al (2) predicted that cytosines that are protonated at N3 should be preferentially methylated because protonation substantially increases the charge on carbon-6 (30). The positively polarized carbon-6 then predisposes the ring to nucleophilic attack at that position (22). Later, Chen et al (10) suggested that formation of a high-energy carbanion intermediate might be avoided by proton transfer from an acidic side chain to the N3 atom of the cytosine, thus forming an endamine intermediate.

In 1992, Smith et al (66) stated that the dihydrocytosine intermediate cannot stack in duplex DNA because it is both nonplanar and nonaromatic. As pointed out by Winkler (79), although not stated explicitly by Chen et al (10), enzyme-assisted formation of the enamine intermediate

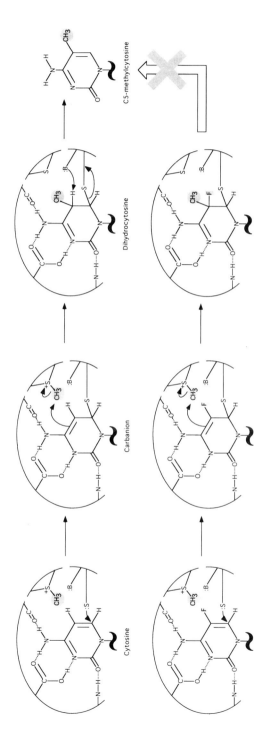

Figure 3 Reaction pathway for C5-cytosine Mtases based on the mechanism proposed by Wu & Santi (80, 81), modified by Baker et al (2). Smith et al (66), and Chen et al (10), and confirmed by the crystallographic work on M.*Hha*I (11, 12, 33).

implies the breakage of Watson-Crick base pairing and, thus, the essentially extrahelical position of the cytosine.

HhaI Methyltransferase

M.*Hha*I, a component of a type II restriction-modification system in the bacterium *Haemophilus haemolyticus* (60), is a C5-cytosine Mtase (EC 2.1.1.73) that methylates the first cytosine of its recognition sequence 5'-GCGC-3' (45) and requires no cofactors other than the methyl donor SAM for enzymatic activity. The enzyme is encoded as a single polypeptide with 327 amino acids (5, 8) (see Figure 2). Overexpression in *E. coli* (34, 82) and the availability of large quantities of pure protein (38) have facilitated the growth of crystals (11, 38).

The structure of M.*Hha*I was solved in a binary complex with SAM (12) and in a covalent ternary complex with a 13-mer oligonucleotide containing methylated 5-fluoro-2'-deoxycytidine at the site of methylation, and the reaction product SAH (11, 33). The ternary complex was formed by incubation of M.*Hha*I, the methyl donor SAM, and a 13-mer oligonucleotide containing the recognition sequence GFGC in which the target cytosine was replaced by 5-fluoro-2'-deoxycytidine (F). The DNA forms a 12-base-pair duplex with single base 5' overhangs. Reaction with this substrate resulted in the formation of an intermediate that contains a dihydrocytosine derivative with a covalent linkage to the protein (55). During this reaction, SAM is converted to SAH, which remains in the complex.

CRYSTAL STRUCTURE OF A C5-CYTOSINE METHYLTRANSFERASE

The M.*Hha*I-SAM binary complex provides insight into the domain organization and its relationship to the conserved sequence motifs (12). The ternary complex reveals the structural basis for DNA-sequence specificity and for the function of amino acids implicated in catalysis and cofactor binding (11, 33).

General Protein Topology: a Two-Domain Structure

The molecule of M.*Hha*I is folded into two domains (Figure 4, *top*): a larger catalytic domain that contains catalytic and cofactor binding sites and a smaller DNA-recognition domain that possesses two glycine-rich loops implicated in sequence-specific DNA recognition and the infiltration of the DNA to flip the target cytosine (11, 12, 33). The DNA is bound in the cleft between the two domains, with the major groove facing the recognition domain and the minor groove facing the catalytic domain (11, 33).

The catalytic domain is an α/β structure, formed around a mixed central β-sheet. The sheet comprises five parallel strands with strand order 5 4 1 2 3, and one antiparallel β-hairpin (strands 6 and 7) next to strand 5 (see Figure 8, *top,* below). The order of the parallel strands is reversed once at a switch point between strands 4 and 1. As one would expect with α/β structures, the active amino acids (motif I: PheX-GlyXGlyPhe and motif IV: ProCys) reside in the loop regions outside the carboxyl ends of these two β-strands. Other functional side chains in this domain reside at the carboxyl ends of the parallel β-strands, lined along the inner surface of the cleft. The six helices within this domain are folded around the β-sheet. The catalytic domain consists of about two-thirds of the protein's amino acids from the N-terminus and a helix from the C-terminus. Thus, at the level of the primary sequence, the two domains are mutually interspersed; i.e. there are two connections between the two domains.

The core of the recognition domain makes up the bulk of the variable region and contains an up-and-down antiparallel five-strand sheet arranged in a circular formation, like the blades of a propeller (12). Two surface loops between the β-strands face the cleft and contact the DNA in the major groove (11, 33).

Induced Fit in Protein-DNA Interactions

A comparison between the structure of M.*Hha*I-SAM and the structure of the ternary complex reveals that both the DNA and the protein have undergone radical structural reorganization, suggesting an induced-fit mechanism for the sequence-specific substrate binding (68).

DNA STRUCTURE: A FLIPPED BASE   The most remarkable feature of the ternary structure is that the target cytosine flips completely out of the DNA helix and positions itself in the active site of the enzyme, next to the cofactor. The exclusion of both the base and sugar of the target cytosine from the helix is accompanied by substantial distortion of the phosphodiester backbone on the same strand (Figure 4, *middle*). Both phosphates flanking the target cytosine deviate significantly (4 Å) from their normal positions in the free oligonucleotide. These changes increase the intrastrand phosphorus-phosphorus distances and provide a pathway for looping the target cytosine out of the helix.

ACTIVE-SITE FORMATION   The major conformational change of the protein lies in the loop (l-4D) located in the catalytic domain (Figure 4, *bottom*). This catalytic loop contains conserved residues in motif IV, including the nucleophile Cys81 and motif V. Upon DNA binding, this loop undergoes a massive conformational change toward the DNA-binding cleft and lies on the minor groove side (11, 33). Another con-

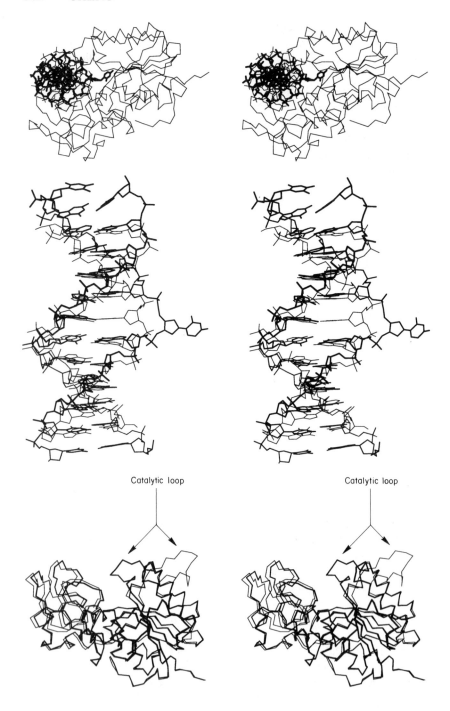

Catalytic loop   Catalytic loop

certed shift in the protein occurs in the recognition domain, which undergoes a small but significant movement toward the DNA-binding cleft.

The catalytic amino acids (Pro80, Cys81, Glu119, and Arg165) rearrange to form the active site. The sulfhydryl group of Cys81 is brought into close proximity to the target cytosine, allowing the direct attack on carbon-6. An ion pair between Arg165 and Glu119, which is present in the binary complex (12), is disrupted, and both side chains of Arg165 and Glu119 now interact with the target cytosine in the ternary complex (33).

Catalytic Domain

The catalytic domain contains nine out of the ten conserved motifs. The majority of the invariant or highly conserved residues occur in loops at the carboxyl ends of the parallel β-strands. Most of these residues are clustered on the inner surface of the cleft and are crucial for function.

Topologically, the catalytic domain can be divided into two halves. A connection between helix αC and strand β4 links the two halves, which are joined by hydrogen bonds between β-strands 1 and 4 (see Figure 8, *top*, below). The first half is formed by three β-α secondary structural elements (β1-αA-β2-αB-β3-αC) containing conserved motifs I–III. This half is mainly responsible for binding the cofactor SAM. Two β-α elements and one β-hairpin (β4-αD-β5-αE-β6-β7) form the second half, which contains conserved motifs IV–VII and is primarily responsible for catalysis. Table 1 lists the possible functions of these conserved residues derived from the structure.

←————————————————————————————

Figure 4   (*Top*) Stereo diagram showing the three-dimensional structure of M.*Hha*I covalently bound to a DNA duplex (11, 33). The protein is drawn with light lines, and the DNA is drawn with heavy lines. View is down the DNA helical axis in which the target cytosine can be seen flipped out from the helix and positioned in the active site. (*Middle*) The structure of classical B-DNA containing the M.*Hha*I recognition sequence GCGC (23) (*thin lines*) and that of the DNA in the ternary complex (*thick lines*). The phosphates on the unmethylated strand can be superimposed with an rms deviation of 1 Å. In contrast, phosphates around the extrahelical cytosine on the methylated strand show a larger deviation (4 Å) from their normal positions. (*Bottom*) The superimposition of the C_α-chains of M.*Hha*I are drawn with light lines (binary complex) or heavy lines (ternary complex). The 20-residue catalytic loop undergoes a large conformational change upon DNA binding. The extreme movement is about 25 Å toward the cleft by the tip of the loop. The DNA-recognition domain is also shifted toward the cleft with a concerted movement of about 3 Å. Generated by the option PLOT in program O (29).

Table 1 Properties of invariant and functional amino acids in M. *Hha*I[a]

Amino acid (structure element)[b]	Possible functions and comments
Motif I	
L17 (β1)	Hydrophobic pack against helices αC and αD
F18 (loop-1A)	Edge-to-face van der Waals (vdw) contact with the adenine of SAM
A19-G-x-G22	Loop-1A, part of the binding pocket for the methionine moiety of SAM
G23 (first aa of αA)	N-H$\cdots$O$_{\eta 1}$ (one of the terminal carboxyl oxygens of SAM)
Mofit II	
E40 (last aa of β2)	O$_{\epsilon 1}\cdots$H-03*, O$_{\epsilon 2}\cdots$H-04* (ribose hydroxyls of SAM)
W41 (β2)	Face-to-face vdw contact with the adenine of SAM
Motif III	
D60 (first aa of αC)	O$_{\delta 1}\cdots$H-N6 (adenine of SAM)
I61 (αC)	N-H$\cdots$N1 (adenine of SAM)
Motif IV	
G78 (last aa of β4)	Part of the binding pocket for the methionine moiety of SAM
F79 (loop-4D)	C=O$\cdots$H-N4 (target cytosine); C=O$\cdots$H-N$_{\delta 2}$ (N120)
P80	Essential for *(a)* the proper orientation of C81, *(b)* H-bond between main chain oxygen of F79 and N4 of target, and *(c)* for forming part of the binding pocket for the methionine moiety of SAM
C81	Covalent bond S$_{\gamma}$-C6 (target cytosine)
Q82	Possibly involved indirectly (through H_2O) in eliminating the 5-position proton
S85	O$_{\gamma}$-H$\cdots$O-P (5′ phosphate of target cytosine)
S87	Insertion into DNA helix from minor groove; O$_{\gamma}\cdots$H-N$_{\epsilon 2}$ (Q237)
G88	Essential for the insertion of S87 into the DNA helix
Motif V	
L100 (loop-4D)	Vdw contact with adenine of SAM on the same side of F18
Motif VI	
P113 (loop-D5)	Structural determinant
E119 (β5)	Interacts with target cytosine, O$_{\epsilon 1}\cdots$H-N4 (target cytosine); O$_{\epsilon 2}\cdots$H$\cdots$N3 (protonated N3)
N120 (β6)	Hydrophobic vdw contact with extrahelical target cytosine, N$_{\epsilon 2}$-H$\cdots$O=C (F79)
V121 (loop-5E)	Hydrophobic vdw contact with extrahelical target cytosine
Motif VII	
D144 (loop-E6)	Located on the outer surface of DNA-binding cleft and facing solvent
Y145 (β6)	Located on the outer surface of DNA-binding cleft and pack against with P113
Motif VIII	
G158 (loop-67)	Structural determinant
P160	Structural determinant

(continued)

Table 1 (continued)

Amino acid (structure element)[a]	Possible functions and comments
Q161	H-bonds with recognition domain, $N_{\epsilon 2}\cdots O{=}C$ (V282); $O_{\epsilon 1}\cdots H\text{-}N$ (L251); $O_{\epsilon 1}\cdots H\text{-}N_{\epsilon}$ (R163)
R163	H-bonds with recognition domain, $N_{\eta 2}\text{-}H\cdots O{=}C$ (L251); $N_{\eta 2}\text{-}H\cdots O{=}C$ (G303); $N_{\eta 1}\text{-}H\cdots O{=}C$ (S305); $N_{\epsilon}\text{-}H\cdots O_{\epsilon 1}$ (Q161)
R165 ($\beta 7$)	Interacts with target cytosine $N_{\epsilon}\text{-}H\cdots O2$ (target cytosine); $N_{\eta 1}\text{-}H\cdots O{=}C$ (E164); $N_{\eta 1}\text{-}H\cdots O\text{-}P$ (5′ phosphate of target cytosine); $N_{\eta 2}\text{-}H\cdots O2$ (target cytosine); $N_{\eta 2}\text{-}H\cdots O4^{*}$ (sugar ring of target)
Motif TRD	
GKGGQGER	First recognition loop
Q237	Interacts with orphan guanine, $N\text{-}H\cdots O6$ (OG); $O_{\epsilon 1}\cdots H\text{-}N1$ (OG); $O_{\epsilon 2}\cdots H\text{-}N2$ (OG); $N_{\epsilon}\text{-}H\cdots O_{\gamma}$ (S87)
R240	DNA-sequence specific interaction, $N_{\eta 2}\text{-}H\cdots O6$ (Gua +1); $N_{\eta 2}\text{-}H\cdots N7$ (Gua +1); $N_{\eta 1}\text{-}H\cdots O{=}C$ (G235)
TLSAYGGG	Second recognition loop
Motif IX	
R272	Ion pairing with E278, $N_{\eta 2}\text{-}H\cdots O_{\epsilon 2}$ (E278); $N_{\eta 1}\text{-}H\cdots O_{\epsilon 1}$ (E278); $N_{\eta 1}\text{-}H\cdots O{=}C$ (K273)
E278	Ion pairing with R272, $O_{\epsilon 1}\cdots H\text{-}N_{\eta 1}$ (R272); $O_{\epsilon 1}\cdots H\text{-}N$ (H275); $O_{\epsilon 1}\cdots H\text{-}N_{\eta 2}$ (R272); $O_{\epsilon 2}\cdots H\text{-}N$ (L197)
R281	Ion pairing with D287, $N_{\eta 2}\text{-}H\cdots O_{\delta 2}$ (D287); $N_{\epsilon}\text{-}H\cdots O_{\delta 2}$ (D287); $N_{\eta 1}\text{-}H\cdots O{=}C$ (L195)
Motif X	
G303	Structural determinant
N304	Possibly involved indirectly (through H_2O) in eliminating 5-position proton

[a] Protein secondary structure and motifs are those shown in Figure 8 (*top*) and Figure 2, respectively.

[b] Abbreviation: aa, amino acid. Standard one-letter abbreviations are used for the residues.

SAM-BINDING SITE   At the surface of the cleft, a pocket embedded in the catalytic domain next to the active site contains the SAM-binding site. The binding involves the insertion of the methionine moiety into the pocket, while the adenosyl moiety is flanked by the hydrophobic side chains (Phe18 of motif I, Trp41 of motif II, and Leu100 of motif V) and two charged side chains (Glu40 of motif II and Asp60 of motif III) (Figure 5). In the ternary complex, the pocket is in a closed form with sides provided by the target cytosine and three stretches of amino acids (Gly303-Asn-Ser-Val306 of motif X, Ala19-Gly-Leu-Gly-Gly23 of motif I, and Gly78-Phe-Pro-Cys81 of motif IV). The bulky side chains,

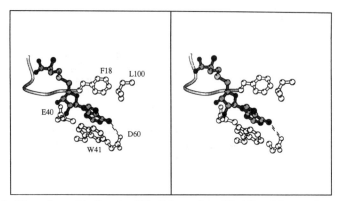

Figure 5   The cofactor binding site (33). Edge-to-face (Phe18) and face-to-face (Trp41) hydrophobic contact with the adenine ring of the cofactor. Glu40 and Asp60 form hydrogen bonds with the ribose and adenine rings, respectively. The glycine-rich loop l-1A is shown as a smooth coil winding through its C_α atom positions. Generated by the program MOLSCRIPT (36).

such as Leu21 and Phe79, point away from the pocket. After the methyl group is transferred, the sulfur atom of SAH is located about 5 Å away from carbon-5 of the target cytosine in the ternary complex (33).

METHYLATION SITE   In the ternary complex, the target cytosine is positioned in the active site formed by the conserved motifs IV (Pro-CysGln), VI (GluAsnVal), and VIII (GlnXArgXArg). Cys81 and SAH lie on opposite sides of the slightly nonpolar dihydrocytosine ring; hence, thiolate addition and methyl transfer originate from opposite faces of the ring. The sulfur atom of the nucleophile Cys81 is linked to carbon-6 covalently (33). The polar groups of the dihydrocytosine ring that normally form the Watson-Crick pair with guanine are now all involved in hydrogen bonds with side-chain and backbone groups of the invariant amino acids (Figure 6, *top*).

The interaction between Glu119 and the N3 and N4 atoms of the cytosine ring is of particular interest in light of (*a*) the N3 protonation and (*b*) the base specificity of two other nucleotide methylases. The distance (2.7 Å) between Glu119 and the N3 atom strongly suggests the presence of a hydrogen bond and therefore the presence of a proton either at the carboxylate oxygen or at N3 (see Figure 3). The most likely source of that proton is a highly ordered water molecule, which is found in direct contact with the side chain of Glu119 (33). This observation directly supports the proposed N3 protonation (see 2, 10, 66).

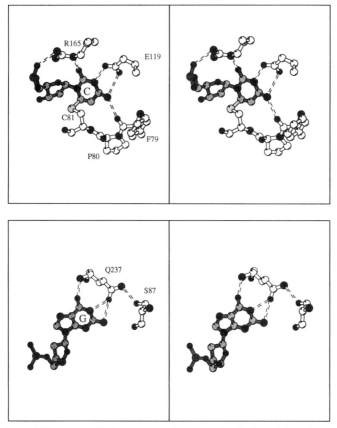

Figure 6   (*Top*) The extrahelical target cytosine is covalently linked through its carbon-6 to the sulfhydryl group of Cys81 and is anchored through hydrogen bonds with the backbone and side-chain atoms of Phe79 (to N4), Glu119 (to N3 and N4), and Arg165 (to O2) in M.*Hha*I. (*Bottom*) The intrahelical orphan guanine, which originally paired with the target cytosine, makes three hydrogen bonds with the side-chain and backbone atoms of Gln237 from the first recognition loop. A hydrogen bond links Gln237 to Ser87 from the catalytic loop. Generated by the program MOLSCRIPT (36).

Comparison of M.*Hha*I with two other nucleotide methylases that have similar catalytic mechanisms reveals the significance of the inter-action between Glu119 and N4 in defining base specificity. In thymidy-late synthase (20, 46), an invariant asparagine makes two hydrogen bonds to the N3 and O4 atoms of its substrate dUMP. Mutation of this asparagine to aspartate or glutamate converts the thymidylate synthase to a deoxycytidylate methylase operating on dCMP (21, 44). Interestingly, the dCMP hydroxymethylase of bacteriophage T4, whose normal substrate is dCMP, naturally contains an aspartate at this position (17). Thus, the base specificity between these two enzymes appears to be determined by the formation of a hydrogen bond either between the terminal NH_2 of an asparagine and the O4 atom on the uridine ring or between the terminal COO^- group of an aspartate or glutamate and the NH_2 group (N4) on the cytosine ring (Figure 7). The presence of an interaction between Glu119 and the N4 atom in M.HhaI indicates that the same mechanism is employed for defining which type of base is to be methylated.

PROTON ELIMINATION   According to the proposed mechanism (80, 81), a base that abstracts a proton from carbon-5 is needed for the β-elimination step (15). Around the target cytosine, the functions of two conserved amino acids in M.HhaI, Gln87 in motif IV and Asn304 in motif X, remain to be accounted for. However, neither the side chain of Gln87 nor that of Asn304 is close enough to carbon-5 to interact directly. In fact, water molecules are bound to the side chains of Asn304 and Gln87 (X Cheng, unpublished results), and such a water molecule may serve as the required general base catalyst.

DNA-Recognition Domain

The recognition domain is dominated by β-strands (12). It contains two glycine-rich sequences (Gly233-Lys-Gly-Gly-Gln-Gly-Glu-Arg240 and Thr250-Leu-Ser-Ala-Tyr-Gly-Gly-Gly-Ile258), which form two loops between β-strands and contact the DNA from the major-groove side. These amino acids are responsible for almost all of the specific interac-

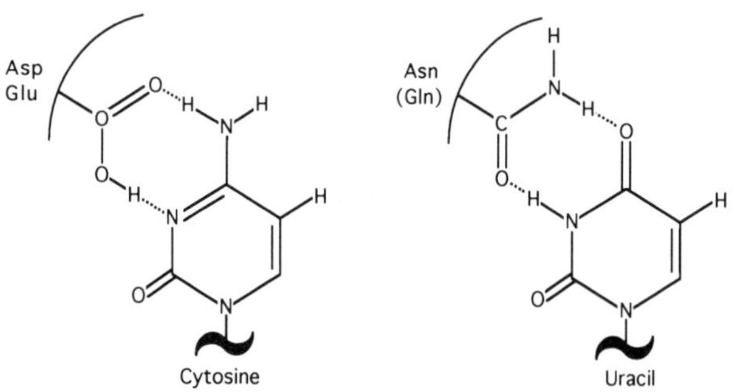

Figure 7   A major determinant of pyrimidine specificity is an asparagine in thymidylate synthase (substrate dUMP, *right*) (21, 44), an aspartic acid in bacteriophage T4 deoxycytidylate hydroxymethylase (substrate dCMP, *left*) (17), and a glutamic acid in M.HhaI (substrate cytosine, *left*) (33).

tions with the four recognition nucleotides 5'-GCGC-3' (33), which confirms the function of the recognition domain in specificity determination.

Interestingly, the two glycine-rich recognition loops fall within the putative TRD of M.*Hha*I predicted by Lauster et al (41). Given the variability both in size and sequence of the variable region, the accuracy of the prediction is remarkable. In fact, the second loop matches the consensus sequence in the C-terminal portion of the TRD (ThrLeuX$_5$-GlyIle). The first part of the loop (Thr250-Leu-Ser-Ala253) runs nearly parallel to the phosphate backbone and spans the entire length of the four recognition elements of the methylated strand. After a sharp turn, the second part of the loop (Tyr254-Gly-Gly-Gly257) embraces the final C·G base pair at the end of the recognition sequence by extending across the major groove. Close contact between the DNA-recognition sequences and the second loop appears to play an important role in positioning the first loop relative to the target cytosine prior to the enzyme's infiltration of the duplex and/or flipping of the target base.

In general, DNA Mtases may use such a novel two-loop DNA-binding motif to accomplish both specific recognition and flipping of the base to be methylated. In the DNA-docking model of the M.*Taq*I structure, the recognition domain has two loops that lie in the surface of the cleft that can be modeled into the major groove of DNA (G Schluckebier & W Saenger, personal communications).

BASE-FLIPPING MECHANISM   Like most specific DNA-binding proteins (27, 70), Mtases may also bind nonspecifically to DNA and probably locate their target sites through facilitated diffusion along DNA molecules (6). Let us assume that DNA binding precedes base expulsion. The M.*Hha*I structure shows that the target cytosine can flip out only through the minor groove. This is because all of the sequence-specific interactions with the target site occur on the major-groove side, and these interactions would be largely maintained during the selective flipping-out process. The extensive contacts between M.*Hha*I and six phosphates on the methylated strand surrounding the target cytosine (three on each side) can contribute to the localized strand opening. Therefore, part of the binding energy between the protein and the target DNA may be used to strain the DNA in a way that greatly reduces the energy barrier for cytosine expulsion.

In conjunction with the expulsion of the target cytosine, Gln237 of the first glycine-rich loop of the recognition domain penetrates into the DNA duplex from the major-groove side. A similar move followed by the catalytic loop including Ser87 approaches the DNA from the minor-groove side. This movement may close down the active-site cavity, lock the cytosine in an extrahelical position, complete the formation of the catalytic intermediate, and permit initiation of chemical catalysis.

The polar groups of the orphan guanine base are all involved in hydrogen bonds with the backbone and side-chain atoms of Gln237, whose alignment is stabilized through hydrogen bonding with Ser87 (Figure 6, *bottom*). The three glycine residues flanking Gln237, and one glycine following Ser87, appear to be crucial in positioning the side chains of Gln237 and Ser87 for their deep penetration into the helix to ensure the hydrophobic stacking with the methylated strand and the hydrogen bonding with the complementary strand.

Although this is the first structure in which a protein causes a base to flip out of the DNA helix, extrahelical bases have precedent in free DNA structure. An extra, unpaired cytosine or thymidine residue remains extrahelical in NMR structures (51, 52), while a bulged adenine residue can adopt extrahelical as well as intrahelical positions in a crystal structure (31). An NMR study has also shown that a guanine or adenine base facing an abasic site prefers an intrahelical position over flipping-out, presumably to allow continuous base stacking (13). This situation would be comparable to the M.*Hha*I-DNA complex after the cytosine has flipped out. The ability of the orphan guanine to maintain an intrahelical conformation in the absence of protein suggests that the infiltration of Gln237 and Ser87 into the helix may not be of primary importance in stabilizing this configuration and perhaps explains why these amino acids are not conserved among C5-cytosine Mtases.

Summary and Discussion

In summary, the binding of M.*Hha*I to substrate DNA results in large conformational changes of both the DNA and the protein. The distortion apparently begins as the localized strand opens; then the target cytosine flips out. Subsequent closing of the catalytic loop on the target maintains the extrahelical position of the cytosine, next to the bound cofactor, by a covalent bond formed between Cys81 and the carbon-6 of the cytosine.

Nucleophilic attack by the enzyme's cysteine thiolate on carbon-6 of a cytosine buried in duplex DNA would be stereochemically impossible. A major distortion of the helix at the site of action was therefore expected, but the solution chosen by nature is much more radical than had been generally anticipated. An important consequence of the extrahelical position of the cytosine is that it is now buried in an active site much like those of enzymes acting on small-molecule substrates (for example, catechol O-methyltransferase). We might expect that the mechanisms involving extrahelical bases may be used more generally by other DNA Mtases and base-modifying enzymes, such as repair enzymes. Some potential candidates are: O^6-methylguanine-DNA Mtase, a suicidal DNA-repair protein that removes methyl groups from the promutagenic lesion O^6-methylguanine and whose structure reveals a buried catalytic cysteine (49), and the β-glucosyltransferase (73) that transfers glucose from uridine diphosphoglucose to hydroxymethyl groups of 5-hydroxymethylcytosines in duplex DNA.

THE CATALYTIC DOMAIN IS A STRUCTURAL FRAMEWORK FOR THE SAM-DEPENDENT METHYLTRANSFERASES

Is the structural information on M.*Hha*I likely to be representative of only C5-cytosine Mtases or of all Mtases? The evolutionary relationships within and between the various Mtase families have been explored by using sequence comparisons, and a gene-duplication model has been proposed for the evolution of type II DNA Mtases (40).

At present, the crystal structure is known for only one other DNA Mtase: M.*Taq*I in complex with SAM (39). This structure is also bilobal. In addition, a single domain structure has been determined for catechol O-methyltransferase (COMT) (72). COMT catalyzes the transfer of the methyl group from SAM to one hydroxyl group of catechol. Catechol, like cytosine, contains a six-membered ring. However, in this case the substrate is a small molecule that can readily diffuse into the active site.

*Taq*I Methyltransferase

Thermus aquaticus DNA Mtase, M.*Taq*I, methylates the exocyclic nitrogen-6 of adenine in the double-helical DNA sequence 5'-TCGA-3' (4, 64). The crystal structure of this enzyme shows α/β folding of the protein into two domains of comparable size (39). The two domains are contiguous at the primary sequence level and, unlike M.*Hha*I, are connected by a single loop. The catalytic domain is dominated by a nine-stranded, twisted β-sheet, and as in M.*Hha*I, the first five β-strands are parallel (Figure 8, *middle*). Two antiparallel β-hairpins ($\beta9,\beta8$ and $\beta6,\beta7$) are adjacent to strand $\beta5$ in the parallel β-strands. The two conserved motifs (ProAlaXAlaXGlyPro and AsnProProTyr) are in loops at the carboxyl ends of strands $\beta1$ and $\beta4$, respectively, where the strand order is reversed.

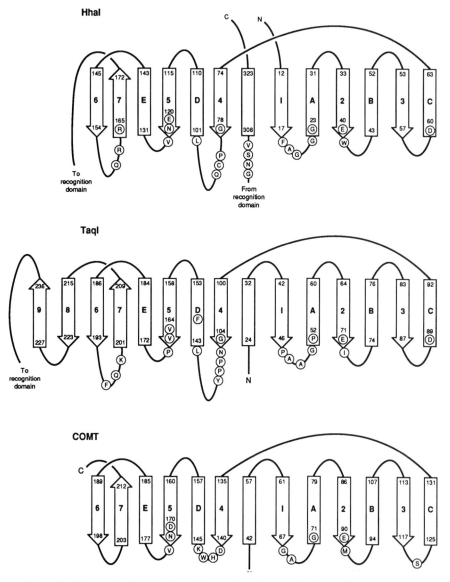

Figure 8 The topological drawing of (*top*) M.*Hha*I, (*middle*) M.*Taq*I, and (*bottom*) COMT indicate their similarity in the catalytic domains. Rectangles (lettered) indicate helices, and broad arrows (numbered) depict strands. Residue numbers indicate the extent of the secondary-structure element. Common elements of secondary structure among the three enzymes are shown in similar positions. Conserved or functionally important amino acids are circled. The unlabeled helix between strands 4 and 1 is folded from the C-terminus in M.*Hha*I, and from the N-terminus in both M.*Taq*I and COMT. Phe146 in helix αD and ValValPro in strand β5 are conserved amino acids found in those N6-adenine Mtases that recognize 5'-TNNA-3' (N = any nucleotide) (28).

Catechol O-Methyltransferase

The structure of COMT in complex with Mg^{2+}, the methyl donor SAM, and a competitive inhibitor shows a typical α/β fold (72). The protein forms one domain of a size roughly equal to that of the catalytic domain of M.*HhaI* and contains a seven-stranded central β-sheet (Figure 8, *bottom*). The parallel arrangement of strands $\beta1-\beta5$ is similar to that found in M.*HhaI* and M.*TaqI*. Loop l-1A contains the consensus sequence associated with SAM binding, while loop l-4D contains some catalytic amino acids.

Common Catalytic-Domain Structure

Comparison of the equivalent secondary structural elements for each protein indicate they share a common central β-sheet (63) (Figure 8). In M.*HhaI* and COMT, this β-sheet comprises five parallel and two antiparallel β-strands. The β-sheet in M.*TaqI* is larger than those in M.*HhaI* or COMT and contains an extra antiparallel β-hairpin ($\beta9$ and $\beta8$). In each structure, the functional residues are located in similar regions, mostly in the loops at the carboxyl ends of the parallel β-strands. Despite some differences in the size of individual secondary-structure elements and the loops in between, equivalent amino acids have strikingly similar functions. The most pronounced difference among these three structures is the helix prior to strand $\beta1$. In M.*TaqI* and COMT, this helix comes from the N-terminus of the protein, while the corresponding helix in M.*HhaI* is from the C-terminus. As a result, the two domains in M.*HhaI* have two connections, but the two M.*TaqI* domains have only one.

Extensive conservation in primary sequence is only evident for C5-cytosine Mtases (see 37). Structure-based sequence alignment, however, reveals that many of the conserved motifs in the catalytic domain of M.*HhaI* have homologues in the other two enzymes (54). Using the nomenclature of Posfai et al (57), motif I (a glycine-rich or closely related consensus sequence, e.g. Ala19-Gly-X-Gly-Gly23 in M.*HhaI*), motif II (represented by an invariant glutamate, Glu40 in M.*HhaI*), motif III (an invariant aspartate, Asp60 in M.*HhaI*), and motif V (an invariant leucine, Leu100 in M.*HhaI*) are easily identified in the M.*TaqI* sequence (Pro46-Ala-X-Ala-X-Gly-Pro52, Glu71, Asp89, and Leu142) and COMT (Gly66-Ala-X-X-Gly70, Glu90, Ser119, and Trp143). These four motifs form a very similar set of interactions with the cofactor for each of the three structures (63).

In contrast, motif IV (ProCysGln in M.*HhaI*), motif VI (GluAsnVal in M.*HhaI*), and motif VIII (GlnXArgXArg in M.*HhaI*) do not have recognizable equivalents with identical amino acids in M.*Taq*I. In M.*Hha*I, these three motifs constitute the active site and catalyze the carbon-5 methylation by interacting with the target cytosine base. Therefore, one would not necessarily expect the same amino acids to interact with the target adenine of M.*Taq*I. However, the amino acids in M.*Taq*I located in the corresponding structural elements (i.e. loops l-4D, l-5E, and l-67) probably have similar functions: For example, ProCysGln in M.*Hha*I and AsnProProTyr in M.*Taq*I are both located in loop l-4D; GluAsnVal in M.*Hha*I and ValValPro in M.*Taq*I are in strand β5 and loop l-5E; and Arg165 in M.*Hha*I and Phe196 in M.*Taq*I are in loop l-67.

N6-Adenine and N4-Cytosine Methylation

The most striking feature of the comparison is the nearly exact overlap of the conserved AsnProProTyr motif in M.*Taq*I and the active site of M.*Hha*I, including the essential amino acids Pro80, Cys81, Glu119, and Arg165, when the two structures are superimposed so that the central β-sheets are coincident (63). Spatially, Asn105 in M.*Taq*I occupies the position analogous to Glu119 in M.*Hha*I; Tyr108 and Phe196 in M.*Taq*I occupy positions similar to Cys81 and Arg165 in M.*Hha*I, respectively.

The mechanism of N6-adenine methylation does not occur via electrophilic attack at N1 followed by Dimroth rearrangement to yield N6-methyladenine (56); instead, it is more likely to occur via direct attack of CH_3^+ on N6. This mechanism would require the activation of N6, or more specifically, direct attack by CH_3^+ would only be possible if N6 became negatively polarized.

Labahn et al (39) have proposed that M.*Taq*I flips the target base out of the DNA helix and positions it into the active site, as occurred in the M.*Hha*I-DNA complex (11, 33). The positions of Asn105 in M.*Taq*I strongly suggest that the N6 (NH_2 group) might hydrogen-bond to the terminal carbonyl group of Asn105 in the AsnProProTyr motif. The invariant proline residues in this AsnProProTyr motif would orient and restrict the conformations of the active-site amino acids (Asn105 and Tyr108). The main-chain oxygens of the two proline residues could also interact with the amine hydrogens, resulting in a more negatively polarized N6. When the target base is bound to the active site, the aromatic rings of Tyr108 and Phe196 in loop l-67 would probably be face to face or edge to face with the planar structure of the target adenine ring. This interaction, and the hydrophobic contacts with Val-ValPro in strand β5 and loop l-56, may be important in orienting the target ring so that the CH_3^+ of the cofactor could attack N6.

Because the (Asp/Asn/Ser)ProPro(Tyr/Phe) motif is conserved in both N4-cytosine and N6-adenine Mtases, N4-cytosine Mtases should have the same catalytic mechanism. However, the conservation of a phenylalanine in loop l-67 (Phe196 in M.*Taq*I) needs further investigation. Of course, the exact mechanisms of methylation by N6-adenine and N4-cytosine Mtases will be facilitated by the determination of the structures of the protein-DNA complexes.

Summary

The catalytic domains of the bilobal proteins M.*Hha*I and M.*Taq*I and the entire single domain of COMT exhibit very similar three-dimensional folding and can serve as structural prototypes. This similarity and the equivalence of amino acids revealed by structural alignment indicate that many SAM-dependent Mtases may share a common catalytic-domain structure. They may either have evolved from a common evolutionary precursor or have converged to a remarkable extent. The fusion of genes has added various substrate-recognition domains to allow for a diversified substrate specificity.

ACKNOWLEDGMENTS

I am grateful to Dr. Richard J Roberts for his encouragement and support. The work from my group was supported in part by a grant from the National Institute of Health (GM 49245).

Literature Cited

1. Arber W, Dussoix D. 1962. Host specificity of DNA produced by *Escherichia coli. J. Mol. Biol.* 5:18–36
2. Baker DJ, Kan JLC, Smith SS. 1988. Recognition of structural perturbations in DNA by human DNA(cytosine-5)methyltransferase. *Gene* 74: 207–10
3. Balganesh TS, Reiners L, Lauster R, Noyer-Weidner M, Wilke K, Trautner TA. 1987. Construction and use of chimeric SPR/φ3T DNA methyltransferases in the definition of sequence recognizing enzyme regions. *EMBO J.* 6: 3543–49
4. Barany F, Slatko B, Danzitz M, Cowburn D, Schildkraut I, Wilson GG. 1992. The corrected nucleotide sequences of the *Taq*I restriction and modification

enzymes reveal a thirteen-codon overlap. *Gene* 112:91–95
5. Barsomian JM, Card CO, Wilson GG. 1988. Cloning of the *Hha*I and *Hin*PI restriction-modification systems. *Gene* 74:5–7
6. Berqerat A, Kriebardis A, Guschlbauer W. 1989. Preferential site-specific hemimethylation of GATC site in pBR322 DNA by Dam methyltransferase from *Escherichia coli. J. Biol. Chem.* 264:4064–70
7. Bestor TH, Coxon A. 1993. Cytosine methylation: the pros and cons of DNA methylation. *Curr. Biol.* 3: 384–86
8. Caserta M, Zacharias W, Nwankwo D, Wilson GG, Wells RD. 1987. Cloning, sequencing, *in vivo* promoter map-

ping, and expression in *Escherichia coli* of the gene for the *Hha*I methyltransferase. *J. Biol. Chem.* 262: 4770–77

9. Chen L, MacMillan AM, Chang W, Ezaz-Nikpay K, Lane WS, Verdine GL. 1991. Direct identification of the active-site nucleophile in a DNA (cytosine-5)-methyltransferase. *Biochemistry* 30:11018–25

10. Chen L, MacMillan AM, Verdine GL. 1993. Mutational separation of DNA binding from catalysis in a DNA cytosine methyltransferase. *J. Am. Chem Soc.* 115: 5318–19

11. Cheng X, Kumar S, Klimasauskas S, Roberts RJ. 1993. Crystal structure of the *Hha*I DNA methyltransferase. *Cold Spring Harbor Symp. Quant. Biol.* 58:331–38

12. Cheng X, Kumar S, Posfai J, Pflugrath JW, Roberts RJ. 1993. Crystal structure of the *Hha*I methylase complexed with S-adenosyl-L-methionine. *Cell* 74:299–307

13. Cuniasse P, Fazakerley GV, Guschlbauer W, Kaplan BE, Sowers LC. 1990. The abasic site as a challenge to DNA polymerase: a nuclear magnetic resonance study of G, C and T opposite a model abasic site. *J. Mol. Biol.* 213:303–14

14. Friedman S, Ansari N. 1992. Binding of the *Eco*RII methyltransferase to 5-fluorocytosine-containing DNA. Isolation of a bound protein. *Nucleic Acids Res.* 20:3241–48

15. Gerlt JA, Gassman PG. 1992. Understanding enzyme-catalyzed proton abstraction from carbon acids: details of stepwise mechanisms for β-elimination reactions. *J. Am. Chem. Soc.* 114: 5928–34

16. Gold M, Hurwitz J. 1964. The enzymatic methylation of ribonucleic acid and deoxyribonucleic acid. *J. Biol Chem.* 239:3858–65

17. Graves K, Butler MM, Hardy LW. 1992. Roles of Cys_{148} and Asp_{179} in catalysis by deoxycytidylate hydroxymethylase from bacteriophage T4 examined by site-directed mutagenesis. *Biochemistry* 31:10315–21

18. Gruenbaum Y, Naveh-Many T, Cedar H, Razin A. 1981. Sequence specificity of methylation in higher plant DNA. *Nature* 292:860–62

19. Hanck T, Schmidt S, Fritz HJ. 1993. Sequence-specific and mechanism-based crosslinking of *Dcm* DNA cytosine-C5 methyltransferase of *E. coli* K-

12 to synthetic oligonucleotides containing 5-fluoro-2'-deoxycytidine. *Nucleic Acids Res.* 21:303–9

20. Hardy LW, Finer-Moore JS, Mountfort WR, Jones MO, Santi DV, Stroud, RM. 1987. Atomic structure of thymidylate synthase: target for rational drug design. *Science* 235:448–55

21. Hardy LW, Nalivaika E. 1992. Asn_{177} in *Escherichia coli* thymidylate synthase is a major determinant of pyrimidine specificity. *Proc. Natl. Acad. Sci. USA* 89:9725–29

22. Hayatsu H. 1976. Bisulfite modification of nucleic acids and their constituents. *Prog. Nucleic Acid Res. Mol. Biol.* 16:75–124

23. Heinemann U, Alings C, Bansal M. 1992. Double helix formation, groove dimensions and ligand binding potential of a G/C stretch in B-DNA. *EMBO J.* 11:1931–39

24. Herman GE, Modrich P. 1982. *Escherichia coli dam* methylase: physical and catalytic properties of the homogeneous enzyme. *J. Biol. Chem.* 257: 2605–12

25. Hotchkiss RD. 1948. The quantitative separation of purines, pyrimidines, and nucleosides by paper chromatography. *J. Biol. Chem.* 168:315–32

26. Ingrosso D, Fowler AV, Bleibaum J, Clarke S. 1989. Sequence of the D-aspartyl/L-isoaspartyl protein methyltransferase from human erythrocytes: common sequence motifs for protein, DNA, RNA, and small molecule S-adenosylmethionine–dependent methyltransferases. *J. Biol. Chem.* 264: 20131–39

27. Jack WE, Terry BJ, Modrich P. 1982. Involvement of outside DNA sequences in the major kinetic path by which *Eco*RI endonuclease locates and leaves its recognition sequence. *Proc. Natl. Acad. Sci. USA* 79: 4010–14

28. Janulaitis A, Vaisvila R, Timinskas A, Klimasauskas S, Butkus V. 1992. Cloning and sequence analysis of the genes coding for *Eco*57I type IV restriction-modification enzymes. *Nucleic Acid. Res.* 20:6051–56

29. Jones TA, Kjeldgaaed M. 1993. Manual for O. Version 5.9. Dept. Molecular Biology, Uppsala Univ., Sweden; Dept. Chemistry, Aarhus Univ., Denmark

30. Jordan F, Sostman HD. 1973. Molecular orbital (CNDO/2 and MINDO) calculations on protonated deoxyribonu-

cleic acid bases: the effects of base protonation on intermolecular interactions. *J. Am. Chem. Soc.* 95:6544–54

31. Joshua-Tor L, Frolow F, Appella E, Hope H, Rabinovich D, Sussman JL. 1992. Three-dimensional structures of bulge-containing DNA fragments. *J. Mol. Biol.* 225:397–431

32. Jost JP, Saluz HP, eds. 1993. *DNA Methylation: Molecular Biology and Biological Significance.* Basel: Birkhäuser

33. Klimasauskas S, Kumar S, Roberts RJ, Cheng X. 1994. *Hha*I methyltransferase flips its target base out of the DNA helix. *Cell* 76:357–69

34. Klimasauskas S, Nelson JL, Roberts RJ. 1991. The sequence specificity domain of cytosine-C5 methylases. *Nucleic Acids Res.* 19:6183–90

35. Klimasauskas S, Timinskas A, Menkevicius S, Butkiene D, Butkus V, Janulaitis A. 1989. Sequence motifs characteristic of DNA (cytosine-N4) methyltransferases: similarity to adenine and cytosine-C5 DNA-methylases. *Nucleic Acids Res.* 17:9823–32

36. Kraulis PJ. 1991. Molscript: a program to produce both detailed and schematic plots of protein structures. *J. Appl. Cryst.* 24:946–50

37. Kumar S, Cheng X, Klimasauskas S, Mi S, Posfai J, et al. 1994. The DNA (cytosine-5) methyltransferases. *Nucleic Acids Res.* 22:1–10

38. Kumar S, Cheng X, Pflugrath JW, Roberts RJ. 1992. Purification, crystallization, and preliminary X-ray diffraction analysis of an M.*Hha*I-AdoMet complex. *Biochemistry* 31:8648–53

39. Labahn J, Granzin J, Schluckebier G, Robinson DP, Jack WE, et al. 1994. Three dimensional structure of the adenine specific DNA methyltransferase M.*Taq*I in complex with the cofactor S-adenosylmethionine. *Proc. Natl. Acad. Sci. USA.* 91:10957–61

40. Lauster R. 1989. Evolution of type II DNA methyltransferases. A gene duplication model. *J. Mol. Biol.* 206:313–21

41. Lauster R, Trautner TA, Noyer-Weidner M. 1989. Cytosine-specific type II DNA methyltransferases. A conserved enzyme core with variable target-recognizing domains. *J. Mol. Biol.* 206:305–12

42. Leonhardt H, Page AW, Weier HU, Bestor TH. 1992. A targeting sequence directs DNA methyltransferase to sites of DNA replication in mammalian nuclei. *Cell* 71:865–73

43. Li E, Bestor TH, Jaenisch R. 1992. Targeted mutation of the DNA methyltransferase gene results in embryonic lethality. *Cell* 69:915–26

44. Liu L, Santi DV. 1992. Mutation of asparagine 229 to aspartate in thymidylate synthase converts the enzyme to a deoxycytidylate methylase. *Biochemistry* 31:5100–4

45. Mann MB, Smith HO. 1979. Specificity of DNA methylases from *Haemophilus* sp. In *Proc. Conf. Transmethylation*, ed. E Usdin, RT Borchardt, CR Creveling, pp. 483–92. New York: Elsevier

46. Matthews DA, Appelt K, Oatley SJ, Xuong NH. 1990. Crystal structure of *Escherichia coli* thymidylate synthase containing bound 5-fluoro-2'-deoxyuridylate and 10-propargyl-5,8-dideazafolate. *J. Mol. Biol.* 214:923–36

47. Mi S, Roberts RJ. 1992. How M.*Msp*I and M.*Hpa*II decide which base to methylate. *Nucleic Acids Res.* 20:4811–16

48. Mi S, Roberts RJ. 1993. The DNA binding affinity of *Hha*I methylase is increased by a single amino acid substitution in the catalytic center. *Nucleic Acids Res.* 21:2459–64

49. Moore MH, Gulbis JM, Dodson EJ, Demple B, Moody PCE. 1994. Crystal structure of a suicidal DNA repair protein: the Ada O^6-methylguanine-DNA methyltransferase from *E. coli. EMBO J.* 13:1495–1501

50. Modrich P. 1991. Mechanisms and biological effects of mismatch repair. *Annu. Rev. Genet.* 25:229–53

51. Morden KM, Chu YG, Martin FH, Tinoco I Jr. 1983. Unpaired cytosine in the deoxyoligonucleotide duplex dCA-$_3$CA$_3$G·dCT$_6$G is outside of the helix. *Biochemistry* 22:5557–63

52. Morden KM, Gunn BM, Maskos K. 1990. NMR studies of a deoxyribocanucleotide containing an extrahelical thymidine surrounded by an oligo (dA)·oligo(dT) tract. *Biochemistry* 29:8835–45

53. Noyer-Weidner M, Trautner TA. 1993. Methylation of DNA in prokaryotes. See Ref. 32, pp. 39–108

54. O'Gara M, McCloy K, Malone T, Cheng X. 1994. Structure-based sequence alignment of three AdoMet-dependent methyltransferases. *Gene.* In press

55. Osterman DG, DePillis GD, Wu JC,

Matsuda A, Santi DV. 1988. 5-Fluoro-cytosine in DNA is a mechanism-based inhibitor of *Hha*I methylase. *Biochemistry* 27:5204–10

56. Pogolotti AL Jr, Ono A, Subramanian R, Santi DV. 1988. On the mechanism of DNA-adenine methylase. *J. Biol. Chem.* 263:7461–64

57. Posfai J, Bhagwat AS, Posfai G, Roberts RJ. 1989. Predictive motifs derived from cytosine methyltransferases. *Nucleic Acids Res.* 17:2421–35

58. Deleted in proof

59. Roberts RJ, Halford SS. 1993. Type II restriction endonucleases. In *Nucleases,* ed. SM Linn, RS Lloyd, RJ Roberts, pp. 35–88. Cold Spring Harbor, NY: Cold Spring Harbor Lab.

60. Roberts RJ, Myers PA, Morrison A, Murray K. 1976. A specific endonuclease from *Haemophilus haemolyticus. J. Mol. Biol.* 103:199–208

61. Rubin RA, Modrich P. 1977. *Eco*RI methylase: physical and catalytic properties of the homogeneous enzyme. *J. Biol. Chem.* 252:7265–72

62. Santi DV, Hardy LW. 1987. Catalytic mechanism and inhibition of tRNA(Uracil-5) methyltransferase: evidence for covalent catalysis. *Biochemistry* 26:8599–8606

63. Schluckebier G, O'Gara M, Saenger W, Cheng X. Universal catalytic domain structure of AdoMet-dependent methyltransferases. *J. Mol. Biol.* In press

64. Slatko BE, Benner JS, Jager-Quinton T, Moran LS, Simcox TG, et al. 1987. Cloning, sequencing and expression of the *Taq*I restriction-modification system. *Nucleic Acid Res.* 15:9781–93

65. Smith HO, Annau TM, Chandrasegaran S. 1990. Finding sequence motifs in groups of functionally related proteins. *Proc. Natl. Acad. Sci. USA* 87:826–30

66. Smith SS, Kaplan BE, Sowers LC, Newman EM. 1992. Mechanism of human methyl-directed DNA methyltransferase and the fidelity of cytosine methylation. *Proc. Natl. Acad. Sci. USA* 89:4744–48

67. Som S, Bhagwat AS, Friedman S. 1987. Nucleotide sequence and expression of the gene encoding the *Eco*RII modification enzyme. *Nucleic Acids Res.* 15:313–32

68. Spolar RS, Record MT Jr. 1994. Coupling of local folding to site-specific binding of proteins to DNA. *Science* 263:777–84

69. Srinivasan PR, Borek E. 1964. Enzymatic alteration of nucleic acid structure. *Science* 145:548–53

70. Terry BJ, Jack WE, Modrich P. 1985. Facilitated diffusion during catalysis by *Eco*RI endonuclease: nonspecific interactions in *Eco*RI catalysis. *J. Biol. Chem.* 260:13130–37

71. Trautner TA, Balganesh TS, Pawlek B. 1988. Chimeric multispecific DNA methyltransferases with novel combinations of target recognition. *Nucleic Acids Res.* 16:6649–57

72. Vidgren J, Svensson LA, Liljas A. 1994. Crystal structure of catechol *O*-methyltransferase. *Nature* 368:354–58

73. Vrielink A, Ruger W, Driessen HPC, Freemont PS. 1994. Crystal structure of the DNA modifying enzyme β-glucosyltransferase in the presence and absence of the substrate uridine diphosphoglucose. *EMBO J.* 13:3413–22

74. Walter J, Trautner TA, Noyer-Weidner M. 1992. High plasticity of multispecific DNA methyltransferases in the region carrying DNA target recognizing enzyme modules. *EMBO J.* 11:4445–50

75. Deleted in proof

76. Wilke K, Rauhut E, Noyer-Weidener M, Lauster R, Pawlek B, et al. 1988. Sequential order of target-recognizing domains in multispecific DNA-methyltransferases. *EMBO J.* 7:2601–9

77. Wilson GG. 1992. Amino acid sequence arrangements of DNA-methyltransferases. *Methods Enzymol.* 216:259–79

78. Wilson GG, Murray NE. 1991. Restriction and modification systems. *Annu. Rev. Genet.* 25:585–627

79. Winkler FK. 1994. DNA totally flipped-out by methylase. *Structure* 2:79–83

80. Wu JC, Santi DV. 1985. On the mechanism and inhibition of DNA cytosine methyltransferases. In *Biochemistry and Biology of DNA Methylation,* ed. GI Cantoni, A Razin, pp. 119–29. New York: Liss

81. Wu JC, Santi DV. 1987. Kinetic and catalytic mechanism of *Hha*I methyltransferase. *J. Biol. Chem.* 262:4778–86

82. Wu JC, Santi DV. 1988. High level expression and purification of *Hha*I methyltransferase. *Nucleic Acids Res.* 16:703–17

83. Wyszynski MW, Gabbara S, Bhagwat AS. 1992. Substitutions of a cysteine conserved among DNA cytosine methylases result in a variety of phenotypes. *Nucleic Acids Res.* 20:319–26

Annu. Rev. Biophys. Biomol. Struct. 1995. 24:319–50
Copyright © 1995 by Annual Reviews Inc. All rights reserved

NUCLEIC ACID HYBRIDIZATION: Triplex Stability and Energetics

G. Eric Plum and Daniel S. Pilch

Department of Chemistry, Rutgers, The State University of New Jersey, Piscataway, New Jersey 08855-0939

Scott F. Singleton

Department of Chemistry, The Pennsylvania State University, University Park, Pennsylvania 16802

Kenneth J. Breslauer

Department of Chemistry, Rutgers, The State University of New Jersey, Piscataway, New Jersey 08855-0939

KEY WORDS: thermodynamics, calorimetry, triple helices and antigene strategies, melting transitions, pH effects, salt effects, ligand-binding effects

CONTENTS

1056-8700/95/0610-0319$05.00

319

ABSTRACT

In this chapter, we review the current state of the thermodynamic database for triple helical oligonucleotide hybridization reactions and present a critical assessment of the methods used to obtain the relevant
data. The thermodynamic stability of triple-helix oligonucleotide constructs is discussed in terms of its dependence on temperature, chain
length, pH, salt, base sequence, base and backbone modifications, and
ligand binding. In particular, we examine the coupling of hybridization
equilibria to proton, cation, and drug-binding equilibria. Throughout
the chapter, we emphasize that a detailed understanding of the endogenous and exogenous variables that control triplex stability is required
for the rational design of oligonucleotides for specific therapeutic, diagnostic, and/or biotechnological applications, as well as for elucidating
the potential cellular roles of these higher-order nucleic acid complexes.

PERSPECTIVES AND OVERVIEW

Nucleic acid molecules can associate via highly specific inter- and intramolecular equilibria to form higher-order structures. Such association
equilibria generally are referred to as hybridization events. This nomenclature underscores the fact that the final complex is a hybrid in which
the associating domains maintain their chemical identities rather than
transform into different chemical states as when, for example, an inorganic acid and base react to form a salt and water.

The most familiar form of hybridization corresponds to the association of two complementary strands or domains to form a duplex structure. The specificity of this association results from the well-known
complementarity between purine (pur) and pyrimidine (pyr) bases (A
with T and G with C). This exquisite complementarity is one of the
primary determinants of genetic expression and regulation. The first
description of the three-dimensional structure of double-stranded DNA
(172) provided insights into the physicochemical basis of this complementarity. Understanding the fundamental principles underlying the
strength and specificity of the molecular recognition of one nucleic acid

molecule by another continues to be an important endeavor for nucleic acid chemists.

For many years, the Watson-Crick model of DNA duplex hybridization dominated the nucleic acid field. However, over the past two decades, nucleic acids have become recognized as far more polymorphic than originally assumed. These new polymorphs include left-handed and parallel-stranded duplexes, hairpins with ordered loops, triplexes, and quadruplexes. Many of these "new" polymorphs are stabilized by non–Watson-Crick base-base and base-backbone interactions. Clearly, nucleic acids can associate to form a wide range of higher-order structures via hybridization events that utilize a surprisingly diverse set of recognition motifs. Significantly, many of these higher-order structures may have biological functions, so these polymorphs are more than laboratory curiosities.

We obviously cannot review here all known classes of nucleic acid structures that result from hybridization between complementary domains. Instead, for reasons explained below, we have decided to focus this review on triplexes, with particular attention to the thermodynamic properties of this class of structures.

The Triplex Motif

The formation of triple-helical nucleic acid complexes shares many features in common with double-helix formation (10). However, in the case of triplex formation, a third strand hybridizes to a Watson-Crick double helix through hydrogen bonding and stacking between the bases of the third strand and the base pairs of the duplex. Since the initial report of triple-helical nucleic acid complexes by Felsenfeld, Davies & Rich (22) in 1957, two factors have stimulated interest in triple-helical DNA. First was the discovery of novel triplex-containing structures, such as H-form DNA, which may exist in vivo and may play a role in mediating cellular events (54, 92, 173). Second was the insight that oligonucleotide-directed triple-helix formation could serve as a general solution for the sequence-specific recognition of double-stranded DNA (69, 94) and RNA (41, 134). Such recognition will be important in the development of reagents for the physical mapping of chromosomes (156), in the design of nucleic acid–based diagnostic protocols, and in the development of antigene therapeutic agents capable of site-specific inhibition of transcription in vivo (26, 44, 80, 94, 112, 114, 157, 160).

Triple helices fall into at least two families that differ in the sequence composition of the third strand, the relative orientation of the backbones of the three strands, and the base triple interactions. In both structural families, a third strand is bound to the major groove of a homopurine·homopyrimidine Watson-Crick duplex domain. In one class, pyrimidine-rich oligonucleotides bind to purine tracts in the major groove of a host Watson-Crick DNA duplex. In this hybridization motif, the third strand binds through the formation of specific Hoogsteen-type hydrogen bonds (T·AT and C^+·GC base triples) to the purine Watson-Crick bases (14, 76, 94, 97, 122, 126–129, 153) and is parallel to the purine Watson-Crick strand (94). In a second class, purine-rich oligonucleotides bind to purine tracts in the major groove of a host Watson-Crick DNA duplex. In this hybridization motif, the third strand binds antiparallel to the Watson-Crick purine strand by forming reverse Hoogsteen hydrogen bonds [G·GC (121, 125) and A·AT (119) or T·AT base triples (121, 125)]. The general structural features of the two classes of triple-helical complexes were recently reviewed (10, 123) and are not discussed in detail here. Instead, we focus our attention on the thermodynamic behavior of these complexes and how thermodynamic information can be exploited to optimize the design of triplex-forming oligonucleotides.

The Need for Triplex Thermodynamic Data

An elucidation of the possible cellular role of triplexes, as well as the rational design and use of oligonucleotides (or analogues) for the detection and/or modulation of biologically important events at arbitrary DNA sequences, will require an understanding of how the stabilities of triple-helical complexes depend on their double- and single-stranded components, as well as on solution conditions. Characterizing the linkage between thermodynamic parameters and solution conditions represents an essential first step toward such an understanding. Furthermore, a knowledge of how the fundamental properties of triplexes lead to their relative stabilities or instabilities will be of practical utility for the de novo design of oligonucleotides.

Relative to the rather extensive thermodynamic characterizations of nucleic acid duplexes (3, 7, 23, 29, 62, 137), the triplex thermodynamic database is small and even inconsistent. However, the recognition of the importance of such data for biomedical and biotechnological applications has recently stimulated studies designed to develop such a database. To evaluate critically this growing body of literature, one must understand the methods by which thermodynamic data are derived from experimental observables and the nature of the underlying assumptions implicit or explicit in a given method of analysis. Thus, in the sections that follow, we describe various methods of analysis that have been, and that can be, used to obtain the requisite triplex thermodynamic data. We also describe various triplex constructs and discuss the factors that influence the thermodynamic behavior of such systems, particularly emphasizing how these factors can be exploited to modulate the stability of oligonucleotide triple helices.

GENERAL CONSIDERATIONS

Comparison of Thermodynamic States

In any thermodynamic analysis, one evaluates differences in state functions (ΔG, ΔH, ΔS, ΔC_p, etc). Consequently, meaningful comparisons between systems only are possible when one knows or assumes that either the initial or final states of the two systems being compared are identical. Thus, great care must be taken to define the states in any thermodynamic argument. For this reason, it is important to design oligonucleotide sequences and solution conditions that avoid secondary equilibria that compete with the desired primary triplex equilibrium under study. In this regard, one should note that the conformational states available to single-stranded oligonucleotides, particularly at low temperature and pH, may not be consistent with the assumption of random-coil behavior that is made in most thermodynamic analyses. For example, C-rich single-stranded oligonucleotides self-associate via CC^+ interactions to form duplexes (36, 107) and quadruplexes (33, 73). Similarly, oligopurines with several contiguous guanine residues self-associate via G-quadrates to form quadruplexes (140, 141). Each of these self-association events, as well as Watson-Crick hairpin formation and single-stranded stacking (17, 168), can contribute significantly to the thermodynamic behavior of a system and therefore must be considered when evaluating triplex thermodynamics.

Furthermore, thermodynamic analysis, at least as described here, requires the system to be at equilibrium. Consequently, the experimental design must permit sufficient time for the system to equilibrate. This consideration is particularly important for triplex systems because the few studies that have examined the kinetics of triple-helix formation (79, 136, 147) reveal a slower rate compared with duplex formation.

Model Oligonucleotide Triple-Helix Constructs

Several model oligonucleotide triple-helix systems have been described, although few have been subjected to thorough thermodynamic characterization. The primary difference between many of these triplex models resides in the molecularity of the complex, which in turn influences the nature of the duplex and triplex ends. For example, the literature contains reports of three-stranded complexes with contiguous duplex extensions (21, 41, 110, 145, 149–152) and with so-called blunt ends (52, 60, 104, 136, 175, 184). Other triplex constructs include Watson-Crick hairpins paired with oligopyrimidine strands (82, 133, 134, 181), an all-pyrimidine hairpin paired with an oligopurine (180), circular oligonucleotides paired with linear oligonucleotides (64), and single-stranded intramolecular triplexes (9, 42, 74–77, 109, 119–122, 125–127, 153, 169, 170).

The presence of the loops that connect the paired regions in some of these model triplex constructs may not be benign. For example, nuclease digestion experiments suggest that the occupancy of the major groove of the Watson-Crick domain results in disruption of apparent structure in a four-cytosine hairpin loop that joins the Watson-Crick strands (170). This observation is not surprising given the structural perturbation, relative to standard B-form DNA, in the duplex region of intramolecular triplexes reported by Radhakrishnan & Patel (123). Similarly, nonbonded loop residues in hairpins (143) and dangling ends on duplexes (142) can contribute to the overall thermodynamics of oligonucleotide structures possessing these nonbonded regions. One approach for minimizing such complications may be the use of nonnucleotide linkers (19, 138), although these elements also may be perturbing. Clearly, additional studies are required.

Appropriately designed model oligonucleotide triple-helix constructs can be induced to undergo two distinct order-disorder transitions by careful adjustment of solution conditions. In this way, one can decouple the triplex-to-duplex transition from the duplex-to-coil transition. Three-stranded model triplexes that contain duplex extensions afford the most realistic model for triplex-duplex junctions as they would exist in most triplex applications. In this connection, observations of triple-helix binding cooperativity (12) suggest that the effects of third-strand binding do not propagate far beyond the ends of the triple-helical region. Other triplex models, particularly the intramolecular constructs, while unnatural in their treatment of end effects, provide significant advantages for the systematic evaluation of base triple defects, unusual bases, etc. When considering the effects of small perturbations (mismatches, bulges, etc) well removed from the ends, one can employ an analysis based on differences ($\Delta\Delta H$, $\Delta\Delta G$, etc). In this analysis, anomalies contributed by end effects should be independent of the central region and can be subtracted out. Although the primary thermodynamic data (ΔG, ΔH, etc) might be compromised by end effects, the impact of a substitution is well represented by the differential thermodynamic parameters ($\Delta\Delta G$, $\Delta\Delta H$, etc).

As noted above, the intramolecular triple helix is an important model construct. Intramolecular triplex formation has been achieved for both pyr·pur·pyr (42, 74–77, 122, 126, 127, 153, 170) and pur·pur·pyr (9, 119–121, 125) triple-helix motifs. Such intramolecular constructs may serve as models for the biologically interesting triple helices. For pyr· pur·pyr and pur·pur·pyr triplexes, these constructs already have proven valuable in the elucidation of triple-helix three-dimensional structure by NMR (74–77, 119–122, 125–127, 153). In addition to fixing the orientation of the third strand, such constructs have some useful advantages in thermodynamic studies because the molecularity of the order-disorder transitions is fixed at one, thereby removing the dependence of the transitions on oligonucleotide concentration. Consequently, the coupled effects of pH and salt concentration are more clearly observed. In fact, the decoupling of oligonucleotide concentration effects by studies on intramolecular triplexes has allowed construction of detailed phase diagrams (109, 169) and the development of a semi-empirical model for DNA triple-helix phase behavior (109).

Coupled Equilibria in Triple-Helix Hybridization

Coupled equilibria play a large role in the overall thermodynamic behavior of oligonucleotide triple-helix systems. Specifically, the role of salts and pH (if the third strand contains C) are crucial and dependent on each other. A complete thermodynamic description of triplex hybridization equilibria ultimately requires consideration of salt and pH effects, as well as the impact of the uptake or release of associated water molecules (131). Drug binding also can couple to third-strand binding equilibria to either shift the overall equilibrium toward or away from stable triple-helix formation (13, 18, 70, 72, 78, 84, 85, 100, 103, 106, 108, 139).

Hybridization reactions that involve changes in the protonation state of the bases (i.e. cytosine protonation to form the C^+GC triple) require special attention to the nature of the buffer solution, a point emphasized by several groups (133, 175). Many commonly used hydrogen-ion buffers, notably Tris [tris(hyroxymethyl)aminomethane], exhibit large heats of ionization, which results in temperature-dependent changes in pH. When a hybridization equilibrium is coupled to a change in protonation, it will be very sensitive to pH. Thus, thermal melting experiments carried out in buffers such as Tris must be corrected for contributions of buffer protonation and deprotonation. To minimize this correction, one should choose buffers with low heats of ionization. In this regard, we also point out that the pK values of hydrogen-ion buffers depend on the concentration of the supporting electrolyte in solution.

METHODS OF ANALYSIS

Determination of Free Energy

All of the noncalorimetric methods for determining the free energy of hybridization of oligonucleotides depend on the well-known relation $\Delta G^\circ = -RT\ln K$, where R is the gas constant, T is temperature, and K is the equilibrium association constant. The value of K may be determined in a variety of ways. The form of K depends both on the number of nucleic acid species in the complex and on the solution conditions. When solution conditions are constant, K for oligonucleotide hybridization reactions is simply described by the relative concentrations of the component oligonucleotides. For many oligonucleotide systems, the equilibrium is bimolecular (oligo + target ↔ complex). In such cases, the equilibrium constant can be described by $K = [\text{complex}]/[\text{oligo}][\text{target}]$, where [complex] is the concentration of the complex, [oligo] is the free-oligonucleotide concentration, and [target] is the concentration of unbound target. For triple-helix hybridization, the target will be a nucleic acid duplex, although a single-stranded target will bind to two oligonucleotides in some cases. A complete description of any of these equilibria requires knowledge of the numbers of each chemical species, including protons, cations, anions, and waters, that is taken up or released upon hybridization (131). Consequently, one must take care when comparing K values for different triplex-forming equilibria to ensure that the equilibrium constants are comparably defined.

As noted above, when the solution conditions are constant, the equilibrium constant, K, for oligonucleotide hybridization can be described by the relative concentrations of the component oligonucleotides. Methods for measuring the amounts of bound and free oligonucleotide are based on one of three principles: (a) physical separation of the mixture, (b) spectroscopic estimation of relative concentrations, and/ or (c) manipulation of the equilibrium to conditions under which the relative concentrations of the components are known (i.e. at T_m).

Gel electrophoresis has proven invaluable in the qualitative description of oligonucleotide complexes because the electrophoretic mobility of complexes typically differs from that of the constituent oligonucleotides. The use of gel-based methods is attractive because the experiments are rapid and require only trace amounts of radiolabeled material. Separation of equilibrium mixtures by gel electrophoresis and quantitation of the material in each band comprise one method of evaluating equilibrium constants (132). To use this approach, the complexes formed must be sufficiently stable, thermodynamically and kinetically, so that the equilibrium is not disturbed by the gel matrix or the applied electric field over the course of the electrophoresis. For these reasons, the method is best applied to relatively long oligonucleotides under conditions of high stability.

A gel-based method for which potential reequilibration on the gel is not a problem involves chemical marking of one of the components, subsequent separation by gel electrophoresis, and quantitation of the marked molecules. For example, in the method of quantitative affinity cleavage titration developed by Singleton & Dervan (150), an oligonucleotide is attached covalently to an inactive DNA-cleaving agent, in this case an EDTA·Fe moiety, and allowed to equilibrate with the target duplex. Cleavage is activated by the addition of another reagent, dithiothreitol, which promotes cleavage of the Watson-Crick duplex DNA near the site at which the oligonucleotide is bound. The cleavage reaction is allowed to proceed for a short time and then is deactivated. The mixture of cleaved and uncleaved target DNA is separated electrophoretically on a gel and the cleaved strands are quantitated. Because the cleavage is proportional to the fraction of target duplex bound by the oligonucleotide, the equilibrium constant can be determined from the dependence of the cleavage intensity on the oligonucleotide concentration.

Frequently, one only is interested in the difference in free-energy change ($\Delta\Delta G$) associated with small alterations in the oligonucleotide probe [i.e. a perfect Watson-Crick (or Hoogsteen) match vs a single mismatch]. Assuming that the imperfect complex can form under the experimental conditions and can be separated by electrophoresis from the perfect complex, competitive equilibrium binding experiments can provide a means for directly determining relative equilibrium constants and thus $\Delta\Delta G$ (133). When applied to the triple-helix case, the mismatched oligonucleotide is equilibrated at various concentration ratios with the perfectly matched, ^{32}P-labeled strand and the target duplex. The mixture is analyzed using gel electrophoresis, and two bands are observed. The more slowly migrating band is the perfectly matched triplex, and the fast-moving band is the unhybridized perfectly matching oligonucleotide. From quantitation of the bands, one can construct a plot of the fraction of perfectly matched triplex that does not form as a function of the ratio of competitor to matching oligonucleotide. The curve can be analyzed to yield estimates for $\Delta\Delta G$.

In yet another approach, Gralla & Crothers (35) have demonstrated that $\Delta\Delta G$ can be determined from the dependence of T_m on the total strand concentration (C_t). In this method, a significant extrapolation may be required to determine $\Delta\Delta G$ at the desired temperature. As a result, the determination of $\Delta\Delta G$ will be influenced by the quality of the estimate of ΔH, which in turn, is related to the slope of the $1/T_m$ vs $\ln C_t$ curve and the size of the cooperative melting unit.

In general, hybridization events are composed of two processes: helix initiation and helix propagation. For short oligonucleotides, initiation (a bimolecular process) dominates the equilibrium. The bimolecular nature of the reaction leads to a strong dependence of hybridization on oligonucleotide concentration. As the length of the oligonucleotide increases, the equilibrium gradually approaches pseudo-monomolecular behavior; that is, the dependence of the equilibrium on oligonucleotide concentration diminishes and ultimately is lost. The loss of concentration dependence occurs because, as in polymers, hybridization becomes dominated by helix propagation (a monomolecular process). For this reason, methods for determining free energy that depend on interpreting the concentration dependence of T_m (or, equivalently, the bimolecular nature of the equilibrium) yield accurate thermodynamic data only for short oligonucleotides for which initiation dominates the equilibrium. The length of the oligonucleotide at which these methods become unreliable varies with the type of hybridization, the oligonucleotide sequence, and perhaps the solution conditions. In fact, Plum et al (110) present data that suggest that DNA triplex formation approaches pseudo-monomolecular behavior at a shorter chain length than does duplex DNA formation.

It has become common practice to measure T_m differences (ΔT_m) between two processes and then to interpret the ΔT_m value as if it directly reflected free-energy differences $(\Delta\Delta G)$ at some temperature well removed from T_m. This practice should be discouraged for several reasons. Most significantly, this treatment ignores any differences in the temperature dependences of ΔG; that is, it fails to acknowledge or account for the fact that the enthalpy change for the two processes may differ. A useful thermodynamic comparison between two processes, particularly when they occur at different temperatures, requires knowledge not only of the relative free-energy differences, but also the relative enthalpy differences (and ideally any differences in heat capacity).

Shifts in T_m with changes in the concentration of an effector [hydrogen ion (pH), drugs] can give qualitative information regarding the relative affinity of the effector for the initial and final nucleic acid states (13, 78). More specifically, for a triplex-to-duplex transition, if T_m increases with effector concentration, then the effector binds with higher affinity to the initial (triplex) state than to the final (duplex) state. Conversely, if T_m decreases with effector concentration, then the effector binds with higher affinity to the final (duplex) state than to the initial (triplex) state. If no change in T_m is observed as a function of effector concentration, then either the effector binds to neither the initial nor the final state, or it binds to both states with equal affinity. Thus, the failure of an effector to change T_m does not necessarily mean that no binding occurs.

Determination of Enthalpy

While knowledge of the free energy of a hybridization reaction is useful, it applies only to the conditions under which the measurement is made. A complete understanding of the hybridization equilibrium, in addition to exploration of the effects of solution conditions such as pH and salt concentration, requires knowledge of the temperature sensitivity of the equilibrium. The temperature sensitivity of the free energy of a process is reflected in the enthalpy term (ΔH).

Enthalpies of hybridization reactions are measured directly by using calorimetric techniques. Isothermal mixing calorimetry (8, 177) provides a direct measure of the heat of a hybridization reaction, ΔH, and its temperature dependence, ΔC_p (when carried out at multiple temperatures). Unfortunately, equilibrium association constants for oligonucleotide binding reactions generally are too large for determination of K by isothermal mixing calorimetry. Differential scanning calorimetry (DSC) (8, 83, 115, 158) differs from other calorimetric techniques in its direct measurement of the transition temperature, T_{max}, and the changes in enthalpy, $\Delta H;$ heat capacity, ΔC_p; and, less directly, entropy, ΔS, and free energy, ΔG, associated with a thermally induced transition, which can be thought of as a dehybridization event. However, caution should be exercised when comparing such data with those derived from isothermal mixing experiments because, in isothermal mixing experiments, the single-stranded states exist at lower thermal energy (kT), whereas in DSC experiments the single strands only are released at a higher thermal energy. For duplex formation, Vesnaver & Breslauer (168) have shown that data derived from isothermal and scanning calorimetry can be quite different because of differences in the low- and high-temperature single-stranded states. Similar effects should prevail for triplex formation and disruption events.

As an alternative to calorimetric methods, model-dependent van't Hoff enthalpies can be obtained by measuring the temperature dependence of some equilibrium property and applying the equation $\partial \ln K / \partial (1/T) = -\Delta H / R$. In general, techniques for determining van't Hoff enthalpies relate the temperature dependence of some observable to the temperature dependence of the equilibrium constant for the reaction under consideration. A variety of methods have been applied to monitor the temperature course (melting) of hybridized complexes.

Spectroscopic techniques sensitive to most hybridization equilibria include optical spectroscopies, such as ultraviolet (UV) and circular dichroism (CD), and nuclear magnetic resonance (NMR). The most widely applied method for monitoring hybridization equilibria is temperature-dependent UV absorbance spectroscopy. The resulting absorbance vs temperature curve may be analyzed in several ways (6, 83, 102, 117) to derive thermal (T_m) and thermodynamic (ΔH, ΔS, ΔG) parameters. Because these are not direct measures of the heat of a process, each method must incorporate assumptions about the nature of the reaction under study. The quality of the resultant data depends ultimately on the appropriateness of the assumptions for the particular system under study. The derivation and application of these methods has been reviewed extensively (6, 83, 102, 117).

As noted above in the context of free-energy measurements, as oligonucleotide chain length increases, hybridization equilibria approach concentration-independent, pseudo-monomolecular, polymer-like behavior. This feature reduces the slope of a $1/T_m$ vs $\ln C_t$ plot. Consequently, van't Hoff enthalpy values derived from the slopes of such curves will be systematically higher than the correct enthalpy value. This discrepancy underscores the need to exercise care in applying methods for enthalpy determinations that depend on true bimolecular behavior.

In principle, the van't Hoff analysis can be extended to determine the free energy (ΔG) of the transition in addition to the enthalpy (ΔH). However, the statistical coupling of the parameters (68) and the propagation of error through the analysis make this method less reliable than determination of ΔG via measurement of association constants. The use of differential scanning calorimetric data to compute ΔG presents a similar situation.

DETERMINANTS OF OLIGONUCLEOTIDE TRIPLE-HELIX STABILITY AND THE SPECIFICITY OF HYBRIDIZATION

The thermodynamic stability of a triplex ($\Delta G°$) depends on the chain length (94, 150), the base sequence (61), and the nature of the oligonucleotide backbone (41, 134). The magnitudes of these effects depend on the strengths of stacking and hydrogen-bonding interactions formed when the third strand binds, on the energetic cost of rearrangement of the target duplex and its associated solvent, and on the sequence dependence of the heat of protonation if third-strand cytosines are involved.

To realize the full potential of triple-helix formation in the manipulation of megabase DNA, the third-strand oligonucleotides must be designed that are able to distinguish among similar sequences, some of which may differ by only one or two base pairs. Using a number of techniques, several laboratories studying various sequences under different conditions have found that triplex stability is significantly influenced by defects, including base triple mismatches and looped-out third-strand bases (25, 76, 86, 88, 94, 133, 150, 183). In fact, the free-energy penalty for a single internal base triple mismatch or bulge has been measured to be near 3 kcal/mol (133, 150), whereas double mismatch or bulge defects are even more destabilizing (133). Interestingly, the enthalpic contribution to mismatch destabilization is apparently small (136). In addition to the identity of a base triple mismatch (25, 37, 86, 88, 183), the location of the mismatch is also important, with central mismatches being more destabilizing than those near the end (86).

To address the problem of imperfectly matched sequences, Roberts & Crothers (133) have exploited a competitive equilibrium between the probe, the target sequence, and a so-called stringency clamp. Enhanced specificity is achieved by selection of an alternative complex (either with an additional complementary oligonucleotide or potential self structure) whose stability is intermediate to that of the perfect and defectively matched triplexes. This method of enhancing specificity (particularly when implemented by attachment of a covalently linked competitor) is potentially of value in therapeutics because manipulations of solution conditions (pH, salt concentrations, temperature, etc) to achieve high levels of stringency, while simple in the laboratory, are not easily effected in vivo.

The stability of a triple-helical complex can be modulated by changing the temperature, the solution conditions, the chain length, or the structure of the oligonucleotide. Increasing the number of base triples at the target site increases the theoretical specificity of the complex. However, when the free-energy penalty of a defect is small relative to the total free energy of formation of the complex, then the observed specificity of binding may be reduced relative to the theoretical specificity. Because the goal is to optimize rather than maximize the affinity of the oligonucleotide for the target, care must be taken to achieve practical specificity. The design of cooperative domains between triplex-forming oligonucleotides is one strategy that has been employed to enhance the specificity of DNA complexation (15). Pyrimidine oligonucleotides bind cooperatively to abutting sites on duplex DNA with an interaction energy near 2 kcal/mol (12, 155). The interaction energy can be enhanced by modifying the bases at the junction (11) or by incorporating discrete dimerization domains into the triplex-forming oligonucleotides (15, 16). When the dimerization domains are nucleotide segments capable of forming short Watson-Crick duplexes, the dimerization of the two triplex-forming oligonucleotides at adjacent sites on the target DNA can be mediated by an exogenous DNA-binding ligand (15). Coupling the energetic contributions from two triplex-forming oligonucleotides through cooperative interactions between them improves the theoretical specificity for simultaneous binding to both DNA target sites.

Temperature Sensitivity of Triple-Helix Stability

As discussed above, the free energy of triplex formation strongly depends on the solution conditions. This dependence primarily is entropic in origin because the uptake and release of counterions and hydrating water molecules are dominated by entropic effects (81, 131). Thus, the dependence of the free energy of hybridization on solution conditions mainly reflects changes in the entropy of formation. Consequently, to avoid differences resulting simply from solution conditions rather than intrinsic triplex properties, there is merit in focusing comparisons on the enthalpy of triple-helix hybridization reactions. Some early scanning (66, 95) and mixing (135) calorimetric studies on RNA pyr·pur·pyr polymer triple helices revealed that the formation of UAU triples from U and AU was less enthalpic than the formation of AU doublets from A and U. Subsequent DSC studies on the corresponding DNA polymers led to similar conclusions (51, 100). Unfortunately, only a few calorimetric studies of oligonucleotide triple helices have appeared in recent years, in contrast to the relatively large number of studies that have relied on van't Hoff analyses and/or T_m comparisons.

As noted above, enthalpy data are less dependent on solution conditions than are free-energy data. Nevertheless, meaningful quantitative comparisons of the available enthalpy data for oligonucleotide triplex hybridization is complicated by the fact that many of the triplex systems studied are formed by different inter- and intramolecular constructs, possess different base compositions and sequences, and have been studied using different experimental techniques. Despite these problems, inspection of the enthalpy data reveals some patterns that may prove to be general. To be specific, calorimetric studies of oligo(pyrimidine) DNA third-strand hybridization with mixing calorimetry (175) and DSC (52, 109, 110, 170), at or near neutral pH, yield enthalpy values of 2.0–4.2 kcal/mol of Hoogsteen-forming nucleotide. Comparisons of these model-independent calorimetric enthalpies with the corresponding model-dependent van't Hoff values under identical conditions reveal that ΔH_{vH} is systematically larger than ΔH_{cal} (52, 109, 110, 170). Interestingly, at low pH, the apparent disparity between the calorimetric and van't Hoff data disappears (170, 180, 181). Although the reported van't Hoff enthalpy values of DNA third-strand hybridization range from about 2 to 8 kcal/mol of Hoogsteen-forming nucleotide (19, 82, 93, 104, 110, 133, 136, 159, 170, 180, 181, 184), most cluster in the range of 5 to 7 kcal/mol.

Several explanations for the apparent inconsistencies in van't Hoff and calorimetric enthalpies are possible; these caveats center on aggregation, kinetics, and heats of protonation. When one finds that ΔH_{cal} $< \Delta H_{vH}$, intermolecular cooperativity (i.e. aggregation) is customarily implicated (115, 158). However, no evidence of aggregation has been reported for these systems. Interestingly, the situation in which ΔH_{cal} $< \Delta H_{vH}$ does not result from aggregation has precedent in the protein literature. Specifically, when under appropriate conditions, the molten-globule protein state forms, a similar enthalpy anomaly occurs and purportedly indicates an unusual intermediate state in thermal denaturation (24, 45, 116, 178, 179). Because the kinetics of triplex formation are slower than those for formation of comparable duplexes (79, 136, 147), one could argue that some enthalpy measurements are compromised because of incomplete triplex formation or failure to reach equilibrium. The protocols associated with calorimetric studies, including variations in scan rates, make this an improbable explanation. A potential additional source of the enthalpy disparity may be the fact that many of the reported enthalpies do not include corrections for deprotonation of cytosine residues (if present) or protonation of buffers. Depending on experimental conditions and on the value used for ΔH of cytosine protonation (82, 130), such corrections could be significant. However, these protonation and deprotonation effects cannot account entirely for the apparent inconsistency in the enthalpy data from calorimetric and van't Hoff analyses. In short, none of the caveats noted above satisfactorily accounts for the behavior of oligonucleotide DNA triples helices. Thus, the origin of the disparity in the calorimetric and van't Hoff enthalpy data remains unclear.

Consideration of a specific example can highlight the issues raised above. A combination of DSC and optically monitored melting experiments on a three-stranded 15-mer triple helix with duplex extensions composed of three base pairs at each end demonstrated many of the important features of oligonucleotide triple-helix thermodynamics (110). Specifically, DSC revealed the enthalpy for the triplex-to-duplex + single-strand transition at pH 6.5 to be 2.0 kcal/mol Hoogsteen interaction. This value is significantly lower than the corresponding van't Hoff enthalpy value of 6 kcal/mol Hoogsteen interaction that was derived from analysis of both the DSC heat capacity curves and the UV melting curves at a concentration approximately 36-fold lower (110). However, because of the concentration independence of the van't Hoff enthalpies determined by analysis of the UV melting curves and the lack of anomalous electrophoretic bands (148), the apparent disparity between the calorimetric and van't Hoff enthalpies cannot be attributable to aggregation. Possible kinetic explanations are not likely because sufficient time was allowed for formation of the structure even given the slow kinetics of triplex formation (79, 136). Furthermore, circular dichroism spectra revealed no evidence of competing pyrimidine strand structures. The observed difference between the van't Hoff and calorimetric enthalpies also cannot be explained by cytosine deprotonation and buffer protonation heats (133, 175). We (109) and others (170) have observed a similar disparity in calorimetric and van't Hoff enthalpies for intramolecular triple helices. Thus, end effects cannot be invoked to explain the apparent anomaly.

Recently, direct application of the van't Hoff equation to binding constants determined as a function of temperature by the affinity cleavage titration method (152) resulted in an enthalpy value of -2 kcal/mol Hoogsteen interaction for the formation of the identical triplex previously shown calorimetrically to exhibit an enthalpy value of 2.0 kcal/mol Hoogsteen interaction. This agreement between the van't Hoff and calorimetric values is gratifying and may reflect a yet-to-be-defined inherent advantage of temperature-dependent affinity cleavage-titration measurements for van't Hoff analysis of triplex structures.

Taken together, the above observations, as well as the additional observation that the concentration dependence of the T_m of the 15-mer triple helix is markedly reduced relative to a duplex melting transition of comparable enthalpy (110), suggest that the van't Hoff analysis should be reserved only for short triple helices for which one can be confident of the all-or-none nature of the thermally induced order-disorder transition. Despite a current lack of consensus regarding the precise values of the enthalpies of formation of the Hoogsteen interactions, the preponderance of evidence suggests that the enthalpy per Hoogsteen base is less than the enthalpy of formation of Watson-Crick base pairs.

Salt Dependence of Triplex Stability

The stabilities of triple-helical complexes are influenced relative to component duplex and single strands by the presence of monovalent cations (19, 52, 60, 104, 110, 136, 145, 151, 175); divalent cations (104,

151); and polyvalent cations, such as hexaamine cobalt(III) (94) and spermine (40, 94, 145, 151, 160, 164). The formation of a local triplex containing 15 base triples was not observed in the presence of up to 10 mM Mg^{2+} (94) or 500 mM K^+ (151) when hexaamine cobalt(III) or spermine was absent from solution. Interestingly, Thomas & Thomas (164) have demonstrated that the stabilization afforded poly(dA)·2poly(dT) by polyamines depends on the length of the methylene chains of the polyamine. Duplex DNA does not exhibit such structure-dependent interactions with polyamines.

For monocations, increasing the sodium ion concentration typically increases the stabilities of triplexes in solution. Triple helices formed by T-rich third strands show a markedly greater salt sensitivity than those containing C^+ in the third strand (170, 175). Because of their higher negative charge, T-rich triple-helical nucleic acids are expected to bind counterions in larger numbers than do double helices of identical length (131). The counterion release upon dissociation and thus $\partial T_m/\partial \ln[Na^+]$ are greater for T-rich triplexes than for duplexes (19, 60). Because the C^+-containing triplexes have a reduced charge density relative to T-rich triple helices, the salt-concentration dependence of the thermal stability ($\partial T_m/\partial \ln[Na^+]$) of these triplexes may be positive (110, 145, 170, 175), approximately zero (169), or even negative (109), depending on the C^+GC base triple content.

In contrast to the situation in solutions containing a single cationic species, the stabilization of triple-helical complexes in mixed valence salt solutions is cation specific. In the presence of millimolar concentrations of spermine and magnesium, increasing the concentration of a monovalent cation decreases the stabilities of triple helices (79, 151). In solutions containing >100 mM concentrations of sodium or potassium, magnesium affords a modest increase in the stabilities of triplexes (79, 151). In the presence of both mono- and divalent cations, increasing the spermine tetracation concentration dramatically increases triplex stability (151). These effects are qualitatively consistent with the coupling of spermine binding affinity for duplex DNA to the monovalent cation concentration (5). Clearly, an understanding of such combined cation effects on triplex stability requires further study.

pH Dependence of Triplex Stability

The requirement for protonation of third-strand cytosines for triplex formation makes the thermal stabilities of triple helices that include C^+GC triples sensitive to pH (34, 110, 170, 175). For isolated C residues, this pH sensitivity is linearly dependent on the fraction of cytosines in the third strand (169).

From the pH dependence of T_m and knowledge of the enthalpy of the transition the number of protons released upon triplex disruption can be estimated (131). Generally, investigators have found that the number of released protons is smaller than the number of cytosines in putative $C^+ \cdot GC$ base triples (109, 175, 181). This observation could indicate partial protonation of the cytosines in the resultant single strands, a plausible explanation at low pH. Alternatively, triplex formation might be characterized by only partial protonation of the cytosines, an explanation that must be favored at high pH. NMR evidence appears to be consistent with protonation at each third-strand cytosine (123); however, these data cannot rule out an equilibrium between protonated and nonprotonated sites that on average results in partial protonation.

The potential application of oligonucleotide-directed triple-helix formation to the modulation of biological events in vivo, where the pH is tightly regulated, has stimulated several efforts to stabilize the C^+GC base triple by modification of the oligonucleotide and to incorporate nucleosides capable of pH-independent recognition of GC base pairs. Substitution of 5-methylcytosine for cytosine—the most widely used base modification—increases the stabilities of polymeric (71) and oligomeric triplexes (110, 181) over a range of pH, thereby increasing the pH range over which stable triplexes are observed. Some nucleosides produce pH-independent hybridization to sequences containing GC base pairs. These nucleosides contain heterocycles with two hydrogen-bond donors that interact with N7 and O6 of guanine without needing protonation at neutral pH (63, 67, 87, 98a). Triplexes formed by hybridization of purine-rich oligonucleotides to duplex targets also possess pH-independent stabilities near neutral pH.

Base Modifications Can Enhance Triplex Stability

Modification of third-strand pyrimidines at the C5 position enhances the stability of triple helices of the pyr·pur·pyr motif. Methylation of both 2'-deoxyuridine and 2'-deoxycytidine (dU → dT and dC → m⁵dC) extends the pH range over which affinity cleavage reveals triplex formation (112) and thus enhances the apparent stabilities of triplexes. Substitution of either 5-bromouracil (112) or 5-(1-propynyl)uracil (11, 32) for thymidine further increases triplex stability. In contrast, substitution of either bromine (111) or 1-propyne (32) at the C5 position of cytosine dramatically reduces the apparent stabilities of the corresponding triplexes.

The methylation of third-strand cytosines also results in an increase in triplex T_m (34, 110, 181) and a modest increase in the affinity constant

(79, 150). The temperature-independent increase of 0.5 units in the apparent pK_a of a 15-mer triplex [d(TTTTTCTCTCTCTCT)] (110) upon dC methylation, despite a minimal methylation-induced change in the dC monomer pK_a, suggests that a pK_a shift is not the origin of methylation-induced enhancement of triplex stability. Furthermore, methylation-induced enhancement in triplex stability is not associated with a change in enthalpy (180, 181). Taken together, these results suggest that methylation causes a favorable entropic contribution to the triplex free energy without significantly altering the enthalpy of triplex formation. Plum et al (110) have found that $\partial T_m/\partial pH$ is unaffected by third-strand methylation. Thus, if we assume that $\Delta\Delta H = 0$ is general for the contribution of third-strand methylation to triplex formation, then the number of protons taken up by the complex upon triplex formation also must be independent of third-strand methylation. This conclusion is consistent with the observation that $\partial \log K/\partial pH$ is independent of third-strand methylation for the same 15-mer sequence under different solution conditions (149).

The increased hydrophobicity imparted by methylation might explain the effect of m^5dC on triplex stability (110, 112, 181). The observed favorable entropy of triplex formation caused by dC methylation is consistent with the postulated hydrophobic origin of the effect on triplex stability. In this connection, particularly long-lived hydration sites are observed in the groove into which the third-strand pyrimidine C5 position substituents project (123, 124). However, substitution of either hydrophobic bromine or propyne moieties at the C5 of cytosine disfavors triple-helix formation. In general, the influence of cytosine methylation on triplex stability does not appear to result from a direct influence of methylation on heterocycle protonation. However, the exact origin of the effect remains to be established (149).

Effects of the Oligonucleotide Backbone

Efforts to engineer oligonucleotides with greater degrees of nuclease resistance and cell membrane permeability have included modifications of both the sugar and phosphate moieties of the backbone. The incorporation of these modifications into antisense and antigene oligonucleotides has been discussed in detail (50, 154, 162, 174).

One class of backbone modifications involves substitution on the deoxyribose sugar moiety. The difference between RNA and DNA molecules provides the most obvious example of this class. Specifically, the presence in RNA of an $-OH$ group at the 2' position of third-strand oligonucleotides (21, 41, 134) thermally stabilizes triplexes relative to triplexes containing the corresponding 2'-deoxy DNA third strands. A similar effect is observed for the corresponding $-OCH_3$ substitution (21). Replacement of the furan oxygen of a deoxyribose with a methylene group also can stabilize a triplex (30). Importantly, the magnitude of such changes depends on the sequence context (30) as well as the presence of base modifications.

Using different triplex constructs, the Crothers (134), Dervan (41), and Hélène (21) groups independently studied the relative stabilities of triplexes composed of various combinations of DNA and RNA strands. The qualitative agreement observed in these very different systems is gratifying. However, given the elaborate coupling of the effects of solution conditions and differences in sequence, triplex constructs, and experimental methodology, it is not surprising that quantitative differences in relative free energies are reported for the various triplex combinations of DNA and RNA strands. Interestingly, when the duplex purine strand is RNA and the Hoogsteen pyrimidine strand is DNA, triplex formation is not observed whether the duplex pyrimidine strand is DNA or RNA (21, 41, 134). However, as discussed in a later section, coupling triplex formation with drug binding can induce formation of this class of triplex that does not form in the absence of the drug (103).

Another type of backbone modification focuses on the phosphoryl group of the phosphate backbone. The thermal stabilities of DNA triplexes containing methylphosphonate-substituted oligonucleotides strongly depend on length; shorter lengths (<19 base triples) favor triplex formation (60, 89–91). The effects of methylphosphonate substitution on the thermal stability and salt sensitivity of duplex DNA depend on both the base sequences and chain lengths of the modified strands (4, 60, 118). Phosphorothioate oligo(pyrimidine)nucleotides bind target duplex DNA with drastically reduced affinities ($\Delta\Delta G > 0.17$ kcal/mol of substitution) when compared with unmodified oligonucleotides at neutral pH and room temperature (39). In contrast, the same substitution affords a modest increase in the stability for pur·pur·pyr triplexes formed by the hybridization of oligo(purine)nucleotides to duplex DNA (39).

Peptide nucleic acids (PNA) represent a novel class of oligonucleotide analogues in which the phosphodiester backbone is replaced by a polyamide backbone. When the bases are complementary, a PNA strand will bind to its DNA complement to form both 1(PNA):1(DNA) and 2(PNA):1(DNA) complexes (20, 43, 96).

Recent studies on oligonucleotides containing 2',5"-phosphodiester linkages instead of the conventional 3',5"-phosphodiester linkages demonstrate that these modified oligomers hybridize to form only triple-helical and not double-helical complexes (59). Interestingly, the triplexes formed by the 2',5"-modified oligomers are less stable thermo-dynamically than the triplexes formed by the corresponding unmodified oligomers.

Effect of Ligand Binding on Formation of Triple-Helical Nucleic Acids

As noted above, considerable research currently focuses upon oligonu-cleotide-directed triplex formation, partly because of its potential use-fulness in therapeutic, diagnostic, and biotechnological applications (for reviews, see 46, 162, 165). The advancement of such applications requires control of the affinity and specificity of third strands for their target duplexes. One approach for achieving this control is through the use of nucleic acid–binding ligands to modulate the hybridization of third strands to their duplex targets. Investigation of this approach has begun with numerous studies probing the influence of both intercalating (70, 72, 84, 85, 106, 108, 139, 163, 171, 176) and minor groove-binding (18, 100, 167) ligands on triplex formation.

The minor groove-binding ligands netropsin (18, 100) and distamycin (167) bind and thermally destabilize intermolecular DNA triplexes that contain only TAT base triples. In contrast, a variety of intercalating ligands, including ethidium (139), coralyne (70), and derivatives of quin-oline (176) and benzopyridoindole (85, 106, 108), bind and thermally stabilize TAT DNA triplexes. Although ethidium intercalation ther-mally stabilizes TAT DNA triplexes, it thermally destabilizes DNA triplexes containing both TAT and C^+GC triples (84, 144). An excep-tion to this trend is the enhancement of thermal stability observed for an alternate-strand triplex containing both TAT and C^+GC triples formed by hybridization of a 5'-5'-linked oligonucleotide with a target duplex (98). Interestingly, ethidium binding has little or no effect on the thermal stability of the corresponding alternate-strand triplex formed by hybridization of a 3'-3'-linked oligonucleotide with the same target duplex. Unlike ethidium, intercalation of coralyne (70) and the family of benzopyridoindole derivatives (85, 106, 108) thermally stabi-lizes intermolecular DNA triplexes containing both TAT and C^+GC triples. However, only coralyne achieves this stabilization without re-quiring a minimum number of contiguous TAT triples as a binding site. The effects of berenil binding on triplex thermal stability with both RNA and DNA triple helices depend on both the [berenil]/[nucleotide] ratio and the solution conditions (105). For example, depending on the Na^+ concentration, berenil binding either enhances or reduces the thermal stability of the poly(dA)·2poly(dT) triplex.

A striking example of a ligand-binding effect on hybridization of a third strand to its duplex target is the demonstration that binding of berenil, 4',6-diamidino-2-phenylindole (DAPI), ethidium, or netropsin induces formation of the $(dT)_n \cdot (rA)_n (dT)_n$ and/or $(rA)_n \cdot (rA)_n (dT)_n$ hybrid triplexes (103), neither of which form in the absence of ligand.

Taken together, these observations emphasize that the effect of a nucleic acid–binding ligand on the hybridization of a third strand to its target duplex depends not only on the mode of ligand binding, but also on the nature of the nucleic acid strands and the solution conditions.

Hybridization Involving Oligonucleotide-Ligand Covalent Conjugates

Covalent attachment of prosthetic groups has been employed to alter the affinity of a third-strand probe for a target-binding site or to deliver a chemical reagent to a unique target sequence. The ligand may be attached covalently to either terminus (3' or 5') (1, 49, 99, 160) or less commonly to a base (often guanine or adenine) within the oligonucleotide (74, 182). Targets for oligonucleotide-ligand covalent conjugates include both single- and double-stranded nucleic acids, with applications in antiviral, antisense, and antigene therapies (for reviews, see 47, 49, 50, 154, 165).

Much of the research probing the hybridization of oligomer-ligand covalent conjugates has centered on oligonucleotide-intercalator conjugates (1, 47–49, 99, 160, 161, 182). Attachment of intercalating ligands, such as phenanthroline (26–28, 146), acridine (1, 48, 99, 160, 161), and ellipticine derivatives (101), to either terminus of the oligonucleotide results in thermal stabilization of the complexes relative to those formed by nonderivatized oligonucleotides. The structure of the linker, as well as its effective length, has a significant effect on the affinity of such conjugates for their target duplexes (99). Site-specific intercalation into an intramolecular DNA triplex by a natural anthracycline (SN-07) attached covalently to the 2-amino group of a guanine residue has been demonstrated (182), although the effect on triplex stability remains to be determined.

Duocarmycin A, when attached covalently at the N3 position of adenine, binds site specifically in the minor groove of an intramolecular triplex (74). Duocarmycin A binding reduced both the apparent pK_a (74) and thermal stability (DS Pilch, DJ Patel & KJ Breslauer, unpublished results) of the triplex.

The enhancement of triplex thermal stability associated with inclusion of oligovalent cations in the solution can be exploited further by covalently attaching oligocationic moieties to the 3' or 5' termini of the oligonucleotides. Polyamine-5'-linked oligonucleotides can form triplexes by hybridization with their DNA duplex targets, under conditions in which the corresponding nonderivatized oligomers do not form triple helices (166).

EXPANDING THE LEXICON OF TRIPLE-HELIX RECOGNITION

To afford maximum flexibility in developing applications of oligonucleotide-directed triplex formation, the current rigid sequence requirements must be overcome. Several strategies have been directed toward this objective, including the discovery of novel base triples formed by natural bases, the design of modified nucleotides and nonnatural heterocyclic bases that form novel base triples, and the use of oligonucleotides that provide alternate-strand duplex recognition.

The requirement for homopurine·homopyrimidine duplex DNA sequences as targets for third-strand hybridization has been eased by the identification of base triple interactions beyond TAT and C^+GC. Guanosine (37) and thymidine (34, 88, 183) can recognize TA and CG base pairs, respectively. When incorporated into an oligodeoxypyrimidine, the base analogue N^4-(3-acetamidopropyl)-deoxycytosine interacts with the cytosine residue of a CG base pair in the target duplex (55). The nonnatural deoxyribonucleoside 1-(2-deoxy-D-ribofuranosyl)-4-(3-benzamidophenyl)-imidazole (D$_3$) recognizes both TA and CG base pairs within pyr·pur·pyr triplexes (38, 61) by means of intercalation (65). Although each of these noncanonical base triples allows triplexes to form at sequences where a homopurine run is interrupted, none has proven to be a general solution to duplex DNA recognition, which will likely require base triple interactions that are as strong and as specific as those of TAT and C^+CG (25).

Oligodeoxyribonucleotides capable of recognizing flanking purine domains on opposing strands of a target duplex have been synthesized with (31, 53, 98) and without (2, 56–58, 97) synthetic phosphodiester linkages (3'-3' or 5'-5') as spacers. Oligonucleotides linked 3'-3' form alternate-strand triplexes with greater thermal stabilities than those formed by the corresponding 5'-5'-linked oligonucleotides (98). The requirement of a synthetic or nucleotide linker between the triplex-forming domains of the third strand to achieve stable triplex formation also appears to be sequence dependent (2, 56–58).

CONCLUDING REMARKS

The development and expanded use of oligonucleotides (or their analogues) for modulating biochemical activities through site-specific triplex formation demands an understanding of how triplex stability depends on temperature, chain length, pH, salt, base sequence, base and backbone modifications, and ligand binding. Compiling the requisite body of thermodynamic data is a minimum first step toward making these assessments. This chapter has reviewed the current state of this database, while critically assessing some of the methods used to obtain the requisite data. Ultimately, such data would be used to construct multidimensional phase diagrams for triplexes that allow the rational design of oligonucleotides for specific therapeutic, diagnostic, and/or biotechnological applications.

Literature Cited

1. Asseline U, Delarue M, Lancelot G, Toulmé F, Thuong NT, et al. 1984. Nucleic acid binding molecules with high affinity and base sequence specificity: intercalating agents covalently linked to oligodeoxynucleotides. *Proc. Natl. Acad. Sci. USA* 81: 3297–3301
2. Beal PA, Dervan PB. 1992. Recognition of double helical DNA by alternate strand triple helix formation. *J. Am. Chem. Soc.* 114:4976–82
3. Bloomfield VA, Crothers DM, Tinoco I Jr. 1974. *Physical Chemistry of Nucleic Acids.* New York: Harper & Row. 517 pp.
4. Bower M, Summers MF, Powell C, Shinokuza K, Regan JB, et al. 1987. Oligodeoxyribonucleoside methylphosphonates. NMR and UV spectroscopic studies of Rp-Rp and Sp-Sp methylphosphonate (Me) modified duplexes of {d(GGAATTCC)}₂. *Nucleic Acids Res.* 15:4915–30
5. Braunlin WH, Strick TJ, Record MT Jr. 1982. Equilibrium dialysis studies of polyamine binding to DNA. *Biopolymers* 21:1301–14
6. Breslauer KJ. 1994. Extracting thermodynamic data from equilibrium melting curves for oligonucleotide order-disorder transitions. In *Methods in Molecular Biology,* Vol. 26. *Protocols for Oligonucleotide Conjugates,* ed. S Agrawal, pp. 347–72. New Jersey: Humana
7. Breslauer KJ, Frank R, Blöcker H, Marky LA. 1986. Predicting DNA duplex stability from the base sequence. *Proc. Natl. Acad. Sci. USA* 83: 3746–50
8. Breslauer KJ, Freire E, Straume M. 1992. Calorimetry: a tool for DNA and ligand-DNA studies. *Methods Enzymol.* 211:533–67
9. Chen F-M. 1991. Intramolecular triplex formation of the purine·purine·pyrimidine type. *Biochemistry* 30:4472–79
10. Cheng Y-K, Pettitt BM. 1992. Stabilities of double- and triple-strand helical nucleic acids. *Prog. Biophys. Mol. Biol.* 58:225–57
11. Colocci N, Dervan PB. 1994. Cooperative binding of 8-mer oligonucleotides containing 5-(1-propynyl)-2'-deoxyuridine to adjacent DNA sites by triple-helix formation. *J. Am. Chem. Soc.* 116:785–86
12. Colocci N, Distefano MD, Dervan PB. 1993. Cooperative oligonucleotide-directed triple helix formation at

adjacent DNA sites. *J. Am. Chem. Soc.* 115:4468–73

13. Crothers DM. 1971. Statistical thermodynamics of nucleic acid melting transitions with coupled binding equilibria. *Biopolymers* 10:2147–60

14. de los Santos C, Rosen M, Patel D. 1989. NMR studies of DNA $(R+)_n \cdot (Y-)_n \cdot (Y+)_n$ triple helices in solution: imino and amino proton markers of $T \cdot A \cdot T$ and $C \cdot G \cdot C^+$ base-triple formation. *Biochemistry* 28:7282–89

15. Distefano MD, Dervan PB. 1992. Ligand-promoted dimerization of oligonucleotides binding cooperatively to DNA. *J. Am. Chem. Soc.* 114:11006–7

16. Distefano MD, Dervan PB. 1993. Energetics of cooperative binding of oligonucleotides with discrete dimerization domains to DNA by triple helix formation. *Proc. Natl. Acad. Sci. USA* 90:1179–83

17. Dolinnaya NG, Braswell EH, Fossella JA, Klump H, Fresco JR. 1993. Molecular and thermodynamic properties of $d(A^+-G)_{10}$, a single-stranded nucleic acid helix without paired or stacked bases. *Biochemistry* 32:10263–70

18. Durand M, Nguyen TT, Maurizot JC. 1992. Binding of netropsin to a DNA triple helix. *J. Biol. Chem.* 267:24394–99

19. Durand M, Peloille S, Thuong NT, Maurizot J-C. 1992. Triple-helix formation by an oligonucleotide containing one $(dA)_{12}$ and two $(dT)_{12}$ sequences bridged by two hexaethylene glycol chains. *Biochemistry* 31:9197–9204

20. Egholm M, Buchardt O, Nielsen PE, Berg RH. 1992. Peptide nucleic acids (PNA). Oligonucleotide analogues with an achiral peptide backbone. *J. Am. Chem. Soc.* 114:1895–97

21. Escudé C, François J-C, Sun J-S, Ott G, Sprinzl M, et al. 1993. Stability of triple helices containing RNA and DNA strands: experimental and molecular modeling studies. *Nucleic Acids Res.* 21:5547–53

22. Felsenfeld G, Davies DR, Rich A. 1957. Formation of a three-stranded polynucleotide molecule. *J. Am. Chem. Soc.* 79:2023–24

23. Felsenfeld G, Miles HT. 1967. The physical and chemical properties of nucleic acids. *Annu. Rev. Biochem.* 36:407–48

24. Filimonov VV, Prieto J, Martinez JC, Bruix M, Mateo PL, Serrano L. 1993. Thermodynamic analysis of the chemotactic protein from *Escherichia coli*, CheY. *Biochemistry* 32:12906–21

25. Fossella JA, Kim YJ, Richards EG, Fresco JR. 1993. Relative specificities in binding of Watson-Crick base pairs by third strand residues in a DNA pyrimidine triplex motif. *Nucleic Acids Res.* 21:4511–15

26. François J-C, Saison-Behmoaras T, Barbier C, Chassignol M, Thuong NT, Hélène C. 1989. Sequence-specific recognition and cleavage of duplex DNA via triple-helix formation by oligonucleotides covalently linked to a phenanthroline-copper chelate. *Proc. Natl. Acad. Sci. USA* 86:9702–6

27. François J-C, Saison-Behmoaras T, Chassignol M, Thuong NT, Hélène C. 1989. Sequence-targeted cleavage of single- and double-stranded DNA by oligothymidylates covalently linked to 1,10-phenanthroline. *J. Biol. Chem.* 264:5891–98

28. François J-C, Saison-Behmoaras T, Chassignol M, Thuong NT, Sun J-S, Hélène C. 1988. Periodic cleavage of poly(dA) by oligothymidylates covalently linked to the 1,10-phenanthroline-copper complex. *Biochemistry* 27:2272–76

29. Freier SM, Kierzek R, Jaeger JA, Sugimoto N, Caruthers MH, et al. 1986. Improved free energy parameters for prediction of RNA duplex stability. *Proc. Natl. Acad. Sci. USA* 83:9373–77

30. Froehler BC, Ricca DJ. 1992. Triple-helix formation by oligodeoxynucleotides containing the carbocyclic analogs of thymidine and 5-methyl-2′-deoxycytidine. *J. Am. Chem. Soc.* 114:8320–22

31. Froehler BC, Terhorst T, Shaw JP, McCurdy SN. 1992. Triple-helix formation and cooperative binding by oligodeoxynucleotides with a 3′-3′ internucleotide junction. *Biochemistry* 31:1603–9

32. Froehler BC, Wadwani S, Terhorst TJ, Gerrard SR. 1992. Oligodeoxynucleotides containing C-5 propyne analogs of 2′-deoxyuridine and 2′-deoxycytidine. *Tetrahedron Lett.* 33:5307–10

33. Gehring K, Leroy J-L, Guéron M. 1993. A tetrameric DNA structure

with protonated cytosine·cytosine base pairs. *Nature* 363:561–65

34. Giovannangélı C, Rougée M, Garestier T, Thuong NT, Hélène C. 1992. Triple-helix formation by oligonucleotides containing the three bases thymine, cytosine, and guanine. *Proc. Natl. Acad. Sci. USA* 89:8631–35

35. Gralla J, Crothers DM. 1973. Free energy of imperfect nucleic acid helices. II. Small hairpin loops. *J. Mol. Biol.* 73:497–511

36. Gray DM, Vaughn M, Ratcliff RL, Hayes FN. 1980. Circular dichroism spectra show that repeating dinucleotide DNAs may form helixes in which every other base is looped out. *Nucleic Acids Res.* 8:3695–3707

37. Griffin LC, Dervan PB. 1989. Recognition of thymine·adenine base pairs by guanine in a pyrimidine triple helix motif. *Science* 245:967–71

38. Griffin LC, Kiessling LL, Beal PA, Gillespie P, Dervan PB. 1992. Recognition of all four base pairs of doublehelical DNA by triple-helix formation: design of nonnatural deoxyribonucleosides for pyrimidine·purine base pair binding. *J. Am. Chem. Soc.* 114:7976–82

39. Hacia JG, Wold BJ, Dervan PB. 1994. Phosphorothioate oligonucleotide-directed triple helix formation. *Biochemistry* 33:5367–69

40. Hampel KJ, Crosson P, Lee JS. 1991. Polyamines favor DNA triplex formation at neutral pH. *Biochemistry* 30:4455–59

41. Han H, Dervan PB. 1993. Sequencespecific recognition of double-helical RNA and RNA·DNA by triple helix formation. *Proc. Natl. Acad. Sci. USA* 90:3806–10

42. Häner R, Dervan PB. 1990. Singlestrand DNA triple-helix formation. *Biochemistry* 29:9761–65

43. Hanvey JC, Peffer NJ, Bisi JE, Thomson SA, Cadilla R, et al. 1992. Antisense and antigene properties of peptide nucleic acids. *Science* 258:1481–85

44. Hanvey JC, Shimizu M, Wells RD. 1990. Site-specific inhibition of *Eco*RI restriction/modification enzymes by a DNA triple helix. *Nucleic Acids Res.* 18:157–61

45. Haynie DT, Freire E. 1993. Structural energetics of the molten globule state. *Proteins Struct. Funct. Genet.* 16:115–40

46. Hélène C. 1991. Rational design of sequence-specific oncogene inhibitors based on antisense and antigene oligonucleotides. *Eur. J. Cancer* 27:1466–71

47. Hélène C. 1992. Control of gene expression by antisense and antigene oligonucleotide-intercalator conjugates. In *Gene Regulation: Biology of Antisense RNA and DNA*, ed. RP Erickson, JG Izant, pp. 109–18. New York: Raven

48. Hélène C, Montenay-Garestier T, Saison T, Takasugi M, Toulmé JJ, et al. 1985. Oligodeoxynucleotides covalently linked to intercalating agents: a new class of gene regulatory substances. *Biochimie* 67:777–83

49. Hélène C, Thuong NT. 1989. Control of gene expression by oligonucleotides covalently linked to intercalating agents. *Genome* 31:413–21

50. Hélène C, Toulmé JJ. 1990. Specific regulation of gene expression by antisense, sense and antigene nucleic acids. *Biochim. Biophys. Acta* 1049:99–125

51. Hopkins HP, Hamilton DD, Wilson WD, Campbell J, Fumero J. 1993. Effects of C_2H_5OH, Na^+(aq), $N(CH_2CH_3)_4^+$(aq), and Mg^{2+}(aq) on the thermodynamics of double-helix–to–random-coil transitions of poly(dA)·poly(dT) and poly(dAdT). *J. Chem. Thermodyn.* 25:111–26

52. Hopkins HP, Hamilton DD, Wilson WD, Zon G. 1993. Duplex and triplehelix formation with dA_{19} and dT_{19}: thermodynamic parameters from calorimetric, NMR, and circular dichroism studies. *J. Phys. Chem.* 97:6555–63

53. Horne DA, Dervan PB. 1990. Recognition of mixed-sequence duplex DNA by alternate-strand triple-helix formation. *J. Am. Chem. Soc.* 112:2435–37

54. Htun H, Dahlberg JE. 1989. Topology and formation of triple-stranded H-DNA. *Science* 243:1571–76

55. Huang C-Y, Cushman CD, Miller PS. 1993. Triplex formation by an oligonucleotide containing N^4-(3-acetamidopropyl)cytosine. *J. Org. Chem.* 58:5048–49

56. Jayasena SD, Johnston BH. 1992. Intramolecular triple-helix formation at $(Pu_nPy_n)·(Pu_nPy_n)$ tracts: recognition of alternate strands via Pu·PuPy and Py·PuPy base triples. *Biochemistry* 31:320–27

57. Jayasena SD, Johnston BH. 1992. Oligonucleotide-directed triple helix formation at adjacent oligopurine and

oligopyrimidine DNA tracts by alternate strand recognition. *Nucleic Acids Res.* 20:5279–88

58. Jayasena SD, Johnston BH. 1993. Sequence limitations of triple helix formation by alternate-strand recognition. *Biochemistry* 32:2800–7

59. Jin R, Chapman WH Jr, Srinivasan AR, Olson WK, Breslow R, Breslauer KJ. 1993. Comparative spectroscopic, calorimetric, and computational studies of nucleic acid complexes with $2',5''$- versus $3',5''$-phosphodiester linkages. *Proc. Natl. Acad. Sci. USA* 90:10568–72

60. Kibler-Herzog L, Kell B, Zon G, Shinozuka K, Mizan S, Wilson WD. 1990. Sequence dependent effects in methylphosphonate deoxyribonucleotide double and triple helical complexes. *Nucleic Acids Res.* 18:3545–55

61. Kiessling LL, Griffin LC, Dervan PB. 1992. Flanking sequence effects within the pyrimidine triple-helix motif characterized by affinity cleaving. *Biochemistry* 31:2829–34

62. Klump HH. 1988. Conformational transitions in nucleic acids. In *Biochemical Thermodynamics,* ed. MN Jones, pp. 100–44. Amsterdam: Elsevier. 2nd ed.

63. Koh SK, Dervan PB. 1992. Design of a nonnatural deoxyribonucleoside for recognition of GC base pairs by oligonucleotide-directed triple helix formation. *J. Am. Chem. Soc.* 114:1470–78

64. Kool ET. 1991. Molecular recognition by circular oligonucleotides: increasing the selectivity of DNA binding. *J. Am. Chem. Soc.* 113:6265–66

65. Koshlap KM, Gillespie P, Dervan PB, Feigon J. 1993. Nonnatural deoxyribonucleoside D_3 incorporated in an intramolecular DNA triplex binds sequence-specifically by intercalation. *J. Am. Chem. Soc.* 115:7908–9

66. Krakauer H, Sturtevant JM. 1968. Heats of the helix-coil transitions of the poly A–poly U complexes. *Biopolymers* 6:491–512

67. Krawczyk SH, Milligan JF, Wadwani S, Moulds C, Froehler BC, Matteucci MD. 1992. Oligonucleotide-mediated triple helix formation using an N^3-protonated deoxycytidine analog exhibiting pH-independent binding within the physiological range. *Proc. Natl. Acad. Sci. USA* 89:3761–64

68. Krug RR, Hunter WG, Grieger RA. 1976. Enthalpy-entropy compensation. 1. Some fundamental statistical problems associated with the analysis of van't Hoff and Arrhenius data. *J. Phys. Chem.* 80:2335–41

69. Le Doan T, Perrouault L, Praseuth D, Habhoub N, Decout JL, et al. 1987. Sequence-specific recognition, photo cross-linking, and cleavage of the DNA double helix by an oligo-α-thymidylate covalently linked to an azidoproflavine derivative. *Nucleic Acids Res.* 15:7749–60

70. Lee JS, Latimer LJP, Hampel KJ. 1993. Coralyne binds tightly to both $T \cdot A \cdot T$- and $C \cdot G \cdot C^+$-containing DNA triplexes. *Biochemistry* 32:5591–97

71. Lee JS, Woodsworth ML, Latimer LJP, Morgan AR. 1984. Poly(pyrimidine)·poly(purine) synthetic DNAs containing 5-methylcytosine form stable triplexes at neutral pH. *Nucleic Acids Res.* 12:6603–14

72. Lehrman E, Crothers DM. 1977. An ethidium induced double helix of poly(rA)·poly(rU). *Nucleic Acids Res.* 4:1381–92

73. Leroy J-L, Gehring K, Kettani A, Guéron M. 1993. Acid multimers of oligodeoxycytidine strands: stoichiometry, base-pair characterization and proton exchange properties. *Biochemistry* 32:6019–31

74. Lin CH, Patel DJ. 1992. Site-specific covalent duocarmycin A–intramolecular DNA triplex complex. *J. Am. Chem. Soc.* 114:10658–60

75. Macaya R, Wang E, Schultze P, Sklenář V, Feigon J. 1992. Proton magnetic resonance assignments and structural characterization of an intramolecular DNA triplex. *J. Mol. Biol.* 225:755–73

76. Macaya RF, Gilbert DE, Malek S, Sinsheimer JS, Feigon J. 1991. Structure and stability of $X \cdot G \cdot C$ mismatches in the third strand of intramolecular triplexes. *Science* 254:270–74

77. Macaya RF, Schultze P, Feigon J. 1992. Sugar conformations in intramolecular DNA triplexes determined by coupling constants obtained by automated simulation of P.COSY cross peaks. *J. Am. Chem. Soc.* 114:781–83

78. McGhee JD. 1976. Theoretical calculations of the helix-coil transition of DNA in the presence of large, cooperatively binding ligands. *Biopolymers* 15:1345–75

79. Maher LJ III, Dervan PB, Wold BJ. 1990. Kinetic analysis of oligodeox-

yribonucleotide-directed triple-helix formation on DNA. *Biochemistry* 29:8820–26

80. Maher LJ III, Wold B, Dervan PB. 1989. Inhibition of DNA binding proteins by oligonucleotide-directed triple helix formation. *Science* 245:725–30

81. Manning GS. 1978. The molecular theory of polyelectrolyte solutions with applications to the electrostatic properties of polynucleotides. *Q. Rev. Biophys.* 11:179–246

82. Manzini G, Xodo LE, Gasparotto D, Quadrifoglio F, van der Marel GA, van Boom JH. 1990. Triple helix formation by oligopurine-oligopyrimidine DNA fragments: electrophoretic and thermodynamic behavior. *J. Mol. Biol.* 213:833–43

83. Marky LM, Breslauer KJ. 1987. Calculating thermodynamic data for transitions of any molecularity from melting curves. *Biopolymers* 26:1601–20

84. Mergny J-L, Collier D, Rougée M, Montenay-Garestier T, Hélène C. 1991. Intercalation of ethidium bromide into a triple-stranded oligonucleotide. *Nucleic Acids Res.* 19:1521–26

85. Mergny J-L, Duval-Valentin G, Nguyen C-H, Perrouault L, Faucon B, et al. 1992. Triple helix-specific ligands. *Science* 256:1681–84

86. Mergny J-L, Sun J-S, Rougée M, Montenay-Garestier T, Barcelo F, et al. 1991. Sequence specificity in triple-helix formation: experimental and theoretical studies of the effect of mismatches on triplex stability. *Biochemistry* 30:9791–98

87. Miller PS, Bhan P, Cushman CD, Trapane TL. 1992. Recognition of a guanine-cytosine base pair by 8-oxoadenine. *Biochemistry* 31:6788–93

88. Miller PS, Cushman CD. 1993. Triplex formation by oligodeoxyribonucleotides involving the formation of X·U·A triads. *Biochemistry* 32:2999–3004

89. Miller PS, Dreon N, Pulford SM, McParland KB. 1980. Oligothymidylate analogues having stereoregular, alternating methylphosphonate/phosphodiester backbones. *J. Biol. Chem.* 255:9659–65

90. Miller PS, McParland KB, Jayaraman K, Ts'o POP. 1981. Biochemical and biological effects of nonionic nucleic acid methylphosphonates. *Biochemistry* 20:1874–80

91. Miller PS, Yano J, Yano E, Carroll C, Jayaraman K, Ts'o POP. 1979. Nonionic nucleic acid analogues. Synthesis and characterization of dideoxyribonucleoside methylphosphonates. *Biochemistry* 18:5134–43

92. Mirkin SM, Lyamichev VI, Drushlyak KN, Dobrynin VN, Filippov SA, Frank-Kamenetskii MD. 1987. DNA H form requires a homopurine-homopyrimidine mirror repeat. *Nature* 330:495–97

93. Mooren MMW, Pulleyblank DE, Wijmenga SS, Blommers MJJ, Hilbers CW. 1990. Polypurine/polypyrimidine hairpins form a triple helix structure at low pH. *Nucleic Acids Res.* 18:6523–29

94. Moser HE, Dervan PB. 1987. Sequence-specific cleavage of double-helical DNA by triple helix formation. *Science* 238:645–50

95. Neumann E, Ackerman T. 1969. Thermodynamic investigation of the helix-coil transition of a ribonucleotide system. *J. Phys. Chem.* 73:2170–78

96. Nielsen PE, Egholm M, Berg RH, Buchardt O. 1991. Sequence-selective recognition of DNA by strand displacement with a thymine-substituted polyamide. *Science* 254:1497–1500

97. Olivas WM, Maher LJ III. 1994. DNA recognition by alternate strand triple helix formation: affinities of oligonucleotides for a site in the human p53 gene. *Biochemistry* 33:983–91

98. Ono A, Chen CN, Kan LS. 1991. DNA triplex formation of oligonucleotide analogues of linker groups and octamer segments that have opposite sugar-phosphate backbone polarities. *Biochemistry* 30:9914–21

98a. Ono A, Ts'o POP, Kan L. 1991. Triplex formation of oligonucleotides containing 2'-O-methylpseudoisocytidine in substitution for 2'-deoxycytidine. *J. Am. Chem. Soc.* 113:4032–33

99. Orson FM, Kinsey BM, McShan WM. 1994. Linkage structures strongly influence the binding cooperativity of DNA intercalators conjugated to triplex forming oligonucleotides. *Nucleic Acids Res.* 22:479–84

100. Park Y-W, Breslauer KJ. 1992. Drug binding to higher ordered DNA structures: netropsin complexation with a nucleic acid triple helix. *Proc. Natl. Acad. Sci. USA* 89:6653–57

101. Perrouault L, Asseline U, Rivalle C, Thuong NT, Bisagni E, et al. 1990. Sequence-specific artificial photo-induced endonucleases based on triple

helix-forming oligonucleotides. *Nature* 344:358–60

102. Petersheim M, Turner DH. 1983. Base-stacking and base-pairing contributions to helix stability: thermodynamics of double-helix formation with CCGG, CCGGp, CCGGAp, ACCGGp, CCGGUp, and ACCGGUp. *Biochemistry* 22:256–63

103. Pilch DS, Breslauer KJ. 1994. Ligand-induced formation of nucleic acid triple helices. *Proc. Natl. Acad. Sci. USA* 91:9332–36

104. Pilch DS, Brousseau R, Shafer RH. 1990. Thermodynamics of triple helix formation: spectrophotometric studies on the $d(A)_{10} \cdot 2d(T)_{10}$ and $d(C_3^+ T_4 C_3^+) \cdot d(G_3A_4G_3) \cdot d(C_3T_4C_3)$ triple helices. *Nucleic Acids Res.* 18:5743–50

105. Pilch DS, Kirolos MA, Plum GE, Breslauer KJ. 1994. II. Berenil [1,3-bis(4'-amidinophenyl)triazene] binding to higher order nucleic acid structures: evidence for non-intercalative binding to both a DNA and an RNA triple helix. *Biochemistry*. Submitted

106. Pilch DS, Martin M-T, Nguyen C-H, Sun J-S, Bisagni E, et al. 1993. Self-association and DNA-binding properties of two triple helix-specific ligands: comparison of a benzo[e]pyridoindole and a benzo[g]pyridoindole. *J. Am. Chem. Soc.* 115:9942–51

107. Pilch DS, Shafer RH. 1993. Structural and thermodynamic studies of $d(C_3T_4C_3)$ in acid solution: evidence for formation of the hemiprotonated $CH^+ \cdot C$ base pair. *J. Am. Chem. Soc.* 115:2565–71

108. Pilch DS, Waring MJ, Sun J-S, Rougée M, Nguyen C-H, et al. 1993. Characterization of a triple helix-specific ligand: BePI {3-methoxy-7H-8-methyl-11-[(3'-amino)propylamino]-benzo[e]pyrido[4,3-b]indole} intercalates into both double-helical and triple-helical DNA. *J. Mol. Biol.* 232:926–46

109. Plum GE, Breslauer KJ. 1994. Thermodynamics of an intramolecular DNA triple helix: a calorimetric and spectroscopic study of the pH and salt dependence of thermally induced structural transitions. *J. Mol. Biol.* In press

110. Plum GE, Park Y-W, Singleton SF, Dervan PB, Breslauer KJ. 1990. Thermodynamic characterization of the stability and the melting behavior of a DNA triplex: a spectroscopic and calorimetric study. *Proc. Natl. Acad. Sci. USA* 87:9436–40

111. Povsic TJ. 1992. *Oligonucleotide-directed sequence specific recognition and alkylation of double helical DNA by triple helix formation*. PhD thesis. Calif. Inst. Technol. Pasadena, CA. 283 pp.

112. Povsic TJ, Dervan PB. 1989. Triple helix formation by oligonucleotides on DNA extended to the physiological pH range. *J. Am. Chem. Soc.* 111:3059–61

113. Deleted in proof

114. Praseuth D, Perrouault L, Le Doan T, Chassignol M, Thuong NT, Hélène C. 1988. Sequence-specific binding and photo cross-linking of α and β oligodeoxynucleotides to the major groove of DNA via triple-helix formation. *Proc. Natl. Acad. Sci. USA* 85:1349–53

115. Privolov PL, Potekhin SA. 1986. Scanning microcalorimetry in studying temperature-induced changes in proteins. *Methods Enzymol.* 131:4–51

116. Ptitsyn OB, Pain RH, Semisotnov GV, Zerovnik E, Razgulyaev OI. 1990. Evidence for a molten globule state as a general intermediate in protein folding. *FEBS Lett.* 262:20–24

117. Puglisi JD, Tinoco Jr I. 1989. Absorbance melting curves of RNA. *Methods Enzymol.* 180:304–25

118. Quartin RS, Wetmur JG. 1989. Effect of ionic strength on the hybridization of oligodeoxynucleotides with reduced charge due to methylphosphonate linkages to unmodified oligodeoxynucleotides containing the complementary sequence. *Biochemistry* 28:1040–47

119. Radhakrishnan I, de los Santos C, Patel DJ. 1993. Nuclear magnetic resonance structural studies of $A \cdot AT$ base triple alignments in intramolecular purine·purine·pyrimidine DNA triplexes in solution. *J. Mol. Biol.* 234:188–97

120. Radhakrishnan I, de los Santos C, Live D, Patel DJ. 1991. Nuclear magnetic resonance structural studies of intramolecular purine·purine·pyrimidine DNA triplexes in solution: base triple pairing alignments and strand direction. *J. Mol. Biol.* 221:1403–18

121. Radhakrishnan I, de los Santos C, Patel DJ. 1991. Nuclear magnetic resonance structural studies of intramolecular purine·purine·pyrimidine DNA triplexes in solution. *J. Mol. Biol.* 221:1403–18

122. Radhakrishnan I, Gao X, de los Santos C, Live D, Patel DJ. 1991. NMR

structural studies of intramolecular $(Y+)_n \cdot (R+)_n (Y-)_n$ DNA triplexes in solution: imino and amino proton and nitrogen markers of G·TA base triple formation. *Biochemistry* 30: 9022–30

123. Radhakrishnan I, Patel DJ. 1994. DNA triplexe: solution structures, hydrations sites, energetics, interactions, and function. *Biochemistry* 33: 11405–16

124. Radhakrishnan I, Patel DJ. 1994. Hydration sites in purine·purine·pyrimidine and pyrimidine·purine·pyrimidine DNA triplexes in aqueous solution. *Structure* 2:395–405

125. Radhakrishnan I, Patel DJ. 1993. Solution structure of a purine·purine·pyrimidine DNA triplex containing G·GC and T·AT triples. *Structure* 1:135–52

126. Radhakrishnan I, Patel DJ. 1994. Solution structure of a pyrimidine·purine·pyrimidine DNA triplex containing T·AT, C$^+$·GC and G·TA triples. *Structure* 2:17–32

127. Radhakrishnan I, Patel DJ, Gao X. 1992. Three-dimensional homonuclear NOESY-TOCSY of an intramolecular pyrimidine·purine·pyrimidine DNA triplex containing a central G·TA triple: nonexchangeable proton assignments and structural implications. *Biochemistry* 31:2514–23

128. Rajagopal P, Feigon J. 1989. NMR studies of triple-strand formation from the homopurine-homopyrimidine deoxyribonucleotides d(GA)$_4$ and d(TC)$_4$. *Biochemistry* 28:7859–70

129. Rajagopal P, Feigon J. 1989. Triple-strand formation in the homopurine: homopyrimidine DNA oligonucleotides d(G-A)$_4$ and d(T-C)$_4$. *Nature* 339:637–40

130. Rawitscher M, Sturtevant JM. 1960. The heats of ionization of deoxynucleotides and related compounds. *J. Am. Chem. Soc.* 82:3739–40

131. Record MT Jr, Anderson CF, Lohman TM. 1978. Thermodynamic analysis of ion effects on the binding and conformational equilibria of proteins and nucleic acids: the roles of ion association or release, screening, and ion effects on water activity. *Q. Rev. Biophys.* 11:103–78

132. Revzin A. 1991. Gel retardation assays for nucleic acid-binding proteins. In *Methods in Nucleic Acid Research*, ed. JD Karam, L Chao, GW Warr, pp. 205–26. Boca Raton, FL: CRC

133. Roberts RW, Crothers DM. 1991. Specificity and stringency in DNA triplex formation. *Proc. Natl. Acad. Sci. USA* 88:9397–9401

134. Roberts RW, Crothers DM. 1992. Stability and properties of double and triple helices: dramatic effects of RNA or DNA backbone composition. *Science* 258:1463–66

135. Ross PD, Scruggs RL. 1965. Heat of reaction forming the three-stranded poly(A+2U) complex. *Biopolymers* 3:491–96

136. Rougée M, Faucon B, Mergny JL, Barcelo F, Giovannangeli C, et al. 1992. Kinetics and thermodynamics of triple-helix formation: effects of ionic strength and mismatches. *Biochemistry* 31:9269–78

137. Saenger W. 1984. *Principles of Nucleic Acid Structure*. New York: Springer-Verlag. 556 pp.

138. Salunkhe M, Wu T, Letsinger RL. 1992. Control of folding and binding of oligonucleotides by use of a nonnucleotide linker. *J. Am. Chem. Soc.* 114:8768–72

139. Scaria PV, Shafer RH. 1991. Binding of ethidium bromide to a DNA triple helix: evidence for intercalation. *J. Biol. Chem.* 266:5417–23

140. Sen D, Gilbert W. 1988. Formation of parallel four-stranded complexes by guanine-rich motifs in DNA and its implications for meiosis. *Nature* 334:364–66

141. Sen D, Gilbert W. 1991. The structure of telomeric DNA: DNA quadriplex formation. *Curr. Opin. Struct. Biol.* 1:435–38

142. Senior MM, Jones RA, Breslauer KJ. 1988. Influence of dangling thymidine residues on the stability and structure of two DNA duplexes. *Biochemistry* 27:3879–85

143. Senior MM, Jones RA, Breslauer KJ. 1988. Influence of loop residues on the relative stabilities of DNA hairpin structures. *Proc. Natl. Acad. Sci. USA* 85:6242–46

144. Shafer RH, Pilch DS, Scaria PV. 1992. Structure and stability studies on short DNA triple helices. In *Structure & Function*, Vol. 1. *Nucleic Acids*, ed. RH Sarma, MH Sarma, pp. 15–28. New York: Adenine. 275 pp.

145. Shea RG, Ng P, Bischofberger N. 1990. Thermal denaturation profiles and gel mobility shift analysis of oligonucleotide triplexes. *Nucleic Acids Res.* 18:4859–66

146. Shimizu M, Inoue H, Ohtsuka E. 1994. Detailed study of sequence-specific DNA cleavage of triplex-forming oligonucleotides linked to 1,10-phenanthroline. *Biochemistry* 33:606–13

147. Shindo H, Torigoe H, Sarai A. 1993. Thermodynamic and kinetic studies of DNA triplex formation of an oligo-homopyrimidine and a matched duplex by filter binding assay. *Biochemistry* 32:8963–69

148. Singleton SF. 1994. *The thermodynamics of oligonucleotide-directed triple helix formation at single DNA sites.* PhD thesis. Calif. Inst. Technol., Pasadena, CA. 268 pp.

149. Singleton SF, Dervan PB. 1992. Influence of pH on the equilibrium association constants for oligodeoxyribonucleotide-directed triple helix formation at single DNA sites. *Biochemistry* 31:10995–11003

150. Singleton SF, Dervan PB. 1992. Thermodynamics of oligodeoxyribonucleotide-directed triple helix formation: an analysis using quantitative affinity cleavage titration. *J. Am. Chem. Soc.* 114:6957–65

151. Singleton SF, Dervan PB. 1993. Equilibrium association constants for oligonucleotide-directed triple helix formation at single DNA sites: linkage to cation valence and concentration. *Biochemistry* 32:13171–79

152. Singleton SF, Dervan PB. 1994. Temperature dependence of the energetics of oligonucleotide-directed triple helix formation at a single DNA site. *J. Am. Chem. Soc.* 116:10376–82

153. Sklenář V, Feigon J. 1990. Formation of a stable triplex from a single DNA strand. *Nature* 345:836–38

154. Stein CA, Cohen JS. 1988. Oligodeoxynucleotides as inhibitors of gene expression: a review. *Cancer Res.* 48:2659–68

155. Strobel SA, Dervan PB. 1989. Cooperative site specific binding of oligonucleotides to duplex DNA. *J. Am. Chem. Soc.* 111:7286–87

156. Strobel SA, Doucette-Stamm LA, Riba L, Housman DE, Dervan PB. 1991. Site-specific cleavage of human chromosome 4 mediated by triple-helix formation. *Science* 254:1639–42

157. Strobel SA, Moser HE, Dervan PB. 1988. Double-stranded cleavage of genomic DNA at a single site by triple-helix formation. *J. Am. Chem. Soc.* 110:7927–29

158. Sturtevant JM. 1987. Biochemical applications of differential scanning calorimetry. *Annu. Rev. Phys. Chem.* 38:463–88

159. Sugimoto N, Shintani Y, Tanaka A, Sasaki M. 1992. Thermodynamics of triple-helix and double-helix formations by octamers of deoxyriboadenylic and deoxyribothymidylic acids. *Bull. Chem. Soc. Jpn.* 65:535–40

160. Sun J-S, François JC, Montenay-Garestier T, Saison-Behmoaras T, Roig V, et al. 1989. Sequence-specific intercalating agents: intercalation at specific sequences on duplex DNA via major groove recognition by oligonucleotide-intercalator conjugates. *Proc. Natl. Acad. Sci. USA* 86: 9198–9202

161. Sun JS, Giovannangeli C, François JC, Kurfurst R, Montenay-Garestier T, et al. 1991. Triple-helix formation by oligodeoxynucleotides and α oligodeoxynucleotide-intercalator conjugates. *Proc. Natl. Acad. Sci. USA* 88:6023–27

162. Sun J-S, Hélène C. 1993. Oligonucleotide-directed triple-helix formation. *Curr. Opin. Struct. Biol.* 3:345–56

163. Sun J-S, Lavery R, Chomilier J, Zakrzewska K, Montenay-Garestier T, Hélène C. 1991. Theoretical study of ethidium intercalation in triple-stranded DNA and at triplex-duplex junctions. *J. Biomol. Struct. Dyn.* 9: 425–36

164. Thomas T, Thomas TJ. 1993. Selectivity of polyamines in triplex DNA stabilization. *Biochemistry* 32: 14068–74

165. Thuong NT, Hélène C. 1993. Sequence-specific recognition and modification of double-helical DNA by oligonucleotides. *Angew. Chem. Int. Ed. Engl.* 32:666–90

166. Tung C-H, Breslauer KJ, Stein S. 1993. Polyamine-linked oligonucleotides for DNA triple helix formation. *Nucleic Acids Res.* 21:5489–94

167. Umemoto U, Sarma MH, Gupta G, Luo J, Sarma RH. 1990. Structure and stability of a DNA triple helix in solution: NMR studies on $d(T)_6 \cdot d(A)_6 \cdot d(T)_6$ and its complex with a minor groove binding drug. *J. Am. Chem. Soc.* 112:4539–45

168. Vesnaver G, Breslauer KJ. 1991. The contribution of DNA single-stranded order to the thermodynamics of duplex formation. *Proc. Natl. Acad. Sci. USA* 88:3569–73

169. Völker J. 1994. *The impact of global and local composition on the stability*

of triple helical DNA. PhD thesis. Univ. Cape Town, Cape Town, South Africa. 235 pp.

170. Völker J, Botes DP, Lindsey GG, Klump HH. 1993. Energetics of a stable intramolecular DNA triple helix formation. *J. Mol. Biol.* 230:1278–90

171. Waring MJ. 1974. Stabilization of two-stranded ribohomopolymer helices and destabilization of a three-stranded helix by ethidium bromide. *Biochem. J.* 143:483–86

172. Watson JD, Crick FHC. 1953. A structure for deoxyribose nucleic acid. *Nature* 171:737–38

173. Wells RD, Collier DA, Hanvey JC, Shimizu M, Wohlrab F. 1988. The chemistry and biology of unusual DNA structures adopted by oligopurine·oligopyrimidine sequences. *FASEB J.* 2:2939–49

174. Wickstrom E, ed. 1991. *Prospects for Antisense Nucleic Acid Therapy of Cancer and AIDS.* New York: Wiley-Liss

175. Wilson WD, Hopkins HP, Mizan S, Hamilton DD, Zon G. 1994. Thermodynamics of DNA triplex formation in oligomers with and without cytosine bases: influence of buffer species, pH, and sequence. *J. Am. Chem. Soc.* 116:3607–8

176. Wilson WD, Tanious FA, Mizan S, Yao S, Kiselyov AS, et al. 1993. DNA triple-helix specific intercalators as antigene enhancers: unfused aromatic cations. *Biochemistry* 32:10614–21

177. Wiseman T, Williston S, Brandts JF, Lin L-N. 1989. Rapid measurement of binding constants and heats of binding using a new titration calorimeter. *Anal. Biochem.* 179:131–37

178. Xie D, Bhakuni V, Freire E. 1991. Calorimetric determination of the energetics of the molten globule intermediate in protein folding: apo-α-lactalbumin. *Biochemistry* 30:10673–78

179. Xie D, Bhakuni V, Freire E. 1993. Are the molten globule and the unfolded states of apo-α-lactalbumin enthalpically equivalent? *J. Mol. Biol.* 232:5–8

180. Xodo LE, Manzini G, Quadrifoglio F. 1990. Spectroscopic and calorimetric investigation on the DNA triplex formed by d(CTCTTCTTTCTTTT-CTTTCTTCTC) and d(GAGAA-GAAAGA) at acidic pH. *Nucleic Acids Res.* 18:3557–64

181. Xodo LE, Manzini G, Quadrifoglio F, van der Marel GA, van Boom JH. 1991. Effect of 5-methylcytosine on the stability of triple-stranded DNA—a thermodynamic study. *Nucleic Acids Res.* 19:5625–31

182. Ye X, Kimura KI, Patel DJ. 1993. Site-specific intercalation of an anthracycline antitumor antibiotic into a Y·RY DNA triplex through covalent adduct formation. *J. Am. Chem. Soc.* 115:9325–26

183. Yoon K, Hobbs CA, Koch J, Sardaro M, Kutny R, Weis A. 1992. Elucidation of the sequence-specific third-strand recognition of four Watson-Crick base pairs in a pyrimidine triple-helix motif: T·AT, C·GC, T·CG, and G·TA. *Proc. Natl. Acad. Sci. USA* 89:3840–44

184. Yoon K, Hobbs CA, Walter AE, Turner DH. 1993. Effect of a 5′-phosphate on the stability of triple helix. *Nucleic Acids Res.* 21:601–6

Annu. Rev. Biophys. Biomol. Struct. 1995. 24:351–78

MEMBRANE-STRUCTURE STUDIES USING X-RAY STANDING WAVES

Martin Caffrey and Jin Wang

Department of Chemistry and Chemical Physics Program, The Ohio State University, Columbus, Ohio 43210-1173

KEY WORDS: membrane-protein structure, cytochrome c, lipid-phase transitions, membrane electrostatics, Langmuir-Blodgett films

CONTENTS

ABSTRACT

The principle and unique features of X-ray standing waves as a means for investigating membrane structure are described in this review. Thus far, X-ray standing waves have been used in structural studies of Langmuir-Blodgett and self-assembled monomolecular lipid films. Most recently, the method has been used in studies of supported membranes hosting the peripheral membrane protein, cytochrome c. Structural

1056-8700/95/0610-0351$05.00

rearrangements occurring in membranes and at surfaces driven by temperature and composition changes have been monitored as well. Finally, ion distribution in the diffuse-double layer next to a charged membrane has been determined using this approach. The review addresses the manner in which these and related measurements were made. What is not covered in the review is a critical appraisal of the limitations of the X-ray standing wave method. Such limitations (which are pronounced and introduce significant mensuration ambiguities at short distances on silver mirrors as used in the membrane protein topology study) have just recently come to our attention and will be reported on separately (S Kirchner, Z Yin, J Wang & M Caffrey, in preparation).

PERSPECTIVES AND OVERVIEW

Understanding membrane structure and how this relates to the biological function of membrane components currently represents one of the grand challenges in structural biology research. By knowing the impact of structure on function, we can hope to manipulate structure to our advantage. This review discusses membrane structure from the perspective of membrane lipid and protein topology and of the aqueous region at and next to the membrane surface. Studying such disparate aspects of membrane topology is not a trivial undertaking. The problem arises primarily from the lack of suitable methods of membrane characterization, i.e. methods that provide direct structural information with atomic resolution in an element-specific manner on samples that may take the form of isolated membranes or lipid monolayers and that can be used with intrinsically ordered and disordered systems. In other words, we seek a method that can work with molecularly thin films where the amount of material examined in the course of measurement is extremely small. The X-ray standing wave (XSW) technique introduced in this review is such a method.

To date, membrane topology studies have largely tended to use the reductionist approach and to examine components in isolation. This valuable experimental tack has contributed enormously to our understanding of the components themselves and has shed light on their behavior in natural membranes. The thrust now must be to examine structure in intact biological membranes and reconstituted systems where the major constituents present in vivo are in place during the measurements. Techniques that are beginning to provide structural information on such systems include molecular biology (46); chemical cross-linking (40); hydrophobicity analysis (47); absorption linear dichroism (45); the assorted new microscopies (15, 20, 26, 33); X-ray (18,

19, 39, 54), neutron (12), and electron (25, 27, 31, 37) diffraction; X-ray (24) and neutron (28, 42) reflectivity; X-ray interferometry (2); fluorescence (14, 32), infrared (11), NMR (44), and ESR (1) spectroscopy; and electrophoresis (35). Each technique has its own strengths and weaknesses, which are not detailed here. Suffice it to say that some of the limitations include sensitivity, the need to work with bulk samples and with potentially perturbing labels, an incompatibility with samples in thin-film form, and an inability to provide useful information on systems that are inherently disordered.

The XSW technique offers many of the advantages of a surface technique provided we can suitably dispose the membrane to be analyzed on a solid substrate for examination. The XSW measurement provides structural information through the location of a marker atom in the profile structure of the sample. The profile structure comprises the one-dimensional projection of the spatially averaged in-plane structure along the normal to the supporting solid surface. The method offers element specificity and spatial resolution on an atomic scale, and although it does not provide direct in-plane structural information, such can be obtained by using data collected normally in the course of an XSW measurement. Another attractive feature is that the method can be applied with equal ease to systems that are inherently ordered and disordered. An example of the former is a two-dimensional crystalline array of bacteriorhodopsin in the purple membrane or in a Langmuir-Blodgett (LB) film of calcium stearate. Ion or protein distribution in the aqueous medium bathing the membrane is an example of the latter. In addition to being useful in determining the structure of systems at equilibrium, the method can also be used to monitor membrane-related dynamic processes. In this regard, it has found application in studies of membrane-lipid phase transitions and of ion movement in membrane systems. Future applications include protein folding, membrane-protein insertion, surface potential–driven rearrangements in membrane-associated ion, lipid, and/or protein distributions, and surface binding.

This review summarizes the progress made in developing and in applying the XSW approach for studying membrane topology. It chronicles a series of measurements made on relatively simple model systems by way of demonstrating definitively the utility and versatility of this new structural tool. What emerges is an information-rich technique for investigating systems that do not naturally or easily lend themselves to detailed structural investigations. Parenthetically, we note that the applicability of the method is not limited to biomembranes. Indeed, the XSW approach, as described here, is finding application in the characterization of other biological and nonbiological thin films, surfaces, and interfaces. The same principles outlined in this review also apply to these systems, which include polymers, chemical and biochemical sensors, and corrosion-prevention and nonlinear optical devices.

MEMBRANE MENSURATION USING X-RAY STANDING WAVES

Introduction

An XSW can be generated by the interference between two coherently related X-ray beams. Conventional XSW measurements (3, 4, 9, 16, 22, 23) use dynamic Bragg diffraction from perfect single crystals for generating XSW with d-spacing periods ranging from 1 to 4 Å. This technique was first applied to the study of implanted heavy-atom layers (3, 4, 22). Interest in the method broadened with the report (3) that the standing wave extended above the surface and could therefore be used for examining adsorbed surface layers (9, 16, 23). Such measurements have proven to be very precise in determining where, and how well, heavy-atom distributions register with respect to the perfect crystal diffraction planes. This information is obtained by observing the modulation in the impurity atom X-ray fluorescence yield as the standing-wave antinodes shift inward by one-half of a d-spacing during a scan in angle θ through the Bragg reflection. This same approach would also be useful for studying the layered arrangement of atoms in LB films. However, the characteristic modulo-d length scale of a few Ångstroms, which makes the XSW technique so appropriate for studying bond-length distances between atom layers at single crystal surfaces, is too short for measuring the spacing between heavy-atom layers in LB films. For this reason, XSW with periods at and above 20 Å are needed to better match the thickness of LB films of biologically relevant materials. In the following two sections, we show how such long-period XSWs can be generated by Bragg diffraction from layered synthetic microstructures (6) or by total external reflection from mirror surfaces (6–8, 51).

Fixed Period XSW

For Bragg diffraction purposes, a layered synthetic microstructure (LSM) is fabricated as a depth-periodic layered structure consisting of 10 to 200 layer pairs of alternating high and low electron density materials (such as tungsten and silicon or platinum and carbon). The layer thicknesses remain sufficiently uniform within the range of 5–100 Å.

The corresponding fundamental diffraction plane spacing can therefore be $d = 10$–200 Å. Owing to the low number of layer pairs that effect Bragg diffraction, these optical elements have a rather large X-ray–energy bandpass and angular reflection width. The quality of LSMs is such that experimental Bragg reflection curves compare well with dynamic diffraction theory, and peak reflectivities are as high as 80%. Therefore, a well-defined standing wave can be generated and used to probe structures deposited on an LSM surface with a periodic scale equivalent to this rather large d-spacing. As this technique allows the investigator to choose the standing-wave period and material composition of the uppermost layer, it has great potential for resolving various surface and interface structures.

During Bragg diffraction, the standing wave nodes coincide with the diffraction planes on the low-angle side of the strong reflection condition, and as the angle θ is increased through the Bragg angle, the standing wave moves inward until the antinodes reach the diffraction planes (Figure 1). To a good approximation, the first-order Bragg diffraction planes coincide with the centers of the heavy-atom layers in the LSM. Above the surface of the LSM, the period D of the standing wave is simply related to the wavelength λ and angle 2θ between the two interfering plane waves as $D = \lambda/(2\sin\theta)$. Because the angular width of the Bragg peak is on the order of a fraction of a milliradian ($0.0573°$), D remains approximately fixed and equal to the d-spacing of the LSM during the course of a typical XSW measurement. As the standing wave moves inward, the fluorescence yield from a layer of marker atoms sitting above the LSM surface shows a characteristic modulation (6). The phase of this modulation (or coherent position) is a measure of the atom layer's average position $\langle z \rangle$, modulo the d-spacing of the LSM. The amplitude of this modulation (or coherent fraction) is a measure of the width of the atom layer, $\langle z^2 \rangle^{1/2}$. If all of the marker atoms were contained in a plane that was parallel to the diffraction planes the coherent fraction would equal unity. On the other hand, if the marker atoms were randomly distributed in a very thick overlayer, the coherent fraction would be zero.

Variable Period XSW

Because X-ray frequencies are greater than the natural frequencies for most bound electrons in matter, the refractive index for X rays is less than unity. Therefore, if the incident angle at an optical boundary is smaller than the critical angle, X rays will undergo total external reflection in the same manner as visible light undergoes total internal reflection.

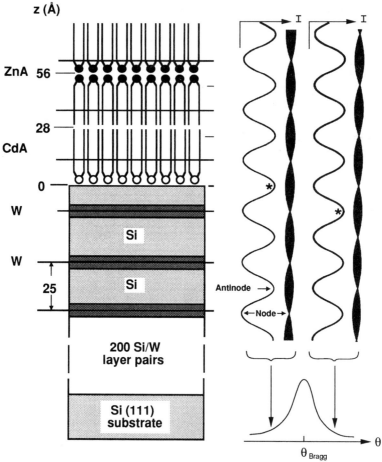

Figure 1   Schematic showing fully extended untilted zinc and cadmium arachidate LB layers deposited on the plasma-cleaned silicon surface of a W/Si LSM with a 25-Å *d*-spacing. The standing waves generated on the low- and high-angle side of the Bragg reflection (*bottom right*) are depicted along the right side. The asterisk marks the position of a particular antinode (maximum) as it moves inward by one half a *d*-spacing upon changing incident angle from below to above θ_{Bragg}.

Not only can an XSW be generated by the interference between the incident and Bragg-diffracted traveling plane waves, but a standing wave can also be established by the interference between the incident and specularly reflected traveling plane waves. During specular (or total external) reflection, the XSW forms in the more optically dense medium above the mirror surface, and an evanescent (or exponentially damped) wave forms below the mirror surface with a very short penetration depth into the less optically dense medium. Although much attention has focused on the evanescent wave (5, 10, 34), the long-period property of this standing wave has only recently been utilized for structure determination (7, 8, 50, 51).

The total external reflection condition constitutes the zeroth-order Bragg diffraction condition with a diffraction plane at the mirror surface and an infinite d-spacing; this realization is the key to understanding standing waves under the specular condition. As in the above description for normal Bragg diffraction, a standing wave node lies at the mirror surface at the low-angle side of the strong specular reflection condition, i.e. at $\theta = 0$, with the first antinode infinitely far above the mirror surface (Figure 2). As the incident angle θ advances through the reflection, the first antinode moves inward until it coincides with the mirror surface at the critical angle θ_c. The remaining antinodes of the standing wave follow behind like a compressing bellows as θ increases with a period of $D = \lambda/(2\sin\theta)$. Advancing above θ_c, the first antinode remains at the mirror surface while the amplitude of the standing wave dies off rapidly because of the abrupt reduction in intensity of the specularly reflected plane wave.

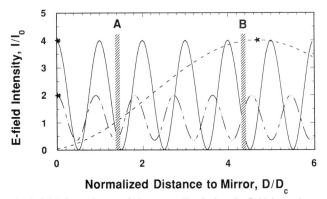

Figure 2 The height dependence of the normalized electric field intensity generated during specular reflection of an X-ray plane wave from the surface of an X-ray mirror at three different incident angles. The asterisk identifies the first antinode (maximum), which at low angles of incidence is quite distant from the surface and is next to the surface at the critical angle. Thus, a marker-atom marker layer at position A above the mirror surface will experience the passage of two E-field maxima and give rise to a corresponding number of peaks in the fluorescence yield curve as the incident angle is adjusted in the range $0 < \theta \leq \theta_c$. In contrast, a marker-atom layer at position B will exhibit five peaks in the fluorescence yield curve in the same angular range.

The standing waves generated at $\theta = 0.1\theta_c$, θ_c, and $1.1\theta_c$ during specular reflection of an X-ray plane wave from an X-ray mirror used in a preliminary study are shown in Figure 2. The distance scale on the abscissa is normalized to the critical period $D_c = \lambda/(2\theta_c)$, the period of the XSW at the critical angle, which is typically tens of Ångstroms. The method used to calculate these curves makes use of Parratt's recursion formulation with Fresnel coefficients (41). Typically, measurements are made by scanning in angle θ and simultaneously monitoring the reflectivity and the fluorescence yields from atoms sitting on, or above, the surface. An equivalent scan in energy can be made (50). However, θ scans are preferred because of the relative ease with which they can be performed. Because the photoelectric effect is proportional to the electric field intensity at the center of an atom, the variation in electric field intensity predicted from this calculation can be used in comparison to the measured fluorescence yields to determine how far an atom sits above the reflecting surface. This length scale, which is inherently longer than the first-order Bragg standing wave period from an LSM, has proven to be invaluable for removing the modulo-d ambiguity from first-order Bragg XSW measurements (6; Figure 3 in Ref. 13).

Data Analysis

In a typical XSW measurement, a data set consists of a fluorescence yield and a reflectivity profile in the angular range of interest. In the ideal case, the complete X-ray fluorescence spectrum is recorded at each step in the profile, and the fluorescence peak from the element of interest is well resolved from scattered incident X rays and other fluorescence signals in the spectrum. The area beneath the fluorescence peak, determined using a χ^2-fitting program, gives an accurate measure of total fluorescence counts. The next step in the analysis is to determine the distribution of the marker atom above the substrate surface by matching the theoretical model to the experimental fluorescence yield and reflectivity data. Initially, a layered model of refractive index based on the known structure of the sample is used. By adjusting the interfacial roughness value, a χ^2-fitting program fits the theoretical reflectivity (41) to the experimental reflectivity profile. The interfacial roughness value giving the best fit is used in the subsequent E-field and fluorescence calculations. In the simplest case, the model distribution of the marker atom layer above the substrate surface is Gaussian with two fitting parameters, the mean position above the surface and the half-width at half-height (HWHH) of the Gaussian.

PROGRESS TO DATE

The following sections describe a series of successfully completed XSW studies. These analyses highlight the utility and versatility of the XSW approach in tackling problems related to membrane topology.

A Molecular Yardstick for Model Biomembranes

LB films have been used extensively as models for biomembranes. Several techniques have been used to probe the molecular structure of such membrane films. The most detailed information is derived from neutron-diffraction and magnetic-resonance studies used in combination with selectively deuterated amphiphiles (38, 43, 55). Neutron-diffraction experiments derived the mean positions of the labeled chain segments in both solid and fluid lipid bilayers with a resolution of 6 Å. Except for single-crystal diffraction measurements, neutron diffraction has produced the highest position resolution available to date. In this study, we developed and implemented an approach that uses XSWs for determining the position and width of marker-atom layers in LB films with sub-Ångstrom resolution (6). Specifically, structural information on an atomic scale was obtained for an LB trilayer system by means of long-period XSWs. The LB trilayer of zinc and cadmium arachidate was deposited on an LSM consisting of 200 tungsten-silicon layer pairs with a 25-Å period (Figure 1). A 30-Å thermally induced inward collapse of the zinc-atom layer that was initially located in the LB trilayer at 53 Å above the LSM surface was observed. The mean position and width of the zinc-atom layer was determined with a precision of ± 0.3 Å. This study represented a first in terms of using XSW with a probing length scale comparable to the dimensions of the biological membrane. It set the stage for the following series of definitive demonstration experiments.

Structure Studies of Membranes up to 1000 Å Thick with Ångstrom Resolution

The success of the measurements described above led to speculation about the utility of the XSW approach in structure studies of supramolecular aggregates and assemblies commonly found in, for example, membrane receptor–ligand interactions and multimembrane stacks. Measurements of this type would require that the probing XSW be well defined at distances much farther from the standing wave–generating mirror surface than those demonstrated previously for such systems. Given the biological import of such structure studies and the enormous potential afforded by the method, we set out to establish that an XSW can be generated that is well defined at close to 1000 Å above the mirror surface. This length scale was chosen in light of the biological systems likely to be investigated using XSW in the foreseeable future. The samples examined in this study consisted of an octadecylthiol (ODT)–coated gold mirror on which we had deposited, using the LB technique, a variable number (0, 14) of ω-tricosenoic acid (ωTA, C23)

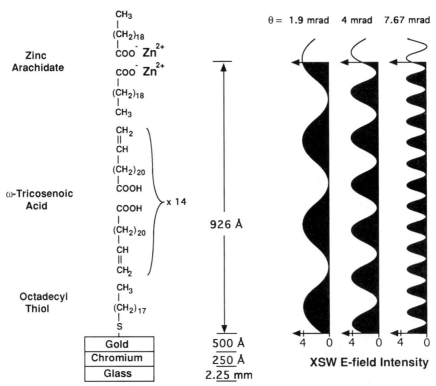

Figure 3   Schematic of the gold mirror and deposited films. Gold was deposited on a piece of chromium-coated float glass by means of thermoevaporation techniques and was plasma cleaned in preparation for treatment with an octadecylthiol solution. Films of ω-tricosenoic acid and zinc arachidate were deposited by the Langmuir-Blodgett method. Transfer ratios were close to unity for each deposition. The dimensions shown were obtained from ellipsometry in the case of deposited films and from manufacturers' specifications in the case of the mirror. On the right is the electric field intensity distribution normal to the mirror surface at three different angles of incidence. Thus, when the incident angle inside the organic overlayer falls within the range $0 < \theta \le 7.67$ mrad, the corresponding fluorescence yield curve should contain a total of 13 maxima for such a sample. In fact, only $11\frac{1}{2}$ peaks are seen experimentally in the range $0 < \theta \le \theta_c$ because of refraction caused by the organic overlayer (51).

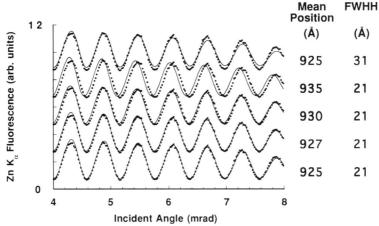

Figure 4 The experimental (*dots*) and theoretical (*solid lines*) angular dependence at 9.8 keV of the zinc K_α fluorescence yield for the sample shown in Figure 3. The sensitivity of the fluorescence yield profile to heavy-atom layer mean position above the surface and to the distribution about the mean position is illustrated. Theoretical curves were generated by assuming the indicated mean zinc positions and spread about the mean position [full-width at half-height (FWHH)]. Curves are displaced on the ordinate for clarity. The data are best fit with a zinc mean position of 925 Å and a FWHH of 21 Å. Changing the mean position by as little as 5 Å or the FWHH by 10 Å introduces a significant mismatch between the experimental and the theoretical data. This mismatch illustrates the structure sensitivity of the XSW approach.

bilayers followed by a single, upper inverted bilayer of zinc arachidate (ZnA, C20) (Figure 3). The results (Figure 4) demonstrate convincingly that the XSW field is well defined at close to 1000 Å above the mirror surface and can be used to establish the mean position and width of the heavy-atom layer with Ångstrom resolution (51). The quality of these data demonstrates the enormous potential of XSW methods as structure probes of membranes and of thin film and interface-related phenomena.

Structure Changes in Model Membranes

As noted above, variable period XSW measurements were previously used to monitor and interpret structural rearrangements undergone during a phase transition in a model membrane with Ångstrom resolution (6, 8). In another study, an extended length scale ranging from 40 Å up to ~1000 Å was used without sacrificing resolution to address the question of whether the phase-transition characteristics of a lipid multilayer are sensitive to the number and identity of the lamellae in the membrane stack. The system chosen for examination consisted of a variable number (0, 2, 8, and 16) of ωTA bilayers followed by a single, upper inverted bilayer of ZnA deposited, by means of the LB technique, on an ODT-coated gold mirror. Variable-period XSW measurements provided precise position information on the zinc layer mean position and width and were used to track the collapse of the heavy-atom layer during the thermotropic phase transition. Samples with and without the ωTA layers showed disparate pretransitional rearrangements, transition temperatures, and apparent cooperativity, as well as final, high-temperature zinc distributions. At sufficiently high temperatures, the ODT desorbed from the gold mirror surface and was replaced by a layer of zinc. In all samples containing ωTA, the cooperative transition occurred at ~70°C, which, as shown by separate low- and wide-angle, time-resolved X-ray diffraction and differential scanning calorimetry measurements, corresponds to the melting temperature of bulk ωTA. Thus, we have the remarkable result that bulk behavior is displayed by as little as two LB bilayers of ωTA. With all thin-film samples, the thermally induced structure change was not reversed upon cooling to and subsequent storage at room temperature. The success of these measurements indicates that the variable period XSW method might now be used to study membrane-related processes and to obtain precise structural information not only in membranes but also in peripheral components such as membrane-associated antibodies and cytoskeletal and peripheral proteins, part of which can be quite distant from the supporting or interacting membrane.

Heavy-Atom Interlayer Diffusion in Langmuir-Blodgett Films

Interlayer diffusion of metallic selenium and of zinc ions has been observed in LB films using variable period XSW generated above a silver mirror (52). The two films used in this study had the following structure: Sample A—hydrophobic silver mirror, 5 bilayers of ωTA, alternate bilayer of ZnA and seleno-dipalmitoylphosphatidylcholine (Se-DPPC); Sample B—silver mirror, Se-DPPC monolayer deposited from a zinc chloride–containing aqueous subphase. In freshly prepared Sample A, selenium was found in a well-defined layer ~3 Å above the zinc layer located 300 Å above the mirror surface. In Sample B, the zinc and selenium layers were essentially coincident. Upon incubation of Sample A in air at 23°C for ≥4 days, selenium had apparently dissociated from the DPPC headgroup and had diffused into an otherwise structurally unaltered film. No such movement of selenium was observed in Sample B, although the zinc layer did undergo diffusion away from the mirror surface. These results suggest that heavy-atom diffusion along the normal of the LB film depends on the form and the environment in which the heavy atom exists in the original film. They also demonstrate the utility of the XSW approach for studying diffusion phenomena in organic thin films and the intriguing possibility of using XSW to monitor ion transport across membranes.

Membrane-Protein Topology

The elucidation of the structure and function of membrane proteins remains one of Biology's grand challenges. Given the demonstrated utility of XSW in studying model membranes, this technique should serve as a means for uncovering key features of membrane-protein structure. This effort aims to determine how membrane proteins such as receptors and transport, light-harvesting, and signal- and energy-transducing proteins are arranged in and on their supporting lipid bilayer membrane and, by extension, how they function in such an environment. To address these fundamental issues, we must prepare a series of lipids and proteins specifically labeled with appropriate marker atoms. Because many membrane proteins contain heavy atoms naturally, they are ideal candidates for structural biology studies. In other cases, marker-atom substitutions can be made that do not perturb the structure or the activity of the protein. For example, selenomethionine can be site-selectively substituted for methionine, a sulfur-containing amino acid, using modern semisynthetic chemistry and recombinant DNA technology. Our immediate objective is to apply these and other methodologies to establishing the membrane topological relationship of the electron-transfer protein, cytochrome c; the biotin-streptavidin complex; protein kinase C; phospholipase A2; and the light-driven proton pump, bacteriorhodopsin. These fundamental investigations lead directly into longer-term projects aimed at the more demanding membrane-protein complexes such as the cystic fibrosis transmembrane conductance regulator and the photosynthetic reaction center.

Cytochrome c is a small ($\sim$100 amino acids long), compact, approximately spherical peripheral membrane protein (36). It is an essential component of the mitochondrial respiratory chain. The protein binds to charged membranes by long-range electrostatic and nonspecific interactions. At neutral pH, it bears a large net charge of approximately $+8$ and has a dipole moment of $\sim$300 Debye (29). The principle upon which the membrane cytochrome c topology measurements are based is as follows: With cytochrome c bound as a monolayer to a flat supported lipid adlayer on an XSW-generating surface, the plane containing the heme iron (or zinc in the case of zinc cytochrome c) serves as an internal reference benchmark plane from and to which distance measurements are made. A series of cytochromes c is prepared, and each member is singly labeled with selenomethionine at a defined site in the protein. Each cytochrome c preparation is in turn adsorbed onto a lipid adlayer deposited on an appropriate LSM or X-ray mirror. By suitably tuning the energy of the incident X-ray beam, one can stimulate (and record) simultaneously the X-ray fluorescence of both the reference iron (or zinc) and the reporter selenium atoms. Fluorescence and reflectivity data are collected in the appropriate angular range and analyzed to calculate the coherent position and fraction of each heavy atom in the bound layer of cytochrome c. For each cytochrome c, the selenium-to-iron (or zinc) distance is calculated. Such measurements, in conjunction with the known three-dimensional structure of the protein, will suggest a unique orientation for the protein at the membrane surface. The orientation information yields the identity of the site of interaction and thus the amino acids in contact with the membrane.

An initial round of XSW and reflectivity measurements on cytochrome c deposited directly on a freshly prepared silver surface and on lipid films has been made. The purpose was to evaluate the suitability of silver mirrors as standing wave–generating substrates for use in XSW measurements on selenomethionine-labeled (SeMet) cytochrome c and to determine if the method is sufficiently sensitive to the heavy-atom signal in a cytochrome c monolayer, where the marker-atom surface density is considerably lower than had been used previously.

Figure 5 shows the results of the XSW measurements on a sample where cytochrome c is situated directly on the mirror surface (Sample

---

→

Figure 5 (*A*) Experimental (*dots*) and theoretical (*lines*) angular dependence of the selenium K_α fluorescence yield from SeMet[80] cytochrome c at a silver mirror surface at 13.3 keV. (*B*) The calculated selenium distribution above the mirror that best fits the fluorescence yield data (*solid line* in *A*). The inset in *B* shows a hexagonally close-packed arrangement of cytochrome c molecules with an average diameter of 34 Å. Separate theoretical fluorescence yield profiles have been generated simulating an unfolded protein with the selenium marker atom at the mirror surface (*dotted line* in *A*) and a film consisting of a protein bilayer (*dashed line* in *A*). (*C*) The α-carbon trace of horse heart cytochrome c with the protein oriented so as to position the selenium marker atom (assumed to replace isomorphously the sulfur in the native protein) 11.5 Å above the silver mirror surface. This particular arrangement has the heme plane perpendicular to the mirror surface while the exposed heme edge faces the surface. The α-carbon backbone of several lysines are in bold-face type, and the N- and C-termini are indicated. Note that the side chains of the amino acid residues fill the 4-Å space between the mirror surface and the α-carbon backbone of the protein in contact with the surface. This is just one of the possible, and physically reasonable, orientations for cytochrome c at the mirror surface, consistent with the XSW data above.

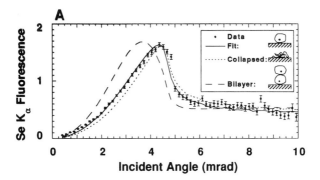

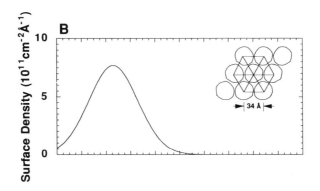

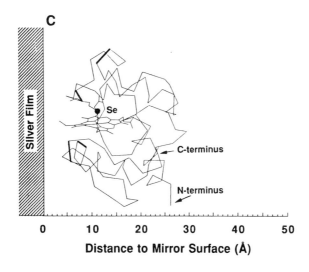

1). The data show that the selenium in the protein is suspended as a monolayer with a mean position of 11.5 ± 2 Å above the mirror surface and with a HWHH spread of 6 Å (53). This result suggests that the protein retains its globular shape while adsorbed at the mirror surface. In support of this statement, we have shown independently that the surface density of cytochrome c in this sample is 1040 ± 10 Å^2 per molecule (53). This is based on a comparison of the fluorescence yield values recorded above the critical angle with a similar fluorescence measurement on a reference sample of known selenium surface density. Because the average diameter of cytochrome c is 34 Å, in a hexagonally close-packed arrangement, each cytochrome c molecule occupies 1000 Å^2. This measurement suggests, therefore, that the protein maintains its globular shape and is hexagonally close-packed at the silver mirror surface.

Figure 5a includes two theoretical fluorescence yield profiles that support the above conclusions and demonstrate the sensitivity of the XSW technique. These profiles simulate an unfolded cytochrome c molecule with the selenium tag at the mirror surface (*dotted line*) and a cytochrome c organized as a protein bilayer (*dashed line*). Clearly, the experimental data are best fit by the model containing a monolayer of globular protein, as described above, with the selenium located 11.5 Å above the mirror surface (*solid line*). Strong evidence indicates that the selenium occupies the same position in the protein as the sulfur in native Met^{80} cytochrome c (49), so this 11.5-Å distance measurement suggests the orientation for the protein at the mirror surface shown in Figure 5c. Thus, four positively charged lysine residues, located at positions 13, 27, 72, and 79, form a ring around the exposed heme edge and thereby a platform, of sorts, for the protein to dock on the metal surface (29). This model has the heme plane oriented perpendicular to the mirror surface and the exposed heme edge facing the surface.

XSW data have also been collected on cytochrome c bound to lipid films as adlayers on a silver mirror. With the protein on a self-assembled monolayer (SAM) of ω-thiolundecanoic (Sample 2), the distribution of protein at the SAM surface is very similar to that found in Sample 1, i.e. a hexagonally close-packed monolayer (53). However, in addition, a small amount of protein (<10%) resides above the first protein monolayer, presumably as domains of protein pauci- and multilayers. In the first protein monolayer, the selenium is located 23 Å above the silver mirror. This relatively short distance might be accounted for by protein penetration into the SAM, by a slight flattening of the protein, and/or by a tilting of the molecules in the SAM. In future studies, a reference marker atom in the SAM and in the protein will help distinguish between these possibilities.

The third sample in the series (Sample 3) posits the protein atop an LB film of dimyristoylphosphatidylserine (DMPS), which in turn is above a SAM of ODT. The fluorescence-yield profile for this sample peaks at 3.3 and 4.5 mrad, which indicates the presence of two protein pools. The first, a monolayer, represents 68% of the protein and places the selenium atom ~25 Å above the silver mirror surface. The remaining 32% is distributed as higher-order protein aggregates above the first protein monolayer. Our immediate objective is to develop methods for preparing samples in the likeness of Sample 3, but with a single monolayer of protein on the LB surface.

These results and the simulations shown in Figures 5 and 6 demonstrate clearly the utility of the XSW approach for studying the topology of surface-adsorbed and membrane proteins. The method has the inherent sensitivity to allow high spatial resolution and element-specific measurements on protein monolayers where surface density is intrinsically low. In addition to making accurate measurements of heavy-atom distribution in the direction perpendicular to the binding interface, we have obtained information about in-plane protein structure from the XSW fluorescence data (53). Thus, in two samples used in this study, the protein adopted a hexagonally close-packed arrangement at the metal or SAM surface. The data also suggest that cytochrome c is quite robust in that its globular structure is stable at disparate interface types for a considerable period of time.

Diffuse Double Layer at the Membrane-Aqueous Interface

The properties of the interface formed by an electrolyte in contact with a charged surface govern numerous processes, including electrodeposition, colloidal suspension, and ion transport to and through biological membranes. The separation of charge at an interface causes a gradient in electrostatic potential that polarizes the solution and affects ion distribution in the interfacial region (Figure 7a). Because the interface resides below a relatively thick aqueous overlayer, high-resolution structure–determining techniques, which rely on charged particle beams or a vacuum, cannot be used to profile the ion distribution in the solution immediately above a charged surface. Consequently, the treatment of this interfacial region has, up until now, been idealized and was based on models such as those given by Helmholtz, Gouy-Chapman, and Stern.

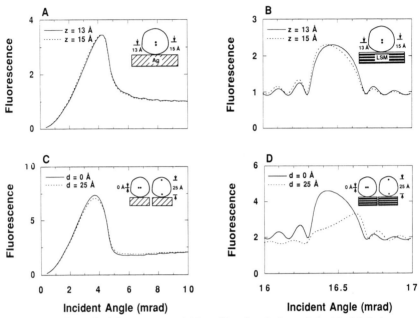

Figure 6   Theoretical fluorescence-yield profiles for singly and doubly labeled cytochrome *c* on a silver mirror and on a Mo/Si LSM. The enhanced spatial resolving power of the fixed (Bragg diffraction from an LSM) compared with the variable period (specular reflection from a mirror) XSW approach is apparent in the sample shown when the yield profiles in Panels *A* and *B* are compared. (*A*) The fluorescence yield profile for a marker atom 13 Å above the mirror surface is virtually indistinguishable from that for a marker atom located 15 Å above the surface. (*B*) The corresponding LSM-based profiles are distinct. (*C*) The insensitivity of variable-period XSW as a tool for distinguishing marker-atom distribution in a small protein containing two identical marker atoms. Obviously, if the two marker atoms represent different atomic elements, they can be examined independently based on their distinct X-ray fluorescence characteristics. (*D*) The fixed-period XSW has ample spatial resolution to distinguish between two possible arrangements of a pair of identical marker atoms in a small protein.

X rays, which can penetrate through millimeters of water, should, in principle, be ideal for solving this long-standing problem in membrane electrostatics and electrochemistry. In the study described below, we measured directly the ion distribution in an electrolyte solution in contact with a charged polymerized phospholipid membrane by using long-period XSWs. The 27-Å thick lipid monolayer was supported on a tungsten-silicon mirror. XSWs were generated above the mirror surface by total external reflection of a 9.8 keV X-ray beam from a synchrotron undulator. The membrane surface, which contained negatively charged phosphate headgroups, was bathed in a dilute zinc chloride solution

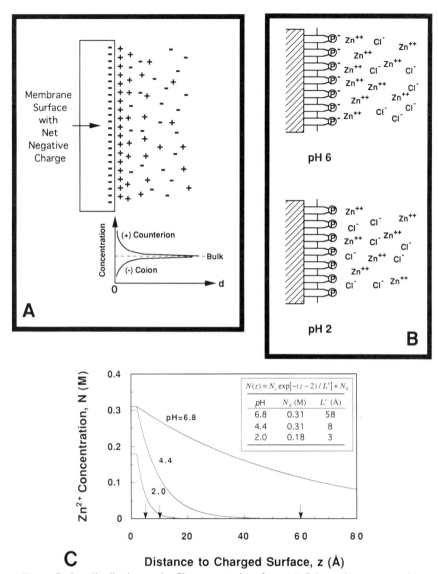

Figure 7 Ion distribution at the film-aqueous interface. (*A*) Schematic representation of the counterion and co-ion distribution in the aqueous phase next to a surface bearing a net negative charge. (*B*) Schematic of the cross-linked phospholipid membrane deposited on a silanated W/Si LSM. The exposed part of the lipid has a phosphate headgroup that bears a net negative charge at high pH and attracts zinc ions from the solution. At low pH, the phosphate headgroup is protonated and rendered uncharged. (*C*) Zinc ion distribution in the aqueous phase next to a cross-linked phospholipid membrane at different pH values as measured using XSW generated under specular conditions. The equation describing the exponential decay distribution is shown in the inset, where N is the zinc concentration at distance z from the surface, N_c is the excess surface zinc concentration, L' is the ion Debye length, and N_0 is the zinc concentration in bulk solution.

(Figure 7*b*). The concentration of zinc ions in the condensed layer at the membrane surface and the zinc ion distribution in the diffuse layer were measured as a function of headgroup charge (7). The Debye length of the diffuse layer varied between 3 and 58 Å depending on the pH of the solution above the phospholipid monolayer. The results agree qualitatively with the Gouy-Chapman-Stern model that predicts that the charged surface can be partially neutralized by a condensed (or adsorbed) layer of counterions and that the ion distribution in the solution will form a diffuse layer with an exponential decay functional form (Figure 7*c*). In a related study, a series of measurements were carried out on this same system at the following pH values in the following order: 5.8, 4.2, 2.0, 4.2, and 5.8. The results demonstrate the thermodynamic reversibility of the pH-induced changes in the diffuse double layer profile (J Wang & M Caffrey, in preparation).

Such a direct measure of ion distribution above a charged membrane surface at this level of sensitivity has not heretofore been possible. At this stage, the method is limited to measuring distributions of ions with X-ray fluorescence energies high enough to penetrate through the outer water layer and encapsulate plastic film. In addition, the total amount of zinc in the interfacial region had to be large compared with the total volume of zinc in the remaining 2 μm of solution. Otherwise, the zinc fluorescence yield data scans would have been indistinguishable from the constant zinc distribution yield curve (7).

This study demonstrates how long-period X-ray standing waves can be used to directly measure the ion distribution profile in an electrolyte solution in contact with a charged membrane surface. With this new method in hand and its utility established, we can now begin experimentally testing almost a century's worth of theory.

FEATURES OF XSW

The XSW approach for studying organic thin films and their interfaces offers several attractive features. The first is resolution. The spatial resolution of XSWs generated by Bragg diffraction is 1% of the layer-pair spacing, *d,* in the substrate LSM. Thus, for example, in our earlier work on zinc and cadmium arachidate trilayers on a W/Si LSM (d = 25 Å), the measured resolution in locating the zinc layer at ~50 Å above the LSM surface was 0.3 Å. Our most recent work (Figure 4) shows that with the heavy-atom layer located 925 Å above the mirror surface, the resolution is on the order of 3 Å. The second advantage is element specificity. Tuning the incident X-ray beam to an energy just above the absorption edge of the element of interest excites its fluorescence.

Elements with absorption energies below and close to the incident beam energy will also be induced to fluoresce under these conditions. In fact, this situation necessitates the use of molybdenum (Mo)/Si as opposed to tungsten (W)/Si LSMs in the selenium XSW measurements. As a result, absolute element specificity cannot be claimed for the method. Furthermore, the lighter elements, such as oxygen, phosphorus, and sulfur, are not currently appropriate for these measurements because of intrinsically low fluorescence, high absorbance, and low detection efficiency at low energies (30).

The third advantage is the ability to make structure-determining measurements on isolated lipid membranes. Given that most membranes exist in the cell in isolation or as pairs of membranes, the samples used in these XSW experiments can more closely model in vivo conditions than, for example, multilamellar vesicles. The ability to make these measurements on essentially a monolayer of protein (or lipid) representing ~10 pmol (100 ng) of cytochrome c in the X-ray beam points to the considerable sensitivity of the method. Such sensitivity originates in the naturally collimated nature of synchrotron radiation. The fourth advantage derives from the direct nature of the XSW measurement. For a given LSM or X-ray mirror, the angle-dependent electric-field profile normal to the surface can be calculated exactly as can the fluorescence-yield profile for a model distribution of heavy atoms above the surface. In most cases, adjusting just two parameters, the position and width of the heavy-atom layer, reduces the number of assumptions needed to match the observed and theoretical fluorescence yield and reflectivity. The fifth advantage refers to the proposed membrane protein–topology measurements, which can be performed on minimally perturbed systems. The iron XSW measurements on iron cytochrome c represent a zero perturbation, whereas the zinc measurements constitute a minimal one. Selenomethionine substitutions in cytochrome c and other membrane proteins involve a conservative substitution of one Group VIA element, selenium (row 4 in the Periodic Table of Elements; atomic number 34), for another, sulfur (row 3, atomic number 16). For systems that are inherently disordered, the XSW method affords an additional important advantage: it can be used to profile ion and/or solute distributions in a solution that is in the immediate vicinity of a surface.

While the XSW method itself does not provide information regarding in-plane structure, data normally collected in the course of an XSW measurement can be used to this end. This feature was exploited in the membrane-topology study on cytochrome c described above that enabled a determination of the hexagonally close-packed arrangement for adsorbed cytochrome c and shed light on the structural stability of this globular protein. We expect to make use of this additional feature of the XSW measurements in future studies of membrane topology.

The strengths of the XSW approach for studying membrane topology are many. Thus far, however, we have discussed only those features that address time-averaged structure. Of course, XSWs can also be used to examine dynamic processes. To date, we have used the method to monitor thermally induced structure changes and to track ion and marker-atom vectorial movement in lipid membranes. These measurements highlight an additional advantage of the XSW method, namely the ability to study processes occurring in or next to membranes in a time-resolved manner.

QUO VADIS

The foregoing discussion clearly shows that the XSW approach to studying membrane topology works and that the means for extracting new and useful static and kinetic structural information from XSW data are in hand. As far as future applications and developments are concerned, the following issues concerning X rays, substrates, and samples must be addressed.

Fortunately, enhanced XSW measurement sensitivity is imminent since the introduction of brighter, third-generation sources such as the European Synchrotron Radiation Facility and the Advanced Photon Source, the planned use of wide bandpass LSM monochromators, and the implementation of a recently discovered resonance enhanced XSW effect (50). In parallel with these developments, we still need to extend the useful X-ray range to lower energies so that the lighter (lower atomic number) elements, P, S, and Ca, for example, can be monitored. Parenthetically we note that we have successfully performed an experiment in which synchrotron-based XSWs were used to locate the position of Ca^{2+} in the profile structure of a model membrane with atomic resolution under ambient conditions (J Wang & M Caffrey, submitted). These advances will reduce our dependence on potentially perturbing heavy-atom substitutions and/or labeling. We also need to improve existing X-ray detection capabilities to the point where most, if not all, of the fluorescent photons emanating from a sample are counted in high resolution, energy-dispersive detectors. The current arrangement incorporates just a single detector that intercepts a mere 1–2% of the fluorescence signal output from the sample. The implementation of these improvements will enormously enhance measurement sensitivity and will enable us to examine more dilute and biologically more relevant systems and to perform kinetic measurements with greater time and spatial resolution.

Substrates are important because their characteristics determine the feasibility of a given XSW measurement and the quality of the data so-derived. The substrates referred to here are LSMs and mirrors serve as XSW-generating and X ray–reflecting surfaces as well as solid supports for the membrane system under investigation. For the X-ray measurement itself, these substrates should ideally be highly reflecting, atomically flat (low roughness value), and of extremely high purity. For LSMs, the substrates should be strongly diffracting and large in size with d-spacings in the range of 10–200 Å and should have selectable internal and upper surface composition. They should also be commercially available and affordable. The substrate surfaces should have the proper hydrophobic and hydrophilic characteristics, be chemically stable and easily handled, and exhibit a suitable surface reactivity so that they can be conveniently chemically and physically modified with self-assembling and/or LB films. The high purity referred to above is needed to minimize the contribution of background fluorescence from the substrate itself. Table 1 lists substrate-marker atom compatibilities. Thus, for example, when working with SeMet cytochrome c, we originally set out to make measurements on a Mo/Si as opposed to a W/Si LSM because of the interference between Se and W fluorescence. However, the Mo/Si LSM available at the time was not usable because of contaminating W in the Mo layer!

Table 1   Substrate-marker atom compatibility

Substrate (mirror, LSM) composition	Substrate-compatible marker element	Substrate-incompatible marker element
Au[a]	Zn, Cu, Mn, I, Cd, Ru, Cs, Tb, Mo, Gd, Fe, La, Ba, Ca	Se, As, Br, Pb, Re, Rb, Sr, (S, P, Cl)[b]
Ag	Se, As, Br, Au, Os, Hg, Pb, Re, Rb, Sr, (S, P)	I, Cd, Ca, (Cl)
Si/W	Zn, Cu, Ni, Mn, Cr, I, Ru, Cs, Tb, Mo, Gd, Fe, La, Ba, Ca	Se, As, Br, Hg, Pb, Re, Rb, Sr, (S, P, Cl)
Si/Mo	Se, As, Br, Au, Os, Hg, Pb, Re, Rb, Sr, Ca	I, Cd, (S, P, Cl)
C/Pt	Zn, Cu, Mn, I, Ru, Cd, Cs, Tb, Mo, Gd, Fe, La, Ba, Ca	Se, As, Br, Hg, Pb, Re, Rb, Sr, (S, P, Cl)

[a] Atomic numbers: P[15], S[16], Cl[17], Ca[20], Cr[24], Mn[25], Fe[26], Ni[28], Cu[29], Zn[30], As[33], Se[34], Br[35], Rb[37], Sr[38], Mo[42], Ru[44], Cd[48], I[53], Cs[55], Ba[56], La[57], Tb[65], Gd[64], Re[75], Os[76], Au[79], Hg[80], Pb[82].

[b] Elements in parentheses currently are not useful in XSW measurements under physiologically relevant conditions. See text for details.

The overall success of the XSW method for studying membrane topology and related systems rests on our ability to prepare suitable samples. Such systems harbor heavy atoms intrinsically and/or have been labeled with suitable marker atoms in a minimally perturbed way. The latter may involve a substitution of one element for another, as in the Se-for-S substitution used with cytochrome c, or a direct chemical labeling of the target molecule. The advantage of using SeMet in place of Met is that the substitution is conservative because both S and Se are Group VIA elements. Furthermore, the average frequency of occurrence of Met in proteins is quite low, i.e. ~2% (17). SeMet can be introduced site specifically in various ways, including by means of semisynthetesis (48), by the judicious use of site-directed mutagenesis and SeMet-containing growth media, and by a method that involves suppressing the amber nonsense codon (21). Ideally, the target molecule would contain several different marker atoms, one serving as a benchmark to which all other distance measurements are referenced. In this way, the topology of the target molecule in or on the membrane can be deciphered. SeMet cytochrome c is one such example because it incorporates two different marker atoms, Fe and Se.

Having suitably labeled the target molecule, the next step is to prepare the corresponding membrane on a solid substrate surface so that useful questions can be addressed with the XSW technique. Transmembrane proteins pose the real challenge: the substrate must be readied to accept either a membrane in which such proteins already exist or one in which a transmembrane protein has been or will be reconstituted. Thus, these more complex and demanding membrane components and systems require the development of new and versatile reconstitution methods, of methods for depositing natural and reconstituted membranes on disparate solid substrates, and of the chemistry required to render the solid substrate surfaces compatible with the analyte membranes. Rendering these surfaces and films chemically stable and mechanically robust will also be important to the success of future studies. The realization of these goals requires an interdisciplinary approach encompassing biochemistry, biophysics, and chemistry. While the challenges ahead are nontrivial, the rewards in terms of insight into membrane structure and how this relates to function will surely make the Herculean effort worthwhile.

CONCLUSIONS

The XSW method represents a new approach to studying the internal and interfacial structure of organic thin films and membrane topology.

It offers an impressive array of advantages and unique features. The structural information and insights into function so garnered will certainly complement and can only extend that available from other membrane-structure and function studies.

ACKNOWLEDGMENTS

We are grateful to our colleagues and collaborators MJ Bedzyk, GM Bommarito, DH Bilderback, K Bruzik, I Clark-Lewis, TL Penner, JS Schildkraut, and C Wallace for assistance with the experiments and for innumerable discussions and advice on the issues raised here. This work was supported by grants from the National Institutes of Health (DK 36849 and DK 45295).

Literature Cited

1. Altenbach L, Marti T, Khorana HG, Hubbell WL. 1990. Transmembrane protein structure: spin labeling of bacteriorhodopsin mutants. *Science* 248:1088–92
2. Amador SM, Pachence JM, Fischetti R, McCauley JJP, Smith IAB, et al. 1993. Use of self-assembled monolayers to covalently tether protein monolayers to the surface of solid substrates. *Langmuir* 9:812–17
3. Andersen SK, Golovchenko JA, Mair G. 1976. New application of X-ray standing-wave fields to solid state physics. *Phys. Rev. Lett.* 37:1141–45
4. Batterman BW. 1964. Effect of dynamical diffraction in X-ray fluorescence scattering. *Phys. Rev.* 133:A759–64
5. Becker RS, Golovchenko JA, Patel JR. 1983. X-ray evanescent-wave absorption and emission. *Phys. Rev. Lett.* 50:153–56
6. Bedzyk MJ, Bilderback DH, Bommarito GM, Caffrey M, Schildkraut JS. 1988. X-ray standing waves: a molecular yardstick for biological membrane. *Science* 241:1788–91
7. Bedzyk MJ, Bommarito GM, Caffrey M, Penner TL. 1990. Diffuse-double layer at a membrane-aqueous interface measured with X-ray standing waves. *Science* 248:52–56
8. Bedzyk MJ, Bommarito GM, Schildkraut JS. 1989. X-ray standing waves at

a reflecting mirror surface. *Phys. Rev. Lett.* 62:1376–79
9. Bedzyk MJ, Materlik G. 1985. Determination of the position and vibrational amplitude of an adsorbate by means of multiple-order X-ray standing wave measurements. *Phys. Rev. B* 31:4110–12
10. Bloch JM, Sanson M, Rondelez F, Peiffer P, Pincus P, et al. 1985. Concentration profile of a dissolved polymer near the air-liquid interface: X-ray fluorescence study. *Phys. Rev. Lett.* 54:1039–42
11. Braiman MS, Rothschild KJ. 1988. Fourier transform infrared techniques for probing membrane protein structure. *Annu. Rev. Biophys. Biophys. Chem.* 17:541–70
12. Büldt G, Gally HU, Seelig J, Zaccai G. 1979. Neutron diffraction studies on phosphatidylcholine model membranes. I. Headgroup conformation. *J. Mol. Biol.* 134:673–91
13. Caffrey M, Wang J. 1992. Internal and interfacial structure of membranes using X-ray standing waves. *Faraday Discuss. Chem. Soc.* 94:283–93
14. Chattopadhyay A, London E. 1987. Parallax method for direct measurement of membrane penetration depth utilizing fluorescence quenching by spin-lableled phospholipids. *Biochemistry* 26:39–45
15. Chiu W. 1993. What does electron cry-

omicroscopy provide that X-ray crystallography and NMR spectroscopy cannot? *Annu. Rev. Biophys. Biomol. Struct.* 22:233–55

16. Cowan PL, Golovchenko JA, Robbins MF. 1980. X-ray standing waves at crystal surfaces. *Phys. Rev. Lett.* 44: 1680–83

17. Dayhoff MO. 1978. *Atlas of Protein Sequence and Structure,* Vol. 5. Washington, DC: Natl. Biomed. Res. Found. 363 pp.

18. Deisenhofer J, Michel H. 1991. High-resolution structures of photosynthetic reaction centers. *Annu. Rev. Biophys. Biophys. Chem.* 20:247–66

19. DeLong L, Blasie JK. 1993. Effect of Ca^{2+} binding on the profile structure of the sarcoplasmic reticulum membrane using time-resolved X-ray diffraction. *Biophys. J.* 64:1750–60

20. Egger M, Ohnesorge F, Weisenhorn AL, Heyn SP, Drake B, et al. 1990. Wet lipid-protein membranes imaged at submolecular resolution by atomic force microscopy. *J. Struct. Biol.* 103: 89–94

21. Ellman J, Mendel D, Cahill SA, Noren CJ, Schultz PG. 1991. Biosynthetic method for introducing unnatural amino acids site-specifically into proteins. *Methods Enzymol.* 202:301–36

22. Golovchenko JA, Batterman BW, Brown WL. 1974. Observation of internal X-ray wave fields during Bragg diffraction with an application to impurity lattice location. *Phys. Rev. B* 10:4239–43

23. Golovchenko JA, Patel JR, Kaplan DR, Cowan PL, Bedzyk MJ. 1982. Solution to the surface registration problem using X-ray standing waves. *Phys. Rev. Lett.* 49:560–63

24. Helm CA, Möhwald H, Kjaer K, Als-Nielsen J. 1987. Phospholipid monolayer density distribution perpendicular to the water surface. A synchrotron X-ray reflectivity study. *Europhys. Lett.* 4:697–703

25. Henderson R, Baldwin JM, Ceska TA, Zemlin F, Beckmann E, et al. 1990. Model for the structure of bacteriorhodopsin based on high-resolution electron cryo-microscopy. *J. Mol. Biol.* 213:899–929

26. Holzenburg A, Wilson FH, Finbow ME, Ford RC. 1992. Structural investigations of membrane proteins: the versatility of electron microscopy. *Biochem. Soc. Trans.* 20:591–97

27. Jap BK, Walian PJ, Gehring K. 1991. Structural architecture of an outer membrane channel as determined by electron cyrstallography. *Nature* 350: 167–70

28. Johnson SJ, Bayerl TM, Weihan W, Noack H, Penfold J, et al. 1991. Coupling of spectrin and polylysine to phospholipid monolayers studied by specular reflection of neutrons. *Biophys. J.* 60:1017–25

29. Koppenol WH, Margoliash E. 1982. The asymmetric distribution of charges on the surface of horse cytochrome *c. J. Biol. Chem.* 257:4426–37

30. Krause MO. 1979. Atomic radiative and radiationless yields for K and L shells. *J. Phys. Chem. Ref. Data* 8:307

31. Kühlbrandt W, Wang DN. 1991. Three dimensional structure of plant light-harvesting complex determined by electron crystallography. *Nature* 350: 130–34

32. Lakey JH, Baty D, Pattus F. 1991. Fluorescence energy transfer distance measurements using site-directed single cysteine mutants. *J. Mol. Biol.* 218: 639–53

33. Lal R, Yu L. 1993. Atomic force microscopy of cloned nicotinic acetylcholine receptor expressed in *Xenopus* oocytes. *Proc. Natl. Acad. Sci. USA* 90:7280–84

34. Marra WC, Eisenberger P, Chou AY. 1979. X-ray total-external-reflection-Bragg diffraction: a structural study of the GaAs interface. *J. Appl. Phys.* 50: 6927–33

35. McLaughlin S. 1989. The electrostatic properties of membranes. *Annu. Rev. Biophys. Biophys. Chem.* 18:113–36

36. Moore GR, Pettigrew GW. 1990. *Cytochrome* c. Berlin: Spinger-Verlag. 478 pp.

37. Mosser G, Mallouh V, Brisson A. 1992. A 9 Å two-dimensional projected structure of cholera toxin B-subunit G_{M1} complexes determined by electron crystallography. *J. Mol. Biol.* 226: 23–28

38. Oldfield E, Meadows M, Rice D, Jacobs R. 1978. Spectroscopic studies of specifically deuterium labeled membrane systems. Nuclear magnetic resonance investigation of the effects of cholesterol in model systems. *Biochemistry* 17:2727–40

39. Pachence JM, Blasie JK. 1991. Structural investigation of the covalent and electrostatic binding of yeast cytochrome *c* to the surface of various ultrathin lipid multilayers using X-ray diffraction. *Biophys. J.* 59:894–900

40. Pakula AA, Simon MI. 1992. Determi-

nation of transmembrane protein structure by disulfide cross-linking: the *Escherichia coli* Tar receptor. *Proc. Natl. Acad. Sci. USA* 89: 4144–48

41. Parratt LG. 1954. Surface studies of solids by total reflection of X rays. *Phys. Rev.* 95:359–69

42. Penfold J, Thomas RK. 1990. The application of the specular reflection of neutrons to the study of surfaces and interfaces. *J. Phys. Condens. Matter* 2:1369–1412

43. Seelig A, Seelig J. 1974. The dynamic structure of fatty acyl chains in a phospholipid bilayer measured by deuterium magnetic resonance. *Biochemistry* 13:4839–45

44. Smith SO, Peersen OB. 1992. Solid-state NMR approaches for studying membrane protein structure. *Annu. Rev. Biophys. Biomol. Struct.* 21: 25–47

45. Stayton PS, Olinger JM, Jiang M, Bohn PW, Sligar SG. 1992. Genetic engineering of surface attachment sites yields oriented protein monolayers. *J. Am. Chem. Soc.* 114:9298–99

46. Stühmer W. 1991. Structure-function studies of voltage-gated ion channels. *Annu. Rev. Biophys. Biomol. Struct.* 20:65–78

47. von Heijne G. 1992. Membrane protein structure prediction. Hydrophobicity analysis and the positive-inside rule. *J. Mol. Biol.* 225:487–94

48. Wallace CJA. 1993. Understanding cytochrome *c* function: engineering protein structure by semisynthesis. *FASEB J.* 7:505–15

49. Wallace CJA, Clark-Lewis I. 1992. Functional role of heme ligation in cytochrome *c*. *J. Biol. Chem.* 267: 3852–61

50. Wang J, Bedzyk M, Caffrey M. 1992. Resonance-enhanced X-rays in thin films: a structure problem for membranes and surface layers. *Science* 258:775–78

51. Wang J, Bedzyk M, Penner T, Caffrey M. 1991. Structural studies of membranes up to 1,000 Å thick using X-ray standing waves. *Nature* 354:377–80

52. Wang J, Caffrey M, Bruzik K, Penner TL, Bedzyk MJ. 1992. Heavy atom diffusion in Langmuir-Blodgett films studied by X-ray standing waves. *Bull. Am. Phys. Soc.* 37:655

53. Wang J, Wallace CJA, Clark-Lewis I, Caffrey M. 1994. Structure characterization of membrane bound and surface adsorbed protein. *J. Mol. Biol.* 237: 1–4

54. Weiss MS, Schulz GE. 1992. Structure of porin refined at 1.8 Å resolution. *J. Mol. Biol.* 227:493–509

55. Zaccai G, Buldt G, Seelig A, Seelig J. 1979. Neutron diffraction studies on phosphatidylcholine model membranes. *J. Mol. Biol.* 134:693–706

Annu. Rev. Biophys. Biomol. Struct. 1995. 24:379–404

EXCEPTIONALLY STABLE NUCLEIC ACID HAIRPINS

Gabriele Varani

MRC Laboratory of Molecular Biology, Hills Road, Cambridge CB2 2QH, United Kingdom

KEY WORDS: nucleic acid structure, nucleic acid thermodynamics, RNA hairpins, DNA hairpins

CONTENTS

ABSTRACT

Hairpins represent the dominant secondary structure element in RNA. Certain sequences are found with exceptional frequency in many RNAs and are characterized by exceptionally high thermodynamic stability. Stable RNA hairpins define nucleation sites for folding, determine tertiary interactions in RNA enzymes, protect mRNAs from degradation, and are recognized by RNA-binding proteins. The structures of several stable DNA and RNA hairpins have revealed networks of stabilizing interactions within the hairpin loop: non–Watson-Crick base pairs and base-phosphate and base-sugar contacts. The unusual stability of these structural elements can be used to stabilize RNA and DNA structures

1056-8700/95/0610-0379$05.00

and to protect antisense oligonucleotides and mRNAs against exonucleolytic degradation.

PERSPECTIVES AND OVERVIEW

Hairpins are the predominant element of RNA secondary structure (64, 72): Approximately 70% of the 16S rRNA folds into 31 different stem loops (Figure 1). RNA hairpins serve as nucleation sites for RNA folding (65), protein-recognition signals, and sites of tertiary interactions (39, 51). In addition to playing these roles, RNA hairpins are involved in mRNA localization (20), retroviral encapsidation and packaging (60, 74), and regulation of mRNA degradation (1, 41). Because only a few RNA structures have been solved, the structures of RNA hairpins pro-

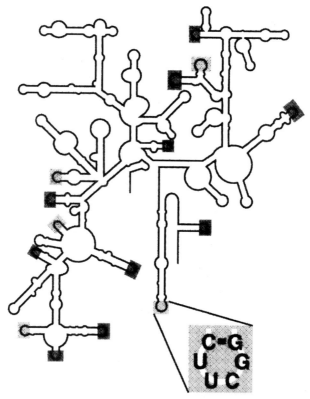

Figure 1 Hairpins represent the dominant element of RNA secondary structure, as shown in this secondary structure of *E. coli* 16S rRNA. Certain sequences (GCAA, UUCG, and related sequences, *shaded*) are found with exceptional frequency.

vide valuable information for studies of RNA folding and structure prediction (17).

The biological importance of DNA hairpins is less obvious. Palindromic DNA sequences form hairpin structures at replication origins or operator sequences, which suggests a functional role for cruciform structures in the regulation of gene expression (45, 46, 51). Hairpin formation has been established in vitro (45, 51) and in vivo (50) by the enhanced chemical and enzymatic reactivity of loop residues upon negative supercoiling. Unusually stable hairpins capable of cruciform extrusion at physiological superhelical densities are found—the colyphage N4 polymerase promoters—and are involved in the recognition of the promoter by the N4 RNA polymerase (insect) (54). Long inverted repeats stimulate recombination in *Escherichia coli* (cruciform structures are analogous to intermediates of homologous recombination) and cause plasmid instability, suggesting that cruciforms occur in vivo (50). Single-stranded DNA is present during several stages of the viral life cycle of filamentous phages, and hairpins present near the replication origin may direct interactions with factors necessary for viral replication (68).

The number and sequence of unpaired nucleotides in hairpin loops vary, but certain sizes and sequences are found with surprising frequency in ribosomal and other RNAs. Tetraloops are common, and UUCG and GCAA loops are especially favored (65, 72). This preference has both thermodynamic and structural origins: The compact structures of tetraloops lend them unusually high thermal stability and nuclease resistance. This article reviews structural, functional, and thermodynamic properties of exceptionally stable DNA and RNA hairpins.

THERMODYNAMICS OF HAIRPIN FORMATION

Effect of Loop Sequence and Size on Hairpin Stability

Thermodynamic studies of RNA and DNA hairpins are necessary to understand the energetics of nucleic acid folding and to derive accurate parameters for RNA secondary-structure prediction. The traditional view of nucleic acid hairpins regarded the helical stem as highly structured and the loop nucleotides as disordered. The sequence dependence of hairpin-loop thermodynamic stability was attributed only to the stem: Single-stranded loops were assumed to destabilize entropically the folded molecule by an amount dependent only on the length of the single-stranded region (37). DNA hairpin loops of four to five nucleotides were shown to have higher stability than smaller or larger loops

(6, 24, 25), whereas early thermodynamic data suggested that RNA hairpin loops have optimal stability with six to seven unpaired nucleotides (21, 67). These results correlated well with a simple structural principle (25): The dominant steric requirement for hairpin-loop folding is that the hairpin bridge the gap between the opposite sides of the stem. The cross-strand phosphate-phosphate distance is approximately 18 Å in both A-RNA and B-DNA helices and is determined by the width of a Watson-Crick base pair. If the unpaired nucleotides are stacked in a single-stranded helix that preserves the pattern of the stem, shorter phosphate-phosphate distances will occur across either the major or the minor groove (Figure 2). In A-form RNA, the minimal phosphate-phosphate distance occurs across the major groove after five to six nucleotides are stacked in A-form fashion on the 3' side of the stem. In B-form DNA, the minimal phosphate-phosphate distance occurs across the minor groove after two to three nucleotides are stacked in helical fashion on the 5' side of the stem. Thus, loops of four to five nucleotides in DNA could maximize stacking interactions while satisfying steric constraints, whereas loops of six to seven nucleotides should satisfy the optimal conditions in RNA (25).

Hairpin loops in tRNAs generally contain six to seven unpaired nucleotides (55), but in ribosomal RNA, loops are smaller, usually containing four to five (72). When more extensive data were collected for hairpins containing three to nine unpaired As, Cs, or Us (22), loops of four to five nucleotides were found to be more stable than hairpins with smaller or larger loops. For DNA hairpins, loops containing four to five nucleotides were also more stable than smaller or larger loops (6, 24, 25). At increasing loop size, the enthalpy of hairpin formation decreases to a minimal value for loops of five to seven nucleotides.

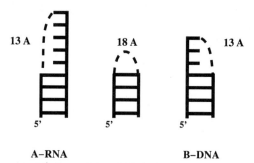

A–RNA   B–DNA

Figure 2   Folding principle for nucleic acid hairpins (25). Stacking of loop nucleotides on either the 3' (A-RNA) or the 5' (B-DNA) side of the stem leads to optimal stacking interactions and minimal cross-strand distances.

However, the melting temperature (the midpoint of the transition from folded hairpin to single strand) decreases at increasing loop size as a result of a more unfavorable entropy of loop formation. The enthalpy associated with hairpin formation is 5–10 kcal/mol greater than that expected from the stem contribution alone, which suggests the presence of stacking interactions within the loop (25).

Sequence effects on loop stability are much smaller than length effects for homonucleotide loops. Between RNA loops of identical size but different sequence, the largest difference in T_m was 5°C between U9 and C9 loops (22), and Cn hairpins were slightly less stable than either An or Un hairpins. In DNA hairpins with four unpaired nucleotides the order of stability was T4 > C4 > G4 > A4, and 5–6°C was the difference in melting temperature between the most stable and least stable loop (59). The small differences in stability between loops of different sequence are entirely enthalpic in origin. The order of stability observed in free energy was parallel to the trend in the calorimetrically determined enthalpies of hairpin formation (59).

Unusually Stable Nucleic Acid Hairpins

The analysis of the effect of loop sequence on hairpin stability has obvious limitations if only homonucleotide loops are studied. Certain sequences, namely UNCG, GNRA, and CUUG (where N is any of the four nucleotides and R is purine), are often found in 16S rRNA (Figure 1) and in other RNAs (72). The unusual thermodynamic properties of these sequences were first observed by Tuerk and coworkers (65), and careful thermodynamic analyses revealed the contribution of individual nucleotides to the thermodynamic stability of UNCG and GNRA loops (2, 3).

The C(UUCG)G hairpin loop (with a stem of three additional base pairs) has a melting temperature approximately 20°C higher than a hairpin with purportedly normal thermodynamic stability, such as the G(U-UUU)C hairpin. In 16S rRNA sequences, the UUCG loop is almost invariably closed by a C·G base pair that should be considered part of the structural unit. The difference in melting temperature corresponds to a 2-kcal/mol decrease in the free energy of hairpin formation at 37°C. The corresponding DNA sequence, dC(TTCG)G, had normal stability, but both r(GAAA) and d(GAAA) sequences are unusually stable. The RNA UUCG loop has a very stable and compact structure (10, 69), whereas the corresponding DNA sequence has considerable flexibility and lacks well-defined interactions within the loop (39). Both RNA and DNA GNRA sequences are exceptionally stable in comparison with other DNA loops (with the exception of the UUCG family of structures, stable RNA hairpin sequences have their counterpart in stable DNA hairpins).

Interactions that stabilize the tetraloop sequences are equivalent to approximately two base pairs of thermodynamic stability: A mini hairpin containing the C(UUCG)G loop sequence closed by a single base pair was as stable as a hairpin with a four–base pair stem and a U4 loop (3). A more quantitative estimate was obtained by subtracting the contribution of the stem residues using nearest-neighbor parameters from the thermodynamic database for RNA secondary-structure prediction (3). Although even these extra-stable sequences have a destabilizing effect on RNA secondary structure, UUCG loops are 2 kcal/mol less destabilizing than hairpin loops containing neither this loop sequence nor the C·G loop-closing base pair. This new information has increased the accuracy of the nearest-neighbor thermodynamic prediction algorithm from 73 to 77%, a significant improvement (37). The destabilizing free energy associated with hairpin loops is entirely entropic and is only partially compensated by a favorable enthalpic contribution. Only for Cn loops are $\Delta H°$ and $\Delta S°$ both positive. Unfortunately, this anomalous sequence was for many years the only source of experimental information available for the construction of a thermodynamic database (21, 67).

The enthalpic contribution from tetraloop hairpins to RNA folding is more favorable than that from other hairpins, which implies that tetraloops have more hydrogen bonding or stacking interactions. This change in enthalpy is partially but not entirely compensated by a smaller entropy of hairpin-loop formation, indicating that the tetraloop structure has a more restricted conformation. With the exception of the loop-closing base pair, which nucleotides compose the stem sequence has little effect on the overall stability of the tetraloop. This result is consistent with the observation that there is no preference in ribosomal RNA sequences for any base pair besides the often conserved loop-closing base pair (72).

UNCG LOOPS   Table 1 shows the effects of loop substitution on UUCG hairpin stability; in most cases, the effects of base substitutions correlate directly with specific interactions observed in the NMR-derived structure. The nonconserved second nucleotide can be mutated to any of the four nucleotides without reducing the hairpin stability. Mutations of the third loop nucleotide from the almost invariant C to U leads to a loss of ~2 kcal/mol in free energy, or 9°C in melting temperature. Similarly, the last loop nucleotide must be a guanosine: Even the simple replacement of the exocyclic amino group of that G to inosine leads to

Table 1 Melting temperatures and free energies of hairpin formation for members of the UUCG family of stable RNA hairpins[a]

RNA loop sequence	T_m (°C)	$\Delta G°_{37}$ (kcal/mol)
C(U U C G)G	71.7	− 5.7
C(U A̲ C G)G	69.3	− 5.2
C(U U U̲ G)G	64.0	− 3.8
C(U U U̲ U̲)G	60.4	− 3.0
G̲(C U U G)C̲	62.4	− 3.6
C(G̲ C U U)G	62.2	− 3.2
G̲(G̲ C U U)C̲	52.3	− 1.7
C(G A A A)G	65.9	− 4.2

[a] Adapted from Reference 2. Underlined letters denote mutations from the wild-type sequence.

a loss in melting temperature of 8°C (56). Reversal of the loop-closing base pair from C·G to G·C leads to a loss of 10°C in melting temperature, or a $\Delta G° \approx +1.5$ kcal/mol in free energy.

The role of the 2'-hydroxyl in the folding of the UUCG family of tetraloops was investigated by assessing the stability of different oligonucleotides containing all ribose and all deoxyribose sugars. In addition, the stability was assessed of chimeric molecules containing a loop of ribose sugars with a deoxyribose stem and of those containing a ribose stem with a deoxyribose loop (56). Deoxyribose sugars in the loop had a large effect ($\Delta T_m = 8$°C) on the hairpin stability but little effect when in the stem. Specific interactions involving the loop 2'-hydroxyl groups are therefore important for loop structure and stability. The thermodynamic stabilities of DNA UUCG loop mutants were approximately the same regardless of the sequence and were comparable to those observed with homopyrimidine loops (2).

GNRA LOOPS   The GNRA sequences confer an additional stability of $\Delta G° \approx -1$ kcal/mol over the stability of homopyrimidine loops (2, 3, 29). The nonconserved second loop nucleotide can be mutated to A, C, or T without any loss in stability, but mutation of the first loop nucleotide from G to A leads to a 15°C decrease in T_m. The favorable free energy contribution derived from the tetraloop structure is more modest for the GNRA family than for the UNCG family. Functional reasons (for instance the involvement in tertiary interactions) rather than thermodynamics alone may explain why these loops are so common in RNA.

All possible nucleotide combinations were tested in a DNA GAAA tetraloop with a stem of only two base pairs (31), and Table 2 summarizes the results (the small two–base pair stem magnifies the influence of the loop sequence on hairpin stability). The melting temperature of the stable hairpin, 76°C, was 30–40°C higher than for hairpins with identical stems but TTTT, GCCC, or GTTT loops. The stem sequence did not influence the loop stability, and the differences observed for varying combinations of G·C base pairs in the stem could be entirely attributed to stacking interactions within the stem. Mutations of the second or third nucleotides from the AA sequence to any other base led to a decrease in melting temperature of 4–5°C. Changing the A at the 3' end of the loop produced greater effects, with $\Delta T_m \approx$ 6–10°C. The most dramatic effects were observed for the first G nucleotide. Substitution with A led to a loss of over 50°C in stability, and pyrimidine substitutions also led to 15–20°C changes in T_m. A comparable effect was observed when the last G in the stem was mutated to inosine. The loss of stability for the G → I mutant was comparable to that observed in regular DNA helices.

Table 2 Melting temperatures for members of the GNRA family of stable DNA hairpins[a]

DNA stem-loop sequence	T_m (°C)
GC(GAAA)GC	76.5
I	59–62
A T	<30
T	55–58
C	60–63
A	<30
T	71.5
C	72.0
G	71.0
T	71.0
C	72.0
G	71.5
T	70.0
C	67.0
G	70.5
T T	69.5
T T T T	33.0
C C C	41–44

[a] Adapted from Reference 31. Only mutations from the wild-type sequence are explicitly indicated.

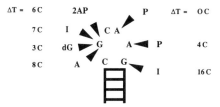

Figure 3   Effect of functional group substitution on the thermodynamic stability of the GCAA loop (57). The decrease in melting temperature is reported next to each substitution; P is purine, I inosine, 2AP two-amino purine, and dG deoxyguanosine.

Functional substitutions by means of chemically synthesized RNAs allowed a finer analysis of the contribution of individual functional groups to hairpin stability (Figure 3) (57). Each functional group makes a relatively modest contribution to the hairpin stability; the largest effect is associated with the removal of the exocyclic amino from the first G ($\Delta G° = +0.7$ kcal/mol). Even this effect is smaller than that observed for G $\rightarrow$ I substitutions within helical regions. The NMR-determined structure shows that each of the functional groups removed in the thermodynamic analysis is involved either in a direct or a water-mediated hydrogen bond (27). Thus, each hydrogen bond contributes relatively little to hairpin stability. In more rigid helical regions, each hydrogen bond makes a greater contribution, so perhaps the absence of strong hydrogen-bonding effects in the hairpin results from the structure's relative flexibility. Furthermore, the thermodynamic comparison is always made between the folded hairpin structure and the denatured single strand, in which hydrogen bonding to solvent water may contribute some offsetting energy. The importance of stacking interactions offers yet another explanation for the relatively small effects observed. Substitutions of functional groups may not only alter the hydrogen-bonding pattern, but may also more subtly affect stacking energies by modifying charge distribution within the heteroaromatic ring. In at least some cases, stacking effects may partially offset loss of hydrogen-bonding ability.

STABLE DNA HAIRPINS

Sequences that form stable DNA hairpins (namely GAA and GAAA loops) are found at the replication origins of phage ϕX174 and herpes simplex virus, in the promoter region of an *E. coli* heat-shock gene, at the replication origin of G_4 phage ssDNA, and at virion RNA polymerase promoters (54). These sequences may be utilized because of their propensity for stabilizing hairpin structures. The structural features of the GAAA DNA loop are qualitatively consistent with the structure determined for its RNA analogue (30). The heptanucleotide dGC(GAA)GC is anomalous, because a stable DNA hairpin with a high melting temperature corresponds to a low-stability RNA counterpart (30). In the NMR-derived structure, the loop of the GAA mini hairpin was composed of a single nucleotide, the central A (29). The first and third loop nucleotides form an *anti-anti* G·A base pair observed in the GCAA RNA loop (Figure 4, *left*) and in a DNA duplex (27, 43). Involvement of the N7 position of the adenine from the G·A pair was confirmed by a 12°C decrease in melting temperature for a 7-deaza substitution. Extensive stacking provided additional stabilizing interactions. The exceptional stability of this sequence may be the result of an optimal compromise between stacking interactions and the bendability necessary to connect the two sides of the stem (29).

Base pairs can form within nucleic acid hairpin loops. Molecular mechanics simulations and NMR studies suggest that base pair formation is possible for YTTR hairpins but not for RTTY sequences (where R indicates purine and Y pyrimidine) (6). A C·G base pair formed in the CTTG hairpin but not in the GTTC sequence (6). Similarly, a T·A

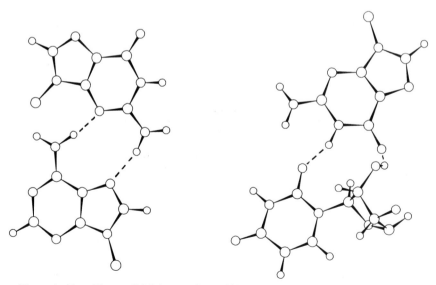

Figure 4   Non–Watson-Crick base pairs stabilizing the UUCG (G·U pair, *right*) and GCAA (*anti-anti* G·A pair, *left*) structures.

base pair formed in the TTTA loop but not in the ATTT loop (6). The identity of the last base pair in the stem did not affect base pair formation, but replacement of the two unpaired Ts with As led to the loss of base pairing. The additional base pair adds thermodynamic stability to the hairpin—sequences with an extra base pair were approximately 7–10°C more stable than sequences without a base pair (6), largely because of more favorable enthalpy. The stabilization conferred by the extra base pair to the DNA hairpins is roughly comparable to that observed in the thermodynamic analysis of RNA tetraloops. The T·A pair was a Hoogsteen base pair with a *syn* adenine, and the C·G base pair was considerably buckled, presumably to reduce the distance to be bridged between the two sides of the stem. Changes in the conformation of the γ (C4'-C5') backbone torsion angle [from the normal *gauche*$^+$ range to the *trans* range (5)] just before the last loop nucleotide facilitated bridging of the cross-strand gap.

EXCEPTIONALLY STABLE RNA HAIRPINS

Biological Functions of Stable RNA Hairpins

PHYLOGENETIC ANALYSIS OF HAIRPIN SEQUENCES   Phylogenetic analysis is a very powerful technique for defining RNA secondary structure (23, 72). Secondary-structure formation dominates the subsequent, less energetically favorable tertiary interactions that are responsible for RNA three-dimensional folding (4). Therefore, phylogeny can be used not only to determine what nucleotides within an RNA sequence are involved in Watson-Crick and wobble pairs, but also to identify more complex tertiary interactions, such as noncanonical base pairs, base triples, pseudoknots, and common hairpin sequences (23).

The phylogenetic analysis of hairpin loop sequences in 16S-like rRNAs revealed a striking preference for loops of four nucleotides (Figure 1). Within all existing 16S-like rRNA sequences, 55% of all hairpin loops contain four unpaired nucleotides (72). The second most common number, five, was present in only 13% of all hairpin loops. This preference is not limited to 16S rRNA: In 23S rRNA, 38% of all hairpin loops are tetraloops and 24% are pentaloops. Within tetraloop sequences, three motifs occur with exceptional frequency: GNRA, UNCG, and CUUG. For example, the hexanucleotide C(UUCG)G occurs 13 times in the 55-kb genome of bacteriophage T4 (12 times within intercistronic regions), which is much more often than would be expected if the sequence occurred randomly and was always flanked by palindromic repeats (65). These three sequences appear to have arisen independently several times during the evolutionary process.

The tetraloop sequences sometimes act as a unit; in closely related organisms, a UNCG-type loop at a particular position is sometimes changed into a GNRA loop, or vice versa (66). Variants of the tetraloop motif often include a one-nucleotide addition, for instance a change from CUUG to CUUGU or from UUCG to UUCGG. The most common triloops have the UUU sequence, but evolutionary pressure appears to prevent most triloops and smaller loops (72).

The phylogenetic analysis reveals a bias for certain loop-closing base pairs. The UUCG loop is almost always closed by a C·G base pair, whereas the CUUG loop is generally closed by a G·C base pair. However, GNRA loops are not closed by a set base pair. Base pairs after the loop-closing pair vary without any correlation (72), but loop sequence and stem length are statistically correlated. Shorter stems are most often closed by the UUCG sequence, perhaps because of its higher thermodynamic stability (73). This evolutionary pressure is stronger in bacteria than in eukaryotes.

The variable regions of 16S rRNA provide ideal sequences to analyze the evolutionary pressure for tetraloop hairpins (73). Because considerable variations in length and sequence are observed in these regions, protein interactions are either absent or sequence independent, and any preference for a particular sequence should not reflect protein-binding requirements. Stem loops in these regions probably provide nucleation sites for folding of the RNA as it is transcribed, and the physical stability of these sequences is a primary determinant of selectivity. Phylogenetic analysis of loop sequences within these regions may therefore provide a relatively unbiased view of the evolutionary pressure in favor of certain loop sequences and of any correlation with stem size and sequence. The preference for tetraloop sequences is particularly strong in the variable regions. The bias is stronger for organisms with lower ribosomal protein content: ~55–60% of all hairpins in archaebacteria, and ~45% in eukaryotes, are tetraloops (73). The loss of secondary proteins protecting the hairpin structures against the cellular environment may be the cause of the stronger requirement for tetraloop sequences.

TERTIARY INTERACTIONS   In self splicing RNAs, tetraloops are involved in tertiary interactions that are critical to formation of the three-dimensional structure of these enzymes (38, 48). Structural insight into these novel tertiary interactions was recently provided by the crystal structure of an intermolecular complex between a GAAA tetraloop and an RNA helix (52). The observed tetraloop-helix interactions correlate well with the specificity of GNRA tetraloops, suggesting that this structure could be a close model for tertiary interactions mediated by GNRA loops in large structured RNAs.

The conserved stem loop P5b in group I self-splicing introns (48) interacts with a helical region within the P6 subdomain. In all sequences containing that secondary structure element, only the second nucleotide is variable (but it is an A in >90% of the cases), and the other three nucleotides are almost invariably G, A, and A, respectively. The second nucleotide can be mutated to an U without significantly disrupting the ribozyme structure, but an increased Mg^{2+} concentration is required to fold the RNA. When the conserved third and fourth nucleotides were mutated from A to G, or when the loop was changed as a unit to UUCG, folding of the group I intron core was disrupted. Thermodynamic stability is therefore not important in group I intron folding. Rather, the ability of the loop nucleotides to participate in tertiary contacts with the P6 region is important. The observation that binding of a tRNA synthetase can substitute for the tertiary interactions between the P5 extension and the core (50) provides an example of how an RNA enzyme might evolve into a ribonucleoprotein enzyme.

Another tetraloop involved in tertiary contacts in the folding of group I intron ribozymes is the L9 loop in the phage T4 *td* intron. This GNRA loop interacts with two base pairs in the minor groove of the P5 helix, as has been proven by its replacement with two Watson-Crick base pairs to generate a pseudoknot (38). The mutated ribozyme had enzymatic activity superior to the wild-type RNA. The thermodynamic contribution to RNA folding from this interaction was remarkably large ($\Delta G^\circ > 3.5$ kcal/mol) (38). As in the previous case, this tertiary interaction requires a precise sequence rather than a thermodynamically stable structure. Substitution of the GNRA-type loop with a UUCG loop led to loss of ribozyme activity (38). Chemical modification analysis above and below the enzyme inactivation temperatures suggests that the tetraloop at the L9 position undergoes a conformational change. At temperatures where the enzyme is active, the Watson-Crick pairing positions of the last two nucleotides are not accessible to chemical modifying agents, presumably as a result of their involvement in tertiary contacts in the minor groove of the P5 helix. At higher temperature, those positions become accessible when only the interactions observed by NMR (27) within the isolated tetraloop are present.

Another common type of long-range interaction involving hairpin loops are the so-called kissing hairpins. This folding motif is recognized by the helix-loop-helix rop protein dimer during regulation of ColE1 plasmid replication and is probably involved in viral recombination. This motif has also been proposed for HIV-1 dimerization and packaging (60). A stable kissing-hairpin structure can also form between the HIV-1 TAR element and a complementary sequence within the *gag* coding region (7).

PROTEIN RECOGNITION   Several RNA-binding proteins recognize tetraloop structures. In all cases, disruption of the stem and mutations of the loop sequence are deleterious for tetraloop recognition.

Antibodies against the UUCG-type stem loop IV of U1 snRNA are found in the sera of patients with systemic lupus erythematosus overlap syndrome (33, 34), and antigenic determinants are localized in the UUCG sequence and in the intact stem structure.

A GNRA loop is recognized by the cytotoxin ricin within the so-called ricin-sarcin loop in the large subunit ribosomal RNA. The loop is thought to be involved in the elongation step of protein synthesis (49, 62) and is footprinted by elongation factors EF-Tu and EF-G within *E. coli* 23S rRNA (47). The loop contains a highly conserved internal loop (71) capped by a GAGA tetraloop structure (62). Ricin recognizes the GAGA loop and depurinates the first A in the loop in the full-length ribosome and even within a minimal hairpin with a two-base-pair stem and a GAGA loop (15, 18, 49).

Signal recognition particle protein components recognize two conserved tetraloops (42) within the signal recognition particle RNA (44, 58, 78). Among these proteins is SRP-19, the only SRP component capable of binding SRP RNA in the absence of other proteins (78). Like SRP-19, ribosomal protein S15 binds to a GNAR tetraloop (76). The similarities in the RNA substrate, and a weak similarity in protein sequence, have led to the proposal of a family of tetraloop-binding proteins (76).

Structures of Stable RNA Hairpins

UUCG LOOPS   The structure of the UUCG hairpin was determined at high resolution using NMR (10, 69). The same UUCG molecule crystallizes as a duplex containing an internal loop (12, 36), but the structural features observed with NMR are in good agreement with the mapping of intact hairpins in ribosomal RNA.

The high resolution of the structure showed that the helical stem is in the A-form family of double helices. The regular A-form features of the stem provide a useful contrast to the unusual backbone conformation and intramolecular interactions seen in the loop. The first loop nucleotide, a uracyl, stacks on the stem A-form structure. No stabilizing interaction can be identified involving the second loop nucleotide, which can be substituted with any nucleotide without significant loss of thermodynamic stability (Table 1). The last nucleotide, a guanosine, also stacks on the stem, but the *syn* conformation of this residue leads to an unusual backbone conformation. An unusual U·G base pair involving both base-base and base-sugar hydrogen bonds (Figure 4, *right*) forms between the first and last loop nucleotide. The interaction between the guanosine base and the uracyl sugar provides a structural basis for the loss of thermodynamic stability (56) and structural features (39) of hairpins containing deoxyribose sugars.

A sharp turn occurs in the phosphodiester backbone between the first and second loop nucleotide and is produced when the phosphate C3'-O3'-P-O5' angle α assumes the *trans* conformation (Figure 5). This motif is very similar to the π-turn observed in the anticodon loop of tRNA (55). Disruption of the common *gauche⁻-gauche⁻* phosphate conformation is energetically costly (loss of the *gauche* effect is esti-

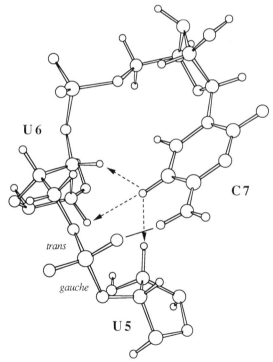

Figure 5   Stabilization of sharp turns in the phosphodiester backbone by base-phosphate interactions. This detail of the structure of the UUCG tetraloop (69) shows the interaction between the C exocyclic amino group and a phosphate in the unusual *gauche-trans* conformation that reverses the direction of the phosphodiester backbone.

mated at 2 kcal/mol). This energetic loss is partially offset by a hydrogen bond between the exocyclic amino of the C and an oxygen of the turning phosphate. Replacement of that cytosine with uracyl, and the substitution of a carbonyl for the exocyclic amino, leads to a loss of 1.5 kcal/mol of thermodynamic stability (65). As a consequence of the base-phosphate contact, the loop cytosine has extensive stacking overlap with the U·G base pair. Differences in stacking between U and C (in the UUUG mutant) may also contribute to the different thermodynamic stabilities of these hairpins. As observed in several other RNA structural elements (14, 53, 71), both loop nucleotides adopt the extended 2'-*endo* sugar conformation, and other torsion angles assume unusual values in the loop. As in DNA hairpins (5, 6), the O5'-C5'-C4'-C3' γ torsion angle in the CpG step of the last loop nucleotide is in the *trans* conformation instead of the *gauche*$^+$ (28), presumably to help bridge the two sides of the stem.

GNRA LOOPS   The structures of GAAA and GCAA hairpin loops were determined at high resolution for the isolated hairpin (27), and more qualitatively for the apical loop in the ricin-sarcin loop (62). As in the UUCG loop, an extra G·A base pair closes the stem (Figure 4, *left*) leaving a loop of only two unpaired nucleotides. This *anti-anti* base pair has been observed in both DNA (43) and RNA structures (49, 62, 71). Base-phosphate contacts and extensive base stacking provide additional stabilizing interactions. A contact between the 2'-hydroxyl group of the first G and the N7 position of the next-to-last purine has also been proposed, and a similar contact has been observed in the UUCG tetraloop (F Allain & G Varani, submitted). However, deoxy-GNRA loops are also thermodynamically stable, and therefore interactions involving this 2'-hydroxyl may not contribute significantly to the thermodynamic stability of the structure. Although the GATA sequence violates the consensus, this sequence also forms a stable hairpin within a deoxynucleotide hairpin loop (3), further weakening the thermodynamic significance of the contact between the purine N7 and the guanine sugar hydroxyl group.

COMPARISON OF TETRALOOP STRUCTURES   Despite significant local structural differences, the overall fold and appearance of UUCG and GCAA are similar (Figure 6). An extra base pair forms within the nominally single-stranded nucleotides, leaving a loop of only two unpaired bases that is constrained sterically by the requirements for loop closing. The second loop nucleotide is poorly structured and in a flexible conformation. Each loop is further stabilized by extensive stacking and by

UUCG   GCAA

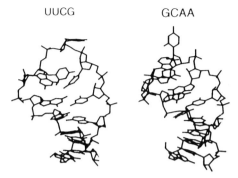

Figure 6   Comparison of the solution structures of UUCG and GCAA loops.

sequence-specific base-phosphate contacts (Figure 7). A comparable motif is also found for the third tetraloop, CUUG, in which a C·G base pair closes the stem and leaves a loop of only two nucleotides (A Pardi, personal communication).

Perhaps the most significant difference between the two families is dynamic rather than structural, which may reflect the different biological roles of these two hairpins. UUCG loops have little flexibility in the loop; both single-stranded nucleotides are essentially in a pure 2'-

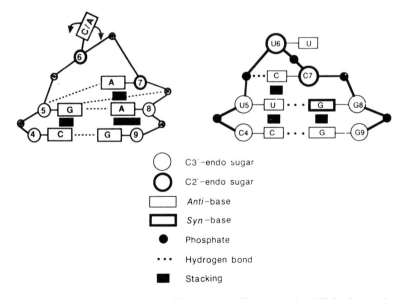

Figure 7   Schematic representation of the structural features and stabilizing interactions of the UNCG and GNRA families of loop structures.

endo sugar conformation. On the other hand, the second and third nucleotides of GNRA loops have highly flexible sugar conformations alternating between nearly equally populated 2'-*endo* and 3'-*endo* conformers. GNRA loops are often used for tertiary contacts (38, 48) and for protein-binding sites (15, 18, 76, 77). UNCG loops have so far not been observed to participate in tertiary interactions, and very few examples of UNCG protein recognition have been found. Tertiary interactions involving GNRA loops may require conformational changes in the loop (38), and the flexibility of this structure may be the factor that allows such changes. The generally more accessible structural features of GNRA loops may reflect these different functional requirements.

OTHER STABLE RNA HAIRPINS   The UUU loop sequence is the most common alternative to tetraloop sequences within 16S-like rRNAs (72). NMR and thermodynamic studies have been conducted on a chemically synthesized 9-mer containing the UUU loop sequence and a stem of three G·C base pairs (14). The entire enthalpy of hairpin formation ($\Delta H°$ = -24 kcal/mol) can be accounted for by the contribution of the three base pairs in the stem (37). Consistent with this observation, the loop structure was poorly defined by the NMR data, which presumably reflects a flexible structure.

Reducing the size of large loops through the formation of non-Watson-Crick base pairs may be very common in RNA. An example was observed in a model hairpin forming one of the stem loops of an RNA pseudoknot (53) and in the TAR element of the EIAV retrovirus (35). A trinucleotide hairpin loop was generated by the formation of several non–Watson-Crick base pairs in a nominally large loop containing nine unpaired nucleotides. A G·U wobble pair, a Watson-Crick A·U pair, and an A·C$^+$ base pair (53) were stabilized at lower pH by protonation of the A·C$^+$ pair.

STABLE HAIRPINS AS TOOLS

Stabilization of RNA Structural Elements

The high thermodynamic stability of tetraloop hairpins makes them ideal tools for stabilizing nucleic acid structures. At the very high concentrations required by NMR and crystallography, RNA molecules often form duplexes instead of monomolecular hairpins. Furthermore, other types of stabilizing elements present in the full-length RNA are often removed to reduce the size of the molecule to be investigated. This problem is illustrated by studies of the HIV TAR RNA element, a hairpin containing a stem of about 20 base pairs and the target of the HIV tat protein (11). To study the interaction between tat and TAR using NMR, the size of the stem must be reduced. However, removal of bases destabilizes the RNA structure, and alternative conformers appear in the NMR spectrum. Although the wild-type TAR sequence is properly folded under certain solvent conditions, the RNA-protein complex may not be stable or soluble under those conditions. To overcome this problem, a stable UUCG sequence was substituted for the wild-type apical loop. The quality of the NMR spectrum improved remarkably, and the observation of characteristic chemical shifts showed that the structure of the tat-binding site was unaffected. Binding of the tat protein was reduced by a factor of four (11), and because no direct interaction between tat and the TAR apical loop occurs, the decrease in affinity probably results from indirect effects on RNA flexibility.

Stabilization of mRNAs and Antisense Oligonucleotides by Stable Hairpin Loops

Tetraloop hairpins stabilize plant mRNAs against degradation by exonucleases (1). Plant plastid mRNAs contain inverted repeats in their 3' end that can form stable hairpins. These sequences are the likely product of posttranscriptional processing and stabilize the mRNAs against 3'-5' exonucleases. Different mRNAs accumulate in distinct ways despite identical constitutive levels of transcription, thereby providing a mechanism by which to regulate translational efficiency. Insertion of a UUCG tetraloop near the 3' end of spinach chloroplast mRNA leads to enhanced mRNA accumulation that results from increased stability (1). The thermodynamic stability of the hairpin is not sufficient by itself to explain the resistance to nucleases. The special structural features of the UUCG loop are responsible for the protection of these mRNAs from nucleases.

The resistance to nucleases of stable RNA and DNA hairpins suggests their use in the stabilization of antisense oligonucleotides or mRNAs. Because degradation of antisense oligonucleotides occurs predominantly by 3'-5' exonuclease activity, RNA and DNA oligonucleotides can be stabilized by tagging stable hairpin structures at their 3' end (Figure 8) (32, 40, 63, 75). This technique can be used either as an alternative or a complement (63) to the stabilization of antisense oligonucleotides by phosphate or ribose analogues.

Both GAA and GAAA DNA hairpins are resistant to nuclease digestion because of their highly stacked and relatively inaccessible structures (nuclease resistance roughly correlates with thermal stability for this class of hairpins). The GAA loop was used to stabilize the dihydrofolate reductase mRNA (Figure 8a) (75), thereby increasing the efficiency of translation approximately twofold in an *E. coli* cell-free translation system as a result of the longer half-life of the mRNA. This technique can be used to increase the yield of proteins expressed in continuous-flow cell-free translation systems. Although a large excess (400-fold) of DNA was required, the specific stabilization required base complementarity between the hairpin and the mRNA (32).

In the approach described in the previous paragraph, the mRNA was stabilized by an intermolecular hairpin complementary to the 3' end of the mRNA. Alternatively, a hairpin can be included at the 3' end of antisense oligonucleotides containing modified phosphorothioate or normal phosphate linkages (Figure 8b) (63). Such self-stabilized oligonucleotides displayed longer half-lives both in vitro and in vivo and better pharmacokinetic properties than their unstabilized counterparts (63). For both natural DNA and phosphorothioate analogues, inclusion of a hairpin at the 3' end led to a 10-fold increase in nuclease resistance. The increase in half-life correlated with the length of the base-paired region. Stable nucleotide sequences were not chosen for the single-stranded loops, so the stabilization can probably be improved by including nuclease-resistant loop sequences.

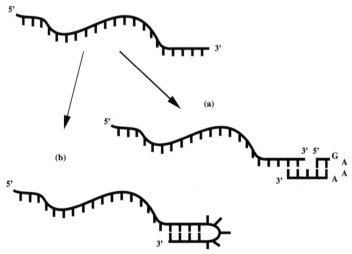

Figure 8 Stabilization of antisense oligonucleotides or mRNAs by stable hairpin tails. Degradation by nucleases can be reduced either by forming an intermolecular hairpin with a second oligonucleotide (*a*) or by including a stable hairpin at the 3' end of the antisense oligonucleotide (*b*).

Engineering Stable Nucleic Acid Hairpins

DNA and RNA hairpins can be artificially stabilized by the introduction of cross-linkable groups (19). Perhaps the least perturbing way to do this is to modify uridine (or thymidine) to N3-ethylthiol uridine and to incorporate the cross-link at the end of the stem. The cross-link adds additional stability to the structure; an NMR study demonstrated that the cross-link's introduction disrupted the regular helical structure very little (70).

This elegant technique allows the stabilization of hairpins over duplexes (or other structures) for studies of protein–nucleic acid interactions and other applications. Chemical synthesis allows the site of cross-linking to be located away from sites of protein contacts. Consequently, the direct disruption of protein binding by steric clashes or other effects can be minimized, and any increase or reduction in the strength of the interaction can be attributed to the extra thermodynamic stability of the hairpin. This technique was applied to the study of how induced fit contributes to an antibody-DNA complex (61).

CONCLUSION

The traditional view of hairpin-loop folding was summarized in a simple and elegant folding principle (25) that neglected any sequence effects on loop structure and stability. In that view, maximization of stacking interactions within the loop and the structure of the stem dominated loop formation. However, other factors influence hairpin structure and their thermodynamic stability in addition to the steric constraints imposed by the loop-closure condition: stem-loop stacking interactions and base stacking and base pairing within the loop. A complex interplay of stacking interactions and base pairing determines the structure of the loop, subject to the steric constraints.

In most DNA and RNA hairpins, extensive stacking interactions are found at the stem-loop junction. A sharp reversal in the direction of the phosphodiester backbone is needed to connect the two sides of the stem and is facilitated by changes in the backbone geometry. The sugar in RNA hairpin loops is almost always in the extended 2'-*endo* conformation, rather than the 3'-*endo* geometry of A-form RNA helices, to lengthen the distance that can be spanned by each individual nucleotide. The interplay between backbone structural rearrangement and stabilizing interactions illustrates how nucleic acids adjust their structures to accommodate local energetic needs and optimize favorable stacking and base-pairing interactions. In nucleic acid helices, the hydrophilic character of the backbone dominates, but the partitioning of hydrophobic and hydrophilic surfaces in hairpin-loop sequences (16, 70) may be important for protein recognition of hairpin structures.

Certain hairpin sequences contain a surprising degree of structural features and interactions that contribute to very high thermodynamic stability. Hydrogen bonding between nucleotides not involved in Watson-Crick pairing and between bases and backbone functional groups, as well as stacking interactions between the loop nucleotides, defines a precise geometry for many loops. These structural features and consequently the hairpin stability depend on the loop sequence and the identity of the sugar (2, 3, 10, 39, 56). As clearly revealed by the UUCG and GCAA structures and thermodynamics, base stacking interactions and base-to-backbone contacts within RNA (and DNA) single-stranded regions determine nucleic acid folding with specificities as great as Watson-Crick base pairing.

Unusually stable hairpins are found with exceptional frequency in RNA (72) and represent ubiquitous building blocks of RNA structure. Loop sequences with exceptional thermodynamic stability (2, 3, 65) provide nucleation sites for folding (65, 66) and sites of tertiary interactions in RNA enzymes (38, 48) are present in termination signals for transcription (13) and reverse transcription (65), are recognized by RNA-binding proteins (33, 76), and protect mRNAs from exonucleolytic degradation (1). These hairpins are found in ribosomal RNAs (72), snRNPs (33), the signal-recognition particle (42), the catalytic component of RNase P, and self-splicing RNAs. Stable RNA loops have been used for structural studies to stabilize RNA structural elements, including hammerhead ribozymes (26) and a triple-stranded domain from group I introns (8, 9). The thermodynamic stability and compact structure of these sequences make them resistant to cleavage by nucleases. This property has been used to enhance the stability of antisense oligonucleotides (40, 63) and mRNAs (32, 75). Chemically modified bases can be used to engineer exceptionally stable hairpins of any sequence (19, 70). More applications will undoubtedly be found for these stable nucleic acid structures.

ACKNOWLEDGMENTS

It is a pleasure to thank Professors Ignacio Tinoco, Jr, University of California at Berkeley, and Arthur Pardi, University of Colorado, for communicating unpublished results from their laboratories, and Dr. Fareed Aboul-ela and Mr. Charles Gubser for critical reading of the manuscript.

Literature Cited

1. Adams CC, Stern DB. 1990. Control of mRNA stability in chloroplasts by 3′ inverted repeats: effects of stem and loop mutations on degradation of psbA mRNA *in vitro*. *Nucleic Acids Res*. 18: 6003–10
2. Antao VP, Lai SY, Tinoco I Jr. 1991. A thermodynamic study of unusually stable RNA and DNA hairpins. *Nucleic Acids Res*. 19:5901–5
3. Antao VP, Tinoco I Jr. 1992. Thermodynamic parameters for loop formation in RNA and DNA hairpin loops. *Nucleic Acids Res*. 20:819–24
4. Banerjee AR, Jaeger JA, Turner DH. 1993. Thermal unfolding of a group I ribozyme: the low-temperature transition is primarily disruption of tertiary structure. *Biochemistry* 32:153–63
5. Blommers MJJ, van de ven FJM, ven der Marel GA, Ven Boom JH, Hilbers CW. 1991. The three-dimensional structure of a DNA hairpin in solution. Two-dimensional NMR studies and structural analysis of d(ATCCTATT-TATAGGAT). *Eur. J. Biochem*. 201: 33–51
6. Blommers MJJ, Walters JALI, Haasnoot CAG, Aelen JMA, van der Marel GA, et al. 1989. Effects of base sequence on the loop folding in DNA hairpins. *Biochemistry* 28:7491–98
7. Chang KY, Tinoco I Jr. 1994. A "kissing" hairpin complex derived from the HIV genome. *Proc. Natl. Acad. Sci. USA*. 91:8705–9
8. Chastain M, Tinoco I Jr. 1992. A base triple structural domain in RNA. *Biochemistry* 31:12733–41
9. Chastain M, Tinoco I Jr. 1993. Nucleoside triples from the group I intron. *Biochemistry* 32:14220–28
10. Cheong C, Varani G, Tinoco I Jr. 1990. Solution structure of an unusually stable RNA hairpin, 5′GGAC(UUCG)-GUCC. *Nature* 346:680–82
11. Churcher MJ, Lamont C, Hamy F, Dingwall C, Green SM, et al. 1993. High affinity binding of TAR RNA by the human immunodeficiency type-1 tat protein requires base-pairs in the RNA stem and amino acid residues

flanking the basic region. *J. Mol. Biol.* 230:90–110
12. Cruse WBT, Saludijan P, Biala E, Strazewski P, Prange′T, Kennard O. 1994. Structure of a mispaired RNA double helix at 1.6 Å resolution and implications for the prediction of RNA secondary structure. *Proc. Natl. Acad. Sci. USA* 91:4160–64
13. D'Aubenton-Carafa Y, Brody E, Thermes C. 1990. Prediction of Rho-independent *E. coli* transcription terminators: a statistical analysis of their RNA stem-loop structures. *J. Mol. Biol.* 216:835–58
14. Davis PW, Thurmes W, Tinoco I Jr. 1993. Structure of a small RNA hairpin. *Nucleic Acids Res.* 21:537–45
15. Endo Y, Gluck A, Wool IG. 1991. Ribosomal RNA identity element for ricin A-chain recognition and catalysis. *J. Mol. Biol.* 221:193–207
16. Erie DA, Suri AK, Breslauer KJ, Jones RA, Olson WK. 1993. Theoretical predictions of DNA hairpin loop conformations: correlations with thermodynamic and spectroscopic data. *Biochemistry* 32:436–54
17. Gautheret D, Major F, Cedergren R. 1993. Modeling the three-dimensional structure of RNA using discrete nucleotide conformational sets. *J. Mol. Biol.* 229:1049–64
18. Glück A, Endo Y, Wool IG. 1992. Ribosomal RNA identity element for ricin α-chain recognition and catalysis. Analysis with tetraloop mutants. *J. Mol. Biol.* 226:411–24
19. Goodwin JT, Glick GD. 1994. Synthesis of a disulfide stabilized RNA hairpin. *Tetrahedron Lett.* 35:1647–50
20. Gottlieb E. 1992. The 3′ untranslated region of localized materal messages contains a conserved motif involved in mRNA localization. *Proc. Natl. Acad. Sci. USA* 89:7164–68
21. Gralla J, Crothers DM. 1973. Free energy of imperfect nucleic acid helices. II. Small hairpin loops. *J. Mol. Biol.* 73:497–11
22. Groebe DR, Uhlenbeck OC. 1988. Characterization of RNA hairpin loop

stability. *Nucleic Acids Res.* 16: 11725–35

23. Gutell RR. 1993. Comparative studies of RNA: inferring higher-order structure from patterns of sequence variation. *Curr. Opin. Struct. Biol.* 3: 313–22

24. Haasnoot CAG, de Bruin SH, Berendsen RG, Janssen HGMJ, Binnendijk TJJ, et al. 1983. Structure, kinetics and thermodynamics of DNA hairpin fragments in solution. *J. Biomol. Struct. Dyn.* 1:115–29

25. Haasnoot CAG, Hilbers CW, van der Marel GA, van Boom JH, Singh UC, et al. 1986. On loop folding in nucleic acid type structures. *J. Biomol. Struct. Dyn.* 25:843–57

26. Heus H, Uhlenbeck OC, Pardi A. 1990. Sequence-dependent structural variations of hammerhead RNA enzymes. *Nucleic Acids Res.* 18:1103–8

27. Heus HA, Pardi A. 1991. Structural features that give rise to the unusual stability for RNA hairpins containing GNRA loops. *Science* 253:191–94

28. Hines JV, Landry SM, Varani G, Tinoco I Jr. 1994. Carbon-proton scalar couplings in RNA: 3D heteronuclear and 2D isotope-edited NMR of ^{13}C-labeled extra stable hairpin. *J. Am. Chem. Soc.* 116:5823–31

29. Hirao I, Kawai G, Yoshizawa S, Nishimura Y, Ishido Y, et al. 1994. Most compact hairpin-turn structure exerted by a short DNA fragment, d(GCGAAGC) in solution: an extraordinarily stable structure resistant to nucleases and heat. *Nucleic Acids Res.* 22:576–82

30. Hirao I, Nishimura Y, Naraoka T, Watanabe K, Arata Y, Miura K. 1989. Extraordinarily stable structure of short single-stranded DNA fragments containing a specific base sequence: d(GCGAAAGC). *Nucleic Acids Res.* 17:2223–31

31. Hirao I, Nishimura Y, Tagawa Y-I, Watanabe K, Miura K-I. 1992. Extraordinarily stable mini-hairpins: electrophoretical and thermal properties of the various sequence variants of d(GCGAAAGC) and their effect on DNA sequencing. *Nucleic Acids Res.* 20:3891–96

32. Hirao I, Yoshikawa S, Miura K-I. 1993. Stabilization of mRNA in an *Escherichia coli* cell-free translation system. *FEBS Lett.* 321:169–72

33. Hoet RM, De Weerd P, Klein Gunnewiek J, Koorneef I, Van Venrooij

WJ. 1992. Epitope recognition on U1 small nuclear RNA recognized by anti-U1RNA-specific autoantibodies. *J. Clin. Invest.* 90:1753–62

34. Hoet RM, Koornneef I, de Rooij DJ, van de Putte LB, van Venrooij WJ. 1992. Changes in anti-U1 RNA antibody levels correlate with disease activity in patients with systemic lupus erythematosus overlap syndrome. *Arthritis Rheumat.* 35:1202–10

35. Hoffman DW, Colvin RA, Garcia-Blanco MA, White SW. 1993. Structural features of the trans-activation response RNA element of equine infectious anemia virus. *Biochemistry* 32:1096–1104

36. Holbrook SR, Cheong C, Tinoco I Jr, Kim S-H. 1991. Crystal structure of an RNA double helix incorporating a track of non–Watson-Crick base pairs. *Nature* 353:579–81

37. Jaeger JA, Turner DH, Zuker M. 1989. Improved predictions of secondary structures for RNA. *Proc. Natl. Acad. Sci. USA* 86:7706–10

38. Jaeger L, Michel F, Westhof E. 1994. Involvement of a GNRA tetraloop in long range RNA tertiary interactions. *J. Mol. Biol.* 236:1271–76

39. James JK, Tinoco I Jr. 1993. The solution structure of a d[C(TTCG)G] DNA hairpin and comparison to the unusually stable RNA analogue. *Nucleic Acids Res.* 21:3287–93

40. Khan IM, Coulson JM. 1993. A novel method to stabilize antisense oligonucleotides against exonuclease degradation. *Nucleic Acids Res.* 21:2957–58

41. Klausner RD, Rouault TA, Harford JB. 1993. Regulating the fate of mRNA: the control of cellular iron metabolism. *Cell* 72:19–28

42. Larsen N, Zwieb C. 1991. SRP-RNA sequence alignment and secondary structure. *Nucleic Acids Res.* 19: 209–15

43. Li Y, Zon G, Wilson WD. 1991. NMR and molecular modeling evidence for a GA mismatch in a purine-rich DNA duplex. *Proc. Natl. Acad. Sci. USA* 88:26–30

44. Liao X, Brennwald P, Wise JA. 1989. Genetic analysis of *Schizosaccharomyces pombe* 7SL RNA: A structural motif that includes a conserved tetranucleotide loop is important for function. *Proc. Natl. Acad. Sci. USA* 86: 4137–41

45. Lilley DMJ. 1980. The inverted repeat as a recognizable structural feature in

supercoiled DNA molecules. *Proc. Natl. Acad. Sci. USA* 77:6468–72

46. Mizuuchi K, Mizuuchi M, Gellert M. 1982. Cruciform structures in palindromic DNA are favored by DNA supercoiling. *J. Mol. Biol.* 156:229–43

47. Moazed D, Robertson JM, Noller HF. 1988. Interaction of elongation factors EF-G and EF-Tu with a conserved loop in 23S RNA. *Nature* 334:362–64

48. Murphy FL, Cech TR. 1994. GAAA tetraloop and conserved bulge stabilize tertiary structure of a group I intron domain. *J. Mol. Biol.* 236:49–63

49. Orita M, Nishikawa F, Shimayama T, Taira K, Endo Y, Nishikawa S. 1993. High-resolution NMR study of a synthetic oligoribonucleotide with a tetranucleotide GAGA loop that is a substrate for the cytotoxic protein, ricin. *Nucleic Acids Res.* 21:5670–78

50. Panayotatos N, Fontaine A. 1987. A native cruciform DNA structure probed in bacteria by recombinant T7 endonuclease. *J. Biol. Chem.* 262:11364–68

51. Panayotatos N, Wells RD. 1981. Cruciform structures in supercoiled DNA. *Nature* 289:466–70

52. Pley HW, Flaherty KM, McKay DB. 1994. Model for an RNA tertiary interaction from the structure of an intermolecular complex between a GAAA tetraloop and an RNA helix. *Nature* 372:111–13

53. Puglisi JD, Wyatt JR, Tinoco I Jr. 1990. Solution conformation of an RNA hairpin loop. *Biochemistry* 29:4215–26

54. Rothman-Denes LB. 1995. DNA supercoiling, DNA hairpins and single stranded DNA binding proteins in bacteriophage N4 transcription regulation. *Sem. Virol.* In press

55. Saenger W. 1984. *Principles of Nucleic Acid Structure.* New York: Springer-Verlag

56. Sakata T, Hiroaki H, Oda Y, Tanaka T, Ikehara M, Uesugi S. 1990. Studies on the structure and stabilizing factor of the CUUCGG hairpin RNA using chemically synthesized oligonucleotides. *Nucleic Acids Res.* 18:3831–39

57. Santa Lucia JJ, Kierzek R, Turner DH. 1992. Context dependence of hydrogen bond free energy revealed by substitutions in an RNA hairpin. *Science* 256:217–19

58. Selinger D, Liao X, Wise JA. 1993. Functional interchangeability of the structurally similar tetranucleotide loops GAAA and UUCG in fission yeast signal recognition particle RNA. *Proc. Natl. Acad. Sci. USA* 90:5409–13

59. Senior MM, Jones RA, Breslauer KJ. 1988. Influence of loop residues on the relative stabilities of DNA hairpin structures. *Proc. Natl. Acad. Sci. USA* 85:6242–46

60. Skripkin E, Paillart J-C, Marquet R, Ehresmann B, Ehresmann C. 1994. Identification of the primary site of the human immunodeficiency virus type 1 RNA dimerization *in vitro*. *Proc. Natl. Acad. Sci. USA* 91:4945–49

61. Stevens SY, Swanson PC, Voss EWJ, Glick GD. 1993. Evidence for induced fit in antibody-DNA complexes. *J. Am. Chem. Soc.* 115:1585–86

62. Szewczak AA, Moore PB, Chan Y-L, Wool IG. 1993. The conformation of the sarcin/ricin loop from 28S ribosomal RNA. *Proc. Natl. Acad. Sci. USA* 90:9581–85

63. Tang JY, Temsamani J, Agrawal S. 1993. Self-stabilized antisense oligodeoxynucleotide phosphorothioates: properties and anti-HIV activity. *Nucleic Acids Res.* 21:2729–35

64. Tinoco I Jr, Puglisi JR, Wyatt JR. 1990. RNA folding. *Nucleic Acid Mol. Biol.* 4:206–26

65. Tuerk C, Gauss P, Thermes C, Groebe DR, Gayles M, et al. 1988. CUUCGG hairpins: extraordinarily stable RNA secondary structures associated with various biochemical processes. *Proc. Natl. Acad. Sci. USA* 85:1364–68

66. Uhlenbeck OC. 1990. Nucleic acid structures—tetraloops and RNA folding. *Nature* 346:613–14

67. Uhlenbeck OC, Borer PN, Dengler B, Tinoco I Jr. 1973. Stability of RNA hairpin loops: $A_6\text{-}C_m\text{-}U_6$. *J. Mol. Biol.* 73:483–96

68. van Belkum A, Blommers MJJ, van der Elst H, van Boom JH, Hilbers CW. 1990. Biochemical and biophysical studies on the folding of the core region of the origin of replication of bacteriophage M13. *Nucleic Acids Res.* 18:4703–10

69. Varani G, Cheong C, Tinoco I Jr. 1991. Structure of an unusually stable RNA hairpin. *Biochemistry* 30:3280–89

70. Wang H, Osborne SE, Zuiderweg ERP, Glick GD. 1994. Three-dimensional structure of a disulfide-stabilized non-ground-state DNA hairpin. *J. Am. Chem. Soc.* 116:5021–22

71. Wimberly B, Varani G, Tinoco I Jr.

1993. The conformation of loop E of eukaryotic 5S ribosomal RNA. *Biochemistry* 32:1078–87

72. Woese CR, Winker S, Guttell RR. 1990. Architecture of ribosomal RNA: constraints on the sequence of "tetraloops." *Proc. Natl. Acad. Sci. USA* 87:8467–71

73. Wolters J. 1992. The nature of preferred hairpin structures in 16S-like rRNA variable regions. *Nucleic Acids Res.* 20:1843–50

74. Yang S, Temin HM. 1994. A double hairpin structure is necessary for efficient encapsidation of spleen necrosis virus retroviral RNA. *EMBO J.* 13:713–26

75. Yoshikawa S, Ueda T, Ishido Y, Miura K-I, Watanabe K, Hirao I. 1994. Nuclease resistance of an extraordinarily thermostable mini-hairpin DNA fragment, d(GCGAAGC) and its application to *in vitro* protein synthesis. *Nucleic Acids Res.* 22:2217–21

76. Zwieb C. 1992. Conformity of RNAs that interact with tetranucleotide loop binding proteins. *Nucleic Acids Res.* 20:4397–4400

77. Zwieb C. 1992. Recognition of a tetranucleotide loop of signal recognition particle RNA by protein SRP19. *J. Biol. Chem.* 267:15650–56

78. Zwieb C. 1994. Site-directed mutagenesis of signal recognition particle RNA. Identification of the nucleotides in helix 8 required for interaction with protein SRP19. *Eur. J. Biochem.* 222:885–90

Annu. Rev. Biophys. Biomol. Struct. 1995. 24:405–34
Copyright © 1995 by Annual Reviews Inc. All rights reserved

FLUORESCENT PROTEIN BIOSENSORS: Measurement of Molecular Dynamics in Living Cells

Kenneth A. Giuliano* and Penny L. Post

Center for Light Microscope Imaging and Biotechnology and Department of Biological Sciences, Carnegie Mellon University, Pittsburgh, Pennsylvania 15213 and *University of Pittsburgh School of Medicine, Department of Neurological Surgery, Suite B-400, Presbyterian University Hospital, Pittsburgh, Pennsylvania 15213-2582

Klaus M. Hahn

Scripps Research Institute, Department of Neuropharmacology IMM 6, La Jolla, California 92037

D. Lansing Taylor

Center for Light Microscope Imaging and Biotechnology and Department of Biological Sciences, Carnegie Mellon University, Pittsburgh, Pennsylvania 15213

KEY WORDS: light microscopy, intracellular probes, cell physiology

---

CONTENTS

1056-8700/95/0610-0405$05.00

405

ABSTRACT

A new generation of reagents that report on specific molecular events in living cells, called fluorescent protein biosensors, has evolved from in vitro fluorescence spectroscopy and fluorescent analogue cytochemistry. Creative designs of fluorescent protein biosensors to measure the molecular dynamics of macromolecules, metabolites, and ions in single cells emerge from the integrative use of contemporary synthetic organic chemistry, biochemistry, and molecular biology. Future advances in fluorescent probe design, computer-driven optical instrumentation, and software will allow us to engineer endogenous cellular components that localize and function as reporters of their activities, thus moving molecular measurement beyond the single cell to living tissues and the whole organism.

PERSPECTIVES AND OVERVIEW

A powerful set of tools based on the interactions of proteins with ligands such as other proteins and macromolecules, metabolites, and ions are being used to explore the molecular basis of life functions. We can now genetically modify the structure and function of specific proteins, overexpress or completely knock out selected proteins, or incorporate foreign proteins into cells, tissues, organs, and organisms. High-resolution spectroscopic tools such as X-ray crystallography and nuclear magnetic resonance (NMR) coupled to molecular modeling allow us to define the relationship between the structure and function of proteins in vitro.

An important challenge in biology is to extend our knowledge of protein structure and function in vitro to the level of molecular interactions in living cells because all life functions originate at the cellular level (76, 114, 118). This extension has a strong foundation in the fields of molecular biology, biochemistry, and fluorescence spectroscopy. The investigation of the molecular basis of cellular function in cell-free systems has led to the purification and characterization of numerous proteins. Using this classical in vitro approach, investigators have amassed data concerning the structure of proteins, how they respond to regulatory signals, and how they associate with other proteins, all in the hope of extrapolating this information to uncover how proteins function in the living cell (61). While the information gained from dilute-solution studies performed in vitro is needed to help interpret the results from living systems, a great challenge is to understand the nonideal chemistry that occurs in the concentrated-fluid and solid phases known to comprise the cell environment (76). Therefore, the goal of the cell biologist is to complete the continuum of information from the high-resolution studies on purified cellular proteins in vitro to the temporal-spatial molecular interrelationships in living cells, tissues, organs, and organisms.

Investigating the molecular dynamics of living systems from cells to organisms is difficult as it requires techniques that minimally perturb normal physiological activities. Historically, biologists have used electromagnetic radiation to study the chosen living biological sample. The earliest use of light microscopes and X-ray scattering demonstrated that this approach was valuable (133). Today, we can explore the temporal-spatial dynamics within living samples with light (29, 114), NMR (31, 35, 54), and a growing list of scanning probe methods based on a variety of physical and chemical properties of the sample (10, 133). Each of these methods has advantages and disadvantages based on type and extent of perturbation, sensitivity, and spatial and temporal resolution, as well as specificity. We believe that future studies will take advantage of more than one of these modes of analysis to simultaneously dissect a multitude of molecular processes in living samples.

This review focuses on the use of labeled proteins, called fluorescent protein biosensors, to explore functional living samples. These biosensors report the functional activity of intracellular proteins through an alteration in the fluorescence spectroscopic properties of the attached probe that reflects some conformational change, reversible ligand binding, or covalent modification.

Proteins are well suited to act as intracellular sensors because their activities are believed to mediate all the chemical reactions in cells (61). However, the approaches discussed here for fluorescence can also be used with chemiluminescence (18), NMR (31, 54), and electron spin resonance (105). The use of fluorescent protein biosensors as sensitive and specific sensors of chemical and molecular changes in living cells has its roots in classical solution spectroscopic studies and fluorescent analogue cytochemistry (118). Fluorescent analogue cytochemistry creates fluorescently labeled, functional protein analogues that have been used to define the distribution and dynamics of molecular processes in living cells (63, 112, 117, 118, 127). Fluorescent protein biosensors have been the natural outgrowth of fluorescent analogue cytochemistry and are a component of this approach (43, 118).

Here, we discuss the theory behind and design of fluorescent protein biosensors and point out chemical and fluorescence-based methodologies that we believe will lead to the newest members of this growing family of biosensors. We begin by dissecting protein activities into their molecular components and discuss how these activities form the basis of the design of fluorescent protein biosensors. We then describe how fluorescence-based reagents are coupled to methodologies designed to detect and analyze their information-rich fluorescence signals. We follow with sections concerning the design and construction of fluorescent protein biosensors, keeping in mind their use in the unique environment of the living cell. Finally, we discuss the major issues in the future of fluorescent protein biosensors.

APPROACHES TO SENSING PROTEIN ACTIVITY IN LIVING CELLS

The activity of intracellular proteins encompasses many sorts of chemical interactions that include the binding and release of ligands, assembly and disassembly of macromolecular structures, the interaction with membranes or organelles, and the catalytic conversion of specific substrates into metabolic or macromolecular products (see 23 for overview). The activity of a protein is defined by the environmental changes that occur either internally or on its surface. This is true whether the protein is an enzyme with catalytic activity or a cellular structural component that must interact with other macromolecules or organelles. Molecular associations that change protein conformation can dramatically alter protein structure, or they can act locally, causing only subtle environmental changes (34). In both cases, the effects on protein activity may be profound. For example, phosphorylation of a single serine residue on the light chain located in the head region of smooth muscle myosin II converts a compact 10S particle with little ATPase activity into an extended 6S, fully active enzyme (120). In contrast, phosphorylation of a single serine residue in the active site of isocitrate dehydrogenase causes no long-range conformational change in the free enzyme, yet it inhibits enzymatic activity by preventing the enzyme from interacting with its negatively charged substrate (52). Regardless of the extent of reversible conformational changes, proteins stabilize these changes by dynamically rearranging molecular dipoles, hydrogen bonds, and ionic and hydrophobic interactions. Many of these activity-dependent molecular rearrangements can be sensed by fluorescence-based reagents and thus form the basis of fluorescent protein biosensor design.

Fluorescent Analogues of Proteins

Fluorescent analogue cytochemistry involves the preparation of functional, fluorescent analogues of proteins used to define the dynamic distribution and activity of these proteins in living cells (117, 127). Three classes of fluorescent chromophores (probes) in proteins are potentially useful in engineering fluorescent analogues: intrinsic, coenzyme, and extrinsic (107).

Intrinsic probes consist of the aromatic side chains of tyrosine, phenylalanine, and tryptophan residues, whereas coenzyme probes are comprised of molecules such as flavin-adenine dinucleotide. Fluorescence spectroscopic investigations of intrinsic and coenzyme probes have revealed important structural information and interactions of selected proteins (60, 132). Unfortunately, intrinsic and coenzyme-based probes have two major limitations: The location of the probe is rarely in the optimal region of the protein to sense key environmental changes, and the excitation spectra are very broad and generally do not permit selective investigation of proteins containing these fluorophores in complex mixtures that include living cells.

Weber (129) introduced the approach of extrinsic fluorescent labeling of proteins. The incorporation of extrinsic fluorescent probes at a specific location in a protein allows for site selection as well as spectral selection. The idea of extrinsic labeling was extended by the discovery of Weber & Laurence (134) that a variety of polycyclic aromatic compounds that were nonfluorescent in aqueous media became fluorescent upon binding serum albumin. A series of classic papers by Weber and his colleagues led the way in the use of fluorescence spectroscopy as a tool to study the structure and dynamics of proteins and other macromolecules (24, 93, 107, 133). A wide range of reactive fluorescent dyes is now available that can be used to target specific sites, exhibit environmental sensitivities, and fit into specific spectral regions (45, 125).

To prepare fluorescent protein analogues, a protein of interest is isolated, covalently modified with a reactive fluorescent dye, and characterized in vitro to determine if the covalent modification somehow affected the original activity (102, 112, 118, 127). Although optimization of the labeling process to produce bright, biologically relevant fluorescent analogues varies with each protein, many analogues have already been prepared and characterized based on general guidelines (63, 102, 128). The characterized fluorescent protein analogue is then introduced into living cells (85), where the fluorescence signal demonstrates the distribution of the analogue in time and space.

Fluorescent protein analogues have been most often used to describe the dynamics of the actin-based cytoskeleton in living cells. For example, to measure the assembly and disassembly of actin (38) and myosin II (59), they have also been used to localize several accessory proteins (64, 84, 87, 119). Fluorescent analogues have now been prepared for numerous structural proteins (39, 88, 99), enzymes (89, 90), and other proteins and peptides (75, 83). When coupled with fluorescence photobleaching recovery methods, they can be used to measure the physical characteristics of the surrounding cytoplasm (59, 64, 74, 111, 128). Similar experiments can be performed using photoactivation of fluorescence that exhibits a higher signal-to-noise ratio (101).

Fluorescent analogue cytochemistry will continue to guide us in our analysis of the dynamics of living cells. Figure 1 demonstrates the use of multiple probes over a spectral range to map the dynamics of multiple proteins. The living human glioblastoma cell shown here was microinjected with three distinctly labeled components: dextran, to map the accessible cytoplasmic volume of the cell; actin, which incorporates into the dynamic actin cytoskeleton; and vinculin, to map the dynamics of focal adhesions. Figure 1a is a video-enhanced differential interference contrast image that depicts glioblastoma morphology and organelle structure. The actin analogue shown here is a fluorescent protein biosensor in that it belongs to a new generation of fluorescent actin analogues that interact optimally with endogenous actin-binding proteins and that therefore report accurately the dynamics of actin assembly in living cells (38). Combining fluorescent analogues and fluorescent protein biosensors in the same cells will give us a powerful set of cell biological reagents. In addition, the fluorescent protein biosensors

---

Figure 1 Multiparameter fluorescence analogue cytochemistry. Living human glioblastoma cells (SNB-19) were microinjected with three distinctly labeled fluorescent analogues and observed with video-enhanced differential interference contrast microscopy (A) or fluorescence microscopy (B–D) using the multimode microscope (29, 37). The nuclei of three cells in the field of view are denoted in A with the letters n and N. The cell marked with N was microinjected with fluorescent analogues that included: (B) an M_r 10,000 dextran (38), (C) nonmuscle actin (38), and (D) smooth muscle vinculin (KA Giuliano, in preparation). The arrowheads in C and D denote the colocalization of stress fibers containing actin and vinculin fluorescent analogues. Using a time series of fluorescence ratio images, data from this type of experiment can be used to measure a temporal and spatial map of actin assembly (38) or the dynamics of focal contact formation and dissolution.

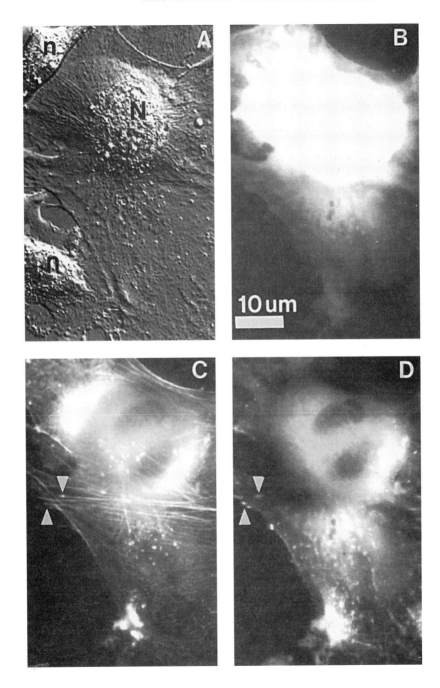

described below can simultaneously be used as fluorescent protein analogues in the same experiment, thus yielding a wealth of information from a single reagent.

Fluorescent Protein Biosensors

Proteins express activity through their interaction with various ligands, from ions and metabolites to macromolecules and organelles. To induce activity, some proteins require an interaction with metal ions (e.g. Ca^{2+}, Mg^{2+}, Fe^{2+}, etc) or metabolites (e.g. cAMP, phosphoinositides, and diacylglycerol). Small ligands can directly induce protein activity, as in iron ions binding to myoglobin, diacylglycerol binding to protein kinase C, or a small ligand interacting with one protein that induces complex formation with other proteins. The reversible binding of ligands, interaction with other macromolecules, and posttranslational modifications are activities for which fluorescent protein biosensors have been designed.

Enzyme activity represents an interesting target for intracellular analysis. Fluorogenic substrates for several enzymes are commercially available that have the potential for widespread use in measuring enzyme activity in living cells (46). Moreover, enzyme-based, fluorescent protein biosensors report the modulation of catalytic activity in living cells (2, 91). Therefore, the activity of an enzyme in a living cell can be mapped using fluorescent substrates and to quantify conformational changes of the same enzyme resulting from the interaction with modulators of activity, such as metabolites or other macromolecules.

Intracellular proteins also interact with a myriad of other macromolecules including other proteins, DNA, RNA, complex carbohydrates, and lipids in the plasma membrane and organelles. Fluorescent protein biosensors can be designed to measure the conformational changes that accompany these interactions, specifically in three general classes of activity-dependent conformational changes: spatial rearrangements of the peptide backbone that alter the distance between specific amino acid residues; activity-dependent changes in the exposure of certain amino acid residues to solvent; and changes in the hydrodynamic radius of a protein (e.g. macromolecular shape changes or macromolecular complex formation). The distinctions between these general classes of protein interactions are not clear-cut, and overlap between them is most likely the rule rather than the exception. For instance, a change in the spatial distance between specific amino acid residues within a protein will most likely be accompanied by a change in protein shape or exposure of a previously hidden region of the protein to solvent, or both. Therefore, one must carefully interpret the signals derived from fluorescent protein biosensors because these reagents can report a combination of environmental changes, especially in the milieu of living cytoplasm.

Fluorescence Reagents and Spectroscopic Methodologies

Just as we generally classified protein activity–dependent conformational changes, we can also loosely group fluorescent reagents and spectroscopic methodologies used to construct and observe fluorescent protein biosensors in living cells. Three types of fluorescence spectroscopy can be used in conjunction with fluorescence ratio imaging microscopy, a major tool in quantifying fluorescence (1, 14, 40). The following ratio imaging methods are independent of cytoplasmic path length, accessible volume, and local concentration: (*a*) Fluorescence resonance energy transfer (FRET) and fluorescence quenching techniques are sensitive to intra- and intermolecular distances and can therefore sense relatively small changes in protein conformation; (*b*) solvent-sensitive fluorescent reagents can detect intracellular changes in protein-ligand binding; and (*c*) fluorescence anisotropy imaging microscopy relies on the modulation of fluorescence polarization to report macromolecular complex formation or alterations in macromolecular shape.

MECHANISMS OF ACTION AND APPLICATIONS OF FLUORESCENT PROTEIN BIOSENSORS

Solvent Sensitivity

BACKGROUND   Molecules that surround fluorophores in solution can exert powerful and useful effects on fluorescence intensities, excitation and emission spectra, and lifetimes. Besides interacting with solvent, dye molecules covalently attached to proteins interact with many other molecules in their immediate environment, including protein amino acid side chains, lipids, nucleic acids, carbohydrates, metabolites, and ions. The diverse mechanisms underlying solvent effects can be divided into general and specific solvent effects (66, 73). General solvent effects result from the interaction of the dipole moment of the dye with the electromagnetic field produced by surrounding solvent molecules, whereas specific solvent effects constitute a diverse class of distinct chemical interactions between a dye and one or more surrounding solvent molecules. Solvent sensitivity manifests itself as an alteration of fluorescence wavelength, intensity (67), or both, changes that are readily detectable in living cells with fluorescence ratio imaging (14).

The sensitivity of fluorescence to its environment has been used to great advantage in the molecular dissection of biological processes. Solvent-sensitive fluorophores have been harnessed in vitro to study protein structure and ligand binding, membrane structure and dynamics, changes in free ion concentration, and many other biological interactions (66). Solvent-sensitive dyes were originally used to probe the hydrophobic microenvironments of macromolecules (106, 134). These free dyes were also used to measure the equilibria of macromolecular interactions (79) but have since been augmented with protein-reactive solvent-sensitive fluorescent dyes (45). Covalently modified proteins have, for example, been used to measure the binding of Ca^{2+} to calmodulin (44, 80, 137) and parvalbumin (92), the binding of calmodulin to target proteins (86), and the assembly of actin subunits into microfilaments (26, 62). Fluorescently labeled proteins with the ability to provide information about the environment surrounding the fluorophore in dilute solution are the predecessors of the present generation of solvent-sensitive fluorescent protein biosensors.

KEY EXAMPLES OF BIOSENSORS   The use of solvent-sensitive fluorophores has recently been extended to the design of protein-based biosensors for studying biochemistry in vitro and in individual, living cells. For example, Hahn et al (44) developed merocyanine fluorophores with long-wavelength, solvent-sensitive fluorescence characteristics specifically for use in live cells. One such fluorophore, modified with side chains that cause it to bind specifically to the calcium-bound conformation of calmodulin, is covalently attached to calmodulin. When calcium binds to the derivatized protein, the dye moves from an aqueous to a hydrophobic environment, with consequent changes in fluorescence (44). This calmodulin analogue is used as an indicator of calmodulin activation in individual living cells, revealing the kinetics and spatial distribution of calmodulin activity during serum stimulation and wound healing (42).

The strengths of biochemistry and molecular biology must sometimes be combined to produce a solvent-sensitive fluorescent protein biosensor. Specific labeling of Cys108 of the regulatory light chain of myosin II with solvent-sensitive dyes was not successful in producing a fluorescent protein biosensor of myosin II phosphorylation (91). Therefore, site-directed mutagenesis was used to introduce a single cysteine-labeling site next to a phosphorylation site on the protein. Myosin light chain kinase activity caused a measurable change in the fluorescence spectrum of labeled myosin II in dilute solution and in isolated muscle fibrils (91).

A new fluorescent protein biosensor for the measurement of submicromolar inorganic phosphate anions in solution represents a new class of ion indicator that has potential for use in living cells. Brune et al (16) developed a genetically engineered phosphate-binding protein to measure the kinetic release of inorganic phosphate from enzymes such as phosphatases. The protein-bound coumarin-based dye exhibits a 5.2-fold increase in fluorescence with a 10-nm peak-wavelength shift in the presence of saturating inorganic phosphate. The authors used the probe to measure the rate of inorganic phosphate release from solutions of actomyosin subfragment 1 during ATPase activity. The design of this in vitro fluorescent probe is echoed in the solvent sensitivity–based fluorescent protein biosensors described below.

Kleinfeld and coworkers used a similar approach to produce fluorescent indicators for the concentration of specific fatty acids. An intestinal fatty acid–binding protein, I-FABP, was labeled with the solvent-sensitive dye acrylodan (94). Fluorescent changes in this indicator are used to monitor concentrations of the fatty acid during activation of living cytotoxic T lymphocytes (4).

CAVEATS OF THE PRESENT METHODOLOGY   Solvent-sensitive fluorescent dyes have found widespread use in the analysis of protein chemistry in dilute solution studies. To study actin assembly in vitro, Kouyama & Mihashi (62) used covalently bound pyrene to measure the assembly of globular actin molecules into actin microfilaments, while Detmers et al (26) produced a similar reagent by reacting 7-chloro-4-nitrobenzeno-2-oxa-1,3 diazole (NBD)–Cl with filamentous actin. Pyrene-actin has since become the reagent of choice for dissecting the assembly and disassembly of actin in vitro because of its large change in fluorescence intensity upon polymerization (22). The limitations of pyrene-actin and other protein-based fluorescent reagents as fluorescent protein biosensors are twofold: the lack of an actin assembly–specific spectral change and the incompatibility of the fluorophore with live cell studies. As originally reported, globular pyrene-actin exhibits a 25-fold increase in fluorescence intensity upon assembly into filamentous actin (62). In the same report, the authors found that the binding of subfragment 1 of myosin II to filamentous pyrene-actin reduced the fluorescence intensity to a level near that of globular pyrene-actin. The fluorescence signal emanating from the pyrene-actin–subfragment 1 complex therefore appeared to be globular actin–like, although actin filaments still predominated. Furthermore, the site of actin modification by pyrene, Cys374, resides in a region of the molecule where several actin-binding proteins interact (56). This modification may either prevent other proteins from interacting with actin (38, 81) or cause unknown spectral changes in the fluorescence spectrum of pyrene-actin if it were to be used in a living cytoplasm.

The photophysical characteristics of the most popular solvent-sensitive fluorophores used to describe dilute-solution protein chemistry preclude their use in living cells (see "Construction of Fluorescent Protein Biosensors," below), whereas the commercially available fluorophores most compatible with live cells show little solvent sensitivity (45). Overcoming this paradox of practicality will require new strategies in both protein and fluorophore engineering (see "Future," below). Genetic engineering of proteins to direct fluorophore labeling and the development of fluorescence reagents appropriate for use in living cells could make newer versions of solvent-sensitive fluorescent protein biosensors more sensitive and specific (21, 28, 91).

Fluorescence Quenching

BACKGROUND   Several processes fall under the general heading of quenching, including energy transfer (see "FRET," below), complex formation, collisional quenching, and excited-state reactions (11, 93, 133). These processes are usually divided into viscosity-dependent dynamic quenching (11) and viscosity-independent static quenching (93). Dynamic quenching results from the interaction of fluorophores in the excited state and affects only the emission spectrum of the fluorophore, whereas static quenching results from the interaction of a fluorophore in the ground state with other molecules and often results in alterations in the absorption spectrum.

The exposure to solvent of small molecules bound to proteins has been assayed using fluorescence quenching induced by solvent perturbation (50). The extent of fluorescence quenching is considered an excellent indicator of this exposure, because fluorescence is quenched by a variety of ions and other molecules (71). For example, Vaughan & Weber (124) used 1-pyrenebutyric acid as a probe attached to proteins together with fluorescence lifetime measurements to determine the quenching by oxygen. The quenching efficiency was taken as a measure of the accessibility of the 1-pyrenebutyric acid probe to O_2. The analysis showed that hydrophobic ligands are buried within the structure of bovine serum albumin. These results suggest that 1-pyrenebutyric acid could be used to measure oxygen concentration under physiological conditions. Based on this work, a fluorescence quenching technique was developed to determine the local oxygen concentration in living liver cells (58). Benson et al (7) extended this approach using video microscopy and measured the Stern-Volmer quenching constants at different locations within liver cells. The quenching constants were calculated for each pixel by taking the ratio of the fluorescence intensity under nitrogen to the fluorescence intensity for all other pO_2 levels. The spatial variation in the quenching constants was interpreted as variations in the solubility coefficient of oxygen in different locations within the liver cells.

KEY EXAMPLES OF BIOSENSORS   Chemiluminescence quenching, which is mechanistically related to fluorescence quenching, has been used to measure protein phosphorylation in living cells. Sala-Newby & Campbell (98) used genetic engineering to develop a luciferase-based reagent to measure protein-kinase activity in a population of living cells. Because quenching of luciferase chemiluminescence is mediated by phosphorylation of the reagent by protein kinase, it formed the basis of the assay.

A quenching-based fluorescent peptide biosensor for calpain protease activity in live hepatocytes was recently described (97). Proteolysis of the intracellularly trapped peptide results in the release of a deprotonated and therefore unquenched coumarin, which is then quantified with video fluorescence microscopy. Calpain protease activity increases concomitantly with intracellular free calcium ion concentration, an observation consistent with the proposed role this protease plays in calcium-mediated signal transduction.

Fluorescence resonance energy transfer (FRET) is a valuable tool for creating quench-based biosensors because of its ability to measure the quenching of the donor fluorescence and the appearance of sensitized fluorescence from the acceptor probe (see "FRET," below). The sensitized fluorescence permits a donor-to-acceptor fluorescence ratio that normalizes the cell signal for variable path length, accessible volume, and local concentration. Alternatively, fluorescence lifetime imaging can be used to map the changes in fluorescence lifetime that accompany fluorescence quenching (68, 123). Because this latter technique provides a spatial map of the lifetime of a particular fluorophore, it does not require that the fluorescent protein biosensor exhibit activity-dependent shifts in light absorption or emission. This technology is also compatible with many presently available intracellular fluorescent probes and promises to spur the development of new fluorescence reagents (68).

The following in vitro study suggests some interesting ways to design biosensors for use in living cells. Tropomyosin is a coiled coil of two parallel α-helical polypeptide chains that functions as a component of the calcium regulation of skeletal and cardiac muscle. Tropomyosin was specifically labeled at Cys190 with *N*-(1-pyrene)-maleimide. Two structural states of tropomyosin were identified: an excimer-forming state and a nonexcimer state. The excimer was identified by the appearance of a wavelength band at 480 nm, which was long compared with the structured fluorescence emission bands at 383 nm and 403 nm. Steric considerations indicated that chain separation of tropomyosin was required for the pyrenes to form an excimer (41). Conformational changes or assembly-disassembly dynamics of various protein subunits could be studied using reversible excimer formation measured either by a ratio of excimer emission to fluorescence emission or by fluorescence-lifetime imaging.

CAVEATS OF THE PRESENT METHODOLOGY   The major limitation to the use of quenching-based fluorescent protein biosensors is the specificity of intracellular quenching. Predicting nonspecific fluorescence quenching in the complex compartments of cytoplasm is problematic because several molecules may participate unpredictably. As described above, oxygen is an efficient quencher, yet its removal may lead to abnormal physiological conditions that would be difficult to predict or quantify. The ability of a constitutive intracellular molecule, pyruvate, to quench fluorescence is predictable enough to form the basis of an in vitro assay for pyruvate reactions (3). Consequently, simple fluorescence-quenching measurements in living cells are difficult to interpret. The release of intracellular quenching may be no easier to decipher. The coumarin-fluorophore–based reagent described above that induces fluorescence as a result of calpain action is also subject to endogenous molecules that may requench its fluorescence. Moreover, coumarin fluorescence is pH sensitive, so a change in intracellular pH concomitant with calpain activation would bias the results. By coupling fluorescence quenching to energy transfer to another fluorophore, or to the formation of eximers, one could take advantage of the benefits of fluorescence ratio imaging microscopy, thus enhancing the specificity of the method. Furthermore, development of new dyes whose fluorescence is chemically protected from oxygen quenching will also improve the specificity of the next generation of quench-based fluorescent protein biosensors.

Fluorescence Resonance Energy Transfer (FRET)

BACKGROUND   Protein activities that involve either significant rearrangement of intramolecular domains or reversible association with a ligand can potentially be sensed in living cells with FRET methodology. The theory of FRET was first described by Förster in 1948 and has been experimentally verified (33, 70, 108, 109). Upon excitation of a donor fluorophore, absorbed energy is transferred in a nonradiative manner to a proximal acceptor fluorophore. Depending on several parameters, this transfer may quench the donor fluorescence and enhance the acceptor fluorescence (30, 48, 66, 136). Most importantly for biological systems, the rate of transfer varies as the inverse sixth power of the distance between donor and acceptor, making FRET extremely sensitive to changes in molecular distances over the range of approximately 1–7 nm. Advances in digital image acquisition and image processing have allowed steady-state and lifetime-dependent (48, 55, 68) FRET measurements to be made with the light microscope. Using this type of microscopy, decreases in the fluorescence intensity and lifetime of the donor caused by specific quenching by the acceptor are temporally and spatially mapped in living cells.

Marsh & Lowey (82) also used FRET to define the interaction between specific sites on the light and heavy chains of the catalytic head region of skeletal muscle myosin II. Huang et al (51) labeled pairs of 30S ribosomal proteins with naphthalene-based and fluorescein dyes and reconstituted 30S particles in vitro. The proximity of 20 ribosomal proteins in the particles was measured and found to agree with previous chemical cross-linking results. Thus, FRET methodology can potentially be used to measure association reactions such as those required for cytoskeletal assembly within living cells (116).

KEY EXAMPLES OF BIOSENSORS   FRET-based fluorescent protein biosensors have been used in living cells to measure protein dynamics at the plasma membrane (49), within intracellular compartments (27, 122), and in the cytoplasm during signal transduction (2). To study lectin receptor topography and mobility in single cells during myoblast fusion, Herman & Fernandez (49) incubated chick muscle cells with a mixture of concanavalin A molecules labeled with pyrene (donor) and fluorescein (acceptor). The authors observed a dramatic reorganization of concanavalin A receptors during myogenesis, suggesting a temporal correlation between changes in membrane fluidity and the onset of myoblast fusion. Young et al (138) coupled fluorescence photobleaching and FRET in living cells to describe the differential membrane-binding effects of concanavalin A and succinyl concanavalin A. Uster & Pagano (122) also used a fluorescently labeled lectin as a fluorescence donor but employed a fluorescent analogue of phosphatidylcholine as an acceptor to measure lectin and lipid sorting in living fibroblasts. Those endocytic cellular compartments containing both lectin and lipid exhibited FRET, whereas those compartments subject to sorting contained only acceptor fluorescent lipids. Adams et al (2) labeled the catalytic and regulatory subunits of cAMP-dependent kinase with an energy-transfer pair that allowed FRET to occur in the holoenzyme complex. However, upon binding of cAMP to the regulatory subunit, the holoenzyme dissociates and FRET is lost as the enzyme becomes active. This fluorescent protein biosensor (1) has been used in several types of living cells to measure changes in intracellular cAMP concentration with high temporal and spatial resolution (2, 100).

Post et al have designed a biosensor of myosin II regulatory light chain phosphorylation that employs energy transfer between fluorescein-labeled regulatory light chains and rhodamine-labeled myosin heavy and essential light chains (PL Post, RL DeBiasio & DL Taylor, in preparation). Phosphorylation of the regulatory light chain produces a change in the energy transfer efficiency. The biosensor has been used in living cells under different conditions to map the spatial distribution of myosin II. An advantage of this method is that both dyes of the energy-transfer pair are on one protein, which eliminates problems of diffusion of donor and acceptor upon mixing with endogenous unlabeled proteins.

CAVEATS OF THE PRESENT METHODOLOGY   Several requirements restrict the design of FRET-based fluorescent protein biosensors for use in vivo. First, donor and acceptor molecules must have sufficient spectral overlap and be optimally oriented within 1–7 nm of each other. Specific protein labeling with two different reactive fluorophores to satisfy these conditions is problematic. Donor and acceptor macromolecules are usually labeled separately and recombined before use in living cells (1, 122). Generally applicable methods for labeling specific amino acid residues will facilitate the future construction of FRET-based fluorescent protein biosensors (see "Construction of Fluorescent Biosensors," below).

Second, dilution with endogenous unlabeled proteins is theoretically a major obstacle to the construction of multisubunit FRET-based fluorescent protein biosensors (115). Once separated, acceptor and donor protein subunits are not likely to interact with each other again in a cytoplasm crowded with endogenous unlabeled protein subunits. However, Adams et al (2) found that their FRET-based optical probe for cAMP is reversible in living cells and suggest that exogenous levels of microinjected probe are sufficiently greater than those of endogenous kinase to statistically favor recombination of labeled subunits. Furthermore, Adams et al (1) discuss the possibility that this excess of exogenous holoenzyme may also perturb the cAMP-response pathway. To avoid the delivery of supraphysiological doses of FRET-based optical probes, Adams et al (1) suggest a chemically tethered version of the biosensor to facilitate recombination of the labeled subunits in living cells. In contrast, the observed reversibility of the multisubunit fluorescent protein biosensor might also be attributed to the structure of the surrounding cytoplasm.

Fluorescence Anisotropy

BACKGROUND   Encoded within the rotational Brownian motion of intracellular proteins is information about their size and shape, interactions with other cellular components, and the viscosity of the surrounding cytoplasm (130). Measurement of this rotational diffusion in living cells would yield temporal and spatial maps of the interaction of proteins with ions, metabolites, and other macromolecular structures that would affect the rotational diffusion of the protein. The rotational diffusion coefficient of a protein in solution is directly related to temperature but inversely related to both the first power of the viscosity of the surrounding medium and the cube of the hydrodynamic radius of the protein (40). Inversely related to the rotational diffusion coefficient of a protein is its rotational correlation time, usually in the range of nanoseconds to tens of nanoseconds (66). If a dye with a fluorescence lifetime on the order of the rotational correlation time of a protein is immobilized on that protein, then significant randomization of its emission dipole occurs during the excited state. This randomization is measured by exciting the dye with plane-polarized light and measuring the fluorescence emission through a variable-angle polarizer. Altering the steady-state polarization of a labeled protein therefore provides a sensitive measure of changes in its hydrodynamic radius; these changes may result from protein peptide chain rearrangements or the interaction of the protein with other cellular components.

Fluorescence polarization has emerged as a primary technique for the measurement of the rotational diffusion of biomolecules in dilute solution, and as such, has been extensively reviewed (9, 17, 65, 103, 130). The technique has been used to measure the rotational diffusion of proteins for more than 40 years (129). Although the aromatic amino acids intrinsic to the proteins can be used as fluorescence polarization probes (131), extrinsic fluorophores are the most useful because they can be selected to have fluorescence lifetimes that closely match the rotational correlation times of proteins (20, 129). For example, fluorescence polarization of extrinsically labeled proteins has been used to measure protein molar volumes and their interaction with small and macromolecular ligands (66).

KEY EXAMPLES OF BIOSENSORS   Recent efforts have applied fluorescence polarization methods to the measurement of specific components or processes of living cells. For example, organic molecules have been used to probe the structure of cytoplasm (57) and membrane dynamics (9) while small proteins have been used to describe cellular signaling pathways (19, 40).

Fluorescence anisotropy imaging microscopy (FAIM), which is related linearly to solution-based fluorescence polarization techniques, is a simple yet powerful mode of light microscopy that is easily added to existing light microscope–based imaging systems (40). For example, FAIM was performed on fluorescein-labeled calmodulin (M_r 16,790) that was microinjected into migrating and growth factor–stimulated fibroblasts (40). FAIM produced temporal and spatial maps showing gradients of calmodulin activation that correlate well with the time course of the elevation and decline of free–calcium ion concentration and with the previously known dynamics of the actin-cytoskeleton in these cells (36, 42). In another example, temporal anisotropy measurements were made of the interaction of fluorescein-labeled epidermal growth factor (M_r ~6000) with its cellular receptor on living cells (19). Upon binding of the growth factor to its receptor on the cell, a rapid quenching of growth factor fluorescence was detected and attributed to changes in its rotational diffusion. The rapid fluorescence decay during growth factor stimulation was used to determine the rate constants for the interaction of the fluorescent growth factor with its receptor on the cell surface.

CAVEATS OF THE PRESENT METHODOLOGY   The limitations of FAIM parallel those of solution-based fluorescence polarization methods and include interferences from light scattering, fluorophore photobleaching, and fluorescence-energy transfer. Methods for dealing with many of these limitations have been described (9, 40), but the photophysics and photochemistry of commonly used protein-reactive fluorophores have thus far hindered full application of FAIM. For fluorescence-polarization techniques to indicate changes in the hydrodynamic radius of proteins or protein complexes, the fluorescence lifetime of the dye used to label the protein of interest must be of the same order as the protein's expected rotational correlation time (40). Prevalent protein-reactive fluorophores able to measure changes in the rotational correlation time changes of medium to large proteins (M_r > 20,000) have molar extinction coefficients and excitation wavelengths that are unfavorable for live cell imaging (40). For example, solutions of globular actin labeled with naphthalene-based dyes that have fluorescence lifetimes of about

10 ns show little change in fluorescence anisotropy when induced to undergo self-assembly to a highly structured filamentous state (77, 121, 130). Nevertheless, actin labeled with the triplet probe erythrosin-5-iodoacetamide, which has a phosphorescence lifetime of >100 μs, shows a significant increase in delayed luminescence anisotropy upon polymerization to filamentous actin (77). Unfortunately, experiments using erythrosin-labeled actin are performed under nonphysiological anoxic conditions in vitro to prevent quenching of the phosphorescence, thus limiting the usefulness of delayed luminescence anisotropy in living cells. Clearly, fluorescent and phosphorescent dyes with physical characteristics more amenable to FAIM need to be explored to extend the applicability of the method to a wider range of proteins.

Future enhancements in the design of the instrumentation and fluorescent protein biosensors used for fluorescence anisotropy microscopy will make the technique more flexible and sensitive. Time-resolved or phase-modulation measurements of anisotropy yield more information about the degree of fluorophore rotation and the environment surrounding the fluorophore than steady-state polarization experiments (66). Time-resolved microscopic instrumentation has already been developed to explore intracellular chemistry (32, 69, 123). The recent development of fluorescence lifetime-resolved two-photon microscopy could be a major breakthrough in time-lapse measurements of living systems (123).

CONSTRUCTION OF FLUORESCENT PROTEIN BIOSENSORS

The central challenge in production of fluorescent protein biosensors is site-selective attachment of dyes to proteins. To date, most protein analogues have been made with environmentally insensitive dyes to simplify quantification of dye distribution within cells. Production of such adducts requires only that the dye be attached at a position where biological activity would be minimally perturbed. In the most widely used method, semirandom labeling, the attachment site depends on the relative reactivities of native amino acid side chains and on the reactive group of the dye.

Although many valuable protein adducts have been produced by means of semirandom labeling, this method largely fails in the generation of more sophisticated analogues that have environmentally sensitive dyes precisely placed to respond to protein activity. A few such probes have been produced using more specific methods, as described below. The future of probe development lies in presently available methods for labeling specific protein amino acid residues, including genetic engineering (91), enzyme-mediated protein labeling (110), and C-terminus labeling (96); in promising new technologies that enable incorporation of nonnative residues, including fluorescently labeled amino acids, during protein synthesis (28); and in the preparation of chimera proteins using the green fluorescent protein or its derviatives as a molecularly targeted fluorophore (21).

To date, all methods use reactive groups on dyes that produce some selectivity for specific amino acid side chains. Dyes with a wide range of reactive groups are now commercially available. Their chemistry and the selection of reaction conditions to maximize selectivity for particular amino acids have been extensively reviewed (15, 45). Although many amino acid side chains can be derivatized or turned into useful labeling sites through chemical or enzymatic modification (47, 78), dyes are usually attached to cysteine or lysine because the nucleophilic side chains of these amino acids are most readily labeled in the presence of other residues. Selectivity for cysteine vs lysine is usually influenced by the pH of the reaction mixture, as cysteine remains in a reactive, deprotonated form at a pH where protonated lysine residues are unreactive. Selection of one lysine over another can be effected by manipulating pH because local protein environments strongly influence the pK_a of individual residues. Finally, ligands that alter protein conformation can be used to alter the relative reactivity of different residues.

When a dye is attached near a ligand-binding site (i.e. to report ligand binding), an affinity-labeling approach can be used to direct the dye to the desired site. Hahn et al (44) produced an indicator of calmodulin conformational change by attaching a dye to the protein where it would bind a hydrophobic pocket found only in the protein's calcium-bound form. A dye was synthesized containing side chains conferring affinity for the pocket. This binding affinity was used to direct the reactive dye to the desired site. A slowly reacting group was used on the dye, so that the dye bound first to the pocket and then covalently attached to a nearby residue. The dye has a strong affinity for the pocket, and its solvent-sensitive fluorescence is affected whenever it moves into the pocket during calcium binding.

Jackson & Puett (53) used a different affinity-labeling tactic to attach a spin label near the active site on calmodulin. This approach may be used to place reporter dyes where they will interact with bound ligands without blocking their binding sites. An inhibitor of calmodulin phosphodiesterase activation was attached to a spin label through a cleavable bridge. The reactive residue for covalent attachment was on the spin label. During labeling, the ligand sat in the binding pocket, directing the reactive group and spin label to a nearby site. The labeled calmodulin could not activate phosphodiesterase until cleavage of the inhibitor. Cleavage led to an active calmodulin with a spin label covalently attached near the active site.

Affinity labeling has also been used to attach a reactive residue at a desired site for later selective derivatization with dye. Bock (12, 13) synthesized a reactive derivative of a peptide that bound to the active site of thrombin. The peptide contained a blocked sulfhydryl function that was released after covalent attachment of the peptide. The sulfhydryl group was then specifically labeled with fluorescent dyes.

An interesting hybrid of intrinsic and extrinsic labeling emerged recently that uses the tools of genetic engineering to increase the power of fluorescence. This method could allow the insertion of a sequence of the *Aequorea victoria* green fluorescent protein and related proteins into target proteins, thus creating a genetically engineered, fluorescent, chimeric protein (21). Another possible technique would be to use a small portion of the the green fluorescent protein sequence containing the hexapeptide chromophore to label specific domains of proteins.

New technologies offer the promise that dyes can be incorporated during in vitro translation and chemical synthesis of proteins, thus overcoming the need to selectively derivatize a protein site. tRNAs can now be charged with unnatural amino acids and incorporated at precise positions in a protein during in vitro translation (6, 28). The many unnatural amino acids introduced by this method include a residue labeled with the fluorescent dye NBD (28). To produce novel protein probes for microinjection in cells, these methods still require optimization. They suffer primarily from the need for extensive synthesis of reagents and from the small scales on which proteins can be produced. New methods for linking synthetic peptides offer a promising alternative to labeling intact proteins. Large-scale synthesis of proteins using automated peptide synthesis has already been reported (95). Adaptation of this chemistry to accommodate peptides bearing dyes should be possible. The coupling of our ability to routinely engineer dyes into specific positions within a protein using biochemical, genetic, and synthetic methods with our increasing knowledge of protein structure should lead to production of many new analogues probing a wide range of protein functions.

DESIGN CONSIDERATIONS OF FLUORESCENT PROTEIN BIOSENSORS UNIQUE TO IN VIVO USES

Although issues relating to the site-specific labeling of proteins dominate the design of fluorescent protein biosensors (see previous section), the use of these reagents in the unique environment of living cells bears some consideration. Fluorophores with properties appropriate for a particular spectroscopic methodology must also exhibit properties favorable for use in live cells (63, 83, 102, 112, 118).

Fluorophore Considerations

For reviews of the fluorophore properties needed for live-cell studies, see Waggoner (126) and Simon & Taylor (102). Here, we summarize the key points:

BRIGHTNESS   Fluorophores should retain a high extinction coefficient and high quantum yields when conjugated to a protein to maximize intracellular detection. Unfortunately, many of the commercially available, environmentally sensitive fluorescent dyes, such as those based on naphthalene or pyrene, have fairly low extinction coefficients when compared with the environmentally insensitive xanthenes (45). Nevertheless, new classes of environmentally sensitive fluorescent dyes have been synthesized to construct solvent-sensitive fluorescent protein biosensors (44).

WAVELENGTH OF EXCITATION   Optimally, dyes for live cell investigations should absorb light at $\lambda > 500$ nm. Excitation of fluorophores at $\lambda < 500$ nm produces cellular autofluorescence (5, 8). Ultraviolet and near-ultraviolet radiation cause cellular photodamage from the byproducts of irradiation of media components (104) as well as induce fluorescence from endogenous components in the cells and from optical components of the microscope.

PHOTOSTABILITY   If a fluorescent protein biosensor is to undergo repeated excitation during a live-cell experiment, then the photostability of the fluorescent protein biosensor becomes one of the most important experimental parameters. Excitation of many dyes in the presence of oxygen may irreversibly photobleach them (102), lead to oxygen-mediated quenching (see "Fluorescence Quenching," above), or generate toxic photoproducts. To help minimize these events, free oxygen can be removed, but the photophysical and physiological effects of such perturbations must also be assessed. Clearly, new approaches are necessary to engineer bright, photostable, and nonphototoxic fluorophores. In addition, new approaches to excitation, such as two-photon excitation, show great promise (25).

SPECIFICITY OF FLUORESCENCE CHANGE   The specificity of a biosensor's spectroscopic change must be well characterized before in vivo data can be interpreted. Concurrent environmental changes may cause spectroscopic changes in the fluorophore (see "Solvent Sensitivity," above). In addition, interactions of the dye with aromatic amino acids present in the cell, other dye molecules, or molecular oxygen can cause unexpected quenching of the fluorophore (see "Fluorescence Quenching," above). Experimental results can be misleading unless these effects are identified first with dilute solution studies.

Protein Considerations

A main consideration in the production of most fluorescent protein biosensors using traditional labeling schemes is the purification of enough protein to synthesize the reagent. Because protein purification from the experimental cells or tissue of interest can be difficult, a protein is often purified from a closely related species or a recombinant expression system.

The protein of interest is usually introduced into living cells and delivered to its proper subcellular location. It must be soluble in a physiological buffer so that it can be either microinjected or bulk loaded into cells (85). Taylor et al (113) have used immunoelectron microscopy to demonstrate molecular incorporation of microinjected fluorescein actin into the stress fibers of living cells. Other proteins, such as organellar proteins, may require attachment of an intracellular targeting signal. The use of chimeras produced between target proteins and the green fluorescent protein (21) or its technical derivative should simplify the methodology dramatically.

The complexity of engineering physiologically relevant fluorescent protein biosensors appears to be daunting at first. Nevertheless, the experience gained in refining fluorophores, genetically manipulating proteins, and performing light microscope–based fluorescence spectroscopy will help focus resources toward developing a straightforward and generally applicable methodology for fluorescent protein biosensor design and use.

FUTURE

Fluorescent analogues of proteins should have an important impact on defining the chemical and molecular dynamics responsible for cell and tissue functions. Advances are expected in four areas: (*a*) the use of molecular biological methods to fluorescently label proteins site specifically; (*b*) the development of new classes of extrinsic luminescent probes designed for wider ranges of excitation and emission spectra, fluorescence lifetimes, and two-photon excitation; (*c*) the development of methods to encapsulate fluorescent probes to minimize photobleaching; and (d) the evolution of user-friendly, yet powerful instrumentation to measure temporal-spatial dynamics in living cells and tissues.

The use of the green fluorescent protein and derivative fluorescent peptides should make the labeling of proteins with a fluorescent marker as simple as making any protein chimera (21). The potential revolutionary impact of using molecular biology to label proteins will be realized if a minimum-length peptide can be incorporated into target proteins in one or more sites. In fact, the green fluorescent protein fluorophore could be used as the probe for fluorescent protein biosensors if the peptide sequence can be incorporated into target proteins near binding and active sites. Similarly, the incorporation of fluorescent analogues of amino acids into specific sites during protein synthesis could create a new class of exciting fluorescent protein biosensors (6, 28; see also 85a, this volume).

The new labeling tools based on molecular biology will complement extrinsic dye options rather than make them obsolete. As these tools simplify labeling, we expect more investigators to prepare fluorescent analogues and fluorescent protein biosensors. However, new extrinsic dyes will be needed to span the full range of the useful spectrum (~360–1000 nm), to create luminescent probes with a wide range of lifetimes for use in measuring the anisotropy of proteins, and to optimize two-photon excitation (25).

The photostability of the luminescent probes will continue to be a major challenge. The real value of this technology is based on the ability to measure changes in cells and tissues during life functions. The present fluorescent probes are at least a factor of 10 less photostable than required for many experiments over time. Therefore, creative methods for protecting the fluorophores from destruction will be needed. Finally, the instrumentation will need to continue to evolve toward increased power and user-friendliness, but decreased cost and complexity.

Although we view fluorescent protein biosensors as some of the most potentially powerful tools for dissecting cellular interrelationships at the molecular level, they are clearly intermediates in the evolution of modern biological discovery. Lewis & Lewis (72), using transmitted light microscopy to observe some of the first cultured mammalian cells, deduced some of the intracellular relationships that we can now molecularly dissect with fluorescent protein biosensors. We are witnessing the development of completely synthetic fluorescent probes for a wide range of physiological parameters, an expansion in the number and sophistication of fluorescent protein biosensors, and molecular techniques to prepare fluorescent analogues of proteins. By engineering endogenous components that constitutively localize and function as reporters of their own activities, we will move beyond the single cell and be able to measure and manipulate molecular dynamics in living tissues and whole organisms.

ACKNOWLEDGMENTS

This work was supported by National Institutes of Health Grants AR32461 (DLT) and AI34929 (KMH), National Science Foundation Science and Technology Center Grant MCB-8920118, Grant 2044BR1 from the Council for Tobacco Research—USA, Inc., and the Pittsburgh Cancer Institute. This is publication 8920-NP of the Division of Virology, Department of Neuropharmacology, Scripps Clinic and Research Foundation.

Literature Cited

1. Adams SR, Bacskai BJ, Taylor SS, Tsien RY. 1993. Optical probes for cyclic AMP. See Ref. 82a, p. 133
2. Adams SR, Harootunian AT, Buechler YJ, Taylor SS, Tsien RY. 1991. Fluorescence ratio imaging of cyclic AMP in single cells. *Nature* 349:694
3. Ando T, Miyata H. 1983. Pyruvate as a fluorescence quencher: a new spectroscopic assay for pyruvate reactions. *Anal. Biochem.* 129:170
4. Anel A, Richieri GV, Kleinfeld AM. 1993. Membrane partition of fatty acids and inhibition of T cell function. *Biochemistry* 32:530
5. Aubin JE. 1979. Autofluorescence of viable cultured mammalian cells. *J. Histochem. Cytochem.* 27:36
6. Bain JD, Switzer C, Chamberlin AR, Benner SA. 1992. Ribosome-mediated incorporation of a non-standard amino acid into a peptide through expansion of the genetic code. *Nature* 356:537
7. Benson DM, Knopp JA, Longmuir IS. 1980. Intracellular oxygen measurements of mouse liver cells using quantitative fluorescence video microscopy. *Biochim. Biophys. Acta* 591:187
8. Benson RC, Meyer RA, Zaruba ME,

McKhann GM. 1979. Cellular autofluorescence—is it due to flavins? *J. Histochem. Cytochem.* 27:44
9. Bentley KL, Thompson LK, Klebe RJ, Horowitz PM. 1985. Fluorescence polarization: a general method for measuring ligand binding and membrane microviscosity. *BioTechniques* 3:356
10. Betzig E, Chicester RJ, Lanni F, Taylor DL. 1993. Near-field fluorescence imaging of cytoskeletal actin. *Bio-Imaging* 1:129
11. Birks JB. 1970. *Photophysics of Aromatic Molecules*. New York: Wiley-Interscience. 704 pp.
12. Bock PE. 1992. Active-site-selective labeling of blood coagulation proteinases with fluorescence probes by the use of thioester peptide chloromethyl ketones. I. Specificity of thrombin labeling. *J. Biol. Chem.* 267:14963
13. Bock PE. 1992. Active-site-selective labeling of blood coagulation proteinases with fluorescence probes by the use of thioester peptide chloromethyl ketones. II. Properties of thrombin derivatives as reporters of prothrombin fragment 2 binding and specificity of the labeling approach for other proteinases. *J. Biol. Chem.* 267:14974
14. Bright GR, Fisher GW, Rogowska J,

Taylor DL. 1989. Fluorescence ratio imaging microscopy. *Methods Cell Biol.* 30:157

15. Brinkley M. 1992. A brief survey of methods for preparing protein conjugates with dyes, haptens, and cross-linking reagents. *Bioconjug. Chem.* 3:2

16. Brune M, Hunter JL, Corrie JET, Webb MR. 1994. The direct, real-time measurement of rapid inorganic phosphate release using a novel fluorescent probe and its application to actomyosin subfragment 1 ATPase. *Biochemistry* 33:8262

17. Burghardt TP, Ajtai K. 1991. Fluorescence polarization from oriented systems. See Ref. 66a, p. 307

18. Campbell AK, Sala-Newby G. 1993. Bioluminescent and chemiluminescent indicators for molecular signalling and function in living cells. See Ref. 82a, p. 58

19. Carraway KL III, Cerione RA. 1993. Fluorescent-labeled growth factor molecules serve as probes for receptor binding and endocytosis. *Biochemistry* 32:12039

20. Chadwick CS, Johnson P. 1961. Depolarisation of the fluorescence of proteins labelled with various fluorescent probes. *Biochim. Biophys. Acta* 53:482

21. Chalfie M, Tu Y, Euskirchen G, Ward WW, Prasher DC. 1994. Green fluorescent protein as a marker for gene expression. *Science* 263:802

22. Cooper JA, Walker SB, Pollard TD. 1983. Pyrene actin: documentation of the validity of a sensitive assay for actin polymerization. *J. Mus. Res. Cell Motil.* 4:253

23. Creighton TE. 1993. *Proteins: Structures and Molecular Properties*. New York: Freeman. 507 pp. 2nd ed.

24. Dandliker WB, Portmann AJ. 1971. Fluorescent protein conjugates. In *Excited States of Proteins and Nucleic Acids*, ed. RF Steiner, I Weinryb, p. 199. New York: Plenum

25. Denk W, Strickler JH, Webb WW. 1990. Two-photon laser scanning fluorescence microscopy. *Science* 248:73

26. Detmers P, Weber A, Elzinga M, Stephens RE. 1981. 7-Chloro-4-nitrobenzeno-1,3-diazole actin as a probe for actin polymerization. *J. Biol. Chem.* 256:99

27. Dunn KW, Mayor S, Myers JN, Maxfield FR. 1994. Applications of ratio fluorescence microscopy in the study of cell physiology. *FASEB J.* 8:573

28. Ellman J, Mendel D, Anthony-Cahill S, Noren CJ, Schultz PG. 1991. Biosynthetic method for introducing unnatural amino acids site-specifically into proteins. *Methods Enzymol.* 202:301

29. Farkas DL, Baxter G, DeBiasio RL, Gough A, Nederlof MA, et al. 1993. Multimode light microscopy and the dynamics of molecules, cells, and tissues. *Annu. Rev. Physiol.* 55:785

30. Förster TH. 1967. Mechanisms of energy transfer. In *Comprehensive Biochemistry*, ed. M Florkin, EH Statz, 22:61. New York: Elsevier

31. Frank S, Lauterbur PC. 1993. Voltage-sensitive magnetic gels as magnetic resonance monitoring agents. *Nature* 363:334

32. Fushimi K, Verkman AS. 1991. Low viscosity in the aqueous domain of cell cytoplasm measured by picosecond polarization microfluorimetry. *J. Cell Biol.* 112:719

33. Gabor G. 1968. Radiationless energy transfer through a polypeptide chain. *Biopolymers* 6:809

34. Gerstein M, Lesk AM, Chothia C. 1994. Structural mechanisms for domain movements in proteins. *Biochemistry* 33:6739

35. Gillies RJ. 1992. Nuclear magnetic resonance and its applications to physiological problems. *Annu. Rev. Physiol.* 54:733

36. Giuliano KA, Kolega J, DeBiasio R, Taylor DL. 1992. Myosin II phosphorylation and the dynamics of stress fibers in serum-deprived and stimulated fibroblasts. *Mol. Biol. Cell* 3:1037

37. Giuliano KA, Nederlof MA, DeBiasio R, Lanni F, Waggoner AS, Taylor DL. 1990. Multi-mode light microscopy. In *Optical Microscopy for Biology*, ed. B Herman, K Jacobson, p. 543. New York: Wiley-Liss

38. Giuliano KA, Taylor DL. 1994. Fluorescent actin analogs with a high affinity for profilin in vitro exhibit an enhanced gradient of assembly in living cells. *J. Cell Biol.* 124:971

39. Gorbsky GJ, Sammak PJ, Borisy GG. 1988. Microtubule dynamics and chromosome motion visualized in living anaphase cells. *J. Cell Biol.* 106:1185

40. Gough AH, Taylor DL. 1993. Fluorescence anisotropy imaging microscopy maps calmodulin binding during cellular contraction and locomotion. *J. Cell Biol.* 121:1095

41. Graceffa P, Lehrer SS. 1980. The ex-

imer fluorescence of pyrene-labeled tropomyosin. A probe of conformational dynamics. *J. Biol. Chem.* 255: 11296

42. Hahn K, DeBiasio R, Taylor DL. 1992. Patterns of elevated free calcium and calmodulin activation in living cells. *Nature* 359:736

43. Hahn K, Kolega J, Montibeller J, DeBiasio R, Post P, et al. 1993. Fluorescent analogues: optical biosensors of the chemical and molecular dynamics of macromolecules in living cells. See Ref. 82a, p. 349

44. Hahn KM, Waggoner AS, Taylor DL. 1990. A calcium-sensitive fluorescent analog of calmodulin based on a novel calmodulin-binding fluorophore. *J. Biol. Chem.* 265:20335

45. Haugland RP, ed. 1992. *Handbook of Fluorescent Probes and Research Chemicals.* Eugene, OR: Molecular Probes. 421 pp. 5th ed.

46. Haugland RP. 1992. Enzyme substrates. See Ref. 45, pp. 81–88

47. Heithier H, Ward LD, Cantrill RC, Klein HW, Im MJ, et al. 1988. Fluorescent glucagon derivatives. I. Synthesis and characterization of fluorescent glucagon derivatives. *Biochim. Biophys. Acta* 971:298

48. Herman B. 1989. Resonance energy transfer microscopy. *Methods Cell Biol.* 30:219

49. Herman BA, Fernandez SM. 1982. Dynamics and topographical distribution of surface glycoproteins during myoblast fusion: a resonance energy transfer study. *Biochemistry* 21:3275

50. Herskovits TT, Laskowski M Jr. 1962. Location of chromophoric residues in proteins by solvent perturbation. I. Tyrosyls in serum albumins. *J. Biol. Chem.* 237:2481

51. Huang KH, Fairclough RH, Cantor CR. 1975. Singlet energy transfer studies of the arrangement of proteins in the 30S *Escherichia coli* ribosome. *J. Mol. Biol.* 97:443

52. Hurley JH, Dean AM, Thorsness PE, Koshland DEJ, Stroud RM. 1990. Regulation of isocitrate dehydrogenase by phosphorylation involves no long-range conformational change in the free enzyme. *J. Biol. Chem.* 265: 3599

53. Jackson AE, Puett D. 1984. Specific acylation of calmodulin. Synthesis and adduct formation with a fluorenyl-based spin label. *J. Biol. Chem.* 259:14985

54. Jacobs RE, Fraser SE. 1994. Magnetic resonance microscopy of em-

bryonic cell lineages and movements. *Science* 263:681

55. Jovin TM, Arndt-Jovin DJ. 1989. FRET microscopy: digital imaging of fluorescence resonance energy transfer. Application in cell biology. In *Cell Structure and Function by Microspectrofluorometry,* ed. E Kohen, JG Hirschberg, 30:99. San Diego: Academic

56. Kabsch W, Vandekerckhove J. 1992. Structure and function of actin. *Annu. Rev. Biophys. Biomol. Struct.* 21:49

57. Kao HP, Abney JR, Verkman AS. 1993. Determinants of the translational mobility of a small solute in cell cytoplasm. *J. Cell Biol.* 120:175

58. Knopp JA, Longmuir IS. 1972. Intracellular measurement of oxygen by quenching of fluorescence of pyrenebutyric acid. *Biochim. Biophys. Acta* 279:393

59. Kolega J, Taylor DL. 1993. Gradients in the concentration and assembly of myosin II in living fibroblasts during locomotion and fiber transport. *Mol. Biol. Cell* 4:819

60. Konev SV. 1967. *Fluorescence and Phosphorescence of Proteins and Nucleic Acids.* New York: Plenum. 204 pp.

61. Kornberg A. 1990. Why purify enzymes? *Methods Enzymol.* 182:1

62. Kouyama T, Mihashi K. 1981. Fluorimetry study of N-(1-pyrenyl)iodoacetamide-labelled F-actin. Local structural change of actin protomer both on polymerization and on binding of heavy meromyosin. *Eur. J. Biochem.* 114:33

63. Kreis TE, Birchmeier W. 1982. Microinjections of fluorescently labeled proteins into living cells with emphasis on cytoskeletal proteins. *Int. Rev. Cytol.* 75:209

64. Kreis TE, Geiger B, Schlessinger J. 1982. Mobility of microinjected rhodamine actin within living chicken gizzard cells determined by fluorescence photobleaching recovery. *Cell* 29:835

65. Lakowicz JR. 1983. Fluorescence polarization. See Ref. 66, p. 111

66. Lakowicz JR, ed. 1983. *Principles of Fluorescence Spectroscopy.* New York: Plenum

66a. Lakowicz JR, ed. 1991. *Topics in Fluorescence Spectroscopy,* Vol. 2. *Principles.* New York: Plenum

67. Lakowicz JR, Gryczynski I. 1991. Frequency-domain fluorescence spectroscopy. In *Topics in Fluorescence*

Spectroscopy, Vol. 1. *Techniques*, ed. JR Lakowicz, p. 293. New York: Plenum

68. Lakowicz JR, Szmacinski H, Nowaczyk K, Berndt KW, Johnson M. 1992. Fluorescence lifetime imaging. *Anal. Biochem.* 202:316

69. Lakowicz JR, Szmacinski H, Nowaczyk K, Johnson ML. 1992. Fluorescence lifetime imaging of free and protein-bound NADH. *Proc. Natl. Acad. Sci. USA* 89:1271

70. Latt SA, Cheung HT, Blout ER. 1965. Energy transfer. A system with relatively fixed donor-acceptor separation. *J. Am. Chem. Soc.* 87:995

71. Lehrer SS. 1967. The selective quenching of tryptophan fluorescence in proteins by iodide ion: lysozyme in the presence and absence of substrate. *Biochem. Biophys. Res. Commun.* 29:767

72. Lewis WH, Lewis MR. 1924. Behavior of cells in tissue cultures. In *General Cytology. A Textbook of Cellular Structure and Function for Students of Biology and Medicine*, ed. EV Cowdry, p. 383. Chicago: Univ. Chicago Press

73. Lippert VE. 1957. Spektroskopische Bestimmung des Dipolmomentes aromatischer Verbingungen im ersten angeregten Singulettzustand. *Z. Elektrochem.* 61:962

74. Luby-Phelps K, Castle PE, Taylor DL, Lanni F. 1987. Hindered diffusion of inert tracer particles in the cytoplasm of mouse 3T3 cells. *Proc. Natl. Acad. Sci. USA* 84:4910

75. Luby-Phelps K, Lanni F, Taylor DL. 1985. Behavior of a fluorescent analogue of calmodulin in living 3T3 cells. *J. Cell Biol.* 101:1245

76. Luby-Phelps K, Lanni F, Taylor DL. 1988. The submicroscopic properties of cytoplasm as a determinant of cellular function. *Annu. Rev. Biophys. Biophys. Chem.* 17:369

77. Ludescher RD, Liu Z. 1993. Characterization of skeletal muscle actin labeled with the triplet probe erythrosin-5-iodoacetamide. *Photochem. Photobiol.* 58:858

78. Lundblad RL. 1991. *Chemical Reagents for Protein Modification.* Boca Raton, FL: CRC. 345 pp. 2nd ed.

79. Malencik DA, Anderson SR, Bohnert JL, Shalitin Y. 1982. Functional interactions between smooth muscle myosin light chain kinase and calmodulin. *Biochemistry* 21:4031

80. Malencik DA, Anderson SR, Shalitin

Y, Schimerlik MI. 1981. Rapid kinetic studies on calcium interactions with native and fluorescently labeled calmodulin. *Biochem. Biophys. Res. Commun.* 101:390

81. Malm B. 1984. Chemical modification of Cys374 of actin interferes with the formation of the profilactin complex. *FEBS Lett.* 173:399

82. Marsh DJ, Lowey S. 1980. Fluorescence energy transfer in myosin subfragment-1. *Biochemistry* 19:774

82a. Mason WT, ed. 1993. *Fluorescent and Luminescent Probes for Biological Activity.* San Diego: Academic

83. Maxfield FR. 1989. Fluorescent analogs of peptides and hormones. *Methods Cell Biol.* 29:13

84. McKenna NM, Wang Y, Konkel ME. 1989. Formation and movement of myosin-containing structures in living fibroblasts. *J. Cell Biol.* 109:1163

85. McNeil PL. 1989. Incorporation of macromolecules into living cells. *Methods Cell Biol.* 29:153

85a. Mendel D, Cornish VW, Schultz PG. 1995. Site-directed mutagenesis with an expanded genetic code. *Annu. Rev. Biophys. Biomol. Struct.* 24:435–62

86. Mills JS, Walsh MP, Nemcek K, Johnson JD. 1988. Biologically active fluorescent derivatives of spinach calmodulin that report calmodulin target protein binding. *Biochemistry* 27:991

87. Mittal B, Sanger JM, Sanger JW. 1987. Binding and distribution of fluorescently labeled filamin in permeabilized and living cells. *Cell Motil. Cytoskelet.* 8:345

88. Mittal B, Sanger JM, Sanger JW. 1989. Visualization of intermediate filaments in living cells using fluorescently labeled desmin. *Cell Motil. Cytoskelet.* 12:127

89. Pagliaro L, Kerr K, Taylor DL. 1989. Enolase exists in the fluid phase of cytoplasm in 3T3 cells. *J. Cell Sci.* 94:333

90. Pagliaro L, Taylor DL. 1988. Aldolase exists in both the fluid and solid phases of cytoplasm. *J. Cell Biol.* 107:981

91. Post PL, Trybus KM, Taylor DL. 1994. A genetically engineered, protein-based optical biosensor of myosin II regulatory light chain phosphorylation. *J. Biol. Chem.* 269:12880

92. Prendergast FG, Meyer M, Carlson GL, Iida S, Potter JD. 1983. Synthesis, spectral properties, and use of

6-acryloyl-2-dimethylaminonaphtha-lene (acrylodan). *J. Biol. Chem.* 248: 7541

93. Radda GK. 1975. Fluorescent probes in membrane studies. *Methods Membr. Biol.* 4:97

94. Richieri GV, Ogata RT, Kleinfeld AM. 1992. A fluorescently labeled intestinal fatty acid binding protein. Interactions with fatty acids and its use in monitoring free fatty acids. *J. Biol. Chem.* 267:23495

95. Rose K. 1994. Facile synthesis of homogeneous artificial proteins. *J. Am. Chem. Soc.* 116:30

96. Rose K, Vilaseca LA, Werlen R, Meunier A, Fisch I, et al. 1991. Preparation of well-defined protein conjugates using enzyme-assisted reverse proteolysis. *Bioconjug. Chem.* 2:154

97. Rosser BG, Powers SP, Gores GJ. 1993. Calpain activity increases in hepatocytes following addition of ATP. Demonstration by a novel fluorescent approach. *J. Biol. Chem.* 268: 23593

98. Sala-Newby G, Campbell AK. 1992. Engineering firefly luciferase as an indicator of cyclic AMP–dependent protein kinase in living cells. *FEBS Lett.* 307:241

99. Salmon ED, Wadsworth P. 1986. Fluorescence studies of tubulin and microtubule dynamics in living cells. See Ref. 116, p. 377

100. Sammak PJ, Adams SR, Harootunian AT, Schliwa M, Tsien RY. 1992. Intracellular cyclic AMP, not calcium, determines the direction of vesicle movement in melanophores: direct measurement by fluorescence ratio imaging. *J. Cell Biol.* 117:57

101. Sawin KE, Theriot JA, Mitchison TJ. 1993. Photoactivation of fluorescence as a probe for cytoskeletal dynamics in mitosis and cell motility. See Ref. 82a, p. 405

102. Simon JR, Taylor DL. 1986. Preparation of a fluorescent analog: acetamidofluoresceinyl-labeled *Dictyostelium discoideum* α-actinin. *Methods Enzymol.* 134:487

103. Steiner RF. 1991. Fluorescence anisotropy: theory and applications. See Ref. 66a, p. 1

104. Stoien JD, Wang RJ. 1974. Effect of near-ultraviolet and visible light on mammalian cells in culture. II. Formation of toxic photoproducts in tissue culture medium by blacklight. *Proc. Natl. Acad. Sci. USA* 71:3961

105. Stone TJ, Buchman T, Nordio PL,

McConnell HM. 1965. Spin-labeled biomolecules. *Proc. Natl. Acad. Sci. USA* 54:1010

106. Stryer L. 1965. The interaction of a naphthalene dye with apomyoglobin and apohemoglobin. A fluorescent probe of non-polar binding sites. *J. Mol. Biol.* 13:482

107. Stryer L. 1968. Fluorescence spectroscopy of proteins. *Science* 162:526

108. Stryer L. 1978. Fluorescence energy transfer as a spectroscopic ruler. *Annu. Rev. Biochem.* 47:819

109. Stryer L, Haugland RP. 1967. Energy transfer: a spectroscopic ruler. *Proc. Natl. Acad. Sci. USA* 58:719

110. Takashi R. 1988. A novel actin label: a fluorescent probe at glutamine-41 and its consequences. *Biochemistry* 27:938

111. Tansey MG, Luby-Phelps K, Kamm KE, Stull JT. 1994. Ca^{2+}-dependent phosphorylation of myosin light chain kinase decreases the Ca^{2+} sensitivity of light chain phosphorylation within smooth muscle cells. *J. Biol. Chem.* 269:9912

112. Taylor DL, Amato PA, Luby-Phelps K, McNeil P. 1984. Fluorescent analog cytochemistry. *Trends Biochem. Sci.* 9:88

113. Taylor DL, Amato PA, McNeil PL, Luby-Phelps K, Tanasugarn L. 1986. Spatial and temporal dynamics of specific molecules and ions in living cells. See Ref. 116, p. 347

114. Taylor DL, Nederlof MA, Lanni F, Waggoner AS. 1992. The new vision of light microscopy. *Am. Sci.* 80:322

115. Taylor DL, Reidler J, Spudich JA, Stryer L. 1981. Detection of actin assembly by fluorescence energy transfer. *J. Cell Biol.* 89:362

116. Taylor DL, Waggoner AS, Murphy RF, Lanni F, Birge RR, eds. 1986. *Applications of Fluorescence in the Biomedical Sciences.* New York: Liss

117. Taylor DL, Wang Y-L. 1978. Molecular cytochemistry: incorporation of fluorescently labeled actin into cells. *Proc. Natl. Acad. Sci. USA* 75: 857

118. Taylor DL, Wang Y-L. 1980. Fluorescently labelled molecules as probes of the structure and function of living cells. *Nature* 284:405

119. Theriot JA, Rosenblatt J, Portnoy DA, Goldschmidt-Clermont PJ, Mitchison TJ. 1994. Involvement of profilin in the actin-based motility of L. monocytogenes in cells and in cell-free extracts. *Cell* 76:505

120. Trybus KM, Lowey S. 1984. Conformational states of smooth muscle myosin. Effects of light chain phosphorylation and ionic strength. *J. Biol. Chem.* 259:8564

121. Tsao TC. 1953. The molecular dimensions and the monomer-dimer transformation of actin. *Biochim. Biophys. Acta* 11:227

122. Uster PS, Pagano RE. 1986. Resonance energy transfer microscopy: observations of membrane-bound fluorescent probes in model membranes and in living cells. *J. Cell Biol.* 103:1221

123. van de Ven M, Gratton E. 1993. Time-resolved fluorescence lifetime imaging. In *Optical Microscopy*, ed. B Herman, JJ Lemasters, p. 373. New York: Academic

124. Vaughan WM, Weber G. 1970. Oxygen quenching of pyrenebutyric acid fluorescence in water. A dynamic probe of the microenvironment. *Biochemistry* 9:464

125. Waggoner AS. 1986. Fluorescent probes for analysis of cell structure, function, and health by flow and imaging cytometry. See Ref. 116, p. 3

126. Waggoner AS. 1990. Fluorescent probes for cytometry. In *Flow Cytometry and Sorting,* ed. MR Melamed, T Lindmo, ML Mendelsohn, p. 209. New York: Wiley-Liss. 2nd ed.

127. Wang Y-L. 1989. Fluorescent analog cytochemistry: tracing functional protein components in living cells. *Methods Cell Biol.* 29:1

128. Wang Y-L, Heiple J, Taylor DL. 1982. Fluorescent analog cytochemistry of contractile proteins. *Methods Cell Biol.* 24:1

128a. Wang Y-L, Taylor DL. 1981. Prob-
ing the dynamic equilibrium of actin polymerization by fluorescence energy transfer. *Cell* 27:429

129. Weber G. 1952. Polarization of the fluorescence of macromolecules. 2. Fluorescent conjugates of ovalbumin and bovine serum albumin. *Biochem. J.* 51:155

130. Weber G. 1953. Rotational Brownian motion and polarization of the fluorescence of solutions. *Adv. Protein Chem.* 8:415

131. Weber G. 1960. Fluorescence-polarization spectrum and electronic-energy transfer in proteins. *Biochem. J.* 75:335

132. Weber G. 1961. Excited states of proteins. In *Light and Life,* ed. WD McElroy, B Glass, p. 82. Baltimore: Johns Hopkins Univ. Press

133. Weber G. 1976. Practical applications and philosophy of optical spectroscopic probes. *Horizons Biochem.* 2:163

134. Weber G, Laurence DJR. 1954. Fluorescent indicators of adsorption in aqueous solution and on the solid phase. *Biochem. J.* 56:31P

135. Deleted in proof

136. Wu P, Brand L. 1994. Resonance energy transfer: methods and applications. *Anal. Biochem.* 218:1

137. Yao Y, Schoneich C, Squier TC. 1994. Resolution of structural changes associated with calcium activation of calmodulin using frequency domain fluorescence spectroscopy. *Biochemistry* 33:7797

138. Young RM, Arnett JK, Roess DA, Barisas BG. 1994. Quantitation of fluorescence energy transfer between cell surface proteins via fluorescence donor photobleaching kinetics. *Biophys. J.* 67:881

Annu. Rev. Biophys. Biomol. Struct. 1995. 24:435–62
Copyright © 1995 by Annual Reviews Inc. All rights reserved

SITE-DIRECTED MUTAGENESIS WITH AN EXPANDED GENETIC CODE

David Mendel

Lilly Research Laboratories, Eli Lilly and Company,
Lilly Corporate Center, Indianapolis, Indiana 46285-0540

Virginia W. Cornish and Peter G. Schultz

Department of Chemistry, University of California, Berkeley,
California 94720

KEY WORDS: unnatural amino acids, site-directed mutagenesis, in vitro suppression, protein structure-function

CONTENTS

ABSTRACT

A biosynthetic method has been developed that makes possible the site-specific incorporation of a large number of amino acids and analogues within proteins. In this approach, an amber suppressor tRNA chemically aminoacylated with the desired amino acid incorporates this amino acid site specifically into a protein in response to an amber codon introduced at the corresponding position in the protein's DNA sequence. Using this method, precise changes within a protein can be

435

made to address detailed structure-function questions. A series of fluorinated tyrosine analogues and linear, branched, and cyclic hydrophobic amino acids have been used to determine the impact of hydrogen bonding and hydrophobic packing, respectively, on protein stability. Glutamate analogues and conformationally restricted amino acids have been used to probe the mechanisms of staphylococcal nuclease and ras. In addition, this technique has been used to construct photocaged proteins and proteins containing photoaffinity labels, spin labels, and isotopic labels at specific positions in the protein sequence suitable for biophysical studies.

INTRODUCTION

Although proteins are involved in virtually every biological process, relatively little is understood about the detailed mechanisms by which these biopolymers, composed of 20 simple building blocks, carry out their remarkable functions. One important tool for probing the forces that govern protein structure and folding, biomolecular recognition, and catalysis is site-directed mutagenesis, in which a specific amino acid in a protein can be replaced with any of the other 19 common amino acids (57, 112). In contrast to small molecule synthesis where myriad changes in structure can be made, changes in protein structure are limited to the 20 natural amino acids. For example, few isostructural (e.g. Thr → Val) or isofunctional (e.g. Glu → Asp) substitutions can be made, making it difficult to dissect out the effects of a given mutation in terms of the specific steric or electronic features of a given amino acid. Ideally, the investigator would tailor replacements to address the particular structure-function question at hand. Such replacements would modify the size, acidity, nucleophilicity, or hydrogen-bonding or hydrophobic properties of an amino acid side chain or would modify the protein backbone itself. Alternatively, analogues could be introduced that have altogether new properties, beyond those specified by the genetic code. These novel molecules include spin labels, affinity labels, and redox-active or metal-chelating amino acids. The ability to substitute such unnatural amino acids into proteins would greatly expand the scope of physical organic studies on proteins.

Several methods can be used to incorporate unnatural amino acids into proteins. Solid-phase synthesis, particularly recent advances in the segment synthesis-condensation approach, has allowed for the synthesis of small proteins containing novel amino acids in milligram quantities (24, 44, 48, 76, 99). Protein semisynthesis, in which a synthetic peptide is ligated to a protein fragment to produce a full-length protein,

has also been used to incorporate unnatural amino acids into proteins
(12, 82). In addition, chemical modification has been used to introduce
a variety of unnatural side chains, including cofactors, spin labels, and
oligonucleotides, into proteins (19, 49, 50, 77, 88, 89). Alternatively,
biosynthetic methods that employ chemically modified aminoacyl-
tRNAs have been used to incorporate several biophysical probes into
proteins synthesized in vitro (11, 59). In general, these approaches are
limited by difficulties in achieving site-specific incorporation of the
amino acids, by the requirement that the amino acids be simple derivatives of the common 20 amino acids, or by problems inherent in the
synthesis of large proteins or peptide fragments. However, recent developments in the stepwise enzymatic condensation of peptides to generate modified proteins show considerable promise (45).

Recently, a biosynthetic approach was developed that allows for the
relatively facile site-specific incorporation of unnatural amino acids into
proteins (Figure 1) (3, 27, 79). This method takes advantage of the fact
that the genetic code contains three stop codons (23). Because only
one stop codon is needed for translation termination, the other two

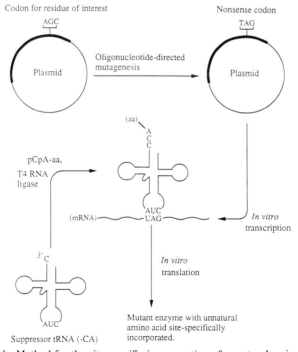

Figure 1   Method for the site-specific incorporation of unnatural amino acids.

can in principle be used to encode nonproteiogenic amino acids. A suppressor tRNA is prepared that recognizes the stop codon UAG (UAG is suppressed in vivo with relatively high efficiency) and that is chemically aminoacylated with the desired unnatural amino acid. Conventional site-directed mutagenesis (96) is used to introduce the stop codon UAG at the site of interest in the protein gene. When the acylated suppressor tRNA and the mutant gene are combined in an in vitro transcription-translation system, the unnatural amino acid is incorporated in response to the UAG codon to give a protein containing that amino acid at the specified position. Early experiments using [^{3}H]-Phe and later experiments with α-hydroxy acids demonstrated that only the desired amino acid is incorporated at the position specified by the UAG codon and that this amino acid is not incorporated at any other site in the protein (28, 79). More recent work has shown that the *Escherichia coli* protein biosynthetic machinery (the in vitro transcription-translation system) can tolerate a broad range of amino acids (27). α,α-Disubstituted amino acids, amino acids in which the side chain is a large reporter group, and even analogues in which the backbone is modified, such as lactic acid, have all been incorporated using this methodology. In vitro protein synthesis is inefficient relative to in vivo synthesis; however, this method, though labor intensive, can yield hundreds-of-microgram to single-milligram quantities of purified protein containing an unnatural amino acid. We have produced several such proteins in quantities sufficient for their characterization using circular dichroism (CD), nuclear magnetic resonance (NMR) spectrometry, and three-dimensional X-ray crystallography (28, 30, 47, 69).

METHODOLOGY

The biosynthetic site-specific incorporation of an unnatural amino acid or amino acid analogue into a protein requires generation of the requisite suppressor tRNA, a general method for acylating the tRNA with unnatural amino acids or amino acid analogues, and the demonstration that sufficient protein can be synthesized in vitro to carry out meaningful mechanistic or structural studies. The suppressor tRNA must be recognized by the protein biosynthetic machinery sufficiently well to suppress a stop codon with high efficiency and at the same time cannot be a substrate for any of the aminoacyl-tRNA synthetases present in the in vitro protein-synthesis extract. If the suppressor tRNA were recognized by any of the aminoacyl-tRNA synthetases, the tRNA could be subject to proofreading (deacylation of the noncognate amino acid) and/or aminoacylation with one of the common 20 amino acids. Such recognition would result in either low suppression efficiencies or in the incorporation of a common amino acid, as well as the desired unnatural amino acid, in response to the stop codon.

Using the above criteria, we constructed an amber suppressor tRNA derived from yeast phenylalanine-tRNA (tRNA$_{CUA}$), in which residues 34–37 in the anticodon loop were replaced by 5'-CUAA-3', for use in an E. coli in vitro protein transcription-translation system (2, 9, 10, 60, 74). Alternatively, a suppressor tRNA derived from E. coli tRNA^{Gly} (92) has been used to suppress UAG codons in short peptides in a rabbit reticulocyte translation system (3). Runoff transcription can readily generate both suppressor tRNAs in relatively large quantities (75, 80). Even though these tRNAs are produced in vitro and may not be modified biochemically (40), both incorporate unnatural amino acids efficiently and exhibit little read-through (incorporation of any amino acid other than the desired unnatural one in response to the UAG codon) at optimal Mg^{2+} concentrations.

Given the high specificity of the aminoacyl-tRNA synthetases for their cognate amino acids (35, 97), an alternative method for acylation of the tRNA had to be developed to ensure that a wide range of unnatural amino acids could be incorporated using this methodology (Figure 2). A modification of the two-step method originally developed by Hecht (42) was used in which the dinucleotide pCpA is first chemically

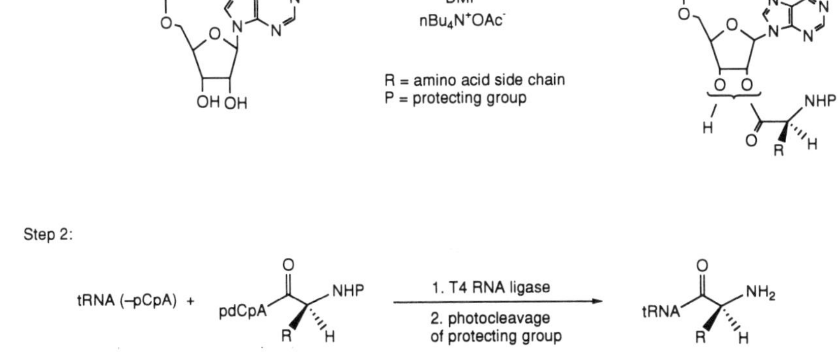

Figure 2   Strategy for the chemical aminoacylation of tRNA$^{Phe}_{CUA}$.

acylated with an Nα-protected amino acid and then enzymatically ligated to a truncated tRNA (tRNA^{-CA}) missing the terminal dinucleotide pCpA at the 3'-acceptor stem (94). We found that the cyanomethyl ester of an Nα-protected amino acid reacts selectively at the 2',3' hydroxyl functions of the ribose to give the desired monoacylated product, obviating the need to protect and deprotect the dinucleotide (Figure 2) (93). In addition, cytidine was replaced with deoxycytidine in the dinucleotide; this replacement significantly simplified the synthesis and eliminated another reactive 2'-OH group without affecting biological activity. Prior to acylation of the dinucleotide, the α-amino group of the amino acid and any reactive side chain functions are protected as their nitroveratryloxy (NVOC) carbamate, ester, or ether derivatives (1, 85). These protecting groups can be removed photochemically from the intact aminoacyl-tRNA (after ligation) in high yield under mildly acidic conditions; acid pH prevents deacylation of the aminoacyl-tRNA because aminoacyl-tRNAs hydrolyze rapidly at neutral pH (93). For light-sensitive amino acids, the biphenylisopropyloxycarbonyl (BPOC) protecting group can be used instead of the NVOC group. The BPOC group is cleaved with mild acid from the aminoacyl-pdCpA prior to ligation to tRNA^{-CA} (3, 93). This aminoacylation protocol is relatively straightforward, proceeds in high yield (both the aminoacylation and ligation reactions), and applies to amino acids with various side chains (27, 37). Nevertheless, the generation of a nonspecific aminoacyl tRNA synthetase—either a lipase, mutagenized synthetase, or a catalytic antibody—could significantly simply this step (13, 53, 54).

Mutagenesis with the chemically acylated suppressor tRNA is currently carried out in vitro because no general methodology exists for introducing large quantities of the aminoacylated suppressor tRNA into intact, dividing cells (38). An *E. coli* in vitro transcription-translation protein synthesis system is being used in our laboratory, consisting of an *E. coli* S-30 extract containing all of the proteins and RNAs required for transcription and translation, nucleotide triphosphates, phosphoenolpyruvate, pyrophosphatase, a variety of salts (Mg^{2+} and Ca^{2+} concentration can significantly affect protein yields) and cofactors, and the DNA encoding the gene of interest. Typically, the gene of interest is placed under a strong T7 or bacterial RNA polymerase promoter. The in vitro reaction can be carried out on a 5-ml scale. The requisite S-30 can be prepared fairly easily on a 2-liter scale; the suppressor tRNA, on a 30-mg scale; the aminoacyl-pdCpA, on a 0.2-mmol scale; and the plasmid, on a 12-mg scale (27). In vitro protein synthesis remains limited by the relatively small quantities of protein that can be obtained. In general, protein yields greater than 100 μg ml^{-1} have not been achieved with either plasmid DNA using an *E. coli* transcription-translation system or with mRNA using a rabbit reticulocyte translation system (27). Unfortunately, in vitro protein yields do not necessarily correlate with those obtained in vivo, and we have found no simple and general rules for ensuring high levels of protein expression in vitro.

In order for this methodology to be useful, the protein biosynthetic machinery must be capable of incorporating a wide variety of amino acids into proteins (14, 41). In fact, approximately 70 different amino acids and analogues have been tested thus far with the *E. coli* system, and a large majority (>50) of these are accepted with reasonable efficiency by that system (Figure 3) (27). The structural and electronic requirements of the rabbit reticulocyte in vitro system are less well defined than the *E. coli* protein-synthesis apparatus (just over 10 nonnative amino acids and analogues have been tested) (5), but the available data suggest rather broad similarities. Conformationally restricted amino acids (e.g. methanoproline, cyclopropylglycine, and α-methyl-L-leucine), amino acids with spin labels and photoaffinity labels as side chains, amino acids with altered pK_a values and hydrogen-bonding properties, photocaged amino acids, α-hydroxy acids, and amino acids with unusual steric properties (e.g. *t*-butylglycine) have all been incorporated into proteins (Figure 3). Suppression efficiencies can vary widely depending on the nature of the amino acid, ranging from 100% for substitution of L-norleucine for Gln28 in 434 repressor (104) to 14% for incorporation of α-methyl-L-leucine in T4 lysozyme (68). Although the suppression efficiency of a given amino acid cannot be predicted a priori, several trends emerge when the identities of the amino acids tested are correlated with their suppression efficiencies (20, 68). In general, large hydrophobic amino acids such as *p*-benzoyl-L-phenylalanine are inserted with higher efficiency than are small amino acids such as alanine and glycine, or charged amino acids such as homoglutamate or ornithine. This correlation is in agreement with reports that large, hydrophobic amino acids such as Trp and Phe bind more tightly to *E. coli* elongation factor-Tu (EF-Tu) than do other natural amino acids such as Ala, Glu, and Lys (64).

The stereochemistry of an amino acid also affects suppression efficiency. L-amino acids and some α,α-disubstituted amino acids such as α-aminoisobutyric acid (AIB) and cyclopropyl through cyclohexylglycine can be incorporated into proteins (68). Neither the *E. coli* nor the rabbit reticulocyte in vitro protein-synthesis system seems able to accommodate D-amino acids or α-methyl-D-amino acids (5, 68). These stereochemical requirements are in agreement, for the most part, with previous studies on the affinity of a variety of unnatural aminoacyl-

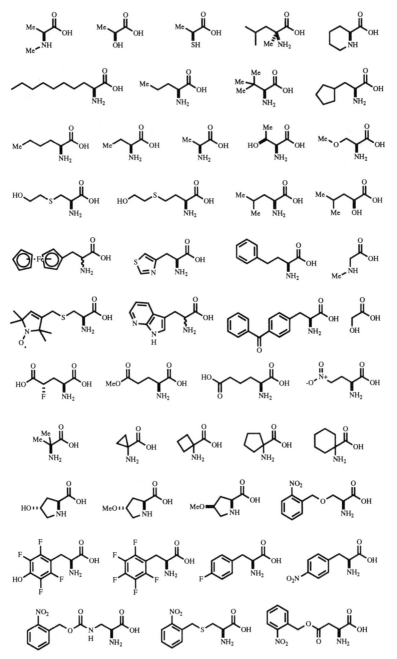

Figure 3 Examples of natural and unnatural amino acids successfully incorporated into proteins via in vitro suppression.

tRNAs for *E. coli* EF-Tu and the ribosome (14). Interestingly, previous experiments that examined the ability of an aminoacyl-tRNA or aminoacyl-CA to bind to the *E. coli* ribosomal A-site and participate in peptide elongation suggested that achiral amino acids such as AIB could not be used as substrates by the *E. coli* protein-biosynthetic machinery (91).

Both the *E. coli* and the rabbit reticulocyte protein biosynthetic machinery also incorporate α-hydroxy acids such as lactic, glycolic, and phenyllactic acid as well as mercapto acids (14, 22, 31). The resulting ester linkages, while similar in structure, are much easier to hydrolyze than amide linkages. A novel feature of mutants containing α-hydroxy acids is their clean and rapid hydrolysis under the SDS-PAGE conditions (17, 28). For example, T4 lysozyme (T4L) containing an Ala82 → Lac replacement retained wild-type enzymatic activity, and a band at the expected 18.7 kDa was observed when SDS-PAGE was carried out in a neutral pH buffer system. When the standard pH 8.8–9.0 buffer was used, a band at ~8 kDa was observed, which is consistent with hydrolysis at position 82. If any of the 20 natural amino acids had been inserted in response to the UAG signal at position 82 in this mutant, an amide linkage would have been formed that is stable to the alkaline conditions of conventional SDS-PAGE. The fact that no 18.7-kDa band was observed even when the gel was heavily overloaded reinforces the fact that heterogenous incorporation of natural amino acids does not occur.

The translational machinery accommodates various other backbone mutations. *N*-methyl-L-phenylalanine (rabbit reticulocyte), *N*-methyl-glycine (*E. coli*), and *N*-methyl-L-alanine (*E. coli*) are site-specifically incorporated into proteins, whereas *N*-ethyl-L-alanine is not (28). The *E. coli* system accepts pipecolinic acid, the six-membered version of proline, but will not incorporate the ring-contracted proline analogues aziridine-2-carboxylic acid and azetidine-2-carboxylic acid (this exclusion may stem from chemical instability rather than from discrimination by the biosynthesis machinery). However, other investigators (36; DA Tirrell & TJ Deming, personal communication) have reported the successful biosynthetic incorporation of L-azetidine-2-carboxylic acid into polypeptides. Other types of backbone replacements for α-amino acids that have been examined include β- and γ-amino acids such as β-alanine, γ-aminobutyric acid, and longer variants (D Mendel, JA Ellman & PG Schultz, unpublished results) as well as dipeptides and dipeptide mimetics (5). To date, attempts to incorporate these amino acids using either *E. coli* or rabbit reticulocyte lysate systems have proven unsuccessful.

The precise structure of an amino acid also influences its suppression efficiency dramatically. For example, even though the spin labels in Figure 10 (analogues 24 and 25, see Figure 10, below) both contain the 1-oxyl-2,2,5,5-tetramethylpyrroline N-oxide group, only analogue 24 could be incorporated in vitro (Figure 10, below) (20). In addition, suppression efficiencies may vary with the nature of the in vitro protein-synthesis system (prokaryotic vs eukaryotic). Both systems prohibit D-amino acid integration into peptide chains, and both systems readily accept α-hydroxy acids and N-methylamino acids. However, significant differences exist between the two systems for specific amino acids: L-2-amino-3,3-dimethylbutanoic acid is efficiently incorporated in the *E. coli* system but functions poorly in a rabbit reticulocyte system (5, 68). The situation is reversed for 2-amino-4-phosphonobutyric acid, a nonhydrolyzable phosphoserine analogue that is well tolerated in the rabbit reticulocyte system but that failed completely when tested with the *E. coli* extract (5; JA Ellman & PG Schultz, unpublished results). Finally, in contrast to in vivo results (9, 74), there appears to be little correlation between the codons adjacent to the UAG codon and suppression efficiencies (20). As the range of unnatural amino acids that are substituted into proteins expands, this methodology should provide additional insights into the specificity of the translational machinery and the factors governing in vitro suppression efficiency.

Future work will focus on broadening the scope of the methodology by increasing protein yields, by minimizing the effect of the amino acid identity on suppression efficiency, and by developing ways to introduce more than one unnatural amino acid into a protein at a time. Efforts to improve protein yields will require improvements in in vitro protein synthesis. Higher protein yields may be achieved using in vitro systems derived from other sources (38) or alternative approaches, such as continuous flow in vitro systems (103). Alternatively, because the *E. coli* transcription-translation system is active at 37°C for only ~1 hour, protein expression levels may be increased by using other lysates, such as lysed spheroplasts, capable of supporting protein synthesis for longer periods (61, 78).

Suppression efficiencies may be improved by (*a*) altering nucleotides in the tRNA molecule involved in tRNA recognition by the elongation factors, the ribosome, or the aminoacyl-tRNA synthetases; (*b*) utilizing suppressor tRNAs from different species; (*c*) deleting release factor-1 (*E. coli*), which competes with the suppressor tRNA for recognition of the UAG codon, from the in vitro extract (55); or (*d*) modifying the specificity of EF-Tu. The production of proteins containing several unnatural amino acids is another goal. A single unnatural amino acid can be incorporated at more than one position in a protein simply by introducing several UAG codons in the coding sequence (VW Cornish & PG Schultz, unpublished results). Preliminary efforts to insert different unnatural amino acids into the same protein have focused on using the other nonsense codons (D Mendel & PG Schultz, unpublished results), infrequently occurring codons (in the latter approach the tRNA must be engineered to eliminate recognition by the corresponding aminoacyl-tRNA synthetase) (18), or a sixty-fifth codon composed of nonstandard nucleotides (4).

Finally, in an exciting recent development in the field, the stop codon–suppression methodology has been extended to the incorporation of unnatural amino acids into intact eukaryotic cells (81). A *Xenopus laevis* oocyte was coinjected with two mutant RNA species: (*a*) mRNA that was synthesized in vitro from a mutated cDNA clone and that contained the stop codon UAG at the residue of interest and (*b*) a suppressor tRNA that had been synthetically acylated with a series of unnatural amino acids. During translation by the oocyte's protein synthetic machinery, the unnatural amino acids were specifically incorporated at position 198 in the binding site of the nicotinic acetylcholine receptor α-subunit. Subtle changes in the structures of the amino acids resulted in readily detectable changes in the function of this ligand-gated ion channel as determined by electrophysiological analysis. This work suggests that unnatural amino acid mutagenesis may be applied to many questions concerning the structural and functional aspects of ion channels, receptors, and transporters.

APPLICATIONS

This section discusses several applications of the methodology in order to illustrate its scope as well as questions that can be addressed when unnatural amino acids are incorporated into proteins. These examples include studies of protein stability, enzyme mechanism, and signal transduction; the construction of photocaged proteins; and the site-specific incorporation of biophysical probes into proteins.

Protein Stability

Site-directed mutagenesis has contributed significantly to our understanding of the factors that determine the stability of proteins. However, because few structurally and electronically conservative changes can be made using the 20 natural amino acids, it is difficult to break down the energetic effects of a given mutation in terms of the contributions from van der Waals interactions, conformational entropy, hydrogen bonds, and other forces. The use of unnatural amino acids should allow us to make more defined mutations in proteins, thereby gaining a more precise picture of the forces that govern protein stability.

An outstanding issue in the protein stability and folding literature is the role of hydrogen bonding. Although hydrogen bonds clearly play an important role in determining the secondary and tertiary structure of proteins (86, 87), the magnitude of their contribution to protein stability has been difficult to assess (46, 95). Values of hydrogen-bond stabilization determined from mutational studies, in which one member of a hydrogen-bonded pair is deleted, vary considerably depending upon the nature and local environment of the hydrogen bond (25, 32). For example, two nondisruptive hydrogen-bond deletions (Tyr78 → Phe and Ser91 → Ala) in barnase each account for 1.4–1.9 kcal mol^{-1} in protein stabilization (33). On the other hand, deletion of a hydrogen bond in the active site of barnase had no effect on protein stability (67). As pointed out above, a concern in all such mutational studies is the possibility of introducing additional destabilizing interactions by leaving unfilled hydrogen-bond donors or acceptors and/or altering local solvation and packing interactions.

In an effort to determine the degree to which side-chain hydrogen bonding stabilizes the folded state of proteins while minimizing the steric and electronic perturbations associated with deleting one member of a hydrogen-bonded pair, Tyr27 in staphylococcal nuclease was substituted with each of several isosteric, fluorinated tyrosine analogues, including 2-fluorotyrosine (analogue 1), 3-fluorotyrosine (analogue 2), and tetrafluorotyrosine (analogue 3), as well as 2,3,5,6-tetrafluorophenylalanine (analogue 4) and phenylalanine (analogue 5) (Figure 4a) (105). These mutants were designed in order to examine the effect of increasing the strength of the Tyr27-Glu10 hydrogen bond on protein stability. Denaturation studies of the corresponding mutants revealed a unique free-energy correlation between $\Delta\Delta G_{H_2O}$ ($\alpha = 0.35$) and the pK$_a$ of the Tyr27 hydroxyl group (Figure 4b). Indeed, substitution of Tyr (pK$_a \approx 10$) with tetrafluoro-L-tyrosine (pK$_a \approx 5$) increased the stability of staphylococcal nuclease (SNase) by 2.3 kcal mol^{-1}. This experiment provides strong evidence that side-chain intramolecular hydrogen bonds can preferentially stabilize the folded state of a protein relative to the unfolded state in water.

The role of backbone hydrogen bonds in determining the stability of the folded state of a protein was also examined (25). The surface amino acid Ala82 in T4L was replaced with the isostere lactic acid (Figure 4c) (28). Ala82 resides at a break between two helices where its NH group and side chain are exposed to water. The Ala82 → lactate mutaa)

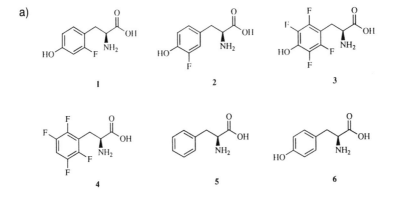

b)

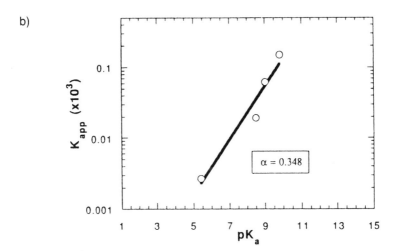

c)

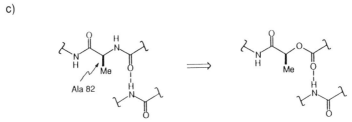

Figure 4   (*a*) Tyrosine and phenylalanine analogues incorporated at site Tyr27 in SNase. The numbered molecules in all figures are referred to as "analogue *n*" in the text. (*b*) Free energy relationship between the pK$_a$ of the site 27 side chain and the stability of SNase. (*c*) Substitution of Ala82 in T4 lysozyme (T4L) with lactic acid.

tion effectively replaces a good hydrogen-bond acceptor, the amide carbonyl group, with a considerably weaker hydrogen-bond acceptor, the ester carbonyl group (51). Because both esters and amides usually adopt the *trans* conformation (110), the 3.7°C (1.0 kcal mol^{-1}) decrease in melting temperature (stability) caused by this substitution again likely reflects the stabilization energy associated with variations in hydrogen-bond strength.

Site-directed mutagenesis studies have also contributed much to our understanding of the role the hydrophobic effect plays in protein stabilization (25, 66). However, the limited substitutions that can be made with the common amino acids quite often lead to changes in factors other than hydrophobicity. For example, in T4 lysozyme (T4L), a relatively large cavity extends beyond the side chains of Leu133 and Ala129 into the core of the enzyme (52). In an attempt to increase hydrophobic-core packing density and, as a consequence, thermal stability, proteins containing the mutations Leu133 → Phe and Ala129 → Val were constructed (52). In both cases, the mutant enzymes were less thermally stable than the wild-type enzyme because of unfavorable packing interactions that increased local strain energy. In contrast, mutagenesis with nonproteiogenic amino acids successfully extended the aliphatic side chain of Leu133 into the T4 lysozyme core without increasing strain energy, thereby affording mutants significantly more stable than wild-type (69). Specifically, when Leu133 was replaced with S,S-2-amino-4-methylhexanoic acid (analogue 7) and S-2-amino-3-cyclopentylpropanoic acid (analogue 8) (Figure 5), the mutant T4Ls melted at temperatures 1.9°C (0.6 kcal mol^{-1} more stable) and 4.3°C (1.2 kcal mol^{-1} more stable) higher, respectively, than wild-type. Interestingly, the surface areas of these two amino acids differ by only ~1 Å^2, demonstrating that burial of hydrophobic surface area was not the sole factor contrib-

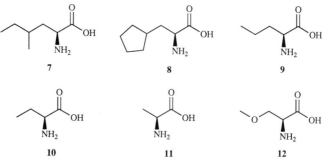

Figure 5 Structure of amino acids substituted for Leu133 in T4L.

uting to increased stability. Relative to the unfolded state, the cyclic variant loses less conformational entropy during folding than does the open chain variant, thus leading to a more stably folded protein.

A complement to experiments aimed at increasing packing density involved systematic pruning of the Leu133 side chain to determine the effect of enlarging the cavity within T4L. Substitution of S-2-aminopentanoic acid (analogue 9), S-2-aminobutyric acid (analogue 10), or alanine (analogue 11) for Leu133 (Figure 5) resulted in a nonlinear relationship between hydrophobic side-chain length and enzyme stability, in which the enzyme became increasingly unstable with removal of each methylene unit from its core (69). Semiquantitative estimates of $\Delta\Delta G$ values agreed well with the experimental values and suggest that stabilization results not only from hydrophobic effects, but also from entropic-, packing-, and cavity-energy terms.

Mutagenesis with nonproteiogenic amino acids has also been used to examine the effects of side-chain solvation on protein stability. We found that T4L containing S-2-aminopentanoic acid-133 (analogue 9) was more stable than the O-methylserine-133 (analogue 12) mutant by 1.7 kcal mol^{-1} (Figure 5) (69). This stabilization can be ascribed almost totally to the less polar nature of norvaline compared with O-methylserine because such isostructural replacements are unlikely to have significantly different packing interactions or side-chain conformational entropies. Similarly, the difference in the octanol-water partitioning ratios obtained with the N-acetyl amide derivatives of S-2-aminopentanoic acid and O-methylserine favored S-2-aminopentanoic acid in octanol by 1.8 kcal mol^{-1} and provided further evidence that octanol-water partitioning values accurately reflect solvation effects on protein stability (69).

The effect of β-branched amino acids on protein stability was examined by comparing mutant proteins containing alanine (analogue 11), L-2-aminobutanoic acid (analogue 10), L-2-aminopentanoic acid (analogue 9), valine (analogue 13), L-2-aminohexanoic acid (analogue 14), and L-2-amino-3,3-dimethylbutanoic acid (analogue 15) at two surface-exposed sites in the middle of two α-helices in T4L (Figure 6) (21). The natural β-branched amino acids valine, isoleucine, and threonine are thought to destabilize α-helices. These amino acids occur infrequently relative to amino acids such as leucine in α-helices in known protein structures, and they destabilize α-helical peptides and protein α-helices (7, 100). For example, when a series of linear and branched amino acids were incorporated into an α-helical peptide, the β-branched amino acids were destabilizing relative to the linear and γ-branched amino acids (65). Substitution of L-2-amino-3,3-dimethylbutanoic acid for L-2-aminohex-

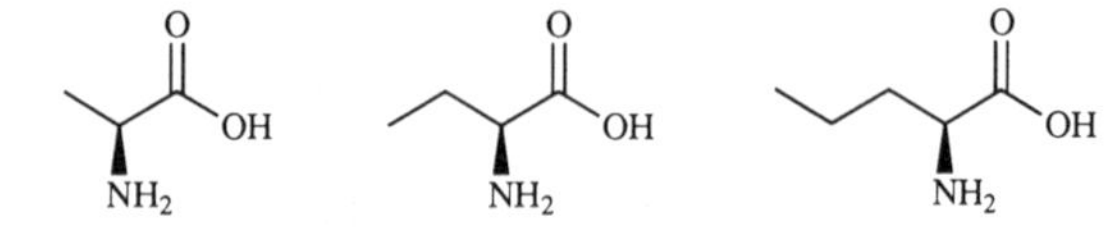

Figure 6 Examples of molecules designed to probe the effects of β-substitution on helix stability in a protein.

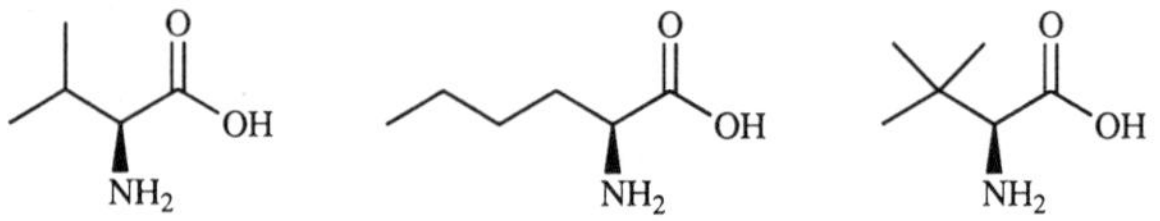

anoic acid or alanine destabilizes the peptide by 0.9 kcal mol^{-1}. The same substitution, however, either destabilizes T4L by 0.69 kcal mol^{-1} (2.5°C) at site Ser44 or stabilizes the protein by 0.27 kcal mol^{-1} (1.0°C) at site Asn68. This difference illustrates the difficulty of delineating simple rules as to which factors stabilize or destabilize proteins given the influence of context effects. In addition, the stabilities and simulated structures of the L-2-amino-3,3-dimethylbutanoic acid mutants have provided insight into the effects of β-branched side chains on α-helix stability in proteins (69). These results underscore the difficulty in interpreting mutagenesis data when more than one property of an amino acid is being altered at once. The ability to precisely alter the structure of an amino acid should allow us to better dissect the individual contributions of hydrophobicity, packing, entropy, and cavity formation on protein stability. We are currently extending these studies to hydrogen-bonding, π-π, and π-ion interactions in protein interiors.

Enzyme Mechanism

Unnatural amino acid mutagenesis also is being used to probe the catalytic mechanisms of several enzymes including staphylococcal nuclease, aspartate aminotransferase, methionine aminopeptidase, and ribonucleotide reductase. The enzyme staphylococcal nuclease (SNase) accelerates the hydrolysis of phosphodiester bonds in nucleic acids some 10^{16}-fold over the uncatalyzed rate. This enzyme has been the subject of many structural, mechanistic, and mutagenesis studies aimed at understanding how enzymes can achieve such extraordinary rate enhancements (63, 108, 109). Based on these studies, it has been suggested that general base catalysis contributes significantly to the catalytic efficiency of this enzyme. Specifically, Glu43 in SNase is thought to act as a general base to activate a water molecule for attack on the phosphodiester backbone of DNA. Glu43 is known to be important for catalysis because replacement by the natural amino acids Asp and Gln results in a significant loss in activity (43).

Surprisingly, substitution of Glu43 with either homoglutamate (analogue 18) or the nitro analogue S-4-nitro-2-aminobutyric acid (analogue 17), which is both isoelectronic and isosteric to glutamate (analogue 16) but a much poorer base, yielded mutant enzymes with kinetic constants markedly similar to those of wild-type SNase under normal assay conditions (Figure 7) (47). The catalytic efficiencies of these mutants, coupled with their pH behavior and the crystal structure of the HGlu43 mutant, suggest that Glu43 may not be acting as a base but rather may play a structural role, serving as a bidentate hydrogen-bond acceptor to fix the conformation of the neighboring loop. Independent studies by Gerlt, in which the loop adjacent to Glu43 was deleted from SNase, have led to the same conclusion (39). Homoglutamate replacements would be of interest in other proteins as well. Conventional mutagenesis on triose phosphate isomerase (TIM) revealed that the Glu165 $\rightarrow$ Asp mutation dramatically decreases the catalytic efficiency of TIM (56).

Amino Acid	Vmax (A_{260} min^{-1} μg^{-1})	K_M^{DNA} ($\mu g/mL$)	K_M^{Ca2+} (μM)
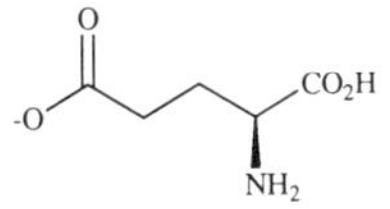 16	6.7 ± 0.7	8 ± 3	320 ± 30
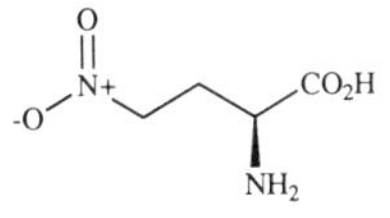 17	3.0 ± 0.5	26 ± 8	470 ± 40
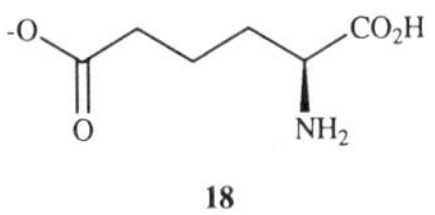 18	5.2 ± 0.2	10 ± 2	290 ± 30

Figure 7 Catalytic efficiencies of wild-type SNase and the mutant enzymes Glu43 $\rightarrow$ S-2-amino-4-nitrobutanoic acid and Glu43 $\rightarrow$ homoglutamate.

It would be of interest to ask how the Glu165 → HGlu replacement would affect the catalytic power of TIM.

As with staphylococcal nuclease, we also asked how varying the pK_a of active site residues affected T4L activity. γ-Fluoroglutamic (FGlu) acid has a pK_a about 2–3 units lower than glutamic acid. Not only did the Glu11 → FGlu T4L retain a high degree of enzyme activity, but also the pH optimum for cell wall hydrolysis was not significantly shifted (D Mendel, JA Ellman & PG Schultz, unpublished results). These results suggest that Glu11 is active in the fully deprotonated state in wild-type T4L, possibly providing electrostatic stabilization to the transition state. The glutamate esters δ-methylglutamate and δ-methyl-γ-fluoro-glutamate were also substituted for Glu11 in T4L, but both yielded inactive enzyme (D Mendel, JA Ellman & PG Schultz, unpublished results).

Signal Transduction

Unnatural amino acid mutagenesis has been used to probe the role of ras p21 in cellular signal-transduction pathways. Mammalian proteins encoded by the *ras* genes are thought to function as regulators of various signal-transduction processes involved in cell growth and differentiation (6, 8, 102). The chemical basis for signal regulation involves cycling of the protein between the inactive guanosine diphosphate (GDP)–bound state and the active guanosine triphosphate (GTP)–bound state. Point mutations that result in a decrease in the intrinsic GTPase activity of ras or of the GTPase-activating protein (GAP)–stimulated GTPase activity are associated with approximately 30% of human cancers (8, 107). In order to better understand the molecular basis by which mutations in ras lead to switch inactivation, we have substituted a series of unnatural amino acids (Figure 8) for residues in

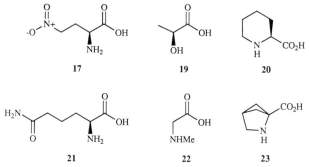

Figure 8   Structures of some unnatural amino acids used to probe the switch function of ras.

loop L4 (the switch II region), loop L2 (the switch I region), and loop L1 (the phosphate-binding loop) (15–17).

Mutations at Gln61 commonly lead to impaired intrinsic GTPase activity. This residue lies in loop L4 of ras, a region that undergoes conformational change upon GTP-GDP exchange. Biochemical studies and the elucidation of the three-dimensional X-ray crystal structures of the GTP-, Gpp(CH_2)p-, and Gpp(NH)p-bound forms of ras have led to the proposal that Gln61 is critical for γ-phosphate binding and catalysis (58, 73, 83, 90). Specifically, it has been proposed that the γ-carboxamide of Gln61 either polarizes water molecule 175 for attack on the γ-phosphate or stabilizes the incipient pentacoordinate transition state. To test these mechanistic hypotheses, we replaced Gln61 with the isoelectronic, isosteric nitro analogue (analogue 17) and with homoglutamine (analogue 21) (Figure 8) (17). Whereas 17 natural mutants at position 61 have reduced GTPase activity and are not activated by GAP, both Glu $\rightarrow$ analogue 17 and Glu $\rightarrow$ analogue 21 mutants had GTPase activity similar to that of the wild-type protein and were activated by GAP. The fact that these mutants retained activity suggests that residue 61 plays some other role in catalysis, perhaps serving to distort the bound GTP toward the transition-state geometry.

Mutations at Gly12 of ras also result in impaired intrinsic GTPase activity and are commonly associated with oncogenic activation (8, 101). Gly12 occurs in a highly conserved type II β-turn, a phosphate-binding loop found in many nucleotide-binding proteins (34, 111). Mutation of Gly12 to any common amino acid other than proline results in diminished GTPase activity (101). To more fully understand the role of Gly12 in switch function, several residues with backbone modifications were inserted at this site, including lactic acid (Lac) (analogue 19), pipecolic acid (Pip) (analogue 20), and N-methylglycine (MeGly) (analogue 22) (Figure 8) (17). The pipecolic acid mutant, which was expected to have a much more negative ϕ value than Gly12, retained GTPase activity similar to that of wild-type ras. The N-methylglycine mutant also had wild-type GTPase activity (Nα methyl substitution also decreases ϕ values). Whereas the Ala12 mutant had reduced GTPase activity, the isosteric lactic acid mutant, in which the backbone amide linkage is replaced by an ester linkage, had normal GTPase activity. The fact that only mutants that can adopt unusual backbone conformations are active suggests that a specific conformation of the loop L1 backbone may be required to avoid unfavorable side-chain interactions in the transition state for GTP hydrolysis. However, even though the Pro12, Pip12, Lac12, and MeGly12 mutants had intrinsic GTPase activity similar to that of wild-type ras, they were not activated by GAP.

Moreover, the Gly13 → Thr, Gly13 → *allo* Thr, and Gly13 → Ser mutants, which have intrinsic GTPase activity two to three times that of wild-type ras (attributable to the β-hydroxyl group), were not activated by GAP and were not transforming in a germinal vesicle breakdown assay with *X. laevis* oocytes. One interpretation of these results is that loop L1 can adopt two or more conformations in solution and that its positioning by one or more effector proteins modulates GTPase activity and oncogenic activation. The unusual backbone structures of the Gly12 and Gly13 mutants may prevent switch function.

The role of Pro34 in loop L2 function was also probed by substituting amino acids containing novel backbone structures for Pro34. The most significant difference between the GTP- and GDP-bound forms of ras is in the region encompassing residues 32–40 (58, 73, 84, 90). It has been proposed that Pro34, which is conserved in ras and is close to the active site, may play a role in controlling the conformation of loop L2, perhaps via a *cis-trans* isomerization of the Pro34 amide bond (84). To examine the structural and mechanistic role of this residue more precisely, Pro34 was replaced with 2,4-methanoproline (analogue 23) (Figure 8), which is strongly biased toward the *trans* configuration by virtue of the Cα substitution (15). The fact that this mutant has wild-type intrinsic and GAP-activated GTPase activity strongly suggests that a *cis-trans* isomerization of Pro34 does not play a key role in signal transduction. Similar substitutions may be useful in probing the role of backbone isomerization in protein-folding pathways.

Novel Functional Substitutions

Unnatural amino acid mutagenesis also allows the substitution of amino acids possessing novel spectroscopic properties including fluorescent, photoactivatable, or EPR- or NMR-active amino acid replacements.

PHOTOACTIVE RESIDUES   Photoactivatable, or caged molecules, possess inactivating protecting groups that can be rapidly removed (<1 ms) to generate the active form of an agonist, substrate, or inhibitor. Caged molecules provide a noninvasive method for controlling a variety of biochemical and cellular processes, including intracellular second-messenger concentrations (85, 98). In the past, such studies have usually used low-molecular-weight caged compounds. Unnatural amino acid mutagenesis simplifies the construction of caged macromolecules bearing one or more blocked side-chain groups (71). For example, active-site residue Asp20, which is essential for catalytic activity in T4 lysozyme, when masked as the β-nitrobenzyl ester (NBAsp) in T4L yielded an enzyme that could be photoactivated. Although the nitrobenzyl ester was incorporated with much better efficiency than native aspartic acid, enzymes containing the ester were completely inactive. Photolysis at 350 nm rapidly converted the ester to its parent acid, resulting in full enzymatic activity. In a second example, a serine residue thought to be involved in the self-splicing reaction of the protein vent DNA polymerase was replaced by *O*-nitrobenzylserine (Figure 9) (18a). The resulting caged polymerase did not undergo the self-splicing reaction, allowing the full-length protein to be isolated. Photolysis of the unspliced protein resulted in loss of the nitrobenzyl protecting group and subsequent protein splicing. This result demonstrates unequivocally

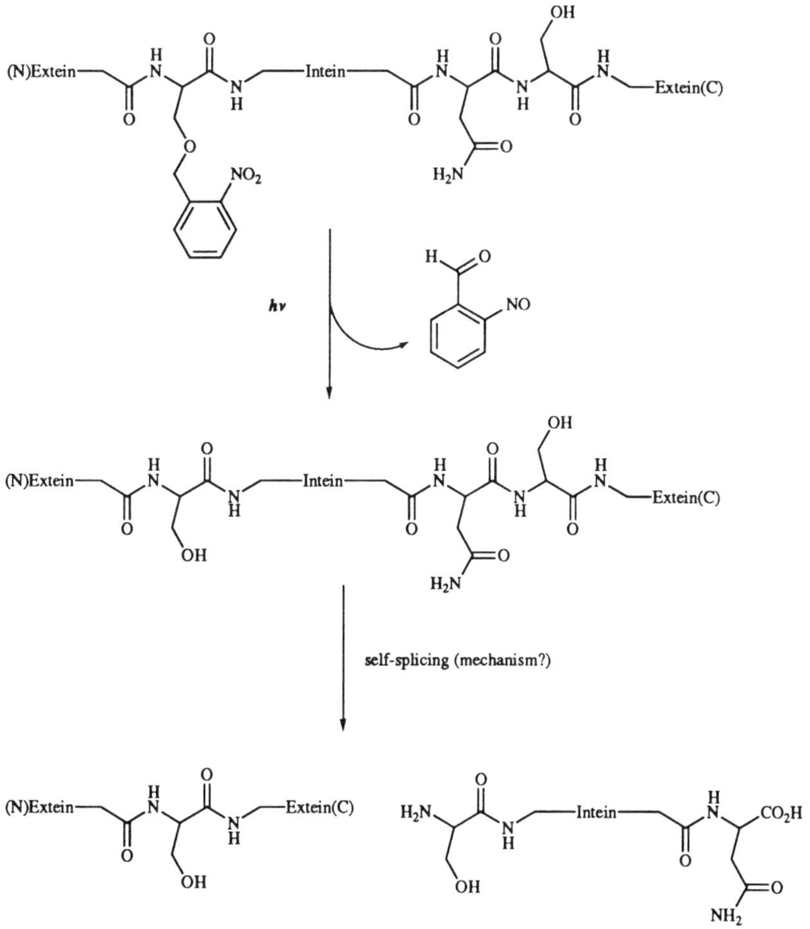

Figure 9   Photactivated self-splicing of vent polymerase using a caged serine analogue.

that protein splicing occurs at the posttranslational level. The ability to construct caged proteins of this sort should make possible a broad range of time-resolved experiments relevant to catalytic mechanism, biomolecular recognition, and protein folding.

Beyond simply masking native side chains, photoactivatable side chains can be used to cross-link proteins with unknown target molecules. Thus far, amino acids that form nitrene, carbene, and ketyl radical active species have been successfully incorporated into p21ras and T4L at specific positions (20; JA Ellman, DR Benson & PG Schultz, unpublished results). Photoaffinity probes can in principle be used to identify key components involved in complex biochemical processes, e.g. signal transduction or gene activation.

REPORTER GROUPS   Biophysical probes have been incorporated into proteins using unnatural amino acid mutagenesis. For example, spin labels and fluorescent amino acids have been site-specifically incorporated into T4L (Figure 10) (20). Taking advantage of recent loop-gap resonator technology, we (20) measured the ESR spectrum of approximately 10 μl of a 1 μM solution of purified T4L containing a spin-labeled amino acid (analogue 24) at position 44. Linewidth analysis of the ESR spectrum revealed that the label was immobilized, consistent with it being protein-bound. Replacement of one of the tryptophans in T4L by 7-azatryptophan (analogue 26) resulted in a red shift in T4L's fluorescent emission maxima. The red shift, however, was not as large as seen in model systems in which water was the solvent, not a protein.

Unnatural amino acid mutagenesis has been employed to site-specifically insert isotopically enriched amino acids into proteins for NMR

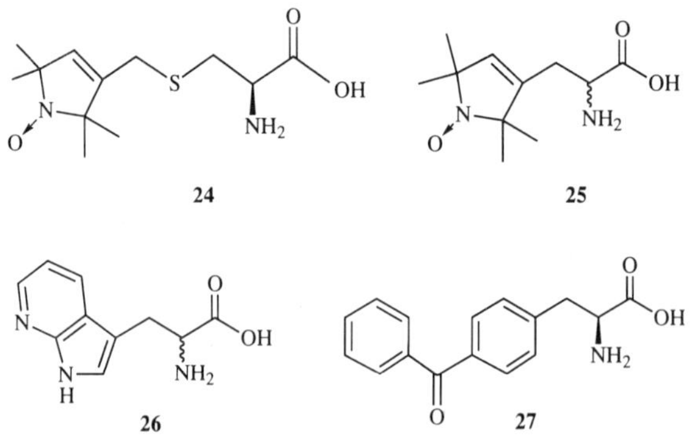

Figure 10   Structure of some biophysical probes tested for incorporation in T4L.

a)

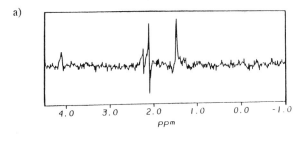

b)

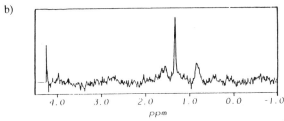

Figure 11 (*a*) ^{13}C-filtered ^{1}H NMR spectrum of the T4L mutant Ala82 → [^{13}C]Ala. (*b*)
^{13}C-filtered ^{1}H NMR spectrum of the denatured form of the same T4L mutant.

studies. A sufficient quantity of purified T4L specifically labeled at site
Ala82 with [^{13}C]Ala was produced to observe the proton resonances
of the selectively labeled protein, in both the native and denatured
states, using ^{13}C-filtered NMR (Figure 11) (30). The ability to site-specifically incorporate probes capable of detecting local structure and
dynamics into proteins should allow for more precise studies of protein
folding and stability; conformational changes in proteins; and the interaction of proteins with other proteins, small molecules, and membranes. For example, it should be possible to carry out spectroscopy on
both the folded and unfolded states of proteins, compare denaturation
curves for various regions of a protein, or probe local structural changes
that occur during protein translocation.

CONCLUSION

The ability to incorporate unnatural amino acids into proteins site-specifically makes it possible to carry out detailed physical organic studies
on this important class of molecules. Mutations can be made to probe
the precise nature of an individual amino acid's contribution to protein
structure or function, often without dramatic losses in activity. This
methodology should provide new insights into and perhaps challenge

assumptions about the nature of protein structure and function. In addition, it may be possible to generate mutant proteins with novel functions. What remains is to increase the protein quantities obtainable and to find ways to bypass the specificity of the protein-biosynthetic machinery so that more diverse amino acid structures can be incorporated to add to the power of this approach.

ACKNOWLEDGMENTS

We are grateful for financial support for this work from the National Institutes of Health (Grant No. R01 GM49220) and the Director, Office of Energy Research, Division of Material Sciences and Division of Energy Biosciences, Office of General Life Sciences, Structural Biology Division, of the US Department of Energy under Contract No. DE-AC03-76SF00098. VWC thanks the National Science Foundation for a predoctoral fellowship.

Any *Annual Review* chapter, as well as any article cited in an *Annual Review* chapter, may be purchased from the Annual Reviews Preprints and Reprints service.
1-800-347-8007;415-259-5017;email:arpr@class.org

Literature Cited

1. Adams SR, Kao JPY, Tsien RY. 1989. Biologically useful chelators that take up Ca^{2+} upon illumination. *J. Am. Chem. Soc.* 111:7957–68
2. Ayer D, Yarus M. 1986. The context effect does not require a fourth base pair. *Science* 231:393–95
3. Bain JD, Glabe CG, Dix TA, Chamberlin AR, Diala ES. 1989. Biosynthetic site-specific incorporation of a non-natural amino acid into a polypeptide. *J. Am. Chem. Soc.* 111: 8013–14
4. Bain JD, Switzer C, Chamberlin A, Benner S. 1992. Ribosome-mediated incorporation of non-standard amino acids into a peptide through expansion of the genetic code. *Nature* 356: 537–39
5. Bain JD, Wacker DA, Kuo EE, Chamberlin AR. 1991. Site-specific incorporation of non-natural residues into peptides: effect of residue structure on suppression and translational efficiencies. *Tetrahedron* 47: 2389–2400
6. Barbacid M. 1987. *ras* genes. *Annu. Rev. Biochem.* 56:779–281
7. Blaber M, Zhang XJ, Lindstrom JD, Deprot SD, Baase WA, Matthews BW. 1994. Determination of α-helix

propensity within the context of a folded protein. *J. Mol. Biol.* 235: 600–24
8. Bos JL. 1989. *ras* oncogenes in human cancer: a review. *Cancer Res.* 49:4682–89
9. Bossi L. 1983. Translation of UAG codon by suppressor tRNA is affected by the sequence following UAG in the message. *J. Mol. Biol.* 164:73–87
10. Bruce A, Atkins J, Wills N, Uhlenbeck O, Gesteland R. 1982. Replacement of anticodon loop nucleotides to produce functional tRNAs: amber suppressors derived from yeast tRNA^{Phe}. *Proc. Natl. Acad. Sci. USA* 79:7127–31
11. Brunner J. 1993. New photolabeling and crosslinking methods. *Annu. Rev. Biochem.* 62:483–514
12. Chaiken IM. 1981. Semisynthetic peptides and proteins. *CRC Crit. Rev. Biochem.* 11:255–301
13. Chinsky N, Margolin AL, Klibanov AM. 1989. Chemoselective enzymatic monoacylation of bifunctional compounds. *J. Am. Chem. Soc.* 111: 386–88
14. Chladek S, Sprinzl M. 1985. The 3'-end of tRNA and its role in protein

biosynthesis. *Angew. Chem. Int. Ed. Engl.* 24:371–91

15. Chung HH, Benson DR, Cornish VW, Schultz PG. 1993. Probing the role of loop 2 in ras function with unnatural amino acids. *Proc. Natl. Acad. Sci. USA* 90:10145–49

16. Chung HH, Benson DR, Schultz PG. 1993. Probing the role of lysine 16 in ras p[21] protein with unnatural amino acids. *J. Am. Chem. Soc.* 115: 6414–15

17. Chung HH, Benson DR, Schultz PG. 1993. Probing the structure and mechanism of ras protein with an expanded genetic code. *Science* 259: 806–9

18. Chunhua M, Kudlicki W, Odom OW, Kramer G, Hardesty B. 1993. In vitro protein engineering using synthetic tRNA[Ala] with different anticodons. *Biochemistry* 32:7937–45

18a. Cook SN, Jack WE, Xiong X, Danley LE, Ellman JA, et al. 1995. Photochemically-initiated protein splicing. *Cell.* In press

19. Corey DR, Schultz PG. 1987. Generation of a hybrid sequence-specific single-stranded deoxyribonuclease. *Science* 233:1401–3

20. Cornish VW, Benson DR, Altenbach CA, Hideg K, Hubbell WL, Schultz PG. 1994. Site-specific incorporation of biophysical probes into proteins. *Proc. Natl. Acad. Sci. USA* 91: 2910–14

21. Cornish VW, Kaplan MI, Veenstra D, Kollman PA, Schultz PG. 1994. Destabilizing and stabilizing effects of placing β-branched amino acids in protein α-helices. *Biochemistry* 33: 120221–31

22. Cornish VW, Mendel D, Schultz PG. 1995. Probing protein structure and function with an expanded genetic code. *Angew. Chem. Int. Ed. Engl.* In press

23. Crick FHC, Barrett L, Brenner S, Watts-Tobin R. 1961. General nature of the genetic code for proteins. *Nature* 192:1227–32

24. Dawson PE, Muir TW, Clark-Lewis I, Kent SBH. 1994. Synthesis of proteins by native chemical ligation. *Science* 266:776–79

25. Dill KA. 1990. Dominant forces in protein folding. *Biochemistry* 29: 7133–55

26. Deleted in proof

27. Ellman JA, Mendel D, Anthony-Cahill S, Noren CJ, Schultz PG. 1992. Biosynthetic method for introducing unnatural amino acids site-specifically into proteins. *Methods Enzymol.* 202:301–36

28. Ellman JA, Mendel D, Schultz PG. 1992. Site-specific incorporation of novel backbone structures into proteins. *Science* 255:197–200

29. Deleted in proof

30. Ellman JA, Volkman BF, Mendel D, Schultz PG, Wemmer DE. 1992. Site-specific isotopic labeling of proteins for NMR studies. *J. Am. Chem. Soc.* 114:7959–61

31. Fahnestock S, Neumann H, Shashoua V, Rich A. 1970. Ribosome-catalyzed ester formation. *Biochemistry* 9:2477–83

32. Fersht AR. 1987. The hydrogen bond in molecular recognition. *Trends Biochem. Sci.* 12:301–4

33. Fersht AR, Shi J-P, Knill-Jones J, Lowe D, Wilkinson A, et al. 1985. Hydrogen bonding and biological specificity analysed by protein engineering. *Nature* 314:235–38

34. Gay NJ, Walker JE. 1983. Homology between human bladder carcinoma oncogene product and mitochondrial ATP-synthase. *Nature* 301:262–64

35. Giege R, Puglisi JD, Florentz C. 1993. tRNA structure and aminoacylation efficiency. *Progr. Nucleic Acids Res. Mol. Biol.* 45:129–206

36. Grant MM, Brown AS, Corwin LM, Troxler RF, Franzblau C. 1975. Effect of L-azetidine 2-carboxylic acid on growth and proline metabolism in *Escherichia coli. Biochim. Biophys. Acta* 404:180–87

37. Griffith MC. 1990. *Chemical aminoacylation of tRNA's with unnatural amino acids.* PhD thesis. Univ. Calif., Berkeley

38. Haines BD, Higgins SJ. 1984. *Transcription and Translation: A Practical Approach.* Oxford: IRL

39. Hale SP, Poole LB, Gerlt JA. 1993. Mechanism of the reaction catalyzed by staphylococcal nuclease: identification of the rate-determining step. *Biochemistry* 32:7479–87

40. Harrington KM, Nazarenko IA, Dix DB, Thompson RC, Uhlenbeck OC. 1993. In vitro analysis of translational rate and accuracy with an unmodified tRNA. *Biochemistry* 32:7617–22

41. Hecht SM. 1992. Probing the synthetic capabilities of a center of biochemical catalysis. *Acc. Chem. Res.* 25:545–52

42. Heckler TG, Chang LH, Zama Y, Naka T, Chorghade MS, Hecht SM. 1984. T4 RNA ligase mediated preparation of novel "chemically misacy-

lated" tRNA^{Phe}s. *Biochemistry* 23: 1468–73

43. Hibler DW, Stolowich NJ, Reynolds MA, Gerlt JA, Wilde JA, Bolton PH. 1987. Site-directed mutants of staphylococcal nuclease. Detection and localization by ^{1}H NMR spectroscopy of conformational changes accompanying substitutions for glutamic acid-43. *Biochemistry* 26:6278–86

44. Hofmann K, Bohn H. 1966. Studies on polypeptides. XXXVI. The effect of pyrazole-imidazole replacements on the S-protein activating potency of an S-peptide fragment. *J. Am. Chem. Soc.* 88:5914–19

45. Jackson DY, Burnier J, Quan C, Stanley M, Tom J, Wells JA. 1994. A designed peptide ligase for total synthesis of Ribonuclease A with unnatural catalytic residues. *Science* 266: 243–47

46. Jeffrey GA, Saenger W. 1991. *Hydrogen Bonding in Biological Molecules*. New York: Springer-Verlag

47. Judice JK, Gamble TR, Murphy EC, deVos AM, Schultz PG. 1993. Probing the mechanism of staphylococcal nuclease with unnatural amino acids: kinetic and structural studies. *Science* 261:1578–81

48. Kaiser ET. 1989. Synthetic approaches to biologically active peptides and proteins including enzymes. *Acc. Chem. Res.* 22:47–54

49. Kaiser ET, Lawrence DS. 1984. Chemical mutation of enzyme active sites. *Science* 226:505–11

50. Kaiser ET, Lawrence DS, Rokita SE. 1985. The chemical modification of enzymatic specificity. *Annu. Rev. Biochem.* 54:565–95

51. Kamlet MJ, Abboud JLM, Abraham MH, Taft RW. 1983. Linear solvation energy relationships. 23. A comprehensive collection of the solvatochromic parameters, π^*, α, and β, and some methods for simplifying the generalized solvatochromic equations. *J. Org. Chem.* 48:2877–87

52. Karpusas M, Baase WA, Matsumura M, Matthews BW. 1989. Hydrophobic packing in T4 lysozyme probed by cavity-filling mutants. *Proc. Natl. Acad. Sci. USA* 86:8237–41

53. Kast P, Hennecke H. 1991. Amino acid substrate specificity of *Escherichia coli* phenylalanyl-tRNA synthetase altered by distinct mutations. *J. Mol. Biol.* 222:99–124

54. Kern D, Giege R, Ebel JP. 1972. Incorrect aminoacylations catalysed by the phenylalanyl- and valyl-tRNA synthetases from yeast. *Eur. J. Biochem.* 31:148–55

55. Kleina LG, Masson JM, Normanly J, Abelson J, Miller JH. 1990. Construction of *E. coli* amber suppressor tRNA genes. II. Synthesis of additional tRNA genes and improvement of suppressor efficiency. *J. Mol. Biol.* 213:705–18

56. Knowles J. 1991. Enzyme catalysis: not different, just better. *Nature* 350: 121–24

57. Knowles JR. 1987. Tinkering with enzymes: what are we learning? *Science* 236:1252–58

58. Krengel U, Schlichting I, Scherer A, Schumann R, Frech M, et al. 1990. Three-dimensional structures of H-*ras* p21 mutants: molecular basis for their inability to function as signal switch molecules. *Cell* 62:539–48

59. Krieg UC, Walter P, Johnson AE. 1986. Photocrosslinking of the signal sequence of nascent preprolactin to the 54-kilodalton polypeptide of the signal recognition particle. *Proc. Natl. Acad. Sci. USA* 83:8604–8

60. Kwok Y, Wong JT. 1980. Evolutionary relationship between *Halobacterium cutirubrum* and eukaryotes determined by use of aminoacyl-tRNA synthetases as phylogenetic probes. *Can. J. Biochem.* 58:213–18

61. Landman O, Spiegelman S. 1955. Enzyme formation in protoplasts of *Bacillus megaterium*. *Proc. Natl. Acad. Sci. USA* 41:698–704

62. Deleted in proof

63. Loll PJ, Lattman EE. 1989. The crystal structure of the ternary complex of staphylococcal nuclease, Ca^{2+}, and the inhibitor pdTp, refined at 1.65 Å. *Proteins* 5:183–201

64. Louie A, Jurnak F. 1984. Kinetic studies of *E. coli* elongation factor Tu–guanosine 5'-triphosphate-aminoacyl-tRNA complexes. *Biochemistry* 24:6433–39

65. Lyu PC, Sherman JC, Chen A, Kallenbach NR. 1991. α-Helix stabilization by natural and unnatural amino acids with alkyl side chains. *Proc. Natl. Acad. Sci. USA* 88:5317–20

66. Matthews BW. 1993. Structural and genetic analysis of protein stability. *Annu. Rev. Biochem.* 62:139–60

67. Meiering EM, Serrano L, Fersht AR. 1992. Effect of active site residues in barnase on activity and stability. *J. Mol. Biol.* 225:585–89

68. Mendel D, Ellman J, Schultz PG. 1993. Protein biosynthesis with conformationally restricted amino acids. *J. Am. Chem. Soc.* 115:4359–60

69. Mendel D, Ellman JA, Chang Z, Veenstra DL, Kollman PA, Schultz PG. 1992. Probing protein stability with unnatural amino acids. *Science* 256:1798–1802

70. Deleted in proof

71. Mendel D, Ellman JA, Schultz PG. 1991. Construction of a light-activated protein by unnatural amino acid mutagenesis. *J. Am. Chem. Soc.* 113:2758–60

72. Deleted in proof

73. Milburn MV, Tong L, de Vos AM, Brunger A, Yamaizumi Z, et al. 1990. Molecular switch for signal transduction: structural differences between active and inactive forms of protoon-cogenic *ras* proteins. *Science* 247: 939–45

74. Miller A, Albertini A. 1983. Effects of surrounding sequence on the suppression of nonsense codons. *J. Mol. Biol.* 164:59–71

75. Milligan JF, Groebe DR, Witherell GW, Uhlenbeck OC. 1987. Oligoribo-nucleotide synthesis using T7 RNA polymerase and synthetic DNA templates. *Nucleic Acids Res.* 15: 8783–98

76. Nakatsuka T, Sasaki T, Kaiser ET. 1987. Peptide segment coupling catalyzed by the semisynthetic enzyme thiosubtilisin. *J. Am. Chem. Soc.* 109:3808–10

77. Neet KE, Nanci A, Koshland DE. 1968. Properties of thiol-subtilisin. *J. Biol. Chem.* 243:6392–6401

78. Nomura M, Hosoda J, Nishimura S. 1958. Enzyme formation in lysozyme lysate of *Bacillus subtilis*. *Biochim. Biophys. Acta* 29:161–67

79. Noren CJ, Anthony-Cahill SJ, Griffith MC, Schultz PG. 1989. A general method for site-specific incorporation of unnatural amino acids into proteins. *Science* 244:182–88

80. Noren CJ, Anthony-Cahill SJ, Suich DJ, Noren KA, Griffith MC, Schultz PG. 1990. *In vitro* suppression of an amber mutation by chemically aminoacylated transfer RNA prepared by runoff transcription. *Nucleic Acids Res.* 18:83–88

81. Nowak MW, Kearny PC, Sampson JR, Saks ME, Lavarca GC. 1995. Side chain contributions at the nicotinic receptor binding site probed with unnatural amino-acid incorporation in intact cells. *Science.* Submitted

82. Offord RE. 1987. Protein engineering by chemical means? *Protein Eng.* 1: 151–57

83. Pai EF, Kabsch W, Krengel U, Homes KC, John J, Wittinghofer A. 1989. Structure of the guanine-nucleotide-binding domain of the Ha-ras oncogene product p21 in the triphosphate conformation. *Nature* 341: 209–14

84. Pai EF, Krengel U, Petsko GA, Goody RS, Kabsch W, Wittinghofer A. 1990. Refined crystal structure of the triphosphate conformation of H-ras p21 at 1.35 Å resolution: implications for the mechanism of GTP hydrolysis. *EMBO J.* 9:2351–59

85. Patchornik A, Amit B, Woodward RB. 1970. Photosensitive protecting groups. *J. Am. Chem. Soc.* 92: 6333–35

86. Pauling L, Corey RB. 1951. Configurations of polypeptide chains with favored orientations around single bonds: two new pleated sheets. *Proc. Natl. Acad. Sci. USA* 37:729–40

87. Pauling L, Corey RB, Branson HR. 1951. The structure of proteins: two hydrogen-bonded helical configurations of the polypeptide chain. *Proc. Natl. Acad. Sci. USA* 37:205–11

88. Polgar L, Bender ML. 1966. A new enzyme containing a synthetically formed active site, thiol-subtilisin. *J. Am. Chem. Soc.* 88:3153–54

89. Pollack SJ, Nakayama G, Schultz PG. 1988. Introduction of nucleophiles and spectroscopic probes into antibody combining sites. *Science* 242:1038–40

90. Prive GG, Milburn MV, Tong L, de Vos AM, Yamaizumi Z, et al. 1992. X-ray crystal structures of transforming p21 ras mutants suggest a transition-state stabilization mechanism for GTP hydrolysis. *Proc. Natl. Acad. Sci. USA* 89:3649–53

91. Quiggle K, Kumar G, Oh TW, Ryu EK, Chladek S. 1981. Donor site of ribosomal peptidyltransferase: investigation of substrate specificity using 2′(3′)-O-(N-acylaminoacyl)-dinucle-oside phosphates as models of the 3′ terminus of N-acylaminoacyl transfer ribonucleic acid. *Biochemistry* 20: 3480–85

92. Roberts JW, Carbon J. 1975. Nucleotide sequence studies of normal and genetically altered glycine transfer ribonucleic acids from *Escherichia coli*. *J. Biol. Chem.* 250:5530–41

93. Robertson SA, Ellman JA, Schultz PG. 1991. A general and efficient route for chemical aminoacylation of transfer RNAs. *J. Am. Chem. Soc.* 113:2722–29

94. Robertson SA, Noren CJ, Anthony-Cahill SJ, Griffith MC, Schultz PG.

1989. The use of 5'-phospho-2-deoxyribocytidylylriboadenosine as a facile route to chemical aminoacylation of tRNA. *Nucleic Acids Res.* 17: 9649–60

95. Rose GD, Wolfenden R. 1993. Hydrogen bonding, hydrophobicity, packing, and protein folding. *Annu. Rev. Biophys. Biomol. Struct.* 22: 381–415

96. Sayers JR, Schmidt W, Eckstein F. 1988. 5'-3' Exonuclease in phosphorothioate-based oligonucleotide-directed mutagenesis. *Nucleic Acids Res.* 16:791–802

97. Schimmel P. 1987. Aminoacyl tRNA synthetases: general scheme of structure-function relationships in the polypeptides and recognition of transfer RNAs. *Annu. Rev. Biochem.* 56:125–58

98. Schlichting I, Almo SC, Rapp G, Wilson K, Petratos A, et al. 1990. Time-resolved x-ray crystallographic study of the conformational change in Ha-*ras* p21 protein on GTP hydrolysis. *Nature* 345:309–15

99. Schnolzer M, Kent SBH. 1992. Constructing proteins by dovetailing unprotected synthetic peptides: backbone-engineered HIV protease. *Science* 256:221–25

100. Scholtz JM, Baldwin RL. 1992. The mechanism of α-helix formation by peptides. *Annu. Rev. Biophys. Biomol. Struct.* 21:95–118

101. Seeburg PH, Colby WW, Capon DJ, Goeddel DV, Levinson AD. 1984. Biological properties of human c-Ha-*ras*1 genes mutated at codon 12. *Nature* 312:71–75

102. Spandidos D. 1989. *Ras Oncogenes.* New York: Plenum

103. Spirin AS, Baranov VI, Ryabova LA, Ovodov SY, Alahhov YB. 1988. A continuous cell-free translation system capable of producing polypep-

tides in high yield. *Science* 242: 1162–64

104. Suich D. 1993. *Mutagenesis of the recognition helix of 434 repressor with nonproteinogenic amino acids.* PhD thesis. Univ. Calif., Berkeley

105. Thorson JS, Judice JK, Chapman E, Murphy EC, Schultz PG. 1994. A linear free energy analysis of hydrogen bonding in proteins. *J. Am. Chem. Soc.* Submitted

106. Deleted in proof

107. Trahey M, McCormick F. 1987. A cytoplasmic protein stimulates normal N-*ras* p21 GTPase, but does not affect oncogenic mutants. *Science* 238: 542–45

108. Tucker PW, Hazen EE Jr, Cotton FA. 1979. Staphylococcal nuclease reviewed: a prototypic study in contemporary enzymology. II. Solution studies of the nucleotide binding site and the effects of nucleotide binding. *Mol. Cell. Biochem.* 23:3–16

109. Weber DJ, Serpersu EH, Shortle D, Mildvan AS. 1990. Diverse interactions between the individual mutations in a double mutant at the active site of staphylococcal nuclease. *Biochemistry* 29:8632–42

110. Wiberg KB, Laidig KE. 1987. Barriers to rotation adjacent to double bonds. 3. The C-O barrier in formic acid, methyl formate, acetic acid, and methyl acetate. The origin of ester and amide "resonances." *J. Am. Chem. Soc.* 109:5935–43

111. Wierenga RK, Terpstora P, Hol WG. 1986. Prediction of the occurrence of the ADP-binding (bab)-fold in proteins, using an amino acid sequence fingerprint. *J. Mol. Biol.* 187:101–7

112. Zoller MJ, Smith M. 1983. Oligonucleotide-directed mutagenesis of DNA fragments cloned into M13 vectors. *Methods Enzymol.* 100:468–500

Annu. Rev. Biophys. Biomol. Struct. 1995. 24:463–93
Copyright © 1995 by Annual Reviews Inc. All rights reserved

COMPLEXES OF THE MINOR GROOVE OF DNA[1]

Bernhard H. Geierstanger and David E. Wemmer

Department of Chemistry, University of California at Berkeley, California 94720

KEY WORDS: DNA structure, DNA-drug interactions, DNA-ligand recognition, sequence-specific recognition of DNA

CONTENTS

---

[1] Abbreviations: G, deoxyguanosine; A, deoxyadenosine; T, deoxythymidine; C, deoxycytidine; I, deoxyinosine (deoxy-2-desamino-guanosine); Val, valine; Cys, cysteine; Ser, serine; Ala, alanine; Thr, threonine; NMR, nuclear magnetic resonance spectroscopy; NOE, nuclear Overhauser effect.

1056-8700/95/0610-0463$05.00

ABSTRACT

An increasing number of high-resolution structures suggest that both the minor and major grooves of DNA can function as receptors for proteins and small molecules. In this review, we try to illustrate the diversity of small molecule ligands that are capable of specifically recognizing the minor groove of DNA. Complex formation results in varying degrees of conformational changes in both DNA and ligands. The discussion focuses on intermolecular interactions that contribute to binding affinity and specificity. There probably is no simple general recognition code that explains the binding specificity of minor-groove ligands. To understand DNA recognition by small molecules, characterization of the binding mode at near-atomic resolution must be combined with thermodynamic data on the energetics of ligand binding to short oligonucleotides.

OVERVIEW AND PERSPECTIVES

The original model of Watson & Crick predicted many of the key features of DNA structure, such as base pairing, which explained much about DNA replication, and the basic features of the major and minor grooves. Later research showed that more functional groups are accessible in the major groove than in the minor, suggesting that in most cases sequence-specific recognition would therefore occur in the major groove (99). This idea has been generally borne out, but the determination of more structures of DNA complexes has revealed a wide variety of both small-molecule ligands and proteins that interact with DNA in the minor groove. In this review, we describe some recently studied minor-groove complexes and consider features that might contribute to their stability. As has been true of major-groove recognition, no simple rules have emerged. In many cases, the recognition process leads to structural rearrangement of both the ligand and the target DNA. These rearrangements make it difficult to identify individual molecular interactions that are exclusively responsible for the specificity of binding. Nevertheless, there has been progress in the design of sequence-specific DNA ligands.

DNA AS A LIGAND RECEPTOR

DNA in aqueous solution is in the B family of conformations, a right-handed helix with 10.5 base pairs per turn and a rise of 3.5 Å per base pair. The major groove of DNA is quite wide, exposing numerous functional groups on the edges of the bases (Figure 1). The minor groove is narrower and exposes a more limited array of functional groups. Although the B-form structure provides a rough picture of the DNA double helix, diffraction and NMR studies have revealed substantial deviations from this idealized structure for many DNA sequences (20, 94). The DNA structure is clearly sequence dependent; for example runs of adenosines lead to a very narrow minor groove and to a high propeller twist of base pairs and introduce a bend into the helix axis (18, 21, 51, 81, 122, 125). Mixed A,T/G,C sequences have a more normal groove width but vary in other local helical parameters (20, 41–44, 125). Many different kinds of evidence indicate considerable flexibility in the conformation of DNA. This flexibility further complicates consideration of DNA as a receptor, because the target may become distorted in response to ligand binding.

DNA COMPLEXES WITH SMALL MOLECULES: OVERVIEW

Proteins typically form a large contact surface with DNA. Binding of smaller antibiotics and mutagens occurs more locally via intercalation

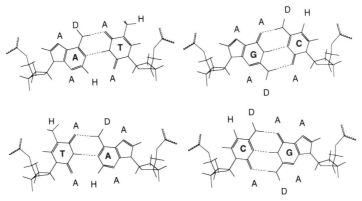

Figure 1 Watson-Crick base pairing and recognition patterns in DNA. View down the helical axis. Adenosine base-pairs with thymidine, while guanosine pairs with cytosine. Hydrogen bond acceptors (A) and donors (D) and hydrophobic groups (H) are indicated in both minor (below the base pairs) and major grooves (above the base pairs). (Adopted from Reference 99.)

between adjacent base pairs or groove binding (97, 128). The majority of small molecules bind to the narrow minor groove of B-DNA (128), presumably because of better van der Waals contacts. Many minor-groove ligands prefer A,T sites, whereas many intercalators have a preference for G,C regions of DNA. As with protein complexes, numerous interactions contribute to ligand binding. Distortions of the DNA structure observed in the complexes reinforce the view that DNA is flexible. Hydrogen bonds are frequently seen between the ligand and DNA and certainly contribute to but do not fully determine sequence specificity. Binding can induce substantial changes in both ligand and DNA conformation. This so-called induced fit (102) seems to be important for ligand-DNA recognition, but it is very difficult to dissect energetically. We discuss examples of the classes of minor-groove ligands for which the binding mode is known at high resolution.

MONO-INTERCALATOR COMPLEXES WITH SUGARS IN THE MINOR GROOVE: ANTHRACYCLINE ANTIBIOTICS

Some very potent antitumor drugs intercalate between adjacent base pairs with bulky oligosaccharides or with peptide or aromatic groups positioned in the grooves (97). Many anthracycline antibiotics, such as arugomycin (Figure 2) (98), nogalamycin (113), and the pluramycins (104), have bulky oligosaccharides in both grooves. Complex formation is a dramatic example of the flexibility of DNA because the stacking of the DNA base pairs must be disrupted at least transiently to allow the ligand to thread through DNA, which explains the very slow binding kinetics of these molecules (97).

The widely used anticancer drugs daunomycin and adriamycin are examples of mono-intercalators that have sugars only in the minor groove. Although the interactions of the chromophore dominate the binding, the minor-groove substituents may make binding affinity dependent on the flanking sequence (29) or may carry reactive groups (126) but do not distort the DNA structure significantly.

MONO-INTERCALATOR COMPLEXES WITH PEPTIDE GROUPS IN THE MINOR GROOVE: ACTINOMYCIN D

Actinomycin D is a commonly used chemotherapeutic agent, with a phenoxazone chromophore and two identical cyclic pentapeptides (Figure 2). Actinomycin D specifically intercalates at d(GpC) steps (28,

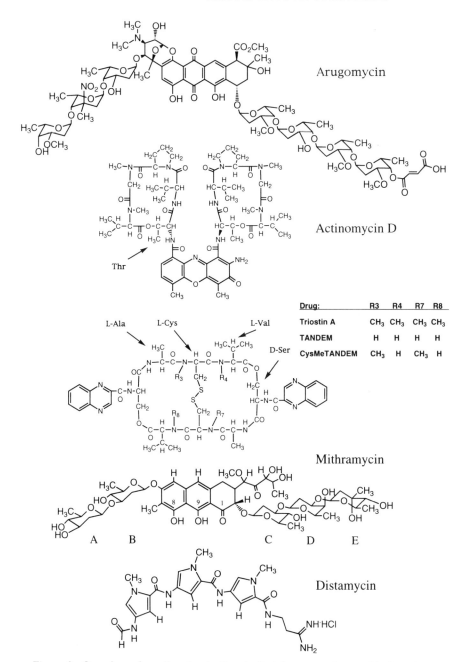

Figure 2 Overview of small-molecule ligands that form complexes with the minor groove.

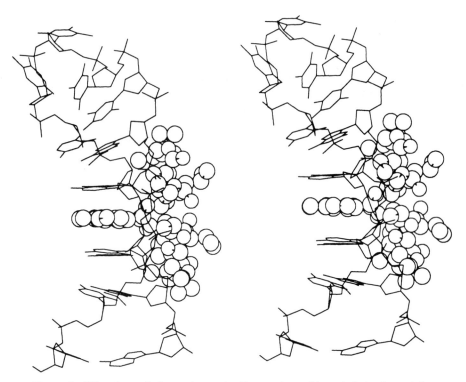

Figure 3 Side view of the actinomycin D complex with a hairpin formed by d(TCGCGTTTTCGCGA) studied by NMR. The nonhydrogen atoms in the actinomycin molecule are displayed as spheres (= 0.5 van der Waals radius), and protons are omitted for clarity. (From Reference 11. Reprinted with permission, © 1994, American Chemical Society.)

112). The solution structures of actinomycin D with d(AAAGCTTT)$_2$ (70) and with a DNA hairpin stem containing a 5'-CGCG-3' site (Figure 3) (11) were determined by NMR. Actinomycin D intercalates at the d(GpC) step in both complexes. The bulky peptides are in the minor groove and point in opposite orientations. They adopt strikingly similar conformations that also resemble the conformation seen in the crystal structure of uncomplexed actinomycin D (70). Hydrogen bonds and van der Waals contacts between the peptide rings make the peptide moiety a rigid right-handed structural domain. Each ring contacts both DNA strands, extending over two base pairs from the intercalation site. Actinomycin D therefore spans a total of four base pairs with good complimentarity between DNA and peptide surfaces.

The DNA remains B-form in the complex (11, 70). Intercalation causes an unwinding of ~20° between the flanking base pair and the

G·C base pairs at the intercalation site (11, 70). The G·C base pairs sandwiching the chromophore are almost parallel (70), with the long axis of the chromophore roughly parallel to the long axis of the base pairs. To accommodate the bulky peptide rings, the minor groove widens substantially to a cross-strand P-P separation of 16.4 Å at the intercalation site and 18.2 Å between A3-G4 and C5-T6 phosphates (70), compared with 10–14 Å for normal drug-free uncomplexed DNA sequences (42).

The specificity for d(GpC) steps is attributed to intermolecular hydrogen bonds between the backbone carbonyl of the threonine residues and the amino group of guanosines as well as a weaker hydrogen bond between the threonine amides and N3 of the guanosines. The van der Waals interactions between the surface of the peptide and the minor groove may determine the preference for the sequence adjacent to the GpC intercalation site. The peptide group of actinomycin D does not undergo significant conformational changes upon complex formation, but the DNA is greatly distorted to fit the bulky peptide group.

BIS-INTERCALATOR COMPLEXES WITH PEPTIDE GROUPS IN THE MINOR GROOVE: TRIOSTIN A, ECHINOMYCIN, CysMeTANDEM, TANDEM, AND LUZOPEPTIN

The quinoxaline antibiotics triostin A, echinomycin, TANDEM, and CysMeTANDEM (Figure 2) bind to DNA through bis-intercalation. Although all these molecules have similar structures, triostin A and its analogue echinomycin bind specifically to d(CpG) steps while CysMeTANDEM and TANDEM recognize d(TpA) sites (1, 2, 72, 73, 111, 120).

Each ligand consists of two quinoxaline chromophores linked by a bicyclic octa-depsipeptide ring. The complexes of these ligands with DNA are very similar in structure. The bulky peptide ring resides in the minor groove, resulting in significant widening of the groove (Figure 4). The two chromophores of CysMeTANDEM intercalate at the d(ApT) steps of a d(GATATC)$_2$ duplex (2), whereas for triostin A and echinomycin (31, 38, 39, 109, 118, 119), the two chromophores intercalate parallel to the stacked base pairs at either side of d(CpG) steps. Two intermolecular hydrogen bonds between the amides of the alanine residues on the peptide rings and the amino groups and/or the N3 nitrogens of guanosines were suggested to be responsible for the sequence specificity of triostin A and echinomycin for 5'-NCGN-3' sites (109, 118, 119). CysMeTANDEM, however, forms analogous intermolecular hydrogen bonds with the N3 of A4 when complexed to d(GATATC)$_2$

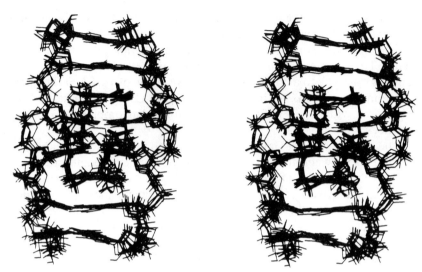

Figure 4 Stereo view of the CysMeTANDEM complex with d(GATATC)$_2$ from the major groove. Ten superimposed final NMR-derived structures are shown. The two chromophores are intercalated parallel to the A·T base pairs. (From Reference 2. Reprinted with permission, © 1993, American Chemical Society.)

(2), an observation that argues against this explanation for the specificity of the complexes.

The basis for the sequence discrimination lies in the chemical differences in the peptide ring. For echinomycin and triostin A, the amides at positions 3, 4, 7, and 8 of the peptide are methylated (Figure 2), whereas in TANDEM no amides are. CysMeTANDEM is identical to triostin A except that it has methylated amides only at cystines 4 and 7. Differences in bridging groups do not explain the different specificity of echinomycin and CysMeTANDEM/TANDEM (73). However, two intramolecular hydrogen bonds between each valine amide and alanine carbonyl reduce the width of the TANDEM peptides (2) compared with triostin A, in which these hydrogen bonds cannot form because the valines are N-methylated. While the valine methyls are in van der Waals contacts with the edges of the thymine in the d(TpA) step, they are not in close proximity to the corresponding cytosine in the d(CpG) step (2). The wider peptide group of triostin A may not fit into a narrower minor groove at d(TpA) steps, but it may form good contacts with a wider d(CpG) groove of free DNA. In the drug-DNA complexes, however, little difference in groove width is apparent (2).

A similar A,T-specific complex is formed by luzopeptin (26, 127), which has two quinoline rings connected by a cyclic depsipeptide (Figure 5). The structure of the symmetric complex with 5′-CATG-3′ (127) appears to have enough room to accommodate the G amino group when

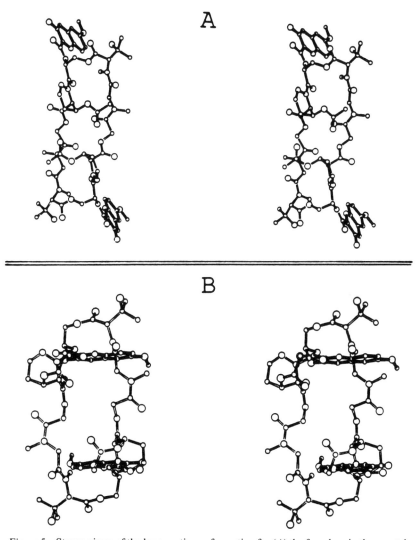

Figure 5   Stereo views of the luzopeptin conformation for (*A*) the free drug in the crystalline state (3) and (*B*) the luzopeptin-d(CATG)$_2$ complex in aqueous solution. Note the dramatic conformational change of the cyclic decadepsipeptide. (From Reference 127. Reprinted with permission, © 1994, American Chemical Society.)

replacing the A·T base pairs with G·C base pairs in 5'-CGCG-3'. As in triostin-TANDEM complexes, intermolecular hydrogen bonds between glycine amides and the thymidine O2 of the sandwiched A·T base pairs stabilize the complex but do not explain its sequence specificity (127). In the free crystalline drug (3), intramolecular hydrogen bonds across the ring, not unlike those seen in the CysMeTANDEM complex, are observed (119), but they are not seen in the luzopeptin-DNA complex. Upon complex formation, both DNA and luzopeptin undergo pronounced conformational changes (Figure 5). This observation suggests that the surface complementarity of receptor and ligand in the complex and the energetics of the induced fit may determine the sequence specificity of these ligands.

COMPLEXES WITH NONINTERCALATING MINOR-GROOVE LIGANDS AND MAJOR DISTORTIONS OF THE DNA: CHROMOMYCIN AND MITHRAMYCIN

The cytotoxic effect of the aureolic acid class of anticancer drugs is believed to result from DNA binding facilitated by Mg^{2+}. Chromomycin and mithramycin (Figure 2) bind in the minor groove without intercalation, in spite of the aromatic chromophore. Binding of the drug dimer results in a major distortion and opening of the minor groove (30, 95). Chromomycin binds to C,G-rich sites of at least three base pairs; of these, 5'-GGG-3' and 5'-CGA-3' are the strongest sites (27, 110). Chromomycin and mithramycin form similar complexes (30, 32, 33, 95) that have comparable but not identical sequence specificity. A d(GpC) step at the center of the binding site appears to be an absolute requirement for binding. Both drugs bind as head-to-tail dimers in the minor groove of the G,C region of d(TTGGCCAA)$_2$, d(TGGCCA)$_2$, and d(TCGCGA)$_2$ (Figure 6). The complexes retain two-fold symmetry. NOE and coupling data are consistent with a wide (~14.5 Å) (95) and shallow minor groove resulting from complex formation.

The hydrophilic edges of two chromomycin or two mithramycin molecules bind next to the G residues, the ligands pointing in opposite directions (Figure 6). The C-D-E sugars (Figure 2) on each molecule point toward the 3' end of the duplex, whereas the A-B sugars and the side chain of the chromophore align with the phosphate backbone (30, 32, 33, 95). The aglycon C9 and C1 groups are coordinated to the Mg^{2+} ion in the minor groove of the d(GpC) step such that the planes of the rings are almost perpendicular (Figure 6). The two symmetry-related C8 hydroxyl groups can form hydrogen bonds to the G amino groups. This interaction may be responsible for the sequence specificity for

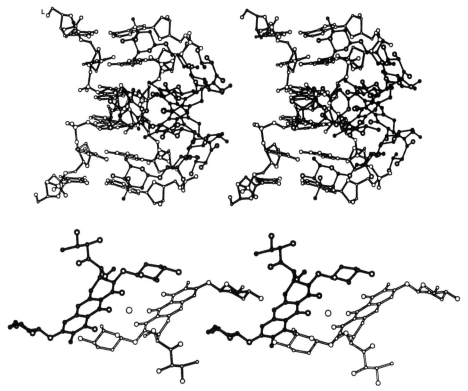

Figure 6   Stereo drawing of the Mg^{2+}-coordinated mithramycin dimer complex with d(TCGCGA)₂. (*Top*) View emphasizing the antiparallel arrangement of the drug molecules in the minor groove. The DNA is drawn with open lines, while the drug molecules are drawn with filled lines. (*Bottom*) View emphasizing the coordination geometry of the mithramycin dimer. A circle indicates the position of the Mg^{2+} cation. (From Reference 95. Reprinted with permission, © 1994, American Chemical Society.)

d(GpC) steps, although differences in DNA conformation and flexibility may also determine the specificity (30, 32, 33, 95). The C and D sugars of one drug stack on top of the chromophore of the other (Figure 6). As a result, the chromophore lies against one wall of the groove, while the sugars interact with the opposite strand. The E sugar stabilizes the complex through contacts that include hydrogen bonds to both strands at the terminal A·T base pairs.

   Mithramycin and chromomycin differ in sugars A, B, and E, and this variation may cause different preferences for flanking DNA sequences. Mithramycin forms a mixture of two different complexes when bound to d(TTGGCCAA)₂ or d(AAGGCCTT)₂ (95), whereas chromomycin only forms one at the central 5'-GGCC-3' sites (32, 33), which suggests that mithramycin is less sequence selective (95). Binding of the bulky ligand dimers may be aided by a wide minor groove, as observed in G,C sequences (41–44, 125). The combination of the wider groove and ligand-DNA hydrogen bonds to the G aminos may determine the G,C specificity. Mithramycin and chromomycin are unusual minor-groove ligands because the binding occurs at G,C sites as a magnesium-coordinated dimer and because binding causes a drastic opening of the minor groove.

COMPLEXES WITH NONINTERCALATING MINOR-GROOVE LIGANDS AND MINOR DISTORTIONS OF THE DNA

Netropsin and distamycin (Figure 7) represent classical examples of nonintercalating minor-groove binders (128). These ligands bind preferentially at sequences of four to five consecutive A·T base pairs without major distortion of the DNA structure. Other members of this class include Hoechst 33258, berenil, DAPI, and SN-6999 (Figure 7).

The binding preference of these ligands for A,T sequences has been attributed to the properties of A,T sites. The computed negative electrostatic potential of A,T sequences in the minor groove suggests that these sites are a likely target for positively charged ligands (90, 91). Poly-A sequences exhibit a narrower minor groove than canonical B-form DNA and thereby promote good van der Waals contacts of the ligand to the sides of the groove (21, 81, 122, 125). Hydrogen bonds between ligand and DNA contribute to the binding affinity and replace a network of hydrogen bonds from the spine of hydration (52, 53). The first X-ray structure of netropsin complexed to DNA suggested that the amino group of G, at the bottom of the minor groove, would sterically interfere with binding at sites containing G·C base pairs (52, 53). All members of this class bind edge-on in the narrow minor groove and have a shape complementary to the helical surface of the minor groove (40). Structural differences between these ligands affect the details of their interactions with DNA, and separating contributions to the stability of these complexes is difficult.

Hoechst 33258

Hoechst 33258 is a fluorescent dye that binds with an affinity of $\sim 5 \times 10^8$ M^{-1} at 5°C to minor-groove sites that have at least four A·T pairs (71). Different ligand conformations and locations have been identified in X-ray (88, 92, 103, 106) and NMR (25, 97) studies of complexes at

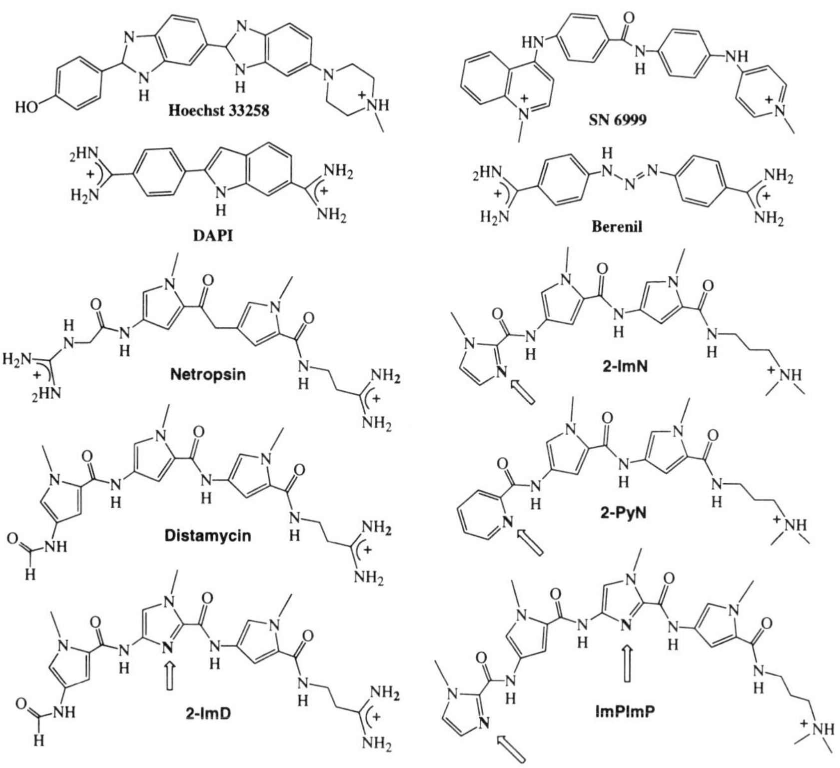

Figure 7 Nonintercalating minor-groove ligands and G·C-specific distamycin analogues. Arrows indicate G-specific hydrogen bond acceptor groups.

a 5'-AATT-3' site. The emerging view is that the terminal phenol ring
flips rapidly and the piperazine ring adopts variable conformations (Figure 8). These two groups exhibit a higher degree of mobility than the
aromatic core, although different orientations of the benzimidazole
rings with respect to each other and the terminal groups also occur.
The position and conformation of the drug in a 5'-AATT-3' binding site
varies considerably in the different complexes, possibly because the
piperazine ring may not be a strict A,T recognition element (25, 88, 92,
103, 106). Hoechst 33258 binding to the minor groove indicates that
various dynamic processes may remain even in tightly bound minor-
groove complexes.

DAPI

DAPI is widely used to stain DNA and chromosomes and has .. binding
constant of 10^7 to 10^8 M^{-1} at 5°C (71) for minor-groove sites of three

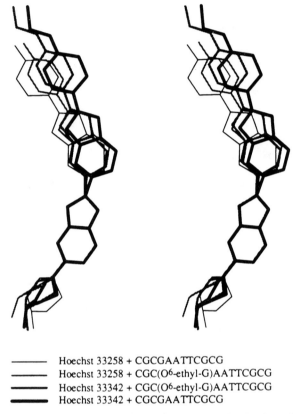

<table>
<tr><td>————</td><td>Hoechst 33258 + CGCGAATTCGCG</td></tr>
<tr><td>————</td><td>Hoechst 33258 + CGC(O[6]-ethyl-G)AATTCGCG</td></tr>
<tr><td>————</td><td>Hoechst 33342 + CGC(O[6]-ethyl-G)AATTCGCG</td></tr>
<tr><td>▅▅▅▅</td><td>Hoechst 33342 + CGCGAATTCGCG</td></tr>
</table>

Figure 8 Stereo view of the superposition of Hoechst molecules from four different drug-DNA crystal structures. The conformation is different in all cases, reflecting the flexibility of the ligand. See Reference 25 for a comparison with NMR structures and a comparison of the locations of the ligand in the binding site. (From Reference 103. Reprinted with permission, © 1992, Oxford University Press.)

or more A·T pairs. In the X-ray structure of the complex with d(CGCGAATTCGCG)$_2$ (59), DAPI spans the 5'-AAT-3' site with the phenyl-amidine at the 5' end. The phenyl and indole rings are coplanar. NMR studies of DAPI binding to d(GCGATCGC)$_2$ indicate a similar binding mode at the 5'-ATC-3' site, but with about 10^3 lower affinity (107).

Berenil

Berenil also binds asymmetrically to the 5'-AAT-3' sequence of d(CGCGAATTCGCG)$_2$ (10). The phenyl rings are aligned parallel with the minor-groove walls. The triazene group is centered at the d(ApT) step. Binding of berenil has also been studied by NMR, and titrations indicate fast exchange between free and bound ligand (45, 48, 58). The binding constant derived from CD measurements is ~1 × 10^6 M^{-1} at 25°C (58). Molecular modeling suggests that asymmetric ligand binding occurs at the 5'-AAT-3' site, but rapid exchange (48) between symmetrically equivalent sites must occur to explain the NMR data.

SN-6999

SN-6999 is a synthetic drug with potential antitumor activity (34). The binding constant of SN-6999 to poly[d(AT)] is ~2 × 10^6 M^{-1} (8); NMR titrations (14, 67) indicate intermediate-to-fast exchange between free and bound ligand. The crystal structure of the SN-6999 complex with

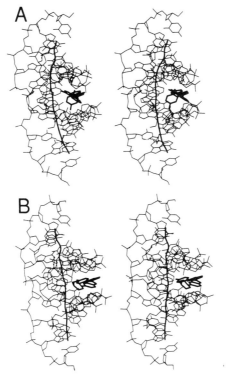

Figure 9 Stereo view down the minor groove of (*A*) the SN-6999 complex with d(CGC[e⁶G]AATTCGCG)₂ and (*B*) the Hoechst 33258 complex with d(CGCGAATTCGCG)₂ (106). The reduced curvature of SN-6999 compared to Hoechst 33358 results in a bend helix as the DNA adjusts its minor groove to fit the ligand. (From Reference 34. Reprinted with permission, © 1993, American Chemical Society.)

the d(CGC[e⁶G]AATTCGCG) duplex (34) provides insight into the interactions of SN-6999 with DNA. In contrast to other minor-groove binders, SN-6999 has a less distinct crescent shape. The terminal pyridinium and methylquinolinium groups are distinctively out of the plane of the coplanar central benzamido and anilino rings (Figure 9). As for other nonintercalating minor-groove ligands, the two central rings sit edge-on in the minor groove of the 5'-AA-3' sequence. The amide hydrogen points into the groove and forms a hydrogen bond with O2 of T20. The rings form extensive van der Waals contacts with the walls of the groove. The terminal rings do not form contacts as strong, but their positive charges contribute to the overall affinity. The methylquinolinium ring is near the center of the helix, whereas the methylpyridinium ring is close to the $e^6G4{\cdot}C23$ and $C3{\cdot}G22$ base pairs at the end of the six–base pair 5'-AATTCG-3' site. The DNA tilts upon SN-6999 binding (Figure 9), presumably to optimize contacts with this ligand, which has a shallower curvature than Hoechst 33258 or distamycin (Figure 7).

Netropsin and Distamycin

NMR (50, 84, 85) and X-ray (16, 17, 52, 53) studies indicate that tight binding of distamycin and netropsin [binding constant, $\sim 1 \times 10^7 \text{ M}^{-1}$ (93)] requires a site of four A·T base pairs with a narrow minor groove. Distamycin binding at asymmetric sites is directional with the N-terminal formyl group pointing toward the 5' end of the A-rich strand (121) (Figure 10).

Two distamycin ligands can bind simultaneously to sites with at least five A·T base pairs. In these 2:1 complexes, two ligands are stacked side by side, and the positively charged end groups point in opposite directions (Figure 10) (15, 86). The formyl group of each ligand lies at the 5' end of the adjacent strand. To accommodate the second ligand in this 2:1 motif, the minor groove must widen by approximately 3.5 Å relative to the 1:1 complex. The 2:1 motif spans five base pairs, and in six-base-pair sites, 2:1 complexes rapidly slide between overlapping five-base-pair sites (24, 36, 87, 121). The relative binding constants of the ligands and the preference for the 2:1 over the 1:1 mode vary highly with the DNA sequence. The narrow groove in poly(A)-type sequences (21, 81, 122, 125), such as 5'-AAAAA-3', favors 1:1 binding, and 2:1 binding occurs only after the saturation of 1:1 binding sites. The wider or more flexible groove of an alternating 5'-ATATA-3' site (66, 125) exhibits binding only in the 2:1 motif (121). The binding cooperativity is intermediate for 5-'AAATT-3' (86). Only 2:1 binding is observed with 5'-IIICC-3'·5'-IICCC-3', even at low ligand:DNA ratios (24). Because the functional groups in the minor groove of A·T and I·C base pairs are identical, the different binding behavior must result from structural differences in the DNA sites. Consistent with this interpretation, only highly cooperative 2:1 distamycin binding to 5'-AAGTT-3' (35), 5'-AAAGT-3', 5'-AAACT-3' (121), 5'-TACGTA-3' (13, 121), and 5'-TAA-CAA-3' (36) is observed. These results suggest that a single G·C base pair locally widens the minor groove.

The binding affinity in these 2:1 complexes is still high because free ligand and complex are in slow exchange on the NMR time scale. Titration calorimetry shows that distamycin binding to 5'-AAGTT-3' occurs with affinity comparable to 5'-AAATT-3' (L Marky, D Rentzeperis & DE Wemmer, unpublished results), which indicates that good van der Waals contacts and shape complementarity of the peptides with the groove are more important than the depth of the groove, and that steric clashes with the G amino group (52, 53) can be avoided in the 2:1 mode. Clearly, the binding behavior of distamycin depends on sequence-dependent variations in minor-groove geometry and/or flexibility.

Summary

Comparison of the structures of the nonintercalating ligands (Figure 7) reveals the complexity of factors contributing to the stability of minor-

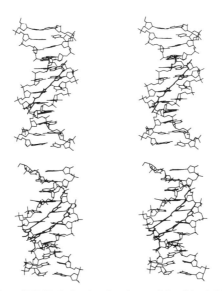

Figure 10 Stereoview of NMR-derived molecular models of the 1:1 distamycin complex with d(CGCGAATTCGCG)₂ (85) (*top*) and the 2:1 distamycin complex with d(CGCAAATTGGC)·d(GCCAATTTGCG) (86). Protons are omitted for clarity, and the distamycin molecules are shown in thick lines.

groove complexes. Berenil and DAPI are both doubly charged and of similar size but differ significantly in binding affinity. Berenil has a binding constant similar to that of SN-6999 (8). The more extended ring system of SN-6999 should have increased affinity because of more extensive van der Waals contacts. However, all three ligands form complexes that are less stable than those of Hoechst 33258, a ligand with one positive charge and with a size equal to SN-6999. Netropsin and distamycin bind with affinities comparable to Hoechst 33258 but have a larger array of hydrogen-bonding groups. The contributions from van der Waals interactions may be affected by the intrinsic curvature of these ligands (19, 40) and by the ability of the DNA to distort upon ligand binding. Electrostatic interactions, hydrogen bonding, and effects of desolvation of DNA and ligand all contribute to the overall affinity, but the relative contributions will vary from ligand to ligand.

COMPLEXES OF LIGANDS DESIGNED FOR SEQUENCE SPECIFICITY

Dickerson (53) and Lown (74) proposed that the A,T-specific netropsin- or distamycin-like molecules could be altered to specifically recognize the G amino group through a hydrogen bond. Lown and others have synthesized many such "lexitropsins" in which N-methylimidazole rings are substituted for N-methylpyrrole rings to introduce a G-specific hydrogen-bond acceptor (12, 49, 60–63, 65, 74). Bis-furan lexitropsins (64), thiazole compounds (54, 89), and analogues of Hoechst 33258 in which benzoxale or pyridoimidazole groups substitute for the benzimidazole rings of Hoechst 33258 (55, 57) were also synthesized and studied. Experimental studies have shown that most of these molecules lose their preference for A,T sites but are not G,C specific (91).

The minor-groove geometry depends strongly on the sequence, and hence the structure of the target sequence must be considered in the design of sequence-specific ligands. A narrow groove, e.g. in 5'-AAAAA-3', can best be targeted with planar molecules, such as netropsin, Hoechst 33258, and distamycin, whose shape matches that of a narrow groove. The wider groove of mixed A,T/G,C- or G,C-rich sequences must be filled with a bulkier but rigid molecule, e.g. the peptide rings of the intercalator actinomycin D, or by a dimeric motif, e.g. the chromomycin-Mg^{2+} dimer. Distamycin can fill the groove of mixed sequences in an antiparallel 2:1 complex that spans five base pairs. This motif is therefore a good platform for the design of sequence-specific minor-groove binders.

Combining this consideration with the lexitropsin idea led to a new set of sequence-specific minor-groove ligands (Figure 7). 1-Methylimid-azole-2-carboxamide-netropsin (2-ImN) specifically binds 5'-(A,T)-G(A,T)C(A,T)-3' sequences as a side-by-side antiparallel dimer (80, 115), an arrangement very similar to that of the dimeric complexes of distamycin (86, 121). Each ligand makes a specific hydrogen bond to one DNA strand in which the imidazole nitrogen specifically interacts with the G amino (Figure 11a). Distamycin and 2-ImN can be combined in a heterodimer to target a 5'-(A,T)G(A,T)$_3$-3' site (36, 76) (Figure 11b). An analogous heterodimer is formed by distamycin and 2-imidazole-distamycin (2-ImD) at a 5'-AAGTT-3' site (22, 35) (Figure 11c). Dista-mycin and 2-ImD each form homodimeric complexes with this site, but the 2-ImD/Dst heterocomplex is the most stable compex. Pyridine nitrogens can also recognize guanosines; pyridine-2-carboxamide-ne-tropsin (2-PyN) binds with high cooperativity as a 2:1 complex to 5'-AGTCA-3'·5'-TGACT-3' (23), but it also footprints at purely A,T sites (114–116), presumably with a C-H rather than the nitrogen pointing into the groove. Covalently linking two 2-PyN ligands has increased the apparent binding affinity and specificity of these ligands in the 2:1 motif (23, 77) (Figure 11d). A similar linked 2-ImN-distamycin molecule (78) and head-to-tail linked ligands (79) (Figure 11e) have also been characterized.

A four-ring (imidazole-pyrrole-imidazole-pyrrole) ligand, ImPImP,

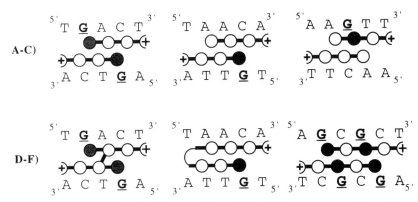

Figure 11 Schematic of designed G·C-specific complexes. (A) 2-ImN homodimer, (B) 2-ImN–distamycin heterodimer, (C) 2-ImD–distamycin heterodimer, (D) covalently linked 2-PyN dimer, (E) head-to-tail linked 2-ImN–distamycin dimer, (F) ImPImP homo-dimers. Shaded circles indicate N-methylimidazole or pyridine rings while N-methylpyr-role rings are shown as open circles. The specifically recognized guanosines are high-lighted. See Figure 7 for the chemical structures of the ligands.

has been designed to bind specifically to an all-G,C recognition site (Figure 11*f*) (37). Using the 2:1 motif, ImPImP targets 5′-(A,T)GCG-C(A,T)-3′ sites with high specificity, completely reversing the specificity of distamycin for A,T sequences. NMR studies of ImPImP binding to d(CGTAGCGCTACG)$_2$ indicate cooperative formation of a tight, symmetric 2:1 complex. The ligands span the nucleotides G5-C6-G7-C8-T9, and the positively charged C-terminus points toward the 3′ end of the adjacent DNA strand. Each imidazole nitrogen forms a specific hydrogen bond with the G amino proton on the adjacent DNA strand. These hydrogen bonds determine the sequence specificity of this ligand.

In summary, although the molecular mechanism of sequence specificity is generally not well understood, the specificity of distamycin-like ligands can be altered rationally. The original lexitropsin concept (53, 74) proved to be correct and valuable. The initially designed lexitropsins, however, were not G·C specific because their design did not consider sequence-dependent variations in the structure of the DNA target. Based on the NMR-derived models of 2:1 distamycin complexes, hydrogen bond acceptors were selectively introduced in this binding motif. Adding an extra specific interaction to a tightly bound 2:1 ligand·DNA complex then results in G·C-specific minor-groove ligands.

COMPLEXES OF CHEMICALLY REACTIVE LIGANDS

A great promise of sequence-specific DNA ligands lies in their ability to deliver reactive groups to a specific binding site to cause covalent modification or degradation. This principle has found wide application in the affinity cleavage approach, wherein an Fe(II)·EDTA group is attached to the ligand to study its binding specificity (19). Ideally, the specificity of binding could be combined with a very selective chemical reaction. A set of natural antibiotics have inspired synthetic approaches to produce site-selective alkylation and DNA-cleavage agents.

Enediyne Antibiotics

Enediyne chromophores, such as C1027 (Figure 12), calicheamicin (Figure 12), neocarzinostatin, and esperamicin (83, 108, 124), are natural antibiotics with antitumor activity that are produced by *Streptomyces* strains. Enediynes bind DNA in the minor groove. Upon activation, a benzenoid diradical abstracts hydrogen atoms from the deoxyribose sugar on both strands causing DNA cleavage. The diversity of the struc-

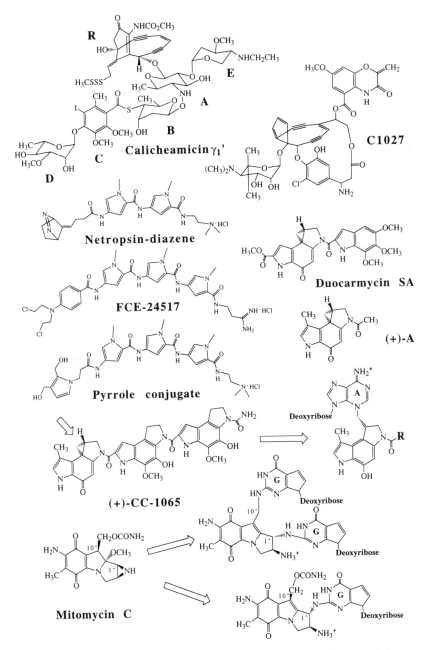

Figure 12 Reactive minor-groove ligands (examples): netropsin-diazene and the ene-diyne antibiotics calicheamicin and C1027, which cause DNA cleavage; the pyrrole conjugate and FCE-24517, which cross-link bases adjacent to A,T sequences; CC-1065 antibiotics and their analogues duocarmycin SA and (+)-A, which adduct DNA at adenosines; and mitomycin C, which adducts DNA at guanosines.

tures of these antibiotics is reflected in the wide range of sequences at which binding and hence cleavage occur. Neocarzinostatin causes double-strand breaks preferentially at 5'-AGT-3', while calicheamicin cuts at 5'-TCCT-3' sites (83, 124). Xu et al (124) identified 5'-GTTAT-3'·5'-ATAAC-3' as a strong cleavage site for C1027 (the cleaved residues are underlined). The selectivity of cleavage is attributed to the contacts formed by the enediyne moiety as well as the rest of the molecule.

Recently, NMR was used to characterize a complex of calicheamicin with d(GCATCCTAGC)·d(GCTAGGATGC) (83). This complex is similar to that of the oligosaccharide moiety of calicheamicin alone, thus supporting the conclusion that the oligosaccharide part of the drug determines the binding mode and specificity, although the aglycone increases the affinity (68). The oligosaccharide follows the curvature of the minor groove covering the TCCT-3' site. All residues, with the exception of sugar E, make DNA contacts (83). The aglycone resides close to the A3·T18 and T4·A17 base pairs. Ring E lies outside the groove. The aromatic ring C contacts G15 and G16 across the strand of the 5'-TCCT-3' segment of the duplex. Four specific hydrogen bonds are identified between the ligand and DNA. Stabilizing interactions between the iodine on ring C and the amino of G15 were inferred from NMR data. Purportedly, the drug does not undergo major conformational changes upon complex formation; instead the DNA adjusts its conformation to fit the rigid drug (117).

Reactive Groups Attached to Distamycin or Netropsin Analogues

Recently Little and coworkers (9) designed and synthesized netropsin-diazene (Figure 12) that combines the binding specificity of netropsin for A,T sequences with the high reactivity of a σ-diyl group. This functionality was suggested by the enediyne antitumor agents. Abstraction of a hydrogen from the sugar-phosphate backbone by an allyl radical leads to DNA cleavage. Photoactivation of the netrospin-diazene to a diyl in a mixture with a DNA restriction fragment produces cleavage at A,T-rich netropsin-binding sites. NMR studies of unactivated netropsin-diazene have been performed with d(CGCAAAAGGC)·d(GCCTTTTGCG) and d(CGCGAATTCGCG)$_2$ (101). NMR titrations and NOESY experiments indicate binding to the central four A·T base pairs. The ligand is in fast exchange between free and complexed forms. As observed for netropsin and distamycin (121), binding of the netropsin-diazene is directional. In the dominant orientation, the diazene group points toward the 5' end of the A-rich strand (located close to

C3·G18 and A4·T17 base pair), while the positively charged N,N-di-methyl group lies at the 3' end. The position of the diazene group with respect to the DNA could, however, not be determined.

The phenyl mustard derivative FCE-24517 (Figure 12) of distamycin slowly forms covalent adducts with bases in the vicinity of A,T sites (75). NMR studies (75) show that the pyrrole rings of FCE-24517 bind to the 5'-TATA-3' segment of the $d(CGTATACG)_2$ duplex. The phenyl mustard group reaches into flanking G·C base pairs. Contrary to netrop-sin-diazene, exchange between free and bound FCE-24517 ligand is slow, indicating that the additional pyrrole ring and the amidinium groups of FCE-24517 increase the binding constant significantly. Hop-kins and coworkers have combined the polypyrrole system of dista-mycin with a pyrrole-derived cross-linking agent (100, 123) (Figure 12) that connects the two guanosines in the 5'-AATTCG-3'·5'-CGAATT-3' target sequence.

CC-1065 and Analogues

(+)-CC-1065, a very potent cytotoxic agent, is a fermentation product of *Streptomyces zelensis* (47) and has been studied extensively. Many analogues with significant pharmacological potential have been synthe-sized (47). (+)-CC-1065 consists of three amide-bridged pyrroloindole units (Figure 12) and binds to the minor groove of A,T rich sites. The exocyclic carbon on the cyclopropane ring reacts with the N3 nitrogen of adenosines. The neutral (+)-CC-1065 fits into the minor groove and spans three base pairs on the 5' and one base pair on the 3' side of the modified adenosine (underlined), e.g. 5'-ATT<u>A</u>G-3' (96) and 5'-GTT<u>A</u>G-3' (69). (+)-CC-1065 induces a bend at the binding site that results in narrowing of the minor groove (105). Hurley and coworkers also propose that DNA flexibility contributes to the sequence recogni-tion of (+)-CC-1065.

Hurley & Draves (47) believe the observed specificity of (+)-CC-1065 alkylation does not entirely result from the A,T specific binding of the nonreactive part because no alkylation occurred at certain A,T-rich sites that were strong noncovalent binding sites. Furthermore, ana-logues that consist only of the reactive cyclopropane ring, such as (+)-A (Figure 12), have the same alkylation specificity as (+)-CC-1065. The alkylation efficiency, however, increases with the binding affinity of the drugs, i.e. longer ring systems that bind more tightly appear to be more efficient. The (−)-enantiomers of CC-1065 and its analogues, e.g. duocarmycin SA (5) (Figure 12), are nonreactive or less reactive. In covalent adducts, the ring system points in the direction opposite to that of the (+)-enantiomers, suggesting that the geometry of the noncovalently bound (−)-enantiomer is unfavorable for the alkylation reaction. The covalent reaction will occur only if DNA and the reactive group of the ligand can adopt the conformation of the transition state of the alkylation reaction. Therefore, Hurley & Draves (47) conclude that, although the specificity and affinity of the nonreactive part of the molecule can selectively deliver a reactive group, part of the selectivity of these DNA alkylating agents is intrinsic to the covalent reaction.

Mitomycin C and Analogues

Whereas CC-1065 and its analogues form adducts at the N3 of adenosine, the anticancer chemotherapeutics mitomycin C (4, 56) (Figure 12), anthramycin (6), and tomaymycin (7) alkylate the N2 of guanosines through binding in the minor groove. Mitomycin C and its analogues (4, 46, 56) are bifunctional reagents capable of adducting two neighboring guanosines through the N2 amino group and the C1″ and C10″ positions of the drug. The bifunctional drug can also cause interstrand cross-links. Norman et al (82) characterized such a cross-link with the d(TAC-GTA)$_2$ duplex. The G4 is adducted to the C1″ position, and N2 of G10 is linked to the C10″ position of the drug. Although the conformation of the cross-linked drug could not be determined accurately, the authors suggested the presence of a widened minor groove at the cross-linking site and that the Watson-Crick base pairing is not disrupted (82).

Summary

For reactive ligands that carry a nonspecific functionality, such as the netrospin-diazene or calicheamicins, the site specificity of the DNA damage is determined by the binding specificity of the ligands. For agents that covalently modify DNA, such as (+)-CC-1065 and mitomycin C, the selectivity of the chemical reaction plays a major role in determining the sequence of the modification site. The stereochemistry of the different enantiomers has important implications for the mutagenic and cytotoxic activity of these ligands. The noncovalent binding specificity and affinity of the ligands will, however, determine and modulate the efficiency of the modification based on the sequence context of the intrinsically reactive DNA site.

CONCLUDING REMARKS

Several high-resolution structures of drug-DNA complexes are now available. In many systems, large conformational changes for both the ligand and the receptor are observed. These conformational changes, the induced fit or folding of receptor and/or ligand, are in addition to specific intermolecular hydrogen bonds, probably the main contributors to binding affinity and specificity (102). Systematic binding studies with small oligonucleotide duplexes of various sequences are needed to derive thermodynamic data on the energetics of binding. Determinations of ligand-binding modes at high resolution are simultaneously needed to approach an understanding of sequence specificity. In most cases, there will probably be no simple recognition code. Nevertheless, the design of new sequence-specific DNA binding and/or modifying ligands has progressed steadily. Success depends heavily on structural characterization of complexes, which argues for the continuation of such work.

Literature Cited

1. Addess KJ, Gilbert DE, Olsen RK, Feigon J. 1992. Proton NMR studies of [N-MeCys^3,N-MeCys^7]TANDEM binding to DNA oligonucleotides: sequence-specific binding at the TpA site. *Biochemistry* 31:339–50
2. Addess KJ, Sinsheimer JS, Feigon J. 1993. Solution structure of a complex between [N-MeCys^3,N-MeCys^7] TANDEM and [d(GATATC)]$_2$. *Biochemistry* 32:2498–2508
3. Arnold E, Clardy J. 1981. Crystal and molecular structure of BBM-928 A, a novel antitumor antibiotic from *Actinomadura luzonesis*. *J. Am. Chem. Soc.* 103:1243–44
4. Bizanek R, McGuinness BF, Nakanishi K, Tomasz M. 1992. Isolation and structure of an intrastrand cross-link adduct of mitomycin C and DNA. *Biochemistry* 31:3084–91
5. Boger DL, Johnson DS, Yun W. 1994. (+)- and ent-(−)-duocarmycin SA and (+)- and ent-(−)-N-BOC-DSA DNA alkylation properties. Alkylation site models that accommodate the offset AT-rich adenine N3 alkylation selectivity of the enantiomeric agents. *J. Am. Chem. Soc.* 116: 1635–56
6. Boyd FL, Cheatham SF, Remers W, Hill GC, Burley LH. 1990. Characterization of the structure of the anthramycin-d(ATGCAT)$_2$ adduct by NMR and molecular modeling studies. Determination of the stereochemistry of the covalent linkage site, orientation

in the minor groove of DNA, and effect on local DNA structure. *J. Am. Chem. Soc.* 112:3279–89
7. Boyd FL, Stewart D, Remers WA, Barkley MD, Burley LH. 1990. Characterization of a unique tomaymycin-d(CICGAATTCICG)$_2$ adduct containing two drug molecules per duplex by NMR, fluorescence and molecular modeling studies. *Biochemistry* 29:2387–2403
8. Braithwaite AW, Baguley BC. 1980. Existence of an extended series of antitumor compounds which bind to DNA by nonintercalative means. *Biochemistry* 19:1101–6
9. Bregant TM, Groppe J, Little RD. 1994. New class of DNA-cleaving agents based on trimethylenemethane. *J. Am. Chem. Soc.* 116:3635–36
10. Brown DG, Sanderson MR, Skelly JV, Jenkins TC, Brown T, et al. 1990. Crystal structure of a berenil-dodecanucleotide complex: the role of water in sequence-specific ligand binding. *EMBO J.* 9:1329–34
11. Brown DR, Kurz M, Kearns DR, Hsu VL. 1994. Formation of multiple complexes between actinomycin D and a DNA hairpin: structural characterization by multinuclear NMR. *Biochemistry* 33:651–64
12. Burckhardt G, Luck G, Zimmer C, Störl J, Krowicki K, Lown JW. 1989. Variation of DNA sequence specificity of DNA-oligopeptide binding ligands related to netropsin: imidazole-

containing lexitropsins. *Biochim. Biophys. Acta* 1009:11–18

13. Capobianco ML, Colonna FP, Forni A, Garbesi A, Iotti S, et al. 1991. Interactions of nucleic acids with distamycins. Binding of Dst-3 to d(CGTTTAAACG)₂ and d(CGTAC-GTACG)₂. *Nucleic Acids Res.* 19:1695–98

14. Chen SM, Leupin W, Rance M, Chazin WJ. 1992. Two-dimensional NMR studies of d(GGTTAATGCG-GT)·d(ACCGCATTAACC) complexed with the minor groove binding drug SN6999. *Biochemistry* 31:4406–13

15. Chen X, Ramakrishnan B, Rao ST, Sundaralingam M. 1994. Binding of two distamycin A molecules in the minor groove of an alternating B-DNA duplex. *Nat. Struct. Biol.* 1:169–75

16. Coll M, Aymami J, van der Marel GA, van Boom JH, Rich A, Wang AH-J. 1989. Molecular structure of the netropsin-d(CGCGATATCGCG) complex: DNA conformation in an alternating AT segment. *Biochemistry* 28:310–20

17. Coll M, Fredrick CA, Wang AHJ, Rich A. 1987. A bifurcated hydrogen-bonded conformation in the d(A·T) base pairs of the DNA dodecamer d(CGCAAATTTGCG) and its complex with distamycin. *Proc. Natl. Acad. Sci. USA* 84:8385–89

18. Crothers DM, Drak J, Kahn JD, Levene SD. 1992. DNA bending, flexibility, and helical repeat by cyclization kinetics. *Methods Enzymol.* 212:3–29

19. Dervan PB. 1986. Design of sequence-specific DNA binding molecules. *Science* 232:464–71

20. Dickerson RE. 1992. DNA structure from A to Z. *Methods Enzymol.* 211:67–111

21. DiGabriele AD, Sanderson MR, Steitz TA. 1989. Crystal lattice packing is important in determining the bend of a DNA dodecamer containing an adenine tract. *Proc. Natl. Acad. Sci. USA* 86:1816–20

22. Dwyer TJ, Geierstanger BH, Bathini Y, Lown JW, Wemmer DE. 1992. Design and binding of a distamycin A analog to d(CGCAAGTTGGC)·d(G-CCAACTTGCG): synthesis, NMR studies, and implications for the design of sequence-specific minor groove binding oligopeptides. *J. Am. Chem. Soc.* 114:5911–19

23. Dwyer TJ, Geierstanger BH, Mrksich M, Dervan PB, Wemmer DE. 1993. Structural analysis of covalent peptide dimers, bis(pyridine-2-carboxamidonetropsin)(CH₂)₃₋₆, in complex with 5′-TGACT-3′ sites by two-dimensional NMR. *J. Am. Chem. Soc.* 115:9900–6

24. Fagan PA, Wemmer DE. 1992. Cooperative binding of distamycin-A to DNA in the 2:1 mode. *J. Am. Chem. Soc.* 114:1080–81

25. Fede A, Billeter M, Leupin W, Wüthrich K. 1993. Determination of the NMR solution structure of the Hoechst 33258-d(GTGGAATTCC-AC)₂ complex and comparison with the X-ray structure. *Struct. Curr. Biol.* 1:177–86

26. Fox KR, Davies H, Adams GR, Portugal J, Waring M. 1988. Sequence-specific binding of luzopeptin to DNA. *Nucleic Acids Res.* 16:2489–2507

27. Fox KR, Howarth NR. 1985. Investigations into the sequence-selective binding of mithramycin and related ligands to DNA. *Nucleic Acids Res.* 13:8695–8714

28. Fox KR, Waring MJ. 1984. DNA structural variations produced by actinomycin and distamycin as revealed by DNase I footprinting. *Nucleic Acids Res.* 12:9271–85

29. Frederick CA, Williams LD, Ughetto G, van der Marel GA, van Boom JH, et al. 1990. Structural comparison of anticancer drug-DNA complexes: adriamycin and daunomycin. *Biochemistry* 29:2538–49

30. Gao X, Mirau P, Patel DJ. 1992. Structure refinement of the chromomycin dimer-DNA complex in solution. *J. Mol. Biol.* 223:259–79

31. Gao X, Patel DJ. 1988. NMR studies of echinomycin bisintercalation complexes with d(A1-C2-G3-T4) and d(T1-C2-G3-A4) duplexes in aqueous solution: sequence-dependent formation of Hoogsteen A1·T4 and Watson-Crick T1·A4 base pairs flanking the bisintercalation site. *Biochemistry* 27:1744–51

32. Gao X, Patel DJ. 1989. Solution structure of the chromomycin-DNA complex. *Biochemistry* 28:751–62

33. Gao X, Patel DJ. 1990. Chromomycin dimer-DNA oligomer complexes. Sequence selectivity and divalent cation specificity. *Biochemistry* 29:10940–56

34. Gao YG, Sriram M, Denny WA,

Wang AH-J. 1993. Minor groove binding of SN6999 to an alkylated DNA: molecular structure of d(CGC[e^6]AATTCGCG)-SN6999 complex. *Biochemistry* 32:9639–48

35. Geierstanger BH, Dwyer TJ, Bathini Y, Lown JW, Wemmer DE. 1993. NMR characterization of a hetero-complex formed by distamycin and its analog 2-ImD with d(CGCA-AGTTGGC):d(GCCAACTTGCG): preference for the 1:1:1 2-ImD:Dst: DNA complex over the 2:1 2-ImD: DNA and the 2:1 Dst:DNA complexes. *J. Am. Chem. Soc.* 115: 4474–82

36. Geierstanger BH, Jacobsen JP, Mrksich M, Dervan PB, Wemmer DE. 1994. Structural and dynamic characterization of the heterodimeric and homodimeric complexes of dista-mycin and 1-methylimidazole-2-car-boxamide-netropsin bound to the minor groove of DNA. *Biochemistry* 33:3055–62

37. Geierstanger BH, Mrksich M, Der-van PB, Wemmer DE. 1994. Design of a G·C-specific DNA minor groove binding peptide. *Science* 266:646–50

38. Gilbert DE, Feigon J. 1991. The DNA sequence at echinomycin binding sites determines the structural changes induced by drug binding: NMR studies of echinomycin binding to [d(ACGTACGT)]$_2$ and [d(TCGAT-CGA)]$_2$. *Biochemistry* 30:2483–94

39. Gilbert DE, Feigon J. 1992. Proton NMR study of the [d(ACGTA-TACGT)]$_2$-2echinomycin complex: conformational changes between echinomycin binding sites. *Nucleic Acids Res.* 20:2411–20

40. Goodsell D, Dickerson RE. 1986. Isohelical analysis of DNA groove-binding drugs. *J. Med. Chem.* 29: 727–33

41. Goodsell DS, Kopka ML, Cascio D, Dickerson RE. 1993. Crystal structure of CATGGCCATG and its implications for A-tract bending models. *Proc. Natl. Acad. Sci. USA* 90: 2930–34

42. Grzeskowiak K, Yanagi K, Privé GG, Dickerson RE. 1991. The structure of B-helical CGATCGATCG and comparison with CCAACGTTGG. *J. Biol. Chem.* 266:8861–83

43. Heinemann U, Alings C. 1989. Crys-tallographic study of one turn of G/C rich B-DNA. *J. Mol. Biol.* 210: 369–81

44. Heinemann U, Alings C, Bansal M.

1992. Double helix conformation, groove dimensions and ligand binding potential of a G/C stretch in B-DNA. *EMBO J.* 11:1931–39

45. Hu S, Weisz K, James TL, Shafer RH. 1992. ^{1}H-NMR studies on d(GCTTAAGC)$_2$ and its complex with berenil. *Eur. J. Biochem.* 204: 31–38

46. Huang H, Pratum TK, Hopkins PB. 1994. Covalent structure of the DNA-DNA interstrand cross-link formed by the reductively activated FR66979 in synthetic DNA duplexes. *J. Am. Chem. Soc.* 116:2703–9

47. Hurley LH, Draves PH. 1993. Molec-ular aspects of the interaction of (+)-CC-1065 with DNA. In *Molecular Aspects of Anticancer Drug-DNA Inter-actions*, ed. S Neidle, M Waring, 1: 89–133. Boca Raton: CRC

48. Jenkins TC, Lane AN, Neidle S, Brown DG. 1993. NMR and molecu-lar modeling studies of the interaction of berenil and pentamidine with d(CGCAAATTTGCG)$_2$. *Eur. J. Bio-chem.* 213:1175–84

49. Kissinger K, Krowicki K, Dabrowiak JC, Lown JW. 1987. Molecular rec-ognition between oligopeptides and nucleic acids. Monocationic imidaz-ole lexitropsins that display enhanced GC sequence dependent DNA bind-ing. *Biochemistry* 26:5590–95

50. Klevit RE, Wemmer D, Reid BR. 1986. ^{1}H NMR studies on the interac-tion between distamycin A and a symmetrical DNA dodecamer. *Bio-chemistry* 25:3296–3303

51. Koo H-S, Wu H-M, Crothers DM. 1986. DNA bending at adenine·thy-mine tracts. *Nature* 320:501–6

52. Kopka ML, Yoon C, Goodsell D, Pjura P, Dickerson RE. 1985. Binding of an antitumor drug to DNA: netrop-sin and CGCGAATT^{Br}CGCG. *J. Mol. Biol.* 183:553–63

53. Kopka ML, Yoon C, Goodsell D, Pjura P, Dickerson RE. 1985. The molecular origin of DNA-drug speci-ficity in netropsin and distamycin. *Proc. Natl. Acad. Sci. USA* 82: 1376–80

54. Kumar S, Jaseja M, Zimmerman J, Yadagiri B, Pon RT, Sapse A-M, Lown JW. 1990. Molecular recogni-tion and binding of a GC site–avoid-ing thiazole-lexitropsin to the decade-oxynucleotide d(CGCAATTGCG)$_2$: ^{1}H-NMR evidence for thiazole inter-calation. *J. Biomol. Struct. Dyn.* 8: 99–121

55. Kumar S, Joseph T, Singh MP, Yadagiri B, Lown JW. 1992. Structure and dynamics of ligand-template interactions of topoisomerase inhibitory analogs of Hoechst 33258: high field ^{1}H-NMR and restrained molecular mechanics studies. *J. Biomol. Struct. Dyn.* 9:853–80

56. Kumar S, Lipman R, Tomasz M. 1992. Recognition of specific DNA sequences by mitomycin C for alkylation. *Biochemistry* 31:1399–1407

57. Kumar S, Yadagiri B, Zimmerman J, Pon RT, Lown JW. 1990. Sequence specific molecular recognition and binding by a GC recognizing Hoechst 33258 analogue to the decadeoxyribonucleotide d-[CATGGCCATG]$_2$: structural and dynamic aspects deduced from high field ^{1}H-NMR studies. *J. Biomol. Struct. Dyn.* 8:331–57

58. Lane AN, Jenkins TC, Brown T, Neidle S. 1991. Interaction of berenil with the EcoR1 dodecamer d(CGCGAATTCGCG)$_2$ in solution studied by NMR. *Biochemistry* 30:1372–85

59. Larsen TA, Goodsell DS, Cascio D, Grzeskowiak K, Dickerson RE. 1989. The structure of DAPI bound to DNA. *J. Biomol. Struct. Dyn.* 7:477–91

60. Lee M, Chang DK, Hartley JA, Pon RT, Krowicki K, Lown JW. 1988. Structural and dynamic aspects of binding of a prototype lexitropsin to the decadeoxyribonucleotide d(CGCAATTGCG)$_2$ deduced from high-resolution ^{1}H NMR studies. *Biochemistry* 27:445–55

61. Lee M, Coulter DM, Pon RT, Krowicki K, Lown JW. 1988. Sequence specific molecular recognition and binding of a monocationic bis-imidazole lexitropsin to the decadeoxyribonucleotide d-[(GATCCGTATG)·(CATACGGATC)]: structural and dynamic aspects of intermolecular exchange studied by ^{1}H-NMR. *J. Biomol. Struct. Dyn.* 5:1059–87

62. Lee M, Hartley JA, Pon RT, Krowicki K, Lown JW. 1988. Sequence specific molecular recognition by a monocationic lexitropsin of the decadeoxyribonucleotide d-[CATGGCCATG]$_2$: structural and dynamic aspects deduced from high field ^{1}H-NMR studies. *Nucleic Acids Res.* 16:665–84

63. Lee M, Krowicki K, Hartley JA, Pon RT, Lown JW. 1988. Molecular recognition between oligopeptides and nucleic acids: influence of van der Waals contacts in determining the 3'-terminus of DNA sequences read by monocationic lexitropsins. *J. Am. Chem. Soc.* 110:3641–49

64. Lee M, Krowicki K, Shea R, Lown JW, Pon RT. 1989. Molecular recognition between oligopeptides and nucleic acids. Specificity of binding a monocationic bis-lexitropsin to DNA deduced from footprinting and ^{1}H NMR studies. *J. Mol. Recognit.* 2:84–93

65. Lee M, Rhodes AL, Wyatt MD, Forrow S, Hartley J. 1993. GC base sequence recognition by oligo(imidazolecarboxamide) and terminus-modified analogues of distamycin deduced from circular dichroism, proton nuclear magnetic resonance, and methidiumpropylethylenediaminetetraacetate-iron(II) footprinting studies. *Biochemistry* 32:4237–45

66. Leroy JL, Charretier E, Kochoyan M, Gueron M. 1988. Evidence from base-pair kinetics for two types of adenine tract structures in solution: their relation to DNA curvature. *Biochemistry* 27:8894–98

67. Leupin W, Chazin WJ, Hyberts S, Denny WA, Wüthrich K. 1986. NMR studies of the complex between the decanucleotide d(GCATTAATGC)$_2$ and a minor-groove-binding drug. *Biochemistry* 25:5902–10

68. Li TH, Zeng ZJ, Estevez VA, Baldenius KU, Nicolaou KC, Joyce GF. 1994. Carbohydrate-minor groove interactions in the binding of calicheamicin γ_1^I to duplex DNA. *J. Am. Chem. Soc.* 116:3709–15

69. Lin CH, Beale JM, Hurley LH. 1991. Structure of the (+)-CC-1065-DNA adduct: critical role of ordered water molecules and implications for involvement of phosphate catalysis in the covalent reaction. *Biochemistry* 30:3597–3602

70. Liu X, Chen H, Patel DJ. 1991. Solution structure of actinomycin-DNA complexes: drug intercalation at isolated G-C sites. *J. Biomol. NMR* 1:323–47

71. Lootiens FG, McLaughlin LW, Diekmann S, Clegg RM. 1991. Binding of Hoechst 33258 and DAPI to self-complementary decadeoxynucleotides with modified exocyclic base substituents. *Biochemistry* 30:182–89

72. Low CML, Drew HR, Waring MJ. 1984. Sequence-specific binding of echinomycin to DNA: evidence for

conformational changes affecting flanking sequences. *Nucleic Acids Res.* 12:4865–79

73. Low CML, Fox KR, Olsen RK, Waring MJ. 1986. DNA sequence recognition by under-methylated analogues of triostin A. *Nucleic Acids Res.* 14:2015–33

74. Lown JW, Krowicki K, Bhat UG, Skorobogaty A, Ward B, Dabrowiak JC. 1986. Molecular recognition between oligopeptides and nucleic acids: novel imidazole-containing oligopeptides related to netropsin that exhibit altered DNA sequence specificity. *Biochemistry* 25:7408–16

75. Mazzini S, Musco G, Ragg E. 1994. Binding modes of the distamycin analog FCE-24517 to d(CGTATACG)$_2$. ^{1}H and ^{13}C sequence-specific assignments. *Magn. Reson. Chem.* 52:139–50

76. Mrksich M, Dervan PB. 1993. Antiparallel side-by-side heterodimer for sequence-specific recognition in the minor groove of DNA by a distamycin/1-methylimidazole-2-carboxamide-netropsin pair. *J. Am. Chem. Soc.* 115:2572–76

77. Mrksich M, Dervan PB. 1993. Enhanced sequence specific recognition in the minor groove of DNA by covalent peptide dimers: bis(pyridine-2-carboxamidonetropsin)(CH$_2$)$_{3-6}$. *J. Am. Chem. Soc.* 115:9892–99

78. Mrksich M, Dervan PB. 1994. Design of a covalent peptide heterodimer for sequence-specific recognition in the minor groove of double-helical DNA. *J. Am. Chem. Soc.* 116:3663–64

79. Mrksich M, Parks ME, Dervan PB. 1994. Hairpin peptide motif. A new class of oligopeptides for sequence-specific recognition in the minor groove of double-helical DNA. *J. Am. Chem. Soc.* 116:7983–88

80. Mrksich M, Wade WS, Dwyer TJ, Geierstanger BH, Wemmer DE, Dervan PB. 1992. Antiparallel side-by-side dimeric motif for sequence-specific recognition in the minor groove of DNA by the designed peptide 1-methylimidazole-2-carboxamide netropsin. *Proc. Natl. Acad. Sci. USA* 89:7586–90

81. Nelson HCM, Finch JT, Luisi BF, Klug A. 1987. The structure of an oligo(dA)·oligo(dT) tract and its biological implications. *Nature* 330:221–26

82. Norman D, Live D, Sastry M, Lipman R, Hingerty BE, et al. 1990. NMR and computational characterization of mitomycin cross-linked to adjacent deoxyguanosines in the minor groove of the d(TACGTA)·d(TACGTA) duplex. *Biochemistry* 29:2861–75

83. Paloma LG, Smith JA, Chazin WJ, Nicolaou KC. 1994. Interaction of calicheamicin with duplex DNA: role of the oligosaccharide domain and identification of multiple binding modes. *J. Am. Chem. Soc.* 116:3697–3708

84. Patel DJ. 1982. Antibiotic-DNA interactions: intermolecular nuclear Overhauser effects in the netropsin-d(C-G-C-G-A-A-T-T-C-G-C-G) complex in solution. *Proc. Natl. Acad. Sci. USA* 79:6424–28

85. Pelton JG, Wemmer DE. 1988. Structural modeling of the distamycin A-d(CGCGAATTCGCG)$_2$ complex using 2D NMR and molecular mechanics. *Biochemistry* 27:8088–96

86. Pelton JG, Wemmer DE. 1989. Structural characterization of a 2:1 distamycin A·d(CGCAAATTGGC) complex by two-dimensional NMR. *Proc. Natl. Acad. Sci. USA* 86:5723–27

87. Pelton JG, Wemmer DE. 1990. Binding modes of distamycin A with d(CGCAAATTTGCG)$_2$ determined by two-dimensional NMR. *J. Am. Chem. Soc.* 112:1393–99

88. Pjura PE, Grzeskowiak K, Dickerson RE. 1987. Binding of Hoechst 33258 to the minor groove of B-DNA. *J. Mol. Biol.* 197:257–91

89. Plouvier B, Bailly Ch, Houssin R, Rao KE, Lown JW, et al. 1991. DNA-sequence specific recognition by a thiazole analogue of netropsin: a comparative footprinting study. *Nucleic Acids Res.* 19:5821–29

90. Pullman A, Pullman B. 1981. Molecular electrostatic potential of the nucleic acids. *Q. Rev. Biophys.* 14:289–380

91. Pullman B. 1990. Molecular mechanisms of specificity in DNA-antitumor drug interactions. In *Theoretical Biochemistry and Molecular Biophysics,* ed. DL Beveridge, R Lavery, pp. 193–205. Guilderland, NY: Adenine

92. Quintana JR, Lipanov AA, Dickerson RE. 1991. Low temperature crystallographic analysis of the binding of Hoechst 33258 to the double-helical DNA dodecamer CGCGAATTCGCG. *Biochemistry* 30:10294–10306

93. Rentzeperis D, Marky LA. 1993. Netropsin binding as a thermodynamic

probe of the grooves of parallel DNA. *J. Am. Chem. Soc.* 155:1645–50

94. Saenger W. 1984. *Principles of Nucleic Acid Structure.* New York: Springer-Verlag. 556 pp.

95. Sastry M, Patel DJ. 1993. Solution structure of the mithramycin dimer-DNA complex. *Biochemistry* 32:6588–6604

96. Scahill TA, Jensen RM, Swenson DH, Hatzenbuhler NT, Petzold G, et al. 1990. An NMR study of the covalent and noncovalent interactions of CC-1065 and DNA. *Biochemistry* 29:2852–60

97. Searle M. 1993. NMR studies of drug-DNA interactions. *Prog. NMR Spectrosc.* 25:403–80

98. Searle MS, Bicknell W, Wakelin LP, Denny WA. 1991. Anthracycline antibiotic arugomycin binds in both grooves of the DNA helix simultaneously: an NMR and molecular modelling study. *Nucleic Acids Res.* 19:2897–2906

99. Seeman NC, Rosenberg JM, Rich A. 1976. Sequence-specific recognition of double helical nucleic acids by proteins. *Proc. Natl. Acad. Sci. USA* 73:804–8

100. Sigurdsson ST, Rink SM, Hopkins PB. 1993. Affinity cross-linking of duplex DNA by a pyrrole-oligopeptide conjugate. *J. Am. Chem. Soc.* 115:12633–34

101. Spielmann HP, Fagan PA, Bregant TM, Little RD, Wemmer DE. 1994. The binding modes of a rationally designed photoactivated DNA nuclease. *Nucleic Acids Res.* Submitted

102. Spolar RS, Record MT. 1994. Coupling of local folding to site-specific binding of proteins to DNA. *Science* 263:777–84

103. Sriram M, van der Marel GA, Roelen HLPF, van Boom JH, Wang AH-J. 1992. Conformation of B-DNA containing O^6-ethyl-G-C base pairs stabilized by minor groove binding drugs: molecular structure of d(CGC[e⁶]G-AATTCGCG) complexed with Hoechst 33258 or Hoechst 33342. *EMBO J.* 11:225–32

104. Sun D, Hansen M, Clement JJ, Hurley LH. 1993. Structure of the altromycin B (N7-guanine)-DNA adduct. A proposed prototypic DNA adduct structure for the pluramycin antitumor antibiotics. *Biochemistry* 32:8068–74

105. Sun D, Lin CH, Hurley LH. 1993. A-

tract and (+)-CC-1065-induced binding of DNA. Comparison of structural features using non-denaturing gel analysis, hydroxyl-radical footprinting, and high-field NMR. *Biochemistry* 32:4487–95

106. Teng MK, Usman N, Fredrick CA, Wang AH-J. 1988. The molecular structure of the complex of Hoechst 33258 and the DNA dodecamer d(CGCGAATTCGCG). *Nucleic Acids Res.* 16:2671–90

107. Trotta E, D'Ambrosio E, Del Grosso N, Ravagnan G, Cirilli M, Paci M. 1993. ¹H NMR study of d(GCGATCGC)₂ and its interaction with minor groove binding 4′,6′-diamidino-2-phenylindole. *J. Biol. Chem.* 268:3944–51

108. Uesugi M, Sugiura Y. 1993. New insights into sequence recognition process of esperamicin A_1 and calicheamicin $γ_1^I$: origin of their selectivities and "induced fit" mechanism. *Biochemistry* 32:4622–27

109. Ughetto G, Wang AH-J, Quigley GJ, van der Marel GA, van Boom JH, Rich A. 1985. A comparison of the structure of echinomycin and triostin A complexed to a DNA fragment. *Nucleic Acids Res.* 13:2305–23

110. Van Dyke MW, Dervan PB. 1983. Chromomycin, mithramycin, and olivomycin binding sites on heterogeneous deoxyribonucleic acid. Footprinting with (methidiumpropyl-EDTA)iron(II). *Biochemistry* 22:2372–77

111. Van Dyke MW, Dervan PB. 1984. Echinomycin binding sites on DNA. *Science* 225:1122–27

112. Van Dyke MW, Hertzberg RP, Dervan PB. 1982. Map of distamycin, netropsin, and actinomycin binding sites on heterogeneous DNA: DNA cleavage-inhibition patterns with methidiumpropyl-EDTA·Fe(II). *Proc. Natl. Acad. Sci. USA* 79:5470–74

113. van Houte LPA, van Garderen CJ, Patel DJ. 1993. The antitumor drug nogalamycin forms two different intercalation complexes with d(GCGT)·d(ACGC). *Biochemistry* 32:1667–74

114. Wade WS, Dervan PB. 1987. Alteration of the sequence specificity of distamycin on DNA by replacement of an N-methylpyrrolecarboxamide with pyridine-2-carboxamide. *J. Am. Chem. Soc.* 109:1574–75

115. Wade WS, Mrksich M, Dervan PB.

1992. Design of peptides that bind in the minor groove of DNA at 5′-(A,T)-G(A,T)C(A,T)-3′ sequences by a dimeric side-by-side motif. *J. Am. Chem. Soc.* 114:8783–94

116. Wade WS, Mrksich M, Dervan PB. 1993. Binding affinities of synthetic peptides, pyridine-2-carboxamidonetropsin and 1-methylimidazole-2-carboxamidonetropsin, that form 2:1 complexes in the minor groove of double-helical DNA. *Biochemistry* 32:11385–89

117. Walker S, Murnick J, Kahne D. 1993. Structural characterization of a calicheamicin-DNA complex by NMR. *J. Am. Chem. Soc.* 115:7954–61

118. Wang AH-J, Ughetto G, Quigley GJ, Hakoshima T, van der Marel GA, et al. 1984. The molecular structure of a DNA-triostin A complex. *Science* 225:1115–21

119. Wang AH-J, Ughetto G, Quigley GJ, Rich A. 1986. Interactions of quinoxaline antibiotic and DNA: the molecular structure of a triostin A–d(-GCGTACGC) complex. *J. Biomol. Struct. Dyn.* 4:319–42

120. Waterloh K, Olsen RK, Fox KR. 1992. Bifunctional intercalator [N-MeCys³,N-MeCys⁷]TANDEM binds to the dinucleotide TpA. *Biochemistry* 31:6246–53

121. Wemmer DE, Geierstanger BH, Fagan PA, Dwyer TJ, Jacobsen JP, et al. 1994. Minor groove recognition of DNA by distamycin and its analogs. In *Structural Biology: The State of the Art, Proc. Eighth Conversation*

on *Biomolecular Stereodynamics,* ed. SM Sarma, MH Sarma, 2:301–23. Guilderland, NY: Adenine

122. Wing R, Drew H, Takano T, Broka C, Tanaka S, et al. 1980. Crystal structure analysis of a complete turn of B-DNA. *Nature* 287:755–58

123. Woo J, Sigurdsson ST, Hopkins PB. 1993. DNA interstrand cross-linking reactions of pyrrole-derived, bifunctional electrophiles: evidence for a common target site in DNA. *J. Am. Chem. Soc.* 115:3407–15

124. Xu YJ, Zhen YS, Goldberg IH. 1994. C1027 chromophore, a potent new enediyne antitumor antibiotic, induces sequence-specific double-strand DNA cleavage. *Biochemistry* 33:5947–54

125. Yoon C, Privé GG, Goodsell DS, Dickerson RE. 1988. Structure of an alternating–B DNA helix and its relationship to A-tract DNA. *Proc. Natl. Acad. Sci. USA* 85:6332–36

126. Zhang H, Gao YG, van der Marel GA, van Boom JH, Wang AH-J. 1993. Simultaneous incorporations of two anticancer drugs into DNA. *J. Biol. Chem.* 268:10095–10101

127. Zhang XL, Patel DJ. 1991. Solution structure of the luzopeptin-DNA complex. *Biochemistry* 30:4026–41

128. Zimmer C, Wähnert U. 1986. Nonintercalating DNA-binding ligands: specificity of the interaction and their use as tools in biophysical, biochemical and biological investigations of the genetic material. *Prog. Biophys. Mol. Biol.* 47:31–112

Annu. Rev. Biophys. Biomol. Struct. 1995. 24:495–522

COMPACT INTERMEDIATE STATES IN PROTEIN FOLDING

Anthony L. Fink

Department of Chemistry and Biochemistry, University of California, Santa Cruz, California 95064

KEY WORDS: molten globule, partially folded intermediate, denatured state

CONTENTS

ABSTRACT

The number of observations of both stable and transient partially folded intermediates is now sufficient for us to assume that all proteins, under the appropriate conditions, will form such species. These intermediates are characterized by substantial secondary structure and little tertiary structure; a collapsed conformation more compact than the unfolded state; exposed hydrophobic surfaces, which lead to binding of hydro-

1056-8700/95/0610-0495$05.00

phobic dyes and a propensity to aggregate; and a heat capacity similar to that of the unfolded state. The term compact intermediates encompasses a broad range of conformations and degrees of folding and compactness: compact intermediates have no single, unique conformation, but rather a whole plethora of structures that range from being very similar to the native state to being substantially expanded and significantly unfolded. The properties of compact intermediates from different proteins, and in some cases from the same protein under different conditions, may be significantly different. Equilibrium compact intermediates may be good models for transient intermediates formed during folding.

PERSPECTIVES AND OVERVIEW

Compact intermediates of proteins have been observed under both transient and equilibrium conditions. In addition, evidence for the existence of compact substates of the unfolded state is growing. The numerous papers published in the past two or three years on this subject means that this review must be selective rather than comprehensive; mostly, it focuses on equilibrium intermediates, which have been the subject of several previous reviews (6, 20, 27, 28, 32, 42, 64, 77, 80, 81, 110, 111). Sufficient numbers of different proteins forming stable-equilibrium, partially folded conformations have been observed that we can make the generalization that all proteins, under the appropriate conditions, will form such species. Although the number of reports is much smaller for transient intermediates observed during refolding, a similar generalization can be made for such transient species. In fact, the so-called molten globule has been proposed to be a universal intermediate in protein folding (112).

Considerable controversy has surrounded the nature of compact intermediates, particularly the molten globule. The major source of the apparently contradictory aspects of compact intermediates from different studies probably stems from significant differences in the conformational state of a partially folded intermediate, either from the same protein under different conditions or from different proteins. A further complication arises from the fact that the conditions used to examine a putative compact intermediate may result in an equilibrium mixture of intermediate and unfolded (or native) species.

Stable compact intermediates have most frequently been observed under conditions of low pH and moderate salt concentration (A states) (43, 50), high pH and moderate salt concentration (51), or low to moderate concentration of denaturant (often at neutral pH) (111). In many cases, removal of ligands, disruption of disulfide bonds, or mutations can result in destabilization of the native state, also leading to formation of an intermediate conformation. Thermally denatured proteins frequently exhibit evidence of residual structure, which in some cases may result from the presence of compact intermediates. With moderate concentrations of denaturant, a mixture of the intermediate and unfolded or native states may be present. Unfortunately the size of many experimentally detected intermediates has not been measured, and thus it is a presumption that they are compact.

The key properties of compact-intermediate states are: (a) substantial secondary structure—in most cases the secondary structure present is probably also present in the native state; (b) absence of much of the native-like tertiary structure, especially as detected with near-UV circular dichroism (CD) and one-dimensional (1D) NMR; (c) a collapsed structure manifested by a hydrodynamic radius more similar to that of the native state than that of the unfolded state; (d) a hydrophobic core; (e) a variable amount of structure and compactness, depending on the particular protein and the particular experimental conditions; (f) substantial exposure of hydrophobic surfaces, leading to binding of hydrophobic dyes such as 8-anilinonaphthalene-1-sulfonic acid (ANS) and a propensity to aggregate; (g) a lack of functional properties; (h) a heat capacity similar to that of the unfolded state; and finally, (i) a less-cooperative unfolding transition than that of the native state, although the degree of cooperativity may vary substantially depending on the amount of structure present in the intermediate. The transition may or may not be a first-order phase transition.

Several additional important points can also now be made about compact denatured states of proteins. (a) There is no single, general compact intermediate with a common structure; instead, each individual protein will have one or more significantly stable compact intermediates. Thus, the properties of compact intermediates from different proteins vary, and even compact intermediates from the same protein may differ, depending on the conditions used to observe the protein. (b) Many compact intermediates are likely to consist of one of two basic structural types: either native state–like regions of secondary structure connected by disordered regions of polypeptide, but still retaining a relatively native state–like topology, or a core of native-like structure, surrounded by unfolded or relatively unfolded polypeptide. (c) Compact intermediates are difficult to distinguish from compact substates of the unfolded protein (especially because the energetic difference between relatively expanded compact intermediates and compact unfolded states resides mostly in the entropy and not the enthalpy).

The most widely described compact denatured state of proteins is the molten globule. This term was first used in the literature by Ohgushi & Wada (104) to describe the acid-denatured state of cytochrome c, which resembled a compact state with native-like secondary structure, but fluctuating tertiary structure, and was similar to a species previously reported by Ptitsyn and coworkers for α-lactalbumin (34). The major distinguishing characteristics of the theoretical molten globule are near-native-like secondary structure, little rigid tertiary structure, and a compactness very similar to that of the native state ($\sim 10\%$ expansion in hydrodynamic radius). However, the term is now used in a rather general way, at least by many authors, to describe any denatured (nonnative) state with significant secondary structure and a propensity to bind hydrophobic dyes such as ANS. Because the only detailed characterization of the molten globule is the theoretical one (45, 109), the term should probably be restricted to species that clearly fit the definition (however, its widespread use as a synonym for folding intermediate is well-entrenched).

Among the controversial and unanswered issues regarding compact intermediates are the following: (a) Whereas the molten globule is by definition quite compact (45, 110), the observed properties of compact intermediates from different proteins (43), and in some cases from the same protein under different conditions (KA Oberg, S Seshadri & AL Fink, submitted), vary significantly. This variation suggests multiple types of intermediate, some of which are quite expanded. Thus, rather than a single unique type of general intermediate a wide variety is observed, ranging from very compact, highly structured forms (119) to collapsed forms of the unfolded state (substantially expanded) (105). In addition, in some cases the conditions used to stabilize a compact intermediate have been ones that led to an equilibrium mixture of compact-intermediate and unfolded states [e.g. apomyoglobin at pH 2, 0.15 M NaCl (13)—at least twice this much salt is required to complete the transition to the A state (52); similarly, studies on cytochrome c in D_2O (73) were performed at a pH in which substantial unfolded protein would be present (53)]. (b) Several investigations have led to the conclusion that the intermediates detected under equilibrium conditions are similar to the transient kinetic intermediates observed during refolding (7, 37, 69, 71, 103), but this question remains to be answered unambiguously and in detail. (c) Is the transition from intermediate to unfolded state a first- or second-order phase transition? Again, there are conflicting claims (e.g. 55, 57). (d) For a given protein, how many (meta-)stable compact intermediates exist? (e) Are the observed compact intermediates true intermediates or are they compact substates of the unfolded state? (f) What are the common structural (and dynamic) features of compact intermediates?

An additional complication arises from the nomenclature in this field. The variety of names for partially folded intermediates reflects the confusion regarding the underlying structure. Although the terms compact intermediate, molten globule, and compact denatured states, among others, have often been used interchangeably, along with the term A state for such species found at low pH, it is desirable that in future more careful attention be paid in describing these species. Preferably the term molten globule should be limited to species that fit its definition (see above). Compact intermediate should be restricted to those species that have been shown, in fact, to be compact. Partially folded intermediate is one possible generic term, when specific details of the structure are unknown; compact denatured state is another, although it has certain connotations that make it less desirable.

MULTIPLE FORMS OF COMPACT-INTERMEDIATE STATES

To account for observations of intermediates that are clearly more expanded than the molten globule, the description of the molten globule has been extended to include both expanded and compact versions (6, 26, 113, 136). It is clearly a mistake to lump all compact intermediates or molten globules together and consider them a single intermediate with common features. On the contrary, it has become apparent that compact intermediates encompass a broad range of conformations and degrees of folding and compactness.

We can reasonably assume that a few conformational states of a given protein will correspond to significant minima in the potential energy surface, in addition to the global minimum. These more stable species would correspond to the observed transient and equilibrium intermediates in folding. The structural factors that lead to the particular stability of these species probably reflect a limited number of metastable arrangements of the polypeptide chain (probably involving the interactions of secondary structural units and hydrophobic clustering). Thus, intermediate conformations observed under both transient and equilibrium conditions will likely exhibit common structural elements.

Strong support for the existence of multiple, stable compact intermediates of the same protein comes from investigations of the A states of apomyoglobin. The addition of anions to the acid-unfolded state of apomyoglobin (pH 2, no salt) leads to formation of the A state. Furthermore, different anions result in A states with different amounts of secondary structure, as detected using CD or Fourier transform infrared (FTIR) spectroscopy (54; KA Oberg, S Seshadri & AL Fink, submitted); regardless of the anion, one of three levels of secondary structure was seen, corresponding to approximately 38, 48, or 60% of the sequence as helix (the native state has 71% and the acid-unfolded 6% helix). Characterization of these three A states showed that they differed significantly in their structure and were monodisperse. For example, the A state with trichloroacetate is the most compact and has the most secondary structure, that with chloride has the least structure and is the most expanded, and that with trifluoroacetate has intermediate properties. Other anions induced A states with properties equivalent to one of these three, indicating that the three are particularly favored conformations. Note that the anion concentrations required are usually in the low to mid-millimolar range (54). The near-UV CD and Trp fluorescence signals indicated that the two Trp residues (on the A helix) are in a nonpolar environment in all the A states. Of particular interest is the fact that the three equilibrium compact intermediates appear to correspond to the three transient intermediates seen in the refolding experiments (74) and to a core of the A, G, and H helices in the most expanded A state. Additional stable helices are present in the more structured A states. Not surprisingly, the data show that the more compact A states have more native-like structure than the expanded ones. Preliminary observations on the acid-denaturation properties of staphylococcal nuclease show that different anions yield A states of different degrees of folding (44), suggesting a similar situation for other proteins. At least two other cases have been reported in which more than one form of compact intermediate is apparent for a given protein: β-lactamase (136) and α-lactalbumin (86).

Various structural probes suggest that the α-lactalbumin molten globule is similar to the native state (107). On the other hand, data from, for example, disulfide trapping (31) and calorimetric studies (55) indicate that the α-lactalbumin molten globule is more akin to a compact unfolded state. One potential complication is that the α-lactalbumin molten globule has been studied under various conditions: neutral (in the absence of Ca^{2+}) to acidic or basic pH, low denaturant concentration, and from different sources (human, bovine, guinea pig) (80, 111). Therefore, we must consider the possibility that different structural forms of the intermediate may be present under different conditions. In fact, the molten globule of apo-α-lactalbumin at neutral pH is probably more structured than the compact intermediate at acidic pH. For example, fluorescence studies on the solvent exposure of tryptophan residues indicate that the pH denaturation of α-lactalbumin results in two forms of compact intermediate corresponding to the classical α-lactalbumin molten globule and to a less compact premolten-globule conformation (86).

COMPACT INTERMEDIATES VS SUBSTATES OF THE UNFOLDED STATE

Are compact intermediates true intermediates, or are they compact forms of the unfolded state? The answer is, it depends—some compact species clearly are true intermediates, and others clearly are not. Since Shortle's (126) seminal observations regarding microsubstates of denatured staphylococcal nuclease, the importance of structure in the denatured state has been the focus of considerable attention. An interesting approach to the question has been that designed on the principle of increasing the stability of the denatured state through site-directed mutagenesis and thus decreasing the apparent stability of the native state (14, 15).

Several recent investigations indicate that for both intermediates and unfolded states the degree of folding and compactness can vary over a wide range depending on the experimental conditions. A particularly good example of this is the *Escherichia coli* molecular chaperone DnaK. In the presence of low concentrations of guanidine hydrochloride (Gdn.HCl), the native state is converted into a compact intermediate whose hydrodynamic radius increases monotonically with increasing denaturant; when first detected at low Gdn.HCl concentration (0.25 M), the Stokes radius (R_s) is 43 Å, and when last observed at higher denaturant (1.4 M) the R_s is 55 Å (105). Similarly, for the unfolded state when first detected at relatively low denaturant concentration, R_s is 53 Å, whereas at concentrations of Gdn.HCl above 4 M, R_s is 69 Å. Other possible examples of compact unfolded states include denatured staphylococcal nuclease (72) and reduced bovine pancreatic trypsin inhibitor (BPTI) (5, 58), which is relatively compact, as detected by fluorescence-energy transfer, but lacks secondary structure and ANS binding.

Although detailed studies on thermally denatured proteins have been relatively few, it is clear that, at least in some cases, such species are quite compact. For example, the hydrodynamic radius of thermally denatured ribonuclease A has a radius of gyration only 30% larger than that of the native state (131). The amount, if any, of residual structure after thermal denaturation has been controversial. NMR studies (121) suggest the absence of structure, whereas CD, FTIR, dynamic light scattering, and small-angle X-ray scattering (SAXS) experiments suggest some remaining secondary structure and significant compactness (125, 131).

TRANSIENT INTERMEDIATES

Rapid-mixing kinetics experiments, mostly using CD and NMR amide protection, reveal the formation of intermediates with substantial secondary structure and presumed compact conformations on a time scale of milliseconds or less (25, 74, 82, 83, 85, 88, 91, 93, 112, 116, 122, 135, 139). The general picture emerging is:

$$U \rightarrow I_1 \rightarrow I_2 \rightarrow I_3 \rightarrow N, \qquad\qquad 1.$$

where U represents the unfolded state, I_i an intermediate, and N the native state. In general, I_1 is formed on a submillisecond time scale and involves both collapse and formation of unstable secondary structure; I_2 represents a relatively compact intermediate with stable secondary structure; and I_3 represents an intermediate with native-like secondary structure and topology but one that lacks the tight side-chain packing of the native state. The refolding of a particular protein may show more or fewer intermediates than in Scheme 1, depending on the relative kinetics of the intermediate conversions and also as a result of the possible presence of parallel folding pathways. Particularly well-studied systems include interleukin-1β (139), lysozyme (116), apomyoglobin (74), cytochrome c (36, 122), barnase (40), staphylococcal nuclease (71), and ubiquitin (16). Not only does some evidence support the existence of parallel pathways analogous to the intermediates in Scheme 1, but recent studies of the folding of cytochrome c raise the question of whether many detected intermediates in folding are not productive intermediates on the folding pathway, but instead kinetically trapped off-pathway species (130)!

The lack of suitable methods for measuring the hydrodynamic size of proteins on millisecond time scales has made it difficult to measure the compactness of early formed intermediates in refolding experiments. Advances in technology relating to small-angle X-ray scattering measurements may solve this problem, given a recent report (35) in which the refolding of myoglobin from urea-denatured solution was monitored with stopped-flow SAXS.

Experiments to monitor the formation of secondary structure by far-UV circular dichroism invariably show the formation of substantial secondary structure within the dead time of mixing. The amount of secondary structure in this initially formed intermediate varies from as low as 30% in staphylococcal nuclease to more than 80% in α-lactalbumin (84, 135). Reasons for this variation undoubtedly include less than the native amount of secondary structure in the intermediate; contributions from the side chains and disulfide bonds to the far-UV CD signal, which only appear as the tertiary structure is formed; and the possibility of nonnative-like secondary structure in the early-folding intermediate (90).

Studies comparing the rates of lysozyme refolding with reduced disulfides vs with intact disulfides indicate that native-like tertiary contacts or interactions must exist at least some of the time in the early intermediate to allow formation of the disulfides. Additional support for early native-like topology comes from studies on barnase, one of the most characterized early kinetic intermediate systems (summarized in 40) in which site-directed mutagenesis techniques were used to stabilize and characterize the transient folding intermediate (94, 124).

Considerable evidence suggests that the equilibrium compact intermediates may be good models for the transient intermediates formed during folding (9, 69, 80, 83, 95, 103). Kinetic studies of apomyoglobin folding (74), which involved amide protection and CD, showed that an intermediate was formed within the dead time of the rapid-mixing system (5 ms) that had the CD spectrum and amide proton–exchange properties of the molten globule intermediate detected under conditions of pH ~4 and low salt (9, 10, 68). The exchange data reveal that the amide protons of the A, G, and H helices were fully protected within 6 ms after refolding was initiated. Part of the B helix is also protected in this time range, and the rest is protected within 1 s. The protons of the E and C helices become protected only after 2.5 s. Thus, the kinetic folding pathway involves an intermediate that strongly resembles the equilibrium compact intermediate, both of which have 35% helix, and the folding pathway involves initial formation of an intermediate with a core of the A, G, and H helices and part of the B helix, followed subsequently by formation of the C/D and E helices (74).

Kuwajima et al (69) suggested on the basis of the similarity of far-UV CD spectra that the molten globule closely resembled the transient intermediate in the folding of α-lactalbumin. Lysozymes are closely related structurally to α-lactalbumin, but unlike α-lactalbumin, chicken lysozyme does not readily form a stable compact intermediate, although a comparable transient intermediate does form (80). Despite their homologous structure, c-type lysozymes and α-lactalbumins differ dramatically in their unfolding behavior; the α-lactalbumins readily form a compact intermediate, whereas lysozymes unfold cooperatively to a highly unfolded state. However, equine lysozyme shows an equilibrium intermediate upon heating or in the presence of Gdn.Hcl that strongly depends on the state of calcium binding (100, 138). CD and NMR results indicate that the intermediate state possesses extensive secondary and some tertiary structure, although the latter is substantially disordered. Marked differences in the folding of human and chicken lysozyme have been observed when refolding was monitored with pulsed hydrogen exchange labeling and near- and far-UV circular dichroism (65, 115, 138). Analysis of the folding of hen lysozyme shows that the protein does not become organized in a single cooperative event but that different parts of the structure become stabilized with very different kinetics. In particular, in most molecules the α-helical domain folds faster than the β-sheet domain. Furthermore, different populations of molecules fold by kinetically distinct pathways. Thus, folding is not a simple sequential assembly process but involves parallel alternative pathways, some of which may involve substantial reorganization steps (116).

Roder, Englander, and their coworkers (36) have investigated the early steps in the folding of cytochrome c in detail. Evidence for the formation of tertiary structure during refolding appears on a time scale orders of magnitude longer than that for most of the secondary structure (36). Some question has arisen recently as to whether these "slow" intermediates observed during cytochrome c refolding are on the productive pathway: When refolding is initiated either from the molten globule or at pH 2 (3 M Gdn.HCl), refolding is very fast (<1 ms and 15 ms, respectively) (130).

Studies monitoring the binding of ANS during refolding as a function of quenching agents have shown that the initially formed intermediate in the refolding of dihydrofolate reductase (DHFR) binds ANS and that the ANS-binding sites in this early intermediate are more solvent exposed than those in subsequent intermediates (75).

COMPACT INTERMEDIATES AT LOW pH: A STATES

Compact intermediates have been most frequently observed at low pH and are usually known as A states under these conditions. A systematic investigation of the acid denaturation of several proteins revealed that their behavior could be classified into three types (43), although these classes are all manifestations of the same underlying conformational phase diagram (52) and reflect different phase-boundary positions. On HCl titration of a salt-free solution, some proteins, such as ubiquitin and T4 lysozyme, remain native-like to pH <2; others, such as α-lactalbumin, transform into the A state at pH 3–4; and a substantial number, such as cytochrome c and β-lactamase, unfold in the vicinity of pH 3–4 to the acid-unfolded state and then, below pH 2, refold into the A state (42, 50).

The acid-unfolded state (observed at low pH at very low ionic strength) may be converted into the A state by the addition of anions (42, 43, 50, 54). Different anions vary in their effectiveness (i.e. concentration required) as well as in the degree of folding they induce in the A state. A limited number of measurements indicate that the number of protons involved in the transition from the native to the acid-unfolded state is typically between two and five (21, 54, 59); similarly, the number of anions involved in triggering the transition from the acid-unfolded state to the A state is also in this range, with association constants on the order of 10^2 to 10^5 M^{-1} (43, 54). The small number of relatively tightly bound ions indicates that the conformational transitions are triggered by a few key ionizations and may point to important interactions such as salt bridges, as in T4 lysozyme, or charged histidine interactions, as in apomyoglobin (11). The mechanism leading to protein unfolding at low (or high) pH and the resulting potential formation of compact intermediates is predominantly electrostatic in nature (53, 54, 59).

The exact behavior of a given protein at low pH (or low concentration of denaturant) is a complex interplay between a variety of stabilizing and destabilizing forces, some of which are very sensitive to the environment (anions, denaturants, and temperature). The specific behavior of a particular system is determined by the underlying conformational phase diagram (9, 54). For example, the position of these phase boundaries determines that α-lactalbumin will transform directly to the molten globule (A state) as the pH decreases, whereas lysozyme will remain native and β-lactamase will initially unfold and then at lower pH refold to the compact A state.

STABILITY OF COMPACT INTERMEDIATES

As would be expected, the stabilities of compact intermediates are less than those of the corresponding native states (53, 59, 80, 111, 123, 143). Compact intermediates are probably less frequently observed in the presence of denaturants because the intermediate and native states may be destabilized to a comparable degree by the denaturant.

Although most calorimetric investigations of the transition between the compact-intermediate and unfolded state have shown no significant difference in the heat capacity and enthalpy change for unfolding (80, 111, 114), there are exceptions [e.g. cytochrome c (79), retinol-binding protein (19), α-lactalbumin (140, 141), and apomyoglobin (99)]. The data conflict regarding the thermodynamic properties of the α-lactalbumin molten globule (55, 108, 140, 143). Part of this apparent contradiction may reflect different classes of compact intermediates, some with more ordered structure than others. Several observations indicate that the transitions between a given intermediate and the corresponding native and unfolded states are two-state, or the so-called all-or-none, transitions (114, 137).

Recent studies (99) demonstrating cold-denaturation of the apomyoglobin A state add an additional dimension to the structural properties of compact intermediates. In the absence of salts, apomyoglobin is unfolded at all temperatures at pH 2. On the other hand, the A state shows a maximum stability in the vicinity of 10–20°C (depending on the anion concentration). The apomyoglobin A state undergoes a cooperative unfolding transition in which ΔC_p of the compact intermediate is less than half that of native apomyoglobin, which in turn is less than half that of native myoglobin. Examination of some of the properties of myoglobin are revealing. From the unfolded state, to the A state, to the apo-protein, to the holo-protein, secondary structure and size change relatively uniformly, whereas the change in heat capacity lags, in the sense that it remains more similar to that of the unfolded state (99). Similar results were observed with cytochrome c.

Theoretical calculations indicate that the heat-capacity differences between two different conformations are proportional to the change in solvent-accessible apolar areas (64). Thus, if the structure of the intermediate is known or can be modeled, we can calculate the heat-capacity change expected. Such calculations for the pH 4 intermediate of apomyoglobin, assuming it consists of the AGH helix core, lead to a value of 870 cal K^{-1} mol^{-1}, which may be compared to the observed value of 520 cal K^{-1} mol^{-1} (64).

Nature of the Phase Transition Between Compact Intermediates and Unfolded States

Griko & Privalov (57), using differential scanning calorimetry (DSC), have shown that the heat capacity of the pH 4 intermediate of apomyoglobin is significantly lower than that of the unfolded state; in fact, it is similar to that of the native state of apomyoglobin and is also dependent on the pH. Interestingly, the thermal unfolding of the apomyoglobin pH 4 intermediate, monitored using DSC, does not show an excess heat absorption but just a gradual change in heat capacity. Thus, this transition cannot be considered a first-order phase transition. Instead, the authors argue that the transition must reflect a second-order phase transition, as predicted theoretically for the molten globule (45). The question as to whether the pH-induced unfolding of this intermediate might in fact be a first-order phase transition remains unanswered at this time.

High-sensitivity DSC has been used to show that thermally denatured SNase at pH 8 is fully unfolded but retains some residual structure at pH 2 (22), an observation in agreement with spectroscopic studies (44). A compact intermediate in the thermal denaturation of SNase in the range of pH 4–7 has recently been characterized with DSC and spectroscopic probes (24): This species has distinctly different properties from the A state, i.e. the compact intermediate at low pH and moderate salt. 3D NMR studies have shown that the mutation G88V, which destabilizes the native state, leads to a denatured state that is more stable and more structured (ordered) than that from the wild-type, which accounts for the observed apparent destabilization of the N state (127). Both fluorescence (49) and DSC (56) measurements on the thermal unfolding of a fragment of SNase lacking the last 13 residues indicate that the transition is a first-order phase transition. However, this species has a significant near-UV CD spectrum indicative of tertiary structure, and it may not be a molten globule but instead a conformation in which the C-terminal domain of the molecule has unfolded while the N-terminal domain remains intact (24, 56). Thus, although the species is a compact intermediate, it does not fit the theoretical criteria for a molten globule. The important points are that the transition between a compact intermediate and the unfolded state can be a first-order phase transition and that not all compact intermediates have the properties expected of the theoretical molten globule. The salt-induced transition between the cytochrome c A state and the unfolded state has also been shown to be a first-order phase transition by using isothermal titration calorimetry (61).

STRUCTURAL ASPECTS OF COMPACT INTERMEDIATES

The basic structural properties of typical compact intermediates have been summarized (80, 110, 111). Unfortunately, detailed information about the structures is generally lacking. Direct characterization of compact-intermediate states by NMR is difficult because of potential line broadening from intermediate exchange caused by multiple conformational equilibria, and limited dispersion of chemical shifts resulting from loss of significant tertiary structure (12). Recent advances in heteronuclear 3D NMR, however, provide a potential means to circumvent the latter problem (118), especially in conjunction with the use of site-specific mutants.

The difficulties inherent in the application of NMR to the study of partially folded species are revealed in three studies of the A state of ubiquitin, which exists at pH 2 in 60% methanol (63). Using 2D NMR amide-protection methods, Pan & Briggs concluded that most of the native secondary structure was present (106), whereas Harding et al (63) concluded that only half of the five β-strands in the β-sheet and a partially structured α-helix were present in the A state. Stockman et al (134), using 3D NMR, assigned most of the resonances in the A state in 60% methanol and demonstrated that only the first two strands of the β-sheet were present. Nevertheless, several NMR structural characterizations of compact intermediates have been reported; these have been based mostly on amide-protection experiments (1, 2, 12, 29, 37, 71, 73, 74, 118). In general, the results reveal evidence supporting the presence of rather unstable regions of secondary structure that correspond to the same secondary structure found in the native state. In addition, a few tertiary interactions are also usually observed.

The physical characterization of the molten globule of α-lactalbumin has been detailed in a series of publications from Kuwajima & Ptitsyn's groups and is summarized in several reviews (20, 33, 80, 110, 111). NMR studies of the molten globule of α-lactalbumin reveal that, based on the limited chemical shift dispersion, the conformation of the protein at low pH is significantly unfolded (12). Interestingly, the hydrophobic clusters found in the native state are absent in the A state, but a new hydrophobic cluster is revealed by nuclear Overhauser effects (NOEs) (2, 29). In contrast to CD experiments, additional H-exchange experiments indicate little stable secondary structure in the molten globule (29). Amide-protection experiments on lysozyme denatured in 8 M urea demonstrate the difficulty of determining whether a species is an intermediate or a compact unfolded substate: A maximum protection factor of five was observed, even though the conformation shows residual structure according to CD and 1D NMR (18), and other species with classical molten globule properties show similar protection factors. This apparent discrepancy probably reflects unstable secondary structure and is consistent with a highly dynamic state.

A characteristic of most compact intermediates is the absence of tight packing in the hydrophobic core of the species. This, of course, is a predicted property of the molten globule and a significant difference from the native state, but whether it is a property of all compact intermediates is not clear. The most native-like intermediate formed during folding or refolding will probably be closest in structure to the hypothetical molten globule: This species is likely to be highly compact, with most of the native secondary structure present but lacking the key side-chain interactions and tight packing that result in the native state. The strong partitioning of the hydrophobic fluorescence probe pyrene to the compact intermediate of carbonic anhydrase is consistent with the existence of a hydrophobic core in the compact intermediate (96). The compact intermediates of interleukin-2 and -4 (both are four-helix bundle proteins) at low pH provide an interesting case in which the far- and near-UV CD as well as ANS-binding properties suggest a typical molten-globule intermediate. However, NMR experiments reveal that although almost all the native secondary structure is present, the connecting regions are highly mobile (extensively disordered) (119). Evidence for a compact core in partially folded intermediates comes from several different approaches, including large-angle X-ray scattering experiments (111). Sound velocity measurements have been used to detect differences in the properties of compact intermediates and native or unfolded states (101). NMR amide-protection experiments on compact intermediates typically show the presence of regions of native secondary structure, although these regions have quite low protection factors.

Additional support for the mobility of some compact intermediates is found in data on α-lactalbumin. Selective reduction and carboxymethylation of the disulfide bond between residues 6 and 120 in α-lactalbumin leads to a species with properties similar to those of the intact protein, with the exception that the stability of the corresponding A state is decreased, as detected in both equilibrium and kinetic experiments (70). Ewbank & Creighton (38) have carried out disulfide trapping experiments on α-lactalbumin in which this disulfide was selectively reduced. In the presence of Ca^{2+} at neutral pH, the protein maintains the native conformation. On removal of Ca^{2+}, the molten globule conformation forms with a $t_{1/2}$ of 1.5 s (38). The three disulfide bonds rearrange spontaneously and very rapidly at pH 8.7, because of intramolecular thiol-disulfide exchange. Analysis of the resulting three-disulfide species revealed that most of the possible isomers were present (31). The results indicate that under the experimental conditions the molten globule of α-lactalbumin is very dynamic, does not maintain a native-like topology (in contrast to IL-4, mentioned above), and is more like a collapsed form of the unfolded state.

De novo designed four-helix bundle polypeptides with a core of Leu residues form a molten hydrophobic core that is a good model for many compact intermediates: Apparently, the lack of specific interactions between the side chains in the core allows for substantial mobility (117). The introduction of specific interactions (metal-binding sites) between helices in this core results in the tight specific interaction seen in native proteins, indicating that hydrophobic clusters can provide the driving force for collapse of an unfolded protein, but specific interactions are necessary to achieve the tight binding characteristic of the native fold (62).

Several investigations have examined compact intermediates of apomyoglobin and its mutants (9–11, 52, 57, 66, 67). Equilibrium intermediates have been observed under two sets of conditions: (a) pH 2 and moderate salt concentration and (b) at approximately pH 4–5 with low salt. Details of the dependence of the conformational state on pH, chloride concentration, and urea have been reported in the form of phase diagrams (10, 52). The structure of the intermediate formed at approximately pH 4 has been investigated using amide proton–protection factors; the results show that protons in the A, G, and H helix regions are protected from exchange (68). Unlike the native state, the stability of the intermediate state at pH 4 is relatively insensitive to the effect of mutation (66, 67). The disruption of a hydrogen bond between His24 and His199 appears to be the main cause of the transition between the native and pH 4 intermediate (11). The effects of the H36Q mutation suggest that the simple three-state model is not sufficient to fully describe the system. Yang & Honig have used a new approach to calculate electrostatic free energies for the pH-induced unfolding of apomyoglobin and can account for many, but not all, of the observed effects, including the presence of the pH 4 intermediate (142). Dill and coworkers (133) had previously correctly calculated the phase diagram for the acid denaturation of apomyoglobin.

The dynamic properties of the native, acid-unfolded, and A states of apomyoglobin have been investigated using tryptophan and ANS fluorescence lifetimes (13). Significant differences in the dynamic properties of the Trp and ANS suggested different structural properties in different regions of the A state. This hypothesis was confirmed in studies monitoring the Gdn.HCl-induced unfolding of the A state (129), which revealed a cooperative unfolding as detected by Trp fluorescence, whereas the unfolding monitored with ANS was less cooperative and more complex.

Staphylococcal nuclease forms a typical A state at low pH in the presence of moderate concentrations of anions (44). In the presence of the stabilizers sodium sulfate and glycerol and at low temperature (−15° C), additional structure is induced, leading to a more structured intermediate with native-like secondary structure and several indications of tertiary structure, such as buried Trp and significant heat capacity difference from the unfolded state (23). Truncated SNase, in which the C-terminal 13 residues have been deleted, adopts a compact conformation with many of the properties of a typical compact intermediate (46, 72, 128). It has native-like far-UV CD, a 1D NMR spectrum similar to that of the denatured protein, and a bimodal $P(r)$ plot for the SAXS data, which suggests a dumbbell shape (47). NMR studies indicate loss of the C-terminal helix and reveal that although much of the native secondary structure is present, it is much less stable in the fragment than in the native conformation (1, 3, 46).

The results of an investigation to measure side-chain mobility in the A state of β-lactamase are surprising in that they suggest some regions in a molten globule are far from molten (21). β-Lactamase from *Bacillus licheniformis* forms a stable compact intermediate at low pH and moderate salt concentration. Site-directed mutagenesis was used to introduce a single cysteine residue to which a spin label was attached via a disulfide. The A state of the spin-labeled protein had amounts of secondary structure comparable to that of the native state but lacked significant tertiary structure. Analysis of the ESR spectral line widths showed that the mobility of the spin label in the A state was similar to that in the native state and was much less mobile than in the unfolded state, indicating that the environment of the spin label in the A state is very similar to that in the native state. Thus, substantial structure must remain in the vicinity of the spin label in the A state, which is rather surprising, given the apparent lack of tertiary structure as observed with other methods (21).

Another approach taken to map out the core structure of a compact intermediate is that of chemical accessibility. By selectively incorporating a single cysteine residue into different regions of carbonic anhydrase and measuring the thiol accessibility to SH-specific modification, Martensson et al (92) showed that the central β-sheet core was ordered, whereas the periphery of the β-sheet was less ordered. A large hydrophobic cluster located between the β-sheet core and the surface appeared to be intact in the intermediate, even at high Gdn.HCl. Similar studies have been done on phosphoglycerate kinase (8).

Evidence for the plasticity of intermediate states is apparent in the properties of some apo-proteins. For example, apomyoglobin has most of the characteristics of a native protein [although this conclusion has been questioned recently in studies with various point mutations, some of which result in dramatic decreases in ellipticity at 222 nm (89), the reader should note that the native state of apomyoglobin is sufficiently unique, stable, and rigid that its structure has been determined with NMR (30)]. In contrast, apocytochromes b_5 and b_{562} show many of the typical properties of a compact intermediate (with the possible exception of more tertiary structure), yet NMR investigations reveal a native-like topology, albeit with some differences in secondary-structure packing (39, 97). On the other hand, apocytochrome c exhibits many of the properties of a denatured protein. At low ionic strength, the far- and near-UV CD spectra are typical of an unfolded protein at all pH values between 2 and 9 (60). However, in the presence of high concentrations of salt, substantial secondary structure is present at both neutral and acidic pH. At low pH, the A state has secondary structure similar to that previously observed for the A state of holocytochrome c. Fluorescence energy transfer experiments revealed several salt- and pH-dependent transitions. In the former two apo-proteins, the presence of the prosthetic group introduces the necessary specificity into the hydrophobic core, which leads to the characteristic tight packing of native conformations. An intermediate reported in the folding of apoplastocyanin has several interesting properties (78). This state has a fluorescence signal some 150% larger than that in the unfolded state. 2D NMR and amide-protection experiments indicate that the intermediate is compact, with flexible β-sheets and altered packing of the hydrophobic core, as well as some tertiary contacts. The intermediate does not show native-like β-sheet CD spectral signals.

Cytochrome c forms a compact intermediate at low pH and moderate salt concentration (43, 50, 53, 132). NMR amide-protection experiments indicate maximum protection (more than fivefold) for the residues corresponding to the three native helices. These regions are also those detected in similar experiments involving transient intermediates during refolding, further supporting the idea that equilibrium and transient intermediates may be very similar structures (73). SAXS has provided information on the radius of gyration and shape of the various conformational states of cytochrome c (76). The equilibrium transition at pH 2 from the acid-unfolded state to the compact-intermediate state, which was induced either by the addition of NaCl or the acetylation of lysyl amino groups and determined by Kratky plots, showed an isoscattering point. This result strongly suggests a two-state mechanism between acid-unfolded and compact-intermediate states (76).

This review has stressed the point that there is no single, unique conformation for compact intermediates, but rather a whole plethora of structures, ranging from ones very similar to the native state to others that are substantially expanded and unfolded. Examples of the former include the A state of IL-4 (118); the intermediate formed at low temperature from the hyperthermophilic D-glyceraldehyde-3-phosphate dehydrogenase, which contains most of the stabilizing secondary, tertiary, and quaternary contacts present in the native state (120); and apocy-

tochromes b_5 and b_{562} (39, 97). These highly ordered compact intermediates are probably good models for intermediates formed late in the
folding process. On the other hand, relatively expanded intermediates,
such as the C-terminal domain fragment of the tryptophan synthase β_2-
subunit (25, 26), are probably better models for intermediates formed
earlier in the folding process. The initial stages of folding, involving
rapid collapse to form a hydrophobic core, likely entail many parallel
pathways, whereas the later stages, after this collapse, involve very
few compact intermediates. Consequently, we expect a much broader
range of substates for the less compact intermediates. In many cases,
protein aggregation arises from compact-intermediate states (28).

In addition to the systems discussed above, compact intermediates
have now been observed in many different proteins, both small and
large, monomeric and oligomeric. Space limitations prevent presentation of a complete list and references. In many cases, the monomeric
forms of oligomers are probably compact intermediates (98); evidence
to support this notion is clearest in the case of bacterial luciferase (48).

MODELS FOR COMPACT INTERMEDIATES AND DENATURED STATES

Theoretical Models

Finkelstein & Shakhnovich (45), using polymer solution theory, predicted two forms of compact intermediate in addition to the unfolded
state, namely a "wet," more compact form and a "swollen," more
expanded form of the molten globule. By applying mean-field theory
to a denatured protein, which they considered as a stochastic polymer,
they determined a theoretical phase diagram for stable protein states.
The key disruption in the transition from the native state to the intermediate states was the breakdown of the tight packing in the core of the
native state.

Dill and coworkers use statistical mechanics to model protein stability; by incorporating electrostatics contributions, they accurately predicted the conformational phase diagram for apomyoglobin, showing
the boundaries between native, compact-intermediate, and unfolded
states as a function of pH and ionic strength (4, 133). Dill and coworkers
(87) recently modeled the conformation of compact denatured states
using the hydrophobic-zippers method (41). Their aim was to model
the observed bimodal distribution observed in SAXS distribution plots,
$P(r)$. They conclude that the hydrophobic collapse of many sequences
can yield compact, nonnative conformations that are about 20% ex-

panded relative to the native state and contain hydrophobic clusters of amino acids. The modeled end-state conformations have many different conformations with similar shape and size properties, which suggests that compact denatured states are ensembles of numerous substates.

Molecular dynamics simulations have been run on a few proteins under conditions mimicking a molten globule: Typically a quasistable state in which significant rearrangement of the secondary structure and no evidence for distinct domains was observed (17).

Ptitsyn's models of the molten globule (110, 111) assume a nonuniform expansion of the native state, which allows retention of the frame of the native state in the molten globule. The frame is defined to include the central parts of helices and sheets that carry nonpolar side chains contributing to the hydrophobic core of the native state. According to Ptitsyn's current model, water does not significantly penetrate this hydrophobic core in the molten globule, although the packing may become looser, thereby permitting greater mobility of these side chains. This model, in which the hydrophobic core is retained while much of the rest of the molecule is relatively unfolded, purportedly reconciles experimental data that indicate both some native-like and some unfolded-like properties. However, as discussed above, the lack of a significant heat-capacity difference between compact-intermediate and unfolded state indicates substantial internal solvation of the intermediate.

A Structural Model for Compact Intermediates

The minimum difference between the native and compact-intermediate states is disruption of the hydrophobic interactions binding the structural units together in the native state, with the consequent exposure of nonpolar surfaces to solvent (the expansion seen in even the most compact intermediate corresponds to a volume increase so large that it can only be accounted for by solvent penetration). Experimental data suggest two possible classes of compact intermediate: (a) a molten globule–like species with mostly native secondary structure but disrupted tertiary interactions, i.e. isolated regions of secondary structure connected by regions of disordered structure, and (b) a conformation consisting of a core of structure essentially identical to part of the native state, with the remaining regions of polypeptide unfolded or relatively unfolded. It is anticipated that a range of compact intermediates with conformations in between these extremes and the unfolded state will also be observed. A model that would account for most of the experimental observations of compact intermediates is described in the following (43, 105):

The native state is assumed to consist of several structural units, or building blocks, that are tightly packed together via tertiary (hydrophobic) interactions. These building blocks may consist of regions of secondary structure, or other types of subdomains or autonomous folding units, and will have significant intrinsic stability because of backbone and side-chain interactions. They would consist of at least a helix or β-hairpin and of at most a domain. The transition from the native state to the most compact-intermediate state would correspond to increased flexibility of the polypeptide chain connecting the structural units and to concurrent separation of these building blocks, with concomitant solvent penetration. These changes would lead to expansion of the molecule as a whole and to a species with the properties of the theoretical molten globule.

Thus, the formation of such an intermediate would involve disruption of the interactions between building blocks, but would have little effect on side-chain interactions within the structural unit. Less-compact intermediates would arise subsequently as the individual structural units unraveled. This unfolding may proceed one at a time, with the least stable unfolding first and the most intrinsically stable last (Figure 1). The unfolding of the individual structural units should be quite cooperative. Presumably, as additional structural units unfolded, the stability of the remaining ones would be decreased. Thus, a series of potential intermediates are envisaged that would range from almost as compact as the native state to greatly expanded. Ultimately, the distinction between intermediate and unfolded state should become blurred. This model makes implicit two kinds of tertiary structure: that between

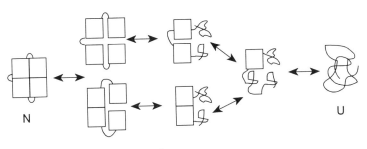

Intermediates

Figure 1 Model for the structure of compact intermediates: Each box represents a structural unit (see text). In the native state, these units are tightly packed and held together by hydrophobic interactions. Compact intermediates arise owing to disruption of these interactions, with greater expansion arising from unfolding of the structural units.

building blocks, which would be the first to be disrupted by the solvent, and that within the building block, which would be more protected from interactions with the solvent and more resistant to denaturation. Compact intermediates are thus pictured as an ensemble of substates ranging from those that are quite compact, with substantial (dynamic) contacts between all or nearly all the building-block units, to those with relatively few contacts between the building blocks, which will thus become unfolded and hence quite expanded. Whereas the building-block units themselves may retain a rather rigid, native-like structure, there will be substantial mobility between them owing to the freely rotating connecting links. Depending on the relative stabilizing or destabilizing forces of the external environment, as well as on the intrinsic structural properties of the protein, the predominant substates may be quite compact and relatively native-like or more expanded.

This model adequately accounts for the known properties of compact intermediates, particularly the retention of substantial secondary structure (within the building blocks), the loss of tertiary structure (contacts between structural units), the solvent penetration and expanded size relative to the native state, the possibility of native-like side-chain environments (in intact structural units with strong neighboring side-chain interactions), and the variation in compactness and amount of secondary structure as a function of environment and protein.

ACKNOWLEDGMENTS

The author is grateful to the many colleagues who communicated manuscripts prior to publication.

Literature Cited

1. Alexandrescu AT, Abeygunawardana C, Shortle D. 1994. Structure and dynamics of a 131-residue fragment of staphylococcal nuclease: a heteronuclear NMR study. *Biochemistry* 33:1063–72
2. Alexandrescu AT, Evans PA, Pitkeathly M, Baum J, Dobson CM. 1993. Structure and dynamics of the acid-denatured molten globule state of alpha-lactalbumin: a two-dimensional NMR study. *Biochemistry* 32:1707–18
3. Alexandrescu AT, Shortle D. 1994.
   Backbone dynamics of a highly disordered 131 residue fragment of staphylococcal nuclease. *J. Mol. Biol.* 42:703–12
4. Alonso DO, Dill KA, Stigter D. 1991. The three states of globular proteins: acid denaturation. *Biopolymers* 31:1631–49
5. Amir D, Krausz S, Haas E. 1992. Detection of local structures in reduced unfolded bovine pancreatic trypsin inhibitor. *Proteins Struct. Funct. Genet.* 13:162–73
6. Baldwin RL. 1991. Molten globules:

specific or nonspecific folding intermediates? *Chemtracts Biochem. Mol. Biol.* 2:379–89

7. Baldwin RL. 1993. Pulsed proton/deuterium exchange studies of folding intermediates. *Curr. Opin. Struct. Biol.* 3:84–91

8. Ballery N, Desmadril M, Minard P, Yon JM. 1993. Characterization of an intermediate in the folding pathway of phosphoglycerate kinase: chemical reactivity of genetically introduced cysteinyl residues during the folding process. *Biochemistry* 32:708–14

9. Barrick D, Baldwin RL. 1993. The molten globule intermediate of apomyoglobin and the process of protein folding. *Protein Sci.* 2:869–76

10. Barrick D, Baldwin RL. 1993. Three-state analysis of sperm whale apomyoglobin folding. *Biochemistry* 32: 3790–96

11. Barrick D, Hughson FM, Baldwin RL. 1994. Molecular mechanisms of acid denaturation. The role of histidine residues in the partial unfolding of apomyoglobin. *J. Mol. Biol.* 237: 588–601

12. Baum J, Dobson CM, Evans PA, Hanley C. 1989. Characterization of a partly folded protein by NMR methods: studies on the molten globule state of guinea pig α-lactalbumin. *Biochemistry* 28:7–13

13. Bismuto E, Irace G. 1994. Unfolding pathway of apomyoglobin. Simultaneous characterization of acidic conformational states by frequency domain fluorometry. *J. Mol. Biol.* 241:103–9

14. Bowler BE, Dong A, Caughey WS. 1994. Characterization of the guanidine hydrochloride-denatured state of iso-1-cytochrome *c* by infrared spectroscopy. *Biochemistry* 33: 2402–8

15. Bowler BE, May K, Zaragoza T, York P, Dong A, Caughey WS. 1993. Destabilizing effects of replacing a surface lysine of cytochrome *c* with aromatic amino acids: implications for the denatured state. *Biochemistry* 32:183–90

16. Briggs MS, Roder H. 1992. Early hydrogen-bonding events in the folding reaction of ubiquitin. *Proc. Natl. Acad. Sci. USA* 89:2017–21

17. Brooks CL. 1993. Molecular simulations of peptide and protein unfolding: in quest of a molten globule. *Curr. Opin. Struct. Biol.* 3:92–98

18. Buck M, Radford SE, Dobson CM. 1993. A partially folded state of hen egg white lysozyme in trifluoroethanol: structural characterization and implications for protein folding. *Biochemistry* 32:669–78

19. Bychkova VE, Berni R, Rossi GL, Kutyshenko VP, Ptitsyn OB. 1992. Retinol-binding protein is in the molten globule state at low pH. *Biochemistry* 31:7566–71

20. Bychkova VE, Ptitsyn OB. 1993. The molten globule in vitro and in vivo. *Chemtracts Biochem. Mol. Biol.* 4: 133–63

21. Calciano LJ, Escobar WA, Millhauser GL, Miick SM, Rubaloff J, et al. 1993. Side-chain mobility of the β-lactamase A state probed by electron spin resonance spectroscopy. *Biochemistry* 32:5644–49

22. Carra JH, Anderson EA, Privalov PL. 1994. Thermodynamics of staphylococcal nuclease denaturation. I. The acid-denatured state. *Protein Sci.* 3:944–51

23. Carra JH, Anderson EA, Privalov PL. 1994. Thermodynamics of staphylococcal nuclease denaturation. II. The A-state. *Protein Sci.* 3:952–59

24. Carra JH, Anderson EA, Privalov PL. 1994. Three-state thermodynamic analysis of the denaturation of staphylococcal nuclease mutants. *Biochemistry* 33:10842–50

25. Chaffotte AF, Cadieux C, Guillou Y, Goldberg ME. 1992. A possible initial folding intermediate: the C-terminal proteolytic domain of tryptophan synthase β chains folds in less than 4 milliseconds into a condensed state with non-native-like secondary structure. *Biochemistry* 31:4303–8

26. Chaffotte A, Guillou Y, Delepierre M, Hinz H-J, Goldberg ME. 1991. The isolated C-terminal (F2) fragment of the *Escherichia coli* tryptophan synthase β₂-subunit folds into a stable, organized nonnative conformation. *Biochemistry* 30:8067–74

27. Christensen H, Pain RH. 1991. Molten globule intermediates and protein folding. *Eur. Biophys. J.* 19:221–30

28. Christensen H, Pain RH. 1994. The contribution of the molten globule model. See Ref. 104a, pp. 55–79

29. Chyan CL, Wormald C, Dobson CM, Evans PA, Baum J. 1993. Structure and stability of the molten globule state of guinea-pig alpha-lactalbumin: a hydrogen exchange study. *Biochemistry* 32:5681–91

30. Coco MJ, Lecomte JTJ. 1994. The

native state of apomyoglobin described by proton NMR spectroscopy: interaction with the paramagnetic probe HyTEMPO and the fluorescent dye ANS. *Protein Sci.* 3: 267–81

31. Creighton TE, Ewbank JJ. 1994. Disulfide-rearranged molten globule state of α-lactalbumin. *Biochemistry* 33:1534–38

32. Dill KA, Shortle D. 1991. Denatured states of proteins. *Annu. Rev. Biochem.* 60:795–825

33. Dolgikh D, Abaturov L, Bolotina I, Brazhnikov E, Bychkova V, et al. 1985. Compact state of a protein molecule with pronounced small-scale mobility: bovine α-lactalbumin. *Eur. Biophys. J.* 13:109–21

34. Dolgikh D, Gilmanshin R, Brazhnikov E, Bychkova V, Semisotnov G, et al. 1981. α-Lactalbumin: compact state with fluctuating tertiary structure? *FEBS Letts.* 136:311–15

35. Eliezer D, Chiba K, Tsuruta H, Doniach S, Hodgson KO, Kihara H. 1993. Evidence of an associative intermediate on the myoglobin refolding pathway. *Biophys. J.* 65:912–17

36. Elöve GA, Chaffotte AF, Roder H, Goldberg ME. 1992. Early steps in cytochrome *c* folding probed by time-resolved circular dichroism and fluorescence spectroscopy. *Biochemistry* 31:6876–83

37. Englander W, Mayne L. 1992. Protein folding studied using hydrogen-exchange labeling and two-dimensional NMR. *Annu. Rev. Biophys. Biomol. Struct.* 21:243–65

38. Ewbank JJ, Creighton TE. 1991. The molten globule protein conformation probed by disulphide bonds. *Nature* 350:518–20

39. Feng Y, Sligar, SG, Wand AJ. 1994. Solution structure of apocytochrome b$_{562}$. *Struct. Biol.* 1:30–5

40. Fersht AR. 1993. Protein folding and stability: the pathway of folding of barnase. *FEBS Letts.* 325:5–16

41. Fiebig KM, Dill KA. 1993. Protein core assembly processes. *J. Chem. Phys.* 98:3475–87

42. Fink AL. 1994. Compact intermediates states in protein folding. In *Sub-Cellular Biochemistry: Protein Structure, Function and Engineering*, ed. S Roy, 24:27–53. New York: Plenum

43. Fink AL, Calciano LJ, Goto Y, Kurotsu T, Palleros DR. 1994. Classification of acid denaturation of proteins: intermediates and unfolded states. *Biochemistry* 33:12504–11

44. Fink AL, Calciano LJ, Goto Y, Nishimura M, Swedberg SA. 1993. Characterization of the stable, acid-induced, molten globule-like state of staphylococcal nuclease. *Protein Sci.* 2:1155–60

45. Finkelstein AV, Shakhnovich EI. 1989. Theory of cooperative transitions in protein molecules. II. Phase diagram for a protein molecule in solution. *Biopolymers* 28:1681–94

46. Flanagan JM, Kataoka M, Fujisawa T, Engelman DM. 1993. Mutations can cause large changes in the conformation of a denatured protein. *Biochemistry* 32:10359–70

47. Flanagan JM, Kataoka M, Shortle D, Engelman DM. 1992. Truncated staphylococcal nuclease is compact but disordered. *Proc. Natl. Acad. Sci. USA* 89:748–52

48. Flynn GC, Beckers CJ, Baase WA, Dahlquist FW. 1993. Individual subunits of bacterial luciferase are molten globules and interact with molecular chaperones. *Proc. Natl. Acad. Sci. USA* 90:10826–30

49. Gittis AG, Stites WE, Lattman EE. 1993. The phase transition between a compact denatured state and a random coil state in staphylococcal nuclease is first-order. *J. Mol. Biol.* 232:718–24

50. Goto Y, Calciano LJ, Fink AL. 1990. Acid-induced folding of proteins. *Proc. Natl. Acad. Sci. USA* 87: 573–77

51. Goto Y, Fink AL. 1989. Conformational states of β-lactamase: molten globule states at acidic and alkaline pH with high salt. *Biochemistry* 28: 945–52

52. Goto Y, Fink AL. 1990. Phase diagram for acidic conformational states of apomyoglobin. *J. Mol. Biol.* 214: 803–5

53. Goto Y, Hagihara Y, Hamada D, Hoshino M, Nishii I. 1993. Acid-induced unfolding and refolding transitions of cytochrome *c*: a three-state mechanism in H$_2$O and D$_2$O. *Biochemistry* 32:11878–85

54. Goto Y, Takahashi N, Fink AL. 1990. Mechanism of acid-induced folding of proteins. *Biochemistry* 29:3480–88

55. Griko YV, Freire E, Privalov PL. 1994. Energetics of the α-lactalbumin states: a calorimetric and statistical thermodynamic study. *Biochemistry* 33:1889–99

56. Griko YV, Gittis A, Lattman EE, Privalov PL. 1994. Residual structure in a staphylococcal nuclease fragment.

Is it a molten globule and is its unfolding a first order phase transition? *J. Mol. Biol.* 243:93–99

57. Griko YV, Privalov PL. 1994. Thermodynamic puzzle of apomyoglobin unfolding. *J. Mol. Biol.* 235:1318–25

58. Gussakovsky EE, Haas E. 1992. The compact state of reduced bovine pancreatic trypsin inhibitor is not the compact molten globule. *FEBS Lett.* 308:146–48

59. Hagihara Y, Tan Y, Goto Y. 1994. Comparison of the conformational stability of the molten globule and native states of horse cytochrome *c*. Effects of acetylation, heat, urea and guanidine-hydrochloride. *J. Mol. Biol.* 237:336–48

60. Hamada D, Hoshino M, Kataoka M, Fink AL, Goto Y. 1993. Intermediate conformational states of apocytochrome *c*. *Biochemistry* 32:10351–58

61. Hamada D, Kidokoro S, Fukada H, Takahashi K, Goto Y. 1994. Salt-induced formation of the molten globule state of cytochrome *c* studied by isothermal titration calorimetry. *Proc. Natl. Acad. Sci. USA* 91:10325–29

62. Handel TM, Williams SA, DeGrado WF. 1993. Metal ion-dependent modulation of the dynamics of a designed protein. *Science* 261:879–85

63. Harding MM, Williams DH, Woolfson DN. 1991. Characterization of a partially denatured state of a protein by two-dimensional NMR: reduction of the hydrophobic interactions in ubiquitin. *Biochemistry* 30:3120–28

64. Haynie DT, Freire E. 1993. Structural energetics of the molten globule state. *Proteins* 16:115–40

65. Hooke SD, Radford SE, Dobson CM. 1994. The refolding of human lysozyme: a comparison with the structurally homologous hen lysozyme. *Biochemistry* 33:5867–76

66. Hughson FM, Baldwin RL. 1989. Use of site-directed mutagenesis to destabilize native apomyoglobin relative to folding intermediates. *Biochemistry* 28:4415–22

67. Hughson FM, Barrick D, Baldwin RL. 1991. Probing the stability of a partly folded apomyoglobin intermediate by side-directed mutagenesis. *Biochemistry* 30:4113–18

68. Hughson FM, Wright PE, Baldwin RL. 1990. Structural characterization of a partly folded apomyoglobin intermediate. *Science* 249:1544–48

69. Ikeguchi M, Kuwajima K, Mitani M, Sugai S. 1986. Evidence for identity between the equilibrium unfolding intermediate and a transient folding intermediate: a comparative study of the folding reactions of α-lactalbumin and lysozyme. *Biochemistry* 25:6965–72

70. Ikeguchi M, Sugai S, Fujino M, Sugawara T, Kuwajima K. 1992. Contribution of the 6-120 disulfide bond of alpha-lactalbumin to the stabilities of its native and molten globule states. *Biochemistry* 31:12695–12700

71. Jacobs MD, Fox RO. 1994. Staphylococcal nuclease folding intermediate characterized by hydrogen exchange and NMR spectroscopy. *Proc. Natl. Acad. Sci. USA* 91:449–53

72. James E, Wu PG, Stites W, Brand L. 1992. Compact denatured state of a staphylococcal nuclease mutant by guanidinium as determined by resonance energy transfer. *Biochemistry* 31:10217–25

73. Jeng MF, Englander SW, Elöve GA, Wand AJ, Roder H. 1990. Structural description of acid-denatured cytochrome *c* by hydrogen exchange and 2D NMR. *Biochemistry* 29:10433–37

74. Jennings PA, Wright PE. 1993. Formation of a molten globule intermediate early in the kinetic folding pathway of apomyoglobin. *Science* 262:892–96

75. Jones BE, Jennings PA, Pierre RA, Matthews CR. 1994. The development of nonpolar surfaces in the folding of *E. coli* dihydrofolate reductase detected by 1-anilinonaphthalene-8-sulfonate binding. *Biochemistry*. In press

76. Kataoka M, Hagihara Y, Mihara K, Goto Y. 1993. Molten globule of cytochrome *c* studied by small angle X-ray scattering. *J. Mol. Biol.* 229:591–96

77. Kim PS, Baldwin RL. 1990. Intermediates in the folding reactions of small proteins. *Annu. Rev. Biochem.* 59:631–60

78. Koide S, Dyson HJ, Wright PE. 1993. Characterization of a folding intermediate of apoplastocyanin trapped by proline isomerization. *Biochemistry* 32:12299–12310

79. Kuroda Y, Kidokoro S-I, Wada A. 1992. Thermodynamic characterization of cytochrome c at low pH: observation of the molten globule state and of the cold denaturation process. *J. Mol. Biol.* 223:1139–53

80. Kuwajima K. 1989. The molten globule state as a clue for understanding the folding and cooperativity of glob-

ular-protein structure. *Proteins Struct. Funct. Genet.* 6:87–103

81. Kuwajima K. 1992. Protein folding in vitro. *Curr. Opin. Biotechnol.* 3: 462–67

82. Kuwajima K, Garvey EP, Finn BE, Matthews CR, Sugai S. 1991. Transient intermediates in the folding of dihydrofolate reductase as detected by far-ultraviolet circular dichroism spectroscopy. *Biochemistry* 30: 7693–7703

83. Kuwajima K, Hiraoka Y, Ikeguchi M, Sugai S. 1985. Comparison of the transient folding intermediates in lysozyme and α-lactalbumin. *Biochemistry* 24:874–81

84. Kuwajima K, Semisotnov GV, Finkelstein AV, Sugai S, Ptitsyn OB. 1993. Secondary structure of globular proteins at the early and the final stages in protein folding. *FEBS Lett.* 334:265–68

85. Kuwajima K, Yamaya H, Miwa S, Sugai S, Nagamura T. 1987. Rapid formation of secondary structure framework in protein folding studied by stopped-flow circular dichroism. *FEBS Letts.* 221:115–18

86. Lala AK, Kaul P. 1992. Increased exposure of hydrophobic surface in molten globule state of alpha-lactalbumin fluorescence and hydrophobic photolabeling studies. *J. Biol. Chem.* 267:19914–18

87. Lattman EE, Fiebig KM, Dill KA. 1994. Modeling compact denatured states of proteins. *Biochemistry* 33: 6158–66

88. Lecomte TJ, Matthews CR. 1993. Unraveling the mechanism of protein folding: new tricks for an old problem. *Protein Eng.* 6:1–10

89. Lin L, Pinker RJ, Forde K, Rose GD, Kallenbach NR. 1994. Molten globular characteristics of the native state of apomyoglobin. *Struct. Biol.* 1: 447–52

90. Liu Z-P, Rizo J, Gierasch LM. 1994. Equilibrium folding studies of cellular retinoic acid binding protein, a predominantly β-sheet protein. *Biochemistry* 33:134–42

91. Mann CJ, Matthews CR. 1993. Structure and stability of an early folding intermediate of *Escherichia coli trp* aporepressor measured by far-UV stopped-flow circular dichroism and 8-anilino-1-naphthalene sulfonate binding. *Biochemistry* 32:5282–90

92. Martensson LG, Jonsson BH, Freskgard PO, Kihlgren A, Svensson M, Carlsson U. 1993. Characterization of folding intermediates of human carbonic anhydrase II: probing substructure by chemical labeling of SH groups introduced by site-directed mutagenesis. *Biochemistry* 32: 224–31

93. Matouschek A, Kellis JT Jr, Serrano L, Bycroft M, Fersht AR. 1990. Transient folding intermediates characterized by protein engineering. *Nature* 346:440–45

94. Matouschek A, Serrano L, Fersht AR. 1992. The folding of an enzyme. IV. Structure of an intermediate in the refolding of barnase analysed by a protein engineering procedure. *J. Mol. Biol.* 224:819–35

95. Matthews CR. 1993. Pathways of protein folding. *Annu. Rev. Biochem.* 62:653–83

96. Mitaku S, Ishido S, Hirano Y, Itoh H, Kataoka R, Saitô N. 1991. Hydrophobic core of molten-globule state of bovine carbonic anhydrase B. *Biophys. Chem.* 40:217–22

97. Moore CD, Al-Misky ON, Lecomte JTJ. 1991. Similarities in structure between holocytochrome b_5 and apocytochrome b_5: NMR studies of histidine residues. *Biochemistry* 30: 8357–65

98. Narhi LO, Rosenfeld R, Wen J, Arakawa T, Prestrelski SJ, Philo JS. 1993. Acid-induced unfolding of brain-derived neurotrophic factor results in the formation of a monomeric "a state." *Biochemistry* 32:10819–25

99. Nishii I, Kataoka M, Tokunaga F, Goto Y. 1994. Cold denaturation of the molten globule states of apomyoglobin and a profile for protein folding. *Biochemistry* 33:4903–9

100. Nitta K, Tsuge H, Iwamoto H. 1993. Comparative study of the stability of the folding intermediates of the calcium-binding lysozymes. *Int. J. Peptide Protein Res.* 41:118–23

101. Nölting B, Jiang M, Sligar SG. 1993. The acidic molten globule state of α-lactalbumin probed by sound velocity. *J. Am. Chem. Soc.* 115:9879–82

102. Deleted in proof

103. Ogasahara K, Yutani K. 1994. Unfolding-refolding kinetics of the tryptophan synthase alpha subunit by CD and fluorescence measurements. *J. Mol. Biol.* 236:1227–40

104. Ohgushi M, Wada A. 1983. 'Molten-globule state': a compact form of globular proteins with mobile side-chains. *FEBS Letts.* 164:21–24

104a. Pain RH, ed. 1994. *Mechanisms of Protein Folding*. Oxford: IRL Press/ Oxford Univ. Press

105. Palleros DR, Shi L, Reid KL, Fink AL. 1993. Three-state denaturation of DnaK induced by guanidine hydrochloride. Evidence for an expandable intermediate. *Biochemistry* 32: 4314–21

106. Pan Y, Briggs MS. 1992. Hydrogen exchange in native and alcohol forms of ubiquitin. *Biochemistry* 31: 11405–12

107. Peng Z, Kim PS. 1994. A protein dissection study of a molten globule. *Biochemistry* 33:2136–41

108. Pfeil W, Bychkova VN, Ptitsyn OB. 1986. Physical nature of the phase transition in globular proteins. *FEBS Letts*. 198:287–91

109. Ptitsyn OB. 1973. Stages in the mechanism of self-organization of protein molecules. *Dokl. Akad. Nauk SSSR*. 210:1213–15

110. Ptitsyn OB. 1987. Protein folding: hypotheses and experiments. *Protein Chem*. 6:273–93

111. Ptitsyn OB. 1992. The molten globule state. In *Protein Folding*, ed TE Creighton, pp. 243–300. New York: Freeman

112. Ptitsyn OB, Pain RH, Semisotnov GV, Zerovnik E, Razgulyaev OI. 1990. Evidence for a molten globule state as a general intermediate in protein folding. *FEBS Letts*. 262:20–24

113. Ptitsyn OB, Semisotnov GV. 1991. The mechanism of protein folding. In *Conformation and Forces in Protein Folding*, ed. BT Nall, KA Dill, pp. 155–68. Washington, DC: AAAS

114. Ptitsyn OB, Uversky VN. 1994. The molten globule is a third thermodynamical state of protein molecules. *FEBS Lett*. 341:15–18

115. Radford SE, Buck M, Topping KD, Dobson CM, Evans PA. 1992. Hydrogen exchange in native and denatured states of hen egg-white lysozyme. *Proteins* 14:237–48

116. Radford SE, Dobson CM, Evans PA. 1992. The folding of hen lysozyme involves partially structured intermediates and multiple pathways. *Nature* 358:302–7

117. Raleigh DP, DeGrado WF. 1992. A de novo designed protein shows a thermally induced transition from a native to a molten globule-like state. *J. Am. Chem. Soc*. 114:10079–81

118. Redfield C, Boyd J, Smith LJ, Smith RAG, Dobson CM. 1992. Loop mobility in a 4-helix bundle protein: ^{15}N NMR relaxation measurements on human IL-4. *Biochemistry* 31: 10431–37

119. Redfield C, Smith RAG, Dobson CM. 1994. Structural characterization of a highly-ordered 'molten globule' at low pH. *Nat. Struct. Biol*. 1:23–28

120. Rehaber V, Jaenicke R. 1993. The low-temperature folding intermediate of hyper-thermophilic D-glyceraldehyde-3-phosphate dehydrogenase from *Thermotoga maritima* shows a native-like cooperative unfolding transition. *FEBS Lett*. 317:163–66

121. Robertson AD, Baldwin RL. 1991. Hydrogen exchange in thermally denatured ribonuclease A. *Biochemistry* 30:9907–14

122. Roder H, Elöve GA. 1994. Early stages of protein folding. See Ref. 104a, 26–54

123. Saab-Rincon G, Froebe CL, Matthews CR. 1993. Urea-induced unfolding of the alpha subunit of tryptophan synthase: one-dimensional proton NMR evidence for residual structure near histidine-92 at high denaturant concentration. *Biochemistry* 32:13981–90

124. Sanz JM, Fersht AR. 1993. Rationally designing the accumulation of a folding intermediate of barnase by protein engineering. *Biochemistry* 32: 13584–92

125. Seshadri S, Oberg KA, Fink AL. 1994. Thermally denatured ribonuclease A retains secondary structure as shown by FTIR. *Biochemistry* 33:1351–55

126. Shortle D. 1987. Equilibrium and kinetic intermediates in protein folding: an alternative explanation. In *Protein Structure, Folding, and Design 2*, ed. DL Oxender DL, pp. 353–61. New York: Liss

127. Shortle D, Abeygunawardana C. 1993. NMR analysis of the residual structure in the denatured state of an unusual mutant of staphylococcal nuclease. *Curr. Biol. Struct*. 1:121–34

128. Shortle D, Meeker AK. 1989. Residual structure in large fragments of staphylococcal nuclease: effects of amino acid substitutions. *Biochemistry* 28:936–44

129. Sirangelo I, Bismuto E, Irace G. 1994. Solvent and thermal denaturation of the acidic compact state of apomyoglobin. *FEBS Lett*. 338:11–15

130. Sosnick TR, Mayne L, Hiller R, Englander SW. 1994. The barriers in protein folding. *Struct. Biol*. 1(3):149–56

131. Sosnick TR, Trewhella J. 1992. Dena-

tured states of ribonuclease A have compact dimensions and residual secondary structure. *Biochemistry* 31: 8329–35

132. Stellwagen E, Babul J. 1975. Stabilization of the globular structure of ferricytochrome *c* by chloride in acidic solvents. *Biochemistry* 14:5135–40

133. Stigter D, Dill KA. 1990. Charge effects on folded and unfolded proteins. *Biochemistry* 29:1262–71

134. Stockman BJ, Euvrard A, Scahill TA. 1993. Heteronuclear three-dimensional NMR spectroscopy of a partially denatured protein: the A-state of human ubiquitin. *J. Biomol. NMR* 3:285–96

135. Sugawara T, Kuwajima K, Sugai S. 1991. Folding of staphylococcal nuclease A studied by equilibrium and kinetic circular dichroism spectra. *Biochemistry* 30:2698–2706

136. Uversky VN, Ptitsyn OB. "Partly folded" state, a new equilibrium state of protein molecules: four-state guanidinium chloride-induced unfolding of beta-lactamase at low temperature. *Biochemistry* 33:2782–91

137. Uversky VN, Semisotnov GV, Pain RH, Ptitsyn OB. 1992. 'All-or-none' mechanism of the molten globule unfolding. *FEBS Lett.* 314:89–92

138. Van Dael H, Haezebrouck P, Morozova L, Arico-Muendel C, Dobson CM. 1993. Partially folded states of equine lysozyme. Structural characterization and significance for protein folding. *Biochemistry* 32:11886–94

139. Varley P, Gronenborn AM, Christensen H, Wingfield PT, Pain RH, Clore GM. 1993. Kinetics of folding of the all-β sheet protein interleukin-1β. *Science* 260:1110–13

140. Xie D, Bhakuni V, Freire E. 1991. Calorimetric determination of the energetics of the molten globule intermediate in protein folding: Apo α-lactalbumin. *Biochemistry* 30: 10673–78

141. Xie D, Bhakuni V, Freire E. 1993. Are the molten globule and the unfolded states of apo-alpha-lactalbumin enthalpically equivalent? *J. Mol. Biol.* 232:5–8

142. Yang A-S, Honig B. 1994. Structural origins of pH and ionic strength effects on protein stability. *J. Mol. Biol.* 237:602–14

143. Yutani K, Ogasahara K, Kuwajima K. 1992. Absence of the thermal transition in apo α-lactalbumin in the molten globule state: a study by differential scanning in microcalorimetry. *J. Mol. Biol.* 228:347–50

Annu. Rev. Biophys. Biomol. Struct. 1995. 24:523–49
Copyright © 1995 by Annual Reviews Inc. All rights reserved

SITE-SPECIFIC DYNAMICS IN DNA: THEORY

B. H. Robinson and G. P. Drobny

Department of Chemistry, University of Washington, Seattle, Washington 98195

KEY WORDS: magnetic resonance, site-specific probes, NMR, EPR

CONTENTS

ABSTRACT

This chapter reviews recent progress in understanding duplex DNA dynamics. The weakly bending rod model of Schurr and coworkers is described and compared to a model-free formulation of DNA dynamics. Numerical trajectory methods for obtaining dynamic information are also discussed. The general principles of magnetic resonance relaxation are then reviewed, and the methods by which molecular motions are incorporated into the calculation of relaxation rates or the simulation of experimental NMR and EPR data are described. The impact that the time scale of the dynamics exerts on various computational methods is considered, and in particular, the implementation of (*a*) the stochastic

1056-8700/95/0610-0523$05.00

Liouville equation, *(b)* the Redfield relaxation matrix, and *(c)* tensorial preaveraging is described. Expressions for direct and cross-relaxation processes are developed by expanding the density matrix in terms of an irreducible tensor basis set.

INTRODUCTION

Knowledge of the internal dynamics of DNA is integral to understanding the function and means of expression of the genetic code. The rigidity of duplex DNA may well control the interaction of DNA with histones and with transcription and translation proteins. Possible long-range allosteric changes in the overall rigidity of DNA may play an integral role in the nature of the secondary structure induced by super-helical stresses or by proteins that bind to supercoiled DNA (12, 15). Thus, both the overall tumbling and the internal-collective modes of DNA need to be determined (24).

Several advancements in our understanding of the dynamics of DNA have come from theoretical, optical, and magnetic-resonance studies. Optical methods include fluorescence polarization anisotropy, depolarized dynamic light scattering, circular dichroism, the electric Kerr effect, and linear dichroism. Schurr et al (30) have reviewed the application of these techniques to the study of DNA. Experiments involving magnetic resonance (MR), including nuclear magnetic resonance (NMR) and electron paramagnetic resonance (EPR), have made many important contributions to the study of the dynamics of DNA, principally duplex DNA. This review discusses novel developments in the use of magnetic resonance as a tool for understanding the dynamics of DNA and the major results from the studies of segments of duplex DNA. We offer suggestions concerning the future of the methodology and the prospects for obtaining information on the dynamics of DNA of arbitrary length and complexity.

This chapter focuses on the utility of site-specific labeling methodologies, such as have been used primarily in MR experiments. In NMR applications, site-specific probes include isotopic substitutions such as ^{15}N for ^{14}N, ^{13}C for ^{12}C, or ^{2}H (or ^{2}D) for ^{1}H. These are, prima facie, nonperturbative alterations of DNA that affect primarily the spin systems and not the structure or dynamics of the DNA. EPR studies of DNA have relied on spin labels covalently incorporated into specific bases that modify the bases and introduce perturbations at the base-pair level. The information obtainable from such site-specific labels cannot be used without two key elements of the data modeling. The first is a simple description of the effects of DNA dynamics [which, at minimum, includes uniform motion, internal collective motions, and local (length-independent) motion], and the second is the incorporation of the DNA dynamics into the framework of the MR data.

The application of site-specific labeling provides a powerful method for determining the local structure and dynamics at specific points within a section of duplex DNA. This approach has not been developed by the optical community; it is our hope that this review will stimulate the development of fluorescent analogues.

THEORIES OF DNA DYNAMICS

Schurr and coworkers have developed a simple and elegant picture of the modes of motion of DNA. Initial efforts considered the collective twisting of base pairs (5, 8, 25, 26). More complete treatments then included the flexural or bending motions as well as various models for the motion of a probe or base pair independent of the DNA to which it is attached (28, 30, 32). DNA is treated, mathematically, as a flexible rod-shaped object. This model has come to be called the weakly bending rod model of DNA. It assumes that although duplex DNA may be curved over a long-distance scale, mean local cylindrical symmetry, arising from the helical nature of duplex DNA, occurs about each base. Each base is connected to its neighbor by bonds that act as Hookean springs, thus providing a potential barrier to both twisting and bending motions. The discussion of dynamics is developed in terms of displacements about a body-fixed axis system that is coincident with the DNA molecule in its canonical form. The principal axis is taken to be the z axis, which coincides with the local helix axis. Therefore, the mean square displacement about the z axis, $\langle \Delta_z(t)^2 \rangle$, corresponds to the twisting of DNA. The mean square displacement about the x axis, $\langle \Delta_x(t)^2 \rangle$, corresponds to the bending of DNA. Because DNA is assumed to have mean local cylindrical symmetry, one can make the simplifying assumption that the mean square displacements about x and y are the same: $\langle \Delta_x(t)^2 \rangle = \langle \Delta_y(t)^2 \rangle$. Moreover, the rotations in the three different directions are assumed to be driven by statistically independent processes, and thus cross-terms in the displacements, such as $\langle \Delta_x(t)\Delta_y(t) \rangle$, are assumed to vanish.

Furthermore, the displacements $\langle \Delta_z(t)^2 \rangle$ and $\langle \Delta_x(t)^2 \rangle$ include all modes: the length independent modes, the internal collective modes, and the uniform or overall tumbling modes of motion. This model forms a basis for discussion of how an idealized piece of duplex DNA may relax. It is very simple and has few adjustable parameters. The extent to which base sequence will cause local alterations of the relaxation is still a matter of experimentation. To date, no evidence indicates that particular sequences differentially cause local structural relaxations that deviate significantly from an average value, although there is much theoretical speculation that this may be the case (14). When such experimental evidence is available, then more detailed theoretical models will be needed to simulate site-specific dynamics. First, however, we must understand what a simple model of relaxation has to say before we can explore more complicated models.

The Weakly Bending Rod

Schurr and coworkers (30 and references therein) have shown that the correlation function for the Wigner rotational matrix elements (WRME) $\mathscr{D}_{n,m}^{\ell}(\Omega)$ associated with a base, when referenced to the laboratory axes in terms of the three Euler angles (Ω), may be written in terms of the displacements of the bases about the local axes. Such a correlation function is given by:

$$\langle \mathscr{D}_{N,M}^{L}(\Omega_0)^* \mathscr{D}_{n,m}^{\ell}(\Omega) \rangle = \frac{\delta_{L\ell}\delta_{M,m}\delta_{N,n}}{(2\ell + 1)}$$

$$\exp -\frac{\{[\ell(\ell + 1) - n^2]\langle \Delta_x(t)^2 \rangle + n^2 \langle \Delta_z(t)^2 \rangle\}}{2}. \qquad 1.$$

This relationship is generally applicable to dynamics in duplex DNA and provides a conceptually elegant framework for understanding the effects of dynamics and the applicability of correlation functions. Correlation functions of this nature are an essential part of understanding and interpreting relaxation phenomena and line shapes in magnetic resonance experiments (see section on effects of dynamics on observables). Equation 1 demonstrates that the dynamics of the WRME do not cross-correlate, which simplifies the nature of the motion. Moreover, the effects of twisting (contained in $\langle \Delta_z(t)^2 \rangle$) are separable from the effects of bending (contained in $\langle \Delta_x(t)^2 \rangle$), and thus the twisting motions can be considered independently from the bending motions. However, when large amplitudes of bending are admitted, this simplification must be abandoned.

Of considerable importance is the realization that the correlation functions depend strongly on position within the linear duplex DNA. In general, the calculation of displacements for a particular base pair from first principles for duplex DNA less than 10,000 base pairs in length is straightforward. We now consider the global tumbling of DNA and the internal, collective motions of twisting and bending. We comment on only the inclusion of length-independent modes, because they are extremely specific for the type and position of the dynamic's probe.

Global Tumbling

If DNA had no internal flexibility (a situation nearly realized for short, less than 20 base pairs, fragments of duplex DNA), the molecule would tumble as a rigid object. Such motion is described by two Stokes-Einstein-Debye rotational diffusion coefficients $D_\parallel$ and $D_\perp$. The mean square displacements are then simply related to the rotational diffusion coefficients (33):

$$\langle \Delta_x(t)^2 \rangle = 2t \cdot D_\perp \quad \text{and} \quad \langle \Delta_z(t)^2 \rangle = 2t \cdot D_\parallel. \qquad 2.$$

For short fragments of DNA, the global tumbling may be described in terms of the dynamics of a right circular cylinder. The motional operator is given as $\Gamma_\Omega = \nabla \cdot \mathbf{D} \cdot \nabla$ where $\mathbf{D}$ is the diagonal diffusion tensor in the frame of the molecule and ∇ is the angular Laplacian operator written in terms of the Euler angles, $\Omega = \Omega_{mol}$ in the molecular frame. The values of the diffusion coefficients for a right circular cylinder of length L and radius R may be calculated using expressions derived by Tirado & de la Torre (33, 34). Therefore, the rotational rates of the uniform modes of motion for short linear segments of duplex DNA of arbitrary length are well characterized. Only the effective hydrodynamic radius R and length L of the DNA must be determined.

The length is taken to be $L = (N + 1) \cdot h$, where $N + 1$ is the number of base pairs and h is the rise per base pair, which is generally accepted to be 3.4 Å. The effective hydrodynamic radius R is often taken to be approximately 10.5 to 12.0 Å. Recent studies (9) indicate that values as low as 10.5 Å are more likely for short DNA containing alternating GC sequences. As sequences become longer ($N > 30$) and more mixed, R appears to approach a limit of approximately 12 Å (24, 36).

The equations of Tirado & de la Torre (33) may be used to calculate the diffusion coefficients $D_\perp$ and $D_\parallel$ for the uniform modes of motion in duplex DNA (9, 17) in buffer. They predict that the two characteristic rotational correlation times for a duplex DNA dodecamer ($R = 12$ and $L = 3.4 \times 12$ Å) at 0°C are 7.5 and 14.3 ns for rotations parallel and perpendicular to the helix axis. The perpendicular correlation time increases roughly quadratically with duplex length, while the parallel component is proportional to the length. At 20°C, the correlation times are about twice as fast as they are at 0°C.

The Twisting Collective Motions

Schurr (7, cf 8) has developed closed-form expressions for the twisting correlation function for a simple dynamic model in which only nearest-neighbor bases are coupled by a Hookean spring characterized by the spring constant α, which is assumed to be the same for all nearest-neighbor pairs. The model therefore depends only on the twisting Hookean spring constant and the diffusion coefficient of the uniform mode, $D_\parallel$, which can be experimentally determined or calculated using the equations of Tirado & de la Torre. Therefore, only a single parameter, α, needs to be determined.

Expressions 1 and 2 reveal that the twisting component of the correlation function is:

$$C_n(t) = \exp\,-\{n^2\langle\Delta_z(t)^2\rangle/2\} = \exp\,-\{n^2 D_\parallel t + n^2\langle\phi_i(t)^2\rangle\}, \qquad 3.$$

where the time dependence of $\langle\phi_i(t)^2\rangle$ models the change in internal twist angle of the ith base as it evolves in time owing to the collective modes. At early times, the mean square oscillation amplitude $\langle\Delta_z(t)^2\rangle$ is dominated by the motion of the individual bases rotating independently of one another, with a diffusion coefficient for a single base pair about the helix axis. As the motion progresses it enters the intermediate motion regime, where $\langle\Delta_z(t)^2\rangle$ is proportional to $t^{1/2}$, which is a characteristic signature of the motion of strongly coupled (one-dimensional) oscillators. The hydrodynamic interactions of the bases with one another have very little influence on the on-axis rotations.

As the bases continue moving, couplings to other bases through the Hookean interactions become more pronounced, and finally the entire system rotates uniformly as a rigid rod with the diffusion coefficient $D_\parallel = k_B T/(N + 1)\gamma_\parallel$. The evolution of the mean square amplitudes of twisting $\langle\phi_i(t)^2\rangle$ can be described by the normal modes, of which there are only N time constants of interest for $N + 1$ base pairs. The time constant, τ_ℓ, and the root mean square displacement, d_ℓ, for the relaxation by the ℓth mode are related to the eigenvalues, Λ_ℓ, of the restoring potential matrix:

$$\tau_\ell = \frac{\gamma_\parallel}{\alpha\Lambda_\ell} \quad \text{and} \quad (d_\ell)^2 = \frac{k_B T}{\alpha\Lambda_\ell}. \qquad 4.$$

The eigenvectors of the restoring potential matrix, which couple the contribution of the ℓth mode to the twisting of the ith base, are needed to fully construct the time dependence of $\langle\phi_i(t)^2\rangle$ as given by:

$$\langle\phi_i(t)^2\rangle = \sum_{\ell\geq2}^{N+1} (d_\ell Q_{i\ell})^2\cdot[1 - \exp(-t/T_\ell)], \qquad 5.$$

where the eigenvalues and eigenvectors are

$$\Lambda_\ell = 4 \sin^2 \left(\frac{\pi(\ell - 1)}{2(N + 1)} \right) \quad \text{and}$$

$$Q_{i\ell}^2 = \left(\frac{2}{(N + 1)} \right) \cos^2 \left[\frac{(2i - 1)(\ell - 1)\pi}{2(N + 1)} \right]. \qquad 6.$$

The evolution of the correlation function $C_n(t)$ represents the complete statistically averaged time course resulting from twisting for each base pair. As the time approaches infinity, (or the amplitudes $\langle \phi_i(t)^2 \rangle$ approach $\langle \phi_i^2(\infty) \rangle$), the motion is dominated by the uniform mode; all of the internal motions have relaxed completely. The amplitude of the uniform mode is reduced because $\langle \phi_i^2(\infty) \rangle$ is nonzero and positive. From the above equations, we can calculate the quantity:

$$\langle \phi_i^2(\infty) \rangle = \sum (d_\ell Q_{i\ell})^2 = \frac{(N + 1)k_B T}{12\alpha} \left[1 + 3 \left(\frac{2i - N - 2}{N + 1} \right)^2 \right]. \qquad 7.$$

This remarkably simple expression for the total maximum mean square displacement is a quantity that can be measured. It is related to the order parameter associated with relaxation due to the twisting component. If we let $S_{\parallel,i}$ be the contribution to the overall order parameter from twisting of the ith base pair, then

$$S_{\parallel,i} = \exp \frac{-\langle \phi_i(\infty)^2 \rangle}{2}. \qquad 8.$$

The square of the order parameter is therefore the amplitude reduction factor for the associated uniform mode (21, 22). The contribution to $C_n(t)$, the nth component of the correlation function, requires only that the order parameter be raised to the n^2 power.

The Bending Collective Motions

The correlation functions for the bending or flexing of DNA have also been developed and solved by Schurr and coworkers (31, 32). In this model, each base pair is restrained from flexing by a spring (represented by a Hookean force constant) connecting each base pair to the neighbor on either side. The spring force constant is assumed to be the same for all bases. The incorporation of bending into the dynamics formulation has been dealt with in different ways: Barkley & Zimm (8) developed an approach that is limited to early times for the central base of an infinitely long section of linear DNA. To extend duplex bending to long times, a mesoscopic approach has been adapted where Brownian dynamics simulations are applied to 9.3 base pair units (6, 10). Song et al (32) have developed an analytic approach to the mesoscopic model that agrees extremely well with the numerical Brownian dynamics simulations when the rod is weakly bending. We review this approach because it offers the physical insight of analytic theory and describes how internal modes contribute to relaxation. Moreover, it is valid in the long time limit. The formal structure is identical to that of twisting, but the eigenvalues and eigenvectors are not analytic. The flexural component of the correlation function for the WRME is

$$F_n(t) = \exp - \left\{ [\ell(\ell + 1) - n^2] \frac{\langle \Delta_x(t)^2 \rangle}{2} \right\},$$

where

$$\frac{\langle \Delta_x(t)^2 \rangle}{2} = D_\perp \cdot t + \langle \eta_i^2(t) \rangle. \qquad 9.$$

The overall displacement in the x direction may be written in terms of the uniform mode displacement plus an internal motion term $\eta_i^2(t)$, which is the angular deformation about the x (or y) axis resulting from internal bending or flexing, referenced to a frame fixed to a rigid rod. The quantity $\langle \eta_i^2(t) \rangle$ is the bending analogue to $\langle \phi_i(t)^2 \rangle$. The uniform mode is separated from the internal modes, and the internal mean square bending angle $\langle \eta_i^2(t) \rangle$ may be written in terms of $N - 1$ modes and $N - 1$ relaxation times for $N + 1$ spheres.

When all of the internal modes of motion relax away, $\langle \eta_i^2(t) \rangle$ becomes $\langle \eta_i^2(\infty) \rangle$, which is the total mean square angular displacement due to bending for the ith sphere. Wu et al (36) have shown that this quantity can be related to the eigenvalues and eigenvectors of the bending potential matrix; working directly with the base pairs (not using the mesoscopic model), they have obtained the infinite time mean square bending amplitude, which is identical in form to that obtained for the mean square angular displacement due to twisting:

$$\langle \eta_i(\infty)^2 \rangle = \Sigma (d_\ell^f Q_{i\ell})^2 = \frac{(N + 1)h}{12P_\beta} \left\{ 1 + 3 \left(\frac{2i - N - 2}{N + 1} \right)^2 \right\}, \qquad 10.$$

where $(d_\ell^f)^2 = h/\Lambda_\ell P_\beta$ is the angular displacement resulting from bending for the ℓth mode, h is the rise per base pair, and P_β is the dynamic flexural persistence length. P_β is related to the bending force constant K_β by $P_\beta = hK_\beta/k_\beta T$, which is the flexural force constant for the Hookean restoring potential responsible for bending. The simplicity of the expression for the total mean square displacements for twisting and bending demonstrate that they are related through the force constants:

$$\frac{\langle \eta_i(\infty)^2 \rangle}{\langle \phi_i(\infty)^2 \rangle} = \frac{\alpha}{K_\beta}.$$ 11.

Just as the total mean square displacement due to twisting is related to a twist-order parameter, the total mean square displacement due to flexing is related to a flexural-order parameter.

$$S_{\perp,i} = \exp \frac{-\langle \eta_i(\infty)^2 \rangle}{2} = (S_{\parallel,i})^{\alpha/K_\beta}.$$ 12.

An amplitude-reduction factor, the result of bending, for the nth component of the uniform mode may be constructed by raising the square of the order parameter to the $\ell(\ell - 1) - n^2$ power.

We now consider the time dependence of the mean square bending angle produced by the hydrodynamic interactions of the spheres with one another and the restoring potential. Song & Schurr (31) have developed an elegant, approximate form for the time dependence of the correlation decay resulting from internal bending using the above mesoscopic model, in which 9.3 individual base pairs are replaced with a hydrodynamically equivalent sphere. The hydrodynamic interactions are considered to occur at the spheres' equilibrium positions (all in a straight line) rather than at their instantaneous positions, and the resulting on-site hydrodynamic interactions are given by the modified Rotne-Prager-Oseen tensor:

$$(\mathbf{H}_\beta)_{\ell m} = \delta_{\ell m} + (1 - \delta_{\ell m}) \frac{3}{8 | \ell - m |} \left\{ 1 + \frac{1}{6 | \ell - m |^2} \right\}.$$ 13.

The effect of the restoring force, which resists bending, requires a matrix $\mathbf{D}_\beta$, which represents a fourth-order central-difference operator. Such a matrix arises from the second central-difference operator, which simulates the harmonic bending potential multiplying the squared angular rotations. The angular rotations of the spheres arise from differences in displacements along x or y and hence appear to be derivatives of the displacements. The net result is that the force on each sphere appears as a fourth-order difference operator operating on the displacement coordinates. Each of these two matrices is of dimension $N + 1$ by $N + 1$ (where $N + 1$ is now the number of spheres, not the number of base pairs). The matrix that must be diagonalized to obtain the normal modes is the product of two matrices: The first matrix accounts for the hydrodynamic interactions, $\mathbf{H}_\beta$, and the second matrix encompasses the restoring forces involved in bending $\mathbf{D}_\beta$. The eigenvalue problem is:

$$Q_\beta^{-1}(\mathbf{H}_\beta \mathbf{D}_\beta)Q_\beta = \Lambda_\beta \qquad\qquad 14.$$

The eigenvalues and eigenvectors cannot be written in closed form, yet because both $\mathbf{H}_\beta$ and $\mathbf{D}_\beta$ are dimensionless, these terms are independent of any physical quantity except the number of spheres and their numerical generation is straightforward. The resulting equation for the time dependence of the mean square displacements is:

$$\langle \eta_i(t)^2 \rangle = \frac{h}{P_\beta} \sum_{\ell=3}^{N+1} (Q_{\beta i+1,\ell} - Q_{\beta i,\ell})^2 \left[1 - \exp\left(-\frac{t}{T_\ell} \right) \right]. \qquad 15.$$

The results are very similar in form to the results obtained from the twisting problem. The time constants for the relaxation of the modes are

$$\tau_\ell = \frac{h^2}{K_\beta \Lambda_{\beta_\ell}} \cdot \frac{k_B T}{(N+1)D_\perp} \qquad\qquad 16.$$

and depend on the bending force constant, K_β, as well as the eigenvalues Λ_{β_ℓ}, from Equation 13. The evolution of $\langle \eta_i(t)^2 \rangle$ in the intermediate regime is proportional to $t^{1/4}$, which follows directly from the fourth central-difference form of $\mathbf{D}_\beta$ and is the characteristic signature of the evolution of the flexure in the strongly coupled region.

The above outline demonstrates that the correlation functions for the WRME (Equation 1) can be calculated within the framework of a simple dynamic model of DNA that considers the uniform modes and the internal collective modes of twisting (Equation 6) and bending (Equation 14). This model has only four adjustable parameters: $D_\parallel$, $D_\perp$, α, and K_β. The first two quantities may be directly measured or may be calculated using the equations of Tirado & de la Torre, whose formulations require simply a knowledge of the hydrodynamic radius R and length L of the DNA duplex. Both L and R can be measured. The only two parameters left to adjust are the twisting and bending force constants, or equivalently, the two order parameters, $S_{\parallel,i}$ and $S_{\perp,i}$. This development represents a simple yet realistic model for DNA dynamics.

The weakly bending rod model developed by Schurr over the past decade makes some rather important predictions that can be tested directly with a local probe for dynamics. The first prediction is that the uniform modes will be the same regardless of where along the DNA the probe is placed. The second is that the mean square angular displacements will increase linearly with increasing length of the DNA.

The third is that the mean square amplitude of angular displacement for both twisting and flexing will be about four times as great as the probe is moved to the ends of the DNA from the center, regardless of length. This prediction can be expressed in terms of order parameters. The order parameter for a probe attached to the end should equal the order parameter measured in the middle raised to the fourth power, regardless of the probe motion with respect to the base pair (i.e. the length- and position-independent contribution to the motion). Because the model specifies the order parameters for the different components in advance, the ratios of order parameters and decay times for each of the components of the relaxation of the WRME are also specified.

The Lipari-Szabo Model-Free Formulation of Molecular Dynamics

Various other treatments of macromolecular dynamics have appeared in the literature. Most notable among them is the so-called model-free formulation of macromolecular dynamics by Lipari & Szabo (LS) (19–22). This approach found early application in the analysis of the high-resolution ^{31}P NMR data obtained by Hogan & Jardetsky (16) from duplex DNA. However, the model-free method has been used most often for interpreting ^{15}N NMR relaxation data in proteins. We now briefly review the methodology of Lipari & Szabo, consider its applicability to the analysis of WRME correlation functions for duplex DNA, and compare its form to the dynamic model developed by Schurr and coworkers.

The LS method is based on the idea that a correlation function will consist of products of the uniform modes and internal dynamics. Moreover, the correlation function for internal dynamics may (when the internal motions are quite rapid) be described by a single correlation time or at most a small set of correlation times, each exhibiting exponential decay. The LS method for describing a generalized correlation function, $C(t)$, separates the uniform modes from the internal dynamics:

$$C(t) = C_o(t)*C_I(t),\qquad 17.$$

where $C_o(t)$ contains the relaxation times resulting from the uniform mode (or modes when the motion is anisotropic), and $C_I(t)$ contains both the generalized order parameters and the relaxation times resulting from internal motions. Lipari & Szabo stress that such a formulation is only approximate and that more rigorous forms must be used when the motions are coupled and the uniform modes are highly anisotropic. Recently, Schurr et al (29) have shown that for these approximations to be valid (*a*) the internal motions must be significantly faster than uniform motions and (*b*) the restrictive potential that controls the internal motions must be uniform in one angle.

Lipari & Szabo write $C_o(t)$ as a sum of exponentials if the motion is anisotropic. Generally, this sum is required because the orientation of the probe relative to the body is arbitrary. To clarify the effect of probe orientation on the correlation function, let us compute the correlation function for the WRME in the frame of the probe, which is assumed to have a specific orientation to that of the molecular-fixed frame. First, we consider the molecule to be a rigid cylinder for which the correlation function for the WRME reduces to:

$$\langle \mathscr{D}^L_{N,M}(\Omega_0)^* \mathscr{D}^\ell_{n,m}(\Omega)\rangle = \frac{\delta_{L\ell}\delta_{M,m}}{(2\ell + 1)} \sum_{p=-\ell}^{\ell} \mathscr{D}^\ell_{N,p}(\Omega_r)^* \mathscr{D}^\ell_{n,p}(\Omega_r)$$

$$\exp - t\{[\ell(\ell + 1) - p^2]D_\perp + p^2 D_\parallel\}. \quad 18.$$

For $\ell = 2$, there are three relaxation rates, only two of which are independent. Notice that we can include some cross-correlation now because the relaxation of the WRME is described in the frame of the probe. This form is simplified by Lipari & Szabo, who argue that it can be treated approximately as generating no cross-correlations and having only two relaxation rates. The amplitudes of these modes are adjustable and not related to the orientation of the probe to the molecular frame of motion. Thus, Lipari & Szabo simplify the above form to:

$$\langle \mathscr{D}^L_{N,M}(\Omega_0)^* \mathscr{D}^\ell_{n,m}(\Omega)\rangle \cong C_o(t)$$

$$= \frac{1}{5}\left[A \exp\left(-\frac{t}{\tau_1}\right) + (1 - A) \exp\left(-\frac{t}{\tau_2}\right)\right], \quad 19.$$

where A and the two relaxation times may be related to the above description in an averaged sense.

Lipari & Szabo express the internal correlation function $C_I(t)$ as a series of single exponential relaxation times:

$$C_I(t) = S^2 + \sum_{k=1}^{P} A_k^2 \exp(-r_k t). \quad 20.$$

This form is an approximation of a more rigorous form for $C_I(t)$. If the internal correlation function is known, Lipari & Szabo suggest that one may find the amplitudes A_k and rates r_k of the internal relaxation components in a least-squares sense. The internal correlation function is understood to always start at unity and end at the order parameter, so the following boundary conditions are satisfied:

$$C_1(0) = 1 \quad \text{and} \quad C_1(\infty) = S^2. \qquad\qquad 21.$$

This methodology provides enough equations to solve for the desired set of rates and amplitudes. An alternative form of the Padé approximants given by Yeramian (37) for analyzing any function in terms of decaying exponentials uses only moments of the function and does not use derivatives.

We now use the Lipari & Szabo formulation to obtain the internal correlation functions for the internal twisting and bending of duplex DNA. Internal motion is characterized in the intermediate motional regime by a $t^{1/s}$ time dependence where $s = 2$ for twisting and $s = 4$ for bending. Therefore, the simplest model for $C_1(t)$ would be: $C_1(t) = \exp - (t/\tau)^{1/s}$. This form satisfies the LS boundary conditions but would suggest the order parameter is zero. Also, the expression for $C_1(t)$ cannot be fit to more than a single exponential because the derivatives of $C_1(t)$ do not exist at $t = 0$ for $s > 1$. The exponential function for $s = 4$ indicates a form very similar to an exponential plus a base line. Therefore, the effective rate of a single exponential is determined to be: $r_1 = (s!\tau)^{-1}$. The order parameter may be found by evaluating the exponential out to two or three time constants, where $C_1(t)$ has decayed to somewhere between 0.15 and 0.05. Clearly, even a simple model for internal dynamics poses problems in the LS formulation.

Comparison of the LS Model-Free Theory and the Theory of Schurr et al

Let us now compare the LS (21, 22) approach to that of Schurr et al (30). The two approaches differ in several ways. First, in the formulation of the uniform modes, Lipari & Szabo truncate the terms from three to two. Second, Lipari & Szabo factor the correlation function into a simple product of $C_o(t)$, the correlation function for the uniform modes, and $C_1(t)$, the correlation function for the internal dynamics. A natural way to write the results of Schurr et al would be to keep the uniform modes and the internal-dynamics components together for each term in the rank expansion of the correlation function. Then one may write the equations of Schurr as:

$$\langle \mathscr{D}_{N,M}^L(\Omega_0)^* \mathscr{D}_{n,m}^\ell(\Omega) \rangle = \frac{\delta_{L\ell}\delta_{M,m}}{(2\ell + 1)} \sum_{p=-\ell}^{\ell} A_p$$

$$\exp - t\{[\ell(\ell + 1) - p^2]D_\perp + p^2 D_\|\} \cdot \{C_{1,\perp}(t)\}^{\ell(\ell + 1) - p^2}\{C_{1,\|}(t)\}^{p^2}, \qquad 22.$$

where $A_p = \mathcal{D}^{\ell}_{N,p}(\Omega_r)^* \mathcal{D}^{\ell}_{n,p}(\Omega_r)$ represents the orientation weighted fractional contributions of the modes, and the perpendicular and parallel contribution to the internal correlation functions, $C_{1,\perp}(t)$ and $C_{1,\parallel}(t)$, are defined above in terms of the relaxation of $\langle \eta_i^2(t) \rangle$ and $\langle \phi_i(t)^2 \rangle$, respectively.

The forms of the WRME correlation functions as given by Lipari & Szabo and Schurr differ little when the internal modes relax rapidly relative to the uniform modes. In the long time limit (long for the internal modes but not for the uniform modes), the uniform modes and the internal modes may be approximately decoupled. However, the form for the correlation function described by Schurr fully encompasses an extended treatment of $C_1(t)$, which is only suggested by the LS functions. Furthermore, the correlation functions of Lipari & Szabo (19–22) and Schurr et al (29, 30) each depend on two parameters. In LS theory, these parameters are the model-free quantities S^2 and an effective internal correlation time, whereas the correlation function of Schurr et al is parameterized by the quantities α and K_β, each of which has a clear physical meaning. In summary, the model-free approach seems to offer little advantage over the approach of Schurr et al in describing the dynamics of duplex DNA, the number of adjustable parameters is equal in each theory and the theory of Schurr et al presents an extended treatment of $C_1(t)$.

A major problem not yet discussed but subsumed by a model-free approach is the length-independent internal motions of the probe relative to the base. This particular issue must be treated separately for each individual probe. Extensions of the Schurr formulation functions of the WRME show that one needs to include an additional internal relaxation term with each C_1 in the above equation (23). Thus, this approach presents a correct mathematical formulation even if individual terms are not known. At this level, model-free terms could be used to simulate the effects of local probe motion without compromising the physical interpretation of the twist and bending force constants. Application of forms that simplify the analysis without compromising the interesting physical features of the problem remains an area of active research.

Localized Motions of the Probe

Thus far, we have developed the dynamics and the correlation functions for the motion of an idealized base pair, which itself is taken to have no internal motion. However, the magnetic resonance spin probe associated with a base may have some mobility relative to the idealized base pair. The source of its motion may come from the motion of moieties within the base (or backbone or sugar) depending upon the nature of the probe or attachment. Such motions are generally on rapid time scales and have been characterized as having rapid relaxation times and limited amplitudes. Several examples of DNA dynamics exist that do not fully adhere to such general conditions on the internal motion (see BH Robinson & GP Drobny, in Volume 25 of this series). Let us now develop a way to incorporate such rapid motions into the form for the correlation function. In the above formalism, we described how to find the spin probe at orientation Ω. This orientation is called the principal axis system (PAS) and is taken to coincide with the CSA spin tensor of the probe with respect to the laboratory axis system. As described above, only two rotations are needed to locate the PAS. The first rotation was by amount Ω_B, which is a rotation from the laboratory frame to the frame of the base pair. The second rotation, by an amount Ω_r, takes one from the rigid base pair to an equilibrium position of the probe. A third rotation, ϵ, is now needed to rotate from the equilibrium position to the actual position of the probe. Ω_B and ϵ are both time-dependent quantities, while Ω_r is time independent. The WRME may be written in terms of these three successive rotations as:

$$\mathscr{D}_{n,m}^{\ell}(\Omega) = \sum_{s,p=-\ell}^{\ell} \mathscr{D}_{n,s}^{\ell}(\epsilon) \cdot \mathscr{D}_{s,p}^{\ell}(\Omega_r) \mathscr{D}_{p,m}^{\ell}(\Omega_B). \qquad 23.$$

The correlation functions for the WRME then may be written as:

$$\langle \mathscr{D}_{N,M}^{L}(\Omega_0)^* \mathscr{D}_{n,m}^{\ell}(\Omega) \rangle$$

$$= \frac{\delta_{L,\ell}\delta_{M,m}}{(2\ell + 1)} \sum_{S,s,p=-\ell}^{\ell} \langle \mathscr{D}_{N,S}^{\ell}(\epsilon_0)^* \mathscr{D}_{n,s}^{\ell}(\epsilon) \rangle \mathscr{D}_{S,p}^{\ell}(\Omega_r)^* \mathscr{D}_{s,p}^{\ell}(\Omega_r) F_p(t) C_p(t). \qquad 24.$$

The values for the time-independent Euler angles Ω_r should be known, given reasonable equilibrium structures for the DNA. The averaging over the motion of the base pair relative to the laboratory was defined above. If the probe has no internal libration relative to the base pair, then

$$\delta_{n,s}\delta_{N,S} = \langle \mathscr{D}_{N,S}^{\ell}(\epsilon_0)^* \mathscr{D}_{n,s}^{\ell}(\epsilon) \rangle \qquad 25.$$

and the equation reduces back to that given previously for two successive Eulerian rotations to find the PAS of the probe. Several possible models may be invoked to describe localized dynamics of the probe relative to the base pair. Woessner's model (35) assumes rapid, uniaxial rotation about a fixed axis. Lipari & Szabo have considered restricted diffusion models (diffusion in and on a cone), whereas Schurr and coworkers have considered both isotropic and anisotropic limited-amplitude libration models. Regardless of the specific model used, such motions are independent of the length of the duplex DNA and are often, but not always, characterized by rapid decay times and limited amplitudes. Assuming that the motion of the spin probe consists of isotropic librations of limited amplitude centered about the equilibrium position, the correlation function takes on a very simple form:

$$\langle \mathcal{D}_{N,M}^{L}(\Omega_0)^* \mathcal{D}_{n,m}^{\ell}(\Omega) \rangle$$

$$= \frac{\delta_{L\ell}\delta_{M,m}\delta_{N,n}}{(2\ell + 1)} \sum_{s,p=-\ell}^{\ell} \langle \mathcal{D}_{n,s}^{\ell}(\epsilon_0)^* \mathcal{D}_{n,s}^{\ell}(\epsilon) \rangle \cdot | \mathcal{D}_{s,p}^{\ell}(\Omega_r)|^2 \cdot F_p(t)C_p(t).$$

26.

The tilt angle Ω_r depends on only one of the three Euler angles. In several examples, Lipari & Szabo (19–22) and Schurr (29, 30) have both shown that only under the most fortuitous circumstances, and applying the most optimistic simplifications, one can write:

$$\langle \mathcal{D}_{N,S}^{\ell}(\epsilon_0)^* \mathcal{D}_{n,s}^{\ell}(\epsilon) \rangle = \left[S^2 + (1 - S^2) \exp\left(-\frac{t}{\tau_\epsilon}\right) \right],$$

27.

where $S = \langle \mathcal{D}_{0,0}^{2}(\epsilon) \rangle$ in this example. In any case, this simple model of localized probe dynamics, when combined with the theory of Schurr et al, incorporates the length-dependent collective modes, the probe orientation, and the internal libration of the probe relative to the idealized base pair. The final correlation function has five adjustable parameters: the tilt angle of the probe relative to the base, the two elastic force constants, the internal order parameter, and the internal relaxation time. Each of these has a clear physical meaning, and the last is probably too fast to be meaningful in most magnetic resonance experiments.

Toward a More Detailed Theory of DNA Dynamics

The model of DNA dynamics developed by Schurr and coworkers provides a means of computing correlation functions based on a small set of adjustable, physically meaningful parameters. These mathematical forms provide insight into the structure of relaxation processes and demonstrate the separability of uniform modes and internal modes. However, several assumptions have been used to keep the model as simple as possible. More robust techniques are available for generating trajectories of the DNA dynamics. Brownian trajectories have been calculated in which segments of the DNA are replaced by spheres of

15.9-Å radius. Trajectories, consisting of the spatial positions of each sphere, are computed according to the stepwise algorithm of Ermak & McCammon (11). These methods take the direct and hydrodynamic interactions into account as described above, except that hydrodynamics are updated at every step of the trajectory. Recently, Elvingson (10) included the effect of hydrodynamics and the effect exerted on the trajectories by an external electric field in Brownian trajectory simulations. The hydrodynamic terms make the DNA more pliable and bendable in the presence of an electric field. Allison et al (5) have examined the triplet anisotropy decay of a 209–base pair DNA as well as the birefringence data of DNA fragments in the range of 130–367 base pairs (4, 6). They concluded that the best-fit Brownian dynamics model requires that the DNA have a persistence length of ~500 Å. However, the calculation reproduces only the effective relaxation times but not the amplitudes of the individual models. Trajectories of this sort may be used to either directly compute the correlation functions of the WRME or to directly simulate magnetic resonance spectra, without computing any correlation functions at all (27). Molecular dynamics simulations are largely restricted to very short times, a limited amount of solvent, and no long-range hydrodynamic interactions. The Brownian trajectory work is the only numerical approach that properly accounts for the long-range (through solvent) hydrodynamic interactions between subunits and can be extended enough to obtain the long-time, uniform mode limits. The lack of local sequence-dependent effects in Schurr's model does not make it incomplete unless experimental evidence demonstrates that DNA dynamics indeed depend on the local sequence. Reports to date have only hinted at this dependence (12, 14, 15, 18), which now constitutes an active area of experimental as well as theoretical research. In the following section, we show how trajectories or correlation functions are used to simulate and analyze magnetic resonance data.

EFFECTS OF DYNAMICS ON OBSERVABLES IN MAGNETIC RESONANCE

The effects molecular motions exert on magnetic resonance observables (such as spin relaxation) depend on the nature of the observable and the details of the experiment. In general, motional information comes from (*a*) the line shape of the magnetic resonance spectrum and (*b*) the relaxation (or cross-relaxation) rate of an observable. The line shape may be calculated from first principles using the stochastic Liouville equation of motion, in which the motional operator is explicitly incorporated into the line-shape equations. An alternative method (when the dynamics are rapid) is to simulate the line shape (or line widths) using the effective tensorial interactions between spins alone or between spins and external fields. The effective interactions differ significantly from the static interactions and are often smaller in magnitude. The methods used to analyze the spectral line shape and relaxation data also appear at first to be quite different. However, both methods of data analysis begin with the stochastic Liouville equation of motion for the density matrix (1) ρ:

$$\dot{\rho} = -i[\mathbf{H}, \rho] - \Gamma_R(\rho - \rho_0) - \Gamma_\Omega(\rho - \rho_0). \qquad 28.$$

The motional process is symbolically represented by Γ_Ω, and the relaxation of observables is contained in Γ_R. $\mathbf{H}$ is the complete Hamiltonian in the laboratory frame, including, if needed, the radio frequency (rf) terms. The Hamiltonian contains terms that depend on the orientation of the spin probe; the dynamics move the molecule, which in turn moves the spin probe and the associated interaction tensor from one orientation to another, thereby changing the resonance position and hence the spin response. Once ρ is known, any observable O, such as $\langle Ix \rangle$ or $\langle Iz \rangle$, which represent the transverse and longitudinal components of the magnetization, may be determined from $\langle O \rangle = \text{tr}\{O \cdot \rho\}$, where tr stands for trace, which is the sum of the diagonal elements of a matrix. Ultimately, a single local spin probe exhibits the magnetic properties of the probe modulated by the stochastic motion of the environment.

Three Hamiltonians are considered in this discussion: (*a*) the orientation-dependent part of the Zeeman Hamiltonian, $\mathbf{H}_Z$, which is the interaction of the probe with the external magnetic field; (*b*) the dipolar Hamiltonian, $\mathbf{H}_{DIP}$, which is a pair-wise, field-independent, direct, through-space interaction between spin dipoles; and (*c*) the quadrupolar Hamiltonian, $\mathbf{H}_Q$, which is the interaction of a spin (greater than 1/2) with the electric-field gradients in the molecule. All Hamiltonians are scalar operators, written as inner products of spin (angular momentum) vector operators coupled through a dyadic tensor (a three-by-three matrix) with either the field or each other, or among themselves. In high field the fundamental term that provides the basic resonance signal is the isotropic part of the Zeeman Hamiltonian. The external field (in frequency units) consists of the dc component along the laboratory z axis, and the rf term along x and y:

$$\mathbf{H} = \begin{pmatrix} \gamma h_0 \cos \omega t \\ \gamma h_0 \sin \omega t \\ \omega_0 \end{pmatrix}, \qquad 29.$$

where ω_0 is the Larmor frequency of the probe, ω is the rf frequency, γ is the gyromagnetic ratio of the probe, and h_0 is the rf, or observer, amplitude. In a particular orientation of the probe, the **G** (or chemical shift anisotropy, CSA) tensor is diagonal; at this orientation the laboratory frame coincides with the principal axis frame (PAF) of the spin. The **G** tensor has the specific form:

$$\mathbf{G} = \begin{pmatrix} g_x & 0 & 0 \\ 0 & g_y & 0 \\ 0 & 0 & g_z \end{pmatrix}.$$

30.

At any other orientation Ω, in the laboratory frame, the **G** tensor is not diagonal but is given as $\mathbf{M}'(\Omega) \cdot \mathbf{G} \cdot \mathbf{M}(\Omega)$ where **M** is the rotation matrix written in terms of the three Euler angles Ω. As a result of absorbing all orientation dependence into the **G** tensor, the spin operators are always referenced to the laboratory frame. Each Hamiltonian contains an orientation-independent part and an orientation-dependent part. The easiest way to write these parts, so that all Hamiltonians have a similar form, is to use the spherical tensor operators for the spin angular momentum operators, I_x, I_y, and I_z:

$$\mathscr{I}_{\pm} = \frac{\mp 1}{\sqrt{2}} (I_x \pm iI_y); \qquad \mathscr{I}_0 = I_z.$$

31.

In this form ($\mathscr{I}_m$) are the three components of a spherical tensor operator of rank 1, where $m = -1, 0,$ or 1. The Zeeman Hamiltonian then is written as $\mathbf{H}_Z = \mathbf{H}_0 + \mathbf{H}_{CSA}$, where $\mathbf{H}_0(h_0 = 0) = \omega_0 I_z$ is the orientation-independent part that provides the fundamental resonance condition. The rf term provides the torque on the spin I by the Hamiltonian:

$$\epsilon(t) = \frac{\gamma h_0}{\sqrt{2}} \sum_{m=-1}^{1} m \exp(im\omega t) \mathscr{I}_{-m}.$$

The orientation-dependent part of the Zeeman Hamiltonian (when $h_0 = 0$), the CSA Hamiltonian (1), is:

$$\mathbf{H}_{CSA} = \sum_{q=-2}^{+2} (-1)^q \mathbf{B}_{-q} \cdot \mathbf{G}_q.$$

32.

This expression is written in terms of a product of two rank 2 spherical tensor operators: The **B** term contains only the spin operators (and constants), while the **G** term contains the elements of the tensorial coupling (which determines the magnitude of the interactions) and the orientation dependence though the WRME (discussed in the previous section). All Hamiltonians can be written in this form. Therefore, we can express the orientation dependence of all Hamiltonians using the same functions as those used to generate correlation functions. This connection will soon become even more evident. The second interaction is that between two spins through a generalized dipolar interaction, characterized by a coupling tensor $\mathbf{A}$, in which the orientation-independent part has been neglected:

$$\mathbf{H}_{DIP} = I \cdot (\mathbf{A} - \bar{a}\mathbf{1}) \cdot \mathscr{S} = \sum_q (-1)^q \mathbf{A}_{-q} \mathbf{F}_q. \qquad 33.$$

The first term is orientation independent and scales as the average of the $\mathbf{A}$ tensor: $\bar{a} = \mathrm{tr}\{\mathbf{A}\}/3$. The term $\mathbf{F}_q$ contains the elements of the dipolar coupling tensor and the WRME, while the spin operators are contained in the $\mathbf{A}_q$ term. For spins greater than 1/2, which is the case for ^{14}N and ^2H nuclei, a quadrupolar interaction Hamiltonian is included and is defined as:

$$\mathbf{H}_Q = I \cdot \mathbf{V} \cdot I = \sum_{q=-2}^{+2} (-1)^q \mathbf{T}_{-q} \mathbf{R}_q. \qquad 34.$$

Because the $\mathrm{tr}\{\mathbf{V}\} = 0$, this interaction contains no scalar part. The spin operators are contained in the elements of $\mathbf{T}_q$, and the quadrupolar coupling constant and WRME are in the elements of $\mathbf{R}_q$. In summary, the $\mathbf{G}_q$, $\mathbf{F}_q$, and $\mathbf{R}_q$ spherical tensor operators include all orientation dependence, and only rank 2 WRMEs are needed. The relationships given above provide us with enough information to solve for a line shape or any other property of the spin system. The computation of a line shape requires knowledge of the $\mathbf{G}$, $\mathbf{A}$, and $\mathbf{V}$ tensors. Such information can often be obtained from model compounds; otherwise, measurements must be done on the same system in the absence of dynamics. If knowledge of the tensors is inaccurate, the dynamics cannot be determined with certainty.

The Hamiltonian is generally divided into two terms, $\mathbf{H} = \mathbf{H}_o + \mathbf{H}'$, where $\mathbf{H}_o$ contains those parts that are either orientation independent or that are stationary (also called secular) in the frame rotating with the rf field. $\mathbf{H}'$ contains terms that are orientationally dependent and often nonstationary as well. This partition is quite useful because the nonstationary terms may be treated by fast-motion relaxation theory, whereas the stationary terms may be retained in the density matrix. The equation of motion for any observable, O_j, in the laboratory frame is:

$$\langle \dot{O}_j \rangle = -i \langle O_j [\mathbf{H}_o, (\rho - \rho_0)] \rangle$$
$$- \langle O_j \Gamma_R (\rho - \rho_0) \rangle - \Gamma_\Omega \langle O_j \rangle - i \langle O_j [\mathbf{H}_o, \rho_0] \rangle. \qquad 35.$$

The operator Γ_Ω represents those long time scale processes that cannot be treated by fast motion averaging and that lead to line-shape changes. Generally, even in the presence of slow dynamics, terms in the Hamiltonian that fluctuate rapidly in the laboratory frame may be incorporated into the fast-motion, or Redfield, relaxation term (also included in Equation 35). Also, the cross correlation of fluctuating and stationary terms in the Hamiltonian are neglected in Equation 35. The relaxation term is given according to fast-motion theory in terms of $\mathbf{H}'$:

$$\langle O_j \Gamma_R (\rho - \rho_0) \rangle = + \int_{\tau=0} \langle [\overline{H'(\tau)}\,[H'(0),\,O_j]] \rangle \, d\tau \qquad 36.$$

where $\mathbf{H}'$ is the orientation-dependent perturbation; $\mathbf{H}'(t)$ is that same perturbation in a frame rotated by $\mathbf{H}_0$. The bar indicates an averaging over the stochastic dynamics. Although this form might seem restrictive, it is the most useful form for computing a line shape or a relaxation time. The equation for a single observable $\langle \dot{O}_j \rangle$ may be written in terms of all other observables by expanding the density matrix in terms of all possible observables:

$$\rho - \rho_0 = \sum_k \langle O_k \rangle O_k^\dagger \qquad 37.$$

where O_k is the operator associated with the observable $\langle O_k \rangle = \mathrm{tr}\{O_k(\rho - \rho_0)\}$. For a single species with spin I, $2I + 1$ operators (including the identity operator) are needed to fully describe ρ in terms of the above expansion. With no loss of generality, the operators can be made orthonormal in the following sense: $\mathrm{tr}\{O_k O_j^\dagger\} = \delta_{kj}$ (38, 39). Thus, we can write the equations of motion of all observables in a very simple form (omitting, for now the rf terms):

$$\langle \dot{O}_j \rangle = - \sum_k \{R_{jk} + i \cdot \omega_{jk}\} \langle O_j \rangle, \qquad 38.$$

where the relaxation terms R_{jk} are given by:

$$R_{jk} = \int_0^\infty \mathrm{tr}\{[O_j,\, \overline{\mathbf{H}'(0),\, [\mathbf{H}'(\tau),\, O_k^\dagger}]]\} \, d\tau \qquad 39.$$

and the frequency terms ω_{jk} are:

$$\omega_{jk} = \mathrm{tr}\{O_j[\mathbf{H}_0, O_k^\dagger]\}. \qquad 40.$$

From the above form for R_{jk}, one may compute the rate of relaxation for any single observable and the cross-relaxation rate between any two observables. For example, R_{ii} is the spin-lattice relaxation rate $R_1 = 1/T_1$ where $O_i = I_z$. The spin-spin relaxation rate for spin I, or R_2, is R_{jj} for $O_j = I_x$. As another example, the rate of quadrupolar relaxation is given for $j = k$ and $O_j = O_k = T_0$ from the quadrupolar tensor operator, defined above. The relaxation is then calculated using the nonsecular terms in the quadrupolar tensor. The nuclear Overhauser cross-relaxation arises from the cross-coupling of the Zeeman magnetization of one spin I with another spin S; in this case $O_j = I_z$ and $O_k = S_z$.

The definition of R_{jk} may be used to understand the connection between the correlation functions developed above and the relaxation observed in the MR experiments. We now take advantage of the form of $\mathbf{H'}$ using as a specific example the orientation-dependent part of the operators given above. The statements are specifically for the quadrupolar operator but apply equally well to the CSA and dipolar operators, or any cross-correlation among them.

Therefore, consider the case where $\mathbf{H'}$ is given by:

$$\mathbf{H'}(\tau) = \sum_{q=-2}^{+2} (-1)^q \tilde{T}_{-q} R_q, \qquad 41.$$

where the tilde denotes that the operator is in the frame of the zeroth-order Hamiltonian. R_{jk} can be calculated. We take advantage of the symmetry of R_q, which applies to $\mathbf{G}_q$ and $\mathbf{F}_q$ as $R_q = (-1)^q R^*_{-q}$ to write out R_{jk} as:

$$R_{jk} = \sum_{qq'} (-1)^{q'} \int_0^\infty \langle R_q^* R_{q'} \rangle \operatorname{tr}\{[O_j, T_q][\tilde{T}_{-q'}, O_k^\dagger]\} \, d\tau, \qquad 42.$$

where the motional averaging takes place only over the orientation-dependent terms in R_q. Writing out the expansion of R_q in terms of the WRME, we find:

$$\langle R_q^* R_{q'} \rangle = \sum_{p,p'} (\rho_{2p}^* \rho_{2p'}) \langle \mathcal{D}^{2*}_{2p,q}(\Omega_0) | \mathcal{D}^2_{2p',q'}(\Omega) \rangle. \qquad 43.$$

This is the connection between a generalized correlation function for a WRME and the relaxation of the spin system. An examination of the forms of the correlation function reveals two important properties: (a) The averaging vanishes unless $q = q'$, and (b) for the dynamic models developed above, the resulting correlation function does not depend on q. However, in some systems, when the uniform modes are suppressed on the MR time scale, the correlation functions do depend on q. The term $\operatorname{tr}\{[O_j, T_q][\tilde{T}_{-q'}, O_k^\dagger]\}$ depends on time in the term $\tilde{T}_q$. In most cases, we may take advantage of the familiar, though not general, relation that: $\tilde{T}_q = T_q \cdot \exp\{iq\omega_0 t\}$. Taking advantage of these relations, the relaxation term becomes:

$$R_{jk} = \sum_q N_q^{j,k} \int_0^\infty \langle \mathbf{R}_q^* \mathbf{R}_q \rangle \exp\{iq\omega_0 t\} \, d\tau, \qquad 44.$$

where the element $N_q^{j,k}$ is just a real, positive number given by:

$$N_q^{j,k} = \text{tr}\{[O_j, T_q][T_q^\dagger, O_k^\dagger]\} \qquad 45.$$

The evaluation of R_{jk} is done by taking the Fourier transform of the sum of the correlation functions to give the total correlation function for R_q. The Fourier transform of a correlation function is called a spectral-density function. By symmetry, the $q = 0$ terms must vanish because $N_q = 0$ when O_j and O_k refer to the z components of the magnetization. Therefore $\langle I_z \rangle$ and the relaxation of $\langle T_0 \rangle$ are given in terms of components at $q = 1$ and $q = 2$ only. The rates are pure real. Defining the spectral density function in the PAS frame as:

$$J_q(\omega) = \frac{2 \cdot Re \left\{ \int_0^\infty \langle R_q^* R_q \rangle \exp\{i\omega t\} \, d\tau \right\}}{|\rho_0|^2}, \qquad 46.$$

it follows that the relaxation rate for the z components (where operator O_j corresponds to either I_z or T_0) is:

$$R_{jj} = |\rho_0|^2 \{ N_1^{j,j} J_1(\omega_0) + N_2^{j,j} J_2(2\omega_0) \}. \qquad 47.$$

By measuring the rates of spin-lattice relaxation and of quadrupolar relaxation, we may uniquely solve for the two spectral-density functions. The description of the spectral-density functions may involve several components. For example, in terms of the model for DNA dynamics described in the preceding section, the spring constants, the relative orientation of the PAS to the molecule, and the uniform modes of motion must be known or estimated. Experimental situations devised to deal with all of these unknowns are discussed below.

Much of the effects of motion on magnetic resonance spectra and observables derives from the correlation functions via the spectral-density functions. Therefore, we have plotted the spectral-density functions associated with a simplified model-correlation function of the form $\exp -\{t/\tau_c\}^{1/s}$ for $s = 1, 2$, and 4. These models approximate the uniform decay ($s = 1$), internal twisting decay ($s = 2$), and internal bending decay ($s = 4$). In Figure 1, the spectral density is plotted as a function of $\omega\tau_c$ for a fixed frequency:

$$J(\omega) = \mathfrak{R} \left\{ \int_{t=0}^\infty \exp - \left\{ \frac{t}{\tau_c} \right\}^{1/s} \cdot \exp -(i\omega t) \, dt \right\}. \qquad 48.$$

As can be seen in Figure 1, the spectral density functions all reach a maximum near $\omega\tau_c = 1$ but the $s = 4$ case is considerably decreased in amplitude, and the roll off at large $\omega\tau_c$ goes approximately as $(\omega\tau_c)^{-1/s}$. In the case of $s = 4$, then, the spectral density covers a very wide range of correlation times.

Preaveraged Tensors

We now discuss the incorporation of dynamics through preaveraged tensors, or dynamically altered effective tensors, as mentioned above.

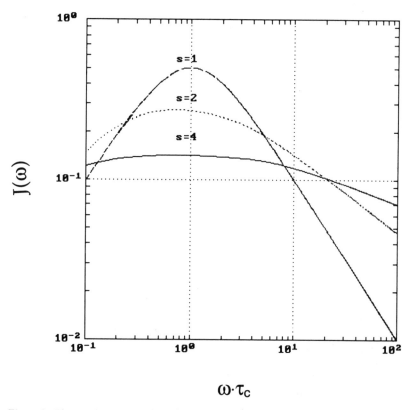

Figure 1 The spectral density functions for the correlation functions given in Equation 48, plotted as a function of correlation time multiplied by the observer frequency, $\{\omega\tau_c\}$ for $s = 1$ (*dashed line*), s = 2 (*dotted line*), and $s = 4$ (*solid line*). For $s = 2$ and $s = 4$, the Fourier transform (FT) is continued into the slow-motion (or high-frequency) regime using appropriate integral approximations. Direct FT methods fail when $\omega\tau_c \gg 1$ or when the correlation functions are slower than simple exponential functions (i.e. $s > 1$) in converging to zero at long times.

In many cases, the internal dynamics are quite rapid relative to the uniform modes. When the internal motions are also rapid relative to the time scale of the MR experiment, the value of the relaxation rate cannot be accurately determined. In this case, we can measure effective tensor elements (or an order parameter) using solid-state NMR or EPR. When the internal dynamics are sufficiently fast, interaction tensors are scaled by the order parameter. Because the tensors contribute to the fast-motion relaxation as the square, the square of the order parameter will be added to the relaxation rates. This relation is also clear in both the LS model-free analysis and the weakly bending rod model. Therefore, rapid internal motion may be accounted for by averaging the tensor over the distribution swept out by the internal motions and otherwise neglecting the internal dynamics in the correlation functions. Tensorial averaging requires a symmetric, time-independent, normalized distribution $P(\Omega)$. The (**A, G,** or **V**) tensor is diagonal in the PAS (or at a known rotation from it). The motion that generated $P(\Omega)$ is diagonal in a different frame. The tensor is then rotated to that frame; the orientation angles are subsequently averaged in that frame over the distribution. The steps are carried out formally by defining a rotation matrix $\mathbf{R}(\Omega^{\tau})$ that rotates the tensor to the averaging frame. The tensor is then averaged in the new frame over the orientation distribution. Often the tensor is left in this frame where it is diagonal or nearly so, and this frame now represents a common frame for all tensors, or the resultant, averaged tensor may be rotated back to its original frame. Griffith & Jost (13) and Hustedt et al (17) have presented examples of this scheme for CSA and dipolar tensors, as have Alam & Drobny (2, 3) for quadrupolar tensors. The major contribution to the order parameter, S, is often given as $S = \langle \mathcal{D}_{0,0}^2 \rangle = \int P(\Omega^{\tau}) \mathcal{D}_{0,0}^2(\Omega^{\tau}) \, d\Omega^{\tau}$. Generally, each WRME will have its own order parameters, but for practicality, the number utilized in any model must be kept to a minimum.

CONCLUSIONS

We have reviewed a simple model for the dynamics of duplex DNA that takes into account the collective, internal processes of bending and twisting as well as length-independent motions. Calculations of correlation functions based on the model are tractable; the model presents a basic picture of DNA dynamics. The model is constructed in terms of meaningful physical constants: the uniform (or overall tumbling) motions and base-pair twisting and flexing force constants. This review has also shown that this weakly bending rod model, as well as any given dynamic model, may be directly incorporated into MR equations of motion. Because of a computationally straightforward relation between correlation functions and MR relaxation times, MR experiments can critically test dynamic models for biopolymers. Some aspects of the weakly bending rod model of DNA dynamics already have been tested by both NMR- and EPR-active site-specific probes (3, 17). The results of those experiments will be reviewed in Volume 25 of this series. Experimentally testing the sequence dependence of the collective modes is now an area of active research, and in particular, future work will be aimed at determining whether or not the weakly bending rod model needs to be augmented to include local sequence-dependent effects.

Literature Cited

1. Abragam A. 1961. Thermal relaxation in liquids and gases. In *The Principles of Nuclear Magnetism*, pp. 264–353. London: Oxford Univ. Press
2. Alam TM, Drobny GP. 1990. Magnetic ordering in synthetic oligonucleotides: a deuterium NMR investigation. *J. Chem. Phys.* 92:6840
3. Alam TM, Drobny GP. 1991. Solid state NMR studies of DNA structure and dynamics. *Chem Rev.* 91:1545–90
4. Allison SA. 1986. Brownian dynamics simulation of worklike chains. Fluorescence depolarization and depolarized light scattering. *Macromolecules* 19:118–24
5. Allison SA, Austin R, Hogan M. 1989. Bending and twisting dynamics of short linear DNAs. Analysis of the triple anisotropy decay of a 209 base pair fragment by Brownian simulations. *J. Chem. Phys.* 90:3843–54
6. Allison SA, Nambi P. 1992. Electric dichroism and birefringence decay of short DNA restriction fragments studied by Brownian dynamics simulation. *Macromolecules* 25:759–68
7. Allison SA, Schurr JM. 1979. Torsion dynamics and depolarization of fluorescence of linear macromolecules. I. Theory and application to DNA. *Chem. Phys.* 41:35–59
8. Barkley MD, Zimm BH. 1979. Theory of twisting and bending of chain macromolecules: analysis of the fluorescence depolarization of DNA. *J. Chem. Phys.* 70:2991–3007
9. Eimer W, Williamson JR, Boxer SG,

Pecora R. 1990. Characterization of the overall and internal dynamics of short oligonucleotides by depolarized dynamic light scattering and NMR relaxation measurements. *Biochemistry* 29:799–811
10. Elvingson C. 1992. Computer simulation of the structure of DNA molecules in an electric field. *Biophys. Chem.* 43:9–19
11. Ermak DL, McCammon JA. 1978. Brownian dynamics with hydrodynamic interactions. *J. Chem. Phys.* 69:1352–60
12. Fujimoto BS, Schurr JM. 1990. Composition dependence of the torsional rigidity of DNA. Relevance to the affinity of 434 repressor for different operators. *Nature* 344:175–78
13. Griffith OH, Jost P. 1976. Lipid spin labels in biological membranes. In *Spin Labeling: Theory and Applications*, ed. LJ Berliner, pp. 453–523. New York: Academic
14. Harrington RE, Vinicov I. 1994. New concepts in protein-DNA recognition: sequence-directed DNA bending and flexibility. *Prog. Nucleic Acid Res. Mol. Biol.* 47:195–270
15. Hogan ME, Austin RH. 1987. Importance of DNA stiffness in protein-DNA binding specificity. *Nature* 329:263–66
16. Hogan ME, Jardetzky O. 1980. Effect of ethidium bromide on deoxyribonucleic acid internal motions. *J. Am. Chem. Soc.* 19:2079–85
17. Hustedt EJ, Spaltenstein A, Kirchner

JJ, Hopkins PB, Robinson BH. 1993. Motions of short duplex DNA: an analysis of DNA dynamics using an EPR-active probe. *Biochemistry* 32:1774–87

18. Kim U-S, Fujimoto BS, Furlong CE, Sundstrom JA, Humbert R, et al. 1993. Dynamics and structures of DNA: long-range effects of a 16 base-pair (GC)$_8$ sequence on secondary structure. *Biopolymers* 33:1725–45

19. Lipari G, Szabo A. 1981. Nuclear magnetic resonance relaxation in nucleic acid fragments: models for internal motion. *Biochemistry* 20:6250–56

20. Lipari G, Szabo A. 1981. Padé approximants to correlation functions for restricted rotational diffusion. *J. Chem. Phys.* 75:2971–76

21. Lipari G, Szabo A. 1982. Model-free approach to the interpretation of nuclear magnetic resonance relaxation in macromolecules. 1. Theory and range of validity. *J. Am. Chem. Soc.* 104: 4546–59

22. Lipari G, Szabo A. 1982. Model-free approach to the interpretation of nuclear magnetic resonance relaxation in macromolecules. 2. Analysis of experimental results. *J. Am. Chem. Soc.* 104:4559–70

23. Nuutero S, Fujimoto BS, Flynn PF, Reid BR, Riberio NS, Schurr JM. 1994. The amplitude of local angular motion of purines in DNA in solution. *Biopolymers* 34:463–80

24. Pecora R. 1991. DNA: a model compound for solution studies of macromolecules. *Science* 251:893–97

25. Robinson BH, Forgacs G, Dalton LR, Frisch HL. 1980. A simple model for internal motions of DNA based upon EPR studies in the slow motion region. *J. Chem. Phys.* 73:4688–92

26. Robinson BH, Lerman LS, Beth AH, Frisch HL, Dalton LR, Auer C. 1980. Analysis of double-helix motions with spin-labeled probes: binding geometry and the limit of torsional elasticity. *J. Mol. Biol.* 139:19–44

27. Robinson BH, Slutsky LJ, Auteri FP. 1992. Direct simulation of CW-EPR spectra from Brownian dynamics trajectories. *J. Chem. Phys.* 96:2609–16

28. Schurr JM. 1984. Rotational diffusion of deformable macromolecules with mean local cylindrical symmetry. *Chem. Phys.* 84:71–96

29. Schurr JM, Babcock HP, Fujimoto BS. 1994. A test of the model-free formulas. Effects of anisotropic rotational diffusion and dimerization. *J. Mag. Reson.* In press

30. Schurr JM, Fujimoto BS, Wu P, Song L. 1992. Fluorescence studies of nucleic acids. In *Topics in Fluorescence Spectroscopy*, Vol 3. *Biological Applications*, ed. JR Lakowicz, pp. 137–229. New York: Plenum

31. Song L, Allison SA, Schurr JM. 1990. Normal mode theory for Brownian dynamics of a weakly bending rod: comparison with Brownian dynamics simulations. *Biopolymers* 29:1773–91

32. Song L, Schurr JM. 1990. Dynamic bending rigidity of DNA. *Biopolymers* 30:229–37

33. Tirado MM, de la Torre JG. 1980. Rotational dynamics of rigid symmetric top macromolecule application to circular cylinders. *J. Chem. Phys.* 73: 1986–93

34. Tirado MM, Martinez C, de la Torre JG. 1984. Comparison of theories for the translational and rotational diffusion coefficients of rod-like macromolecules. Application to short DNA fragments. *J. Chem. Phys.* 81:2047

35. Woessner DE. 1962. Spin relaxation processes in a two-proton system undergoing anisotropic reorientation. *J. Chem. Phys.* 36:1–4

36. Wu P, Fujimoto BS, Schurr JM. 1987. Time-resolved FPA of short restriction fragments. The friction factor for rotation of DNA about its symmetry axis. *Biopolymers* 26:1463–88

37. Yeramian E, Claverie P. 1987. Analysis of multiexponential functions without a hypothesis as to the number of components. *Nature* 326:169–74

38. Zhu L. 1994. *A study of spin dynamics and molecular structure of nucleic acids by NMR*. PhD thesis. Univ. Wash., Seattle, WA. 229 pp.

39. Zhu L, Reid BR, Kennedy M, Drobny GP. 1994. Modulation of J-couplings by cross-relaxation in DNA sugars. *J. Magn. Reson.* In press

Annu. Rev. Biophys. Biomol. Struct. 1995. 24:551–77

LECTIN STRUCTURE

James M. Rini

Departments of Molecular and Medical Genetics and Biochemistry,
University of Toronto, Toronto, Ontario, Canada, M5S 1A8

KEY WORDS: C-type lectins, galectins, animal lectins, plant lectins,
bacterial toxins, influenza virus hemagglutinin

CONTENTS

ABSTRACT

Lectins comprise a structurally very diverse class of proteins characterized by their ability to bind carbohydrates with considerable specificity.
They are found in organisms ranging from viruses and plants to humans
and serve to mediate biological recognition events. Although lectins
bind monosaccharides rather weakly, they employ common strategies
for enhancing both the affinity and specificity of their interactions for
more complex carbohydrate ligands. The terms subsite and subunit

1056-8700/95/0610-0551$05.00

multivalency are defined to describe the ways in which these enhancements are achieved. Analysis of the X-ray crystal structures of different lectin types serves to illustrate how, in structural terms, subsite and subunit multivalency confer context-specific functional properties.

PERSPECTIVES AND OVERVIEW

Lectins are a structurally diverse group of proteins or protein domains capable of binding oligosaccharides with considerable specificity. This property suggests that they play a role in biological-recognition events (66). Although many plant and microbial lectins have been known for some time, only recently has the prevalence of animal lectins also been recognized (4, 22, 26, 32, 36, 47). Animal lectin families include C-type lectins, galectins (S-type lectins), and P-type lectins (3, 19, 22). The X-ray crystal structures of the first examples of C-type lectins and galectins were recently solved. Galectins bear an unexpected structural similarity to plant lectins from the Leguminosae family.

Analysis of the three-dimensional structures of several carbohydrate-binding proteins, including plant lectins, enzymes, Fabs, and the bacterial periplasmic transport proteins, has led to the identification of two major subgroups (58, 78). The group I carbohydrate-binding proteins, typified by the periplasmic binding proteins and some enzymes, completely envelop their carbohydrate ligands in deep binding pockets, whereas the group II carbohydrate-binding proteins bind their ligands in shallow pockets or grooves on the protein surface. In this review, the term lectin describes group II–type carbohydrate-binding proteins or protein domains that are themselves not enzymes or antibodies. Thus, influenza virus hemagglutinin and the B-oligomers of the bacterial toxins are considered lectins, whereas the influenza virus neuraminidase is not. Several recent reviews have dealt with the structural characterization of the periplasmic transport proteins, carbohydrate-binding Fabs and enzymes, and their carbohydrate complexes (10, 11, 75, 78). The importance of oligosaccharide conformation and the role played by water in mediating protein-carbohydrate interactions was also recently reviewed (6, 37).

This review examines the three-dimensional structures of lectins from a wide range of sources to illustrate the structural basis for their carbohydrate-binding affinity and specificity. The geometry of the binding site and the overall tertiary and quaternary structure of these lectins are discussed with particular emphasis on the role played by multivalency.

LECTIN-CARBOHYDRATE INTERACTIONS

Operationally, lectins have often been categorized, within families, according to their mono- or, sometimes, disaccharide binding specificity. These carbohydrates bind in the monosaccharide or primary binding site with dissociation constants in the 0.1–1.0 mM range. However, lectins often show binding-site dissociation constants in the micromolar range for larger, more complex oligosaccharides. In these cases, the oligosaccharide interacts with secondary sites on the lectin surface as well as with the primary binding site. Affinity enhancements of this type arise as a result of what is termed here as subsite multivalency. In contrast, subunit multivalency describes the process that leads to the increases in affinity achieved when more than one lectin subunit, either contained on the same polypeptide chain or from separate chains of an oligomer (e.g. a trimeric lectin), bind a multivalent ligand. Interactions of this type can lead to dissociation constants in the nanomolar range for the appropriate multivalent ligand.

The known lectin structures display a diverse range of three-dimensional architectures. However, the parallel roles played by subsite and subunit multivalency provide a framework for understanding the structural basis for lectin-carbohydrate interactions.

X-RAY CRYSTAL STRUCTURES

Legume Lectins

Members of the legume lectin family show considerable sequence and structural homology (90), but differences in their carbohydrate-binding specificity make them well suited to the study of structure-function relationships (67). The legume lectin monomer has a molecular weight of 25,000 and is composed primarily of a six- and a seven-stranded antiparallel β-sheet. The most common mode of dimerization relates 2 monomers in a 2-fold symmetric fashion to create a continuous 12-stranded antiparallel β-sheet that extends across the dimer interface, as shown in Figure 1 for *Lathyrus ochrus* isolectin I (LOL I) (9). Each monomer binds a manganese and a calcium ion, which are essential for carbohydrate binding.

Concanavalin A (Con A), LOL, and pea lectin all show mannose- and glucose-binding specificity, and the X-ray crystal structures of their carbohydrate complexes (7–9, 17, 60) show a monosaccharide binding–site geometry very similar to that of the LOL I–α-methyl-D-mannopyranoside complex (Figure 2). The C4 and C6 hydroxyl groups, serv-

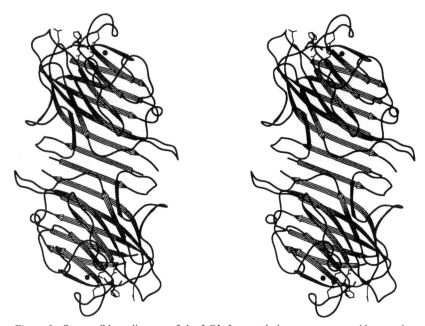

Figure 1 Stereo ribbon diagram of the LOL I–α-methyl-D-mannopyranoside complex showing the bound carbohydrate and the amino acid side chains in the binding site [Protein Data Bank (PDB) entry 1lob]. The manganese and calcium ions are shown as black spheres.

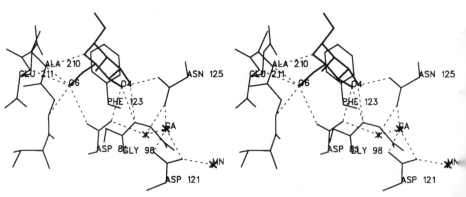

Figure 2 Stereo diagram of the LOL I–α-methyl-D-mannopyranoside complex binding site showing hydrogen-bond interactions (*dotted lines*) (PDB entry 1lob).

ing as both hydrogen-bond donors (to Asp81) and acceptors, form the basis of the interaction. This cooperative hydrogen-bonding scheme is characteristic of the carbohydrate hydroxyl groups most deeply buried in the binding site and is typical of that seen in carbohydrate complexes of type I carbohydrate-binding proteins (78). In fact, complexes of the periplasmic transporter proteins show that all hydroxyl groups of the bound carbohydrate are involved in such cooperative hydrogen bonds. In contrast, this LOL I complex shows that the C3 hydroxyl group serves only as a hydrogen-bond acceptor (from Gly99 NH) and that the C2 hydroxyl, which is completely solvent exposed, has no hydrogen-bond interactions with the protein. The lack of interaction with the C2 hydroxyl group is consistent with the mannose or glucose binding specificity shown by these lectins. Phe123 makes van der Waals contact with the carbohydrate ring in a fashion not unlike that seen in many protein-carbohydrate complexes (56, 78). Both Asp81 (in the *cis* configuration) and Asn125 are involved in carbohydrate interactions as well as in coordinating the bound calcium ion (see Figure 2), which presumably explains the metal ion requirement for carbohydrate binding.

The closely related plant lectin from *Erythrina corallodendron* (EcorL) binds galactose, allowing for an analysis of the structural basis for the change in specificity. The X-ray crystal structure of the EcorL-lactose complex (65) shows that binding is mediated exclusively through the galactose moiety (Figure 3). The carbohydrate ring has rotated in the monosaccharide binding site so that Asp89 (Asp81 in LOL I) now interacts with the C3 and C4 hydroxyl groups even though Asn133, Asp89, Gly107, and Phe131 are in the same positions as their LOL I homologues. Because of an insertion, the conformation of the 220–222 loop in EcorL (see Figures 2 and 3) is completely different

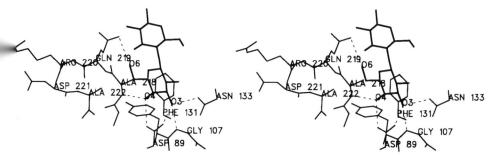

Figure 3   Stereo diagram of the EcorL-lactose complex binding site (PDB entry 1lte). The binding-site orientation is the same as that shown in Figure 2.

from that of the homologous loop in LOL I (residues 210–211). These changes accommodate and stabilize the C6 hydroxyl group of galactose, which now hydrogen bonds to the side chain of Gln219 and to a water molecule. As a result of the rotation, the carbohydrate ring now participates in a galactose-specific stacking interaction with Phe131, as discussed in more detail below. Given the rigidity of the rest of the binding site, the difference in specificity is clearly dictated by the conformation of the 220–222 loop (210–211 in LOL 1) (65).

The legume lectins also show differences in their oligosaccharide-binding properties. The presence of α1,6-linked fucose in the core of N-linked oligosaccharides, for example, is an important determinant for high affinity binding of oligosaccharides to some of the mannose- or glucose-specific legume lectins (14, 38). The X-ray crystal structures of *L. ochrus* isolectin II (LOL II) in complex with the N2 fragment of human lactotransferrin and an isolated glycopeptide (7) have defined the role played by the fucose moiety. In these complexes, the α1,3-linked mannose residue of the biantennary oligosaccharide resides in the monosaccharide binding site, and the fucose residue is hydrogen bonded to a shallow crevice on the distal side of Phe123 (see Figure 2). As a result, extended van der Waals contacts made between the oligosaccharide and the lectin render Phe123 completely inaccessible to solvent. Although soluble fucose is not bound by these lectins, fucosylated glycopeptides bind approximately 100-fold more tightly than their unfucosylated analogues. These structures clearly show the importance of subsite multivalency in determining the carbohydrate-binding specificity of these lectins.

The X-ray crystal structure of *Griffonia simplicifolia* lectin IV (GS4) in complex with the Lewis b (Le^b) blood group substance (15, 16) has shown that the equivalent of the EcorL 220–222 loop is again implicated as a determinant of carbohydrate-binding specificity. Although the galactose moiety of the Le^b tetrasaccharide is bound in the same orientation as that found in the EcorL complex, the equivalent of the EcorL 220–222 loop is truncated so as to completely eliminate this side of the binding site. The α(1,4)-linked fucose moiety of the bound saccharide now occupies this volume. Both hydrogen-bond interactions and van der Waals contacts, involving all residues of the saccharide, stabilize the complex. GS4 shows no measurable affinity for monosaccharides (26), which is consistent with the fact that one side of the monosaccharide-binding site has been structurally deleted. Clearly subsite multivalency is a requirement for carbohydrate binding by this lectin.

The ability to agglutinate cells, stimulate mitosis, and cross-link receptors and substrates are some of the properties associated with the legume lectins (46). In all cases, subunit multivalency is almost certainly a requirement. Several distinct structural patterns of monomer association yielding entirely different binding-site dispositions have been observed among the legume lectins. EcorL (65) and GS4 (15, 16) also form dimers, but unlike the canonical LOL I dimer (see Figure 1), neither display the characteristic continuous 12-stranded antiparallel β-sheet. Two distinct tetramer arrangements also occur. In Con A, two canonical dimers associate to yield a tetramer with 222 symmetry (30), whereas two different dimer types (GS4- and LOL I–like) are found in peanut agglutinin, resulting in a tetramer that shows neither 222 nor four-fold symmetry (2).

Wheat Germ Agglutinin

Wheat germ agglutinin (WGA) is one of the highly conserved chitin-binding lectins of the plant family Gramineae and shows carbohydrate-binding specificity for both N-acetyl-D-glucosamine and N-acetyl-D-neuraminic acid (sialic acid). The X-ray crystal structures of WGA1 and WGA2 (two of the three isoforms) and several of their carbohydrate complexes have been determined (85–88). WGA is a dimeric protein composed of identical 17-kDa polypeptides each containing 32 disulfide-linked cysteine residues. The amino acid sequence of the monomer shows an approximate four-fold sequence repeat, suggesting that the molecule evolved through gene duplication and fusion (89). The repeats define 43-residue isostructural subdomains (A, B, C, D) that are arranged in a pseudo four-fold screw–related fashion (Figure 4). In the two-fold symmetric dimer, the monomers associate in a head-to-tail fashion, resulting in subdomain pairs (A1/D2, B1/C2, C1/B2, and D1/A2) that each possess quasi two-fold symmetry. For each subdomain (A, B, C, D), a principal (pr) and helper (hl) binding site has been defined. However, when carbohydrate binds in the principal site of a given subdomain, the helper interactions come not from the helper site within that subdomain but from the paired subdomain of the two-fold related monomer [e.g. B1(pr)/C2(hl)]. All four unique site types are known to be able to bind carbohydrate (88), and because of differences in sequence and the extent to which the helper domain participates, they are expected to show different carbohydrate-binding affinities.

The X-ray crystal structure of a WGA1-sialylglycopeptide complex (88) shows carbohydrate binding at three of the four unique site types. The glycopeptide contains a branched O-linked tetrasaccharide possessing both α2,3- and α2,6-linked terminal sialic acid moieties that bind in the B1(pr)/C2(hl) and C2(pr)/B1(hl) sites of crystallographically related dimers. The A2(pr)/D1(hl) site also binds carbohydrate, in this

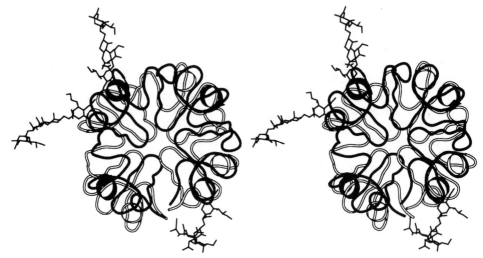

Figure 4 Stereo ribbon diagram of the WGA1-sialylglycopeptide complex viewed down the helical axis (PDB entry 2cwg). The two monomers of the WGA1 dimer are represented by open and filled ribbon types. For clarity, only the saccharide portion of the bound glycopeptide is shown.

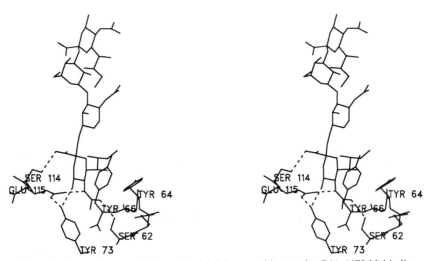

Figure 5 Stereo diagram of the WGA1-sialylglycopeptide complex B1(pr)/C2(hl) binding site (PDB entry 2cwg).

case through the $\alpha2,6$-linked sialic acid moiety of a second glycopeptide molecule. Carbohydrate binding to the highest-affinity B1(pr)/C2(hl) site (Figure 5) is mediated primarily by three Tyr residues of the primary site (also called the aromatic-rich site) and by hydrogen bonds to the side chains of Ser114 and Glu115 of the helper site. Carbohydrate binding to the lower-affinity A2(pr)/D1(hl) site, which contains helper residues unable to make side-chain hydrogen bonds (Pro157 and Gly158), shows that the aromatic-rich principal site can function independently. This observation suggests, contrary to previous belief, that even WGA monomers can bind carbohydrate and that the WGA dimer has eight potential binding sites (88). Analysis of this and other WGA-carbohydrate complexes with sialylated oligosaccharides (87, 88) shows that in all cases binding is determined primarily by interaction with the terminal sialic acid moieties. Even though in some cases helper interactions are important, they define a monosaccharide-binding site, and subsite multivalency is therefore not a factor. However, a helical cluster of eight potential carbohydrate-binding sites makes it likely that subunit multivalency is an important component of WGA function.

Ricin

Ricin is a heterodimeric (AB) cytotoxic glycoprotein found in the seeds of the castor plant. The lectin B-chain binds to oligosaccharide structures on the cell surface and mediates entry of the cytotoxic A-chain. The ricin B-chain (Figure 6) is composed of two globular domains, each of which comprises a link domain and 3 homologous 40-residue subdomains that pack around a pseudo 3-fold rotation axis (61, 62). As in WGA, the ricin B-chain is stabilized by several disulfide-linked cysteine residues and has likely arisen through gene-duplication events (77). The X-ray crystal structure of the ricin-lactose complex (61, 62) shows lactose binding at only two of the six possible sites. At both sites, the C3 and C4 hydroxyl groups of galactose donate hydrogen bonds to the side-chain carboxyl oxygen atoms of an aspartic acid residue. In addition, the C3 hydroxyl group accepts a hydrogen bond from a conserved asparagine residue. Both sites also show a stacking interaction between the plane formed by the C3, C4, C5, and C6 carbon atoms of the galactose and the ring of an aromatic residue (Tyr248/Trp37 in site 2/1). Examination of those sites that do not have carbohydrate in the binding site show that key residues have either been replaced or perturbed. However, this observation does not rule out the possibility that other sites might act as secondary sites, a suggestion consistent with the fact that branched glycopeptides bind much more tightly to

Figure 6   Stereo ribbon diagram of the ricin-lactose complex B-chain, showing the bound carbohydrate (PDB entry 2aai). A conserved Trp residue is also shown to highlight the pseudo three-fold symmetry shown by the two domains. The link peptide of each domain is shown in black.

ricin (1) even though the distance between the lactose-bound sites is too great to be spanned by a single branched oligosaccharide (62).

Bacterial Toxins

Bacterial toxins share with ricin the common feature of a lectin B-domain, which mediates cell attachment, and an A-subunit responsible for the cytotoxic effects (12). Both *Escherichia coli* heat-labile entero-toxin (LT) (Figure 7) and cholera toxin (CT) are AB_5 oligomers in which the five B-subunits form a five-fold rotationally symmetric pentamer. Comparison of the X-ray crystal structures of an LT-lactose complex (68, 69) and the CT-B-pentamer-G_{M1} pentasaccharide complex (CTB-G_{M1}) (52) shows that the carbohydrate-binding sites are structurally very similar, particularly with respect to interactions with the bound galactose moiety. The LT complex shows that interaction with lactose is mediated exclusively by the galactose. The additional interactions with the terminal sialic acid moiety of the G_{M1} pentasaccharide, as seen in the CTB-G_{M1} complex (Figure 8), explain the receptor specificity shown by these toxins. The sialic acid moiety is not very intimately associated with the surface of the protein, making only two direct hydrogen bonds with the backbone and a van der Waals contact with Tyr12. Interaction of the terminal galactose and sialic acid residues,

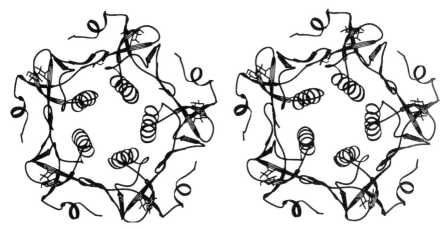

Figure 7 Stereo ribbon diagram of the LT-lactose complex B-pentamer, showing the bound carbohydrate in each of the five monomers (PDB entry 1ltt).

described as a two-fingered grip (52), illustrates the importance of sub-site multivalency in determining the specificity of these interactions. The five carbohydrate-binding sites of the B-pentamers of these toxins form a planar array that, like the carbohydrate-binding sites in the ricin B-chain, is located on the binding-domain face opposite that of the association with the toxic A-subunit. These structural similarities cer-tainly suggest that the bacterial toxins and ricin share a common struc-ture-function relationship.

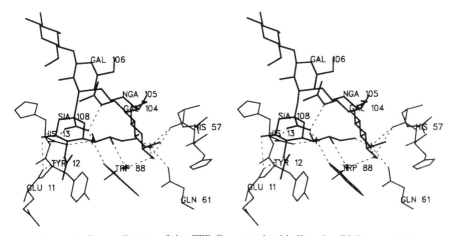

Figure 8 Stereo diagram of the CTB-G_{M1} complex binding site (PDB entry 1chb).

Pertussis toxin (PT) contains a cytotoxic domain, and in this case a heteropentameric (S2, S3, two copies of S4 and S5) binding domain, and shares considerable structural homology with the CT family (70). The X-ray crystal structure of PT in complex with a soluble transferrin oligosaccharide (71) shows carbohydrate bound to equivalent sites in the carboxy terminal portion of subunits S2 and S3 through exclusive interaction with the terminal sialic acid moieties. The N-terminal domains of S2 and S3, which share structural similarity with the C-type lectin family even though they lack the homologous binding-site region, are also thought to contain carbohydrate-binding sites (70, 71).

Influenza Virus Hemagglutinin

Influenza virus hemagglutinin (HA) is the viral surface glycoprotein responsible for host-cell attachment and membrane fusion (83). The molecule is trimeric and characterized by a long, triple-helical coiled coil that supports the globular lectin domains responsible for binding sialic acid–containing cell surface receptors (84). X-ray crystal struc-

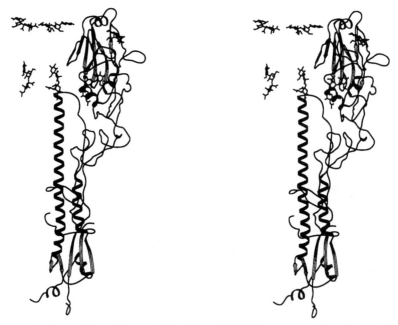

Figure 9   Stereo ribbon diagram of the HA-(α2,3)sialyllactose complex, showing the bound carbohydrate (PDB entry 1hgg). Both saccharide moieties bound to each of the three HA monomers are shown, but for clarity the protein portion of only one monomer is shown.

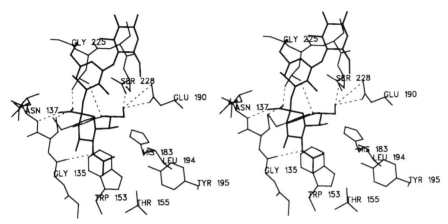

Figure 10   Stereo diagram of the first HA-(α2,3)sialyllactose-binding site (PDB entry 1hgg).

tures of the HA in complex with sialyllactose and several synthetic sialic acid derivatives (64, 80) have defined two (α2,3)sialyllactose-binding sites on each monomer that result in a three-fold symmetric array of six potential receptor-binding sites (Figure 9). The first site resides in a surface pocket close to the end of the globular head group and binds (α2,3)sialyllactose approximately four times more tightly than the second site, which resides in a concave pocket between the HA1 and HA2 polypeptide chains of each monomer. Interactions with the saccharide in the first site are mediated primarily by the terminal sialic acid moiety of the (α2,3)sialyllactose (Figure 10). The glycerol moiety, the N-acetyl NH and the C1 carboxyl group are all involved in hydrogen-bond interactions, whereas the C4 hydroxyl group is not. Trp53 participates in a stacking interaction with the planar N-acetyl group. In contrast, all three residues of the trisaccharide interact with the protein in the second site. The environment of the sialic acid moiety in no way resembles that of the first site. As in the WGA complexes, the interactions in the first site seem to be dominated by the terminal sialic acid residue, which suggests that subsite multivalency has little importance. But again, given the array of six potential carbohydrate-binding sites, subunit multivalency likely plays an important role in HA function.

C-Type Lectins

C-type animal lectins are a family of carbohydrate-binding proteins characterized by a 15-kDa calcium-dependent carbohydrate-recognition domain (CRD) that is usually linked to an accessory domain (19, 21, 22). Among others, the family includes the endocytic glycoprotein receptors (18, 49), the selectins (5, 39), the macrophage mannose receptor, and the soluble collectins (22, 63).

The first three-dimensional structure of a C-type lectin was the X-ray crystal structure of the CRD of rat mannose-binding protein A (MBP-A) (82), one of the soluble collectins responsible for antibody-independent host defense against foreign pathogens. Over 50% of the CRD is formed by loops and extended structure, and the remainder comprises two short α-helices and five β-strands (see Figure 11). A subsequent complex of this domain with an asparagine-linked oligosaccharide (81) defined the carbohydrate-binding site and the critical role played by the bound calcium ion. In this complex (see Figure 12) not only do the C3 and C4 hydroxyl groups of one of the terminal mannose residues interact directly with the calcium ion, but the direct calcium-binding ligands Glu185, Asn187, Glu193, and Asn205 form bridges between the calcium ion and these two hydroxyl groups. His189 makes limited van der Waals contact with the mannose residue but does form one edge of the binding site.

The X-ray crystal structure of the lectin-EGF domain of E-selectin (27) provided the second example of a C-type lectin CRD. The selectins

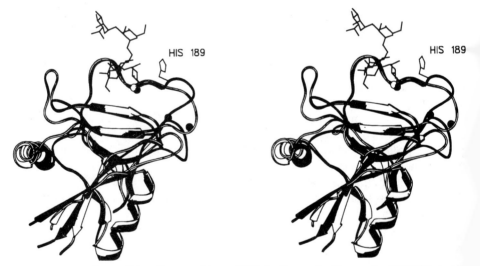

Figure 11   Stereo ribbon diagram of the rat MBP-A-oligosaccharide complex CRD (*filled ribbons*), showing the bound carbohydrate (PDB entry 2msb) superimposed on the E-selectin CRD (*open ribbons*). Calcium ions are shown as spheres. His189 of MBP-A is shown for reference.

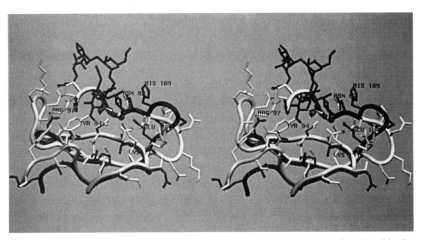

Figure 12   Stereo diagram of the MBP-A–oligosaccharide complex binding site (*black*), showing the bound carbohydrate (PDB entry 2msb) superimposed on the E-selectin binding site (*white*). Calcium ions are shown as spheres. Residue labels 189 and 193 refer to MBP-A.

are endothelial cell surface receptors involved in targeting lymphocyte migration to inflammatory sites (5, 39), and considerable interest focuses on the design of inhibitors to these lectins. Although the three-dimensional structures of the CRDs of MBP-A and E-selectin are very similar, the loop regions flanking the carbohydrate-binding site differ significantly (Figure 11). Figure 12 shows a comparison of the two carbohydrate-binding sites. Although residues 188–193 and in particular His189 in MBP-A define one side of the carbohydrate-binding site, the corresponding loop (residues 82–88) in E-selectin assumes an entirely different conformation, leaving the calcium ion exposed on a relatively flat surface. In contrast, the loop defined by MBP-A residues 199–202 becomes a prominent feature in E-selectin (residues 94–102), directing Tyr94 and Arg97—residues critical for E-selectin function (27)—toward the calcium mediated saccharide-binding site. It has been proposed that the terminal fucose residue of sialyl Lewis x (sLe^x), an E-selectin ligand, binds in the calcium-liganded position (27, 81) and that the terminal sialic acid residue participates in important additional interactions. The complete lack of a pocket around the calcium site suggests that subsite multivalency is a critical component of carbohydrate binding by E-selectin. In this respect, carbohydrate binding by E-selectin may resemble that seen in the GS4-Le^b saccharide complex in which extended interactions with the oligosaccharide compensate for the loss of one edge of the monosaccharide-binding site.

Galectins

The galectins are a family of β-galactoside–binding animal lectins characterized by a highly conserved 15-kDa CRD showing a characteristic set of highly conserved amino acid residues (4). Both intra- (79) and extracellular (13) functions have been proposed for these lectins (32), including a role in modulating cell-cell and cell-matrix interactions (36). To date, the galectin CRD has been found in at least four different structural arrangements, including monomers and dimers, as well as larger polypeptides containing one or two copies of the CRD in association with an accessory domain or linker characterized by proline- and glycine-rich repeat sequences (4, 31, 32, 34, 54, 79).

The X-ray crystal structures of dimeric galectin-1 (45) and galectin-2 (48) in complex with N-acetyllactosamine and lactose, respectively, have recently been solved. They show that the CRD is made up of a five- and a six-stranded antiparallel β-sheet that, in these two-fold symmetric dimers, both form continuous antiparallel β-sheets across the dimer interface (Figure 13). The amino acids forming the lactose-binding site are contained on four adjacent β-strands (48) that are continuous in the linear sequence and are encoded by a single DNA exon conserved among the various galectin structural classes (25, 54) (see Figure 13).

Analysis of the carbohydrate-binding site (Figure 14) shows that the C4 hydroxyl group of galactose is hydrogen bonded to His45, Asn47, and Arg49, residues that are absolutely conserved among all galectins sequenced. The C6 hydroxyl group of the galactose moiety also participates in hydrogen-bond interactions, as do the C2 and C3 hydroxyl groups of glucose. Again, an aromatic residue (Trp65) makes extensive van der Waals contact with the galactose moiety. The C3 hydroxyl group of the galactose moiety is not hydrogen bonded and is sterically accessible for substitution. This observation is consistent with the fact that polylactosaminyl glycans are ligands for the galectins (44, 91). In fact, analysis of the three-dimensional structure of the carbohydrate-binding site (48) shows that the galectins would be able to bind an internal lactose unit of these β1,3-linked repeating structures. The various members of the galectin family show differences in binding affinity for these and other naturally occurring oligosaccharides substituted at the galactose O3 position (44), which indicates a clear role for subunit multivalency in determining binding specificity.

The galectin monomer shows striking structural homology with that of the legume lectin monomer (Figure 15) even though these lectins share no significant sequence homology (45, 48). As shown in the figure,

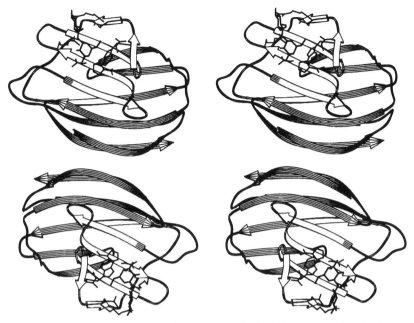

Figure 13 Stereo ribbon diagram of the human galectin-2–lactose complex (PDB entry 1hlc) showing the bound carbohydrate and the amino acid side chains in the binding site. The carbohydrate-binding cassette is shown as an open ribbon.

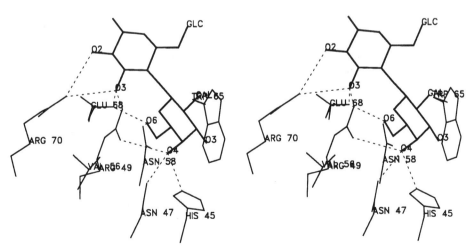

Figure 14 Stereo diagram of the human galectin-2–lactose complex binding site (PDB entry 1hlc).

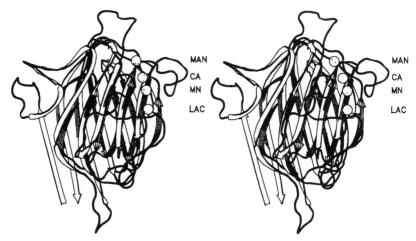

Figure 15   Stereo ribbon diagram of human galectin-2 (*striped ribbons*) superimposed on the pea lectin–trimannoside complex (PDB entry 1rin) (*open ribbons*) showing the location of mannose (MAN), calcium (CA), and manganese (MN) in pea lectin and lactose (LAC) in human galectin-2.

the location of the carbohydrate-binding sites are not conserved, but perhaps significantly, they are positioned on the same face of the lectin. The manganese and calcium ions, essential for carbohydrate binding in the legume lectins, are bound by a loop linking two of the strands homologous to the carbohydrate-binding cassette of the galectins (48).

The X-ray crystal structure of human serum amyloid P component (SAP) provides another example of an animal protein with lectin properties that is structurally similar to the legume lectins (23). However, the carbohydrate-binding site is located in a position yet again different from that found in either the legume lectins or the galectins. SAP is a pentraxin made up of two five-fold symmetric pentamers that associate to form soluble decameric structures. Interestingly, like the bacterial toxin B-pentamers, the carbohydrate-binding sites of the SAP pentamer form a planar array (23).

PRIMARY BINDING-SITE GEOMETRY

In many cases the monosaccharide-binding specificity of a lectin indicates in a broad sense its functional role, although, as we have seen, affinity and fine specificity can be modulated in several ways. Mannose recognition by C-type lectins in higher organisms, for example, provides a mechanism for distinguishing self from nonself (63, 72), and the entire galectin family serves as receptors for β-galactosides (4). Similarly, sialic acid recognition is the primary determinant in influenza virus and pertussis toxin binding to cell surface receptors. To determine whether recognizable, monosaccharide-specific binding-site geometries have emerged, the structural environments of various monosaccharide types in these lectin-carbohydrate complexes have been examined.

Galactose

Alignment of the EcorL-lactose, ricin-lactose, human galectin-2–lactose, and LT-lactose complexes, based on the galactose moiety in the primary binding site, reveals a remarkably well-defined spatial relationship between the plane formed by the C3, C4, C5, and C6 carbon atoms of the galactose moieties and an aromatic side chain in the binding site (Figure 16). In fact, the six-membered rings of the tryptophan side chain in human galectin-2 and LT are very closely aligned with the tyrosine and phenylalanine side chains in the ricin and EcorL complexes. There are few other obvious parallels. In EcorL and ricin, Asp89 and Asp234, respectively, have very similar interactions with the C3 and C4 hydroxyl groups and, as might be expected, the C4 hydroxyl group is hydrogen bonded to the protein in all cases. The C2 and C6 hydroxyl groups are of varying importance in these complexes.

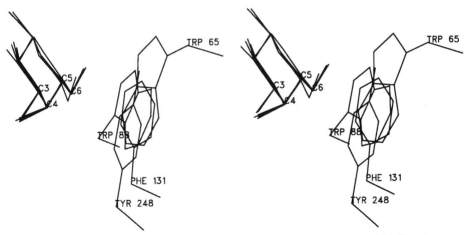

Figure 16 Stereo diagram showing the relative placement of galactose and binding-site residues Trp65 (galectin-2), Phe131 (EcorL), Tyr248 (ricin site 2), and Trp88 (LT).

Sialic Acid

Analysis of the environment of the sialic acid moiety in the HA-sialyl-lactose complex and the WGA-sialylglycopeptide complex reveals little similarity between the two sites (see Figures 5 and 10; in these figures the sialic acid moieties have been aligned in the same orientation). Although an aromatic residue in the HA complex makes a van der Waals interaction with the N-acetyl group, the WGA complex has no equivalent to HA's ring-stacking interaction with Tyr66. In both cases the N-acetyl amide at C5 is hydrogen bonded to the protein, but in the HA complex the glycerol moiety hydrogen bonds to the protein and the C4 hydroxyl group does not, whereas the WGA complex exhibits the reverse.

Mannose

Comparison of the rat MBP-A and LOL I mannose complexes again shows little similarity in binding-site geometry. The direct interaction of the bound carbohydrate with the calcium ion in MBP-A is a unique feature of C-type lectins. MBP-A contains no equivalent of the LOL I Phe123 (see Figure 2); in fact, MBP-A His189 is placed on the opposite face of the mannose ring toward its axial C2 hydroxyl group. Drickamer has pointed out that Glu185 and Asn187, which are calcium- and carbo-hydrate-binding ligands, are determinants of monosaccharide binding specificity among C-type lectins (20, 21). Although Glu and Asn are found at these positions in the C-type lectins specific for mannose or glucose, respectively, galactose-specific members of the family have Gln and Asp. In fact, site-directed mutagenesis of MBP-A (20) has shown that the Gln/Asp mutant shows a 20-fold increase in affinity for galactose. Sequence alignment shows that His189 in MBP-A is replaced by Trp in the galactose-specific rat asialoglycoprotein receptor (21). Given the strong preference for the galactose-ring stacking shown above, efforts should focus on determining whether such a geometry can be incorporated into a model for galactose-specific C-type lectin binding, which would explain the mutagenesis results.

MULTIVALENCY AND FUNCTIONAL ROLES

Toxins

The X-ray crystal structures of several lectins and their carbohydrate complexes have provided numerous examples of how multivalency is manifested at the structural level. Ultimately, investigators should correlate these structural features with functional roles. To some extent this goal has been realized with the cholera toxin–like structures. In addition to understanding the basis for G_{M1} ganglioside-binding specificity, the pentameric-binding subunits and their planar array of carbohydrate-binding sites have led to a model for toxin-membrane interactions (52). Ricin, in what appears to be a functionally related architecture, also presents a toxin subunit distal to a planar array of carbohydrate-binding sites. In this case, although six sites are arranged in two pseudo three-fold symmetric arrays, only two appear to bind carbohydrate. Although subunit multivalency undoubtedly plays an important role in toxin function, given that the oligosaccharide receptors on the host cell are free to diffuse in the plane of the membrane, the intersite separation and spatial distribution of the lectin subunits, barring the planar arrangement, are probably not critical.

C-Type Cell Surface Receptors

In other cases, however, the spatial arrangement of the lectin domains seems to be an important determinant of function. The macrophage mannose receptor and the endocytic glycoprotein receptors, both C-type lectins, have been cited in this regard (21, 72, 74). The macrophage mannose receptor plays a role in the innate immune response and binds glycoconjugates terminating in mannose, fucose, or N-acetylglucosamine, cell surface components typical of pathogenic microorganisms. It is made up of a single polypeptide chain encoding eight C-type lectin CRDs, of which only one shows carbohydrate-binding properties in isolation. High-affinity interactions require a fragment containing two to four subunits, depending on the nature of the ligand (73, 74), and the linear domain organization may reflect the macrophage mannose receptor's role in binding long-chain cell surface polysaccharides such as the yeast mannans. WGA, with a helical array of carbohydrate-binding sites each showing different carbohydrate-binding affinities, provides an example of structural features with interesting parallels.

In contrast, the endocytic receptors for glycoproteins contain one CRD per monomer that associate in the membrane to form trimers or higher-order oligomers (49, 76). The asialoglycoprotein receptor is a heterooligomer that recognizes terminal galactose moieties typical of asialylated serum glycoproteins. A series of experiments with natural and synthetic branched oligosaccharides has shown that the two different CRD types form a compact and precise spatial arrangement that interacts with specific arms of an N-linked oligosaccharide (42, 49, 59). The tightest-binding naturally occurring triantennary structures have dissociation constants in the nanomolar range. Similar studies with the chicken hepatic lectin and N-acetylglucosamine terminating branched oligosaccharides suggest a similar domain organization (41–43). Clearly, subunit multivalency not only produces high-affinity binding but also defines specificity for the branching pattern of a single N-linked oligosaccharide.

Unlike the hepatic receptors, the selectins, which are also membrane bound C-type lectins, have not been found to oligomerize. However, the relatively low affinity expected of interactions involving a monomeric receptor may reflect a functional role, which in the selectins promotes the initial weak interactions resulting in the rolling phase of leukocyte extravasation (39). Of course, in this case both the protein receptor and carbohydrate ligands are on the surface of cells, and therefore multivalency can be achieved through receptor density.

Soluble Lectins

MBP-A also forms trimers, in this case through interactions with its N-terminal collagen-like tails. The resulting coiled-coil structures in turn form higher-order oligomers containing three, four, or six clusters of trimers (22, 63). Unlike the hepatic receptors, MBP-A does not show enhanced affinity for branched oligosaccharides and small synthetic cluster glycosides (40), which is consistent with a different structural organization. However, it does show very high affinity for neoglycoproteins containing multiple, widely spaced carbohydrate moieties (40), a clear indication of the nature of its oligomeric structure and again a reflection of its ability to recognize structures typical of the cell surface of pathogenic microorganisms.

Unlike the C-type animal lectins, several of which are membrane bound, all of the galectins studied to date are soluble, although galectin-3 does show a tendency to oligomerize (35, 51, 53). The dimeric 14-kDa galectins, which have been implicated in modulating cell-cell and cell-substratum interactions (36), show structural similarities with the legume lectins, suggesting a similar structure-function relationship (48). Galectin-4, whose three-dimensional structure has yet to be determined, contains both an N- and a C-terminal lectin domain linked by a short peptide segment (34, 54). This observation raises the possibility that the linker serves as a flexible adapter allowing for a range of relative monomer orientations to be achieved. Interestingly, the formation of oligomers by galectin-3, which is mediated by an N-terminal domain composed of proline- and glycine-rich repeat sequences, results in cooperative binding to multivalent substrates such as laminin (51). The N-terminal domain is degraded very rapidly by endogenous tissue collagenases, raising the interesting possibility that subunit multivalency and the resultant cooperative binding properties might be regulated (31).

Although many lectins agglutinate cells, a physiological role for such a property is not well established. Several C-type lectins in the venom of rattlesnakes, however, may serve to agglutinate various host-cell types (24, 33). These lectins are soluble oligomers of C-type CRDs that are not linked to accessory domains. Sedimentation and preliminary X-ray diffraction analysis have shown that venom lectin from the rattlesnake *Crotalus atrox* forms decamers composed of two five-fold symmetric pentamers (B Nagar, NM Young & JM Rini, unpublished data). Given that the C-type lectin and the SAP monomers are not structurally related, it is truly remarkable that both form five-fold symmetric pentameric arrays that associate to form decamers.

Carbohydrate–Cross-Linked Lectin Arrays

To date, the three-dimensional structure of a lectin-carbohydrate complex that shows a multivalent ligand spanning carbohydrate-binding domains found either on a single polypeptide chain or separate chains of a physiologically relevant oligomer, has not been determined. However, multivalent oligosaccharides have been found that cross-link lectins to produce aggregates or crystal lattices (28, 29, 50, 62, 81, 88). That the number of such examples, which include several lectin types, is rapidly growing clearly indicates the steric and conformational feasibility of such multivalent interactions.

CONCLUSIONS AND SUMMARY

Clearly, Nature has provided a diverse range of structural motifs and domain organizations to mediate lectin-carbohydrate interactions. Given the rather weak interactions between lectins and monosaccharides, it is not surprising that multivalency is used by all lectin structural types. We have seen that both subunit and subsite multivalency are mechanisms used to confer both specificity and affinity upon lectin-carbohydrate interactions.

Although this review has emphasized the structural basis of lectin-carbohydrate interactions, we can rarely attach quantitative significance to the relative importance of a given set or subset of interactions. Our structural data must be interpreted in light of thermodynamic data describing these interactions with particular attention to the role played by solvent and oligosaccharide conformation and flexibility (6, 11, 37, 55, 57, 75).

Although the determination of lectin and oligosaccharide structures has in some ways outpaced our understanding of their physiological functions, the intense interest in the design of carbohydrate-based therapeutic inhibitors of selectin-mediated interactions has certainly signaled the coming of age of the study of lectin-carbohydrate interactions.

ACKNOWLEDGMENTS

I thank Amit Kanigsberg, Ulug Ünligil, and Yuri Lobsanov for help in the preparation of figures and Hakon Leffler for fruitful discussions. I also thank Bradford Graves for access to the E-selectin lec/EGF domain coordinates. This work was supported by grants from the Medical Research Council of Canada and the National Cancer Institute of Canada.

Literature Cited

1. Baenziger JU, Fiete D. 1979. Structural determinants of *Ricinus communis* agglutinin and toxin specificity for oligosaccharides. *J. Biol. Chem.* 254(19):9795–99
2. Banerjee R, Mande SC, Ganesh V, Das K, Dhanaraj V, et al. 1994. Crystal structure of peanut lectin, a protein with an unusual quaternary structure. *Proc. Natl. Acad. Sci. USA* 91:227–31
3. Barondes SH, Castronovo V, Cooper DNW, Cummings RD, Drickamer K, et al. 1994. Galectins: a family of animal β-galactoside-binding lectins. *Cell* 76:597–98
4. Barondes SH, Cooper DNW, Gitt MA, Leffler H. 1994. Structure and function of a large family of animal lectins. *J. Biol. Chem.* 269:1–5
5. Bevilacqua MP. 1993. Endothelial-leukocyte adhesion molecules. *Annu. Rev. Immunol.* 11:767–804
6. Bourne Y, Cambillau C. 1993. The role of structural water molecules in protein-saccharide complexes. *Topics Mol. Biol.* 17:321–37
7. Bourne Y, Mazurier J, Legrand D, Rougé P, Montreuil J, et al. 1994. Structures of a legume lectin complexed with the human lactotransferrin N2 fragment, and with an isolated biantennary glycopeptide: role of the fucose moiety. *Structure* 2:209–19
8. Bourne Y, Rougé P, Cambillau C. 1992. X-ray structure of a biantennary octasaccharide-lectin complex refined at 2.3-Å resolution. *J. Biol. Chem.* 267: 197–203
9. Bourne Y, Roussel A, Frey M, Rougé P, Fontecilla-Camps J-C, et al. 1990. Three-dimensional structures of complexes of *Lathyrus ochrus* isolectin I with glucose and mannose: fine specificity of the monosaccharide-binding site. *Proteins* 8:365–76
10. Bourne Y, van Tilbeurgh H, Cambillau C. 1993. Protein-carbohydrate interactions. *Curr. Opin. Struct. Biol.* 3: 681–86
11. Bundle DR, Young NM. 1992. Carbohydrate protein interactions in antibodies and lectins. *Curr. Opin. Struct. Biol.* 2(5):666–73
12. Burnette WN. 1994. AB_5 ADP-ribosylating toxins: comparative anatomy and physiology. *Structure* 2:151–58
13. Cooper DNW, Massa SM, Barondes SH. 1991. Endogenous lectin inhibits myoblast adhesion to laminin. *J. Cell Biol.* 115:1437–48
14. Debray J, Decout D, Strecker G, Spik G, Montreuil J. 1981. Specificity of twelve lectins towards oligosaccharides and glycopeptides related to N-glycosylproteins. *Eur. J. Biochem.* 117:41–55

15. Delbaere LTJ, Vandonselaar M, Prasad L. 1990. Molecular recognition of a human blood group determinant by a plant lectin. *Can. J. Chem.* 68:1116–21

16. Delbaere LTJ, Vandonselaar M, Prasad L, Wilson Quail J, Wilson KS, Dauter Z. 1993. Structures of the lectin IV of *Griffonia simplicifolia* and its complex with the Lewis b human blood group determinant at 2.0 Å resolution. *J. Mol. Biol.* 230:950–65

17. Derewenda Z, Yariv J, Helliwell JR, Kalb (Gilboa) AJ, Dodson EJ, et al. 1989. The structure of the saccharide-binding site of concanavalin A. *EMBO J.* 8(8):2189–93

18. Drickamer K. 1987. Membrane receptors that mediate glycoprotein endocytosis: structure and biosynthesis. *Kidney Int.* 32(23):S167–80

19. Drickamer K. 1988. Two distinct classes of carbohydrate recognition domains in animal lectins. *J. Biol. Chem.* 263:9557–60

20. Drickamer K. 1992. Engineering galactose-binding activity into a C-type mannose-binding protein. *Nature* 360:183–86

21. Drickamer K. 1993. Evolution of Ca^{2+}-dependent animal lectins. *Prog. Nucleic Acid Res. Mol. Biol.* 45:207–33

22. Drickamer K, Taylor ME. 1993. Biology of animal lectins. *Annu. Rev. Cell Biol.* 9:237–64

23. Emsley J, White HE, O'Hara BP, Oliva G, Srinivasan N, et al. 1994. Structure of pentameric human serum amyloid P component. *Nature* 367:338–45

24. Gartner TK, Ogilvie ML. 1984. Isolation and characterization of three Ca^{2+}-dependent β-galactoside-specific lectins from snake venoms. *Biochem. J.* 224:301–7

25. Gitt MA, Barondes SH. 1991. Genomic sequence and organization of two members of a human lectin gene family. *Biochemistry* 30:82–89

26. Goldstein IJ, Poretz RD. 1986. Isolation, physiochemical characterization, and carbohydrate-binding specificity of lectins. See Ref. 45a, pp. 35–247

27. Graves BJ, Crowther RL, Chandran C, Rumberger JM, Li S, et al. 1994. Insight into E-selectin/ligand interaction from the crystal structure and mutagenesis of the lec/EGF domains. *Nature* 367:532–38

28. Gupta D, Bhattacharyya L, Fant J, Macaluso F, Sabesan S, et al. 1994. Observation of unique cross-linked lattices between multiantennary carbohydrates and soybean lectin. Presence of pseudo-2-fold axes of symmetry in complex type carbohydrates. *Biochemistry* 33(24):7495–7504

29. Gupta D, Brewer CF. 1994. Homogeneous aggregation of the 14-kDa β-galactoside specific vertebrate lectin complex with asialofetuin in mixed systems. *Biochemistry* 33:5526–30

30. Hardman K, Agarwal R, Freiser M. 1982. Manganese and calcium binding sites of concanavalin A. *J. Mol. Biol.* 157:69–86

31. Herrmann J, Turck CW, Atchison R, Huflejt M, Poulter L, et al. 1993. Primary structure of the soluble lactose binding lectin L-29 from rat and dog and interaction of its non-collagenous Pro, Gly, Tyr-rich sequence with bacterial and tissue collagenase. *J. Biol. Chem.* 268:26704–11

32. Hirabayashi J, Kasai K-I. 1993. The family of metazoan metal-independent β-galactoside-binding lectins: structure, function and molecular evolution. *Glycobiology* 3(4):297–304

33. Hirabayashi J, Kusunoki T, Kasai K-I. 1991. Complete primary structure of a galactose-specific lectin from the venom of the rattlesnake *Crotalus atrox*. *J. Biol. Chem.* 266:2320–26

34. Hirabayashi J, Satoh M, Kasai K. 1992. Evidence that *Caenorhabditis elegans* 32-kDa beta-galactoside-binding protein is homologous to vertebrate beta-galactoside-binding lectins. cDNA cloning and deduced amino acid sequence. *J. Biol. Chem.* 267:15485–90

35. Hsu DK, Zuberi RI, Liu F-T. 1992. Biochemical and biophysical characterization of human recombinant IgE-binding protein, an S-type animal lectin. *J. Biol. Chem.* 267:14167–74

36. Hughes RC. 1992. Lectins as cell adhesion molecules. *Curr. Opin. Struct. Biol.* 2(5):687–92

37. Imberty A, Bourne Y, Cambillau C, Rougé P, Perez S. 1993. Oligosaccharide conformation in protein/carbohydrate complexes. *Adv. Biophys.* *Chem.* 3:71–117

38. Kornfeld K, Reitman ML, Kornfeld R. 1981. The carbohydrate-binding specificity of pea and lentil lectins. *J. Biol. Chem.* 256(13):6633–40

39. Lasky LA. 1992. Selectins: interpreters of cell-specific carbohydrate information during inflammation. *Science* 258:964–69

40. Lee RT, Ichikawa Y, Kawasaki T,

Drickamer K, Lee YC. 1992. Multivalent ligand binding by serum mannose-binding protein. *Arch. Biochem. Biophys.* 299(1):129–36

41. Lee RT, Rice KG, Rao NBN, Ichikawa Y, Barthel T, et al. 1989. Binding characteristics of *N*-acetylglucosamine-specific lectin of the isolated chicken hepatocytes: similarities to mammalian hepatic galactose/*N*-acetylgalactosamine-specific lectin. *Biochemistry* 28:8351–58

42. Lee YC. 1992. Biochemistry of carbohydrate-protein interaction. *FASEB J.* 6:3193–3200

43. Lee YC, Lee RT, Rice K, Ichikawa Y, Wong T-C. 1991. Topography of binding sites of animal lectins: ligands' view. *Pure Appl. Chem.* 63(4):499–506

44. Leffler H, Barondes SH. 1986. Specificity of binding of three soluble rat lung lectins to substituted and unsubstituted natural β-galactosides. *J. Biol. Chem.* 261:10119–26

45. Liao D-I, Kapadia G, Ahmed H, Vasta GR, Herzberg O. 1994. Structure of S-lectin, a developmentally regulated vertebrate β-galactoside-binding protein. *Proc. Natl. Acad. Sci. USA* 91:1428–32

45a. Liener IE, Sharon N, Goldstein IJ, eds. 1986. *The Lectins. Properties, Functions, and Applications in Biology and Medicine*. London/Orlando: Academic. 600 pp.

46. Lis H, Sharon N. 1986. Biological properties of lectins. See Ref. 45a, pp. 265–91

47. Lis H, Sharon N. 1991. Lectin-carbohydrate interactions. *Curr. Opin. Struct. Biol.* 1:741–49

48. Lobsanov YD, Gitt MA, Leffler H, Barondes SH, Rini JM. 1993. X-ray crystal structure of the human dimeric S-Lac lectin, L-14-II, in complex with lactose at 2.9 Å resolution. *J. Biol. Chem.* 268:27034–38

49. Lodish HF. 1991. Recognition of complex oligosaccharides by the multisubunit asialoglycoprotein receptor. *Trends Biol. Sci.* 16:374–77

50. Mandal DK, Brewer CF. 1992. Interactions of concanavalin A with glycoproteins: formation of homogeneous glycoprotein-lectin cross-linked complexes in mixed precipitation systems. *Biochemistry* 31:12602–9

51. Massa SM, Cooper DNW, Leffler H, Barondes SH. 1993. L-29, an endogenous lectin, binds to glycoconjugate ligands with positive cooperativity. *Biochemistry* 32:260–67

52. Merritt EA, Sarfaty S, Van Den Akker F, L'Hoir C, Martial JA, Hol WGJ. 1994. Crystal structure of cholera toxin B-pentamer bound to receptor G_{M1} pentasaccharide. *Protein Sci.* 3:166–75

53. Ochieng J, Platt D, Tait L, Hogan V, Raz T, et al. 1993. Structure-function relationship of a recombinant human galactoside-binding protein. *Biochemistry* 32:4455–60

54. Oda Y, Herrmann J, Gitt MJ, Turck C, Burlingame AL, et al. 1993. Soluble lactose binding lectin from rat intestine with two carbohydrate binding domains in the same peptide chain. *J. Biol. Chem.* 268:5929–39

55. Perez S, Imberty A, Carver JP. 1994. Molecular modeling: an essential component in the structure determination of oligosaccharides and polysaccharides. *Adv. Comput. Biol.* 1:147–202

56. Quiocho FA. 1989. Protein-carbohydrate interactions: basic molecular features. *Pure Appl. Chem.* 61(7):1293–1306

57. Quiocho FA. 1993. Probing the atomic interactions between proteins and carbohydrates. *Biochem. Soc. Trans.* 21(2):442–48

58. Quiocho FA, Vyas NK, Spurlino JC. 1989. Atomic interactions between proteins and carbohydrates. *Am. Crystallogr. Assoc.* 25:23–35

59. Rice KG, Weisz OA, Barthel T, Lee RT, Lee YC. 1990. Defined geometry of binding between triantennary glycopeptide and the asialoglycoprotein receptor of rat hepatocytes. *J. Biol. Chem.* 265(30):18429–34

60. Rini JM, Hardman KD, Einspahr H, Suddath FL, Carver JP. 1993. X-ray crystal structure of a pea lectin-trimannoside complex at 2.6 Å resolution. *J. Biol. Chem.* 268(14):10126–32

61. Rutenber E, Katzin BJ, Ernst S, Collins EJ, Mlsna D, et al. 1991. Crystallographic refinement of ricin to 2.5 Å. *Proteins* 10:240–50

62. Rutenber E, Robertus JD. 1991. Structure of ricin B-chain at 2.6 Å resolution. *Proteins* 10:260–69

63. Sastry K, Ezekowitz RA. 1993. Collections: pattern recognition molecules involved in first line host defense. *Curr. Opin. Immunol.* 5:59–66

64. Sauter NK, Glick GD, Crowther RL, Park S-J, Eisen MB, et al. 1992. Crystallographic detection of a second ligand binding site in influenza virus hemagglutinin. *Proc. Natl. Acad. Sci. USA* 89:324–28

65. Shaanan B, Lis H, Sharon N. 1991. Structure of a legume lectin with an ordered N-linked carbohydrate in complex with lactose. *Science* 254: 862–66

66. Sharon N, Lis H. 1989. Lectins as cell recognition molecules. *Science* 246: 227–34

67. Sharon N, Lis H. 1990. Legume lectins—a large family of homologous proteins. *FASEB J.* 4:3198–3208

68. Sixma TK, Kalk KH, van Zanten BAM, Dauter Z, Kingma J, et al. 1993. Refined structure of *Escherichia coli* heat-labile enterotoxin, a close relative of cholera toxin. *J. Mol. Biol.* 230: 890–918

69. Sixma TK, Pronk SE, Kalk KH, van Zanten BAM, Berghuis AM, et al. 1992. Lactose binding to heat-labile enterotoxin revealed by X-ray crystallography. *Nature* 355:561–64

70. Stein PE, Boodhoo A, Armstrong GD, Cockle SA, Klein MH, et al. 1994. The crystal structure of pertussis toxin. *Structure* 2:45–57

71. Stein PE, Boodhoo A, Armstrong GD, Heerze LD, Cockle SA, et al. 1994. Structure of a pertussis toxin-sugar complex as a model for receptor binding. *Struct. Biol.* 1(9):591–96

72. Taylor ME. 1993. Recognition of complex carbohydrates by the macrophage mannose receptor. *Biochem. Soc. Trans.* 21(2):468–73

73. Taylor ME, Bezouska K, Drickamer K. 1992. Contribution to ligand binding by multiple carbohydrate-recognition domains in the macrophage mannose receptor. *J. Biol. Chem.* 267(3): 1719–26

74. Taylor ME, Drickamer K. 1993. Structural requirements for high affinity binding of complex ligands by the macrophage mannose receptor. *J. Biol. Chem.* 268:399–404

75. Toone EJ. 1994. Structure and energetics of protein-carbohydrate complexes. *Curr. Opin. Struct. Biol.* 4: 719–28

76. Verrey F, Drickamer K. 1993. Determinants of oligomeric structure in the chicken liver glycoprotein receptor. *Biochem. J.* 292:149–55

77. Villafranca JE, Robertus JD. 1980. Ricin B chain is a product of gene duplication. *J. Biol. Chem.* 256:554–56

78. Vyas NK. 1991. Atomic features of protein-carbohydrate interactions. *Curr. Opin. Struct. Biol.* 1:732–40

79. Wang JL, Werner EA, Laing JG, Patterson RJ. 1992. Nuclear and cytoplasmic localization of a lectin-ribonucleoprotein complex. *Biochem. Soc. Trans.* 20:269–74

80. Weis WI, Brown JH, Cusack S, Paulson JC, Skehel JJ, Wiley DC. 1988. Structure of the influenza virus haemagglutinin complexed with its receptor, sialic acid. *Nature* 333:426–31

81. Weis WI, Drickamer K, Hendrickson WA. 1992. Structure of a C-type mannose-binding protein complexed with an oligosaccharide. *Nature* 360: 127–34

82. Weis WI, Kahn R, Fourme R, Drickamer K, Hendrickson WA. 1991. Structure of the calcium-dependent lectin domain from a rat mannose-binding protein determined by MAD phasing. *Science* 254:1608–15

83. Wiley DC, Skehel JJ. 1987. The structure and function of the hemagglutinin membrane glycoprotein of influenza virus. *Annu. Rev. Biochem.* 56:365–94

84. Wilson IA, Skehel JJ, Wiley DC. 1981. Structure of the haemagglutinin membrane glycoprotein of influenza virus at 3 Å resolution. *Nature* 289:366–73

85. Wright CS. 1987. Refinement of the crystal structure of wheat germ agglutinin isolectin 2 at 1.8 Å resolution. *J. Mol. Biol.* 194:501–29

86. Wright CS. 1989. Comparison of the refined crystal structures of two wheat germ isolectins. *J. Mol. Biol.* 209: 475–87

87. Wright CS. 1990. 2.2 Å resolution structure analysis of two refined *N*-acetylneuraminyl-lactose-wheat germ agglutinin isolectin complexes. *J. Mol. Biol.* 215:635–51

88. Wright CS, Jaeger J. 1993. Crystallographic refinement and structure analysis of the complex of wheat germ agglutinin with a bivalent sialoglycopeptide from glycophorin A. *J. Mol. Biol.* 232:620–38

89. Wright HT, Brooks DM, Wright CS. 1985. Evolution of the multidomain protein wheat germ agglutinin. *J. Mol. Evol.* 21:133–38

90. Young NM, Oomen RP. 1992. Analysis of sequence variation among legume lectins. A ring of hypervariable residues forms the perimeter of the carbohydrate-binding site. *J. Mol. Biol.* 228:924–34

91. Zhou Q, Cummings RD. 1990. The S-type lectin from calf heart tissue binds selectively to the carbohydrate chains of laminin. *Arch. Biochem. Biophys.* 281(1):27–35

Annu. Rev. Biophys. Biomol. Struct. 1995. 24:579–610

CAPILLARY ELECTROPHORESIS OF PROTEINS AND NUCLEIC ACIDS

B. L. Karger, Y.-H. Chu, and F. Foret

Barnett Institute, Northeastern University, 360 Huntington Avenue, Boston, Massachusetts 02115

KEY WORDS: protein analysis, DNA analysis, binding studies, CE/MS

CONTENTS

ABSTRACT

During the past 30 years, slab gel electrophoresis has been one of the most important tools available to modern biochemistry, biology, and clinical research. However, despite substantial progress in methodology, slab gel techniques typically suffer from laborious, time-consuming and difficult-to-automate procedures. Capillary electrophoresis

(CE), first introduced a decade ago, emerges now as an alternative to slab gel techniques with all the advantages of modern automated technology. Although the first target of CE was analysis of small molecules (it is a highly efficient alternative to HPLC), now a main focus is on biopolymers. Currently, CE can be viewed as a fully automated tool for rapid, highly sensitive, and quantitative analysis of minute (nanoliter) amounts of complex samples. This chapter reviews the most important CE techniques and their use for the analysis and characterization of proteins and DNA.

INTRODUCTION

Traditionally, slab gel electrophoresis has been a primary tool for purification and analysis of biopolymers (2). A variety of slab gel techniques are well established, including molecular-weight determination by SDS-PAGE, blotting (e.g. Southern, Western), and purity assessment via two-dimensional gels. Nevertheless, slab gel electrophoresis is difficult to automate and quantitate and is relatively slow per lane—on the order of hours.

Capillary electrophoresis (CE), although comparatively new, offers the advantages of an instrumental approach to electrophoresis. The capillary format enables the generation of electric fields at least 50-fold more powerful than those of traditional slab gels, which leads to rapid separations—on the order of minutes. Because of its great potential, its suitability for biological mixtures, and its ability to handle precisely nanoliter quantities of material, CE is fast becoming one of the most widely used techniques for analytical separation.

This chapter critically assesses capillary electrophoresis for biopolymer characterization and analysis. It first provides a brief background on CE, followed by a discussion of two major application areas that are under rapid development—protein and DNA analysis. Because of page limitations, we do not discuss carbohydrate analysis. However, a good review of this topic recently appeared (65). More detailed information about specific aspects of capillary electrophoresis can be found in several recently published monographs (20, 25, 28, 55).

BASIC PRINCIPLES AND INSTRUMENTATION

In CE, the column internal diameters typically range between 50 and 100 μm, yielding currents of roughly 10–20 μA for fields of about 300 V/cm with low conductivity buffers. Fused silica capillaries of such diameters are readily available as a result of optical-fiber technology.

In addition, the walls of the capillary provide an anticonvective effect that stabilizes the buffer solution within the tube. Thus, open-tube operation, in which the ionic species are separated solely on the basis of electrophoretic mobility, is easy to implement.

Because fused silica contains free silanol groups that will be ionized when exposed to the background electrolyte at pH values above ~2, the inside surface of the capillary will be negatively charged and the charge density pH dependent. The adjacent layer of hydrated positive ions in the solution will move upon application of the electric field, dragging the bulk liquid inside the capillary towards the negative electrode. A more detailed description of this process, called electroosmosis, can be found elsewhere (20). Here, we note that electroosmotic flow can serve as an important transport mechanism in the open-tube mode of CE, where it facilitates transport by plug flow of low mobile ionic (cationic and anionic) and neutral sample components towards the detector. On the other hand, the bare fused silica is quite active, and the inner capillary wall must frequently be coated with a layer of a polymeric material (e.g. linear polyacrylamide) to eliminate adsorption of proteins and other biopolymers. Such coated capillaries may exhibit little or no electroosmotic flow. Surface-coated capillaries (covalently attached or surface adsorbed) are typically necessary for analyses in which the resolution demands are high, such as in the separation of closely related protein variants and, especially, in DNA sequencing.

Figure 1 shows an example of the high-resolution capabilities of CE; it presents the separation of a protein mixture performed in an open-tube format with a coated capillary to prevent sample adsorption (77). The separation is fast, and the peak widths are quite narrow. When protein adsorption on the capillary wall is minimized, separation efficiencies exceeding 10^6 theoretical plates per meter (a measure of peak broadening) are possible in CE—a factor at least 10–100 times better than the efficiency of high performance liquid chromatography (HPLC). Finally, the reproducibility of both qualitative analysis (migration times) and quantitative analysis (peak area) is excellent with an automated CE instrument. The relative standard deviation of both the migration times and peak areas can, typically, be 1% or better.

The basic instrumentation for CE is quite straightforward. The fused silica separation capillary, which typically has a total length of 20–60 cm, is dipped into background electrolyte (BGE) reservoirs equipped with Pt electrodes for connecting the high voltage power supply, which can typically deliver up to 30 kV. On-column monitoring of UV absorbance is the most common detection mode. Injection can either be accomplished by pressure drop to deliver a fixed volume or by electro-

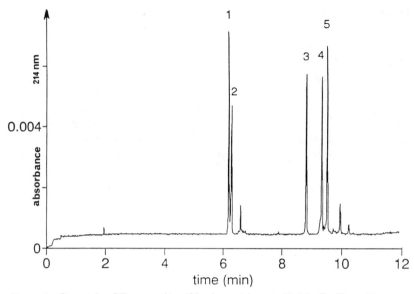

Figure 1   Open-tube CE separation of basic proteins at pH 4.5. Capillary, 50 cm ×
75μm; coated with linear polyacrylamide. Electric field strength 530 V/cm. 1, lysozyme;
2, cytochrome *c;* 3, myoglobin; 4, trypsinogen; 5, α-chymotrypsinogen A. Reproduced
from Reference 77, with permission of Elsevier Publishers.

migration, in which an electric field provides a means for transport of
the ionic species onto the column. When possible, pressure injection
is preferred because it places a known amount of sample on the column,
whereas electrokinetic injection may create sample bias in the injection
process (41).

The amount of sample injected is typically in the nanoliter range.
Hence, CE can be viewed as a nanotechnology tool. This feature is
particularly important in the biological sciences, where the amounts of
material available for study are often quite limited. For example, CE
can be used for analyzing components in single cells, such as erythrocytes (97). (Note the volume of single cells is in the picoliter range.)

Detection

The most common detector is a miniaturized UV detector of HPLC.
For further characterization of the bands migrating into the detection
cell, one can use photodiode array spectrometers. As in HPLC, rapid
scanning spectral analysis provides useful additional information in the
identification and assessment of band purity. Because the optical path
length is very short, only moderate detection limits in terms of initial

sample concentration (10^{-5}–10^{-6} M) can be obtained with on-column absorbance detection. However, because of the miniaturized design, the mass sensitivity is quite low, e.g. on the femtomole scale (10^{-15} mol). When higher concentration sensitivity is required, one can use either on-column sample preconcentration [such as sample stacking (12), isotachophoresis (21), or solid-phase extraction (29)] or a more selective and sensitive detection principle such as fluorescence. With the sample preconcentration approach, the injected sample volume is increased to the low microliter range.

An important development in CE is the utilization of lasers as excitation sources for on-column laser-induced fluorescence detection. This approach, particularly with dye-labeled molecules, provides a means for selective detection at concentrations of 10^{-11} M or lower. Considering the minuscule amount of injected volume (nanoliters), the actual mass detection limits are in the attomole (10^{-18} mole) or zeptomole (10^{-21} mole) ranges. Indeed, at the 1-zm level, 600 molecules are detected; detection levels are at times described in terms of number of molecules analyzed rather than moles.

Besides having high sensitivity, fluorescence detection is also quite selective, requiring the presence of certain fluorescent moieties within the detected molecule. Because only a few molecules possess native fluorescence in the excitation region desired, a suitable tag must be attached to the molecule prior to analysis. The situation is quite straightforward in DNA analysis, in which the use of fluorescently labeled nucleotides or primers is a routine practice. Most common fluorescein and rhodamine derivatives can be easily excited with the argon ion laser (488 nm, 514 nm lines) or by an inexpensive HeNe laser operating at 543 nm. Double-stranded DNA fragments can also be detected with high sensitivity after complexing with an intercalation dye such as ethidium bromide or thiazole orange (79). In protein analysis, the situation is more complicated because derivatization, for example of amino groups, typically provides a range of multiply labeled products, introducing significant heterogeneity to the sample. Thus, new strategies for introducing a single fluorescent label, for example attachment to thiol groups (82), are being investigated. In some cases, native fluorescence of tryptophan-containing proteins can be used with excitation at 275 nm (54).

New advances in tagging chemistries with red or near-infrared dyes allow use of semiconductor lasers with longer excitation wavelengths. Besides being smaller, longer lasting, and more reliable, solid-state lasers are substantially less expensive than respective gas lasers. Another possible advantage stems from the fact that the background fluorescence is much weaker at longer excitation wavelengths. An example of the fluorescent tags suitable for labeling of DNA and proteins are cyanine dyes that can be excited by semiconductor lasers operating in the red region (635, 650, 670 nm). Sensitivities close to those obtained with fluorescein labeling (10^{-11} M) have been reported (10). In cases requiring spectral resolution of the fluorescence, a grating polychromator and an array detector, such as an intensified photodiode array or CCD, can be used (8, 44).

Capillary Electrophoresis and Mass Spectrometry

By coupling a separation technique to a mass spectrometer, we create an incomparable analytical tool. While the separation represents a unique means of sample pretreatment, the mass spectrometer provides information on exact molecular weight. At the same time, the separated molecules can be further fragmented in the mass spectrometer to obtain structural information. The combination of CE and mass spectrometry (CE/MS) is a relatively new but rapidly developing technique (61, 66). In this section, we discuss CE/MS because we believe it adds significant information to CE analysis, and it will surely become a major tool in the years ahead.

Because CE separates the sample in a liquid phase, an important part of the CE/MS instrumentation is the interface by which the sample ions are transferred into a high vacuum inside the mass spectrometer. Although suitable interfaces, such as thermospray, laser desorption, or fast atom bombardment, have been developed, the electrospray interface is currently used in the majority of the CE/MS applications (83). The popularity of the electrospray interface arises from its unique features, which include simple construction, direct coupling under atmospheric pressure conditions, and the production of predominantly molecular ions even with large biopolymers such as proteins. Another unique feature is that it yields a distribution of multiply charged molecular ions. Typically, molecular ions with 20–30 charges or more are obtained. Such multiply charged molecular ions decrease the mass-to-charge ratio of the ions, allowing the use of standard quadrupole mass analyzers for protein analysis. Because the charge difference between the adjacent peaks is known, a very precise molecular mass determination can be obtained. The precision of the molecular mass determination with a quadrupole mass spectrometer is typically better than 0.03% (a substantial improvement over common SDS-PAGE), and even much better precision can be obtained with new high-resolution mass spectrometers, such as ion cyclotron resonance (38).

The sensitivity of the CE/MS analysis is comparable to that of CE with UV detection. Substantially better detection limits can be obtained with electrophoretic preconcentration techniques such as sample stacking (96) or isotachophoresis (ITP) (52, 97), which can improve detection levels by two orders of magnitude or more. Figure 2*a* shows an example of the CE/MS analysis of a protein sample obtained with ITP preconcentration. The mass spectrum in Figure 2*b* shows the distribution of multiply charged ions of lysozyme obtained during the CE separation,

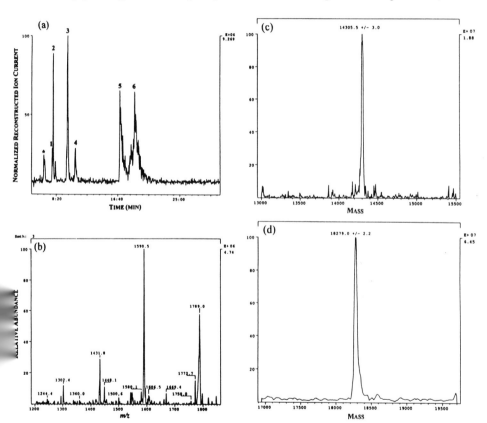

Figure 2 CE/MS analysis of a protein mixture with transient ITP preconcentration. (*a*) The total ion electropherogram—the signal amplitude represents the total current generated by all ions detected in the mass spectrometer. Sample: lysozyme (peak 1), cytochrome *c* (peak 2), ribonuclease A (peak 3), myoglobin (peak 4), β-lactoglobulin A (peak 5), β-lactoglobulin B (peak 6); ~500 nM each, dissolved in 5 mM ammonium acetate buffer. Injection volume 750 nl. (*b*) The spectrum of lysozyme obtained by averaging the scans under the peak in the electropherogram. (*c*) The deconvoluted spectrum of lysozyme. (*d*) The deconvoluted spectrum of β-lactoglobulin B. Capillary, 60 cm × 75 μm; BGE, 6-aminohexanoic acid/acetic acid; pH 4.5; 250 V/cm. Reproduced from Reference 89, with permission of the American Chemical Society.

and Figures 2*c* and 2*d* show deconvoluted mass spectra. The detection limit obtained with ITP preconcentration is better than 10^{-8} M, enabling reliable mass analysis of minor sample components.

In the example shown in Figure 2, CE was interfaced to a quadrupole mass spectrometer; however, CE interfacing to other types of mass spectrometers is also under development. Ion storage devices and time-of-flight instruments should be especially useful. The storage types of mass spectrometers, such as the ion trap (81), can provide both fast scanning and the ability to store ions of a selected mass-to-charge ratio for further mass spectrometric analysis. Time-of-flight instruments are relatively simple and inexpensive devices with high scanning rates (millisecond) and excellent ion throughput. Off-line analysis of fractions collected from CE in conjunction with matrix-assisted laser desorption (MALDI) sample ionization also provides a simple and rapid way for CE/MS of protein samples (45).

In the purity assessment, minor protein modifications such as deamidation or misfolding, as well as a change in the carbohydrate portion of glycoproteins, can be responsible for a different migration in CE. Here, the on-line mass spectrometric analysis can provide immediate information about the type of the protein modification. An important application will undoubtedly be analysis of protein tryptic digests with on-line MS sequence determination (93). Similar applications can also be expected in the analysis of short oligonucleotides, especially antisense DNA. Carbohydrate analysis is yet another emerging application of CE, and again, coupling with MS will provide a more complete picture about the sample.

CE as a Nanopreparative Method

The high speed and resolution of the CE analysis makes this technique very attractive for collection of low levels of samples. Although the maximum quantity of the sample taken for the CE analysis is typically at or below the nanomole level (hence the term nanopreparative), the collection of sample fractions can still be important. In the most simple arrangement, the zones are collected in microvials as they migrate out from the capillary past the detector (71). The collected fractions can be then further characterized by peptide sequencing and mass analysis (33) or by PCR amplification in the case of DNA. Although the analysis must be interrupted as many times as there are fractions to be collected, this method of fraction collection is available on commercial instruments. Another approach to sample collection is to use a moving membrane interface (43). In this case, the detection end of the capillary is in direct contact with the wetted surface of a collection membrane (e.g.

polyvinylidene fluoride or cellulose acetate). The membrane, which also forms an electric contact with the high-voltage power supply during CE analysis, slowly moves, and the sample zones eluting the CE capillary are deposited on its surface as tiny streaks. After analysis, the collected fractions can be either eluted from the membrane or analyzed directly on the surface through specific staining, e.g. Southern blotting (94).

Because fraction collection in CE directly provides highly purified sample components, no gel extraction or blotting is necessary. Moreover, the whole procedure can be fully automated, which provides speed and accuracy in the further characterization of analyzed substances.

PROTEIN ANALYSIS BY CAPILLARY ELECTROPHORESIS

The separation and analysis of proteins by CE is another important application. Slab gel electrophoresis has been used for a long time, not only to analyze protein mixtures, but also to characterize proteins. SDS-PAGE can serve in molecular weight determination and isoelectric focusing for pI determination. Both of these methods have been adopted into the CE format and are discussed here. Affinity electrophoresis, used in the slab gel format, was recently adopted for open-tube CE. Here, we discuss this method, affinity capillary electrophoresis (ACE), along with other areas of protein characterization, including enzyme catalysis. These approaches further allow us to conduct microanalysis in the capillary, either through an enzymatic reaction procedure and/or immunological detection. Because CE is a nanotechnique, these approaches permit facile analysis at very low sample levels, a feature of increasing significance. We believe all of these points will become more important in the future.

A problem with the broad application of CE arose in that many proteins, particularly those of opposite charge to the surface of the capillary, adsorbed to the wall, resulting in either poor efficiency and/or loss of material. The reduction in adsorption for proteins has become an important issue. In the next section, we show that much progress has been made to date and that there are a variety of approaches to achieve high resolution.

Open-Tube CE

Figure 1 shows the high-performance separation of a group of standard proteins using open-tube CE. When the major band-broadening mechanism solely results from diffusion, high-performance separations are possible, in the range of one million plates per meter. As in all aspects of electrophoresis, pH manipulation can be utilized to titrate the net charge on the molecule for selective separation purposes (18). In addition, as described above, the peaks may be collected after the capillary for specific identification using immunological staining reagents or identified by on-line mass spectrometry.

As we have noted earlier, bare silica is negatively charged because of ionization of the silanol groups. The silica surface contains strong acidic groups, and even at pH 2–3, some net negative charge, albeit little, remains. Separation of negatively charged species, such as acidic proteins above their pI, can be effectively achieved using the bare-silica approach (53). However, particularly for basic proteins and, more generally, for proteins as a whole (e.g. hydrophobic interactions), adsorption to the capillary wall can be a significant consideration. Three approaches have been adopted to minimize adsorption: manipulation of pH, dynamic coating of the surface using additives to the electrophoresis buffer, and chemical modification of the surface via coatings.

Operation at low pH has been successfully applied, for example, in the separation of peptides. Figure 3 illustrates the separation at low pH of a tryptic digest of human hemoglobin A (73). In general, migration order differs relative to reversed phase liquid chromatography (LC). The peptides are net positively charged and therefore will migrate towards the negatively charged electrode, the cathode. Adsorption will be minimal because the number of silanol groups that are deprotonated at this pH is small. Hence, the electroosmotic velocity will be low. As in the case of reverse-phase LC, additives can be included in the buffer

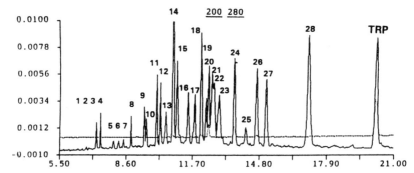

Figure 3   CE separation of tryptic digest of human hemoglobin A. Capillary, 50 cm × 50 μm; BGE, 50 mM phosphate; pH 2.5; 300 V/cm. Tryptophan was used as internal standard. Detection at 200 nm (*solid line*) and 280 nm (*dashed line*). Reproduced from Reference 73, with permission of Elsevier Publishers.

to affect ion-pair selectivity (76). The addition of buffer additives such as amines and/or detergents can effectively reduce protein adsorption (53).

For basic proteins, one can also modify the surface of the wall and convert the negative charge to a positively charged layer. These changes will produce electrostatic repulsion between the basic proteins and the wall, thereby allowing high-performance separations. The surface can be modified by using cationic detergents such as cetyltrimethylammonium bromide (92) or polyethyleneimine additives (90). Alternatively, one may covalently attach a positively charged layer to the silica surface. With such a positively charged surface, extremely basic proteins such as histones can be effectively separated.

A third approach is to attach a neutral covalent coating to the silica surface. The most popular coating today is the attachment of linear polyacrylamide (36). Not only is a hydrophilic surface produced, reducing adsorption, but in addition, the viscosity of the interfacial layer will substantially reduce electroosmotic flow. Separations in such cases are simply based on electrophoretic mobility differences. Several other neutral coatings have been developed for capillary electrophoresis.

An alternative approach that combines both an adsorbed coating and a covalently attached coating is to utilize a hydrophobically coated capillary, such as a C18 layer. The addition of a nonionic detergent such as Brij 35 to the running buffer provides a means to dynamically adsorb the detergent to the hydrophobic surface. A hydrophilic layer is thus presented to the protein. A combination of solvation of the protein by the nonionic detergent and reduction in the hydrophobicity of the surface allows the separation of proteins near neutral pH (91).

SDS-Protein Complexes

SDS-PAGE is one of the most established methods of protein analysis and molecular-weight determination (2). In the early days of CE, investigators demonstrated that cross-linked polyacrylamide gel-filled capillaries could be utilized for SDS-PAGE (16). However, the relative instability of these gels, particularly with respect to high-salt sample matrices, limited the lifetime of the columns. The use of non-cross-linked polymer matrices, e.g. linear polyacrylamide (35), significantly improved the stability of the columns, because the use of matrices with limited viscosity permitted the sieving medium to be replaced after each run.

Another factor is the absorptivity of the polymer itself. UV detection should remain in the wavelength range of roughly 200–210 nm, where the peptide bond is relatively sensitive. Polyacrylamide absorbs significantly in this range and therefore is not a desirable polymer for this application. However, many other polymers can be utilized, and this laboratory has achieved success with dextran (22). Other possible polymers include polyethylene glycol (27) and more recently polyvinyl alcohol. Several companies have commercial CE kits for assessing purity and determining the molecular weight of proteins via SDS complexes.

Figure 4 shows a rapid separation of a series of SDS-protein complexes from 14,000 to 220,000 Daltons (22). Calibration plots of mobility of standard SDS-protein complexes vs log molecular weight are linear. Furthermore, the reproducibility of migration times from run to run are approximately 0.2–0.3% relative standard deviation (rsd), when the matrix is replaced after each run. Thus, not only does the replaceable approach yield longer column lifetimes, but more precise results, as well.

In SDS-PAGE, the molecular weight is only accurate to roughly 10% for well-behaved proteins. Clearly, the use of mass spectrometry to determine molecular weight where the accuracy is generally better than 0.1% is the preferred approach. However, SDS-PAGE yields the ap-

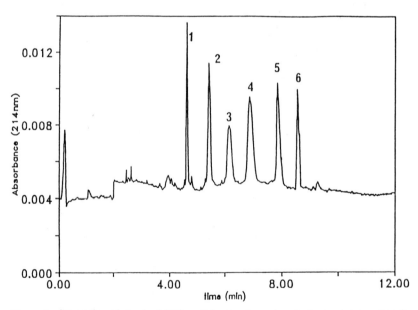

Figure 4 Separation of standard SDS-protein complexes in a dextran polymer network. Buffer: 0.06 M AMPD–cacodylic acid, pH 8.8, 0.1% SDS, 10% w/v dextran (mol wt 2,000,000). Capillary, 18 cm × 75 μm internal diameter (id.), 400 V/cm. Peaks: 1, myoglobin; 2, carbonic anhydrase; 3, ovalbumin; 4, bovine serum albumin; 5-β-galactosidase; 6, myosin. Reproduced from Reference 22, with permission of the American Chemical Society.

proximate molecular weight with simple equipment and particularly above 100,000 Daltons may provide a satisfactory molecular-weight measurement, given the heterogeneity of such molecules.

Not all classes of proteins follow the calibration curve. A particularly important example is that of glycoproteins, in which the sialic acids on the end of the carbohydrate chains, as well as the carbohydrate itself, cause the glycoprotein to lie off the calibration curve of standard proteins. We estimate molecular weight in such cases by using a Ferguson plot, which involves determination of log mobility as a function of concentration of polymer. The slopes of such plots can be related to molecular weight (2). Commercially, kits are available to determine molecular weight of glycoproteins in CE by this procedure.

Capillary Isoelectric Focusing

Isoelectric focusing (IEF) is one of the most powerful methods for the high-resolution separation of protein mixtures (70). Separation is based on differences in isoelectric points (pI) and depends on establishment of a stable pH gradient along the separation path. Such a gradient can be generated either by a suitable liquid mixture of ampholytic components or by proteolytic groups attached to a stabilizing gel (70). During the focusing, proteins move to the pH position in the gradient equal to their respective pI. Conventional IEF is performed using a gel matrix such as agarose, either in slabs or tubes.

The introduction of CE initiated attempts to transfer IEF into the capillary format without using a stabilizing media (the capillary wall is anticonvective) and dispensing with the laborious evaluation of the separation. The first successful attempts by Hjerten demonstrated the capillary isoelectric focusing (cIEF) of human myoglobin and transferrin in a glass capillary (37).

Because IEF is in principle a steady-state technique in which the analytes form fixed sharp concentrated zones, detection in cIEF has generally required mobilization of the zones to the detector after focusing. In most cases the cIEF separation proceeds in two steps. First, the capillary is filled with the sample dissolved in a 3–6% solution of ampholytes, e.g. pH 3–10, and placed between two electrode vessels. The cathodic electrode vessel contains a basic electrolyte, e.g. NaOH, and the anodic one an acidic electrolyte, e.g. H_3PO_4. After the electric current is switched on, the sample components migrate until they reach their pI in the pH gradient established by the ampholyte solution in the capillary. The focusing step typically takes about 5–15 min. During this time the electric current drops to a small fraction (10% or less) of its initial value, which provides a means to monitor the focusing process.

After focusing, the train of focused zones can be mobilized with a pH shift induced by a change of the electrolyte in one of the electrode reservoirs—a process known as salt mobilization (48). The identification of individual analytes is mostly based on a comparison of migration times in the mobilization step with those of standard substances (49). Typical resolution in cIEF is reported to be better than 0.03 pH units (48). Figure 5 presents an example of the cIEF analysis of human transferrins with salt mobilization. Note the excellent resolution of individual variants with a total analysis time of approximately 14 minutes.

Recently, single-step cIEF procedures, combining the focusing and mobilization steps, were described (11, 57, 60). In this case, the whole content of the capillary flows to the detector while focusing simultane-

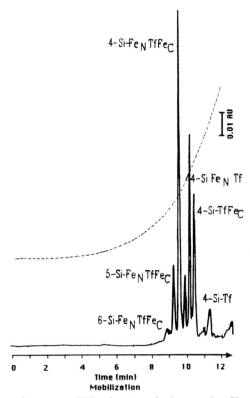

Figure 5 High-performance cIEF of a transferrin sample. Si, sialo; Tf, transferrin—$Fe_N Tf$ and $TfFe_C$ so denote monoferric transferrin forms containing iron at the N- or C-terminal lobe, respectively. $Fe_N TfFe_C$ is diferric transferrin. UV detection at 280 nm. Salt mobilization: the dotted line marks the increase of the electric current during the mobilization. Reproduced from Reference 49, with permission of Elsevier Publishers.

ously occurs. The flow can be generated either by electroosmosis (57, 60) or by a pressure drop applied at the injection end of the capillary (11).

During analysis, the protein zones concentrate from a large injected volume into a small volume of the focused zone. In this respect, cIEF can be considered a sample-concentrating technique, and high-sensitivity quantitative information can be obtained via on-line detection. However, the ability to achieve high concentrations at the isoelectric point can also be a potential problem because of possible protein precipitation. We can avoid this difficulty by using strong solubilizing agents, such as urea and nonionic detergents, in the ampholyte mixture. The separation capillary should also be coated with a hydrolytically stable layer to prevent protein adsorption, precipitation, and changes in electroosmotic flow. Commercial kits for cIEF have recently been introduced for general-purpose use. In summary, cIEF should find value in assessment of isoforms of glycoproteins, clinical assays (e.g. hemoglobin variants), and more generally, high resolution of protein mixtures.

Affinity Capillary Electrophoresis

The functional properties of proteins, e.g. enzymatic catalysis, signal transduction, and energy interconversion, vary enormously. The basis of much of protein function involves protein interaction with other molecules. Among available techniques for studying binding interactions, affinity capillary electrophoresis (ACE) has recently demonstrated its value in the measurement of binding constants, estimation of kinetic rate constants, and determination of binding stoichiometries of receptor-ligand interactions in biochemical systems.

BINDING CONSTANTS   Slab gel electrophoretic techniques have been used to examine interactions of biochemical systems (15, 88). ACE is a new procedure for studying ligand binding with receptors (3, 13, 23, 24, 34, 39, 51). As an outgrowth of affinity gel electrophoresis, ACE measures the electrophoretic mobility of a protein as a function of concentration of the ligand present in the electrophoresis buffer. The attractive features of ACE include the ability to provide a rapid assessment of protein-ligand interactions using very small amounts of substances. The protein need not be pure; simultaneous determination of individual binding constants using a sample composed of a mixture of isozymes or different proteins is possible (14).

Weak-binding systems   Measurement of binding constants of weak binding systems (fast-to-intermediate dissociation rates; ≥ 0.1 s^{-1}) involves determining the migration time of the protein of interest at various concentrations of the ligand present in the electrophoresis buffer. The sample also contains a small, neutral molecule to measure electroosmotic flow (EOF), if an uncoated capillary is used for the binding experiments, as well as to provide noninteracting protein standards. The latter correct for any changes in EOF or conductivity occurring with changes in concentration of the ligand (23, 24). From the dependence of the electrophoretic mobility of the protein on ligand concentration and the difference in mobility of free protein and the protein·ligand complex, the binding constant can be measured by using the classical Scatchard analysis. When the EOF or conductivity of buffers do not change significantly with the addition of the ligand to the electrophoresis buffer, measuring changes in migration time of the protein in order to approximate changes in electrophoretic mobilities facilitates measurement of binding constants (13).

Figure 6 shows a series of electropherograms of bovine carbonic anhydrase isozymes CA-B and CA-A in a buffer containing various concentrations of the monocarboxylated arylsulfonamide ligand 1. The electrophoretic mobilities of horse heart myoglobin (HHM) and mesityl oxide (MO), used as internal standards, were independent of the concentration of 1. The binding constant for CA-B determined by ACE $(0.48 \times 10^6 \text{ M}^{-1})$ agreed well with that obtained from a competitive fluorescence-based assay $(0.51 \times 10^6 \text{ M}^{-1})$. The CA-A isozyme, having a binding constant similar to that of CA-B, gave a value of K_b measured by ACE that was indistinguishable from that for CA-B (CA-B and CA-A differ in one amino acid residue: Arg56 for CA-B, Gln56 for CA-A). Figure 6 illustrates the power of ACE to measure simultaneously binding constants of a mixture of isozymes (13). ACE can also measure binding constants of proteins to neutral, small ligands by allowing the ligand to compete with a charged ligand of known binding constant, i.e. a competitive binding assay.

Tight-binding systems   In cases where proteins associate with ligands with high affinity (slow dissociation rates; $<0.1 \text{ s}^{-1}$), the procedure for determining binding constants is straightforward. Direct measurement of the peak areas of the free and bound protein (or ligand) allows determination of binding constants, provided that the free and bound species have different electrophoretic mobilities (34). Because the protein·ligand complex is assumed to not dissociate within the time of the CE experiment, sensitive detection of both free and complexed species becomes essential to achieving measurement of binding constants in these systems. Laser-induced fluorescence detection of dye-labeled

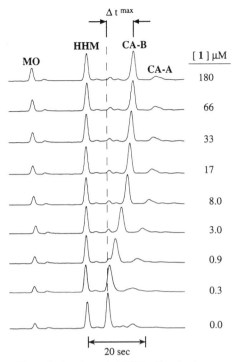

Figure 6 Affinity capillary electrophoresis (ACE) of bovine isozymes of carbonic anhydrase B (CA-B) and A (CA-A) in tris-glycine buffer at pH 8.4 containing various concentrations of the monocarboxylated arylsulfonamide inhibitor 1. Horse heart myoglobin (HHM) and mesityl oxide (MO) were used as internal standards. Reproduced from Reference 13, with permission of the American Chemical Society.

species at subnanomolar concentrations can play a significant role in the measurement of large binding constants ($K_b > 10^9 \, M^{-1}$) (see below).

KINETIC RATE CONSTANTS   In addition to the electrophoretic mobility of the protein being altered upon binding with the ligand, broadening of the peak in the region of mobility between the free and fully bound protein is often observed for weakly bound species (3). This broadening has been previously described in chromatography (59) and results from the compatibility of the rate of equilibration with the time required for the CE experiment. Simulation of the behavior of the protein under conditions of the ACE experiment allows extraction of rate constants (i.e. association and dissociation) from the widths of the peak. For example, CA-B binds a tricarboxylated arylsulfonamide inhibitor with the rate constants of $1.5 \times 10^4 \, M^{-1} \, s^{-1}$ for the association rate and

$0.1 \, s^{-1}$ for the dissociation rate, as determined by computer simulation. These values are comparable to those reported in the literature (10^4–10^6 $M^{-1} s^{-1}$ for the association rates, 0.05–0.5 s^{-1} for the dissociation rates) (3). These results suggest that experimentally obtained electropherograms for associating systems can be described with several variables: association and dissociation rate constants, concentration of the ligand, and the relative mobilities of free and bound proteins. In programs of therapeutic drug discovery, the effectiveness of a lead compound as an enzyme inhibitor depends not only on how tightly the inhibitor is bound by the enzyme but also on the rate of association of the inhibitor to the enzyme and the rate of dissociation of the enzyme·inhibitor complex (69).

BINDING STOICHIOMETRY   Binding stoichiometry is important in many aspects of molecular recognition in biology. ACE can conveniently determine the stoichiometries of protein-ligand interactions (15). It is applicable to both tight- and weak-binding systems.

In systems of weak affinities (i.e. fast dissociation rates), to simplify the determination of binding stoichiometry, the protein (P) is kept in its fully bound state by using concentrations of the ligand (L), both in the sample solution and in the electrophoresis buffer, that are much greater than the dissociation constant (K_d) (i.e. $[L]_{sample}$ and $[L]_{buffer}$ $\gg K_d$). The determination of the peak area from the electropherograms at the migration time of the ligand measures the concentration of the free ligand ($[L]_{free}$). The point of zero peak area, in the plot of the area of the free ligand vs the total ligand concentration, gives a value of ligand in a sample where $[L]_{free} = [L]_{buffer}$. The difference between the total and free ligand concentrations is the amount of the ligand bound to the receptor (i.e. $[L]_{bound} = [L]_{sample} - [L]_{buffer}$). The concentration ratio of the bound ligand to the receptor then permits the determination of the binding stoichiometry. For example, CA-B binds the arylsulfonamide ligand 1 with a stoichiometry of 1:1, which is consistent with values reported in the literature (15).

In tight-binding systems (i.e. slow dissociation rates), the determination of stoichiometry of the protein·ligand complex is straightforward as well. As the concentration ratio of $[L]_{total}/[P]$ in the sample rises, the concentration of the complex, which appears as an additional peak in the electropherogram, increases until the ratio of $[L]_{total}/[P]$ equals its stoichiometry. Beyond this point, no more complex can form because all the protein has been fully titrated and associated with the ligand. Thus, the slope of the plot of the free ligand vs the ratio of

$[L]_{total}/[P]$ abruptly changes, which yields the binding stoichiometry. For example, a monoclonal anti–human serum albumin (anti-HSA) binds to its antigen HSA with an expected stoichiometry of 1:2, and one streptavidin binds four biotins (15). In addition, ACE can also be used to identify the stoichiometry of stable binding intermediates for multivalent systems of high affinity.

Protein Characterization

Because CE is a high-resolution separation technique, studies of protein unfolding by CE have shown that it can distinguish different forms of protein conformations (50, 75, 84). For example, the protein α-lactalbumin undergoes a conformational transition upon temperature increase in the capillary (75).

With a capillary serving as a microreactor, enzyme-catalyzed reactions can take place under nondenaturing conditions to convert substrates to products (4, 5, 30, 31); all relevant events, such as electrophoretic mixing, molecular recognition, and subsequent chemical reaction, take place simultaneously in the capillary. Experimentally, enzymes are injected as plugs. Substrates may be introduced into the capillary as a separate plug or included both in the capillary and in the electrophoresis buffer. Using a glucose-6-phosphate dehydrogenase (G6PDH)–catalyzed oxidation reaction of glucose-6-phosphate (Glc-6-P) with NAD cofactor as the model system, 10 amol (10^{-17} mol) of G6PDH have been indirectly detected through enzymatic conversion of NAD to NADH (4, 5).

Other CE-based microreactors using enzymes immobilized on the wall of the capillary have shown value in the microscale characterization of proteins (1, 62). Using trypsin immobilized on the wall of an activated capillary, an on-column digestion of 0.1 nmol of the denatured β-casein was successfully demonstrated (1).

Immunoassay (e.g. ELISA) is one of the most commonly used techniques because of its ability to measure selectively trace concentrations of the target molecule from mixtures of numerous other components of much higher concentrations. We (82), and others (63, 72, 78, 80), are developing methods of CE-based immunoassays (e.g. affinity probe capillary electrophoresis, APCE). In conjunction with sensitive detection such as laser-induced fluorescence, antigen immunoassays with APCE offer advantages of (a) high speed, (b) high sensitivity of trace analysis of antigen (10^{-11}–10^{-12} M), and (c) the potential of automation. In addition, the method is a homogenous assay, the binding of antibody and antigen taking place in solution.

GENETIC ANALYSIS BY CAPILLARY ELECTROPHORESIS

Slab gel electrophoresis is a major tool today for analysis of oligonucle-otides and DNA fragments (e.g. restriction-fragment mapping, DNA sequencing, and mutational analysis). Many of the procedures conducted in the slab gel format have been incorporated into CE with attendant increases in speed, automation, quantitation, and isolation. As a result of various studies, a basic core design for genetic analysis by CE has emerged—a column utilizing a replaceable sieving matrix and laser-induced fluorescence detection (74). Multiple capillary instrumentation to mimic the multiple lanes in slab gels has been developed (42) and should be commercially available in the near future.

Sieving Matrices for Capillary Electrophoresis

Because of the success of cross-linked polyacrylamide gels in slab gel electrophoresis, initial CE columns involved similar cross-linked gel-filled capillaries (17, 26, 86, 98). High-resolution separation of single-stranded fragments was readily achievable, with efficiencies as high as 30 million theoretical plates per meter (26) and often 3–6 million plates per meter. These high efficiencies, yielding peak widths of only a few seconds, result from the substantial decrease in solute diffusion (>50-fold) in the gel matrix.

Such cross-linked gel columns have been commercialized and can be utilized for successful separation, particularly when the injections (electrokinetic) are from solutions of distilled water or those with very low conductivity. However, with biological mixtures that may contain salt, DNA template, etc, the cross-linked gel columns have limited stability, particularly under the high fields used. In addition, cross-linked gel matrices in capillaries cannot generally be employed above room temperature, because the pressure change in the pores cannot be accommodated, and the gels collapse. Thus, alternative matrices have been developed.

Today, replaceable non-cross-linked polymer networks are the predominant sieving matrix in CE. Furthermore, the viscosity of the polymer matrices is often low enough that the matrix may be replaced after each run on commercial equipment. Linear polyacrylamide is one example of such a polymer matrix (35, 68, 74); others include a variety of celluloses such as hydroxyethyl cellulose (57) and dextran and polyethylene oxide (22, 27). With such entangled polymer matrices, osmotic stress can be effectively accommodated by the movement of fibers. A neutral coating must be attached to the walls to reduce electroosmotic

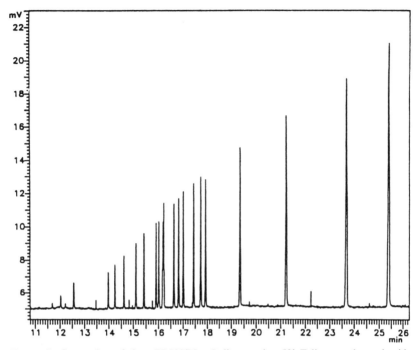

Figure 7 Separation of the pBR322/Msp I digest using 5% T linear polyacrylamide matrix, 1 × trisborate EDTA (TBE). Fragments range from 9 to 622 bp. Capillary, 20 cm × 75 μm id. 300 V/cm. Reproduced from Reference 68, with permission of Elsevier Publishers.

flow to a minimal value. Replaceable polymer networks have a separation performance generally comparable to that of cross-linked gels. Figure 7 shows the separation of a mixture of restriction-fragment digest dsDNA molecules separated by linear polyacrylamide (68).

DNA Sequencing and ssDNA Analysis

Initially, polyacrylamide cross-linked gels were used for analysis of single-stranded short oligonucleotides (17, 26). Because of its high efficiency and relative speed of separation, CE immediately became known as a superior method for the determination of the purity of these oligonucleotides. More recently, because of the relative increased stability of the linear polymers, such matrices have become more widely adopted.

A significant application is the DNA sequencing of Sanger reaction products using fluorescently tagged species in which single-base resolution can be achieved, using both cross-linked and linear polyacrylamide

matrices (43a, 56, 74, 85, 86, 98); however, cross-linked gels have severely limited lifetimes when used in the analysis of DNA-sequencing
mixtures. Recently, our laboratory introduced a replaceable sieving
matrix for DNA sequencing (74). Pressures of only a few hundred PSI
are sufficient for replacing the matrix with fresh material. Figure 8
shows the separation of sequencing-reaction products for an M13mp18
template, utilizing dye-labeled dideoxy terminators. A 4% T column is
employed in which separation can be read to over 500 bases in less
than an hour. The denaturing buffer in the sequencing matrix is 30%
formamide, 3.5 M urea at a temperature of 30°C. Such a buffer system
eliminates many compressions in the separation of the Sanger reaction
products (74, 86). In Figure 8, three hexamer oligonucleotides have
been used as the primer for the specific chain extension, along with a
single-stranded binding protein from *Escherichia coli*. Modular primer

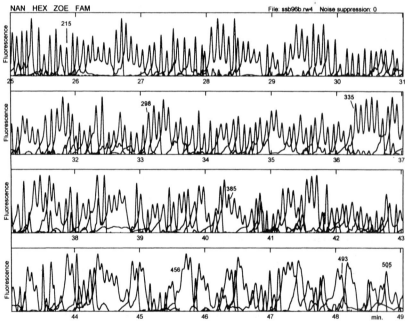

Figure 8   Separation of DNA sequencing reaction products by CE and intensified photodiode array detection. DNA sequencing with hexamer primers, single-stranded binding
protein, and fluorescent labeled dideoxynucleotides was performed on M13mp18. The
electrophoretic conditions for the separation were: capillary, 28 cm × 75 μm; constant
electric field, 200 V/cm; running buffer, 4% T linear polyacrylamide in 1 × TBE; 30%
formamide; 3.5 M urea; column temperature, 30°C. (J Berka, M Ruiz-Martinez, E Carrilho & BL Karger, unpublished data.)

walking, as introduced by Studier and colleagues (47) and Ulanovsky and colleagues (47a), is being developed in our laboratory for efficient CE-directed sequencing along a 40-kb cosmid clone. Such an approach will minimize subcloning steps and thus reduce substantially the front-end chemistry, since only fourfold redundancy will be necessary, vs the usual shotgun sequencing in which the redundancy is eight- to tenfold.

Frequently, one is interested in sequencing only short stretches of DNA, perhaps 100–200 bases in length, e.g. to detect mutations. In such cases, sequencing can be quite fast, and alternative and simplified strategies can be considered. For example, four separate dyes are not necessary for terminator-coding purposes. With the use of manganese rather than magnesium salts and the addition of pyrophosphatase, the relative amounts of sequencing products remain constant over the stretch of DNA sequenced in that run (87). This approach allows coding for specific base terminations, using the relative peak areas of the separated bands. In our laboratory (74), we followed the approach of Dovichi et al (9), with two dyes and two ratios. Specifically, FAM and JOE dye-labeled primers were selected for the two spectral channels, because the mobility-shift differences for the two dyes were minimal. Using a single-laser two-photomultiplier approach and a replaceable linear polyacrylamide matrix, we could read the sequence by eye out to 350 bases in half an hour (74). For 100–200 bases, ~10 min per run should be sufficient time to read the sequence. As already noted, throughput can be increased by parallel processing using a multiple capillary array (42).

dsDNA

Figure 7 shows the speed and resolving power of replaceable polymer sieving matrices for the analysis of dsDNA. A plot of migration time vs base number leads to a linear region up to roughly 400 base pairs, followed by a slow change in slope, ultimately leading to a plateau region where the rate of change in migration time or mobility with base number is small. At low base number, the double-stranded molecules follow the classical sieving mechanism of Ogston (64). Increases in base number lead to reptation in which the DNA molecules follow a snake-like motion through the sieving matrix. In this region, migration time vs base number is linear. The change in slope leading to the plateau region is attributed to the stretching of the DNA by the applied field (64). In a stretched conformation, the differences of DNA molecules with respect to size are substantially reduced. In this analysis, the polymeric matrices are viewed as sieving media with fluctuating pores arising from entanglement of the polymeric chains with one another. The

DNA molecules can also become entangled with the polymer fibers themselves. Particularly at low polymer concentrations, well below the entanglement threshold, this DNA-polymer interaction can result in a size-based separation mechanism (7).

Linear polyacrylamide has become one of the popular matrices to use with capillary electrophoresis for dsDNA (68). A second popular approach is to utilize a cellulose derivative, such as hydroxyethyl cellulose, as a sieving matrix (58). Commercial kits in a replaceable format are available for these matrices. The high-resolution capabilities of such matrices typically lead to roughly a 4–base pair separation. For matrices of slightly higher concentration and thus somewhat higher viscosity, single–base pair resolution is achievable (68). Because pressure injection can be used with the replaceable matrices, one need not desalt the PCR-product solution prior to injection. However, if cross-linked gels or viscous polymer networks are to be used, which would require electrokinetic injection, then a desalting step would be necessary.

Intercalating agents such as ethidium bromide and thiazole orange have been frequently added to the running buffer and sample solutions for dsDNA separation to improve the separation. A particular advantage of thiazole orange is that it is compatible with a commercially available argon ion laser system in which the sensitivity of analysis is enhanced more than 100-fold (79).

The intercalators normalize the conformation or structure of double-stranded DNA molecules. As is well known, DNA bending and flexibility, which are significant biological features of DNA, can cause selective electrophoretic retardation of species (32). Through the use of intercalators, molecules migrate in the general order of increasing base number (68). We should note that although homodimeric intercalators such as TOTO and YOYO have become sensitive staining agents for slab gel electrophoresis (99), success in capillary electrophoresis has been somewhat limited. Often bands appear broadened, owing in part to adsorption of the dye to the capillary wall and the association of DNA strands (99). Thus, to date, most efforts in CE have been with monomeric intercalators.

In the PCR reaction, fluorescently tagged primers are often utilized. Thus, the ultimate PCR product can be sensitively detected by laser-induced fluorescence. Fluorescently tagged PCR products can be also used in a quantitative PCR procedure in which the capillary serves as a quantitative detection system (PM Williams, S Williams, C Schwer, ASM Krishnarao & BL Karger, in preparation). Today, quantitative PCR generally involves the use of a competitive PCR approach in which an internal standard with the same priming site and perhaps slightly different length (but roughly the same GC content) is used.

Beyond quantitative PCR, the applications of dsDNA analysis by CE are numerous. For example, one can assess the relative purity of the obtained PCR product. In addition, the method can be used for restriction-fragment length polymorphism (RFLP) analysis, such as in DNA fingerprinting and diagnostics (57). A rapid detection of polymorphic repeat regions (microsatellite analysis) is also possible using CE.

dsDNA analysis by CE is a commercially available procedure that can be readily utilized for rapid separations. The method provides good resolution up to roughly 1000 base pairs and reasonable resolution up to 20,000–30,000 base pairs. Given the most recent developments in long-range PCR (6), matrices for increased resolution in the range of 1000–20,000 base pairs may soon be necessary. The use of ultradilute polymer matrices may hold promise in this regard (7).

Mutation Detection—Base Substitution

Of various procedures developed in slab gel electrophoresis to recognize single or multiple point differences, two important ones currently in use are SSCP (single-strand conformational polymorphism) (67) and DGGE (denaturing gradient gel electrophoresis) (19).

In SSCP, the two strands are denatured from each other, and then the separate strands are electrophoretically resolved in a sieving medium under nondenaturing conditions (67). The conformation of the strands, differing in sequence but not in length, are sufficiently divergent to allow separation of the two strands. Correspondingly, mutation of one or both of the single strands often yields sufficient conformational difference to allow separation of mutant from wild-type strands. This method of mutant detection is increasingly popular today because of its simplicity. Figure 9 shows the separation of a standard mutation test mixture, with both strands labeled with two different fluorophores (FAM and JOE). In this experiment, a single-laser, two-photomultiplier instrument is used. Relative to slab gels, the CE method offers advantages similar to those discussed earlier—speed, resolution, automation, and fraction collection.

In DGGE, one takes advantage of the differences in the strength of hydrogen bonding as a function of base composition of the complementary strands. In DGGE, a gradient of increasing denaturant strength (or temperature) is established across a slab gel. If we assume a 200–base pair dsDNA molecule with one half of the fragment melting or denaturing at high temperature (i.e. possessing a significant amount

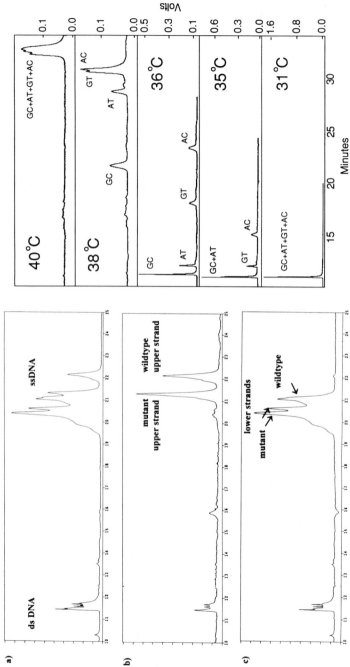

Figure 9 (*Left*) CE-SSCP analysis of wild-type and mutant DNA (276 bp). The sample was prepared with PCR using FAM- and JOE-labeled primers for upper and lower strands, respectively. Two-color LIF detection with excitation at 488 nm and emission collected at 520 nm (FAM) and 560 nm (JOE). (*a*) Total signal from both dyes; (*b*) detection of the FAM-labeled upper strand; (*c*) detection of the JOE-labeled lower strands with two different conformations. Separation conditions: 200 V/cm, 30°C; capillary, 14 cm × 100 μm, 7% linear polyacrylamide (LPA) in 1 × TBE (K Hebenbrock, PM Williams & BL Karger, unpublished data). (*Right*) CDCE (constant denaturant capillary electrophoresis) separation as a function of column temperature. 206-bp long fluorescein-labeled human mitochondrial DNA sample contained an equimolar mixture of two homoduplexes (GC and AT) and two heteroduplexes (GT and AC). Column: 6% T linear polyacrylamide, 3.3 M urea, 20% (v/v) formamide in TBE. Electric field: 250 V/cm. Reproduced from Reference 46, with permission of Oxford University Press.

of GC content) and the investigated 100-base sequence melting at a lower temperature, then the molecule will electrophorese rapidly as a double-stranded molecule to the point at which a significant amount of melting occurs for the studied sequence. At this position, the cross-sectional area of the molecule will increase significantly, substantially retarding the migration of the molecule. The sample components will thus focus at specific places on the slab, depending on their melting temperatures. Clearly, homoduplexes will require a higher melting temperature than heteroduplexes; furthermore, GC pairs (triple hydrogen bonds) will melt at higher temperatures than AT pairs (double hydrogen bonds). A variant of this approach is constant denaturant gel electrophoresis (CDGE) (40), by which we can achieve high resolution within a given melting region.

The recently developed technique of constant denaturant capillary electrophoresis (CDCE) incorporates replaceable linear polyacrylamide matrices and laser-induced fluorescence detection (46). For CDCE, a short heated or constant denaturant zone within the capillary is used. Consider, as above, a mixture of wild-type and mutant homo- and heteroduplexes, consisting of roughly 200 base pairs, with one half of each being a high melting domain and the other a lower melting domain. The homoduplexes will melt at a higher temperature than the heteroduplexes. As seen in Figure 9, at 31°C, in the hot zone, one peak emerges that is a mixture of all four species (see figure caption) and migrates through the column without melting. As the temperature in the denaturant zone rises slightly, first the heteroduplexes and then the homoduplexes separate, with four peaks appearing at 36°C. Further increases in temperature lead to complete denaturation of the low melting domain, with the four peaks emerging together at 38–40°C. In the above example, some denaturant was added in the running buffer; however, the use of nondenaturing conditions and increased temperature (60°C) with the above sample results in widely separated sharp peaks (46). The heteroduplex peaks can be collected separately from the wild-type homoduplex, leading to an enrichment of mutants by approximately three orders of magnitude. This procedure permits the detection of mutants occurring in a frequency quite low relative to the occurrence of the wild-type ($<10^4$–10^5). Furthermore, a high degree of automation is possible.

ACKNOWLEDGMENTS

The authors gratefully acknowledge NIH under GM 15847 for support of this work. This is contribution #616 from the Barnett Institute.

Literature Cited

1. Amankwa LN, Kuhr WG. 1992. Trypsin-modified fused-silica capillary microreactor for peptide mapping by capillary zone electrophoresis. *Anal. Chem.* 64:1610–13
2. Andrews AT. 1986. *Electrophoresis, Theory, Techniques and Biomedical and Clinical Applications.* Oxford: Clarendon. 452 pp.
3. Avila LZ, Chu YH, Blossey EC, Whitesides GM. 1993. Use of affinity capillary electrophoresis to determine kinetic and eqilibrium constants for binding of arylsulfonamides to bovine carbonic anhydrase. *J. Med. Chem.* 36:126–33
4. Avila LZ, Whitesides GM. 1993. Catalytic activity of native enzymes during capillary electrophoresis: an enzymatic microreactor. *J. Org. Chem.* 58:5508–12
5. Bao J, Regnier FE. 1992. Ultramicro enzyme assays in a capillary electrophoretic system. *J. Chromatogr.* 608:217–24
6. Barnes WM. 1994. PCR amplification of up to 35-kb DNA with high fidelity and high yield from bacteriophage templates. *Proc. Natl. Acad. Sci. USA* 91:2216–20
7. Barron AE, Blanch HW, Soane DS. 1994. A transient entanglement coupling mechanism for DNA separation by capillary electrophoresis in ultradilute polymer solutions. *Electrophoresis* 15:597–615
8. Carson S, Cohen AS, Belenkii A, Ruiz-Martinez MC, Berka J, Karger BL. 1993. DNA sequencing by capillary electrophoresis—use of a 2-laser 2-window intensified diode array detection system. *Anal. Chem.* 65:3219–26
9. Chen DY, Harke HR, Dovichi NJ. 1992. 2-label peak-height encoded DNA sequencing by capillary gel electrophoresis—3 examples. *Nucleic Acids Res.* 20:4873–80
10. Chen FTA, Tusak A, Pentoney S, Konrad K, Lew C, et al. 1993. Semiconductor laser-induced fluorescence detection in capillary electrophoresis using a cyanine dye. *J. Chromatogr.* 652:355–60
11. Chen SM, Wiktorowicz JE. 1992. Isoelectric focusing by free solution capillary electrophoresis. *Anal. Biochem.* 206:84–90
12. Chien RL, Burgi DS. 1992. On-column sample concentration using field amplification in CZE. *Anal. Chem.* 64:489A–96A
13. Chu YH, Avila LZ, Biebuyck HA, Whitesides GM. 1992. Use of affinity capillary electrophoresis to measure binding constants of ligands to proteins. *J. Med. Chem.* 35:2915–17
14. Chu YH, Chen JK, Whitesides GM. 1993. Affinity electrophoresis in multisectional polyacrylamide slab gels is a useful and convenient technique for measuring binding constants of aryl sulfonamides to bovine carbonic anhydrase B. *Anal. Chem.* 65:1314–22
15. Chu YH, Lees WJ, Stassinopoulos A, Walsh CT. 1994. Using affinity capillary electrophoresis to determine binding stoichiometries of protein-ligand interactions. *Biochemistry* 33:10616–21
16. Cohen AS, Karger BL. 1987. High-performance sodium dodecyl sulfate polyacrylamide gel capillary electrophoresis of peptides and proteins. *J. Chromatogr.* 397:409–17
17. Cohen AS, Najarian DR, Paulus A, Guttman A, Smith JA, Karger BL. 1988. Rapid separation and purification of oligonucleotides by high-performance capillary gel electrophoresis. *Proc. Natl. Acad. Sci. USA* 85:9660–63
18. Compton BJ, O'Grady EA. 1991. Role of charge suppression and ionic strength in free zone electrophoresis of proteins. *Anal. Chem.* 63:2597–2602
19. Fisher SG, Lerman LS. 1983. DNA fragments differing by single base-pair substitutions are separated in denaturing gradient gels: correspondence with melting theory. *Proc. Natl. Acad. Sci. USA* 80:1579–83
20. Foret F, Krivankova L, Bocek P. 1993. *Capillary Zone Electrophoresis.* Weinheim/New York: VCH. 346 pp.
21. Foret F, Szoko E, Karger BL. 1993. Trace analysis of proteins by capillary zone electrophoresis with on-column

transient isotachophoretic preconcentration. *Electrophoresis* 14:417–28

22. Ganzler K, Greve KS, Cohen AS, Karger BL, Guttman A, Cooke NC. 1992. High-performance capillary electrophoresis of SDS protein complexes using UV-transparent polymer networks. *Anal. Chem.* 64:2665–71

23. Gomez FG, Avila LZ, Chu YH, Whitesides GM. 1994. Determination of binding constants of ligands to proteins by affinity capillary electrophoresis: compensation for electroosmotic flow. *Anal. Chem.* 66:1785–91

24. Gomez FG, Chen JK, Tanaka A, Schreiber SL, Whitesides GM. 1994. Affinity capillary electrophoresis: insights into the binding of SH3 domains by peptides derived from an SH3-binding protein. *J. Org. Chem.* 59:2885–86

25. Grossman PD, Colburn JC, eds. 1992. *Capillary Electrophoresis. Theory & Practice.* New York/London: Academic. 352 pp.

26. Guttman A, Cohen AS, Heiger DN, Karger BL. 1990. Analytical and micropreparative ultrahigh resolution of oligonucleotides by polacrylamide gel high-performance capillary electrophoresis. *Anal. Chem.* 62:137–41

27. Guttman A, Horvath J, Cooke N. 1993. Influence of temperature on the sieving effect of different polymer matrices in capillary SDS gel electrophoresis of proteins. *Anal. Chem.* 65:199–203

28. Guzman NA, ed. 1993. *Capillary Electrophoresis Technology.* New York: Dekker. 857 pp.

29. Guzman NA, Trebilcock MA, Advis JP. 1991. The use of a concentration step to collect urinary components separated by capillary electrophoresis and further characterization of collected analytes by mass spectrometry. *J. Liq. Chromatogr.* 14:997–1015

30. Harmon BJ, Patterson DH, Regnier FE. 1993. Electrophoretically mediated microanalysis of ethanol. *J. Chromatogr.* 657:429–34

31. Harmon BJ, Patterson DH, Regnier FE. 1993. Mathematical treatment of electrophoretically mediated microanalysis. *Anal. Chem.* 65:2655–62

32. Harrington RE. 1993. Studies of DNA bending and flexibility using gel electrophoresis. *Electrophoresis* 14:732–46

33. Hathaway GM. 1992. Preparative capillary electrophoresis for off-line sequence, composition and mass analy-

sis of peptides. *Methods Compan. Methods Enzymol.* 4:244–51

34. Heegaard NHH, Robey FA. 1994. The emerging role of capillary electrophoresis as a tool for the study of biomolecular noncovalent interactions. *Am. Lab.* pp. 28T–28X

35. Heiger DN, Cohen AS, Karger BL. 1990. Separation of DNA restriction fragments by high performance capillary electrophoresis with low and zero crosslinked polyacrylamide using continuous and pulsed electric fields. *J. Chromtogr.* 516:33–48

36. Hjerten S. 1985. High-performance electrophoresis: elimination of electroendosmosis and solute adsorption. *J. Chromatogr.* 347:191–98

37. Hjerten S, Zhu MD. 1985. Adaptation of the equipment for high-performance electrophoresis to isoelectric focusing. *J. Chromatogr.* 346:265–70

38. Hofstadler SA, Bruce JE, Rockwood AL, Anderson GA, Winger BE, Smith RD. 1994. Isotopic beat patterns in fourier transform ion cyclotron resonance mass spectrometry—implications for high resolution mass measurements of large biopolymers. *Int. J. Mass Spectrom. Ion Phys.* 132:109–27

39. Honda S, Taga A, Suzuki K, Suzuki S, Kakehi D. 1992. Determination of the association constant of monovalent model protein-sugar interaction by capillary zone electrophoresis. *J. Chromatogr.* 597:377–82

40. Hovig E, Smith-Sørensen B, Brøgger A, Børresen A. 1991. Constant denaturant gel electrophoresis, a modification of denaturing gradient gel electrophoresis, in mutation detection. *Mutat. Res.* 262:63–71

41. Huang X, Gordon MJ, Zare RN. 1988. Bias in quantitative capillary zone electrophoresis caused by electrokinetic sample injection. *Anal. Chem* 60:375–77

42. Huang XC, Quesada MA, Mathies RA. 1992. DNA sequencing using capillary array electrophoresis. *Anal. Chem.* 64:2149–54

43. Huang X, Zare RN. 1990. Continuous sample collection in capillary zone electrophoresis by coupling the outlet of a capillary to a moving surface. *J. Chromatogr.* 516:185–89

43a. Kambara H, Takahashi S. 1993. Multiple-sheathflow capillary array DNA analyser. *Nature* 361:565–66

44. Karger AE, Harris JM, Gesteland F. 1991. Multiwavelength fluorescence detection for DNA sequencing using

capillary electrophoresis. *Nucleic Acids Res.* 19:4955–62

45. Keough T, Takigiku R, Lacey MP, Purdon M. 1992. Matrix-assisted laser desorption mass spectrometry of proteins isolated by capillary zone electrophoresis. *Anal. Chem.* 64:1594–1600

46. Khrapko K, Hanekamp JS, Thilly WG, Belenkii A, Foret F, Karger BL. 1994. Constant denaturant capillary electrophoresis (CDCE)—a high resolution approach to mutational analysis. *Nucleic Acids Res.* 22:364–69

47. Kieleczawa J, Dunn JJ, Studier FW. 1992. DNA sequencing by primer walking with strings of contiguous hexamers. *Science* 258:1787–91

47a. Kotler LE, Zevin-Sonkin D, Sobolev IA, Beskin AD, Ulanovsky LE. 1993. DNA sequencing: modular primers assembled from a library of hexamers or pentamers. *Proc. Natl. Acad. Sci. USA* 90:4241–45

48. Kilár F. 1994. Isoelectric focusing in capillaries. In *Handbook of Capillary Electrophoresis*, ed. JP Landers, pp. 95–109. Boca Raton/London: CRC

49. Kilár F. 1991. Determination of pI by measuring the current in the mobilization step of high-performance capillary isoelectric focusing. Analysis of transferrin forms. *J. Chromatogr.* 545:403–6

50. Kilár F, Hjerten S. 1993. Unfolding of human serum transferrin in urea studied by high-performance capillary electrophoresis. *J. Chromatogr.* 638:269–76

51. Kuhn R, Frei R, Christen M. 1994. Use of capillary affinity electrophoresis for the determination of lectin-sugar interactions. *Anal. Biochem.* 218:131–35

52. Lamoree MH, Reinhoud NJ, Tjaden UR, Niessen WMA, Van der Greef J. 1994. On-capillary isotachophoresis for loadability enhancement in capillary zone electrophoresis/mass spectrometry of beta-agonists. *Biol. Mass Spectrom.* 23:339–45

53. Lauer HH, McManigill D. 1986. Capillary zone electrophoresis of proteins in untreated fused silica tubing. *Anal. Chem.* 58:166–70

54. Lee TT, Yeung ES. 1992. High-sensitivity laser-induced fluorescence detection of native proteins in capillary electrophoresis. *J. Chromatogr.* 595:319–25

55. Li SFY. 1992. *Capillary Electrophoresis.* Amsterdam/New York: Elsevier. 586 pp.

56. Luckey JA, Drossman H, Kostichka AJ, Mead DA, D'Cunha J, et al. 1990. High speed DNA sequencing by capillary electrophoresis. *Nucleic Acids Res.* 18:4417–21

57. Mazzeo JR, Krull IS. 1991. Coated capillaries and additives for the separation of proteins by capillary zone electrophoresis and capillary isoelectric focusing. *BioTechniques* 10:638–45

58. McCord BR, Jung JM, Holleran EA. 1993. High resolution capillary electrophoresis of forensic DNA using a non-gel sieving buffer. *J. Liq. Chromatogr.* 16:1963–81

59. Miller JM. 1988. Kinetic processes in chromatography. In *Chromatography: Concepts and Constrasts*, pp. 25–39. New York: Wiley

60. Molteni S, Frischknecht H, Thormann W. 1994. Application of dynamic capillary isoelectric focusing to the analysis of human hemoglobin variants. *Electrophoresis* 15:22–30

61. Muck WM, Henion JD. 1989. Determination of leucine enkephalin and methionine enkephalin in equine cerebrospinal fluid by microbore high-performance liquid chromatography and capillary electrophoresis coupled to tandem mass spectrometry. *J. Chromatogr.* 495:41–59

62. Nashabeh W, El Rassi Z. 1992. Enzymophoresis of nucleic acids by tandem capillary enzyme reactor–capillary zone electrophoresis. *J. Chromatogr.* 596:241–64

63. Nielsen RG, Rickard EC, Santa PF, Sharknas DA, Sittampalam GS. 1991. Separation of antibody-antigen complexes by capillary zone electrophoresis, isoelectric focusing and high-performance size-exclusion chromatography. *J. Chromatogr.* 539:177–85

64. Noolandi J. 1991. Theory of DNA gel electrophoresis. In *Advances in Electrophoresis*, ed. A Chrambach, MJ Dunn, BJ Radola, 5:1–57. Weinheim/New York: VCH. 414 pp.

65. Novotny MV, Sudor J. 1993. High-performance capillary electrophoresis of glycoconjugates. *Electrophoresis* 14:373–89

66. Olivares JA, Nguyen NT, Yonker CR, Smith RD. 1987. On-line mass spectrometric detection for capillary zone electrophoresis. *Anal. Chem.* 59:1230–32

67. Orita M, Iwahana H, Kanazawa H, Hayashi K, Sekiya T. 1989. Detection of polymorphisms of human DNA by

gel electrophoresis as single strand conformation polymorphisms. *Proc. Natl. Acad. Sci. USA* 86:2766–70

68. Pariat YF, Berka J, Heiger DN, Schmitt T, Vilenchik M, et al. 1993. Separation of DNA fragments by capillary electrophoresis using replaceable linear polyacrylamide matrices. *J. Chromatogr. A* 652:57–66

69. Paton WDM, Rang HP. 1966. A kinetic approach to the mechanism of drug action. *Adv. Drug Res.* 3:57–80

70. Righetti PG. 1983. *Isoelectric Focusing: Theory, Methodology and Applications.* Amsterdam: Elsevier

71. Rose DJ, Jorgenson JW. 1988. Fraction collector for capillary zone electrophoresis. *J. Chromatogr.* 438:23–34

72. Rosenzweig Z, Yeung ES. 1994. Laser-based particle-counting microimmunoassay for the analysis of single human erythrocytes. *Anal. Chem.* 66:1771–76

73. Ross GA, Lorkin P, Perrett D. 1993. Separation and tryptic digest mapping of normal and variant haemoglobins by capillary electrophoresis. *J. Chromatogr.* 636:69–79

74. Ruiz-Martinez MC, Berka J, Belenkii A, Foret F, Miller AW, Karger BL. 1993. DNA sequencing by capillary electrophoresis with replaceable linear polyacrylamide and laser-induced fluorescence detection. *Anal. Chem.* 65:2851–58

75. Rush RS, Cohen AS, Karger BL. 1991. Influence of column temperature on the electrophoretic behavior of myoglobin and α-lactalbumin in high-performance capillary electrophoresis. *Anal. Chem.* 63:1346–50

76. Rush RS, Derby PL, Strickland TW, Rohde MF. 1993. Peptide mapping and evaluation of glycopeptide microheterogeneity derived from endoproteinase digestion of arythropoietin by affinity high-performance capillary electrophoresis. *Anal. Chem.* 65:1834–42

77. Schmalzing D, Piggee CA, Foret F, Carrilho E, Karger BL. 1993. Characterization and performance of a neutral hydrophilic coating for the capillary electrophoretic separation of biopolymers. *J. Chromatogr. A* 652:149–59

78. Schultz NM, Kennedy RT. 1993. Rapid immunoassays using capillary electrophoresis with fluorescence detection. *Anal. Chem.* 65:3161–65

79. Schwartz HE, Ulfelder KJ. 1992. Capillary electrophoresis with laser-induced fluorescence detection of PCR fragments using thiozole orange. *Anal. Chem.* 64:1737–40

80. Schwartz HE, Ulfelder KJ, Chen F-TA, Pentoney SL Jr. 1994. The utility of laser-induced fluorescence detection in applications of capillary electrophoresis. *J. Capillary Electrophor.* 1:36–54

81. Schwartz JC, Jardine I. 1992. *Proc. ASMS Conf. Mass Spectrometry and Allied Topics, 40th, Washington, DC, May 31–June 5.* pp. 707–8

82. Shimura K, Karger BL. 1994. Affinity probe capillary electrophoresis: analysis of recombinant human growth hormone with a fluorescent labeled antibody fragment. *Anal. Chem.* 66:9–15

83. Smith RD, Wahl JH, Goodlett DR, Hofstadler SA. 1993. Capillary electrophoresis/mass spectrometry. *Anal. Chem.* 65:A574–84

84. Strege M, Lagu A. 1991. Separation of DNA restriction fragments by capillary electrophoresis using coated fused silica capillaries. *Anal. Chem.* 63:1233–36

85. Swerdlow H, Dew-Jager KE, Brady K, Grey R, Dovichi NJ, Gesteland R. 1992. Stability of capillary gels for automated sequencing of DNA. *Electrophoresis* 13:475–83

86. Swerdlow H, Wu S, Harke H, Dovichi NJ. 1990. Capillary gel electrophoresis for DNA sequencing: laser-induced fluorescence detection with the sheath flow cuvette. *J. Chromatogr.* 516:61–67

87. Tabor S, Richardson CS. 1990. DNA sequence analysis with a modified bacteriophage T7 DNA polymerase. Effect of pyrophosphorolysis and metal ions. *J. Biol. Chem.* 265:8322–26

88. Takeo K. 1987. Affinity electrophoresis. In *Advances in Electrophoresis*, ed. A Chrambach, MJ Dunn, BJ Radola, 1:229–79. New York: VCH

89. Thompson TJ, Foret F, Vouros P, Karger BL. 1993. Capillary electrophoresis electrospray ionization mass spectrometry—improvement of protein detection limits using on-column transient isotachophoretic sample preconcentration. *Anal. Chem.* 65:900–6

90. Towns JK, Regnier FE. 1990. Polyethyleneimine-bonded phases in the separation of proteins by capillary electrophoresis. *J. Chromatogr.* 516:69–78

91. Towns JK, Regnier FE. 1991. Capillary electrophoretic separations of proteins using nonionic surfactant coatings. *Anal. Chem.* 63:1126–32

92. Tsuda T. 1987. Modification of electroosmotic flow with cetyltrimethy-

lammonium bromide in capillary electrophoresis. *J. High Resolut. Chromatogr.* 10:622–24

93. Wahl JH, Gale DC, Smith RD. 1994. Sheathless capillary electrophoresis electrospray ionization mass spectrometry using 10 mm i.d. capillaries—analyses of tryptic digests of cytochrome *c. J. Chromatogr.* 659:217–22

94. Warren WJ, Cheng YF, Fuchs M. 1994. Protein immunodetection using capillary electrophoresis with membrane fraction collection. *LC-GC* 12:22

95. Deleted in proof

96. Wolf S, Vouros P. 1995. Incorporation of sample stacking techniques into the capillary electrophoresis. CF FAB mass spectrometry analysis of DNA adducts. *Anal. Chem.* 67: In press

97. Xue QF, Yeung ES. 1994. Indirect fluorescence determination of lactate and pyruvate in single erythrocytes by capillary electrophoresis. *J. Chromatogr.* 661:287–95

98. Zhang JZ, Chen DY, Harke H, Dovichi NJ. 1991. DNA sequencing by capillary gel electrophoresis and laser-induced fluorescence detection. *Anal. Sci.* 7:1485–89

99. Zhu HP, Clark SM, Benson SC, Rye HS, Glazer AN, Mathies RA. 1994. High-sensitivity capillary electrophoresis of double-stranded DNA fragments using monomeric and dimeric fluorescent intercalating dyes. *Anal. Chem.* 66:1941–48

Annu. Rev. Biophys. Biomol. Struct. 1995. 24:611–41

STRUCTURE-FUNCTION OF THE CHANNEL-FORMING COLICINS[1]

W. A. Cramer, J. B. Heymann, and S. L. Schendel

Department of Biological Sciences, Purdue University, West Lafayette, Indiana 47907

B. N. Deriy and F. S. Cohen

Department of Physiology, Rush Medical College, Chicago, Illinois 60612

P. A. Elkins and C. V. Stauffacher

Department of Biological Sciences, Purdue University, West Lafayette, Indiana 47907

KEY WORDS: cytotoxin, immunity protein, ion channel, membrane binding, membrane protein, molten globule

CONTENTS

[1] Abbreviations: ANS, 1-anilinonaphthalene-8-sulfonate; CD, circular dichroism; $\Delta\Psi$, membrane potential; DLPC, DMPC, DOPC, dilauryl-, dimyristoyl-, dioleoyl-phosphatidylcholine; DOPG, dioleoyl-phosphatidylglycerol; EPR, electron paramagnetic resonance; FTIR, Fourier transform infrared spectroscopy; k, Boltzmann's constant; MIR, multiple isomorphous replacement; P190, 190-residue channel polypeptide; SDS, sodium dodecyl sulfate; TNP-PE, trinitrophenyl-phosphatidylethanolamine; TPP$^+$, tetraphenyl-phosphonium ion; UV, ultraviolet.

1056-8700/95/0610-0611$05.00

ABSTRACT

The channel-forming colicins are plasmid-encoded bacteriocins that kill
E. coli and related cells and whose mode of action is of interest in
related problems of protein import and toxicology. Colicins parasitize
metabolite receptors in the outer membrane and translocate across the
periplasm with the aid of the Tol or Ton protein systems. X-ray structure data for the channel domain and colicin are available. Residues
have been identified that affect the channel ion selectivity and particular
helices implicated in channel structure and in conformational changes
required for binding or insertion of the channel into the membrane.
Unique aspects of the colicin channel system are the involvement of
protein import in the gating process, the existence of multiple open and
closed states, and the existence and action of an immunity protein that
involves specific intramembrane helix-helix interactions with transmembrane helices of the colicin channel-forming domains.

PERSPECTIVES AND OVERVIEW

Rationale

Colicins are a subset of the bacteriocins that have several modes of
lethal action, including inhibition of protein and DNA synthesis and
cellular deenergization. This review focuses on the molecular processes
that are associated with the channel-forming colicins and that are responsible for the deenergization. The molecular details of the interac-

tion of colicins with the cell receptor, cytoplasmic membrane, and artificial membranes are relevant to the mechanism of action of toxins, macromolecule translocation, protein unfolding and import, spontaneous and voltage-dependent protein binding and insertion, and ion-channel structure. This review addresses issues of common interest for toxins and colicins that include the structural changes that they undergo in the transition from the water-soluble to the membrane-bound and inserted state and the mechanism by which they enter the cell. Recent reviews of colicin-channel structure-function are available (57, 73).

Colicins and Toxins: Entry into Membranes and Cells

The toxin-like, channel-forming colicins are plasmid-encoded proteins (classified by the receptor and translocation system in Table 1) that are bactericidal to cells of *Escherichia coli* and related strains such as *Shigella sonnei*. Colicins and bacteriophages can enter cells by parasitizing receptors in the outer membrane whose physiological purpose is usually metabolite (e.g. metal or vitamin) transport. For example, colicin E1 binds to the vitamin B_{12} receptor (BtuB), and colicin B uses ferric enterochelin (FepA). Colicin A of the group A colicins utilizes the combination of receptors used by the E-type colicins and colicin N—BtuB and OmpF, respectively. These colicins have been grouped as A (E1, A, N) or B (Ia, Ib, and B) on the basis of the proteins (Tol or Ton system) used in their translocation and uptake.

Bactericidal Effect

The colicins exert their lethal effect through a one-hit mechanism (47) at ≤ 0.1 nM concentration, implying that a single polypeptide can kill,

Table 1 Classification of the channel-forming colicins by receptor and translocation system[a]

Colicin	Size (residues)	Receptor	Translocation/uptake system
E1	522	BtuB	TolA, TolC, TolQ, TolR
Ia	626	Cir	TonB
Ib	626	Cir	TonB
A	592	BtuB, OmpF	TolA, TolB, TolC, TolQ, TolR
B	511	FepA	TonB, ExbB, ExbD
N	387	OmpF	Tol

[a] From References 4, 5, 20, 29, 69, 79, 102.

although not every molecule does so. Studies on colicin E1 have indicated that the one-hit bactericidal action can be explained on an energetic basis by the ability of a single molecule to form a voltage-dependent ion channel (11, 84) in the cytoplasmic membrane (41). The single-
channel ion conductance of this membrane in vitro (11) and in vivo (SL
Schendel, unpublished data) of 3×10^6 ions/s must be sufficient to
depolarize an *E. coli* cell with a H^+ pump rate of approximately 10^6
H^+/cell-s (42). The metabolic events closely coupled to membrane depolarization constitute inhibition of active transport (17, 28) and rapid
depletion of the intracellular ATP (28), potassium (55, 76, 104), and at
least part of the phosphate (43) pools. This leads to cell death. Assays
of the accumulation of the labeled lipophilic cation $[^3H]TPP^+$ (7) have
shown that the depolarization induced by colicin A is not complete but
decreases from -170 mV to -70 mV at pH 7.8, which is sufficient
to cause a 50-fold decrease in the ratio $(ATP)/(ADP)(P_i)$ and in the
concentration of accumulated potassium. Alternatively, the decrease
in intracellular ATP level might result from the cell's net loss of the
intracellular orthophosphate formed by ATP hydrolysis, rather than
exclusively from ATPase activity coupled to membrane depolarization
(43). Efflux of a significant fraction of the intracellular phosphate would
provide some of the counterions needed to balance the potassium efflux
(41).

The colicin-induced decrease of membrane potential and intracellular
ATP level suggests that the bioenergetic action of these colicins resembles that of traditional uncouplers of oxidative phosphorylation (15).
However, unlike such uncouplers, colicin E1 also causes a substantial
(approximately fourfold) inhibition of cellular respiration. Because it
occurs in the absence, but not the presence, of potassium, this inhibition is presumably also associated with the depletion of potassium
stores (SL Schendel, unpublished data; for colicin A, see Reference
58). As summarized elsewhere (58), respiring bacteria in high potassium
medium should retain the main metabolic functions, which would explain the rescue of colicin-treated cells in high potassium medium (55).
The data on potassium rescue in an F_1F_0 ATPase$^-$ strain, but not in
wild-type strains (16, 55), imply that a decrease in intracellular ATP or
potassium increases the probability of cell death.

Functional Domains

The colicin molecule is organized into functional domains whose
boundaries in the polypeptide chain have been approximately defined

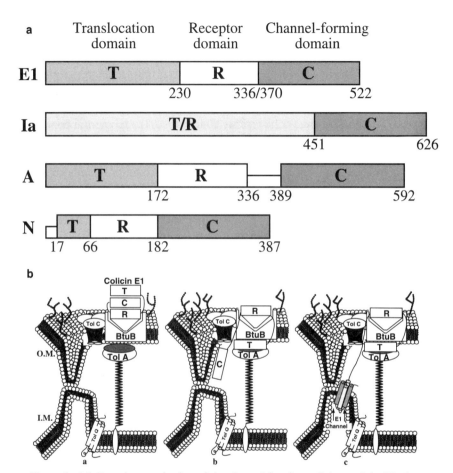

Figure 1 (*A*) Domain organization of the channel-forming colicins: colicin E1, determined by trypsinolysis (17) and cyanogen bromide digestion (10); colicin Ia for which only the boundary for the channel domain has thus far been defined by trypsinolysis (37); colicin A, determined by deletion mutants (2); colicin N, defined by chymotrypsinolysis and thermolysis (25). Shown are the N-terminal translocation domain T, the receptor-binding domain R, and the channel domain C. (*B*) Schematic model for the translocation of colicin E1 across the cell envelope. (*a*) Binding of colicin E1 via its receptor-binding domain (R) to the receptor (BtuB, and perhaps TolC protein) in the outer membrane (OM). (*b*) *Trans*-envelope translocation mediated by the interaction of the N-terminal translocation domain (T) with TolA in the periplasmic space and with TolQ. TolA is anchored to the inner membrane by a putative single *trans*-membrane helix, and TolQ is anchored in the inner membrane (IM) by three *trans*-membrane helices. (*c*) Formation of the four-helix channel (C) in the inner membrane. The presence of adhesion zones between inner and outer membrane is indicated.

for colicins E1, Ia, A, and N (Figure 1A). The N-terminal, central, and C-terminal extended segments of the molecule contain the translocation (T), receptor-binding (R), and channel-forming (C) domains, respectively. It is not known if these domains, particularly the channel domain, function completely independently. The almost identical T and R domain sequences (the N-terminal 426 residues) of colicins Ia and Ib that use the same receptor and translocation system compared to the 60% identity of the ~220-residue C domain (63) support the concept of independent domains. However, there is no similar example of the correlations in the A group of colicins.

The T domain interacts with the intra- and intermembrane macromolecule Tol (colicins E, A, and N) or Ton (colicins Ia, Ib, and B) (Table 1) to accomplish the transport of the channel domain from the outer to inner membrane (Figure 1B). The translocation system, together with the receptor, may also impose an import-competent conformation on the channel polypeptide. A sequence motif—Asp(Glu)-Thr(Ile)-X-Val(X)-Val, called the TonB-box—near the N-terminus of the T domain is shared by the TonB-dependent colicins (Ia, Ib, and B) with a number of receptor proteins, including BtuB, Cir, and FepA (86). This sequence similarity suggests that these colicins may compete with the receptors for interaction with TonB, perhaps to utilize its energy-transducing capability (77) for translocation across the periplasmic space. A functional role of a sequence in a corresponding region of the T domain of colicin A is implied by the translocation defect in a Δ16-29 deletion mutant. This alteration eliminates a region rich in serine and glycine (2) that may confer flexibility to the translocation domain.

The receptor may also be involved in translocation across the outer membrane, as discussed in the case of the OmpF receptor and binding and translocation of colicin N. Studies on the altered colicin sensitivity, X-ray structure, and channel conductance of the OmpF mutant Gly119-Asp, in which the Asp side chain partly occludes the porin channel, indicated that colicin N may traverse the outer membrane through this channel (30, 49).

Figure 2 compares the amino acid sequences of the C domains of the six channel-forming colicins, E1, Ia, Ib, A, B, and N. The six C domains separate into two groups, E1, Ia, Ib and A, B, N, on the basis of sequence identity and the absence and presence, respectively, of a 10-residue segment containing the loop between helices 8 and 9 as defined in the X-ray crystal structure of the C domain of colicin A (Figure 3A).

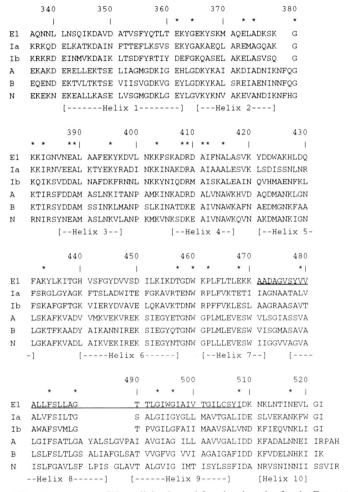

```
            340          350          360          370          380
             |            |           | *  *       |    * *        *
E1   AQNNL LNSQIKDAVD ATVSFYQTLT EKYGEKYSKM AQELADKSK   G
Ia   KRKQD ELKATKDAIN FTTEFLKSVS EKYGAKAEQL AREMAGQAK   G
Ib   KRKRD EINMVKDAIK LTSDFYRTIY DEFGKQASEL AKELASVSQ   G
A    EKAKD ERELLEKTSE LIAGMGDKIG EHLGDKYKAI AKDIADNIKNFQG
B    EQEND EKTVLTKTSE VIISVGDKVG EYLGDKYKAL SREIAENINNFQG
N    EKEKN EKEALLKASE LVSGMGDKLG EYLGVKYKNV AKEVANDIKNFHG
            [-------Helix 1--------] [---Helix 2----]


            390          400          410          420          430
        *  *    **|        *        |   *   **|  ** *      |              |
E1   KKIGNVNEAL AAFEKYKDVL NKKFSKADRD AIFNALASVK YDDWAKHLDQ
Ia   KKIRNVEEAL KTYEKYRADI NKKINAKDRA AIAAALESVK LSDISSNLNR
Ib   KQIKSVDDAL NAFDKFRNNL NKKYNIQDRM AISKALEAIN QVHMAENFKL
A    KTIRSFDDAM ASLNKITANP AMKINKADRD ALVNAWKHVD AQDMANKLGN
B    KTIRSYDDAM SSINKLMANP SLKINATDKE AIVNAWKAFN AEDMGNKFAA
N    RNIRSYNEAM ASLNKVLANP KMKVNKSDKE AIVNAWKQVN AKDMANKIGN
            [--Helix 3--]           [--Helix 4--]    [--Helix 5-


            440          450          460          470          480
        *           |          |      *    *    *      *  |            * |
E1   FAKYLKITGH VSFGYDVVSD ILKIKDTGDW KPLFLTLEKK AADAGVSYVV
Ia   FSRGLGYAGK FTSLADWITE FGKAVRTENW RPLFVKTETI IAGNAATALV
Ib   FSKAFGFTGK VIERYDVAVE LQKAVKTDNW RPFFVKLESL AAGRAASAVT
A    LSKAFKVADV VMKVEKVREK SIEGYETGNW GPLMLEVESW VLSGIASSVA
B    LGKTFKAADY AIKANNIREK SIEGYQTGNW GPLMLEVESW VISGMASAVA
N    LGKAFKVADL AIKVEKIREK SIEGYNTGNW GPLLLEVESW IIGGVVAGVA
         -]        [-----Helix 6------]   [--Helix 7--]    [----


                         490          500          510          520
        *       *        |     *   *     |        *  |          *   |
E1   ALLFSLLAG          T TLGIWGIAIV TGILCSYIDK NKLNTINEVL GI
Ia   ALVFSILTG          S ALGIIGYGLL MAVTGALIDE SLVEKANKFW GI
Ib   AWAFSVMLG          T PVGILGFAII MAAVSALVND KFIEQVNKLI GI
A    LGIFSATLGA YALSLGVPAI AVGIAG ILL AAVVGALIDD KFADALNNEI IRPAH
B    LSLFSLTLGS ALIAFGLSAT VVGFVG VVI AGAIGAFIDD KFVDELNHKI IK
N    ISLFGAVLSF LPIS GLAVT ALGVIG IMT ISYLSSFIDA NRVSNINNII SSVIR
         --Helix 8------]    [------Helix 9-----]    [Helix 10]
```

Figure 2 Aligned sequences of the colicin channel-forming domains for the E-type (E1, Ia, and Ib), and A-type (A, B, and N) colicins. Positions of α-helices in the crystal structure of the colicin A channel-forming domain are indicated (adapted from 75), and the hydrophobic segment of colicin E1 corresponding to helices 8 and 9 is underlined. Numbering is based on the colicin E1 sequence; an asterisk indicates conserved residues.

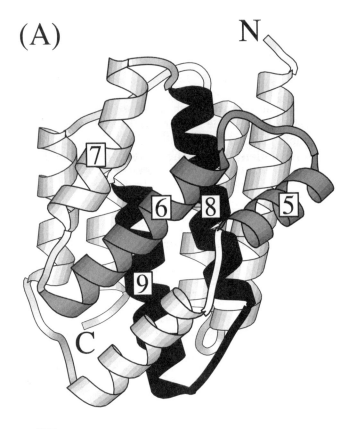

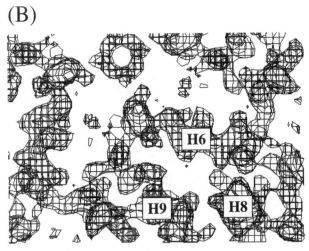

STRUCTURE OF THE SOLUBLE CHANNEL DOMAIN

X-Ray Crystallographic Structural Analysis

Structure analysis of the C-terminal channel domain of colicins A, E1, Ia, and N has been particularly useful in providing information on structure-function relationships. The X-ray crystal structure of a 204-residue C-terminal soluble channel polypeptide of colicin A has been determined at 2.4-Å resolution (74, 75). The overall structure of this channel domain can be described as a bundle of 10 helices, roughly arranged in three layers (Figure 3A). The central helices (helices 8 and 9) of the structure are highly hydrophobic and are surrounded by a ring of eight positively charged residues at one end of the molecule (75).

Crystals of the channel domain of colicin E1 have been grown from the 190-residue polypeptide P190 produced from pSKHY, a plasmid that overexpresses the C-terminal domain of colicin E1 (94). These crystals are tetragonal with space group I4 ($a = b = 87.2$ Å, $c = 59.2$ Å), have one monomer per asymmetric unit, and diffract to 2.2–2.4 Å (23). Similar crystals were grown from proteolytically produced C-terminal fragments that differ from the P190 polypeptide only in five N-terminal residues. Efforts to solve the structure by molecular replacement using the colicin A channel polypeptide coordinates did not produce a unique solution. A strong isomorphous replacement signal could be obtained from a mercury derivative of the single cysteine (Cys505) in the P190 polypeptide, but additional derivatives proved difficult to produce. The combination of data from a tungstate and a platinum derivative, each of which had only a very weak signal, with the mercury data has resulted in a well-phased map at 3.0 Å (Figure 3B), which can be extended to the full 2.4-Å resolution of the native data (PA Elkins, A Bunker, WA Cramer & CV Stauffacher, in preparation).

A preliminary fit to the electron density in this map reveals the basic

---

Figure 3   (A) Ribbon diagram of the 204-residue soluble colicin A C-terminal channel polypeptide solved by Parker et al (75). The preformed hydrophobic and amphipathic helices (helices 8-9 and 5-6, respectively), which may participate in the channel structure for colicin E1 (39, 67, 81, 95), are shaded. (B) 49 × 34 × 12 Å thick section, perpendicular to the c axis, of the electron density in the 3.0-Å MIR map for the P190 colicin E1 polypeptide. The map shown was produced from MIR phases, without solvent flattening or other phase modification. The crystallographic four-fold axis of the I4 space group lies near the upper edge. Portions of three helices—6, 8, and 9—can be clearly seen in the map.

features of the structure of the colicin E1 channel domain. This molecule is composed of 10 helices with the same overall topology as in colicin A, although their arrangement relative to each other has been modified, particularly on the side of the molecule containing helices 1 and 5. This shifting of helical positions is consistent with the 500-MHz ^{1}H NMR data, which established a structural difference between these two colicins (107). The two helical hairpins (8-9 and 5-6), which are predicted to insert into the membrane to form a four-helix channel (16, 109), have orientations in the structure of the soluble channel domain opposite to that predicted in the membrane (Figure 4d), implying a large conformational change. As predicted, the central hydrophobic helices of the E1 structure are shorter by one turn than the corresponding helices in colicin A.

The whole molecule of colicin Ia has been crystallized in the space group C222$_1$ (a = 66.0 Å, b = 176.2 Å, c = 290.2 Å), and the structure was solved to an effective resolution of 4 Å (38). Loop structures were not resolved, and the apparent α-helices could only be modeled using polyalanine chains. The channel domain consists of two subdomains: (a) a C-terminal, 10-helix subdomain with features similar to the corresponding domains of colicins A and E1 and (b) an 8-helix subdomain presumably located just upstream from the 10-helix subdomain. The 8-helix subdomain may modulate the channel activity of the 10-helix subdomain, which would explain the reported electrophysiological differences between the whole molecule and the 18-kDa tryptic fragment, which includes only the 10-helix subdomain (see section on channel formation, below).

In all three structures, the helices corresponding to the proposed hydrophobic hairpin of the membrane channel (Figure 2; helices 8 and 9), as well as two other helices (Figure 2; helices 5 and 6) whose membrane insertion is voltage-dependent, appear to be preformed in the water-soluble form of the molecule. This general pattern of a helical bundle with one or more central hydrophobic helices occurs in several toxins whose activity depends on insertion or translocation across a membrane (73).

Channel Size

The size of the lumen space of the colicin E1 ion channel was estimated using the relative permeability to large organic cations and anions (11, 12, 82). It was concluded that lumen diameter is at least 8-9 Å (12, 89). However, a substantially smaller diameter can be inferred from the following data: (a) The passage of all ions larger than Na$^+$, K$^+$, and Cl$^-$ was impeded. (b) Many of the organic ions in these studies are asymmetric and elongate, and rather than flow through the channel they may thread through. If the minimum diameters of these ions were used for lumen-size calculations, the estimated channel diameter would be substantially smaller, i.e. approximately 4–5 Å using the data of Bullock et al (12). This diameter is accommodated by a channel structure consisting of the four helices discussed in the section on voltage-dependent insertion of the colicin channel.

Mutagenesis Experiments on the Channel Domain with Implications for Structure

Mutagenesis of colicin E1 to produce Thr501Glu and Gly502Glu in helix 9 (89), and Lys510Met and Lys512Tyr in the interhelix (helices 9 and 10) loop, showed that these residues affect the ion selectivity of the channel, which is anion- and cation-selective at low and neutral pH, respectively (89). These two lysines, as well as Lys469 and Lys470 between helices 7 and 8, provide an ideal environment [according to the *cis*-positive rule (99)] for spontaneous insertion into the membrane bilayer of helices 8 and 9 as a hydrophobic hairpin (Figures 3A, 4). Saturation mutagenesis of helices 8 and 9, in which 29 mutations were made at 26 different sites, also indicated that these helices are inserted into the membrane bilayer (95).

The disulfide-bond engineering of the colicin A channel, based on the X-ray structure (75), provides important information on the conformational changes associated with binding and unfolding of the channel at the membrane surface (22). Mutants were constructed with disulfide cross-links between helices 1 and 9, 5 and 6, 7 and 8, and 9 and 10 (Figure 3A). All mutants were not cytotoxic in the cross-linked state, but activity could be restored by the reduction of the disulfide bonds. An assay for binding or insertion in which intrinsic tryptophan fluorescence of the channel polypeptide was quenched by brominated oleoyl fatty acid chains in the DOPG lipid revealed that binding insertion was inhibited only for the helix 1-9 cross-linked mutant. This finding implied either that unfolding of helices 7 and 10 from the central hydrophobic hairpin in the globular state is not required for insertion (22) or that it is not required for binding. A question about whether bromine quenching assays only surface binding (39) arises because the bromine at the 9-10 position of the fatty acid is within 4–10 Å of the interfacial polar head-group region of the membrane (106) where surface-bound helices are located. The uncertainty in position ensues from motion of the lipids along the normal to the membrane plane (103). These experiments imply that unfolding or conformational change of the 1-2 hairpin relative to the 8-9 hairpin is required for binding or insertion.

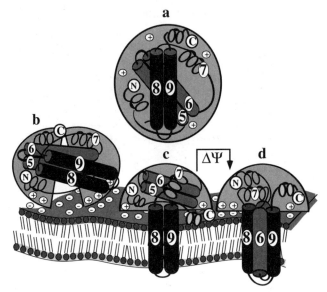

Figure 4 Some intermediate states in the binding and insertion of the 175- to 200-residue colicin channel polypeptide. (*a*) The soluble state. (*b*) Partial unfolding in solution or by the Tol system (not shown) and initial electrostatic binding to the membrane surface. (*c*) Channel unfolding at the membrane surface; the hydrophobic hairpin (helices 8 and 9) spontaneously inserts into the bilayer. (*d*) Membrane potential, $\Delta\Psi$, causes insertion of amphiphilic hairpin (helices 5-6).

APPROACH OF CHANNEL DOMAIN TO THE MEMBRANE

Some major questions about the nature of the interactions of the colicin channel with the cytoplasmic membrane concern the nature of (*a*) intermediate states in the transition between the soluble and membrane-bound states, (*b*) the driving force at the membrane surface for the transition from the soluble to a membrane-bound state, (*c*) the structure of the membrane-bound nonconductive closed-channel state(s) that can accomplish the transition to an integral open conductive channel, and (*d*) the coupling between membrane potential and the membrane-bound polypeptide that causes the closed-to-open transition through a voltage-driven insertion of at least one amphiphilic hairpin segment.

The transition from the water-soluble to a membrane-inserted state involves large structural changes in toxins such as diphtheria (62) and *Pseudomonas* exotoxin A (50); in toxin-like molecules such as the channel-forming colicins (14, 73); and in the human complement glycoprotein, C9 (61). The nature of the structural intermediates involved in these changes is of interest in the context of protein folding and protein insertion into membranes. Protein unfolding–associated structural changes that are relevant to the insertion process are induced by (a) the bulk-phase acidic pH required for activity of toxins such as diphtheria (62) and the channel-forming colicins (18, 66) or (b) the more acidic environment near the negatively charged membrane surface (68, 98). Diphtheria toxin and the colicin E1 channel domain share some common features in response to acidic bulk phase pH: (a) unmasking of the buried hydrophobic domain, as inferred from their partition from water into a nonionic detergent phase, and (b) increased accessibility to probes such as proteases and, for the colicin E1 channel, acrylamide (66).

It has been proposed that the acidic active state of diphtheria toxin can be characterized by a partial (111) or massive (80) unfolding of the protein. In the partially unfolded state, it was reported that tertiary but not secondary structure is disrupted, which corresponds to the behavior of proteins in the molten-globule conformation (62). The loss of tertiary structure of the colicin A channel polypeptide at pH values <2.5, which was indicated by loss of the near-UV CD spectrum, implied that a molten globule of the colicin A channel polypeptide might represent an intermediate in its insertion into 100% anionic (DOPG) membranes (68, 98). The molten-globule state in protein folding is characterized by (a) conservation of the native secondary structure, (b) loss of tertiary structure or poorly defined tertiary-structure contacts, (c) a volume approximately unchanged from that of the native protein, and (d) an increased accessibility of the hydrophobic core to hydrophobic dyes such as ANS (46, 78). The protease- and acrylamide-accessible low pH (pH 3.5) translocation-competent colicin E1 channel domain was described as an unfolded or dynamic conformation (66). The channel polypeptide at pH 3.5 has an effective hydrodynamic radius that is approximately unchanged from the value at neutral pH and an increased hydrophobic character (66). The above properties of the colicin E1 channel have also been described as belonging to a molten-globule state (78).

The requirement of a partly unfolded state for activity has been shown by the coincidence of (a) the onset of channel activity and (b) the decrease in amplitude of the near-UV CD spectrum as a function of pH (85). Tertiary constraints on the three tryptophans of the colicin E1 channel polypeptide are retained down to pH 2. In addition, the tryptophan fluorescence emission spectrum is virtually unchanged over the pH range 2–6. The temperature independence up to 70°C of the near-UV spectrum at pH 3 and 6 implied that the colicin E1 channel polypeptide is more stable than that of colicin A (68), which may explain the total loss of the near-UV CD spectrum of the colicin A channel polypeptide at pH 2 (98). For colicin E1, the unfolded state associated with the presence of activity at acidic pH has the properties of a compact unfolded state, with some, but not all, of the properties of a molten globule.

Local lower pH at the membrane surface probably does not significantly facilitate formation of an unfolded intermediate, given the small effect on local membrane acidity of a physiological acidic membrane lipid content ($\sim$30% for wild-type *E. coli*), the retention of significant near-UV CD amplitude down to pH 2, and the small extent of immersion of a 40-Å globular colicin channel polypeptide in the 10-Å Debye layer of lower pH at the membrane surface (85).

The unfolded active state in vitro can also be created at neutral pH by adding low concentrations ($\sim 10^{-3}$%) of SDS or β-D-octylglucoside (0.44%) (66). Studies of the effect of the latter detergent indicate that it causes some unwrapping of the channel polypeptide near its N-terminus (97). One might infer from these studies that one of the roles of the in vivo intra- and intermembrane Tol and Ton macromolecular systems that translocate the colicin from the receptor in the outer membrane to the cytoplasmic membrane (Figure 1*b*) is to impose a similar unfolded state on the C-terminal channel domain of the colicin.

CHANNEL-DOMAIN BINDING TO THE MEMBRANE

Topography of the Channel Bound to the Membrane Surface

Studies of the surface topography of C-terminal colicin-channel polypeptides bound to liposomes have used the accessibility of the polypeptide to proteases to determine whether the channel structure contains *trans*-membrane segments in addition to the four α-helices previously identified and to discriminate between different topographical possibilities for the surface-bound state. The greatly increased trypsin susceptibility of the bound polypeptide relative to that in aqueous solution indicated the presence of an unfolded surface-bound state (109). The N-terminal 50 residues of the 190-residue colicin E1 membrane-bound peptide are unbound or loosely bound, as indicated by their relative accessibility to proteases, in contrast to the C-terminal 105 residues, which were protease inaccessible. The protease accessibility of the N-terminal segment Ala336–Lys382 would exclude any model for the structure of the closed channel state that includes *trans*-membrane helices on the N-terminal side of Lys382, although this does not preclude a role for such segments in modulation of channel activity (38). An unfolding of the channel domain peptide associated with binding to the membrane surface (Figure 4*b*,*c*) could be detected by the increase in sensitivity to trypsinolysis of the Lys381–Lys382 site relative to the sensitivity of this site in the soluble channel (109). The C-terminal hydrophobic region of colicin Ia bound to membranes at low (1:1500) protein:lipid ratios was also inaccessible to protease (65), but colicin A bound at a high (1:100) ratio was not (64). Figure 4*c* shows a model for the topography of an unfolded monomeric surface-bound intermediate of the colicin channel domain with surface-bound helices. This scheme includes a *trans*-membrane hydrophobic helical hairpin and insertion of the amphiphilic hairpin as a result of the membrane potential (Figure 4*d*).

Optimum Binding Affinity of the Channel Domain

Thermodynamic parameters describing equilibrium binding of the colicin E1 channel polypeptide (P190) to membranes were obtained using resonance energy transfer of fluorescence from the three intrinsic tryptophans to the quencher, TNP, bound to the head group of DOPE and incorporated into DOPG/DOPC vesicles (108). A major role for electrostatic interactions in the initial binding of the fragment to the membranes was inferred from the dependence of the binding parameters on ionic strength, net positive charge of the P190, and negative membrane surface charge. The inability to reverse the binding of P190 to the vesicles by increasing the pH or ionic strength indicated the presence of a significant hydrophobic binding process that follows the initial electrostatic binding. The electrostatic interaction may also have a role in concentrating the channel polypeptide, which is basic at low pH, at the anionic membrane surface (WL Hubbell, personal communication). EPR spin-label studies of the time course of binding and insertion of the colicin E1 at pH 2.7 into neutral DLPC membranes indicated a significant contribution of the hydrophobic component to the energetics of binding (88).

The binding to DOPG/DOPC membranes was characterized by a nanomolar dissociation constant (K_d), which decreased monotonically with increasing anionic lipid content. Maximal activity values occurred over a range of 30–50% in acidic lipid that corresponds to K_d values in the range of 1–5 nM. These data lead to the novel hypothesis that colicin activity requires an optimum acidic lipid content, close to the physiological level (~30%) found in *E. coli* membranes (108).

The inference that the colicin A hydrophobic hairpin does not insert into the bilayer in 100% DOPG membranes (35, 48, 56, 64) may provide an explanation for the acidic lipid optimum of 30–50%: When the electrostatic interactions are too strong, the hydrophobic hairpin would not be able to insert into the bilayer because the density of charged residues on the membrane surface is too high, and/or the protein rearrangement on the membrane surface associated with the insertion process cannot occur. A somewhat similar phenomenon has been demonstrated for the activity of somatostatin as a function of the strength of membrane binding (87). In addition, the acidic lipid optimum provides a reason for the disagreement concerning whether the hydrophobic hairpin does or does not insert into the hydrophobic bilayer in the absence of a membrane potential: The hydrophobic hairpin does not insert into membranes made of 100% DOPG lipid (35, 48, 56) but does insert as might be expected (26) into membranes containing the more physiological level of approximately 20–30% acidic lipid (65, 67, 81, 109).

Insertion of the hydrophobic hairpin is supported by polarized FTIR analysis of the channel polypeptide in oriented membranes that showed an average helix orientation with a significant component normal to the plane of the membrane. This dichroism and an even larger positive one for the colicin A channel polypeptide (40) indicate that at least one hydrophobic hairpin spans the bilayer. The FTIR spectra showed hydrogen-deuterium exchange in the incorporated channel peptide that occurred on a much faster time scale (5–10 min) than that measured (24–48 h) for the intrinsic membrane proteins rhodopsin and bacteriorhodopsin (81). This rapid exchange is consistent with the existence of a multistate dynamic structure (see following section).

CHANNEL FORMATION

Voltage-Dependent Insertion of the Colicin Channel: Channel Gating Involves Protein Translocation

A *trans*-negative membrane potential drives the insertion of an amphiphilic hairpin (Lys420–Lys461) that corresponds to the preformed helical hairpin helices 5-6 in the soluble colicin A channel polypeptide (Figure 2) and is associated with the opening of the channel (67). This translocation was detected through a membrane potential–dependent increase in channel labeling by two different lipophilic radiolabeled photoaffinity probes and by a decrease in tyrosine labeling from the external aqueous solution. The labeling changes were large ($\sim 50\%$) and dependent on membrane potential, implying that the opening-closing of the channel is driven by a reversible insertion-extrusion of the amphiphilic segment (67). No significant labeling changes were detected in other regions of the channel polypeptide (67). However, such alterations may still occur because the -100-mV diffusion potential imposed on the liposomes is not clamped and may decay during the import process. These data provide evidence for a role of protein import in the process of channel gating, previously considered in the electrophysiological experiments of Raymond et al (83) and Slatin et al (93), and the existence of a channel consisting of at least four *trans*-membrane helices (Figure 4*d*). A model of this four-helix colicin E1 ion channel has the helices I (Lys420–Lys436), II (Ser442–Lys461), III (Lys470 –Ala488), and IV (Ile494–Lys510), which contain 18 charged residues, 9 lysines, and 9 aspartates, each the smaller of the basic and acidic charged residues (16). In addition, the aromatic residues are clustered at the ends of the helices, as often found in membrane proteins (19).

Using site-directed mutations to cysteine in this region of the channel domain, cysteines labeled with covalently bound biotin derivatives with spacers, and trapping of the biotin tag with streptavidin on the *trans*-side of the membrane, Slatin et al (92) found that channel gating of colicin Ia is associated with membrane insertion of at least 31 residues, Lys511–Tyr541 (corresponding to Ala407–Ile437 of colicin E1; Figure 2) of the C domain. This region is believed to be translocated across the membrane (92), and this finding implies that $\geq 31 + 2(20) \approx 70$ residues are inserted into the membrane as a result of the potential. Alternatively, different segments of the 31-residue peptide are translocated with different *trans*-membrane helices at different times, consistent with a view of multiple channel states (see section on multiple states and dynamics, below).

Role of a Charged Histidine in the Voltage-Sensitive Helical Hairpin

A histidine (His$^+$), e.g. His440 in the colicin E1 voltage-sensitive segment, with a diameter of 4 Å would have to overcome a Born charging barrier (71) on the order of 30 kT to cross a bilayer with a dielectric constant of 2 (71). Several site-directed mutations producing charge-altered variants at or around His440, including His440Cys, His440Cys + Val441His, and His440Glu, were used to search for a gating charge by measuring the voltage dependence of deactivating tail currents (the decay of current measured with a *trans*-positive voltage)

(1, 72). The voltage dependence of the currents of each mutant, measured at low pH in the presence of a deactivating voltage, was similar to that of the wild-type, suggesting that the His440 is translocated after deprotonation. Deprotonating His$^+$ at the membrane interface at pH 3.5 requires an energy of 5.8 kT, which is significantly less than the 30 kT required to surmount the Born barrier (LI Krishtalik, personal communication) and perhaps explains the unaltered voltage dependence of the mutants.

Multiple States and Dynamics of Open Colicin Channels

Colicin E1 exhibits multiple membrane states at the single-channel level. For the whole colicin, 10-pS channels are initially observed in 1 M KCl (Figures 5A,B). Subsequently, 20-, 40-, and 60-pS channels appear with increased activation, and even larger channels can occur. For P190, the first channels appear between 7 and 13 pS (Figures 5C, D). Thereafter, 30- and 60-pS channels occur. The 60-pS channels have

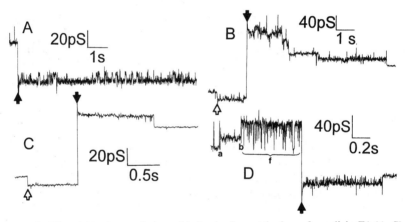

Figure 5 Time dependence of channel behavior by patch clamp for colicin E1 (*A, B*) and the C-terminal P190 channel domain (*C, D*). (*A*) A 10-pS channel repetitively opened (downward direction) and closed after a voltage switch from +60 to −60 mV (*up arrow*). (*B*) In the same experiment, 20-pS channels were subsequently opened (*open arrow*) at −60 mV (last opening shown), and a +60 mV potential (*down arrow*) caused sequential closing. (*C*) With −60 mV, the first P190 channel opened with a conductance of 10 pS (*up arrow*). A switch to +60 mV (*down arrow*) caused it to close about 1.2 s later. (*D*) Subsequently, with +50 mV, a channel recovered from inactivation to a subconductance level of 20 pS (a) before opening to its full 60-pS conductance (b). Thereafter, the channel closed and opened to the full 60-pS level. Flickering (f) and subconductance levels are typical for larger conductances. Switching to −50 mV (*up arrow*) caused inactivation to a subconductance level of 20 pS before the channel became fully inactivated (20).

20- to 30-pS substates. All colicin channels can exhibit very fast (>2 kHz) flickering (f in Figure 5D). However, for large channels, the flickering is much more pronounced. Flickering is more common for the P190 than for the parental colicin. For both colicin and P190 channels, the conductances of the larger open channels are multiples of those seen earlier, which suggests oligomerization. Thus, the receptor-binding and translocation domains alter gating properties, as indicated by flickering. In addition, although it was found to be qualitatively similar for colicin E1 and a channel polypeptide (11, 13), there are quantitative differences in substate conductances (Figures 5A,B vs C,D) and ion selectivity (82).

The multiple open states seen at the single channel level are manifested in the kinetics of tail-current decay. The decay rates of tail currents with increased time of activation and increased activation voltage decrease for colicin but not for P190, presumably because channels must pass through more states to close after increased activation. The tail currents are multi-exponential, in contrast to those described in a previous report, which also indicates several open states. Moreover, analysis of the change in tail currents shows several inactivated states. Multiple closed states have also been identified (1). Thus, colicin has many closed, open, and inactivated states (72); the concept of a single membrane-inserted conformation is clearly incorrect and even a model with a few membrane-inserted forms may be an oversimplification.

The tail currents for the whole molecule and for the channel-forming domain polypeptide, P190, are different. P190 exhibits fewer inactivated states, and the rate of decay of tail currents does not decrease with increased activation time and voltage (72). The properties of tail currents of a 292-residue polypeptide containing both channel-forming and receptor-binding domains (Figure 1A) were intermediate between those of the P190 and the whole molecule. Thus, while translocation and receptor-binding domains are not required for channel activity, they alter the gating properties.

In contrast to P190 and whole colicin E1, whose channel properties are qualitatively similar, colicin Ia and its 18-kDa channel-forming polypeptide have been reported to differ profoundly (37). Single-channel conductances of the polypeptide were an order of magnitude larger than those of the colicin. The 18-kDa polypeptide opened with both trans-(−) and trans-(+) potentials, in contrast to the colicin, which opened only with trans-(−). Some of these differences could be explained by the observation that channel behavior varies with time and history of voltage application (e.g. colicin E1, Figure 5). Differences in the channel behavior of C-terminal polypeptides could also be ascribed to the influence in the whole molecule of the 8-helix subdomain proximal to the 10-helix subdomain on gating properties (vide supra, X-ray crystallographic analysis) (38).

THE TOL AND TON IN VIVO TRANSLOCATION SYSTEMS

The translocation of group A colicins across the cell envelope is aided by the Tol proteins (Table 1, Figure 1*B*), which are required for macromolecular import, specifically of certain colicins and the DNA of filamentous bacteriophages. Group B colicins (Ia, Ib, B) require the presence of the TonB proteins, TonB, ExbB, and ExbD, for translocation. TolA is a 421-residue protein that is indispensable to translocation of the A group colicins. It is anchored in the inner membrane by a hydrophobic stretch of 21 amino acids and is proposed to span the periplasmic space via a unique extended sequence, Lys_{1-2}-Ala_{3-4}-(Glu/Asp), indicative of a long, 330-residue, uninterrupted α-helix (59). This extended region presumably places the C-terminal domain against the outer membrane, where it appears to interact with a component(s) in the periplasm or the inner surface of the outer membrane to maintain outer membrane integrity (60), which suggests that the C-terminal domain of TolA serves as a receiver for the translocation domain of an entering colicin molecule after it crosses the outer membrane.

Several analogies can be drawn between the TonB and TolA systems (Table 1). The TonB proteins, ExbB and ExbD, are highly homologous to TolQ and TolR, respectively. Both ExbB and ExbD are predicted to have the same membrane topology as TolQ and TolR (51–53). In the TonB system, the stability of TonB depends on the presence of intact ExbB and, to a lesser extent, ExbD. In the absence of these two proteins, TonB is rapidly degraded (29), which suggests that ExbB and ExbD perhaps serve as a buttress for TonB anchored in the inner membrane. ExbB has also been shown to possess a chaperonin-like function in that it may stabilize the cytoplasmic TonB in an extended conformation prior to its insertion into the inner membrane (54). Given the sequence similarity between TolQ and ExbB, and TolR and ExbD, it is not unlikely that TolQ and TolR serve a similar function for TolA. Indeed, TolQ can partially restore iron-uptake activity to cells that have no functional ExbB (8).

Another similarity between the TonB and TolA systems is the extended nature of TolA and TonB. TonB interacts with outer membrane receptors such as FhuA and BtuB via the receptor's TonB box (9). TonB is able to reach the outer membrane by virtue of a rigid, extended region that contains multiple X-Pro dipeptide repeats (45). With the exception of their hydrophobic membrane-anchoring domains, TolA and TonB share little sequence homology, but both proteins are predicted to have an extended nature that enables them to span the periplasmic space. It remains to be seen if the extended regions of these two proteins are vital to the uptake of large molecules, or whether they serve as merely a scaffold that properly positions the regions of the protein that interact with outer membrane proteins.

IMMUNITY PROTEINS

Unique Aspect of Colicin Toxin-Like Action: the Immunity Protein

The ability of a single channel–forming colicin to kill a cell (14) is rivaled only by the efficiency of the immunity protein encoded by the same plasmid. This protein can protect a cell against concentrations of the colicin 10^4–10^7 times higher than that required to kill nonimmune cells. This protective mechanism is a unique aspect of the interaction of colicins with cell membranes, compared with other toxins and toxin-like molecules. The activity of the immunity proteins of the channel-forming colicins is poorly understood. The high specificity of each immunity protein for its colicin is reflected in the limited sequence homology between them (Figure 6).

The immunity proteins are constitutively expressed from the natural plasmids at such low levels (10^2 to 10^3 molecules per cell) (96, 110) that they are probably targeted towards the entry sites of the colicin to provide effective protection. The immunity proteins of the channel-forming colicins have been localized to the E. coli cytoplasmic membrane by the ability of inner membrane vesicles from an imm^+ strain to inhibit colicin Ia activity (100), detergent extraction of ImmE1 (6, 90), immunological detection of ImmA modified with a foreign epitope (32), and topology analysis of ImmA and E1 fusion proteins (96).

Topology of Imm

The inner membrane topology of ImmA was determined using PhoA fusions and proteolysis of an N-terminal epitope tag (Figure 7A), and that of ImmE1 from the position of PhoA and complementary LacZ fusions (Figure 7B). ImmA has four trans-membrane α-helices, approximately spanning segments Ala14–Tyr37, Val69–Phe89, Ser-106–Phe123, and Ala143–Phe165, with both the N- and C-termini located in the cytoplasm (32, 33). The shorter ImmE1 has three trans-membrane α-helices, with approximate spans of Tyr5–Ser28,

(A)

```
                    10         20         30         40         50
Imm A    MMNEHSIDTD NRKANNALYL FIIIGLIPLL CIFVVYYKTP DALLLRKIAT
Imm B    MT---SNKDK NKKANEILYA FSIIGIIPLM AILILRINDP YSQVLYYLYN
Imm N    MHNT------ ---------- ---------- ---------- ----LLEKII

                    60         70         80         90        100
Imm A    STENLPSITS SYNPLMTKVM DIYCKTAPFL ALILYILTFK IRKLINNTDR
Imm B    KVAFLPSITS LHDPVMTTLM SNYNKTAPVM GILVFLCTYK TREIIKPVTR
Imm N    AYLSLPGFHS LNNPPLSEAF NLYVHTAPLA ATSLFIFTHK ELELKPKSSP

                   110        120        130        140
Imm A    NTVLRSCLLS PLVYAAIVYL FCFRNFELTT AGRPVRLMAT
Imm B    KLVVQSCFWG PVFYAILIYI TLFYNLELTT AGGFFKLLSH
Imm N    LRALKILTPF TILYISMIYC FLLTDTELTL SSKTFVLIVK

                   150        160        170
Imm A    ND-ATLLLFYI GLYSIIFFTT YITLFTPVTA FKLLKKRQ
Imm B    NV-ITLFILYC SIYFTVLTMT YAILLMPLLV IKYFKGRQ
Imm N    KRSVFVFFLYN TIYWDIYIHI F-VLLVPYRN I-------
```

(B)

```
                             10         20         30
Imm E1    M----SLRYYIKNI LFGLYCTLIY IYLITKNSEG
Imm E1*   M----SLRYYIKNI LFGLYCALIY IYLITKNNEG
Imm Ia    MN----RKYYFNNM WWGWVTGGYM LYMSWDYEFK
Imm Ib    MKLDISVKYLLKSL IPILIILTVF YLGWKDNQEN

                    40         50         60         70
Imm E1    YYFLVSDKML YAI---VISTILC PYSKYAIEYI AFNFIKKDFF
Imm E1*   YYFLASDKML YAI---VISTILC PYSKYAIEHI FFKFIKKDFF
Imm Ia    Y------RLL FWCI-SLCGMVLY PVAKWYIEDT ALKFTRPDFW
Imm Ib    A------RMF YAFIGCIISAITF PFSMRIIQKM VIRFTGKEFW

                    80         90        100        110
Imm E1    ERRKNLNNAP VAKLNLFM-LY NLLCLVLAIP FGLLGL-FISI KNN---
Imm E1*   RKRKNLNKCP RGKIKPYLCVY NLLCLVLAIP FGLLGL-VYIN KE----
Imm Ia    NSGFFAD-TP -GKM-GLLAVY TGTVFILSLP LSMIYILSVII KRLSVR
Imm Ib    QKDFFTN--P VGG--SLTAIF ELFCFVISVP VVAIYLIFILC KALSGK
```

Figure 6 Alignment of the immunity proteins for the A-type (A) and E-type colicins (B). ImmE1* is the ImmE1 homologue from *S. sonnei*. Numbering is based on the ImmA (A) and ImmE1 (B) sequences. The putative *trans*-membrane α-helices are underlined.

Figure 7 Topographical models of (A) ImmA (from 33) and (B) ImmE1 (modified from 96), showing the *trans*-membrane helices (H1, H2, H3, and H4), the loops (L1, L2, and L3), and the termini (T1 and T2). Fusion sites are indicated by bold outlines. Mutant residues are boxed. Loss of immunity activity in ImmA is caused by Leu20Arg + Phe21Ser, Arg92Asp, Arg46Asp + Arg92Asp, Val135Pro + Arg136Asp + Leu137Asp + Met138Asp, Arg136Asp, and Ile155Arg; and in ImmE1 by Ile19Lys + Ile21Lys, Ile121Lys + Met39Lys, Met39Lys + Ile45Lys, and Leu95Asp + Val96Arg).

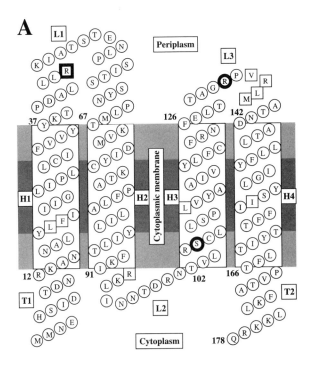

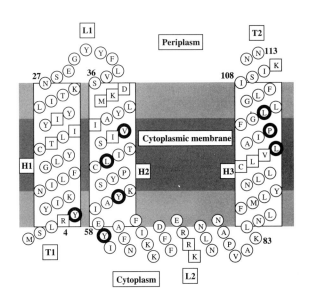

Ser36–Glu58, and Leu84–Ile108. Here, the N- and C-termini are on the cytoplasmic and periplasmic sides of the membrane, respectively (96). The orientation of both immunity proteins is consistent with the inside-positive rule, which describes the topological charge bias of cytoplasmic membrane proteins (99).

The periplasmic loops of ImmA (L1 and L3) are larger than the one periplasmic loop of ImmE1 (L1), while the ImmE1 cytoplasmic loop, L2, is larger and more highly charged (Figure 7). L2 of ImmE1 contains a highly charged segment, Lys66–Lys74—seven charges in a nine-residue segment. Its amphipathic character suggests that it is an α-helix associated with the interfacial region (106) of the cytoplasmic membrane surface.

Specific Intramembrane Helix-Helix Interactions

The specificity in the colicins with respect to immunity has been localized to the C-terminal channel-forming domains by using hybrid colicins (4, 36), truncated colicin E1 (6), and colicin immunity bypass mutants (110). A hybrid consisting of the translocation and receptor domains of colicin Ia and the channel-forming domain of colicin E1 could use the TonB translocation system to kill cells, but was less effective against cells producing ImmE1 (110). Thus, immunity does not seem to be associated with the Tol translocation system, although a close proximity of the Tol and Ton systems in a complex might negate this conclusion. The use of colicin A and B hybrids further narrowed the immunity specificity down to the helix 8-9 hairpin (Figures 4c,d).

ImmA and ImmB are homologous (38% identity, Figure 6A) (33), and ImmA confers partial immunity to colicin B (27). Parts of these proteins were exchanged to determine the particular segments involved generally and specifically in immunity to each colicin (27). Only the first 30 residues, and part of the first periplasmic loop (Tyr37–Ser60) of ImmA could be replaced by the corresponding sequences of ImmB without loss of activity. Exchange of either the cytoplasmic loop or the second periplasmic loop, and efforts to make hybrids with *trans*-membrane helices from both immunity proteins, yielded products in which activity was absent or very small.

Of 65 colicin E1 site-directed mutants in the hydrophobic and amphipathic hairpins of the C domain, 6 could bypass the protective effect of ImmE1 (110). These comprise five different loci (His440, Phe443, Gly444, Ala474, and Ser477) on two proposed membrane-spanning helices of the open colicin channel, one hydrophobic (Ala471–Ala488) and one amphiphilic (Val441–Trp460) (Figure 8). These mutations correspond to loci in the 7-8 interhelix loop and helix 6, respectively, of

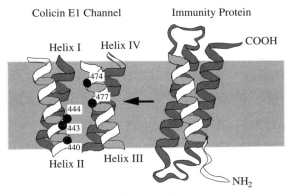

Figure 8 Model for the mechanism of action of immunity protein with the colicin E1 channel showing specific helix-helix interactions of the hydrophobic helices of Imm protein with two of the membrane-spanning helices (Figure 4) of the colicin channel domain (110).

colicin A. Two mutants, Ser477Arg and Ser477Lys, showed activity on immune and nonimmune cells at concentrations that differed by less than 10-fold, indicating almost complete bypass of the function of ImmE1. In contrast, wild-type colicin could not bypass ImmE1 function at concentrations 30,000 times higher than that required to kill nonimmune cells. It is proposed that the immunity protein exerts its specific effect in the cytoplasmic membrane through helix-helix recognition and interaction with at least one integral hydrophobic and one amphipathic helix of the colicin E1 channel (Figure 8). This model can be reconciled with the low expression if the immunity proteins are associated with supermolecular complexes comprised of the receptors and translocation proteins of various systems spanning the cell envelope (i.e. the periplasmic space and the two membranes), structures reminiscent of adhesion zones (3, 44).

Role of the Translocation Complex

ImmE1 and BtuB are expressed to the same levels ($\sim 10^3$/cell) from their natural promoters in JC411(pColE1) (JB Heymann, unpublished data), although in other cell strains, BtuB is only expressed to approximately 200 copies per cell (105). Approximately 400–800 TolA molecules/cell have been reported in logarithmic phase cells (59). The similar levels of expression of these proteins suggest a stoichiometric complex bridging the outer and inner membrane at the colicin entry sites to which the immunity protein may be targeted.

Various receptors and the Tol proteins, TolA, TolB, TolQ, and TolR, have been proposed to form macromolecular complexes in the cyto-plasmic membrane (101), which would be the most likely structure to which ImmE1 is targeted. In an overproduced version of this complex, TolA is present in the smallest amounts, perhaps only one polypeptide per complex, while TolQ contributes the greatest number of molecules [approximately 5–10 per TolA (44)].

TolQ and its homologue from the TonB system, ExbB, exhibit a motif [Leu-Val(Phe)-Ala(X)-Ala-Ile-Pro] in the third *trans*-membrane helix that is reproduced in ImmE1 and in the *E. coli* F_1F_0 ATPase subunit *c*. ExbB and TolQ are integral membrane proteins, with three putative *trans*-membrane helices (although the topology is the reverse of ImmE1). In all cases, the variable residues (Xs) are hydrophobic, except for the Asp in subunit *c*. The occurrence of the motif in subunit *c* may point to a common structural feature associated with helix-helix interactions in the membrane, because subunit *c* forms oligomeric intra-membrane complexes (31). Perhaps ImmE1 binds to TolQ, locating it at the site of colicin entry.

An understanding of the mechanism of action of the immunity pro-teins of the channel-forming colicins will most likely involve elucidation of the processes of intramembrane protein-protein recognition as well as of the colicin translocation systems.

ACKNOWLEDGMENTS

The studies of the authors described in this review were supported by NIH grants GM-18457 (WAC), GM-44001 (CVS), and GM-47828 (FSC). The authors thank LI Krishtalik for helpful discussions, and A Fin-kelstein, V Geli, K Jakes, C Lazdunski, AR Merrill, JM Pages, F Pat-tus, and S Slatin for communicating results of their studies prior to publication.

Literature Cited

1. Abrams CK, Jakes KS, Finkelstein A, Slatin SL. 1991. Identification of a translocated gating charge in a volt-age-dependent channel. Colicin E1 channels in planar phospholipid bi-layer membranes. *J. Gen. Physiol.* 98:77–93
2. Baty D, Frenette M, Lloubès R, Geli V, Howard SP, et al. 1988. Func-tional domains of colicin A. *Mol. Mi-crobiol.* 2:807–11
3. Bayer ME. 1968. Areas of adhesion between wall and membrane of *E. coli. J. Gen. Microbiol.* 53:395–404
4. Benedetti H, Frenette M, Baty D, Knibiehler M, Pattus F, Lazdunski C. 1991. Individual domains confer specificity in colicin uptake, in pore-

properties and in immunity require-ment. *J. Mol. Biol.* 217: 429–39

5. Benedetti H, Lazdunski C, Lloubès R. 1991. Protein import into *Escherichia coli:* colicins A and E1 interact with a component of their transloca-tion system. *EMBO J.* 10:1989–95

6. Bishop LJ, Bjes ES, Davidson VL, Cramer WA. 1985. Localization of the immunity protein-reactive do-main in unmodified and chemically modified COOH-terminal peptides of colicin E1. *J. Bacteriol.* 164:237–44

7. Bourdineaud JP, Boulanger P, Laz-dunski C, Letellier L. 1990. In vivo properties of colicin A: channel activ-ity is voltage dependent but translo-cation may be voltage independent. *Proc. Natl. Acad. Sci. USA* 87: 1037–41

8. Braun V, Hermann C. 1993. Evolu-tionary relationship of uptake sys-tems for biopolymers in *Escherichia coli* cross-complementation between the TonB-ExbB-ExbD and TolA-TolQ-TolR proteins. *Mol. Microbiol.* 8:261–68

9. Brewer S, Tolley M, Trayer IP, Barr GC, Dorman CJ, et al. 1990. Struc-ture and function of X-Pro dipeptide repeats in the TonB proteins of *Salmonella typhimurium* and *Escherichia coli*. *J. Mol. Biol.* 216:883–95

10. Brunden KR, Cramer WA, Cohen FS. 1984. Purification of a small re-ceptor-binding peptide from the cen-tral region of the colicin E1 molecule. *J. Biol. Chem.* 259:190–96

11. Bullock JO, Cohen FS, Dankert JR, Cramer WA. 1983. Comparison of the macroscopic and single channel con-ductance properties of colicin E1 and its C-terminal tryptic peptide. *J. Biol. Chem.* 258:9908–12

12. Bullock JO, Kolen ER. 1992. Anion permeability of colicin E1 in planar lipid bilayers. *Biophys. J.* 61(2):115. (Abstr.)

13. Cleveland MB, Slatin S, Finkelstein A, Levinthal C. 1983. Structure-func-tion for a voltage-dependent ion channel: properties of a C-terminal fragment of colicin E1. *Proc. Natl. Acad. Sci. USA* 80:3706–10

14. Cramer WA, Dankert JR, Uratani Y. 1983. The membrane channel-form-ing bacteriocidal protein, colicin E1. *Biochim. Biophys. Acta* 737:173–93

15. Cramer WA, Knaff DB. 1991. Mem-brane structre and storage of free en-ergy. In *Energy Transduction in Biological Membranes*, pp. 79–138. New York: Springer-Verlag

16. Cramer WA, Zhang Y-L, Schendel S, Merrill AR, Song HY, et al. 1992. Dy-namic properties of the colicin E1 ion channel. *FEMS Lett.* 105:71–82

17. Dankert J, Uratani Y, Grabau C, Cramer WA, Hermodson M. 1982. On a domain structure of colicin E1: a C-terminal peptide fragment active in membrane depolarization. *J. Biol. Chem.* 257:3857–63

18. Davidson VL, Brunden KR, Cramer WA. 1985. An acidic pH requirement for insertion of colicin E1 into artifi-cial membrane vesicles: relevance to the mechanism of action of colicins and certain toxins. *Proc. Natl. Acad. Sci. USA* 82:1386–90

19. Deisenhofer J, Michel H. 1989. The photosynthetic reaction center from the purple bacterium *Rps. viridis*. *Science* 245:1463–73

20. Deriy BN, Cramer WA, Cohen FS. 1995. Kinetic differences in single channel properties of colicin E1 and its C-terminal channel polypeptide. *Biophys. J.* 68: In press (Abstr.)

21. DiMasi DR, White JC, Schnaitman CA, Bradbeer C. 1973. Transport of vitamin B_{12} in *Escherichia coli:* com-mon receptor sites for vitamin B_{12} and the E colicins on the outer mem-brane of the cell envelope. *J. Bacte-riol.* 115:506–13

22. Duché D, Parker MW, Gonzalez-Mañas J-M, Pattus F, Baty D. 1994. Uncoupled steps of the colicin A pore formation demonstrated by disulfide engineering. *J. Biol. Chem.* 269: 6332–39

23. Elkins P, Song HY, Cramer WA, Stauffacher CV. 1994. Crystallization and characterization of colicin E1 channel-forming polypeptides. *Proteins Struct. Funct. Genet.* 19:150–57

24. Deleted in proof

25. El Kouhen R, Fierobe H-P, Sciani-manico S, Steiert M, Pattus F. 1993. Characterization of the receptor and translocator domains of colicin N. *Eur. J. Biochem.* 214:635–39

26. Engelman DM, Steitz TA. 1981. The spontaneous insertion of proteins into and across membranes. The helical hairpin hypothesis. *Cell* 23:411–22

27. Espesset D, Piet P, Lazdunski C, Geli V. 1994. Immunity proteins to pore-forming colicins: structure-function relationships. *Mol. Microbiol.* 10: 1111–20

28. Fields KL, Luria SE. 1969. Effects of colicins E1 and K on cellular metabo-lism. *J. Bacteriol.* 97: 64–77

29. Fisher E, Günter K, Braun V. 1989

Involvement of ExbB and TonB in transport across the outer membrane of *E. coli:* phenotypic complementation of *exbB* mutants by overexpressed *tonB* and physical stabilization of TonB by ExbB. *J. Bacteriol.* 171:5127–34

30. Fourel D, Mizushima S, Bernadac A, Pagès J-M. 1993. Specific regions of *Escherichia coli:* OmpF protein involved in antigenic and colicin receptor sites and in stable trimerization. *J. Bacteriol.* 175:2754–57

31. Fromme P, Boekema EJ, Gräber P. 1987. Isolation and characterization of a supramolecular complex of subunit III of the ATP synthase from chloroplasts. *Z. Naturforsch.* 42c:1239–45

32. Geli V, Baty D, Lazdunski C. 1988. Use of a foreign epitope as a "tag" for the localization of minor proteins within a cell: the case of the immunity protein to colicin A. *Proc. Natl. Acad. Sci. USA* 85:689–93

33. Geli V, Baty D, Pattus F, Lazdunski C. 1989. Topology and function of the integral membrane protein conferring immunity to colicin A. *Mol. Microbiol.* 3:679–87

34. Geli V, Knibiehler M, Bernadec A, Lazdunski C. 1989. Purification and reconstitution into liposomes of an integral membrane protein conferring immunity to colicin A. *FEBS Lett.* 60:239–44

35. Geli V, Koorengevel MC, Demel RA, Lazdunski C, Killian JA. 1992. Acidic interaction of the colicin A pore-forming domain with model membranes of *E. coli* lipids results in a large perturbation of acyl chain order and stabilization of the bilayer. *Biochemistry* 31:11089–94

36. Geli V, Lazdunski C. 1992. An α-helix hydrophobic hairpin as a specific determinant in protein-protein interaction occurring in *E. coli* colicin A,B immunity systems. *J. Bacteriol.* 174:6432–37

37. Ghosh P, Mel SF, Stroud RM. 1993. A carboxy-terminal fragment of colicin Ia forms ion channels. *J. Membr. Biol.* 134:85–92

38. Ghosh P, Mel SF, Stroud RM. 1994. The domain structure of the ion channel-forming protein colicin Ia. *Nat. Struct. Biol.* 1:597–604

39. Gonzalez-Mañas JM, Lakey JH, Pattus F. 1992. Brominated phospholipid as a tool for monitoring the membrane insertion of colicin A. *Biochemistry* 31:7294–7300

40. Goormaghtigh E, Vigneron L, Knibiehler M, Lazdunski C, Ruysschaert JM. 1991. Secondary structure of the membrane-bound form of the pore-forming domain of colicin A: an attenuated total-reflection polarized Fourier-transform infrared spectroscopy study. *Eur. J. Biochem.* 202:1299–1305

41. Gould JM, Cramer WA. 1977. Studies on the depolarization of the *Escherichia coli* cell membrane by colicin E1. *J. Biol. Chem.* 252:5491–97

42. Gould JM, Cramer WA. 1977. Relationship between oxygen-induced proton efflux and membrane energization in cells of *Escherichia coli. J. Biol. Chem.* 252:5875–82

43. Guihard G, Benedetti H, Besnard M. 1993. Phosphate efflux through channels formed by colicins and phage T5 in *Escherichia coli* cells is responsible for the fall in cytoplasmic ATP. *J. Biol. Chem.* 268:17775–80

44. Guihard G, Boulanger P, Benedetti H, Lloubes R, Besnard M, Letellier L. 1994. Colicin A and the tol proteins involved in its translocation are preferentially located in the contact sites between the inner and outer membranes of *Escherichia coli* cells. *J. Biol. Chem.* 269:5874–80

45. Hannavy K, Barr G, Dorman CJ, Adamson J, Mazengera LN, et al. 1990. TonB protein of *S. typhimurium:* a model for signal transduction in membranes. *J. Mol. Biol.* 216:897–910

46. Haynie TT, Freire E. 1993. Structural energetics of the molten globule state. *Proteins Struct. Funct. Genet.* 16:115–40

47. Jacob F, Siminovitch L, Wollman E. 1952. Sur la biosynthése d'une colicine et sur son mode d'action. *Ann. Inst. Pasteur* 83:295–315

47a. James R, Lazdunski C, Pattus F, eds. 1992. *Bacteriocins, Microcins and Lantibiotics.* Heidelberg: Springer-Verlag

48. Jeanteur D, Pattus F, Timmons PA. 1994. Membrane-bound form of the pore-forming domain of colicin A. A neutron-scattering study. *J. Mol. Biol.* 235:898–907

49. Jeanteur D, Schirmer T, Fourel D, Simonet V, Rummer F, et al. 1994. Structural and functional alterations of a colicin-resistant mutant of OmpF-porin from *Escherichia coli. Proc. Natl. Acad. Sci. USA* 91:10675–79

50. Jiang JX, London E. 1990. Involvement of denaturation-like changes in

Pseudomonas exotoxin A hydrophobicity and membrane penetration determined by characterization of pH and thermal transitions. Roles of two distinctly conformationally altered states. *J. Biol. Chem.* 265:8636–41

51. Kampfenkel K, Braun V. 1992. Membrane topology of the *Escherichia coli* ExbD protein. *J. Bacteriol.* 174: 5485–87

52. Kampfenkel K, Braun V. 1993. Topology of the ExbB protein in the cytoplasmic membrane of *Escherichia coli*. *J. Biol. Chem.* 268:6050–57

53. Kampfenkel K, Braun V. 1993. Membrane topologies of the TolQ and TolR proteins of *Escherichia coli*: inactivation of TolQ by a missense mutation in the proposed first transmembrane segment. *J. Bacteriol.* 175: 4485–91

54. Karlsson M, Hannavy K, Higgins CF. 1993. ExbB acts as a chaperone-like protein to stabilize TonB in the cytoplasm. *Mol. Microbiol.* 8: 389–96

55. Kopecky AL, Copeland DP, Lusk JE. 1975. Viability of *Escherichia coli* treated with colicin K. *Proc. Natl. Acad. Sci. USA* 72:4631–34

56. Lakey JH, Duché D, González-Manas J-M, Baty D, Pattus F. 1993. Fluorescence energy transfer distance measurements. The hydrophobic helical hairpin of colicin A. *J. Mol. Biol.* 230:1055–67

57. Lakey JH, van der Goot FG, Pattus F. 1994. All in the family: the toxic activity of pore-forming colicins. *Toxicology* 87:85–108

58. Letellier L, Lazdunski C, Benedetti H, Bourdineaud JP, Boulanger P. 1992. In vivo properties of colicin A: channel activity and translocation. See Ref. 47a, p. 121

59. Levengood SK, Beyer WF, Webster RE. 1991. TolA: a membrane protein involved in colicin uptake contains an extended helical region. *Proc. Nat. Acad. Sci. USA* 88:5939–43

60. Levengood-Freyermuth SK, Click EM, Webster RE. 1993. Role of the carboxyl-terminal domain of TolA in protein import and integrity of the outer membrane. *J. Bacteriol.* 175: 222–28

61. Lohner K, Esser AF. 1991. Thermal unfolding and aggregation of human complement protein C9: a differential scanning calorimetry study. *Biochemistry* 30:6620–25

62. London E. 1992. How bacterial proteins enter cells: the role of partial unfolding in membrane translocation. *Mol. Microbiol.* 6:3277–62

63. Mankovich JA, Hsu C-H, Konisky J. 1986. DNA and amino acid sequence analysis of structural and immunity genes of colicins Ia and Ib. *J. Bacteriol.* 168:228–36

64. Massotte D, Yamamoto M. Scianimanico S, Sorokine O, Dorsselaer AV. 1993. Structure of the membrane-bound form of the pore-forming domain of colicin A: a partial proteolysis and mass spectrometry study. *Biochemistry* 32:13787–94

65. Mel SF, Falick AM, Burlingame AL, Stroud RM. 1993. Mapping a membrane-associated conformation of colicin Ia. *Biochemistry* 32:9473–79

66. Merrill AR, Cohen FS, Cramer WA. 1990. On the nature of the structural change of the colicin E1 channel peptide necessary for its translocation-competent state. *Biochemistry* 29: 5829–36

67. Merrill AR, Cramer WA. 1990. Identification of a voltage-responsive segment of the potential-gated colicin E1 ion channel. *Biochemistry* 29: 8529–34

68. Muga A, Gonzalez-Manas JM, Lakey JH, Pattus F, Surewicz WK. 1993. pH-dependent stability and membrane interaction of the pore-forming domain of colicin A. *J. Biol. Chem.* 268:1553–57

69. Nau C, Konisky CD. 1989. Evolutionary relationship between the TonB-dependent outer membrane transport proteins: nucleotide and amino acid sequences of the *Escherichia coli* colicin I receptor gene. *J. Bacteriol.* 171:1041–47

70. Neidhardt FC. 1987. Chemical composition of *Escherichia coli*. In *Escherichia coli and Salmonella typhimurium Cellular and Molecular Biology*, ed. FC Neidhardt, JL Ingraham, KB Low, B Magasanik, M Schaechter, HE Umbarger, pp. 3–6. Washington, DC: Am. Soc. Microbiol.

71. Neumcke B, Läuger P. 1969. Nonlinear electrical effects in lipid bilayer membranes. II. Integration of the generalized Nernst-Planck equations. *Biophys. J.* 9:1160–70

72. Ok DC, Cohen FS, Zhang Y-L, Cramer WA. 1994. Inactivation of colicin channels with small voltages is affected by an N-terminal domain. *Biophys. J.* 66(2):439 (Abstr.)

73. Parker MW, Pattus F. 1993. Rendering a membrane protein soluble in water: a common packing motif in

bacterial membrane proteins. *Trends Biochem. Sci.* 18:391–94

74. Parker MW, Pattus F, Tucker AD, Tsernoglou D. 1989. Structure of the membrane pore-forming fragment of colicin A. *Nature* 337:93–96

75. Parker MW, Postma JPM, Pattus F, Tucker AD, Tsernoglou D. 1992. Refined structure of the pore-forming domain of colicin A at 2.4 Å resolution. *J. Mol. Biol.* 224:639–57

76. Phillips SK, Cramer WA. 1973. Properties of the fluorescence probe response associated with the transmission mechanism of colicin E1. *Biochemistry* 12:1170–76

77. Postle K. 1990. TonB and the gram-negative dilemma. *Mol. Microbiol.* 4: 2019–25

78. Ptitsyn OB. 1992. The molten globule state. In *Protein Folding,* ed. TE Creighton, pp. 243–300. New York: Freeman

79. Pugsley AP. 1984. The ins and outs of colicins. *Microbiol. Sci.* 1:168–75

80. Ramsay G, Montgomery D, Berger D, Freire E. 1989. Energetics of diphtheria toxin insertion and translocation. Calorimetric characterization of the acid-induced pH transition. *Biochemistry* 28:529–33

81. Rath P, Bousché O, Merrill AR, Cramer WA, Rothschild KJ. 1991. FTIR evidence for a predominantly α-helical structure of the membrane-bound channel forming C-terminal peptide of colicin E1. *Biophys. J.* 59: 516–22

82. Raymond L, Slatin SL, Finkelstein A. 1985. Channels formed by colicin E1 in planar lipid bilayers are large and exhibit pH-dependent ion selectivity. *J. Membr. Biol.* 84:173–81

83. Raymond L, Slatin SL, Finkelstein A, Liu Q-R, Levinthal C. 1986. Gating of a voltage-dependent channel (colicin E1) in planar lipid bilayers. Translocation of regions outside the channel domain. *J. Membr. Biol.* 92: 255–68

84. Schein SJ, Kagan BL, Finkelstein A. 1978. Colicin K acts by forming voltage-dependent channels in phospholipid bilayer membranes. *Nature* 276: 159–63

85. Schendel SL, Cramer WA. 1995. On the nature of the unfolded intermediate in the *in vitro* transition of the colicin E1 channel domain from the aqueous to the membrane phase. *Protein Sci.* In press

86. Schramm E, Mende J, Braun V,

Kamp RM. 1987. Nucleotide sequence of the colicin B activity gene *cba:* consensus pentapeptide among TonB-dependent colicins and receptors. *J. Bacteriol.* 169:3350–57

87. Seelig J, Nebel S, Ganz P, Bruns C. 1993. Electrostatic and nonpolar peptide-membrane interactions. Lipid binding and functional properties of somatostatin analogues of charge $z = +1$ to $z = +3$. *Biochemistry* 32: 9714–21

88. Shin Y-K, Levinthal C, Levinthal F, Hubbell WL. 1993. Colicin E1 binding to membranes: time-resolved studies of spin-labeled mutants. *Science* 259:960–63

89. Shirabe K, Peterson AA, Shiver JW, Cohen FS, Nakazawa A, Cramer WA. 1989. Decrease of anion selectivity caused by mutation of Thr501 and Gly502 to Glu in the hydrophobic domain of the colicin E1 channel. *J. Biol. Chem.* 264:1951–57

90. Shirabe K, Yamada M, Merrill AR, Cramer WA, Nakazawa A. 1993. Overproduction and purification of the colicin E1 immunity protein. *Plasmid* 29:236–40

91. Shiver JW, Cramer WA, Merrill AR, Cohen FS. 1988. Site-directed mutagenesis of the charged residues near the carboxy-terminus of the colicin E1 ion channel. *Biochemistry* 27: 8421–28

92. Slatin SL, Qui X-Q, Jakes KS, Finkelstein A. 1995. Identification of a translocated protein segment in a voltage-dependent channel. *Nature.* In press

93. Slatin SL, Raymond L, Finkelstein A. 1986. Gating of a voltage-dependent channel (colicin E1) in planar lipid bilayers: the role of protein translocation. *J. Membr. Biol.* 92: 247–54

94. Song HY. 1991. *Topography of ColE1 gene products: the channel-forming domain and the immunity protein.* PhD thesis. Purdue Univ., West Lafayette, IN. 205 pp.

95. Song HY, Cohen FS, Cramer WA. 1991. Membrane topography of ColE1 gene products: (I) The hydrophobic anchor of the colicin E1 channel is a helical hairpin. *J. Bacteriol.* 173:2927–34

96. Song HY, Cramer WA. 1991. Membrane topography of ColE1 gene products: (II) The immunity protein. *J. Bacteriol.* 173:2935–43

97. Steer BA, Merrill AR. 1994. The col-

icin E1 insertion-competent state: detection of structural changes using fluorescence energy transfer. *Biochemistry* 33:1108–15

98. van der Goot FG, Gonzalez-Mañas J-M, Lakey JH, Pattus F. 1992. A 'molten-globule' membrane insertion intermediate of the pore-forming domain of colicin A. *Nature* 354:408–10

99. von Heijne G. 1992. Membrane protein structure prediction. Hydrophobicity and the positive-inside rule. *J. Mol. Biol.* 225:487–94

100. Weaver CA, Redborg AH, Konisky J. 1981. Plasmid-determined immunity of *Escherichia coli* K-12 to colicin Ia is mediated by a plasmid-encoded membrane protein. *J. Bacteriol.* 148:817–28

101. Webster RE. 1991. The *tol* gene products and the import of macromolecules into *E. coli. Mol. Microbiol.* 5:1005–11

102. Webster RE, Levengood SK. 1992. TolA: structure, location and role in the uptake of colicins. See Ref. 47a, p. 241

103. Weiner MC, White SH. 1992. Structure of a fluid dioleoylphosphatidylcholine bilayer determined by joint refinement of X-ray and neutron diffraction data. (III) Complete structure. *Biophys. J.* 61:434–47

104. Wendt L. 1970. Mechanism of colicin action: early events. *J. Bacteriol.* 104:1236–41

105. White JC, Di Girolamo PM, Fu ML,

Preston YA, Bradbeer C. 1973 Transport of vitamin B_{12} in *Escherichia coli. J. Biol.Chem.* 248:3978–86

106. White SH, Wimley WC. 1994. Peptides in lipid bilayers: structural and thermodynamic basis for partitioning and folding. *Curr. Opin. Struct. Biol.* 4:79–86

107. Wormald MR, Merrill AR, Cramer WA, Williams RJP. 1990. Solution NMR studies of colicin E1 C-terminal thermolytic peptide: structural comparison with colicin A and the effects of pH changes. *Eur. J. Biochem.* 191:155–61

108. Zakharov S, Zhang Y-L, Heymann JB, Cramer WA. 1995. Colicin E1 in channel binding with the membrane: An optimum interaction is required for activity. *Biophys. J.* 68: In press

109. Zhang Y-L, Cramer WA. 1992. Constraints imposed by protease accessibility on the *trans*-membrane and surface topography of the colicin E1 ion channel. *Protein Sci.* 1:1666–76

110. Zhang Y-L, Cramer WA. 1993. Intramembrane helix-helix interactions as the basis of inhibition of the colicin E1 ion channel by its immunity protein. *J. Biol. Chem.* 268:10176–84

111. Zhao JM, London E. 1986. Similarity of the conformation of diphtheria toxin at high temperature to that in the membrane-penetrating low pH state. *Proc. Natl. Acad. Sci.* 83:2002–6

Annu. Rev. Biophys. Biomol. Struct. 1995. 24:643–75
Copyright © 1995 by Annual Reviews Inc. All rights reserved

ACTIN-BINDING PROTEIN COMPLEXES AT ATOMIC RESOLUTION

P. J. McLaughlin

Department of Biochemistry, Hugh Robson Building, George Square, Edinburgh EH8 9XD, United Kingdom

A. G. Weeds

MRC Laboratory of Molecular Biology, Hills Road, Cambridge CB2 2QH, United Kingdom

KEY WORDS: G-actin–binding proteins, DNase I, profilin, gelsolin, protein crystallography

CONTENTS

643

1056-8700/95/0610-0643$05.00

ABSTRACT

This review describes three structures of actin complexed with different monomer-binding proteins, namely with DNase I, gelsolin segment 1, and profilin. In these proteins, the binding sites are discontinuous in the sequence, and those residues that form intermolecular hydrogen bonds are not well conserved in homologous proteins. The strongly conserved residues that define the family of proteins in gelsolin and profilin reflect the underlying structural fold of each. The binding surfaces for segment 1 and profilin are different, although they peripherally overlap on actin. No extreme features in the binding surfaces of these complexes distinguish them from other globular proteins.

PERSPECTIVES AND OVERVIEW

Dynamic changes in the organization of actin have been closely linked to changes in cell shape and cellular motility (reviewed in 73). The actin-rich cortex, present beneath the cell membrane in eukaryotic cells, has a gel-like consistency that depends on the presence of a variety of actin-binding proteins that associate with either F- or G-actin. Over 60 actin-binding proteins have been identified (60). These include (*a*) proteins such as filamin or α-actinin that cross-link filaments; (b) proteins such as gelsolin or smaller actin-depolymerizing factors (21) that induce breaks in filaments, reduce the viscosity of gels, and effect gel-sol transitions; and (*c*) proteins such as profilin or thymosin $\beta 4$ that sequester G-actin and modulate the ratio of polymer to monomer (reviewed in 78). Other actin-binding proteins include myosin motor proteins and components involved in membrane attachment. This diversity raises the question of whether actin-binding proteins are variations on a few structural themes, as are DNA-binding proteins. We may also ask the reverse, i.e. whether any special feature of the surface of actin makes the molecule so multivalent.

Only three binding proteins have been solved at atomic resolution in complex with actin, but others have been solved in the absence of actin (reviewed in 61). The prediction of actin-binding sites is fraught with difficulty, even when the answer is known from the crystal structure. The scope of this review is limited to the structures of actin in complex with DNase I, gelsolin segment 1, or profilin. Before describing them, we start with a brief primer on actin structure.

ACTIN PRIMER

The structure of G-actin, determined in complex with DNase I, revealed a four-domain protein (Figure 1a) (35). Subdomains 1 and 3 are made from noncontiguous sections of the polypeptide chain. The connection of secondary structural elements in each is similar and the topology of the two together is similar to hexokinase: Like hexokinase,

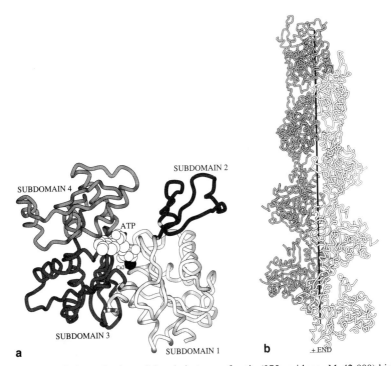

Figure 1 (*a*) Schematic view of the chain trace of actin (375 residues, M_r 42,000) highlighting subdomain 1 (residues 1–32, 70–144, 338–375), subdomain 2 (residues 33–69), subdomain 3 (residues 145–180, 270–337), and subdomain 4 (residues 181–269). (*b*) Eight actin subunits oriented in the filament structure model as described by Holmes et al (23). The actin subunits are from the crystal structure of the actin–gelsolin segment 1 complex. The DNase I–binding loop, which is not ordered in the absence of DNase I, is omitted. The barbed end is at the bottom.

actin binds ATP at a site between domains. The ATP ligates a calcium ion through its β and γ phosphoryl oxygen atoms. Aged crystals containing ADP show little change in protein conformation. The whole molecule is rather asymmetric; it has the dimensions 55 × 55 × 35 Å, and the four subdomains lie roughly in a plane. The standard viewing direction is roughly along the narrowest dimension as defined in the original description of the structure. Here, we respect this convention in schematic ribbon diagrams showing the trace of the actin chain [made using Molscript (37)].

Filamentous actin (F-actin) is not amenable to X-ray crystallography because polymer lengths are not homogeneous. Nevertheless, filament symmetry and low-resolution images were obtained from muscle and in oriented gels of actin by means of X-ray diffraction and in vitreous ice or from negatively stained filaments or paracrystals by electron microscopy (48). The Heidelberg group (23) found a best orientation for the crystal structure actin model that was consistent with X-ray diagram intensities obtained from oriented actin gels (Figure 1b). This model was refined by splitting the structure into four domains to be treated as rigid bodies, each comprised of randomly selected residues that were redefined on each cycle (43). The symmetry is that of a left-handed helix in which 13 subunits repeat every 6 turns in roughly 358 Å along the axis. Thus the operation that relates subsequent subunits is a rotation of $-166°$ and a translation of 27.5 Å, about one-half the molecule length, along the axis. Two such operations place a third molecule on top of the first, related to it by a rotation of 28° in the opposite sense. Hence F-actin appears as a right-handed two-strand helix of 358-Å pitch. A corollary of this symmetry is that strands run parallel and the two filament ends are not equivalent, which is consistent with differences in the critical concentration at the two ends (59). The arrowhead appearance of filaments decorated with myosin subfragments led to monikers for the ends as either *barbed* or *pointed*. The fast growing (+) barbed end is at the bottom, and the pointed (−) end is at the top of the axis in Figure 1b.

The model is consistent with much independent evidence for associations between subunits and continues to be consistent with emerging results (48). However, the maximum resolution of the fiber data is 8.4 Å, and the details of side-chain interactions between subunits are not necessarily correct. Electron diffraction beyond 7.0 Å has been demonstrated for actin filaments in the acrosomal process of *Limulus polyphemus* sperm (66), which should result in independently phased images that show actin helices as rods that can be compared with the crystal structure.

DNase I

Actin-Binding Properties of DNase I

DNase I binds very strongly to G-actin and inhibits its nucleotide exchange. Recent measurements indicated a $K_d \approx 50$ pM (12). DNase I binds and caps the pointed ends of filaments with a K_d of 2 nM (58). Paradoxically, high concentrations of DNase I increase the depolymerization rate at pointed ends, possibly because of steric interference when DNase I binds both subunits (87). This result is consistent with the filament model—we found steric clashes when two DNase I actin complexes were superimposed onto the pointed end of the filament.

Structure of Actin-DNase I

The 2.8-Å resolution atomic structure of DNase I with actin (35) shows that DNase I binds between subdomains 2 and 4 (Figure 2). The major contact is with subdomain 2, where an actin loop—the DNase I–binding loop—is incorporated into an edge β-sheet of DNase I (Figure 3). Residues involved in actin binding are contained within a relatively short sequence between residues 44 and 69. The insertion of strands to continue a β-sheet is not uncommon. In many serine protease–inhibitor complexes, the association is antiparallel (27), but in the thrombin-hirudin complex (65), it is parallel, as in the actin-DNase I complex.

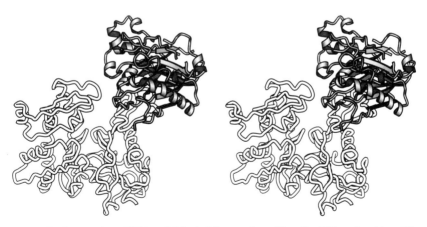

Figure 2 Stereo view of DNase I (*shaded*) in complex with actin. DNase I residues 65, 67, and 69 hydrogen bond to actin residues 41, 43, and 45 in the DNase I–binding loop to form a parallel seventh strand of the DNase I sheet. These residues reside at one edge of the lower of the two central sheets in the β-sandwich that characterizes the structure (see Figure 3). This sheet is roughly perpendicular to the actin surface.

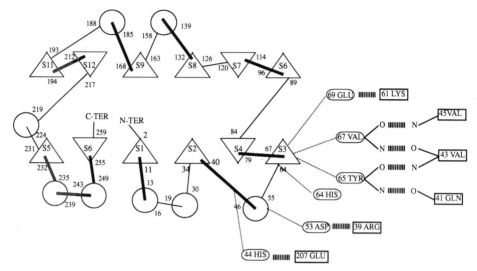

Figure 3 Schematic diagram showing the topology in DNase I of secondary-structural elements, which are viewed normal to the chain direction with α-helices as circles and β-strands represented by triangles whose direction denotes parallel or antiparallel strands. DNase I residues in contact are shown with dotted lines leading to ovals, and the actin residues to which they are bound are enclosed in rectangles.

Actin does not bind at the active site of DNase I; it inhibits enzyme activity by sterically blocking the active site and preventing substrate entry. Figure 4 shows superposition of DNase I in complex with a DNA octamer (89) (Brookhaven Protein Data Bank entry 1DNK) onto DNase I in the actin complex. Only the top loop in subdomain 4 (residues 241–247) makes steric clashes with the first two base pairs of the DNA, while the scissile bond is between the sixth and seventh base pairs. The association between actin and DNase I holds even when actin's nucleotide is removed (63). If as a result of nucleotide dissociation the bonding between the two halves of actin is broken, subdomains 3 and 4 may no longer obstruct the binding of DNA.

Because the DNase I–binding loop is hydrophobic and extends from the underlying actin structure, its conformation is unlikely to be retained in actin alone. The electron density between residues 40 and 49 in the segment 1 complex is nil, whereas in the profilin complex, the density exhibits highest crystallographic B-factors in that structure. In the structure of the profilin complex, the loop position in subdomain 2 is shifted, but the conformation within the loop is roughly similar to that in the DNase I complex. The refined Holmes model for F-actin

(43) has a different conformation for the loop, in which it is packed towards subdomain 4. The starting conformation was modeled, and whether the final position is defined by the experimental measurements is not clear.

In contrast to the changes in actin, the cognate strand, between residues 65 and 69 in DNase I, has changed little from the conformation in the absence of actin. The rms (root mean square) difference in main chain atoms is 1.4 Å, and the largest side-chain difference, for Tyr67, is 2.1 Å.

All actins tested, except for certain protozoan actins, bind DNase I (18, 24). A chimeric actin containing the N-terminal 83 residues of *Tetrahymena* actin and residues 84–375 of *Dictyostelium discoideum*

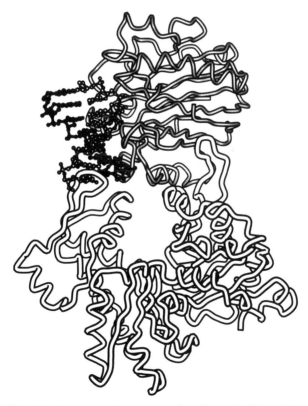

Figure 4   DNase I octamer complex superposed on the actin-DNase I structure. The view shows the DNase I axis roughly vertical and in the plane of the paper and' actin in roughly the standard view.

actin did not bind to DNase I, presumably because it lacks the binding site in subdomain 2 (25). In *Entamoeba histolytica* actin, Ser replaces Gly42, and the structure shows that this serine residue may clash with Tyr65 in the DNase I strand.

GELSOLIN

Substructure of Gelsolin and Related Proteins

Gelsolin severs actin filaments in calcium and caps their barbed ends. It also forms calcium-dependent complexes with two actin monomers, which nucleate polymerization (reviewed in 86, 90). Removal of calcium dissociates only one of the actins from the ternary complexes, thereby leaving binary complexes (9). Gelsolin also binds phosphatidyl-inositol-4,5-bisphosphate (PIP_2) (30), and PIP_2 dissociates the EGTA-stable actin-gelsolin binary complex and removes gelsolin from the barbed ends of actin filaments.

Gelsolin's pattern of conserved residues (85a) indicates that the single polypeptide chain comprises six segments of sequence. Each sequence segment encompasses a separately folded structural domain. Proteins related to gelsolin include adseverin (52) and villin, which has an additional F-actin–binding headpiece that confers cross-linking activity in the absence of calcium (46). Severin from *Dictyostelium discoideum* contains three repeating segments (3) as do the capping proteins gCap39 (92) or macrophage capping protein (MCP) (14).

Actin-Binding Properties

Gelsolin contains three distinct actin-binding sites: two monomer-binding sites in segment 1 and segments 4–6 (8) and a filament-binding site in segment 2 (85). The minimal severing domain is located in segments 1–2, while nucleation requires segments 2–6 (82, 85). Severin also contains three actin-binding sites within its three segments (17), but in contrast to gelsolin, it has poor nucleating activity (91). The dissociation constant of segment 1 from its complex with actin is 4–5 pM with and 1–2 nM without calcium (8). These values compare with dissociation constants of 25 nM for segments 4–6 and ~3 μM for segments 2–3.

Although gelsolin has the properties required to regulate disassembly and assembly of actin filaments in cells (73), and enhanced motility was observed in NIH 3T3 fibroblasts that overexpress gelsolin (13), no evidence shows unambiguously that gelsolin plays an essential role in cell motility. Gelsolin in blood plasma may depolymerize and sequester actin released during cellular damage (32).

Structure of the Actin–Segment 1 Complex

The structure of gelsolin segment 1 has been solved in complex with actin (47). Segment 1 binds between subdomains 1 and 3, on the front face in the standard view (Figure 5a). The longest α-helix bears most of the contacting residues. A Ca^{2+}-binding site, located at its carboxyl-terminal end (Figure 5b), is ligated by the carboxylate of Asp109 and carbonyl groups from the adjacent turn; coordination of this ion is completed by the carboxylate of Glu167 of actin, so both proteins contribute to the site. This is probably the Ca^{2+} ion that is sequestered between actin and gelsolin and that cannot be removed by EGTA (9, 83). A second Ca^{2+} ion has been located at the N-terminal end of the same helix: Its ligands are solely from segment 1, and the carboxylate groups involved are conserved in almost all species from the many phyla for which gelsolin sequences are available. These charged side chains are

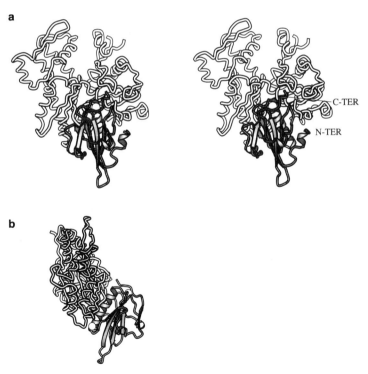

Figure 5 (a) Stereo view of actin–gelsolin segment 1 complex. Ca^{2+} ions are shown as spheres (the intermolecular Ca^{2+} ion is almost hidden in this view). (b) View perpendicular to a, from left to right.

close together in space and buried away from the solvent; thus the Ca^{2+} ion is necessary to maintain the conformation.

ACTIN-BINDING SITE   The footprints of each molecule on the other show complementary chemical composition (Figure 6). Each has a central patch of apolar atoms with a peripheral rim of polar atoms, where most hydrogen-bonding residues are located in the apposed surfaces. The hydrogen-bonding residues are discontinuous in the linear sequence and cluster on the top face, above the central β-sheet (as defined in Figure 7). The salient feature at the center of the contact is the insertion of Ile103 from the major helix between Leu346 and Leu349 of subdomain 1 and Tyr143 of subdomain 3. These actin residues form an apolar pocket and their conformations are unchanged in the other two crystal structures. Thus the site seems ready-made.

STRUCTURE IMPLICATIONS FOR SEVERING FUNCTION   The location of segment 1 overlaps with the periphery of an actin-actin contact between two molecules in the same strand; profilin overlaps more fully in the

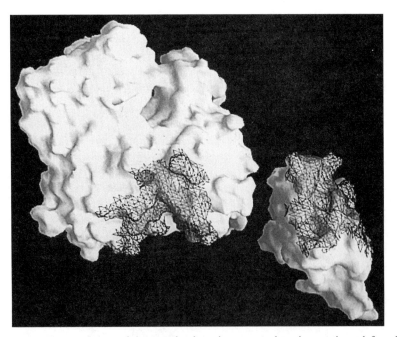

Figure 6   The two halves of the complex have been opened to show actin on left and segment 1 on the right. The contact areas are shown as a net and the apolar areas included within these areas are shown in a darker shade.

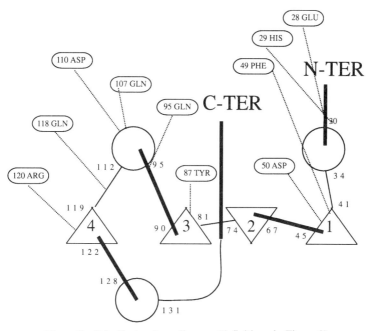

Figure 7   Gelsolin topology diagram (definitions in Figure 3).

same region (Figure 8). Segment 1 is targeted onto F-actin by the other segments of gelsolin, but the structure suggests that it destabilizes the actin-actin contact from the surface of the filament without prizing the subunits apart to insert itself. Thus an attractive mechanism for severing is a glancing interaction that breaks critical bonds, without the large activation energy required to separate subunits. The F-actin–binding sites in segments 2–3 may act solely to increase the local concentration of segment 1 at the correct place on the filament, but an additional role in destabilizing filament subunits has also been proposed (75). A construct spanning segments 2–6, which decorates actin filaments in the presence or absence of calcium, also shows weak severing activity in calcium (in the presence of which segments 4–6 would have capping activity) (82). This observation suggests that the site in segments 4–6 can mimic that of segment 1, albeit inefficiently, or that segments 2–3 may act synergistically with segment 1 to destabilize filaments.

Putative PIP₂-Binding Site

Wild-type segment 1 binds PIP₂, but a mutant lacking the C-terminal 15 residues does not (93). The deleted region contains a sequence of

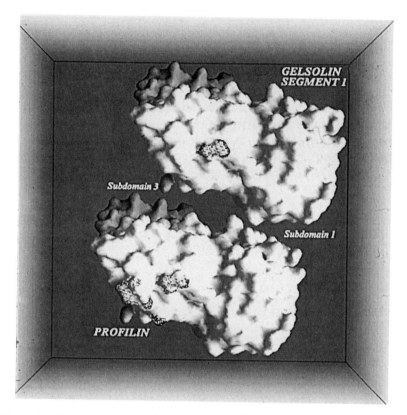

Figure 8 Views of actin approximately along the filament axis in the Holmes model, looking at the barbed end. The areas on an actin subunit contacted by both the binding protein and another subunit in the filament model are shown as a net.

basic side chains that is also found in other PIP$_2$-binding proteins. These may bind the phosphoinositol head groups. The structure shows that this C-terminal sequence also contributes a ligand to the intramolecular Ca^{2+}-binding site. This Ca^{2+} ion has an incomplete coordination sphere and is missing a ligand roughly normal to the protein surface. A similar Ca^{2+} coordination was observed in the structure of annexin V, a Ca^{2+}-controlled phospholipid-binding protein (7). By analogy, the intramolecular Ca^{2+} ion in segment 1 may be a ligand for inositol phosphate groups. The linear sequence of this region of segment 1 is similar to a second PIP$_2$ site at the N-terminus of segment 2 (residues 140–150) (31); these regions may be two halves of the same head group–binding site located at the segment boundary.

Sequence Variation in the Gelsolin Family

The position corresponding to Ile103 in segments 1 and 4 always has a large apolar side chain (Figure 9), but in all other segments this position is deleted, polar, or charged. The close-packed nature of the binding of Ile103 between apolar side chains from actin subdomains 1 and 3 greatly limits the types of side chains that can be accommodated there. In addition, the pattern of residues that form the apolar face of the long helix in segment 1 is also clear in aligned segment 4 sequences. Thus, segment 4 is the only other segment likely to bind actin at the

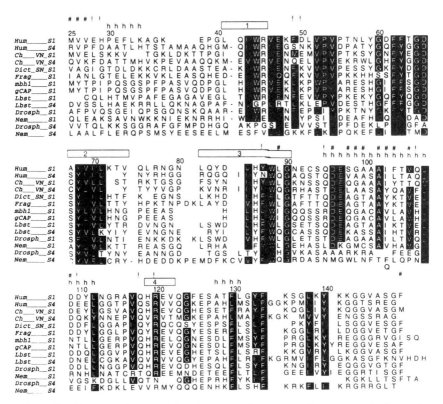

Figure 9 Alignment of segment 1 and segment 4 sequences from some gelsolins and homologues. Abbreviations: S1, segment 1; S4, segment 4. Species: Hum, human; Ch, chicken; Dict, *Dictyostelium discoideum;* Lbstr, lobster; Drosph, *Drosophila melanogaster;* Nem, *Caenorhabditis elegans.* Homologues: VN, villin; SN, severin. Numbering is for plasma form of human gelsolin. Secondary structure is indicated with h for helix and open boxes for strands. On the top line, # denotes contacting residue and ! hydrogen-bonding residue.

same site as segment 1. Recent work suggests that the binding site of segments 4–6 is indeed located in segment 4 (B Pope, SK Maciver & AG Weeds, submitted). Interestingly, the conservation of residues adjacent to Ile103 is not apparent in segment 4 of gelsolin from *Drosophila melanogaster* (22, 72) or in that from the nematode *Caenorhabditis elegans* (81). Both show greater divergence between equivalent segments in the two halves than do other gelsolins. The absence of this conservation in *D. melanogaster* and the nematode suggests that (*a*) gene duplication occurred more recently in the other phyla, and gelsolins have not all descended as a six-segment protein from a more ancient antecedent; (*b*) *D. melanogaster* and nematode segment sequences diverged within each protein to a such an extent that any duplication is no longer apparent; or (*c*) the duplication of segments in *D. melanogaster* and nematodes did not occur in three domain blocks. A comparison of the functions of these gelsolins would be illuminating.

Residues that form the apolar core of segment 1 are conserved in type, as shown by a global alignment of all gelsolin segments. Matsudaira & Janmey (46) predicted that the conserved patterns were not an actin-binding motif because not all gelsolin segments bind actin, but rather that they reflect the presence of the underlying structure. A corollary is that all segments would have the same folding topology. This prediction has been borne out by the solution NMR structures of villin segment 1 (45) and severin segment 2 (67). Figure 10 shows a structural sequence alignment using the algorithm encoded in the computer program O (33) to improve an initial hand fit. In gelsolin segment 1, the C-terminal residue is Phe149, and its side chain is firmly packed against the actin structure. In villin segment 1, the region after residue 120 has very different conformations in the 10 best models, so it may be mobile in the absence of actin. The position in villin equivalent to Phe149 is Met125. Actin binding protects this residue from chemical oxidation (15), which might indicate surface exposure in the uncomplexed form. Nevertheless, this region may be constrained by the other domains in intact villin in a position similar to that found in the segment 1–actin structure.

CONSERVATION OF INTERMOLECULAR HYDROGEN-BONDING RESIDUES IN GELSOLIN SEGMENT 1   Ten residues in segment 1 contribute 12 intermolecular hydrogen bonds to the complex with actin. Only two of these (Phe49 and Tyr87) are part of the conserved pattern found in all gelsolin segments, but Phe49 has only main-chain hydrogen-bonding potential, and the side chain of Tyr87 is completely buried except for the hydrogen-bonding hydroxyl group. The hydrogen-bonding potential is not

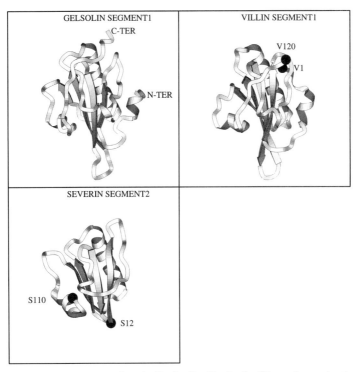

Figure 10 Aligned structures in gelsolin family. For both villin and severin, the first and last ordered residues are denoted with letters and a black sphere. The N- and C-terminal peptides of segment 2 have many conformations and have been omitted. Within a 2.0-Å rms cut off, 79% of villin segment 1 and 84% of severin segment 2 C_α atoms that are ordered superpose on the gelsolin segment 1 structure.

conserved, but the bulky apolar nature of the side chain is, reflecting the role of the residue in packing the interior. Therefore both of the residues that are similar in chemical type in all segments may be conserved for reasons unconnected with binding actin. Only two hydrogen-bonding residues are conserved absolutely: Gln118, which is bonded to actin Glu167 (also involved in the intermolecular Ca^{2+} ligands), and Arg120, which bonds to the main-chain at Gly146. A double mutation, in which two Glu residues replaced His119-Arg120, showed reduced affinity for actin (84), but either or both of these substitutions could primarily affect segment 1 structure rather than the actin-binding interactions. Both Gln118 and Arg120 lie at the edge of segment 1 that may be at an interaction site between segments (47), and their conservation may reflect constraints on the packing between segments in whole gelsolin.

PROFILIN

Actin-Binding Properties

Both *Acanthamoeba castellanii* (76) and bovine profilins (39) bind cytoplasmic actin with a four- to tenfold higher affinity than muscle actin. Profilactin as originally isolated from spleen did not contain bound ATP (10), and profilactin purified on hydroxylapatite lost its bound ATP (70). This loss may explain the apparently greater affinity [$K_d \approx 0.4$ μM (39)] of this complex compared with that of individual components [$K_d \approx 5$–10 μM (41)]. No evidence supports the presence of the high-affinity profilin complex in reconstituted systems, and in steady-state binding assays, the K_d for human platelet profilin binding to platelet actin or muscle actin was ~5 μM or less (20).

Profilin-actin complexes directly elongate actin filaments at their barbed ends (64), and profilin shows weak barbed end–capping activity (20). Because such capping affects the critical concentration at the barbed end of the filament, changes in apparent critical concentration in the presence of profilin will not give a true dissociation constant for the complex. For gelsolin-capped filaments, the affinity of profilin for actin is about 10 times higher than previously thought, i.e. $K_d \approx 0.5$ μM (56).

Profilin increases the rate constant for dissociation of ATP from actin by 1000-fold and catalyzes nucleotide exchange because it exchanges between monomers on a subsecond time scale (20). In the presence of thymosin β4, profilin may play an important role in promoting actin-filament assembly (56). Thus, profilin may modulate the interaction of other monomer-binding proteins.

Profilin may regulate activity of phospholipase C-γ1 and thereby be involved in cell signaling pathways in response to growth factors (reviewed in 44). Recent work suggests that profilin plays an important role in the actin-based motility of *Listeria monocytogenes* (79).

Actin-Binding Site

Schutt et al (68) solved the structure of the complex between bovine profilin and β-actin at 2.55-Å resolution. Profilin binds between subdomains 1 and 3 across the narrower edge of the protein, at the bottom in the standard view (Figure 11). There is substantial overlap with the actin-actin footprint in the filament model. The central region of the actin interface with profilin contains four aromatic residues [often a feature of antibody-antigen complexes (55)], but the area is not completely apolar because the C-terminal carboxylate of Tyr375 and all

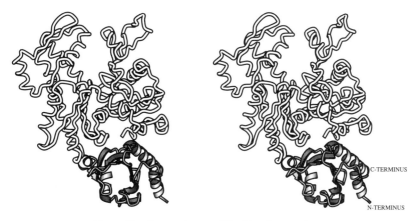

Figure 11   Stereo view profilin–β-actin complex.

the tyrosine hydroxyl groups are solvent accessible. The two ion pairs between the molecules reside at either end of the footprint made by profilin on actin (Figure 12). Hydrogen-bonding residues are from four separate elements of secondary structure (Figure 13). The central anti-parallel β-sheet is roughly perpendicular to the actin surface. The profilin binding face involves helices that pack on either side of this sheet and the penultimate two strands (4 and 5) of the sheet. Thus no single motif in the linear sequence describes the actin-binding residues.

Polyproline-Binding Site

Profilin binds poly (L-proline) (77). The binding sites in *A. castellanii* profilin I (4) and mammalian profilin (49) were recently identified by

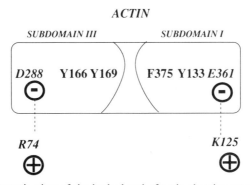

Figure 12   Schematic view of the barbed end of actin showing aromatic and charged residues that contact profilin.

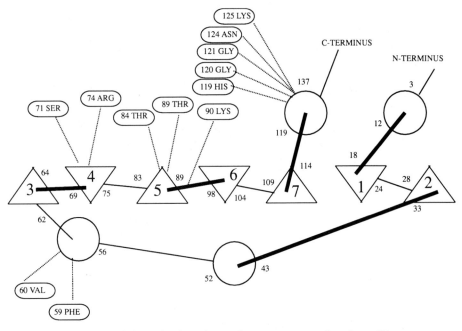

Figure 13   Schematic view of secondary-structure topology in profilin.

means of NMR spectroscopy (Figure 14*a*). In both cases, polyproline binds to an aromatic surface at the top face of the molecule between the N- and C-terminal helices. There is little overlap between the poly(L-proline) and actin-binding sites, which is consistent with solution experiments. Mutagenesis of aromatic residues on the surface of bovine profilin abolished binding (5): The mutated residues correspond to two of those identified in the NMR study (4). A K_d of ~0.4 μM was estimated from the chemical shift in amide resonances (4).

In solution, polyproline forms a type II helix, which is a left-handed helix with three residues per turn and a rise of 3.1 Å per residue. Based on the maximum distance between residues whose chemical shifts were perturbed by polyproline binding (~17 Å) and with the conformation of polyproline in the type II helix, 6 contiguous proline residues would be sufficient to span this distance (49). However, 10 proline residues were the minimum required to record a fluorescence change upon complex formation, and the optimum was at least 15–20 (57). Ten residues would span 31 Å in a type II helix. Although this distance is within the dimensions of a profilin molecule, it is about twice as long as the extent of the residues shown in Figure 14*b*. Perhaps at least 10 proline residues are needed to form a type II helix that can sustain the entropy loss in binding to profilin.

Polyproline type II helical structures are not rare in proteins, but their average length is only three residues (a single turn of α-helix) (1). The longest observed are eight residues in avian pancreatic protein (APP) (6) and nine in a fibronectin tandem domain structure (26). Prolines in these regions are rarely consecutive. In APP they are spaced at three-residue intervals—2, 5, 8 (as in collagen)—thereby forming one face of the polyproline-like helix. This surface packs against the apolar face of an α-helix to form the buried core of the protein (proline pyrolidine side chains are hydrophobic). Although many of the residues implicated in binding polyproline in profilin are aromatic and packed between the N- and C-terminal helices, they do not form a wholly apolar patch, because much of the profilin surface is formed by the polar atoms within these residues. APP is a very stable protein (6), while polyproline binding to actin is weak (57).

Some cytoskeletal proteins contain stretches of more than 6 consecutive proline residues, but such sequences are found in over 200 unrelated proteins (49). Although the physiological significance is unclear, many profilins of greatly different phylogenies bind polyproline, and many of the residues implicated in the binding are conserved. However, many of these are large aromatic amino acids whose conservation may reflect their role in stabilizing the protein fold.

PIP$_2$-Binding Site

In addition to binding actin and polyproline, profilin also binds PIP$_2$ (40). Figure 14b shows residues implicated in PIP$_2$ binding. In summarizing the experimental evidence, Cedergren-Zeppezauer et al (11) de-

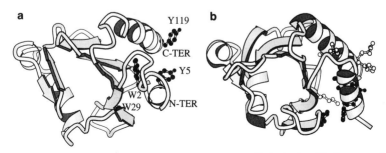

Figure 14   (*a*) Residues implicated in putative poly(L-proline) site (profilin in same orientation as in Figure 11). (*b*) Residues implicated in PIP$_2$ site (basic residues, *open circles,* apolar residues, *closed circles*).

lineate an extensive site that is peripheral to the actin contact. Because PIP$_2$ would be in a membrane or micelle, actin binding could be prevented without direct competition with its binding site. A hydrophobic patch within the site may bind the lipid chain (11). This patch overlaps with the poly (L-proline) site, but simultaneous binding of PIP$_2$ and polyproline to profilin has been observed (49). The energy required to pull a lipid molecule out of a micelle or double membrane is considerable [phospholipases that pull lipid head groups into their active sites have apolar tunnels that completely shield the lipid chain from solvent (69)], but binding the lipid chain may not be necessary. Rather, binding of the polyanionic phosphoinositol head groups by basic residues may be more important even though each may not have its own binding site. Profilin binds about five PIP$_2$ molecules in mixed membranes (19). The spacings between head groups can be estimated using the observed dimensions of isolated PIP$_2$ micelles of packing number 82. Values for their radii have been inferred [24 (88), 30, or 39 Å (74)]. The area occupied by each PIP$_2$ on a sphere with these dimensions is equivalent to square patches of sides of 9–15 Å. Thus, a small protein such as profilin probably does not have distinct sites for each head group but rather organizes a cluster of phosphoinositides around its edge. Even if each head group was only bound weakly, the coordinate binding of five molecules would be much stronger. Because the phospholipid molecules are in a membrane, the association is perforce cooperative since the dimensionality of the reaction volume is reduced after the first has been bound.

Sequence Variation in the Profilin Family

One feature that was emphasized in early studies on profilin was its basic character, in contrast to actin, which has an acidic isoelectric point. More recent work has identified both basic and neutral isoforms of profilin in *A. castellanii,* which show similar interactions with actin (36). Differences in isoelectric point result from two additional basic residues in the middle part of the sequence in the basic isoform (2).

Pollard & Rimm identified 17 residues that are conserved in a diverse family of profilins (62). Figure 15 shows them with a modification, based on the human profilin NMR structure, that avoids breaking strand 5 (50). Most are involved in packing the core of the molecule or occur at the start or end of secondary structural elements, where they may be involved in directing a turn in the conformation. Neither of the two conserved carboxylate groups is involved in a charge pair (as for segment 1). Residue Asp8 points to solution and is not an actin contact. Residue Glu46 is almost completely buried (as is the equivalent residue,

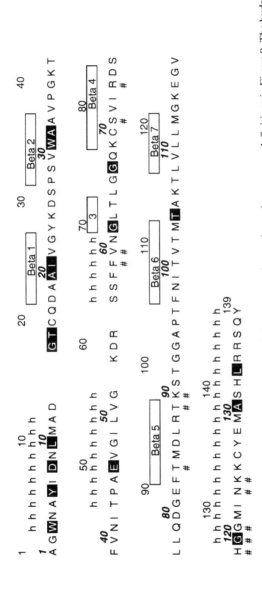

Figure 15 Sequence of bovine profilin. The secondary structural elements are shown above the sequence definitions in Figure 9. The hydrogen-bonding residues are denoted by # below the sequence.

Gln41 in the *A. castellanii* profilin structure), and the charge is uncompensated. None of the residues that hydrogen bonds to actin is conserved, except for Gly121. This residue makes only a main-chain hydrogen bond, and its conservation probably reflects its position at the start of the C-terminal helix. The ion pair at position 90 with actin Asp288 is conserved, because the only change is to histidine. The other ion-pair residue (Lys125 to Glu361) is uncharged in both *A. castellanii* and *Physarum polycephalum* actins. There is no coordinate mutation of Glu361 in actins in these species, and position 360 is also acidic, while it is uncharged in mammalian actins. Perhaps because the ion pairs are at the periphery of the contact, the side chain has the conformational freedom to reach solution and the charge is not unfavorably buried.

Thus, sequence analysis of the profilin family has not predicted the hydrogen-bonding residues and has even been misleading. The binding residues exhibit considerable sequence variation. Of eight profilin side-chain residues involved in hydrogen bonding to actin, none is absolutely conserved and only Lys74 and Lys90 maintain charge type. Before the profilin structure was available, a sequence homology between the profilins and the gelsolin family was shown to delineate the apolar face of the actin-binding helix in the gelsolin segment 1 structure (47). While this result successfully predicted that the C-terminal region of profilin is α-helical, the inference from this and other evidence (80) that profilin and gelsolin segment 1 might bind actin in a similar way was wrong.

COMPARISON OF BINDING SITES

Figure 16 compares actins in the three complexes. In previous experiments, Janin & Chothia have compared antibody-antigen and protease-protease inhibitor complexes with well-refined structures at high resolution (28). Between 600 and 1000 Å^2 of accessible area is buried by

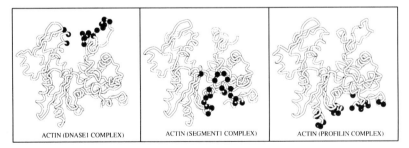

Figure 16   Actins in the three complexes. The contacting residues with each binding protein are denoted by black spheres.

Table 1 Summary of surfaces occluded from solvent in actin complexes[a]

Complex	Surface occluded (Å²) (fraction of total free surface)			Fractional composition of surfaces											
				Actin						Binding protein					
			Binding	Apolar		Polar		Charged		Apolar		Polar		Charged	
	Total	Actin	protein	Bound	Free	Bound	Free	Bound	Free	Bound	Free	Bound	Free	Bound	Free
DNase I	1756	942 (0.06)	814 (0.08)	0.73	0.58	0.18	0.24	0.09	0.18	0.59	0.55	0.27	0.33	0.15	0.12
Segment 1	1986	1034 (0.07)	951 (0.14)	0.62	0.56	0.28	0.23	0.11	0.21	0.67	0.61	0.25	0.28	0.08	0.11
Profilin	2043	1034 (0.07)	1009 (0.15)	0.56	0.56	0.21	0.25	0.22	0.19	0.61	0.58	0.21	0.29	0.19	0.13

[a] Values calculated using the procedures and parameters described in Reference 29.

Table 2 Summary of possible bonds in actin complexes

Complex	Number of contacts (Atomic centers less than sum of VDW radii +0.5 Å)	Aromatic residues		Possible hydrogen bonds			
		Actin	Binding protein	Main chain	Ion pairs not involving histidine	Possible ion pairs involving histidine	Total
DNase I	143	1	3	2	2	2	11
Gelsolin segment 1	129	1	3	6	0	0	15
Profilin	132	5	2	2	3	0	11

each molecule, 1650 ± 350 Å^2 in all. All three actin complexes are thus at the upper boundary (Table 1). The numbers of hydrogen bonds (Table 2) are also high (the normal range is 8–13). These results may be more significant than they first seem, because in the data bank used strong complexes, which may be easier to crystallize and to diffract to high resolution, may be overrepresented.

Certain complexes have individual characteristics that are unusual, e.g. ion pairs are rare. Although segment 1 has none, profilin has three and DNase I two (possibly five if histidines are protonated). The ratio of apolar atoms in the contacting surfaces is usually similar to the rest of the solvent-accessible surface, but both DNase I and segment 1 bury a larger percentage of apolar surface. In the DNase I complex, the interface is significantly more hydrophobic because of the apolar residues in the DNase I–binding loop. In the profilin complex, the interface contains seven aromatic residues, a feature more often found with antibody-antigen complexes (55).

Actin can also be considered an actin-binding protein. In the filament, a single subunit has four binding sites for other actin subunits. If the packing of subunits in the filament model is roughly correct, the total water-accessible area on a single subunit occluded by the others should be not unlike that observed for other oligomeric proteins. Although the fine details of subunit contacts are uncertain, we can estimate how different side chain and domain orientations affect the accessibility changes. We repeated the calculation for each of the actin-structure models, separately made into a test filament using the parameters found for the unrefined filament (23). The areas buried in the interfaces between filament subunits are all similar for the refined and test models (between 2000 and 3000 Å^2). Furthermore, more apolar atoms are buried in the interfaces than are present in the accessible filament surface, and both of these features are characteristic of protein oligomers (29).

Since these results were not implicit in fitting or refining the filament model, they independently confirm that the model is consistent with a normal oligomeric protein.

Except for the mobility of the DNase I–binding loop, the actin structures in the DNase I and gelsolin segment 1 complexes are very similar. In the latter, the largest conformational change is the movement of the side chain of Tyr169 that makes a hydrogen bond to segment 1. This conformational change also occurs in the profilactin structure, but since the residue is close to Phe375, which had been removed in the DNase I crystals, the new position may avoid steric clashes with that residue. The β-actin structure in the profilin complex shows a 5° rotation between subdomains 1 and 3 with respect to 2 and 4. Whether this is inherent in β-actin, or a consequence of profilin binding or the tight packing in that crystal form, awaits clarification.

ACTIN AS A TARGET PROTEIN

Is there anything about the G-actin structure that makes it a target for so many binding proteins? Actin has traditionally been considered a "sticky" protein. Does this property result from the presence of unusual patches of apolar atoms on the surface or from a special distribution of charged residues?

Surface Area

The surface area exposed to solvent is a little higher than average for a protein of its size, but this may merely reflect the medium resolution of the structures. For globular proteins, Miller et al (51) found a relationship between solvent-accessible area A (in Å^2) and relative molecular mass (M_r): $A = 6.3 \times M_r^{0.73}$. The accessible surface areas for the three complexes without their cognate binding proteins, using the same radii as Miller et al (51), showed roughly 9% more accessible area than that predicted by the equation, but deviations of this magnitude have been found in previous work. Thus, no evidence indicates that actin is any more open or loosely packed than is normal for a globular protein.

Chemical Composition

The chemical composition of the monomer surface is also normal. On average, protein surfaces are 57% nonpolar, 24% polar, and 19% charged with a 5% variation (51). The composition of each of the three structures is within these bounds. Two of the proteins (segment 1 and DNase I) bind to noticeably apolar patches on the actin surface. In the actin segment 1 complex, a central patch is formed by four apolar residues exposed on the solvent-accessible face of the helix (residues 341–349) in subdomain 1 and by the tyrosine residue from subdomain 3. The helix residues were noted as an unusual feature that might denote a binding site (34), even before the structure of the segment 1 complex was solved. All four residues are conserved except in the most divergent actins (71). In contrast, the surfaces in the profilin complex are no more apolar than nonbinding surfaces. Hence an unusual cluster of hydrophobic residues is not an essential feature for actin binding (Table 1).

Surface Topography

The binding surfaces in all three complexes are closely opposed so that there are few solvent-filled cavities between them. The free energy change for water that is excluded at the interface in the free protein contributes to the binding energy in the complex. Water molecules at the surface of a protein have lower entropy than water in bulk solvent because each protein atom excludes a solid sector around each water molecule from contact with bulk solvent. The size of the excluded sector depends on the local shape of the protein; hence, differently shaped protein surfaces affect the entropy of water molecules differently (54). Concave protein surfaces exclude a greater solid angle around a water molecule than do plane surfaces, which exclude more than convex surfaces. Thus the entropic contribution to the free energy of association may be more favorable at some surfaces than at others.

We have looked at the shapes of binding interfaces in actin and other protein complexes to see if this feature distinguishes the actin-binding surfaces from the rest of the protein by using a computer program (SURFCV) by S Sridharan (Columbia University) that calculates this local measure. At points in the accessible protein surface, the ratio between the solid angle around a water molecule at the interface that is excluded from bulk solvent and that at a plane surface is computed. A fractional exclusion less than 1.0 means that the surface is locally convex and that the contribution to the free energy of association of a second protein that may bind there is less than for a locally concave surface, for which the fractional exclusion is greater than 1.0. Thus the fractional exclusion can be considered a local measure of hydrophobicity. For larger proteins, it approaches unity (54), the value for a plane surface. We are interested in departures from this average in binding sites.

We calculated the fractional exclusions in the contacting and noncontacting surfaces for the separate proteins in a number of complexes. The noncontacting surfaces were invariably close to unity, but the contacting surfaces were not. Some of the lowest fractional exclusions (that is locally convex surfaces, on average) were for dimer interfaces of superoxide dismutase (2SOD) (0.85) and of citrate synthase (2CSC) (0.73). The lowest was 0.64 for the binding site on lysozyme in a Fab complex (1FDL). The largest value (concave) was only 1.08, for the binding site of *Streptomyces griseus* protease A in complex (3SGB) with ovomucoid inhibitor (0.84). Although the average values in this complex suggest complementary concave-convex binding surfaces, this scheme is not universal, because the dimers are symmetrical and both surfaces are identical, while in the antigen-antibody complex, both are convex.

The binding surfaces in the actin complex are different from the non-contacting surfaces, both for actin and the cognate binding proteins, but the fractional exclusions are not far from unity and none is as large as those observed for other complexes described above. They are actin-DNase I (1.06, concave; 0.98, convex), actin-gelsolin segment 1 (1.06, 0.95), and actin-profilin (1.01, 1.06). Thus local surface topography is not a distinctive marker for the actin-binding sites.

Fractal Dimension

Rough patches on molecular surfaces may denote sites of interaction (16, 42). Fractal dimension has been used as a measure of surface roughness to show that bound water molecules are located in surface grooves (38). The fractal dimension is determined by plotting the numbers of atoms in spheres of increasing radii for points on the molecular surface (38), where the fractal dimension is the slope of log(number of atoms) vs log(radius). For instance, in the extreme case of a point at the tip of a fine projection from the protein surface, the number of atoms is proportional to the radius, and the fractal dimension is 1.0; at the edge of a thin sheet, the number of atoms is proportional to the radius squared (fractal dimension 2.0); at the bottom of a pit with a narrow entrance, the number of atoms is proportional to the radius cubed (fractal dimension 3.0). These extremes rarely occur in protein structures, in which the average fractal dimension is roughly 2.2.

We find that fractal dimensions for noncontacting surfaces in the complexes we examined vary only between 2.17 and 2.29 and that values for contacting and noncontacting surfaces were similar. The outlying values were low rather than high, denoting smoother rather than rougher surfaces. These were for the binding site on actin (2.09) for DNase I and for ovomucoid inhibitor (2.11) in its complex with *S. griseus* protease A (3SGB). Both insert a loop that projects from the rest of the structure, so the shape tends toward a thin sheet and thus has lower fractal dimension. In summary, no evidence indicates an increased surface roughness at actin-binding sites or at the sites of any of the other complexes.

Electrostatic Potential

Actin is characterized as an acidic protein, whereas mammalian profilin is basic. We used a finite difference algorithm (53) to solve Poisson-Boltzmann equations for the separate protein models in all three actin complexes, using dielectric values of 2 and 80 for inside the protein and for the solvent, respectively, and a monovalent salt concentration of 150 mM. Subdomain 1 is the most negative of all four subdomains. We have compared both the electrostatic potentials of the free proteins in each complex and the contact region of each with the rest of its surface. Our analysis shows that neither do actin-binding proteins have to be positively charged nor do they necessarily bind at the most negatively charged sites on actin. [*Acanthamoeba* profilin I has a pI of 5.5, which is much more acidic than profilin II, but the binding constants to actin are similar (36).] None of the binding proteins makes specific interactions with the N-terminal acidic residues of actin, which are most variable between different isoforms.

Summary of Binding Features

The actin-binding surfaces show no extreme features, nor are any common to all three structures that distinguish them from other complexes. Extreme properties such as extensive apolar interfaces between subunits are usually found in proteins that denature when they are separated (29). Actin, in contrast, undergoes repeated cycles of polymerization and is stable in both forms. Nevertheless, all the complexes share one feature in common—each protein binds between two actin subdomains. Nicholls et al (54) have argued that a convex and concave surface release more free energy in occluding bulk solvent from the interface between them than does an equivalent area between flat surfaces. The price is the free energy of maintaining the concave surface, which reduces the entropy of water molecules at the interface. Perhaps this cost is more easily borne by actin because of the interdomain contacts and the bound nucleotide that pins them together. The almost planar arrangement of the subdomains may allow most access to such clefts between domains. In the filamentous form, additional actin-binding sites may occur between the protruding first subdomains on successive actin subunits in the same strand that is adjacent to the more exiguous subdomain 2 that connects the successive first subdomains within the same strand.

CONCLUSION AND FUTURE DIRECTIONS

Actin is fascinating as a target protein because it has binding sites for many different proteins, the basis for which is not apparent from their sequences. From DNA-binding proteins, we might expect some structural principles to simplify our apparent confusion and facilitate predictions. Unfortunately none of the three complexes solved so far has a common binding site, but as three is hardly a quorum, we may not have a representative sample yet. Each protein spans two actin subdomains, and the numbers of hydrogen bonds and area excluded from solvent are both high, but the actin sites show no extremes in surface topography, electrostatics, or fractal dimension. Even given the known crystal structures of actin-binding protein complexes and clear sequence alignments with related proteins, we have seen variability in residues that hydrogen bond to actin and in how conserved residues more often map to the apolar cores of these proteins. Because binding occurs at surfaces, the residue types that can be accommodated there are less likely to destabilize the individual protein folds and so they can be more variable. In one respect however, actin is a favorable model system to understand specificity between binding proteins. Its surface residues are much more conserved throughout evolution than most proteins. Thus, actin may be thought of as a stationary target, and in its complexes we need consider only the sequence variability of one protein and not two. An ensemble of structures from different complexes is clearly needed. Then some or all of the three complexes described here might be seen as paradigms, just as the helix-turn-helix motif or β-ribbon associations are in DNA-binding proteins. An additional challenge is to open up F-actin structures to study at atomic resolution: Forming and crystallizing defined length protofilaments would facilitate attempts to solve complexes with F-actin-binding proteins (such as myosin subfragment 1!).

ACKNOWLEDGMENTS

We thank T Holak and M Rozycki for coordinates before publication; C Chothia, S Maciver, H-G Mannherz, A Nicholls, and S Sridharan for discussions; and E Getzoff and S Sridharan for computer programs. This work was supported by the Commission of the European Communities and the Wellcome Trust.

Literature Cited

1. Adzhubei AA, Sternberg MJE. 1993. Left-handed polyproline II helices commonly occur in globular proteins. *J. Mol. Biol.* 229:472–93
2. Ampe C, Sato M, Pollard TD, Vandekerckhove J. 1988. The primary structure of the basic isoform of *Acanthamoeba* profilin. *Eur. J. Biochem.* 170:597–601
3. André E, Lottspeich F, Schleicher M, Noegel A. 1988. Severin, gelsolin, and villin share a homologous sequence in regions presumed to contain F-actin severing domains. *J. Biol. Chem.* 263:722–28
4. Archer SJ, Vinson VK, Pollard TD, Torchia DA. 1994. Elucidation of the poly-L-proline binding-site in *Acanthamoeba* profilin-I by NMR-spectroscopy. *FEBS Lett.* 337:145–51
5. Bjorkegren C, Rozycki M, Schutt CE, Lindberg U, Karlsson R. 1993. Mutagenesis of human profilin locates its poly(L-proline)-binding site to a hydrophobic patch of aromatic-amino-acids. *FEBS Lett.* 333:123–26
6. Blundell TL, Pitts JE, Tickle IJ, Wood SP, Wu CW. 1981. X-ray-analysis (1.4 Å resolution) of avian pancreatic polypeptide: small globular protein hormone. *Proc. Natl. Acad. Sci. USA* 78:4175–79
7. Brisson A, Mosser G, Huber R. 1991. Structure of soluble and membrane-bound human annexin-V. *J. Mol. Biol.* 220:199–203
8. Bryan J. 1988. Gelsolin has three actin-binding sites. *J. Cell Biol.* 106:1553–62
9. Bryan J, Kurth MC. 1984. Actin-gelsolin interactions. Evidence for two actin-binding sites. *J. Biol. Chem.* 259:7480–87
10. Carlsson L, Nyström L-E, Sundkvist I, Markey F, Lindberg U. 1977. Actin polymerizability is influenced by profilin, a low molecular weight protein in non-muscle cells. *J. Mol. Biol.* 115:465–83
11. Cedergren-Zeppezauer ES, Goonesekere NCW, Rozycki MD, Myslik JC, Dauter Z, et al. 1994. Crystallization and structure determination of bovine profilin at 2.0 Å resolution. *J. Mol. Biol.* 240:459–75
12. Combeau C, Carlier M-F. 1992. Covalent modification of G-actin by pyridoxal 5'-phosphate: polymerization properties and interaction with DNase I and myosin subfragment 1. *Biochemistry* 31:300–9
13. Cunningham CC, Stossel TP, Kwiatkowski DJ. 1991. Enhanced motility in NIH 3T3 fibroblasts that overexpress gelsolin. *Science* 251:1233–36
14. Dabiri GA, Youngs CL, Rosenbloom J, Southwick FS. 1992. Molecular cloning of human macrophage capping protein cDNA. *J. Biol. Chem.* 267:16545–52
15. deArruda MV, Bazari H, Wallek M, Matsudaira P. 1992. An actin footprint on villin. Single site substitutions in a cluster of basic residues inhibit actin severing but not capping activity of villin. *J. Biol. Chem.* 267:13079–85
16. Douglas JF. 1989. How does surface-roughness affect polymer surface interactions. *Macromolecules* 22:3707–16
17. Eichinger L, Schleicher M. 1992. Characterization of actin- and lipid-binding domains in severin, a calcium-dependent F-actin fragmenting protein. *Biochemistry* 31:4779–87
18. Gadasi H. 1982. Isolated *Entamoeba histolytica* actin does not inhibit DNase-I activity. *Biochem. Biophys. Res. Commun.* 104:158–64
19. Goldschmidt-Clermont PJ, Machesky LM, Baldassare JJ, Pollard TD. 1990. The actin-binding protein profilin binds to PIP$_2$ and inhibits its hydrolysis by phospholipase-C. *Science* 247:1575–78
20. Goldschmidt-Clermont PJ, Machesky LM, Doberstein SK, Pollard TD. 1991. Mechanism of the interaction of human platelet profilin with actin. *J. Cell Biol.* 113:1081–89
21. Hawkins M, Pope B, Maciver SK, Weeds AG. 1993. Human actin depolymerizing factor mediates a pH sensitive destruction of actin filaments. *Biochemistry* 32:9985–93
22. Heintzelman MB, Frankel SA, Artavanis-Tsakonas S, Mooseker MS. 1993. Cloning of a secretory gelsolin from *Drosophila melanogaster*. *J. Mol. Biol.* 230:709–16
23. Holmes KC, Popp D, Gebhard W, Kabsch W. 1990. Atomic model of the actin filament. *Nature* 347:44–49
24. Horono M, Kumagai Y, Numata O, Watanabe Y. 1989. Purification of *Tetrahymena* actin reveals some unusual properties. *Proc. Natl. Acad. Sci. USA* 86:75–79
25. Horono M, Sutoh K, Watanabe Y, Ohno T. 1992. A chimaeric actin carrying N-terminal portion of *Tetrahymena*

actin does not bind to DNase I. *Biochem. Biophys. Res. Commun.* 184: 1511–16

26. Huber AH, Wang YME, Bieber AJ, Bjorkman PJ. 1994. Crystal-structure of tandem type-III fibronectin domains from *Drosophila* neuroglia at 2.0 Å. *Neuron* 12:717–31

27. Huber R, Bode W. 1978. Structural basis of the activation and action of trypsin. *Acc. Chem. Res.* 11:114–22

28. Janin J, Chothia C. 1990. The structure of protein-protein recognition sites. *J. Biol. Chem.* 265:16027–30

29. Janin J, Miller S, Chothia C. 1988. Surface, subunit interfaces and interior of oligomeric proteins. *J. Mol. Biol.* 204: 155–64

30. Janmey PA, Iida K, Yin HL, Stossel TP. 1987. Polyphosphoinositide micelles and polyphosphoinositide-containing vesicles dissociate endogenous gelsolin-actin complexes and promote actin assembly from the fast-growing end of actin filaments blocked by gelsolin. *J. Biol. Chem.* 262:12228–36

31. Janmey PA, Lamb J, Allen PG, Matsudaira PT. 1992. Phosphoinositide-binding peptides derived from the sequences of gelsolin and villin. *J. Biol. Chem.* 267:11818–23

32. Janmey PA, Stossel TP, Lind SE. 1986. Sequential binding of actin monomers to plasma gelsolin and its inhibition by vitamin D-binding protein. *Biochem. Biophys. Res. Commun.* 136:72–79

33. Jones TA, Zou JY, Cowan SW, Kjeldgaard M. 1991. Improved methods for building protein models in electron density maps. *Acta Crystallogr.* A47: 110–19

34. Kabsch W, Mannherz HG, Suck D. 1985. 3-Dimensional structure of the complex of actin and DNase-I at 4.5 Å resolution. *EMBO J.* 4:2113–18

35. Kabsch W, Mannherz HG, Suck D, Pai EF, Holmes KC. 1990. Atomic structure of the actin-DNase I complex. *Nature* 347:37–44

36. Kaiser DA, Sato M, Ebert RF, Pollard TD. 1986. Purification and characterization of 2 isoforms of *Acanthamoeba* profilin. *J. Cell Biol.* 102:221–26

37. Kraulis PJ. 1991. Molscript—a program to produce both detailed and schematic plots of protein structures. *J. Appl. Crystallogr.* 24:946–50

38. Kuhn LA, Siani MA, Pique ME, Fisher CL, Getzoff ED, Tainer JA. 1992. The interdependence of protein surface-topography and bound water-molecules revealed by surface accessibility and fractal density measures. *J. Mol. Biol.* 228:13–22

39. Larsson H, Lindberg U. 1988. The effect of divalent-cations on the interaction between calf spleen profilin and different actins. *Biochim. Biophys. Acta* 953:95–105

40. Lassing I, Lindberg U. 1985. Specific interaction between phosphatidylinositol 4,5-bisphosphate and profilactin. *Nature* 314:472–74

41. Lee S, Li M, Pollard TD. 1988. Evaluation of the binding of *Acanthamoeba* profilin to pyrene-labeled actin by fluorescence enhancement. *Anal. Biochem.* 168:148–55

42. Lewis M, Rees DC. 1985. Fractal surfaces of proteins. *Science* 230:1163–65

43. Lorenz M, Popp D, Holmes KC. 1993. Refinement of the F-actin model against X-ray fiber diffraction data by the use of a directed mutation algorithm. *J. Mol. Biol.* 234:826–36

44. Machesky LN, Pollard TD. 1993. Profilin as a potential mediator of membrane-cytoskeletal communication. *Trends Cell Biol.* 3:381–85

45. Markus MA, Nakayama T, Matsudaira P, Wagner G. 1994. Solution structure of villin 14T, a domain conserved among actin-severing proteins. *Protein Sci.* 3:70–81

46. Matsudaira PT, Janmey PA. 1988. Pieces in the actin-severing protein puzzle. *Cell* 54:139–40

47. McLaughlin PJ, Gooch JT, Mannherz HG, Weeds AG. 1993. Structure of gelsolin segment-1-actin complex and the mechanism of filament severing. *Nature* 364:685–92

48. Mendelson RA, Morris E. 1994. The structure of F-actin—results of global searches using data from electron-microscopy and X-ray crystallography. *J. Mol. Biol.* 240:138–54

49. Metzler WJ, Bell AJ, Ernst E, Lavlie TB, Mueller L. 1994. Identification of the poly-L-proline-binding site on human profilin. *J. Biol. Chem.* 269: 4620–25

50. Metzler WJ, Constantine KL, Friedrichs MS, Bell AJ, Ernst EG, et al. 1993. Characterization of the 3-dimensional solution structure of human profilin—H-1, C-13, and N-15 NMR assignments and global folding pattern. *Biochemistry* 32:13818–29

51. Miller S, Janin J, Lesk AM, Chothia C. 1987. Interior and surface of monomeric proteins. *J. Mol. Biol.* 196: 641–56

52. Nakamura S, Sakurai T, Nonomura Y. 1994. Differential expression of bovine adseverin in adrenal-gland revealed by in-situ hybridization—cloning of a cDNA for adseverin. *J. Biol. Chem.* 269:5890–96

53. Nicholls A, Honig B. 1991. A rapid finite-difference algorithm, utilizing successive over-relaxation to solve the Poisson-Boltzmann equation. *J. Comput. Chem.* 12:435–45

54. Nicholls A, Sharp KA, Honig B. 1991. Protein folding and association: insights from the interfacial and thermodynamic properties of hydrocarbons. *Proteins Struct. Funct. Genet.* 11:281–96

55. Padlan EA. 1990. On the nature of antibody combining sites—unusual structural features that may confer on these sites an enhanced capacity for binding ligands. *Proteins Struct. Funct. Genet.* 7:112–24

56. Pantaloni D, Carlier M-F. 1993. How profilin promotes actin filament assembly in the presence of thymosin $\beta 4$. *Cell* 75:1007–14

57. Perelroizen I, Marchand J-P, Blanchoin L, Didry D, Carlier M-F. 1994. Interactions of profilin with G-actin and poly(L-proline). *Biochemistry* 33:8472–78

58. Podolski JL, Steck TL. 1988. Association of deoxyribonuclease I with the pointed ends of actin filaments in human red blood cell membrane skeletons. *J. Biol. Chem.* 263:638–45

59. Pollard TD. 1986. Rate constants for the reactions of ATP- and ADP-actin with the ends of actin filaments. *J. Cell Biol.* 103:2747–54

60. Pollard TD. 1993. Actin and actin binding proteins. In *Guidebook to the Cytoskeletal and Motor Proteins*, ed. T Kreis, R Vale, pp. 3–11. New York: Oxford Univ. Press

61. Pollard TD, Almo S, Quirk S, Vinson V, Lattman EE. 1994. Structure of actin binding proteins: insights about function at atomic resolution. *Annu. Rev. Cell Biol.* 10:207–49

62. Pollard TD, Rimm DL. 1991. Analysis of cDNA clones for *Acanthamoeba* profilin-I and profilin-II shows end-to-end homology with vertebrate profilins and a small family of profilin genes. *Cell Motil. Cytoskeleton* 20:169–77

63. Polzar B, Nowak E, Goody RS, Mannherz HG. 1989. The complex of actin and deoxyribonuclease-I as a model system to study the interactions of nucleotides, cations and cytochalasin-D

64. Pring M, Weber A, Bubb MR. 1992. Profilin actin complexes directly elongate actin-filaments at the barbed end. *Biochemistry* 31:1827–36

65. Rydel TJ, Tulinsky A, Bode W, Huber R. 1991. Refined structure of the hirudin-thrombin complex. *J. Mol. Biol.* 221:583–601

66. Schmid MF, Jakana J, Matsudaira P, Chiu W. 1993. Imaging frozen, hydrated acrosomal bundle from *Limulus* sperm at 7Å resolution with a 400 kV electron cryomicroscope. *J. Mol. Biol.* 230:384–86

67. Schnuchel A, Wiltscheck R, Eichinger L, Schleicher M. 1995. Structure of severin domain 2 in solution. *J. Mol. Biol.* Submitted

68. Schutt CE, Myslik JC, Rozycki MD, Goonesekere N, Lindberg U. 1993. The structure of crystalline profilin beta-actin. *Nature* 365:810–16

69. Scott DL, White SP, Otwinowski Z, Yuan W, Gelb MH, Sigler PB. 1990. Interfacial catalysis—the mechanism of phospholipase-A_2. *Science* 250:1541–46

70. Segura M, Lindberg U. 1984. Separation of non-muscle isoactins in the free form or as profilactin complexes. *J. Biol. Chem.* 259:3949–54

71. Sheterline P, Sparrow JC. 1994. Actin. *Protein Profile* 1:13–21

72. Stella MC, Schauerte H, Straub KL, Leptin M. 1994. Identification of secreted and cytosolic gelsolin in *Drosophila*. *J. Cell Biol.* 125:607–16

73. Stossel TP. 1993. On the crawling of animal cells. *Science* 260:1086–94

74. Sugiura Y. 1981. Structure of molecular aggregates of (3-*sn*-phosphatidyl)-L-myo-inositol 3,4-bis(phosphate) in water. *Biochim. Biophys. Acta* 641:148–59

75. Sun HQ, Wooten DC, Janmey PA, Yin HL. 1994. The actin side-binding domain of gelsolin also caps actin-filaments—implications for actin filament severing. *J. Biol. Chem.* 269:9473–79

76. Tabacman LS, Korn ED. 1982. The regulation of actin polymerization and the inhibition of monomeric actin ATPase activity by *Acanthamoeba* profilin. *J. Biol. Chem.* 257:4166–70

77. Tanaka M, Shibata H. 1985. Poly(L-proline)-binding proteins from chick-embryos are a profilin and a profilactin. *Eur. J, Biochem.* 151:291–97

78. Theriot JA, Mitchison TJ. 1993. The three faces of profilin. *Cell* 75:835–38

79. Theriot JA, Rosenblatt J, Portnov DA.

Goldschmidt-Clermont PJ, Mitchison TJ. 1994. Involvement of profilin in the actin-based motility of *L. monocytogenes* in cells and in cell-free extracts. *Cell* 76:505–17

80. Vinson VK, Archer SJ, Lattman EE, Pollard TD, Torchia DA. 1993. 3-Dimensional solution structure of *Acanthamoeba* profilin-I. *J. Cell Biol.* 122:1277–83

81. Waterston R, Martin C, Craxton M, Huynh C, Coulson A, et al. 1992. A survey of expressed genes in *Caenorhabditis elegans*. *Nature Genet.* 1:114–23

82. Way M, Gooch J, Pope B, Weeds AG. 1989. Expression of human plasma gelsolin in *E. coli* and dissection of actin binding sites by segmental deletion mutagenesis. *J. Cell Biol.* 109:593–605

83. Way M, Pope B, Gooch J, Hawkins M, Weeds AG. 1990. Identification of a region of segment 1 of gelsolin critical for actin binding. *EMBO J.* 9:4103–9

84. Way M, Pope B, Weeds AG. 1992. Are the conserved sequences in segment 1 of gelsolin important for binding actin? *J. Cell Biol.* 116:1135–43

85. Way M, Pope B, Weeds AG. 1992. Evidence for functional homology in the F-actin binding domains of gelsolin and alpha-actinin: implications for the requirements of severing and capping. *J. Cell Biol.* 119:835–42

85a. Way M, Weeds AG. 1988. Nucleotide sequence of pig plasma gelsolin. Comparison of protein sequence with human gelsolin and other actin-severing proteins shows strong homologies and evidence for large internal repeats. *J. Mol. Biol.* 203:1127–33

86. Weeds A, Maciver S. 1993. F-actin capping proteins. *Curr. Opin. Cell Biol.* 5:63–69

87. Weber A, Pennise CR, Pring M. 1994. DNase-I increases the rate-constant of depolymerization at the pointed (−) end of actin filament. *Biochemistry* 33:4780–86

88. Wendoloski JJ, Kimatian SJ, Schutt CE, Salemme FR. 1989. Molecular-dynamics simulation of a phospholipid micelle. *Science* 243:636–38

89. Weston SA, Lahm A, Suck D. 1992. X-ray structure of the DNase I-d(GGTATACC)(2) complex at 2.3-Å resolution. *J. Mol. Biol.* 226:1237–56

90. Yin HL. 1988. Gelsolin: calcium and polyphosphoinositide-regulated actin-modulating protein. *Bioessays* 7:176–79

91. Yin HL, Janmey PA, Schleicher M. 1990. Severin is a gelsolin prototype. *FEBS Lett.* 264:78–80

92. Yu F-X, Johnston PA, Sudhof TC, Yin HL. 1990. gCap39, a calcium ion- and polyphosphoinositide-regulated actin capping protein. *Science* 250:1413–14

93. Yu F-Z, Sun H-Q, Janmey PA, Yin HL. 1992. Identification of a polyphosphoinositide-binding sequence in an actin monomer-binding domain of gelsolin. *J. Biol. Chem.* 267:14616–21

Annu. Rev. Biophys. Biomol. Struct. 1995. 24:677–700

FLEXIBLE DOCKING AND DESIGN

R. Rosenfeld, S. Vajda, and C. DeLisi

Department of Biomedical Engineering, Boston University, Boston, Massachusetts 02215

KEY WORDS: automated molecular docking, computer-aided drug design, empirical free-energy evaluation, peptide antigen–MHC interaction, protease inhibitor design

CONTENTS

ABSTRACT

Docking and design are the major computational steps toward understanding and affecting receptor-ligand interactions. The flexibility of many ligands makes these calculations difficult and requires the development and use of special methods. The need for such tools is illustrated by two examples: the design of protease inhibitors and the analysis and design of peptide antigens binding to specific MHC receptors. We review the computational concepts that have been extended from rigid-body to flexible docking, as well as the following important strategies for flexible docking and design: (*a*) Monte Carlo/molecular dynam-

677

1056-8700/95/0610-0677$05.00

ics docking, (*b*) in-site combinatorial search, (*c*) ligand build-up, and (*d*) site mapping and fragment assembly. The use of empirical free energy as a target function is discussed. Due to the rapid development of the methodology, most new methods have been tested on only a limited number of applications and are likely to improve results obtained by more traditional computational or graphic tools.

INTRODUCTION

A critical factor in virtually all biological processes is the specificity of ligands for larger proteins, such as membrane-bound receptors, or enzymes. Ligands may be flexible; for example, neurotransmitters, inhibitors, and cofactors are often small flexible organic molecules. Many hormones and antigens are small or intermediate-size polypeptides. A predictive understanding of the molecular basis of recognition, which would encompass the ability to design ligands that bind specific receptors and to predict the change in stability caused by site-specific substitutions, is central to developing rational drug- and vaccine-design strategies as well as to elucidating normal and pathological cellular behavior.

Here, we analyze aspects of computational approaches to the docking of flexible molecules to proteins, as well as to the design of oligopeptides and other flexible ligands that would bind with high affinity to a specified receptor site. Design means either determining the chemical composition of a ligand with desired binding properties (e.g. the amino acid sequence of an oligopeptide) or, in a somewhat more restrictive sense, ranking a given set of ligands according to their binding affinities. Docking means determining the geometry of a receptor-ligand complex using the structure of the free receptor.

In general, accurate approaches to docking and design require progress on two major problems: finding a target function (in the most general case, a computationally viable free energy–evaluation model) that can accurately weight any specified conformation of the system and developing an algorithm that efficiently searches a complex energy landscape for the target function's minimum value.

In spite of the complexity of these problems, several experimental systems allow simplifying approximations in the computations. In the simplest systems, the geometries of the reactants remain, to a good first approximation, unchanged by complex formation (2, 16, 34, 40, 51, 52). In such rigid-body systems, an algorithm need only search the six-dimensional rotational/transitional space and can generally make effective predictions with simplified target functions. Because execution time is relatively rapid, these methods can be used to search large structural databases for small molecules that fit the binding site and that can serve as lead compounds for drug design (1, 39, 63, 71).

The rigid-body approach has limited uses, except in the search for small compounds. In almost all test cases, docking accuracy is much greater when one uses the geometries that the receptor and ligand have in the complex than when one uses the geometries of the uncomplexed molecules (70). The difference in accuracy implies that the assumption of rigidity is not fully valid even for protein-protein complexes in which the observed structural changes between the bound and free forms are small (77). In addition, simple scoring functions, such as measures of surface complementarity (34, 84), surface-area burial (85), solvation free energy, electrostatic-interaction energy, or the total molecular-mechanics energy (70), often fail to distinguish between near-native structures and others far from native. Hence, simple methods, though useful, are incomplete.

In the past few years, several groups have tried to improve docking procedures by allowing for flexibility. Introducing local minimization of a molecular-mechanics energy function such as CHARMm (7) yields only limited improvement. A general approach to flexible docking requires an unbiased sampling of the allowed conformational space of the ligand and a concurrent exploration of its six rigid-body degrees of freedom in the anisotropic environment of the receptor. This goal is difficult to achieve using traditional approaches, except perhaps for very small ligands (68). We review several flexible-docking and -design strategies for reducing computational efforts by fully exploiting the available structural and chemical information. Although most of the methods reviewed apply to any flexible ligand, we concentrate on peptides and peptide-like compounds that play a major role in many biological systems (49).

The success of docking depends heavily on the choice of a target function that accounts for the enthalpic, entropic, and solvation interactions that govern ligand-receptor association. The scoring is critical in design, in which the entropy loss of a flexible ligand, and the change in its internal energy upon binding, can greatly affect the binding affinity. In principle, free-energy perturbation (FEP) or thermodynamic-integration (TI) methods should permit accurate determination of the effects of mutagenesis on a receptor-ligand complex (35, 37, 54). In practice, however, such relatively rigorous procedures are computationally intensive and are not likely to be useful in docking or design for at least another five to ten years. The alternative approach to determining free energy is to use empirical functions (31, 58, 60), several of which are reviewed here.

PROBLEMS REQUIRING THE USE OF FLEXIBLE METHODS

Design of Protease Inhibitors

OVERVIEW   Protein cleavage is a ubiquitous aspect of biological processes: for example, the digestion of food, the control of blood pressure, and the activation of many proteins from precursors all require cutting, often at specific locations, of covalent bonds. The enzymes that carry out these diverse cleavage processes are collectively referred to as proteases. Errors in the production or regulation of any number of these enzymes cause serious pathologies. Protease inhibitors can be potential drugs (such as the HIV aspartic protease inhibitor), or investigative tools to elucidate the function of specific proteases.

INHIBITOR DESIGN   The design of high-affinity inhibitors for many proteases has been accomplished already because the enzymatic mechanisms of these families of enzymes are well understood and many derivatives of natural inhibitors have proven to be potent inhibitors. For serine proteases, the existence of a structural binding motif (Figure 1), found in all the small inhibitors of this family (5), may simplify the search for possible inhibitor conformations. The major obstacle to utilizing these inhibitors for therapeutic purposes is specificity. The major-

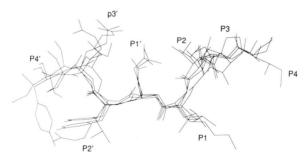

Figure 1   Superposition of four different inhibitors bound to different proteases: bovine pancreatic trypsin inhibitor (BPTI) complexed with kallikrein, chymotripsin inhibitor 2 complexed with subtilisin, eglin C complexed with thermitase, turkey ovomucoid inhibitor complexed with proteinase B from *Streptomyces griseus*. P4′ through P4 denote inhibitor side chains at given positions of the specificity pocket.

ity of known protease inhibitors are not specific for a single protease but rather inhibit, to varying levels, several proteases from a given family.

Because the naturally occurring protease inhibitors are proteins, one obvious approach to inhibitor design is to modify a segment of the inhibitor that is implicated in binding. Peptide inhibitors can occasionally be used directly for therapeutic purposes—for example, topical application of peptide-based inhibitors of proteases blocks parasite penetration through the skin (12). However, they more often serve as first-generation compounds that can be transformed into peptidomimetic inhibitors resistant to proteolysis.

Peptide Binding to Major Histocompatibility Complex Receptors

OVERVIEW   The ability to discriminate foreign from self, the major role of the immune system, is regulated mainly by the major histocompatibility complex (MHC) receptors. These comprise a highly polymorphic set of glycoproteins that bind and display fragments of intracellular proteins on the cell surface, thereby informing other components of the immune system of the protein composition within the cell. The two major classes of MHC receptors, I and II, have highly similar structures. In both, the antigenic binding site—a cleft approximately 20 Å long, 8 Å deep, and 12 Å wide—is formed by a β-sheet floor bounded by α-helical walls. Variations in the amino acids that line the cleft modulate both its shape and chemical nature, thus determining haplotype specificity.

Class I molecules are found on all nucleated cells, displaying 8- to 10-residue-long fragments of cytosolic proteins. In infected cells, a certain fraction of these fragments will have originated in proteins that are not native to the host, thus presenting a foreign molecular arrangement recognized by T-cell receptors (TCR) on CD8$^+$ cytotoxic T lymphocytes. This recognition stimulates, among other things, the release of cytolytic agents that mediate lysis of the infected cell. Class II products are generally confined to cells of the immune system, such as B cells, macrophages, and other dendritic cells. The pathway leading to the presentation of class II receptors on B cells consists of protein recognition by immunoglobulin receptors, followed by endocytosis of the antigen-receptor complex, proteolysis of the antigen, and recycling of 13- to 15-residue-long fragments complexed with class II molecules to the surface. These peptide-MHC complexes, when recognized by the TCR of CD4$^+$ helper T cells, stimulate production of the various lymphokines that regulate a humoral (antibody) immune response.

In contrast to its numerous immunoglobulin receptors and TCRs, the immune system has few MHC haplotypes. To elicit an immune response against the many possible pathogens, each haplotype must be able to bind many different peptides.

VACCINE DESIGN   The central role of MHC-peptide complexes in communicating the health of the cell to TCRs suggests that a predictive understanding of their structure could contribute substantially to progress in applied, as well as in basic, immunological research. Of particular therapeutic and prophylactic importance is the ability to design peptides with desired MHC and TCR specificities. One of the central complications in designing a peptide vaccine is MHC gene polymorphism. Different individuals, even when infected with an identical virus, will generally present different peptide fragments of the antigen. Any attempt to design a peptide vaccine must account for the various MHC haplotypes in the population of interest.

Several studies on HIV have reported a correlation between specific MHC class I alleles and either fast (33) or slow (76) progression of AIDS, which suggests an important role for a cell-mediated immune response. The induction of a strong antibody response may weaken a cell-mediated response caused by the effects of cross-regulatory cytokines, and therefore an effective vaccine strategy may need to specifically target cell-mediated immunity without eliciting neutralizing antibodies.

SEQUENCE AND STRUCTURAL MOTIFS   In peptides that bind a particular MHC haplotype, one or two positions (so-called anchors) tend to be occupied by one or a few specific residues, whereas the other positions tend to permit a relatively high degree of substitution (22, 23). However, the anchor residues are neither sufficient nor always necessary for binding.

Crystallographic studies (24, 47, 48, 72) have shown that class I–bound peptides are relatively extended, with a kink at or near position 3. Although the various peptide structures can be juxtaposed so that their terminal residues are closely aligned at both ends, their backbone conformations and side-chain orientations can differ substantially (Figure 2). Nevertheless, docking peptides to class I receptors is easier than flexible docking in general, because the known structural motif substantially constrains the translational and rotational search space.

The only class II complex that has been crystallized displays a fully extended, twisted peptide conformation (74). Several biochemical stud-

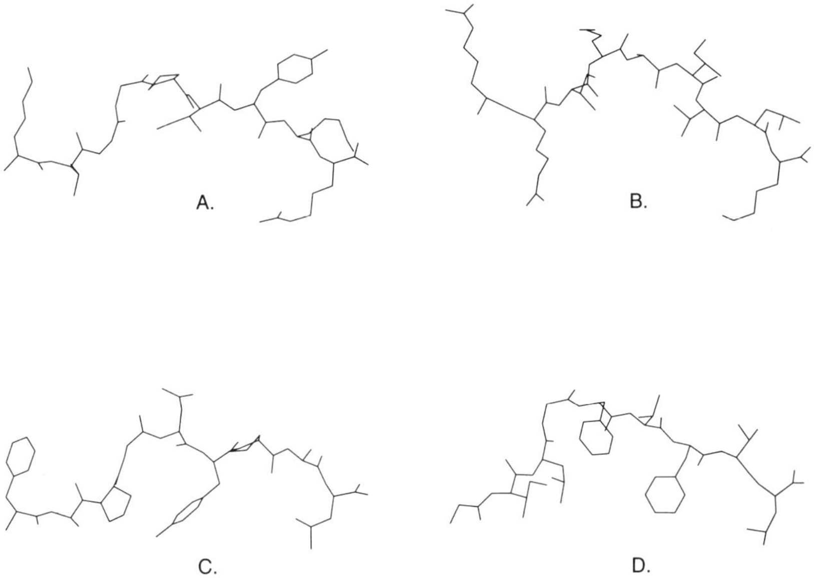

Figure 2   Bound conformation of four peptides bound to different MHC haplotypes. (*A*) HLA-Aw68 bound peptide. (*B*) HLA-B27 bound peptide. (*C*) H2-K^b bound peptide. (*D*) HLA-A2 bound peptide.

ies have suggested that class II–bound peptides share a common three-dimensional structure (50, 61).

METHODS OF DOCKING AND DESIGN

Docking encompasses a variety of different problems. The prediction of the optimum location of a ligand and its free energy of binding would ideally emerge from the crystal structure of the unliganded macromolecule without any a priori restrictions on the structure of the ligand. In practice, computations have been restricted to systems that allow various simplifications.

We assume that the binding sites, structural motifs of bound ligands, and structural variations within a given class of complexes are known, as in the proteases and MHC molecules as targets. Although this information significantly reduces the translational space that must be explored, ligand flexibility introduces substantial complications. Although the structure of the class I MHC has been known since 1987 (3), not even an approximate structure was predicted for the bound peptide, despite several attempts (11, 64), before a high resolution X-ray structure of an MHC-peptide complex was obtained (47).

From Rigid to Flexible Algorithms

Rigid-body docking contributed to the development of the following computational concepts that play important roles in flexible docking and design: (*a*) shape descriptors, (*b*) grid-based energy evaluation, (*c*) soft potentials, (*d*) local minimization, and (*e*) multiple-copy techniques. We discuss these concepts in turn.

SHAPE DESCRIPTORS   Shape descriptors consist of a relatively small number of characteristic points on the surfaces of the two molecules in a complex (69). One can search for the docked conformations by optimally superimposing or matching these points, which is computationally more efficient than matching two molecular surfaces, each defined by hundreds of atoms. In the DOCK program (16, 40), a set of spheres represents the negative image of the receptor, and a fast sphere-matching algorithm docks candidate ligands from a shape database. Katchalski-Katzir and coworkers (34) use three-dimensional discrete functions that distinguish between the surface and the interior of proteins. A correlation function is calculated to assess the extent of geometric match between surfaces of the molecules.

   Shape complementarity alone is a poor target function that frequently fails to distinguish near-native complex conformations from ones that have a different structure but relatively good complementarity (70). Therefore, the concept of shape descriptors has been extended by requiring pairwise interactions. In the directed version of DOCK, a hydrogen-bonding parameter is introduced (43). Jiang & Kim (32) match opposing surface normal vectors. In addition to surface overlap, Bacon & Moult (2) include Coulombic interactions in the scoring function. Pellegrini & Doniach (62) use a full molecular-mechanics interaction potential, but only among relatively few fiducial atoms. Shape descriptors are used for docking molecular fragments in flexible docking programs such as GRID (26), LUDI (6), and CLIX (41) (see below).

GRID-BASED ENERGY EVALUATION   A scoring scheme that accounts for electrostatic and van der Waals interactions as well as solvation effects generally improves accuracy of the docking and reduces the number of false positive solutions, i.e. complex structures that differ from the native (70). However, the use of more realistic potential function increases computational costs. These can be reduced by precomputing terms in the potential of the rigid receptor for each point on a three-dimensional grid (26, 27). Any target function in which the ligand and receptor terms are separable can be treated in this manner. The approach can be combined with the use of shape descriptors (32, 52). Although grid-based energy evaluation applies to rigid receptors only, ligand energy values are not precomputed and hence the ligand can be flexible (27).

SOFT POTENTIALS   Soft potentials are target functions that allow for some penetration of the protein surfaces being matched. Even the most rigid proteins undergo some changes when interacting with another molecule. Thus, rigid docking procedures frequently rank near-native conformations after structures that are far from the native, and a more realistic potential function does not necessarily improve performance. One way to address this difficulty is to use an artificial soft potential (2, 32, 62, 84, 88). Soft potentials can and have been used in conjunction with both shape descriptors and grid-based energy evaluations. Softening of the potential is also beneficial in flexible docking procedures.

LOCAL MINIMIZATION   Another way of introducing limited flexibility involves local minimization. Rigid-body docking with six degrees of freedom is augmented by local energy minimization in the space of N additional continuous variables that describe the conformation of either the ligand only, or both the ligand and receptor (70). The score function in these procedures is usually the potential energy of the complex, based on a molecular-mechanics energy function such as CHARMm (7). Local minimization can be combined both with shape descriptors and soft potentials and also with grid-based energy evaluation if the receptor structure is kept rigid. Although minimization leads to some conformational changes, it yields results that depend heavily on the starting ligand conformation, and hence the method does not qualify as truly flexible docking (68).

MULTIPLE-COPY TECHNIQUES   Several methods use numerous ligand copies, each transparent to the others but subject to the full force of the receptor, to determine energetically favorable positions and orientations of small molecules or functional groups in the binding site of a protein (21, 55, 65). Although the multiple-copy, simultaneous-search (MCSS) method was originally proposed in the context of a rigid receptor (55), it was extended recently to allow for ligand and receptor flexibility (65). In this latter case, several ligand copies and one copy of the receptor are minimized simultaneously, which substantially increases computational efficiency because the internal energy of the receptor is calculated only once for all ligand copies.

Strategies for Flexible Docking and Design

Flexible docking strategies require no a priori knowledge of the ligand conformation and hence consist of searches in the space of $6 + N$ translational, rotational, and conformational variables (11, 27, 28, 42, 88). Such an approach becomes a necessity if there is no useful information on the conformation of the ligand, as in the case of docking short linear peptides. Because flexible design relies heavily on flexible docking procedures, the two problems can be discussed simultaneously.

Four different strategies are currently in use for docking flexible ligands: (a) Monte Carlo or molecular-dynamics docking of complete molecules, (b) in-site combinatorial search, (c) ligand buildup, and (d) site mapping and fragment assembly. Some of the recent docking and design procedures combine several of these strategies. Although the same ideas are also important in pharmacophore-matching programs such as ALLADIN (81), CATALIST (73), and FOUNDATION (30), we restrict our discussion to docking and design for receptors with known three-dimensional structures.

DOCKING BY MONTE CARLO OR MOLECULAR-DYNAMICS METHODS   The number of possible conformations increases exponentially with the conformational degrees of freedom, N. One way to avoid this combinatorial explosion is to sample the $6 + N$ dimensional space by using Monte Carlo or molecular-dynamics simulations. Monte Carlo methods explore the thermodynamically accessible states of a system by generating small random changes that are either accepted or rejected according to the Metropolis algorithm (53). The probability of accepting steps that increase the energy depends on a temperature-like parameter T, which can be decreased according to a schedule known as simulated annealing (36). This popular method was first used for docking by Goodsell & Olson (27), who allowed rotations about a single bond in each step in addition to rigid body rotations and translations. Because a grid-based energy evaluation increased the efficiency of the procedure, the receptor was assumed to be rigid. Yue (88) used simulated annealing with a soft potential given in terms of distance constraints.

Simulated annealing should, in theory, always converge to the global minimum. Guaranteeing this convergence, however, would require an infinite number of temperature decrements, at each of which the system should reach equilibrium. In practice, one can only explore a few temperatures, and the number of equilibration steps at each temperature is also limited. Furthermore, in macromolecular applications the numerous degrees of freedom in a Monte Carlo search limits it to only small regions of the conformational space, and the results depend on the starting conformation. The investigator can reduce this deficiency somewhat by using the method in tandem with a coarse-grain rigid search (11, 28) or by simply repeating the analysis at various starting conformations. One can increase the relatively small acceptance ratio yielded by Monte Carlo calculations by using Monte Carlo minimization, i.e. by combining each Monte Carlo step with local minimization (77).

Molecular-dynamics techniques generally work as well as Monte Carlo methods in the simulation of macromolecules, particularly for calculating thermodynamic properties. Although molecular dynamics is efficient in exploring low-energy states, conformational changes that require the crossing of even relatively low energy barriers are extremely rare, and because of limits on simulation times the analysis is strictly local. Investigators have explored larger regions of the conformational space of free peptides (14) and protein loops (9) simply by running the simulation at artificially high temperatures. High temperatures tend to unfold the receptor, but recent modifications sidestep these unwanted effects (18) by separating the center-of-mass motion of the ligand from its internal and rotational motions and by using different thermal baths to study each type of ligand motion and to assess the receptor motion. Thus, the temperatures and the time constants of coupling to the baths can be arbitrarily varied for these three types of motion, allowing either a frozen or a flexible receptor and allowing control of search rate without disturbing the internal structure of the receptor (18). The new method has been applied to only a single problem, but the idea is certainly appealing.

With increasing degrees of freedom, both Monte Carlo and molecular-dynamics strategies become more unreliable, because of the restricted sampling of the conformational space (11). Even such limited exploration is very time-consuming, and these methods are not very useful for screening large databases for suitable ligands (82).

IN-SITE COMBINATORIAL SEARCH   The conformational space of small molecules, particularly short peptides, can be explored in discrete steps. Thus, in the conformational analysis of an oligopeptide, we assign a conformational state to each residue from a collection of discrete states, which are usually defined as low-energy conformations of isolated amino acids represented by points on the (ϕ, ψ) map (79, 80). Assigning side chains from a table of rotamers is a similar problem (17).

The problem is finding the combination of discrete states that minimizes a target function such as the potential energy. In principle, the optimal assignment can be found by a systematic search, but the number of conformations to be explored increases exponentially with the size of the problem (e.g. the number of residues). Combinatorial optimization algorithms such as branch-and-bound (80) or dead-end elimination (17) can efficiently limit the number of conformations whose energies need to be evaluated during the search for the global minimum.

When we consider a ligand in a given orientation relative to a protein, we can perform a conformational analysis of the ligand directly in the binding site (42) and can extend the analysis to receptor side chains that interact with the ligand (42). Because many of the conformations do not fit into the site, the search is computationally more efficient for a given ligand position than for an isolated molecule. Coupled to a search in the rotational and translational space of the ligand, the method can perform flexible docking that takes a significant portion of the receptor's conformational freedom into account.

LIGAND BUILDUP   An efficient combinatorial strategy for solving stagewise optimization problems, known as ligand buildup (25, 79), involves constructing conformations by sequentially adding building blocks (i.e. fragments or atoms) in various conformations to a seed (i.e. starting) molecular fragment. Building ligands directly in the binding site is a remarkably efficient flexible-docking and -design strategy. With the GROW procedure (56), one can dock and/or design peptide inhibitors using a library of low-energy conformations of isolated amino acid residues as building blocks. The recent addition of a general template library extended this method to nonpeptide ligand design. The building blocks used in GroupBuild (66) are small functional groups such as hydroxy, carbonyl, or benzene rings. The buildup starts from a given ligand fragment or from a given position in the binding site. GenStar (67) and LEGEND (59) are buildup-type design programs that use single atoms rather than functional groups as building blocks.

Both combinatorial minimization and its special, buildup-type implementations are prone to combinatorial explosion, unless a large fraction of all conformations is discarded at every step according to some heuristic considerations. However, if the heuristics are based on valid assumptions, these approaches guarantee finding the lowest-energy structures available to the system, unlike random approaches such as the Monte Carlo technique.

SITE MAPPING AND FRAGMENT ASSEMBLY   Goodford (26) introduced the idea of using molecular probes to map the binding site of a macromolecule to search for energetically favorable positions. Generally, the probes are functional groups (or, in the case of peptide ligands, possibly entire amino acid residues) that are docked to a target site. In particular, GRID (26) places small fragment probes at many regularly spaced grid points within the active site and determines the most favorable scores. Thus, the different groups (water, methyl group, amine nitrogen, carboxy oxygen, and hydroxyl) are used as specialized shape descriptors in a grid-based energy evaluation, and the energy contour surfaces for the various probes delineate regions of attraction between probe and protein. The procedure is well suited to multiple-copy techniques (55).

The output of GRID (and, more generally, the mapping of the receptor) provides information on favorable positions for several functional groups. Using local minimization, one can identify a few positions for each group at which it is both sterically acceptable and is likely to interact favorably with the surrounding side chains of the receptor. The goal of fragment-assembly approaches, pioneered by Lewis & Dean (44, 45), is to connect the individual molecular fragments into a single, viable molecule. The CLIX program (41) performs this task by screening a small molecular database. For each molecule, the program attempts to make a pair of the substituent's chemical groups spatially coincide with a pair of favorable interaction sites proposed by GRID in the binding site of the protein. Some site-mapping and fragment-assembly programs also make use of generalized shape descriptors. LUDI (6) positions molecular fragments into the binding site of an enzyme in such a way that hydrogen bonds with the enzyme are formed and hydrophobic pockets are filled. These fragments are then linked together with suitable spacers. The linked-fragment approach of Verlinde and coworkers (83) is somewhat more general, exploiting several properties (shape, hydrophobicity, hydrogen bonding, etc) as shape descriptors. Caflisch and coworkers (10) used MCSS to map a binding site and constructed possible ligands by building bonds to connect the various minima they found. To build the bonds, they used a simplified energy function that allowed an exhaustive search over all possible connections. In HOOK (19), MCSS is also used in the mapping stage, but the minima are connected by means of a search through a database of molecular scaffolds for possible connectors. In docking or designing peptide ligands, the use of entire residues instead of small functional groups generally increases the specificity of mapping and restricts the necessary considerations to a relatively small number of positions in the assembly stage (65, 68).

COMBINED STRATEGIES   Several factors promote the development of combined strategies. First, in-site ligand buildup can be made more efficient if the building blocks are favorable positions derived from site mapping. Conversely, site mapping results in numerous favorable positions and, in a design problem, in a variety of more or less equally favorable chemical groups at each position. Efforts to link such fragments clearly can profit from the methods of combinatorial optimization. Second, a hierarchical approach, the elements of which appear in almost every procedure, can increase efficiency. A hierarchical approach reduces the region of interest; for example, an initial rigid-body method might be used to search for a manageable number of conformations, which are then subjected to detailed exploration with sophisticated strategies and more realistic target functions. Finally, combining various methods can be very efficient in particular problems. For example, the end groups of peptides bound to class I MHC receptors are confined to small regions at the two ends of the site. As shown below, one can exploit this property by mapping these regions to find favorable positions for the end residues and then determining the conformation of the intervening peptide fragment by chain-closure algorithms (65, 68) based either on combinatorial search (8) or on a multiple copy scaling-relaxation algorithm (90, 91).

Empirical Evaluation of Binding Free Energy

The most natural score function, both in design and docking, is the free energy of binding given by $\Delta G = G^b - G^f$, where G^f and G^b, respectively, denote the free energies of the system before (free) and after (bound) the complex is formed. In design, the objective is to identify the ligand with the lowest attainable value of ΔG, whereas in docking, G^f is a constant, and hence the minimum of the binding free energy is attained at the minimum of G^b.

The established methods of free-energy evaluation by thermodynamic integration or perturbation approaches through molecular-dynamics or Monte Carlo simulations are far too demanding computationally to be used in docking or design (86). Several empirical free-energy evaluation models have been published to overcome this limitation (31, 58, 60, 86). In addition to a molecular-mechanics interaction energy, empirical models estimate the contributions of solvation and entropy loss. If these terms are simple enough, the model enables fast free-energy evaluation and hence can serve as a target function.

Novotny and coworkers (60) calculated the free-energy change accompanying the association of two rigid molecules according to the equation

$$\Delta G = E_{el} + \Delta G_h - T\Delta S_{sc} + \text{const}, \qquad 1.$$

where E_{el} is the electrostatic interaction energy between the ligand and the receptor, ΔG_h is the solvation free energy, and ΔS_{sc} is the loss of side-chain conformational entropy. The constant term includes further entropy loss resulting from changes in rotational and translational degrees of freedom and the cratic contribution to entropy. Equation 1 does not include a van der Waals component because the protein-protein and protein-water van der Waals interactions are assumed to cancel (60). The solvation free energy ΔG_h is assumed to be proportional to the change in solvent-accessible surface area upon binding. The side-chain entropy loss ΔS_{sc} is also calculated by taking into account the change in accessible atomic surface areas. The ΔG values calculated for nine endopeptidase–protein inhibitor complexes showed good agreement with experiments (38).

Horton & Lewis (31) estimated the free energy of rigid binding by

$$\Delta G = \alpha \Delta G_{apolar} + \beta \Delta G_{polar} + const, \qquad 2.$$

where both solvation free-energy terms, ΔG_{apolar} and ΔG_{polar}, are calculated by sums of the form used by Eisenberg & McLachlan (20). The polar term encompasses only atoms that are involved in hydrogen bonds and salt bridges; all other atoms contribute to the apolar term. The coefficients α and β are dimensionless parameters determined by fitting Equation 2 to binding free energies measured in 15 rigid-body complexes (31). On the basis of general relationships in the thermodynamics of protein folding (57), Murphy and coworkers described the structural energetics of angiotensin binding (58) with a similar expression that, in addition to a constant, consists of terms that depend on polar and apolar surface areas.

Whereas Equation 1 can be derived from the general expression $\Delta G = \Delta E - T\Delta S$ by considering the energy and entropy differences between bound and free states and using several simplifying assumptions, the model of Horton & Lewis (Equation 2) is completely empirical. Furthermore, the two expressions differ strongly, because of the Coulombic term E_{el} in Equation 1. However, in analyzing high-resolution X-ray structures of protein complexes, we found that the electrostatic interaction energy E_{el} can be accurately described as a linear combination of polar and apolar surface areas, probably because surface charges dominate the interaction energy (80a). Thus, the two free-energy expressions are, in fact, very similar.

Equations 1 and 2 assume that both the receptor and the ligand are rigid, but this is clearly a very poor approximation for many ligands, such as short peptides. The flexibility of the ligand has two consequences: Neither (*a*) the conformational (internal) energy change of the ligand, ΔE, nor (b) the loss of conformational entropy upon binding are negligible. Because the free ligand adopts many different conformations, one needs to calculate the average energy change $\langle \Delta E \rangle$. The solvation free-energy change ΔG_h also depends on the conformation of the free ligand, and hence in Equation 1 it should be replaced by the ensemble average $\langle \Delta G_h \rangle$ (80a). For peptides, the equation must account for the backbone entropy loss ΔS_{bb}, which can be estimated by an empirical method such as conformational filtering (78). Thus, the free energy of binding of a flexible ligand is calculated by

$$\Delta G = \langle E_{el} \rangle + \langle \Delta G_h \rangle - T \Delta S_{sc} - T \Delta S_{bb} + \text{const.} \qquad 3.$$

Because $\langle E_{el} \rangle$ and $\langle \Delta G_h \rangle$ are averages over the ensemble of free ligand conformations, the evaluation of Equation 3 is far from simple.

Verlinde & Hol (82) recently formulated the most important qualitative rules for the design of high-affinity ligands as follows: (a) The steric and electrostatic complementarity should be excellent; (b) a fair amount of hydrophobic surface should be buried in the complex; and (c) substantial conformational rigidity of the ligand is required to reduce the entropy loss upon binding. The terms in Equation 1 and 3 are in good agreement with these rules. The only difference is that, because of the lack of the van der Waals term, the equations do not measure steric complementarity. In fact, the simplified model assumes good packing of both protein-ligand and protein-solvent interfaces, and hence all steric clashes have to be removed before the free-energy evaluation, e.g. by subjecting the complex to local energy minimization using a traditional molecular-mechanics potential function.

APPLICATIONS OF FLEXIBLE METHODS: CURRENT STATUS

Design of Protease Inhibitors

In each of the major families of proteases, the active site exhibits a high degree of structural conservation. Because the three-dimensional structure of at least one member of each of these families has been determined, attempts to design inhibitors for a protease whose structure is unknown can start by predicting the structure of the protease by means of homologous extension. The first successful study of this kind was the design of antihypertensive drugs—inhibitors of renin and the angiotensin-converting enzyme.

The first inhibitors designed for renin, an aspartic protease, simply incorporated the naturally occurring, small-molecule inhibitor of this enzyme, statin, into an octapeptide from its natural substrate, angiotensinogen. The resulting inhibitor was improved by building a model of the protease through homologous extension, by using molecular graphics to dock the inhibitor, and by creating more potent derivatives by means of chemical intuition (4). A similar approach (13) yielded a potent inhibitor for angiotensin-converting enzyme, a zinc protease whose structure is unknown. This inhibitor is widely used as the antihypertensive drug Captopril. A recent study showed that this compound is highly flexible in its free state (46), and its success as a drug demonstrates that protease inhibitors can be designed using traditional tools. However, Hassall and coworkers (29) later addressed the issue of flexibility and successfully increased Captopril's potency. They fit a model of the molecule, which they considered to have two freely rotatable bonds, to the known structure of the thermolysin active site, and determined its most likely conformation using molecular graphics. They designed a bicyclic derivative based on this conformation, thereby abolishing freedom of rotation about the two rotatable bonds and imposing a conformation that they predicted is the most suitable for binding.

Many other systems have been developed with similar approaches, i.e. by homologous extension from a known protease-inhibitor complex. Cohen and coworkers (12) designed a peptide inhibitor for a serine protease of the blood fluke *Schistosoma mansoni*. A model for the protease was built based on the known structure of porcine pancreatic elastase, and a substrate was designed based on the structure and binding mode of boronic acid inhibitor bound to α-lytic protease. Sumiya and coworkers (75) designed a specific inhibitor for cathepsin B, a lysosomal thiol protease. The structure of the protease was modeled based on the crystal structure of a papain-inhibitor complex (also a thiol protease). The authors then used molecular graphics to dock a known inhibitor to the model and, on the basis of chemical intuition, synthesized 17 derivatives, one of which proved to be both potent and specific.

Similar studies have examined proteases of known structure, of which the best studied is the aspartic protease of HIV (for a review, see 87). The DOCK program (15) was applied to this enzyme to search through approximately 10^4 small molecules for potential inhibitors. An additional visual search among the 200 top-ranked compounds for proximity to the catalytic site, hydrogen-bonding capacity, and chemical synthesizability resulted in a candidate inhibitor. Although the affinity of the final compound is several orders of magnitude too low for clinical use, this molecule can be used as a lead compound for the design of more potent inhibitors.

Ring and coworkers (63) used the same techniques to design inhibitors against proteases crucial to the pathogenicity of the schistosome and malaria parasites, for which the structures are unknown. The two enzymes, a serine and a cysteine protease, were modeled based on the known structure of homologous proteins, and a database of approximately 55,000 compounds was searched for suitable lead compounds. The compounds were ranked according to two target functions: the shape-complementarity function (15) and a simplified molecular-mechanics potential approximating the interaction energy between the protease and ligand. Both functions proved inadequate for choosing high-affinity compounds, and potential lead compounds were chosen based on visual inspection of the 2200 compounds with the best shape complementary and the 2200 with the best interaction energy. This study suggests that the efficacy of determining lead compounds may be sensitive to the accuracy of the proposed structure of the receptor when traditional methods and target functions are used.

Flexible-docking methods have been used only recently. Caflisch and coworkers (10) applied a fragment assembly method to dock a known peptide inhibitor to HIV protease. MCSS was used to find possible minima for functional groups corresponding to backbone and side-chain pieces and for the peptide constructed by connecting these fragments. With GroupBuild, Rotstein & Murcko (66) reconstructed a known inhibitor from a fragment used as a seed. Both studies obtained results in accord with crystallographic data, but the applicability of the methods to the design of novel inhibitors has yet to be demonstrated.

Peptide Binding to Major Histocompatibility Complex Receptors

As noted previously, attempts to dock peptides to class I MHC receptors have clearly demonstrated the limitations of the currently available docking methods. Energy minimization (68), molecular-dynamics (64), and Monte Carlo (11) docking strategies failed dramatically to predict the bound conformation of antigenic peptides: In all cases the peptide, initially put in an α-helical conformation, remained helical throughout the calculations despite the fact that the native conformation is extended. Of the several crystal structures of class I–peptide complexes now available—of the same MHC haplotype with varying peptides and of varying haplotypes—all show a highly conserved hydrogen-bond network between the backbone of the terminal peptide residues and conserved side chains of the receptors. If the peptide termini are in highly favorable energy minima, one can assume that their optimal position and orientation when isolated from the rest of the peptide will significantly overlap their crystallographic position.

This assumption forms the basis for two recent studies (65, 68) in which each of the terminal residues was initially docked in isolation and the conformation of the intervening chain was then calculated using a loop-closure algorithm. In the first study, the terminal residues were docked using a rigid-body grid search augmented by local energy minimization at energetically favorable grid positions; the second study utilized a multiple-copy (21, 55) method to simultaneously minimize the energy of 20 residue copies that had random initial conformations and positions. Because the electrostatic interaction between the ligand (single-residue) backbone and the receptor is strong, both of these methods succeed in finding the ligand's optimal position. The side-chain conformations, on the other hand, are harder to predict. In both methods, the predicted side-chain conformation depends strongly on the initial side-chain conformation and can be found only by testing a large number of starting conformations. The multiple-copy methods, which enhance sampling, address this problem well. In fact, we (R Rosenfeld, Q Zheng, S Vajda & C DeLisi, submitted) recently found the correct side-chain conformations using this method, having chosen as the target function the potential energy of the system augmented by a qualitative entropy-related term derived from the clustering of copies in a multiple-copy simulation (65, 89, 91).

Although the use of loop closure algorithms in determining the conformation of the intervening residues has met with only limited success, largely because of the omission of water from the simulations, it nevertheless is of practical value. These calculations correctly predict the function of each of the peptide side chains (anchor vs T-cell epitope), as well as the overall orientation of the peptide, as measured by the hydrogen bonds between the peptide backbone and the receptor (R Rosenfeld, Q Zheng, S Vajda & C DeLisi, submitted). This information is important for the development of vaccine-design strategies. In contrast, the correct prediction of the atomic coordinates awaits further methodological development.

CONCLUSIONS

The number of available docking and design methods is exploding. Some of the fundamental ideas, such as shape descriptors (40), grid-based energy evaluation, and mapping of the binding site (26), have been known for almost a decade. Nevertheless, essentially all general-purpose docking and structure-based design programs, particularly those explicitly addressing ligand flexibility, have been published in the past four years—most in the past two years (82). Clearly, the importance of designing inhibitors for proteases, particularly the HIV protease, has substantially promoted the development of these programs and has focused efforts on the problem of ligand flexibility.

The recent and explosive developments in methodology have led to an interesting situation. On one hand, some of the most powerful methods available for flexible drug design are so new that they have been tested in only a few relatively simple problems. On the other hand, other research groups have not waited for such state-of-the-art technologies and have solved difficult drug-design problems using traditional tools such as rigid-body docking and visual inspection on the computer screen. As discussed above, these traditional tools have been successful in the design of protease inhibitors, but the problem of docking peptide antigens in MHC receptors requires a genuine flexible methodology. The new programs are likely to result in improved inhibitors and ligands in both types of problems.

In spite of the spectacular rate at which computational tools are being developed, additional work will be required to solve two major difficulties. First, both docking and design as defined here lead to nondeterministic polynomial (NP)–complete combinatorial problems. Solving such problems by any exact method presumably requires computing time that grows faster than any polynomial in N, the number of degrees of freedom. In practice, investigators avoid the combinatorial explosion by using criteria that retain only some top-scoring solutions at various steps of the algorithms. Thus, the final solutions are likely to be suboptimal rather than optimal. Second, a related and even more important problem is selecting a target function that estimates the binding free energy efficiently and with adequate accuracy. Recently developed empirical models seem to satisfy these criteria when tested on complexes of rigid molecules with known structure, but these models have not yet been coupled with search algorithms. In particular, the success of such a procedure depends on the sensitivity of the calculated free energies to inevitable errors in the atomic coordinates. Hence, this sensitivity requires careful analysis. As we have discussed, the use of free energy as a target function can be easily extended to flexible ligands in docking problems, but design requires calculating the free energy of the unbound ligand, a problem that is substantially more difficult.

ACKNOWLEDGMENTS

We thank Zhiping Weng for reading the manuscript. This work was supported by NIH/NIAID grant AI30535 (CD and RR) and DOE grant FG02-93ER61656 (SV).

Literature Cited

1. Alberg DG, Schreiber SL. 1993. Structure-based design of a cyclophilin-calcineurin bridging ligand. *Science* 262: 248–50
2. Bacon DJ, Moult J. 1992. Docking by least-squares fitting of molecular surface patterns. *J. Mol. Biol.* 225:849–58
3. Bjorkman PJ, Saper MA, Samraoui B, Bennet WS, Strominger JL, Wiley DC. 1987. Structure of the human class I histocompatibility antigen, HLA-A2. *Nature* 329:506–12
4. Blundell TL, Cooper J, Foundling SI, Jones DM, Atrash B, Szelke M. 1989. On the rational design of renin inhibitors: X-ray studies of aspartic proteinases complexed with transition-state analogues. In *Perspectives in Biochemistry*, ed. H Neurath, pp. 83–89. Washington, DC: Am. Chem. Soc.
5. Bode W, Huber R. 1991. Ligand binding: proteinase-protein inhibitor interactions. *Curr. Opin. Struct. Biol.* 1: 45–52
6. Bohm HJ. 1992. The computer program LUDI: a new method for the de novo design of enzyme inhibitors. *J. Comput. Aided Mol. Des.* 6:131–47
7. Brooks BR, Bruccoleri RE, Olafson BD, States DJ, Swaminathan S, Karplus M. 1983. CHARMm: a program for macromolecular energy, minimization, and dynamics calculations. *J. Comput. Chem.* 4:187–217
8. Bruccoleri RE, Karplus M. 1987. Prediction of the folding of short polypeptide segments by uniform conformational sampling. *Biopolymers* 26: 137–68
9. Bruccoleri RE, Karplus M. 1990. Conformational sampling using high-temperature molecular dynamics. *Biopolymers* 29: 1847–62
10. Caflisch A, Miranker A, Karplus M. 1993. Multiple copy simultaneous search and construction of ligands in binding sites: application to inhibitors of HIV-1 aspartic proteinase. *J. Med. Chem.* 36:2142–64
11. Caflisch A, Niederer P, Anliker M. 1992. Monte Carlo docking of oligopeptides to proteins. *Proteins* 13: 223–30

12. Cohen FE, Gregoret LM, Amiri P, Aldape K, Railey J, McKerrow JH. 1991. Arresting tissue invasion of a parasite by protease inhibitors chosen with the aid of computer modeling. *Biochemistry* 30:11221–29
13. Cushman DW, Cheung HS, Sabo EF, Ondetti MA. 1977. Design of potent competitive inhibitors of angiotensin-converting enzyme. Carboxyalkanoyl and mercaptalkanoyl amino acids. *Biochemistry* 16:5484–91
14. Daggett V, Levitt M. 1992. Molecular dynamics simulations of helix denaturation. *J. Mol. Biol.* 233: 1121–38
15. DesJarlais RL, Seibel GL, Kuntz ID, Furth PS, Alvarez JC, et al. 1990. Structure-based design of nonpeptide inhibitors specific for the human immunodeficiency virus 1 protease. *Proc. Natl. Acad. Sci. USA* 87: 6644–48
16. DesJarlais RL, Sheridan RP, Seibel, GL, Dixon JS, Kuntz ID. 1988. Using shape complementarity as an initial screen in designing ligands for a receptor binding site of known three-dimensional structure. *J. Med. Chem.* 31: 722–29
17. Desmet J, DeMaeyer M, Hazes B, Lastern I. 1992. The dead-end elimination theorem and its use in protein side-chain positioning. *Nature* 356: 539–42
18. DiNola A, Roccatano D, Berendsen HJC. 1994. Molecular dynamics simulation of the docking of substrates to proteins. *Proteins* 19:174–82
19. Eisen MB, Wiley DC, Karplus M, Hubbard RE. 1994. HOOK: a program for finding novel molecular architectures that satisfy the chemical and steric requirements of a macromolecular binding site. *Proteins* 19:199–221
20. Eisenberg D, McLachlan AD. 1986. Solvation energy in protein folding and binding. *Nature* 319:199–203
21. Elber R, Karplus M. 1990. Enhanced sampling in molecular dynamics: use of the time-dependent Hartree approximation for a simulation of carbon monoxide diffusion through myoglobin. *J. Am. Chem. Soc.* 112:9161–75

22. Falk K, Rotzschke O, Stevanovic S, Jung G, Rammensee H-G. 1991. Allele-specific motifs revealed by sequencing of self-peptides eluted from MHC molecules. *Nature* 351:290–96

23. Falk K, Rotzschke O, Stevanovic S, Jung G, Rammensee H-G. 1994. Pool sequencing of natural HLA-DR, DQ, and DP ligands reveals detailed peptide motifs, constraints of processing, and general rules. *Immunogenetics* 39: 230–42

24. Fremont DH, Matsumura M, Stura EA, Peterson PA, Wilson IA. 1992. Crystal structures of two viral peptides in complex with murine MHC class I H-2 K^b. *Science* 257:919–27

25. Gibson KD, Scheraga HA. 1987. Revised algorithms for the build-up procedure for predicting protein conformations by energy minimization. *J. Comput. Chem.* 8: 826–34

26. Goodford PJ. 1985. A computational procedure for determining energetically favorable binding sites on biologically important macromolecules. *J. Med. Chem.* 28:849–75

27. Goodsell DS, Olson AJ. 1990. Automated docking of substrates to proteins by simulated annealing. *Proteins* 8:195–202

28. Hart TN, Read NJ. 1992. A multiple-start Monte-Carlo docking method. *Proteins* 13:206–22

29. Hassall CH, Krohn A, Moody CJ, Thomas WA. 1982. The design of a new group of angiotensin-converting enzyme inhibitors. *FEBS Lett.* 147: 175–79

30. Ho CMW, Marshall G. 1993. FOUNDATION: a program to retrieve all possible structures containing a user-defined minimum number of matching query elements from three-dimensional databases. *J. Comput. Aided Mol. Des.* 7:3–22

31. Horton N, Lewis M. 1992. Calculation of the free energy of association for protein complexes. *Protein Sci.* 1: 169–81

32. Jiang F, Kim SH. 1992. "Soft docking": matching the molecular surface cubes. *J. Mol. Biol.* 219:79–102

33. Kaslow RA, Duquesnoy R, Van Raden M. 1990. A1, Cw7, B8, DR3 HLA antigen combination associated with rapid decline of T-helper lymphocytes in HIV-1 infection. *Lancet* 335: 927–30

34. Katchalski-Katzir E, Shariv I, Eisenstein M, Friesem A, Aflalo C, Vakser IA. 1992. Molecular surface recognition: determination of geometric fit between proteins and their ligands by correlation techniques. *Proc. Natl. Acad. Sci. USA* 89:2195–99

35. King PM, Richards WG. 1992. Free energy calculations in molecular biophysics. *Mol. Phys.* 76:251–75

36. Kirpatrick S, Gelatt CD Jr, Vecchi MP. 1983. Optimization by simulated annealing. *Science* 220:671–80

37. Kollman PA. 1994. Theory of macromolecule-ligand interactions. *Curr. Opin. Struct. Biol.* 4:240–45

38. Krystek S, Stouch T, Novotny J. 1993. Affinity and specificity of serine endopeptidase-protein inhibitor interactions: empirical free energy calculation based on X-ray crystallographic structures. *J. Mol. Biol.* 234:661–79

39. Kuntz ID. 1992. Structure-based strategies for drug design and discovery. *Science* 257:1078–82

40. Kuntz ID, Blaney JM, Oatley SJ, Langridge R, Ferrin TE. 1982. A geometric approach to macromolecule-ligand interactions. *J. Mol. Biol.* 161:269–88

41. Lawrence MC, Davis PC. 1992. CLIX: a search algorithm for finding novel ligands capable of binding proteins of known three-dimensional structure. *Proteins* 12:31–41

42. Leach AR. 1994. Ligand docking to proteins with discrete side-chain flexibility. *J. Mol. Biol.* 235:345–56

43. Leach AR, Kuntz ID. 1992. Conformational analysis of flexible ligands in macromolecular receptor sites. *J. Comp. Chem.* 13:733–48

44. Lewis RA, Dean PM. 1989. Automated site-directed drug design: the concept of spacer skeletons for primary structure generation. *Proc. R. Soc. London Ser. B* 236:125–40

45. Lewis RA, Dean PM. 1989. Automated site-directed drug design: the formation of molecular templates in primary structure generation. *Proc. R. Soc. London Ser. B* 236:141- 62

46. Luke BT. 1994. A quantum mechanical conformational search of Captopril, a potent inhibitor of the angiotensin-converting enzyme. *J. Mol. Struct.* 309:1–11

47. Madden DR, Garboczi DN, Wiley DC. 1994. The antigenic identity of peptide-MHC complexes: a comparison of the conformations of five viral peptides presented by HLA-A2. *Cell* 75: 693–708

48. Madden DR, Gorga, JC, Strominger JL, Wiley DC. 1992. The three-dimensional structure of HLA-B27 at 2.1 Å

resolution suggests a general mechanism for tight peptide binding to MHC. *Cell* 70:1035–48

49. Marshall G. 1992. Three-dimensional structure of peptide-protein complexes: implications for recognition. *Curr. Opin. Struct. Biol.* 2:904–19

50. Marshall KW, Liu AF, Canales J, Perahia B, Jorgensen B, et al. 1994. Role of the polymorphic residues in the HLA-DR molecules in allele-specific binding of peptide ligands. *J. Immunol.* 152:4946–57

51. Meng EC, Gschwend DA, Blaney JM, Kuntz ID. 1993. Orientational sampling and rigid-body minimization in molecular docking. *Proteins* 17: 266–78

52. Meng EC, Schoichet BK, Kuntz ID. 1992. Automated docking with grid-based energy evaluation. *J. Comput. Chem.* 13:505–24

53. Metropolis N, Rosenbluth AW, Rosenbluth MN, Teller AH, Teller E. 1953. Equation of state calculations by fast computing machines. *J. Chem. Phys.* 21:1087–92

54. Mézei M, Beveridge DL. 1986. Free energy simulations. *Ann. N. Y. Acad. Sci.* 494:1–23

55. Miranker A, Karplus M. 1991. Functionality maps of binding sites: a multicopy simultaneous search method. *Proteins* 1:29–34

56. Moon JB, Howe J. 1991. Computer design of bioactive molecules: a method for receptor-based de novo ligand design. *Proteins* 11:314–28

57. Murphy KP, Freire E. 1992. Thermodynamics of structural stability and cooperative folding behaviours in proteins. *Adv. Protein. Chem.* 43:313–61

58. Murphy KP, Xie D, Garcia KC, Amzel LM, Freire E. 1993. Structural energetics of peptide recognition: angiotensin II/antibody binding. *Proteins* 15: 1120

59. Nishibata Y, Itai A. 1993. Confirmation of usefulness of a structure construction program based on three-dimensional receptor structure for rational lead generation. *J. Med. Chem.* 36: 2921–28

60. Novotny J, Bruccoleri RE, Saul FA. 1989. On the attribution of binding energy in antigen-antibody complexes MCPC603, D1.3, and HyHEL-5. *Biochemistry* 28:4735–49

61. O'Sullivan D, Arrhenius T, Sidney J, Del Guercio M-F, Albertson M, et al. 1991. On the interaction of promiscuous antigenic peptides with different DR alleles: identification of common structural motifs. *J. Immunol.* 147: 2663–69

62. Pellegrini M, Doniach S. 1993. Computer simulation of antibody binding specificity. *Proteins* 15:436–44

63. Ring CS, Sun E, McKerrow HJ, Lee GK, Rosenthal PH, et al. 1993. Structure-based inhibitor design by using protein models for the development of antiparasitic agents. *Proc. Natl. Acad. Sci. USA* 90:3583–87

64. Rognan D, Reddehase MJ, Koszinowski UH, Folkers G. 1992. Molecular modeling of an antigenic complex between a viral peptide and a class I major histocompatibility glycoprotein. *Proteins* 13:70–85

65. Rosenfeld R, Zheng Q, Vajda S, DeLisi C. 1993. Computing the structure of bound peptides: application to antigen recognition by class I MHCs. *J. Mol. Biol.* 234:515–21

66. Rotstein SH, Murcko MA. 1993. GroupBuild: a fragment-based method for de novo drug design. *J. Med. Chem.* 36:1700–10

67. Rotstein SH, Murcko MA. 1993. GenStar: a program for de novo drug design. *J. Comput. Aided Mol. Des.* 7: 23–43

68. Sezerman U, Cornette J, Vajda S, DeLisi C. 1993. Toward computational determination of peptide-receptor structure. *Protein Sci.* 2:1827–46

69. Shoichet BK, Bodian DL, Kuntz ID. 1992. Molecular docking using shape descriptors. *J. Comput. Chem.* 3: 380–97

70. Shoichet BK, Kuntz ID. 1991. Protein docking and complementarity. *J. Mol. Biol.* 221:327–46

71. Shoichet BK, Stroud RM, Santi D, Kuntz ID, Perry KM. 1993. Structure-based discovery of inhibitors of thymidilate synthase. *Science* 259:1145–50

72. Silver ML, Guo HC, Strominger JL, Wiley D. 1992. Atomic structure of a human MHC molecule presenting an influenza virus peptide. *Nature* 360: 367–68

73. Sprague PW. 1991. CATALIST: a computer aided drug design system specifically designed for medicinal chemists. In *Recent Advances in Chemical Information. Proc. 1991 Chemical Information Conf.*, ed. H Coller, pp. 107–11. London: R. Soc. Chem.

74. Stern LG, Brown JH, Jardetsky TS, Gorga JC, Urban RG, et al. 1994. Crystal structure of the human class

II MHC protein HLA-DR1 complexed with an influenza virus peptide. *Nature* 368:215–21

75. Sumiya S, Yoneda T, Kitamura K, Murata M, Yokoo C, et al. 1992. Molecular design of potent inhibitor specific for cathepsin B based on the tertiary structure prediction. *Chem. Pharm. Bull.* 40:299–303

76. Taylor R. 1994. Histocompatibility antigens, protective immunity, and HIV-1. *J. NIH Res.* 6:68–71

77. Totrov M, Abagyan R. 1994. Detailed ab initio prediction of lysozyme-antibody complex with 1.6Å accuracy. *Nat. Struct. Biol.* 1:259–63

78. Vajda S. 1993. Conformational filtering in polypeptides and proteins. *J. Mol. Biol.* 229:125–45

79. Vajda S, DeLisi C. 1990. Determining minimum energy conformations of polypeptides by dynamic programming. *Biopolymers* 29:1755–72

80. Vajda S, DeLisi C. 1994. An adaptive branch-and-bound minimization method based on dynamic programming. In *The Protein Folding Problem and Tertiary Structure Determination,* ed. KM Mertz, SM LeGrand, pp. 409–32. Boston: Birkhauser

80a. Vajda S, Weng Z, Rosenfeld R, DeLisi C. 1994. Effect of conformational flexibility and solvation on receptor-ligand binding free energies. *Biochemistry* 33:13977–88

81. VanDrie JH, Weininger D, Martin YC. 1989. ALLADIN: an integrated tool for computer-assisted molecular design and pharmacophore recognition from geometric, steric, and substructure searching of three-dimensional molecular structures. *J. Comput. Aided Mol. Des.* 3:225–54

82. Verlinde CLMJ, Hol WGJ. 1994. Structure-based drug design: progress, results and challenges. *Structure* 2: 577–87

83. Verlinde CLMJ, Rudenko G, Hol WGJ. 1992. In search of new lead compounds for trypanosomiasis drug design: a protein structure-based linked-fragment approach. *J. Comput. Aided Mol. Des.* 6:131–47

84. Walls PH, Sternberg MJE. 1992. New algorithm to model protein-protein recognition based on surface complementarity: applications to antibody-antigen docking. *J. Mol. Biol.* 228: 277–97

85. Wang H. 1991. Grid-search molecular accessible surface algorithm for solving the protein docking problem. *J. Comp. Chem.* 12:746–50

86. Wilson C, Mace JE, Agard DA. 1991. Computational method for the design of enzymes with altered substrate specificity. *J. Mol. Biol.* 220:495–506

87. Wlodawer A, Erickson JW. 1993. Structure-based inhibitors of HIV-1 protease. *Annu. Rev. Biochem.* 62: 543–85

88. Yue S. 1990. Distance-constrained molecular docking by simulated annealing. *Protein Eng.* 4:177–84

89. Zheng Q, Rosenfeld R, DeLisi C, Kyle DJ. 1994. Multiple copy sampling in protein loop modeling: computational efficiency and sensitivity to dihedral angle perturbations. *Protein Sci.* 3: 493–506

90. Zheng Q, Rosenfeld R, Vajda S, DeLisi C. 1993. Loop closure via bond scaling and relaxation. *J. Comput. Chem.* 14:556–65

91. Zheng Q, Rosenfeld R, Vajda, S, DeLisi C. 1993. Determining protein loop conformation using scaling-relaxation techniques. *Protein Sci.* 2:1242–48

SUBJECT INDEX

A

Acanthamoeba castellanii
  profilin and, 658–59, 662, 664, 670
ACCESS program
  thermodynamics of folding intermediates and, 146
Acetic acid
  glacial
    amino acid polymers and, 7
Acetylcholine
  receptor
    channel proteins and, 34–40, 43, 49, 51
Aconitase
  nuclear magnetic spectroscopy and, 211
Acrylodan
  fluorescent protein biosensors and, 415
Actin
  fluorescent protein biosensors and, 415–16
Actin monomer-binding proteins
  actin as target protein
    binding features and, 670
    chemical composition and, 667–68
    electrostatic potential and, 670
    fractal dimension and, 669–70
    surface area and, 667
    surface topography and, 668–69
  actin primer and, 645–46
  binding site comparisons and, 664–67
  DNase I and, 647–50
  gelsolin and, 650–57
  overview, 644–45
  possible bonds in actin complexes, 666
  profilin and, 658–64
  surfaces occluded from solvent in actin complexes, 665
Actinomycin D
  minor groove complexes and, 466–69
Active-site formation
  DNA methyltransferases and, 301, 303
Adducin
  β-calmodulin and, 89
Adenosine triphosphate (ATP)

actin monomer-binding proteins and, 646, 658
channel-forming colicins and, 614
DNA gyrase and, 194–99, 201–5
S-Adenosyl-apL-ap-methionine-dependent methyltransferases
  DNA methylation and, 296, 298, 300–1, 303, 305–6, 311–15
Adenylyl cyclase
  type I
    calmodulin and, 89
5'-Adenylyl-β,γ-imido-diphosphate (ADPNP)
  DNA gyrase and, 196, 198–203, 205
ADPNP
  See 5'-Adenylyl-β,γ-imido-diphosphate
Adriamycin
  minor groove complexes and, 466
Adseverin
  gelsolin and, 650
Aequorea victoria green fluorescent protein
  fluorescent protein biosensors and, 425
Aerolysin
  channel proteins and, 33
Affinity capillary electrophoresis
  binding constants and
    tight-binding systems, 594–95
    weak-binding systems, 593–94
  binding stoichiometry and, 596–97
  kinetic rate constants and, 595–96
Affinity cleavage approach
  minor groove complexes and, 482
African swine fever virus
  DNA topoisomerases and, 192–93
Aglycone
  minor groove complexes and, 484
Alfrey, T., 8
Alkaline phosphatase
  immobilized enzymes and, 13
Alkanes
  DNA analogues and, 170

ALLADIN program
  flexible docking and design and, 686
Amber codon
  site-directed mutagenesis with expanded genetic code and, 435, 439
Amides
  compact intermediates and, 508–9, 512
  DNA analogues and, 170–71
Amines
  DNA analogues and, 170
Amino acids
  poly-α amino acids, 5–12
  unnatural
    site-directed mutagenesis with expanded genetic code, 435–58
Amino-peptidase P
  amino acid polymers and, 11
Aminopyridine
  channel proteins and, 46
Amira, B., 3
Ampholyte solution
  capillary electrophoresis and, 591, 593
Anabaena spp.
  ferredoxins and, 216–21, 226, 228
Anaphylactic shock
  polytyrosyl gelatin and, 11–12
Anhydrides
  N-carboxy-α-amino acid, 6–7, 10
Anhydroglycine
  derivation of, 6
8-Anilinonaphthalene-1-sulfonic acid (ANS)
  channel-forming colicins and, 623
  compact intermediates and, 497–98, 501, 504, 509–10
Annexin
  gelsolin and, 654
Annexin V
  atomic structure of
    channel proteins and, 47–48
ANS
  See 8-Anilinonaphthalene-1-sulfonic acid
Antihypertensive drugs
  design of, 692–93
Anthracyclines
  minor groove complexes and, 466–67

701

CUMULATIVE INDEXES

CONTRIBUTING AUTHORS, VOLUMES 20–24

CHAPTER TITLES, VOLUMES 20–24

INDEXED BY KEYWORD